UNIVE

Natural Immunity

Natural Immunity

Edited by
David S. Nelson
Kolling Institute of Medical Research,
Royal North Shore Hospital, Sydney

ACADEMIC PRESS
Harcourt Brace Jovanovich, Publishers
Sydney   San Diego   New York   Berkeley
Boston   London   Tokyo   Toronto

ACADEMIC PRESS AUSTRALIA
30–52 Smidmore Street, Marrickville, NSW 2204

United States edition published by
ACADEMIC PRESS INC.
1250 Sixth Avenue
San Diego, California 92101–4311

United Kingdom edition published by
ACADEMIC PRESS, INC. (LONDON) LTD.
24/28 Oval Road, London NW1 7DX

National Library of Australia Cataloguing-in-Publication Data

Natural Immunity.
  Bibliography.   Includes index.
  ISBN 0 12 514555 1.

  1. Natural immunity.   I. Nelson, David S. (David Selwyn).

616.07 9

Library of Congress Catalog Card Number: 88-070924

CONTENTS

1

16 Local Tissue Injury 506
Sigurd J. Normann

17 Effectors and Modulators of Natural Immunity: Discussion 540
David S. Nelson

PART II   NATURAL IMMUNITY IN DISEASE PROCESSES

18 Viral Infections 557
Page S. Morahan and Donna Murasko

CONTRIBUTORS

Jon S. Abramson (39), Bowman Gray School of Medicine of Wake Forest University, Winston-Salem, North Carolina 27103, USA

William H. Adler (392), Clinical Immunology Section, Gerontology Research Center, National Institute on Aging, 4940 Eastern Avenue, Baltimore, Maryland 21224, USA

Bradley S. Bender (392), Clinical Immunology Section, Gerontology Research Center, National Institute on Aging, 4940 Eastern Avenue, Baltimore, Maryland 21224, USA

Michael Bennett (484), Department of Pathology, University of Texas Health Science Center at Dallas, 5323 Harry Hines Blvd, Dallas, Texas 75235, USA

Samuel N. Breit (284), Centre for Immunology, St Vincent's Hospital and University of New South Wales, Sydney NSW 2010, Australia

Gerald I. Byrne (587), Department of Medical Microbiology, University of Wisconsin, Madison, Wisconsin 53706, USA

Christina Cheers (613), Department of Microbiology, University of Melbourne, Parkville, Victoria 3052, Australia

Donna Chow (172), Manitoba Institute of Cell Biology, University of Manitoba, Winnipeg, Manitoba, Canada

I. A. Clark (702), Zoology Department, Australian National University, Canberra, ACT 2601, Australia

John Leslie Collins (147), Salk Institute, PO Box 85800, San Diego, California 92138–9216, USA

W. B. Cowden (702), John Curtin School of Medical Research, Australian National University, Canberra ACT 2601, Australia

R. A. B. Ezekowitz (15), Division of Hematology/Oncology, Childrens Hospital and Dana Farber Cancer Institute, Harvard Department of Pediatrics, 320 Longwood Avenue, Boston, Massachusetts 02115, USA

Nicola Fabris (306), Immunology Centre, Gerontology Research Department, Italian National Research Centres on Aging (INRCA), Via Birarelli 8, Ancona, Italy

Mark P. Fletcher (440), Division of Clinical Immunology and the Departments of Internal Medicine and Nutrition, University of California at Davis, TB 192, Davis, California 95616, USA

M. Eric Gershwin (440), Division of Clinical Immunology and the Department of Internal Medicine and Nutrition, University of California at Davis, TB 192, Davis, California 95616, USA

Elie Gertner (795), Department of Medicine, Division of Clinical Immunology, University of Texas Health Science Center, 7703 Floyd Curl Drive, San Antonio, Texas 78284, USA

David L. Gordon (218), Clinical Microbiology, Royal Newcastle Hospital, Newcastle NSW 2300, Australia

Arnold Greenberg (172), Manitoba Institute of Cell Biology, University of Manitoba, Winnipeg, Manitoba, Canada

David I. Grove (723), Department of Medicine, University of Western Australia Queen Elizabeth II Medical Centre, Nedlands, WA 6009, Australia

Ronald B. Herberman (71), Pittsburg Cancer Institute and Departments of Medicine and Pathology, University of Pittsburgh, School of Medicine, Pittsburg, Pennsylvania 15213, USA

Peter Hersey (123), Immunology and Oncology Unit of the Mater Misericordiae Hospital, Royal Newcastle Hospital, Newcastle, NSW 2300, Australia

David L. Hoover (679), Infectious Disease Service, Walter Reed Army Medical Center, Washington, DC 20012, USA

N. H. Hunt (702), John Curtin School of Medical Research, Australian National University, Canberra, ACT 2601, Australia

Lucille S. Hurley (440), Division of Clinical Immunology and the Departments of Internal Medicine and Nutrition, University of California at Davis, TB 192, Davis, California 95616, USA

Thomas R. Jerrells (587), Walter Reed Army Institute of Research, Washington, DC 20307–5100 USA

Carl L. Keen (440), Division of Clinical Immunology and the Departments of Internal Medicine and Nutrition, University of California at Davis, TB 192, Davis, California 95616, USA

Suzanne Lemieux (348), Immunology Research Centre, Institute Armand-Frappier, Université de Quebec, Laval, Quebec, Canada

Monte S. Meltzer (587 and 679), Infectious Disease Service, Walter Reed Army Medical Center, Washington, DC 20307, USA

Veronica Miller (172), Department of Microbiology and Immunology, UCLA School of Medicine, CA 90024, USA

Page S. Morahan (557), Department of Microbiology and Immunology, Medical College of Pennsylvania, Henry Avenue, Philadelphia, Pennsylvania 19129, USA

Donna M. Murasko (557), Department of Microbiology and Immunology Medical College of Pennsylvania, Henry Avenue, Philadelphia, Pennsylvania 19129, USA

Carol A. Nacy (587 and 679), Infectious Disease Service, Walter Reed Army Medical Center, Washington, DC 20307, USA

James E. Nagel (392), Clinical Immunology Section, Gerontology Research Center, National Institute on Aging, 4940 Eastern Avenue, Baltimore, Maryland 21224, USA

D. S. Nelson (540 and 817), Kolling Institute of Medical Research, Royal North Shore Hospital, St Leonards, NSW 2065, Australia

Sigurd J. Normann (506), Box J-275, JHMHC, Department of Pathology, College of Medicine, University of Florida, Gainesville, Florida 32610, USA

Paul Q. Patek (147), Salk Institute, PO Box 85800, San Diego, California 92138–9216, USA

Jacques J. Proust (392), Clinical Immunology Section, Gerontology Research Center, National Institute on Aging, 4940 Eastern Avenue, Baltimore, Maryland 21224, USA

Mauro Provinciali (306), Immunology Centre, Gerontology Research Department, Italian National Research Centres on Aging (INRCA), Via Birarelli 8, Ancona, Italy

Paul G. Quie (39), Department of Pediatrics, University of Minnesota, Minneapolis, Minnesota 55455 USA

Vernon Riley (473), Pacific Northwest Research Foundation, Seattle, Washington 98194, USA (deceased; summary by Maurice Landy)

Emil Skamene (348), Division of Clinical Immunology and Allergy, Montreal General Hospital Research Institute, Montreal, Quebec, Canada

Phillip D. Smith (241), Cellular Immunology Section, Laboratory of Microbiology and Immunology, National Institute of Dental Research, National Institutes of Health, Bethesda, Maryland 20892, USA

Tania C. Sorrell (645), Department of Medicine, The University of Sydney, and Infectious Diseases Unit, Westmead Centre, Westmead, NSW 2145, Australia

Mary M. Stevenson (348), Division of Clinical Immunology and Allergy, Montreal General Hospital Research Institute, Montreal, Quebec, Canada

Osias Stutman (749), Immunology Program, Memorial Sloan-Kettering Cancer Center, 1275 York Avenue, New York, New York 10021, USA

Norman Talal (795), Division of Clinical Immunology, Clinical Section Audie L. Murphy Memorial Veterans Hospital, and Department of Medicine, University of Texas Health Science Center, 7703 Floyd Curl Drive, San Antonio, Texas 78284, USA

Sharon M. Wahl (241), Cellular Immunology Section, Laboratory of Microbiology and Immunology, National Institute of Dental Research, National Institute of Health, Bethesda, Maryland 20892, USA

J. Gary Wheeler (39), Bowman Gray School of Medicine of Wake Forest University, Winston-Salem, North Carolina 27103, USA

PREFACE

Every successful species on our planet has made an accommodation with an environment that is almost never wholly friendly. Climate and weather, predators and parasites all take their toll, as do genetic mistakes and, inevitably, senescence with its attendant breakdown in homeostasis. Although all individuals must die, the survival of the species can be assured — for some time, at least — by many sorts of adaptation, from the crude strategy of massive reproduction to the development of conscious, intelligent co-operation. Adaptability is almost as important as adaptation, and one of the most effective defences that has evolved is the set of reactions that we know, in higher animals, as adaptive immunity. With quite breathtaking elegance, if not simplicity, the system of adaptive, acquired immunity provides us and our vertebrate cousins with rapid and specific defences against a wide range of microbial pathogens and metazoan parasites. It may also provide defences against the enemy within — the transformed cells whose growth as cancer can threaten the entire body.

In admiring the molecular and genetic mechanisms of adaptive immunity — and the intellectual achievements of those who have revealed many of its secrets — we are, however, apt to forget the existence of another and blunter set of defensive weapons: those of natural immunity. In the strict sense, natural immunity includes those defences that operate in the absence of a specific, adaptive immune response. Some are apparently simple and phylogenetically old, for example, an unbroken integument, the secretion of antibacterial molecules (lysozyme, fatty acids), ciliary action. The effectiveness of mechanical barriers, ciliary action and flushing actions is well illustrated by the ease with which infection can become established in wounds, in bronchi in which ciliary action is impeded, or in blocked tubes of various sorts (Eustachian tubes, bile ducts, ureters).

More commonly studied effectors of natural immunity are phagocytic cells, the 'natural antibodies' that are found in serum in the absence of

12

known antigenic stimulation, components of the complement system, and various naturally occurring cytotoxic cells. These effectors are subject to modulation by many factors: age, nutrition, stress, radiation, tissue damage and the mediators and products of inflammatory reactions. These same modulating factors, however, also affect the efficiency with which adaptive immune responses are mounted and expressed. For many immunologists, therefore, a consideration of 'natural immunity' also includes the non-specific modulation or regulation of adaptive immune responses by those factors. Certainly, an individual who can, at a particular time, make a rapid specific immune response to a pathogen is more likely to escape exposure with little or no overt disease than is one whose response is sluggish or inadequate; such an individual may thus seem to possess more potent 'natural immunity'. For this reason, the brief for contributors to this book was not too prescriptive, and the reader will find that many of the discussions range into that rather grey area between 'natural' and 'acquired' immunity.

The first part of the book deals with the effector mechanisms of natural immunity and the factors that influence them. The second part deals with the operation of natural immunity in a variety of infections and other pathological conditions. Inevitably, this design has led to some overlap. This is to the good, as it allows for some diversity of opinion to be expressed. In one area, that of naturally occurring cytotoxic cells, diversity has been actively sought. This subject is directly treated in three chapters in Part A. It is also of central importance in considering the operation of natural immunity in cancer and some virus infections, and has recently achieved prominence in discussions of certain rheumatic diseases, so these cells appear again in different chapters of Part B.

So that the editor's role is not wholly passive, I have taken it upon myself to offer some personal (and possibly idiosyncratic) comments at the end of each part of the book. These comments include brief discussions of diseases in which natural immunity is less prominent, but in which immunity, in the broadest sense, may operate, or in which the effectors of natural immunity play some part, perhaps in other guises.

This book has its origins in discussions with Dr Maurice Landy, to whom I am greatly indebted for stimulation, suggestions and encouragement. I thank Jeremy Fisher and Roslyn Roberts of Academic Press, for their help and patience during the long gestation of this book, and Justine Roberts for skilled secretarial assistance. In this enterprise, as in many others, Dr Peggy Nelson has given help and support well above and beyond the call of duty.

PART I EFFECTORS AND MODULATORS OF NATURAL IMMUNITY

1

Macrophages

R. A. B. EZEKOWITZ

Division of Hematology/Oncology
Childrens Hospital and Dana Farber Cancer Institute
Harvard Department of Pediatrics
320 Longwood Avenue
Boston, MA 02115, USA

NATURAL IMMUNITY
IBSN 0 12 5145551

I. INTRODUCTION

Macrophages are remarkable cells in many ways. Their wide anatomical distribution and capacity to secrete over 100 different molecules enable them to function beyond their well-known phagocytic and destructive capacities. Their responsiveness to local environmental influences enables them to interact with many other cells and molecules in health and disease. Many biological functions of macrophages fit them for both central effector roles and regulatory roles in natural immunity.

II. ANATOMICAL DISTRIBUTION

A. Definition of Macrophages Using Monoclonal Antibodies

The life history of the macrophage has been extensively studied in the mouse by use of a specific rat monoclonal antibody, F4/80. The differentiation antigen (F4/80) provides an ideal marker to define the precise distribution of macrophages in the tissues of normal developing and adult mice. Antigen F4/80 is found on the surface of all mature mouse macrophages from different sites, and in different states of activation, and also on macrophage-like cell lines (Austyn and Gordon, 1981). All colonies derived from bone-marrow progenitors in the presence of specific colony-stimulating factor (CSF-1) express F4/80 uniformly (Hirsch *et al.*, 1981). The antigen is stable to glutaraldehyde-perfusion fixation and can be detected on paraffin-embedded tissue sections by the avidin–biotin–peroxidase method (Gordon *et al.*, 1986). The specificity and sensitivity of this immunocytochemical procedure combined with excellent preservation of morphology, provides unique information on macrophage localisation.

B. Fetal Macrophages

In the mouse, the committed progenitors for macrophages appear on the fifth day of embryonic life (G. Shia, unpublished), but mature macro-phages detected by the F4/80 antibody are first evident in the yolk sac on day 9 (L. Morris, unpublished). Subsequently, macrophages appear in large numbers in mesenchymal tissues (day 12 on), during organogenesis and progressively in fetal liver, spleen and bone marrow as haemopoietic organs obtain mature stellate macrophages that are closely associated with clusters of immature erythroid cells (Gordon *et al.*, 1986). The seeding of other sites, such as gut, kidney, central nervous system and lung, occurs from the time a circulation is established and continues after birth. The exact mechanism(s) by which macrophages enter these tissues is not known, but it would appear that in the central nervous system blood monocytes are recruited to dispose of senescent neurones and axons undergoing programmed cell death during development (Perry *et al.*, 1985). After phagocytosis of remnants, the macrophages extend spindly plasma membrane processes and mature into microglia, as shown in the plexiform layer of the retina (Hume *et al.*, 1984a). The pattern of distribution of macrophages established in early life seems to persist throughout adult life. The renewal of macrophages at these various sites, and the effects of the local environment on macrophage function and vice versa will be discussed in later sections.

C. Lymphoid Tissues and Haemopoietic Organs

1. Bone marrow

The antigen F4/80 permits identification of early mononuclear phago-cyte precursors in the bone marrow. It is also present on cells lining vascular sinuses (as in liver) and larger cells forming the centre of haemopoietic islands (Hume and Gordon, 1985). These larger cells lie at the centre of clusters of proliferating haemopoietic cells and have been purified by collagenase digestion and adherence to glass. These cells have a novel lectin-like receptor for sheep erythrocytes which is distinct from CD2 (T11; sheep red-cell receptor on T cells and natural killer cells) (Gordon, 1986). It has been suggested that these stromal macrophages have a role in controlling monocytopoiesis and erythropoiesis by secreting specific growth factors.

2. Thymus

The thymus contains several populations of F4/80 cells distinguishable on the basis of morphology and anatomical localisation (Hume *et al.*, 1983). Along the capsule, cells are distributed on connective tissue septa and project into the cortex, where they extend fine membranous processes between thymocytes. The modified epithelial cells forming Hassall's corpuscles are often surrounded by F4/80$^+$ cells and in the medulla there is a population of smaller rounded F4/80$^+$ cells with the classical appearance of macrophages.

3. Spleen, lymph node and gut-associated lymphoid areas

In contrast to the situation in the thymus, cells labelled with F4/80 are rarely seen in association with dense groups of lymphocytes in other lymphoid organs, including spleen, lymph nodes, Peyer's patches and other gut-associated lymphoid follicles. In the spleen the white pulp is initially devoid of macrophages save for isolated examples in the marginal zone. By contrast the red pulp represents a very dense concentration of F4/80$^+$ cells. The cortical regions of lymph nodes and gut-associated lymphoid areas also contain few macrophages. In lymph nodes they are concentrated within medullary sinuses and immediately adjacent paracortical regions (Hume *et al.*, 1983). In Peyer's patches and in lymphoid follicles in the colon and caecum, F4/80$^+$ cells are only seen immediately under the capsule and in the lamina propria. In Peyer's patches and lymph nodes only occasional labelled cells have been observed in presumed germinal centres (tingible body macrophages), but follicular dendritic cells are clearly F4/80 negative (Hume *et al.*, 1983).

D. Central Nervous System

It was originally proposed by del Rio Hortega (1932) that microglial cells were mesodermal in origin. Some authors have argued that microglia are derived from blood monocytes (Baldwin, 1981) but others have claimed they are of neuroectodermal origin (del Rio Hortega, 1932; Fiyita and Kiranura, 1976). Immunohistochemical localisation of the macrophage-specific antibody F4/80 and monoclonal antibodies to the IgG1/2b Fc receptor (2.4G2) and the type 3 complement receptor (Mac 1) have revealed two populations of macrophages in adult mice brains (Perry *et al.*, 1985). Those associated with the choroid plexus, ventricles and leptomeninges, and the microglia. These studies provide strong support for the hypothesis that microglial cells are derived from monocytes, and that the possession of Fc and complement receptors allows them to play a part in the immune defence of the nervous system. If microglia are renewed constitutively by circulating monocytes, then paradoxically they may be responsible for infection of the CNS by certain trans-acting lentiviruses such as the human immunodeficiency virus (HIV, HTLV-III) in humans and visna virus in sheep. This class of viruses appears to infect macrophages without immediate cytopathic effects to the host cell (Gartner *et al.*, 1986).

E. Other Sites

Macrophages are found in large numbers all the way down the lamina propria of the gut, in the epidermis, in subcutaneous tissue, in the bronchoalveolar lining and in the genitourinary tract — i.e., along portals of entry of maximum antigen load. The distribution of macrophages at these strategic places and in serosal cavities is particularly pertinent to the role of macrophage in first-line host defence (Hume *et al.*, 1984b).

Perhaps less well known sites of macrophages are several endocrine organs, including the adrenal and pituitary glands, and parts of the reproductive tract (testis, ovary, uterus). In the normal kidney macrophages are found in the medullar as part of the juxta-glomerular complex and along the tubules (Hume and Gordon, 1985).

The precise localisation of macrophages throughout the body has broadened our concept of macrophage functions beyond its traditional role in chronic inflammation, host defence and tissue remodelling to include trophic interactions with haemopoietic cells, endothelia and epithelia, and the maintenance of local homeostasis. Although a rat analogue has been found, as yet no human analogue for antigen F4/80 has been identified. Therefore, conclusions drawn in rodents can merely be extrapolated to humans, but the use of other monoclonal antibodies directed against human Fc and complement receptors confirms a similar pattern of distribution of macrophages in some human tissues (Witmer and Steinman, 1984; Ugolina *et al.*, 1980).

III. MACROPHAGE HETEROGENEITY

Differences in biological activities and in secretory and surface properties found in macrophages from different anatomical sites and after various infections and stimuli are well documented (Ezekowitz and Gordon, 1984). Out of this identification of macrophage heterogeneity has emerged the question: Do these differences reflect alternative pathways of macrophage differentiation, or can the macrophage modulate its phenotype in response to external environmental stimuli? The answer to this question has emerged from tissue culture systems using defined populations of macrophages and the identification, purification and molecular cloning of specific glycoproteins which control growth, differentiation and activation of macrophages and closely related cells.

A. Resident, Inflammatory and Activated Macrophages

The idea that macrophages need to undergo functional modification in order to express resistance to infection can be traced back to the writings of Metchnikoff (1905) at the turn of the century. The term 'activation' was introduced by Mackaness in the 1960s to describe the intrinsic adaptive changes that enable macrophages to express enhanced antimicrobial resistance (Mackaness, 1970a). He and his collaborators presented evidence that although the acquired microbicidal mechanisms of activated macrophages are non-specific in their expression, their induction depends on the generation of a specific immune response. Acquired immunity to *Listeria monocytogenes*, an intracellular parasite, can be passively transferred to normal mice with living lymphoid cells, but not with serum from the *Listeria* immune donors (Mackaness, 1970b). The responsible lymphocytes are T cells. The demonstration of *in vivo* mediation of macrophage activation by sensitised lymphocytes (Lane and Unanue, 1972) prompted Simon and Sheagren (1972) to reproduce the event *in vitro*. They showed that when macrophages removed from uninfected animals (resident macrophages) were co-cultured with sensitised lymphocytes and specific antigen, the macrophages acquired enhanced listericidal activity. Current evidence indicates that the adaptive changes in macrophages which allow them to express acquired cellular immunity are mediated by lymphokines, of which interferon gamma appears to be the most active (Schreiber, 1984).

The original definition of activated macrophages involved their bactericidal activity and their role in cellular resistance to contain infections. Yet it has become apparent that, when the roles of macrophages in the physiology and pathology of mammals are studied, this is a restricted definition. The basic process of inflammation, tissue remodelling, degradation and turnover of normal body constituents, trophic functions and antitumor resistance may be more general expressions of macrophage activity. With these roles in mind it is necessary to consider the properties which distinguish this acquired state of activation from the non-activated state.

1. Surface properties of macrophages

Several specific receptors and antigens have been defined on macrophages, including a lectin-like receptor that mediates endocytosis of mannose- or fucose-terminated glycoproteins (MFR) (Stahl *et al.*, 1984), several types of Fc receptors which bind and internalise certain classes of immunoglobulin (Kossard and Nelson, 1968), receptors for a cleaved third component of complement (CR1 and CR3) recognised by distinct monoclonal antibodies (Ross, 1985) and F4/80 (Austyn and Gordon, 1981). In addition, macrophages can be induced to express Class II major histocompatibility complex (MHC) antigens (Ia antigens) by various infectious stimuli (Scher *et al.*, 1980; Steinman *et al.*, 1980; Steeg *et al.*, 1982), lymphocyte function antigen LFA-1, and some unique cell-surface antigens (Nathan, 1985).

Peritoneal macrophages obtained from animals after infection with live BCG are considered activated. They spread rapidly in culture, secrete neutral proteinases (but not elastase) (Werb *et al.*, 1986), secrete high levels of reactive oxygen intermediates when stimulated further, and display enhanced ability to kill micro-organisms and tumour cells (Nathan, 1985; Werb *et al.*, 1986). These cells show decreased secretion of apolipoprotein E (Werb *et al.*, 1986), prostaglandins and leukotrienes (Scott *et al.*, 1982). The use of cell-specific ligands and monoclonal antibodies enabled us to define a surface phenotype which distinguishes activated from non-activated macrophages. BCG-activated macrophages express high levels of Ia antigens and Fc receptors for IgG2a (Ezekowitz *et al.*, 1983), but decreased receptors for mannose terminal glycoconjugates and decreased antigen F4/80, whilst their expression of Mac1 (CR3) is unchanged (Ezekowitz *et al.*, 1981). Decreased receptor-mediated endocytosis is associated with active secretion of plasminogen activator and the ability to secrete high levels of superoxide (O_2^-) and hydrogen peroxide (H_2O_2) after further stimulation. Single-cell analysis revealed that the levels of antigen F4/80, mannose receptor and IgG1/IgG2a Fc receptor were decreased on activated macrophages; all cells in the population were positive, but less strongly so than non-activated macrophages.

Supernatant from antigen- or mitogen-stimulated lymphocytes (lymphokines) has been shown to augment macrophage antimicrobial and antitumour activity, increase macrophage spreading in culture, increase the capacity of macrophages to secrete plasminogen activator and reactive oxygen intermediates, and enhance Ia antigen expression (Adams and Hamilton, 1984, Nathan, 1985). We therefore examined the ability of lymphokines to induce the activated phenotype on previously non-activated macrophage populations *in vitro*. Lymphokines mediated the co-ordinate changes in cell surface phenotype and secretory profile found on cells activated *in vivo* (Ezekowitz *et al.*, 1985a). The lymphokine which mediated these effects, macrophage-activating factor (MAF), appears to have physical, biochemical and functional properties identical to interferon gamma (Schreiber, 1984).

The macrophage plasma membrane undergoes selective remodelling during activation. These changes are stable, occur in a co-ordinated manner and are accompanied by specific induction of biosynthetic and secretory responses to interferon gamma and perhaps to other activating agents. This suggests a common mechanism whereby a number of genes are selectively activated and repressed.

Macrophages, therefore, exhibit sets of surface and secretory properties which correlate with their functional state. I believe that macrophage activation represents the state induced by interferon gamma, in which the cell displays enhanced ability to release reactive oxygen intermediates. This should be contrasted to other definitions which consider the macrophages' ability to kill micro-organisms and tumour cells as the determinant of macrophage activation (Adams and Hamilton, 1984). This latter definition fails to take into account that resident macrophages which secrete lysozyme and complement components may effectively eliminate certain classes of susceptible bacteria but do not display any of the other properties associated with an activated macrophage.[1] The role of the macrophage in host defence, against any one agent at any one time, is dependent on the susceptibility of the target to the array of effector molecules intrinsic to the state of the cell at this time. How that cell may alter this array of molecules will be discussed in the following section.

B. Regulation of Macrophage Growth, Differentiation and Activation

Macrophages arise from the bone marrow where pluripotential stem cells under the influence of specific differentiation, growth factors and cytokines mature into circulating monocytes which constitutively leave the bloodstream and renew tissue macrophages (Diesselhoff-den Dulk *et al.*, 1979). Little is understood about the signals required for a monocyte to repopulate tissue macrophages, but the dynamic equilibrium is exemplified by the turnover of Kupffer cells in the liver every 7–10 days (Van Furth *et al.*, 1983). Steady-state production, recruitment and turnover of macrophages can be dramatically altered by an exogenous stimulus. A sterile inflammatory agent, such as thioglycollate, elicits an influx into the peritoneal cavity of a mouse of 10 times as many macrophages as are already resident. This begins within 1 day and reaches a peak after 3–5 days. Rapidly growing pathogens such as *Listeria monocytogenes* (Lepay *et al.*, 1985), or *Plasmodium yoelii* (Lee *et al.*, 1986), evoke the accumulation of up to 10-fold more macrophages in organs such as liver and spleen within a week. Unlike the initial resident populations, which display relatively little microbicidal activity, the newly recruited macrophages display enhanced respiratory burst activity. The examples illustrate that the demands of infection or other inflammatory and injurious agents are met by increased production of macrophages in the bone marrow, increased emigration and accelerated turnover. A satisfactory explanation of these events requires the following features: (1) that stem cells are renewed and give rise to precursor cells throughout the life of the animal; (2) that the production of one or more

---

[1] For further discussion, see Chapter 17.

lineages can be controlled on demand; and (3) that differentiation is progressive and irreversible, but that cells adapting to various conditions are endowed with considerable biosynthetic flexibility, thereby explaining macrophage heterogeneity.

The identification, purification and molecular cloning of specific glycoproteins which control growth, differentiation and activation have provided exciting new insights into these questions. These include interleukin-3 (IL-3) (Yang *et al.*, 1986), macrophage colony stimulating factor (or M-CSF) (Metcalf, 1984), granulocyte–macrophage colony stimulating factor (GM-CSF) (Gough *et al.*, 1984), and granulocyte colony stimulating factor (G-CSF), which enhance macrophage growth; and interferons, which tend to inhibit growth (Trinchieri and Perussia, 1985). These cytokines act at several stages of macrophage differentiation, extend overlapping pleiotropic effects, and bind to specific surface receptors. Growth and some differentiation effects depend on continuous exposure of macrophages to the cytokine and are reversible, accounting for the extrinsic control of primary macrophage proliferation. This information has been derived in large part from in vitro culture systems where a bipotential progenitor (CFU-C) gives rise to both macrophages and granulocytes, and commitment to each lineage can be controlled by the nature and concentration of the growth factor in the medium (Metcalf, 1984). Improved yields and purity of progenitors from fresh bone marrow can be achieved using the FACS multiparameter analyser. Cells cultured in semi-solid agar give rise to macrophage colonies which are powerful tools for analysing diversity among independent clones. Studies of various cell markers in this way support the hypothesis that macrophages are clonally equivalent and that macrophages are a single cell family, albeit a remarkably variable one (Hirsch *et al.*, 1981). This idea is supported by studies using bipotential cell lines (HL60, WEHI-3) which retain their ability to differentiate along either lineage when treated with various agents (CSFs, dimethyl sulfoxide, phorbol esters, interferons, vitamins D3) (Sachs, 1980). Clonal analysis of these and other cell lines treated with specific cytokines has revealed that clones which received similar stimuli are equivalent.

We can, therefore, definitively state that the functional state of macrophage is determined by external regulatory signals. However, the molecules which control the earliest stages of stem cell growth and differentiation have not been defined. Growth factor and cytokine production within the host can be stimulated by endotoxin, antigens and infectious agents, but little is known about the cells responsible for production and the regulatory circuits involved. A better understanding can be expected from the use of specific antibodies, gene probes and recombinant growth factors in vitro and in vivo.

IV. CELL SURFACE RECOGNITION

Macrophages encounter a multiplicity of potential ligands (cells, matrix mediators, organisms) which they are required to recognise and to which they must respond. Unlike lymphocytes, macrophages are not clonally derived and do not possess specific antigen receptors. Macrophages possess distinct receptors which mediate engulfment of large particles as well as a variety of fluid-phase receptors involved in receptor-mediated endocytosis and thus important in cell homeostasis (Silverstein *et al.*, 1977).

The major phagocytic receptors recognise common ligands, for example complement (complement receptors, CR) or the Fc portion of immunoglobulin (Fc-receptor, FcR), or ubiquitous ligands such as mannose (mannose receptor, MR). Silverstein *et al.* (1977) proposed a zipper mechanism to account for opsonin- (antibody and complement) dependent phagocytosis. According to this proposal, receptor–ligand interactions occur in local segments of the plasma membrane that mediate binding of the particle, but ingestion results from involvement of the contractile apparatus. This proceeds if receptors interact sequentially around the full circumference of the target, like a zipper, guiding membrane flow and eventual fusion around the particle.

Macrophage receptors vary in their ability to mediate phagocytosis. Receptors for the cleaved third component of complement (CR1, CR3) exist in two distinct states (Wright and Griffin, 1985), which mediate: (1) binding alone, or (2) binding and ingestion. CR activity depends on the physiological state of the macrophage: ingestion is observed in inflammatory, but not resident macrophages. It can be modulated by lymphokines and fibronectin (Wright *et al.*, 1984). The mechanism by which this occurs in unclear but an interesting homology between the beta chain of CR3 and the fibronectin receptor at the nucleotide level (T. Springer, personal communication) suggests that fibronectin may interact directly with this part of the molecule and thereby influence its function.

By contrast, Fc receptors, among which distinct receptors for different types of immunoglobulin exist (Unkeless *et al.*, 1981), and MR bind and ingest ligands constitutively. In addition to mediating the ingestion of large particles, which cross-link many receptors on the cell surface, directing the ingested particle to the lysosome, both these receptors are able to recognise monomeric ligands. These enter the endosomal compartment where receptor and ligand dissociate; the receptor is then rapidly recycled to the cell surface (Stahl *et al.*, 1980).

Macrophages readily adhere to artificial and physiological substrates. This process has been considered as attempted phagocytosis, but recent studies reveal that phagocytosis and attachment are distinct processes. When macrophages spread on glass, the zone of contact remains accessible to extracellular protein probes, whereas spreading on a specific ligand attached to a substrate creates a zone of exclusion to the probe ('black hole') (Wright and Silverstein, 1984). This resembles the close apposition between macrophage and target, which creates a 'pocket' for vectorial secretion and concentration of macrophage effector molecules.

These 'pockets' may also be important in expanding the macrophage's repertoire of recognition. The dependence on specific antibody and serum complement limits the macrophage's role in first-line host defence as the pathogen infiltrates an epithelial surface for the first time. The macrophages can extend their range of recognition by (1) direct recognition of a ligand on the cell surface of the pathogen, e.g. carbohydrate — specifically, mannose; and (2) by secreting proteins for which they themselves have receptors.

Evidence exists that many pathogens have complex cell walls which are rich in mannose polymer. These include yeasts (Ballou, 1976) and parasites like *Leishmania donovani* (Russell and Wilhelm, 1986), an obligatory intracellular pathogen of macrophages. Uptake of the mannose-rich yeast zymosan (Ezekowitz *et al.*, 1984) and *Leishmania donovani* promastigotes (Blackwell *et al.*, 1985) can proceed by direct sugar recognition or via the alternative pathway of complement. Macrophages have a previously unexplained, but well-known, capacity to synthesise and secrete complement proteins including the regulatory components of the alternative pathway (Stecher *et al.*, 1967; Colten, 1976; Lai *et al.*, 1975; Whaley, 1980). This has been invoked as an unusual local opsonisation mechanism (Ezekowitz *et al.*, 1984). Targets which are efficient activators of the alternative pathway of complement assemble macrophage-derived ligand, C3bi, on their surface and are then recognised by the cells' own CR3.

Evidence for this hypothesis has been obtained by using several CR3-specific inhibitory monoclonal antibodies, including Mac1, MO-1 and OKM10, and Fab anti-C3 monoclonal antibody (Ezekowitz *et al.*, 1985b). Direct evidence comes from: (1) biosynthetic labelling of macrophages and demonstration of C3bi on the particle in the absence of an exogenous source of complement (Ezekowitz *et al.*, 1985b); and (2) by direct visualisation of macrophage-derived C3 on the surface of *Leishmania* promastigotes using an anti-C3 antibody and protein-A gold conjugate on electron microscope sections (Wozencraft *et al.*, 1986). An alternative view holds that, although macrophages can perform these complex functions, the undoubted involvement of the CR3 results from direct reactions with other ligands, as well as C3bi (Ross *et al.*, 1985b). In addition, CR3 and the structurally homologous molecules lymphocyte-function-associated antigen (LFA-1) and p150, 95 have been implicated in the direct binding to macrophages of certain smooth strains of *E. coli* (Wright and Jong, 1986) and *Histoplasma capsulatum* (Bullock and Wright, 1987). Further, the binding to macrophage of several particles, e.g. rabbit erythrocytes, that activate the alternative pathway of complement, can be partially inhibited by soluble beta glucan (Czop and Austen, 1985).

Whatever the mechanism, these studies raise the possibility that neither the macrophage nor the target cell is passive in the process of recognition. The recognition of complex ligands probably occurs via several receptors which can act independently or in concert. The role of leukocyte adhesion molecules like LFA-1 (Jeffries *et al.*, 1985) may be analogous to that of the CD3, CD4 and CD8 (T3, T4, T8) molecules on various classes of T cells. They might enhance contact between the macrophage and the target thereby allowing other receptors to move within the plane of the membrane and engage specific ligands on the target.

Macrophages also express receptors for lipoproteins (Fogelman *et al.*, 1985) and modified sugars (Vlassara *et al.*, 1984) (non-enzymatically glycosylated proteins) and for various peptides, hormones and neurotransmitters (Hartung *et al.*, 1986). Recently, a single class of high-affinity receptors for the neuropeptide substance P has been defined on resident guinea pig peritoneal macrophages (Hartung *et al.*, 1986). Engagement of these receptors results in the release of C3, lysosomal enzymes and arachidonic acid products. These studies suggest a role for macrophages in the neuroinflammatory process.

It is clear that the full repertoire of macrophage discriminatory functions has not been clearly elucidated. The molecular cloning of some of these cell-surface receptors will provide a basis to examine structure–function relationships in macrophage recognition. Expression of full-length receptor cDNA clones in artificial lipid bilayers may be the only definitive way to study the relative roles of receptors in ligand–receptor interaction.

V. MACROPHAGE SECRETION

A. General Features

Over the past decade the macrophage has emerged as a major secretory cell. The rich repertoire of secreted substances (Table 1.1) supports the concept that macrophages constitute a significant and unusually responsive family of secretory cells. Some general features of macrophage secretion include: (1) certain products are constitutively secreted in relatively large amounts (e.g. lysozyme); (2) most secretory responses are regulated by the functional state of the macrophage and their release requires an additional surface trigger; (3) few products arise solely from macrophages, and evaluation of the importance of macrophages as their source requires consideration of each specific circumstance (e.g., in complement biosynthesis, the contribution of the macrophage is quantitatively small compared to that of the hepatocyte); (4) although relative amounts of products may be low, high local concentrations at extravascular sites can be reached by focusing on 'black holes' and responses may be amplified by proteolytic cascades; and (5) single molecules, like interleukin 1 alpha and beta, and tumour necrosis factor (cachectin) have multiple activities. Macrophage secretion products are responsible for interactions with other molecules in the physiological cascades of fibrinolysis and coagulation. They may contribute directly to inflammation and acute hypersensitivity (Type I allergic reactions), as well as mediating many trophic functions.

B. Regulation of Secretion

It is not surprising, given the range of products secreted by macrophages (Table 1.1), that release of bioactive molecules by macrophages is regulated. Perhaps less obvious is that the secretion of sets of proteins is correlated with selective changes in the expression of plasma membrane antigens and receptors. As discussed in an earlier section the cell surface changes are regulated by external molecules. These include growth factors, lymphokines, cytokines and hormones, all of which play a key role in regulating macrophage secretion.

An intriguing aspect of this process is that the same mediators may enhance the secretion of some proteins and decrease the secretion of others (Werb *et al.*, 1986). Interferon gamma, for example, induces synthesis of neutral proteinases, factor B, and a novel thromboglobulin-like chemotactic peptide (Luster *et al.*, 1985), but decreases secretion of apolipoprotein E (Werb *et al.*, 1986). Glucocorticoids induce the release of angiotensin-converting enzyme and of macrocortin, an inhibitor of phospholipase activity, but decrease secretion of neutral proteinases (Werb *et al.*, 1986). By contrast, other products like lysozyme and some complement proteins appear to be constitutively released.

Most macrophage secretion is a response to an external mediator which selectively activates or represses specific genes. The regulation of secretion appears to be co-ordinated with the cell surface changes and may occur at transcriptional, post-transcriptional, translation or post-translational stages. It is not clear whether genes which control differentiation of the cell and activation are coordinately expressed. Nor is it known whether the same macrophages secrete all the different products listed in Table 1.1. There has been no adequate clonal survey to establish this point, and cell lines may be unstable and express only a partial phenotype. Macrophages in different sites do show interesting differences in secretion of complement proteins (Colten *et al.*, 1985), presumably reflecting differences in cell maturation and their response to the local environment. Similarly some products are associated with resident macrophages (prostaglandins, certain leukotrienes, complement products) and are sometimes lost after cell stimulation, while others (neutral proteinase and respiratory burst products) are only released from inflammatory or activated cells.

Plasma membrane receptors and ligands represent another level of control on macrophage secretion. Receptors differ in this regard, as ligation of FcR, but not of CR, triggers a respiratory burst (Yamamoto and Johnston, 1984) and arachidonate metabolism (Aderem *et al.*, 1985). Key events occur at the plasma membrane independent of internalisation, as mere ligation of receptors is sufficient to mediate secretion. Secretion appears to be targeted by mobilisation of specific vessels and orientation of the Golgi complex and microtubule organising centre (Kupfer *et al.*, 1985). The subsequent interaction between receptors and transducing signals, presumably to the nucleus, is unknown. Receptors may open up gated channels (Fc receptor is an ion channel) (Young and Cohn, 1985), interact with second messengers like cyclic guanidine or adenine nucleotides, or themselves translocate to the nucleus, like steroid receptors (Godowski *et al.*, 1987).

The regulated secretion of macrophages products accounts for many local and systemic effects observed in immunity and inflammation. The destructive effects of respiratory burst products and neutral proteinases have received a great deal of attention, but other macrophage products, like interleukin 1 and cachectin (tumour necrosis factor), have multiple different and shared properties, with a wide range of cellular targets (Nathan, 1987). In the next section I will discuss how these and other products of resident tissue macrophages contribute to the role of these cells in natural immunity.

VI. THE MACROPHAGE IN FIRST-LINE HOST DEFENCE

Macrophages are uniquely qualified to play a pivotal role in first-line host defence for the following reasons: (1) they are distributed along the

Table 1.1: Secretory products of mononuclear phagocytes (Nathan, 1987)

POLYPEPTIDE HORMONES

Interleukin-1-α
Tumour necrosis factor α (cachectin)
Interferons α
Interferons γ (confirmation needed)
Platelet-derived growth factor(s)
Fibroblast growth factor
Transforming growth factor α
Insulin-like activity
Thymosin B4
Erythropoietin
Granulocyte–macrophage colony-stimulating factor
Erythroid colony-potentiating factor
Factor inducing monocytosis
β-endorphin
Adrenocorticotropic hormone
Plasmacytoma growth factor
Neutrophil-activating factor

COMPLEMENT COMPONENTS

Classical pathway: C1, C4, C2, C3, C5
Alternative pathway: factor B, factor D, properdin
Inhibitors: C3b inactivator, $\beta-1H$
Active fragments generated by macrophage proteases: C3a, C3b, C5a, Bb

COAGULATION FACTORS

Intrinsic pathway: IX, X, V, prothrombin
Extrinsic pathway: VII
Surface activities: tissue factor, prothrombinase
Prothrombolytic activity: plasminogen activator
Antithrombolytic activities: plasminogen activator inhibitor, plasmin inhibitors

OTHER ENZYMES

Neutral proteases: plasminogen activator, elastase, collagenases, angiotensin convertase, others
Lipases: lipoprotein lipase, phospholipase A2
Glucosaminidase: lysozyme
Lysosomal acid hydrolases: proteases, lipases, (deoxy)ribonucleases, phosphatases, glycosidases, sulfatases
Deaminase: arginase

INHIBITORS OF ENZYMES AND CYTOKINES

Protease inhibitors: alpha-2 macroglobulin, alpha-1 antiprotease, plasminogen activator inhibitor, plasmin inhibitors, collagenase inhibitor
Phospholipase inhibitor: lipomodulin (macrocortin)
Interleukin 1 inhibitors

Table 1.1: *continued*

PROTEINS OF EXTRACELLULAR MATRIX OR CELL ADHESION

Fibronectin
Gelatine-binding protein of 95 kD
Thrombospondin
Chondroitin sulfate proteoglycans

BINDING PROTEINS OTHER THAN FOR CELLS OR MATRIX

For metals: transferrin, acidic isoferritins, transcobalamin II
For lipids: apolipoprotein E, lipid transfer protein

BIOACTIVE OLIGOPEPTIDES

Glutathione

BIOACTIVE LIPIDS

Cyclooxygenase products: PGE2, PGF2, prostacyclin, thromboxane
Lipoxygenase products: monohydroxyeicosatetraenoic acids, dihydroxyeicosatetraenoic
    acids, leukotrienes B4, C, D, E
Platelet-activating factors (1-*O*-alkyl-2-acetyl-sn-glyceryl-3-phosphorylcholine)

STEROL HORMONES

1, 25-dihydroxyvitamin D3

PURINE AND PYRIMIDINE PRODUCTS

Thymidine, uracil, uric acid, deoxycytidine
Neopterin (2-amino-4-oxo-6-trihydroxypropylpteridine)

REACTIVE OXYGEN INTERMEDIATES

Superoxide radical, hydrogen peroxide, hydroxyl radical, hypohalous acids

REACTIVE NITROGEN INTERMEDIATES

Nitrites, nitrates

---

portals of entry of maximum antigen load: (2) they are able to recognise pathogens in the absence of antibody or serum complement; (3) they secrete many potent mediators of acute inflammation and immediate hypersensitivity (Davies *et al.*, 1984), (4) they interact with endothelial cells, mast cells, fibroblasts and polymorphonuclear leukocytes; and (5) they respond to environmental stimuli which modulate their function to adapt to an evolving physiological response.

The macrophage's role in natural immunity is best illustrated by a specific example. Assume that a pathogenic mannose-rich yeast is inhaled. This is probably a common occurrence, although invasive yeast infection is a rare event which appears to occur only in a compromised host. How does the normal host deal with this challenge? Direct recognition of the pathogen by macrophages which underlie the epithelial surface can occur by sugar recognition, i.e. via the mannose receptor (Sung *et al.*, 1983). Macrophages will also secrete complement components which can opsonise the pathogen if it is an activator of the alternative pathway of complement. Recognition of the particle may occur by both these receptors together, leading to binding and ingestion of the yeast. This would serve two purposes: (1) the pathogen would be directed to the lysosome and presumably be destroyed; and (2) ligation of the surface receptors would amplify complement secretion, thereby generating C5a and C3a and cause the release of prostaglandins and leukotrienes, interleukin 1, and perhaps histamine and other vasoactive substances. The mediators may act on neighbouring cells like endothelium to promote vasodilation, oedema, and chemotaxis of acute inflammatory cells, especially polymorphonuclear leukocytes (PMNs) (Davies *et al.*, 1984; Sung *et al.*, 1983). Human PMNs bind and internalise opsonised yeast very poorly; however, if the particle is 'opsonised' by the macrophage the PMN is then able to recognise the yeast particle (Roos *et al.*, 1981; Ezekowitz *et al.*, 1985b). This interaction results in degranulation of the PMN, lysosomal enzymes and reactive oxygen intermediates being liberated. In some instances, at least in vitro, both the pathogen and the macrophage are destroyed (Ezekowitz *et al.*, 1985b). The macrophage would then play a key role in tissue remodelling and repair of the breach in the epithelium — one of its traditional roles.

If the invading pathogen is not an activator of the alternative complement pathway, or does not have a mannose-rich cell wall, direct recognition may be mediated via the LFA-1 family of molecules (Wright and Jong, 1986), beta-glucan receptors (Czop and Austen, 1985), or scavenger receptors (Vlassara *et al.*, 1984). Once specific interaction with the cell surface has occurred, presumably the same pattern of secretion could proceed. If the inoculum was too great and is not destroyed by the tissue macrophages or the acute inflammatory cells PMNs or monocytes, a specific immune response may be mounted either at the site of entry or at a distant site. This would involve the selective migration of lymphocytes (T and B cells) through high endothelial venules (Volkman and Gowans, 1963). These cells may interact: (1) directly with the pathogen, i.e. generate effector T cells, or specific antibody, or (2) indirectly by the release of lymphokines such as interferon gamma, lymphotoxin and certain colony-stimulating factors which may serve to increase bone-marrow production of myeloid cells as well as act locally on cells at the site of infection. Certain pathogens, such as *Mycobacterium tuberculosis*, trypanosomes or *Toxoplasma* (Sharma and Remington, 1981) have evolved mechanisms for avoiding the usual effector molecules. These infections often result in granuloma formation where macrophages, directed by the T cell and aided by fibroblasts, attempt to wall off infection and thereby limit its spread and create an unfavourable local milieu.

VII. CONCLUSIONS

Macrophages, by virtue of this anatomic distribution, versatility and rich repertoire of secreted substances, can influence all aspects of immune and inflammatory responses. They also serve as an excellent model to study cell differentiation, vectorial transport of proteins and receptor-mediated endocytosis. The isolation of cDNA clones which represent macrophage cell-surface proteins (Ravage *et al.*, 1986; Lewis *et al.*, 1986) and secreted products will provide useful tools for further study of the complex regulation of macrophage gene expression. The challenge of the future is the elucidation of macrophage-specific regulatory sequences and or trans-acting proteins. In this knowledge lies the potential to generate cell-specific agents with which to modulate macrophage function at will.

Acknowledgments: This work is supported by NIH ROI AI-23786-OI and by a Child Health Research Grant from Charles H. Foundation. I would like to thank Siamon Gordon for his help and guidance, and for stimulating discussions.

REFERENCES

Adams, D. O. and Hamilton, T. A. (1984). The cell biology of macrophage activators. *Amer. Rev. Immun.* 2: 283.

Aderem, A. A., Wright, S. D., Silverstein, S. D. and Cohn, Z. A. (1985). Ligated complement receptors do not activate the arachidonic acid cascade in resident peritoneal macrophages. *J. Exp. Med.* 161: 617.

Austyn, J. M. and Gordon, S. (1981). F4/80, a monoclonal antibody directed specifically against the mouse macrophage. *Eur. J. Immun.* 11: 805.

Baldwin, F. (1981). Microglia and brain macrophages. In I. Carr and W. T. Daems (eds), *The Reticuloendothelial System*, vol. 1. New York: Plenum Press: 635.

Ballou, C. (1976). Structure and biosynthesis of mannan component of the yeast cell envelope. *Adv. Microb. Physiol.* 14: 93.

Blackwell, J. M., Ezekowitz, R. A. B., Roberts, M. B., Channon, J. Y., Sim, R. B. and Gordon, S. (1985a). Macrophage complement and lectin-like receptors bind *Leishmania* in the absence of serum. *J. Exp. Med.* 162: 324.

Bullock, W. E. and Wright, S. D. (1987). The role of adherence-promoting receptors, C13, LFA-1 and gp150, 95 in binding of *Histoplasma capsulatum* by human macrophages. *J. Exp. Med.* 165: 195.

Colten, R. H. (1976). Biosynthesis of the complement. *Adv. Immun.* 22: 66.

Colten, H. R., Cole, F. S., Sackstein, R. and Auerbach, J. S. (1985). Tissue and species specific regulation of complement biosynthesis in mononuclear phagocytes. In R. van Furth (ed.), *Mononuclear Phagocytes: Characteristics, Physiology and Functions*. Dordrecht, Boston, Lancaster: Martinus Nijhoff: 147–54.

Czop, J. K. and Austen, K. F. (1985). A beta-glucan inhibitable receptor on human monocytes: its identity with the phagocytic receptor for partrenulate activators of the alternative complement pathway. *J. Immun.* 134: 2588.

Davies, P., Bailey, P. J. and Goldenberg, M. (1984). The role of arachidonic acid oxygen products in pain and inflammation. *Ann. Rev. Immun.* 2: 335.

Del Rio Hortega, P. (1932). Microglia. In W. Penfield (ed.), *Cytology and Cellular Pathology of the Nervous System*. New York: Paul B. Hoebes: 432.

Diesselhoff-den Dulk, M. M. C., Grofton, R. and van Furth, R. (1979). Origin and kinetics of Kupffer cells during an acute inflammatory response. *Immunology* 37: 7.

Ezekowitz, R. A. and Gordon, S. (1984). Alterations of surface properties by macrophage activation: Expression of receptors for Fc and mannose-terminal glycoproteins and differentiation antigens. In D. O. Adams and M. G. Hanna Jr (eds), *Contemporary Topics in Immunobiology*, vol. 18. New York: Plenum Press: 35.

Ezekowitz, R. A. B., Austyn, J. A., Stahl, P. and Gordon, S. (1981). Surface properties of Bacillus Calmette-Guerin-activated mouse macrophages. Reduced expression of mannose-specific endocytosis, Fc receptors and antigen F4/80 accompanies induction of Ia. *J. Exp. Med.* 154: 60.

Ezekowitz, R. A. B., Bampton, M. and Gordon, S. (1983). Macrophage activation selectively enhances expression of Fc receptors for IgG2a. *J. Exp. Med.* 157: 807.

Ezekowitz, R. A. B., Sim, R., Hill, M. and Gordon, S. (1984). Local opsonisation by secreted macrophage complement components: Role of receptors for complement in uptake of zymosan. *J. Exp. Med.* 159: 244–60.

Ezekowitz, R. A. B., Hill, M. and Gordon, S. (1985a). In R. van Furth (ed.), *Mononuclear Phagocytes: Characteristics, Physiology and Function.* Dordrecht, Boston, Lancaster: Martinus Nijhoff: 521.

Ezekowitz, R. A. B., Sim, R. B., MacPherson, C. G. and Gordon, S. (1985b). Interaction of human monocytes, macrophages and polymorphonuclear leukocytes with zymosan in vitro: Role of type 3 complement receptors and macrophage-derived complement. *J. Clin. Invest.* 76: 2368–76.

Fiyita, S. and Kitanura, T. (1976). Origin of brain macrophages and the nature of microglia. In H. Zimmerman (ed.), *Progress in Neuropathology*, vol. 3. London: Greve and Stratton: 1.

Fogelman, S. M., VanLenten, B. J., Hokom, M., Seager, J., Wong, H., Navab, M., Shapiro, S., Haberland, M. E. and Edwards, P. A. (1985). In R. van Furth (ed.), *Mononuclear Phagocytes; Characteristics, Physiology and Function.* Dordrecht, Boston, Lancaster: Martinus Nijhoff: 803–9.

Gartner, S., Markovitz, P., Markovitz, D. M., Kaplan, M. H., Gallo, R. C. and Popovic M., (1986). The role of mononuclear phagocytes in HTLV-III/LAV infection. *Science* 233: 215.

Godowski, P. J., Ruscuni, S., Misefeld, R. and Yamamoto, K. R. (1987). Glucocorticoid receptor mutants that are constitutive activators of transciptional enhancement. *Nature* 325: 368.

Gordon, S. (1986). Biology of the macrophage. *J. Cell Sci.* Suppl. 4: 267.

Gordon, S., Crocker, P., Morris, L., Lee, S. H., Perry, V. H. and Hume, D. (1986). Localisation and function of tissue macrophages. In *Biochemistry of Macrophages*, Ciba Fdn. Symp. 118, London: Pitman: 54–67.

Gough, N. M., Gough, J., Metcalf, D. *et al.* (1984). Molecular cloning of a cDNA encoding a murine haematopoietic growth regulator, granulocyte-macrophage colony stimulating factor. *Nature* 309: 763.

Hartung, M. P., Wolters, K. and Toyka, K. (1986). Substance P binding properties and studies on cellular responses in guinea pig macrophages. *J. Immun.* 136: 3826.

Hirsch, S., Austyn, J. M. and Gordon, S. (1981). Expression of the macrophage-specific antigen F4/80 during differentiation of mouse bone marrow cells in culture. *J. Exp. Med.* 154: 157. ·

Hume, D. A. and Gordon, S. (1985). The mononuclear phagocyte system of the mouse defined by immunohistochemical localisation of antigen F4/80. In R. van Furth (ed.), *Mononuclear Phagocytes: Characteristics, Physiology and Function.* Dordrecht, Boston, Lancaster: Martinus Nijhoff: 9–17.

Hume, D. A., Robinson, A. P., MacPherson, G. G. and Gordon, S. (1983). The immunohistochemical localisation of antigen F4/80: The relationship between macrophages, Langerhans cells, reticular cells and dendritic cells in lymphoid and hematopoietic organs. *J. Exp. Med.* 158: 1522.

Hume, D. A., Perry, V. H. and Gordon, S. (1984a). The histochemical localisation of a macrophage-specific antigen in developing mouse retina. Phagocytosis of dying neuron and differentiation of microglial cells to form a regular array in plexiform layers. *J. Cell Biol.* 97: 253.

Hume, D. A., Perry, V. H. and Gordon, S. (1984b). The mononuclear phagocyte system of the mouse defined by immunohistochemical localisation of antigen F4/80: macrophages associated with epithelia. *Anat. Rec.* 210: 503.

Jeffries, W. A., Greem, J. R. and Williams, A. F. (1985). Authentic T helper CD4 (W3/25) antigen on rat peritoneal macrophages. *J. Exp. Med.* 162: 117–27.

Johnson, W. J., Somers, S. D. and Adams, A. D. (1984). Expression and development of macrophage activation for tumor cytotoxicity. In D. O. Adams and M. G. Hanna Jr (eds), *Contemporary Topics in Immunobiology*, vol. 13. New York: Plenum Press: 127.

Kossard, S. and Nelson, D. S. (1968). Studies on cytophilic antibodies IV: The effects of protocytic enzymes (trypsin and papain) on the attachment to macrophages of cytophilic antibodies. *Aust. J. Exp. Biol. Med. Sci.* 46: 63.

Kupfer, A., Dennert, G. and Singer, S. J. (1985). The reorientation of the Golgi apparatus and the microtubule-organizing center in cytotoxic effector cell is a prerequisite in the lysis of bound targets. *J. Mol. Cell Immun.* 2: 37.

Lai A Fat, R. F. M. and van Furth, R. (1975). In vitro synthesis of some complement components (C1a, C3, & C4) by lymphoid tissues and circulating leukocytes in man. *Immunology* 28: 359.

Lane, F. C. and Unanue, E. R. (1972). Requirement of thymus (T) lymphocytes for resistance to listeriosis. *J. Exp. Med.* 135: 1104.

Lee, S. H., Crocker, P. and Gordon, S. (1986). Macrophage plasma membrane and secretory properties in murine malaria. Effects of *Plasmodium yoelii* infection on macrophages in the liver, spleen and blood. *J. Exp. Med.* 163: 54.

Lepay, D. A., Steinman, R. M., Nathan, C. F., Murray, H. W. and Cohn, Z. A. (1985). Liver macrophages in murine listeriosis: Cell-mediated immunity is correlated with an influx of macrophages capable of generating reactive oxygen intermediates. *J. Exp. Med.* 161: 491.

Lewis, V. A., Kock, T., Plutner, H. and Mellman, I. (1986). A complementary DNA clone for a macrophage-lymphocyte Fc receptor. *Nature* 324: 377.

Luster, A. D., Unkeless, J. C. and Ravetch, J. V. (1985). Interferon transcriptionally regulates an early-response gene containing homology to platelet proteins. *Nature* 315: 672.

Mackaness, S. B. (1970a). In R. van Furth (ed.), *Mononuclear Phagocytes.* Dordrecht, Boston, Lancaster: Martinus Nijhoff: 461.

Mackaness, S. B. (1970b). The mechanisms of macrophage activation. In S. Mudd (ed.), *Infectious Agents and Host Reactions.* Eastbourne: W. B. Saunders: 61.

Metcalf, D. (1984). *The Haematopoietic Colony Stimulating Factors* Amsterdam: Elsevier Science Publishers: 1–493.

Metchnikoff, E. (1905). *Immunity to Infectious Diseases.* New York: Cambridge University Press.

Nathan, C. F. (1985). Regulation of macrophage oxidative metabolism and antiparasitic activity. In R. van Furth (ed.), *Mononuclear Phagocytes: Characteristics, Physiology and Function.* Dordrecht, Boston, Lancaster: Martinus Nijhoff: 411–20.

Nathan, C. (1987). Macrophage secretion. *J. Clin. Invest.,* 79:319.

Perry, V. H., Hume, D. A. and Gordon, S. (1985). Immunohistochemical localisation of macrophages and microglia in the adult and developing mouse brain. *Neuroscience* 15: 313.

Ravage, J. V., Luster, D., Weinshank, R., Kochan, J. *et al.* (1986). Structural heterogeneity and functional domains of murine immunoglobin Fc receptors. *Science* 234: 718.

Roos, D., Bot, A. M., Van Schart, M., de Boer, M. and Daha, M. L. (1981). Interaction between human neutrophils and zymosan particles. The role of opsonins and divalent cations. *J. Immun.* 126: 433.

Ross G. D. (1985). Complement receptors. *Immunol. Today* 5: 686.

Ross G. D., Cain, J. A. and Lachmann, P. J. (1985). Membrane complement receptor type 3 (CR3) has lectin-like properties analogous to bovine conglutinin and functions as a receptor for zymosan and rabbit erythrocytes as well as a receptor for iC3b. *J. Immun.* 134: 3307–15.

Russell, D. and Wilhelm, H. (1986). Attachment of *Leishmania* promastigotes to macrophages inhibited by Fab fragments directed against a parasite glycoprotein gp. *J. Immun.* 136: 7613.

Sachs, L. (1980). Constitutive uncoupling of pathways of gene expression that control growth and differentiation in myeloid leukaemia: A model for origin and progression of malignancy. *Proc. Natl. Acad. Sci. (USA)* 77: 6152.

Scher, M., Beller, D. and Unanue, E. R. (1980). Demonstration of a soluble mediator that induces expression in Ia positive macrophages. *J. Exp. Med.* 152: 1684.

Schreiber, R. D. (1984). Identification of gamma interferon as a murine macrophage activating factor for tumor cytotoxicity. In D. O. Adams and M. G. Hanna Jr (eds), *Contemporary Topics in Immunobiology.* New York: Plenum Press: 171.

Scott, W. A., Paulowski, N. A., Murray, H., Andreach, M., Zrike, J. and Cohn, Z. A. (1982). Regulation of arachidonic acid metabolism by macrophage activation. *J. Exp. Med.* 155: 1148.

Sharma, S. D. and Remington, J. S. (1981). Macrophage activation and resistance to intracellular infection. *Lymphokines* 3: 181.

Silverstein, S. C., Steinman, R. M. and Cohn, Z. A. (1977). Endocytosis. *Ann. Rev. Biochem.* 46: 669.

Simon, H. and Sheagren, J. N. (1972). Enhancement of macrophage bactericidal capacity by antigenically stimulated immune lymphocytes. *Cell Immun.* 4: 163.

Stahl, P. D., Schlessinger, P. H., Sigardson, E., Rodman, J. S., Lee, Y-C. (1980). Receptor-mediated endocytosis of mannose glycoconjugates by macrophages: Characterization and evidence for receptor recycling. *Cell* 19: 207.

Stahl, P. D., Wileman, T. E. and Shephard, V. L (1984). The mannose receptor of macrophages: a current perspective. In R. van Furth (ed.), *Mononuclear Phagocytes: Characteristics, Physiology and Function.* Dordrecht, Boston, Lancaster: Martinus Nijhoff: 59–65.

Stecher, V. J., Morse, J. H. and Thorbecke, G. J. (1967). Sites of production of promate serum proteins associated with the complement system. *Proc. Soc. Exp. Biol. Med.* 124: 433.

Steeg, P. S., Moore, R. N., Johnson, H. M. and Oppenheim, J. J. (1982). Regulation of murine macrophage Ia antigen expression by a lymphokine with murine interferon activity. *J. Exp. Med.* 156: 1780.

Steinman, R. M., Nogueria, N., Witmer, D., Tydings, J. D. and Mellman, I. S. (1980). Lymphokine enhances the expression and synthesis of Ia antigens on cultured mouse peritoneal macrophages. *J. Exp. Med.* 152: 1248.

Sung, S. J., Nelson, R. S. and Silverstein, S. C. (1983). Yeast mannose inhibits binding and phagocytosis of zymosan by mouse peritoneal macrophages. *J. Cell Biol.* 96: 160.

Trinchieri, G. and Perussia, B. (1985). Immune interferon: a pleiotropic lymphokine with multiple effects. *Immun. Today* 6: 131.

Ugolina, V., Nuneg, G., Smith, R. G., Stastny, P. and Capra, J. D. (1980). Initial characterization of monoclonal antibodies against human monocytes. *Proc. Natl. Acad. Sci. (USA)* 77: 6764.

Unkeless, J., Fleit, H. and Mellman, I. S. (1981). Structural aspects and heterogeneity of immunoglobulin Fc receptors. *Adv. Immun.* 31: 247.

Van Furth, R., Diessenhoff-Den Dulk, M. M. C. and Mattie, H. (1983). Quantitative study on production and kinetics of mononuclear phagocytes during an acute inflammatory response. *J. Exp. Med.* 138: 1314.

Vlassara, H., Brownlee, M. and Cerami, A. (1984). Accumulation of diabetic rat peripheral nerve myelin by macrophages increases with the presence of advanced glycosylation end product. *J. Exp. Med.* 160: 197–207.

Volkman, A. and Gowans, J. L. (1963). The origin of macrophages from bone marrow in the rat. *Br. J. Exp. Path.* 46: 62–70.

Werb, Z., Banda, M. J., Takemura, R. and Gordon, S. (1986). Secreted proteins of resting and activated macrophages. In D. M. Weir, L. A. Herzenberg and L. A. Herzenberg (eds), *Handbook of Experimental Immunology*, 4th edn. Oxford: Blackwell Scientific Publications: 47.1–47.28.

Whaley, K: (1980). Biosynthesis of the complement components and regulatory proteins of the alternative complement pathway by human peripheral blood monocytes. *J. Exp. Med.* 151: 501.

Witmer, M. D. and Steinman, R. M. (1984). Immunocytochemical studies of human mononuclear phagocytes and dendritic cells. In R. van Furth, (ed.), *Mononuclear Phagocytes*. Dordrecht, Boston, Lancaster: Martinus Nijhoff: 41.

Wozencraft, A. D., Sayers, S. and Blackwell, J. M. (1986). Macrophage type 3 complement receptors mediate serum independent binding of *Leishmania donovani*. Detection of macrophage-derived complement on the parasite surface by immunoelectron microscopy. *J. Exp. Med.* 164: 1332.

Wright, S. D. and Griffin, F. M. Jr (1985). Activation of phagocytic cells' C3 receptors for phagocytosis. *J. Leuk. Biol.* 38: 327.

Wright, S. D. and Jong, M. T. C. (1986). Adhesion-promoting receptors on human macrophages recognize *Escherichia coli* by binding lipopolysaccharide. *J. Exp. Med.* 166: 1876.

Wright, S. D. and Silverstein, S. C. (1984). Phagocytosing macrophages exclude proteins from the zones of contact with opsonized targets. *Nature* 309: 359.

Wright, S. D., Licht, M. R., Craigmyle, L. S. and Silverstein, S. C. (1984). Communication between receptors for different ligands on a single cell: Ligation of fibronectin receptors induces a reversible alteration in the function of complement receptors on cultured human monocytes. *J. Cell Biol.* 99: 336.

Yamamoto, K. and Johnston, R. B. Jr (1984). Dissociation of phagocytosis from stimulation of the oxidative metabolic burst in macrophages. *J. Exp. Med.* 159: 405.

Yang, Y-C., Ciarletta, A. B., Temple, P. A. (1986). Human Il-3 (multi-CSF): identification by expression cloning of a novel hematopoietic growth factor related to murine IL-3. *Cell* 47: 3.

Young, J. D.-E. and Cohn, Z. A. (1985). Nature of transmembrane signal associated with binding to the macrophage. In R. van Furth (ed.), *Mononuclear Phagocytes: Characteristics, Physiology and Function*. Dordrecht, Boston, Lancaster: Martinus Nijhoff: 399–406.

Polymorphonuclear Leukocytes — The Neutrophil

J. GARY WHEELER

*Bowman Gray School of Medicine of
Wake Forest University, Winston-Salem, NC 27103, USA*

JON S. ABRAMSON

*Bowman Gray School of Medicine of
Wake Forest University, Winston-Salem, NC 27103, USA*

PAUL G. QUIE

*Department of Pediatrics
University of Minnesota, Minneapolis, MI 55455, USA*

NATURAL IMMUNITY
ISBN 0 12 5145551

I. INTRODUCTION

The neutrophil is a highly specialised phagocytic cell whose primary function is killing microbes which invade the host. The main events that occur when the neutrophil is stimulated can be categorised into chemotactic, secretory or oxidative responses. Each of these activities helps regulate the others, although certain stimuli at specific concentrations can induce one of these responses without the others (Weissman *et al.*, 1981). Preliminary events which occur before the onset of chemotactic, oxidative or secretory activities include: (1) ligand–membrane receptor interaction, (2) changes at the plasma membrane, (3) ionic fluxes, (4) alterations in the cytoskeleton, (5) changes in cyclic nucleotide levels, (6) initiation of arachidonic acid metabolism. Proteins produced by other types of leukocytes (i.e. lymphocytes, monocytes and macrophages) play an important role in controlling neutrophil activity. In this chapter the function of human neutrophils and the pathway by which preliminary events regulate chemotactic, secretory and oxidative activities of these cells will be discussed.

II. MATURATION

Maturation of neutrophils occurs within two frameworks: (1) the ontogeny of single cells and (2) the development of a mature organ response to microbial challenge.

Single cell development has been carefully delineated through morphological observations of normal and pathological bone marrow processes and the development of tissue culture methodology (see reviews by Wright, 1982; Bainton *et al.*, 1971; Quesenberry and Levitt, 1979; Golde, 1983). A consistent theme of these reports is that full differentiation is necessary for normal neutrophil function to be possible.

Neutrophils are derived from bone-marrow progenitor cells which are yet to be fully characterised. These cells are unipotent derivatives of pluripotent stem cells; i.e. they are committed to neutrophil differentiation. The first observable step in tissue differentiation is the development of the early promyelocyte also referred to as the eogranulocyte (Brederoo *et al.*, 1983). From this stage the earliest granule forms, nucleated granules, have been described. While this granule form is an accepted organelle in other species, the existence of a third granule type and its possible function in human neutrophils has only recently been confirmed (Wright, 1982; Breton-Gorius *et al.*, 1978; Scott and Horn, 1970).

The late promyelocyte develops next. It is characterised by primary or azurophilic cytoplasmic granules containing a variety of hydrolases, proteases, lysozyme and myeloperoxidase. With further cellular differentiation to the myelocytic stage, there is a loss of the deep blue appearance of the granules when stained with Wright-Giemsa, and acquisition of a more neutrophilic character. This change is caused by an increase in the number of secondary or specific granules. The specific staining character of the granules allows one to distinguish neutrophils from basophils and eosinophils. Specific granules of the neutrophil myelocyte contain lactoferrin and vitamin B12 binding protein and, in the mature cell, outnumber the azurophilic granules twofold. The neutrophil granules are generated in the Golgi complex and bud off from the endoplasmic reticulum. Abnormalities in the budding process are reported (e.g. the formation of giant coalesced granules in Chediak-Higashi disease). Early stages of neutrophil development are characterised by the presence of mitochondria and later stages by a proliferation of glycogen with few mitochondria. This change represents a shift from respiration to glycolysis as the major source of cell energy (Beck, 1958; Scott and Horn, 1970).

Granule maturation is undoubtedly accompanied by parallel maturation of glycoproteins on the cell surface and the development of membrane receptors, although little is known of this evolution. Promyelocytic cells of the HL-60 line lack complement receptors (CR3) and Fcγ receptors until the cells are stimulated to differentiate. Examination of bone-marrow samples shows that the Fcγ receptors are not present until the metamyelocyte stage (Fleit *et al.*, 1984) and correlation of neutrophil chemotaxis and degranulation with presence of surface receptors is recognised (Cotter and Henson, 1983; Fontana *et al.*, 1980). Excessive N-acetyl neuraminic acid on the surface of immature cells has been associated with a high negative surface charge inhibiting adhesion and cell–cell interactions (Lichtman and Weed, 1972). Clinical syndromes associated with membrane glycoprotein and receptor activity defects have been discussed by Anderson *et al.*, (1984), Kobayashi *et al.*, (1984), Boxer *et al.*, (1982a), Gallin *et al.*, (1982) and Arnaout *et al.*, (1982).

Other neutrophil functions correlate with maturation. For example, chemotaxis is reduced in early band forms compared with segmented forms (Boner *et al.*, 1982). Immature neutrophils are also more rigid and have delayed microbial ingestion compared with mature forms (Lichtman and Weed, 1972; Altman and Stossel, 1974).

A. Regulation of Neutrophil Numbers

Regulatory factors affect neutrophil differentiation in the bone marrow, determining stem-cell pool size, transformation of the dividing cells in the proliferating pool, and maturation of non-dividing cells. Colony-stimulating factors (CSFs) that activate neutrophil stem cells are part of a complex feedback system which can also involve humoral inhibitors ('chalones'), stimulants from mature monocytes and granulocytes, and cell–cell interaction in the bone-marrow stroma. Various pharmacological agents (e.g. lithium), microbial degradation products (especially endotoxin) and cellular products (e.g. lactoferrin and prostaglandin E) have been noted to inhibit or potentiate CSF activity. Human CSF can be produced by T-lymphocytes, macrophages and endothelial cells (Cline and Golde, 1979; Brennan *et al.*, 1980; Burgess and Metcalf, 1980).

Under physiologically stable conditions about 9–11 days are required for neutrophil maturation and release into the circulation. This estimate is based on generation times of 18 to 24 hours for myeloblasts and promyelocytes and 52 hours for myelocytes, and 96 to 144 hours for appearance in the circulation (Cronkite and Vincent, 1970; Fliedner *et al.*, 1964a,b). Under conditions of stress or infection the turnover time is accelerated; for example, in the neonate; reconstitution of the depleted marrow has occured in less than 24 hours (Christensen *et al.*, 1982; Wheeler *et al.*, 1984a). Once the granulocyte leaves the marrow, half-life in the circulation is 6 to 10 hours (Mauer *et al.*, 1960). Neutrophils have been shown to remain fully functional up to 28 hours when stored in CPD anticoagulated whole blood at 4°C (Wheeler *et al.*, 1984b; McCullough *et al.*, 1969).

B. Neutrophils in Neonates[1]

During fetal development, leukocytes are first produced in the liver at about two months' gestation. At about five months' gestation, the bone marrow assumes its role as the primary haemopoietic centre, and leukocyte production diminishes in the liver (Playfair *et al.*, 1963). Experimental animal models have shown that the bone-marrow neutrophil storage pool of premature and term neonates is considerably smaller

[1] See also Chapter 13

per kilogram than that of adults. Responses to infection in human neonates can cause rapid exhaustion of the storage pool and, in some cases, neutropenia (Christensen *et al.*, 1982; Erdman *et al.*, 1982). It is not yet known at what age the infant storage pool achieves normal adult size, or if attrition occurs with ageing.

In addition to the smaller numbers available, the neutrophils of neonates function abnormally compared with those of older children and adults, a factor which may contribute to the neonate's increased susceptibility to infection. Most studies of neonatal granulocyte function have been done on cord blood, which contains immature forms, and therefore interpretation of the data is difficult. Furthermore, the birth process may affect neutrophils (Frazier *et al.*, 1982). Acidosis, anaesthesia and maternal progesterone (Lippa *et al.*, 1983; White *et al.*, 1983; Cotton *et al.*, 1983) may contribute to neutrophil dysfunction in the peripheral blood of infants during the early hours after delivery.

Neutrophil chemotactic responsiveness is decreased in neonates, and neonatal serum is defective in chemotactic activity (Mohandes *et al.*, 1982; Miller, 1979; Anderson *et al.*, 1983; Sacchi *et al.*, 1982). Klein *et al.* (1977) have presented evidence that neutrophil chemotactic responsiveness does not reach normal adult standards until six years of age. These abnormalities may be more prominent in premature neonates. Abnormal distribution of binding sites on the cell surface and abnormal shape change after stimulation have been noted (Anderson *et al.*, 1981). Deformability, adherence and aggregation, functions necessary for normal chemotaxis, are also abnormal (Olson *et al.*, 1983; Fontan *et al.*, 1981; Krause *et al.*, 1982; Mease *et al.*, 1981).

Conflicting evidence has been presented for abnormalities of other functions of neutrophils in the neonatal period. Frazier *et al.* (1982) noted that neutrophils in cord blood from elective non-labour caesarean sections have normal quantitative nitro-blue tetrazolium reduction, oxygen consumption and hexose monophosphate shunt activity. In contrast, chemiluminescence (a measure of oxidative metabolic function) has been shown to be depressed 12–36 hours after birth (Mills *et al.*, 1979). Although respiratory functions are normal in the resting neutrophil, 'stressed' or stimulated neonatal neutrophils have decreased oxidative metabolism and killing when compared with those of adults (Mills *et al.*, 1979; Anderson *et al.*, 1974; W. C. Wright *et al.*, 1975; Shigeoka *et al.*, 1979). This finding may be explained by the increased immature forms that accompany the neonate's response to stress, or it may represent an independent cellular maturational defect. Phagocytosis has been shown to be normal or supernormal (Mills *et al.*, 1979; Harris *et al.*, 1983). Ambruso and Johnston (1981) have suggested that neutrophil lactoferrin levels are reduced in neonates. Calcium modulation, microtubular function, ATP modulation and other early activation steps, have yet to be thoroughly investigated.

While significant attention has been paid to the maturation of neutrophils at the beginning of life, only recently have efforts been focused on this process as a function of ageing.[2] Suzuki *et al.* (1983) demonstrated that degranulation decreases after the age of 50. Further studies are needed of the effects of aging on both neutrophil maturation and function.

III. NEUTROPHIL CHEMOTAXIS

Migration of neutrophils to sites of microbial invasion is a prerequisite for localising and eliminating infections. The states of cell movement include non-directed migration, stimulated non-directed migration (i.e. chemokinesis), and directed migration (i.e. chemotaxis). Differentiating between these responses is important since a patient's cells may have a defect in the machinery needed for cell movement, be unable to increase the rate of migration, or be incapable of directed migration to a chemoattractant. The type of biophysical defect occurring in the cell determines which of the migration responses will be impaired. Abnormalities of membrane glycoprotein receptors, cytoskeleton assembly, lysosomal granules and cyclic nucleotide levels have all been implicated in affecting chemotaxis (Gallin *et al.*, 1980).

A. Neutrophil Chemoattractants

The initial event in the chemotactic response is the generation of chemotactic stimuli. Chemotactic stimuli include C5a, a complement component generated during activation of the complement cascade, substances secreted from lymphocytes (i.e. lymphokines), arachidonic acid metabolites derived from the oxidation of lipid contained within the neutrophil plasma membrane, proteins involved in the coagulation pathway, and microbial components which can both initiate the complement cascade and induce chemotactic activity themselves. Synthetic oligopeptides (e.g. N-formyl-methionyl-leucyl-phenylalanine) similar to these microbial chemoattractants are potent chemotactic stimuli which have been used extensively to study the chemotactic response (Gallin *et al.*, 1980).

The chemoattractant attaches to a receptor on the plasma membrane of the cell. Most, if not all, chemotactic factors attach to receptors specific

---

[2] See also Chapter 12

for the given chemoattractant (Williams *et al.*, 1977; Harvath and Leonard, 1982; Fletcher and Gallin, 1983). Prior to ligand–receptor binding, neutrophils move in a random fashion, but once the chemoattractant has attached to plasma membrane receptors functional responses such as chemokinesis and chemotaxis can proceed. The neutrophil can sense a 1 per cent gradient from the front to the back of the cell and will move in the direction of the highest concentration of the chemoattractant (Zigmond, 1974; Zigmond, 1977). The oligopeptide chemotactic factor receptors exist in two affinity states (high and low) which are in part interconvertible. The convertibility of the receptor affinity helps determine the intensity of the chemotactic response and is regulated via guanine nucleotides (Snyderman, 1985). In vitro data suggest that fewer than 50 per cent of neutrophils migrate in response to chemoattractants and that the cells that migrate to different chemoattractants are from the same population. The structural or biochemical difference between the migrating and non-migrating cells is not known, but does not appear to be due to ligand–receptor binding (Harvath *et al.*, 1980; Harvath and Leonard, 1982).

B. Neutrophil Response To Chemoattractants

Once ligand–receptor binding occurs, activation of guanine nucleotide proteins, changes in transmembrane potential, shifts in ionic concentrations and cytoskeleton assembly occur. The cell shape becomes bipolar, specific granules associate with plasma membranes and discharge their contents into phagosomes and into the extracellular medium, and changes in cyclic nucleotide levels occur within the cell.

Within 10 seconds after ligand–receptor binding the electrical potential across the plasma membrane increases and the calcium associated with the membrane is mobilised. This change in transmembrane potential precedes alterations in the cytoskeleton, shape changes and degranulation (Weissmann *et al.*, 1981). Increased intracellular calcium levels derived from membrane-bound calcium stores appear to be necessary for stimulation of chemotaxis. Extracellular calcium is not required but may increase the response (Weissmann *et al.*, 1981).

C. Neutrophil Locomotion Machinery

Prior to directed migration, the cell changes its shape from spherical to bipolar. A wide undulating pseudopod containing large amounts of microfilament proteins is at the leading edge of the cell while at the back are the nucleus and long extending fibres (retraction fibres) by which the cell adheres to surfaces. The centriole, which is the organising centre for

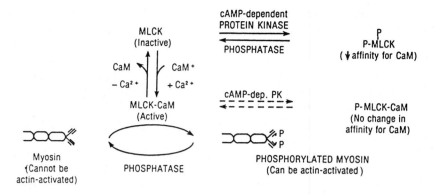

Fig. 2.1: Diagram showing the effects of phosphorylating the myosin hexamer. Phosphorylation is catalysed by a complex of MLCK and calcium-calmodulin (MLCK-CaM). MLCK (myosin light chain kinase) is itself a substrate for cAMP-dependent protein kinase. The rate and stoichiometry of MLCK phosphorylation depends on whether CaM is bound to MLCK. Reproduced from Adelstein, R. S. (1983), Regulation of contractile proteins by phosphorylation, *J. Clin. Invest.* 72: 1863–6.

the microtubule system, is found between the nucleus and the leading front of the cell (Malech *et al.*, 1977, Gallin *et al.*, 1980).

The neutrophil cytoskeleton is composed of microfilaments containing actin and myosin proteins, which provide contractile forces for cell movement (Figure 2.1). Actin has two linear polymers of a globular protein wrapped in a helix shape. Myosin is composed of large molecules which are asymmetrical. One end of the myosin molecule has a globular shape which binds to actin and has an enzymatic site that hydrolyses ATP. Contractile activity is regulated by the rate of hydrolysis of ATP which appears to be controlled by a calcium-calmodulin-dependent enzyme called myosin light chain kinase. Calmodulin contains four calcium-binding sites; it binds to myosin light chain kinase and initiates the phosphorylation of myosin. This increases the rate of ATP hydrolysis and causes contractile activity to occur with the sliding of actin and myosin filaments past each other (Adelstein, 1983). Microtubules which radiate from the centriole provide stability to the cytoskeleton, allowing movement of lysosomal granules and locomotion (Gallin *et al.*, 1980).

IV. NEUTROPHIL SECRETION

Lysosomal granules were thought to be involved solely in the killing and digestion of microbes ingested by the neutrophil. Recent evidence, however, suggests that lysosomal enzymes which associate with the plasma membrane and are secreted into the extracellular medium have an important role in regulating chemotactic activity. Lactoferrin from specific granules of neutrophils may contribute to chemotactic activities, since a patient who lacked specific granules had marked impaired adherence and chemotaxis (Boxer *et al.*, 1982a). Normal function was restored by the addition of lactoferrin to the patient's cells in vitro. Exocytosis of lactoferrin may contribute to neutrophil surface charges and adherence to endothelial cells (Oseas *et al.*, 1981; Boxer *et al.*, 1982b). Other secretory products may also affect neutrophil adherence and chemotaxis (Gordon *et al.*, 1979; Bockenstedt and Goetzl, 1980).

Secretion of neutrophil contents into inflammatory sites appears to contribute to regulation of the inflammatory response. Certain lysosomal enzymes cause cleavage of complement components (Ward and Hill, 1970; Wright and Gallin, 1975, 1977) and formation of C5a by activating the complement cascade (Wright and Gallin, 1975, 1977; Wright and Klock, 1979). Other proteases can inactivate a number of chemotactic factors including C5a (Venge and Olsson, 1975; Wright and Gallin, 1977). Therefore, neutrophil secretory factors can generate or inactivate chemotactic stimuli and thereby regulate migration of cells to sites of inflammation.

Another means whereby neutrophil localise at a site of infection is the process of deactivation. Cells undergoing vigorous degranulation (i.e. release of over 30 per cent of lysosomal enzymes) have decreased numbers of chemotactic receptors, and impaired chemotaxis. In cells undergoing limited degranulation these functions are enhanced (Gallin *et al.*, 1978a). Deactivated cells maintain the capacity to phagocytise and kill microbes (Gallin, 1982). Recent studies suggest that neutrophils have an intracellular pool of chemoattractant receptors many times greater than the number of surface receptors. These intracellular receptors are translocated to the surface when neutrophils are stimulated (Gallin and Seligmann, 1984).

V. NEUTROPHIL ADHERENCE

Adherence of neutrophils to a surface is required for normal chemotactic activity and is facilitated by ligand–receptor interaction (Smith *et al.*, 1979; Smith and Hollers, 1980; Gallin *et al.*, 1982). Reports of patients with absence of one or more high molecular weight protein complexes on leukocytes (Crowley *et al.*, 1980; Bowen *et al.*, 1982; Arnaout *et al.*, 1982; Anderson *et al.*, 1984; Kobayashi *et al.*, 1984) suggest that surface glycoproteins are necessary for various adhesion-dependent neutrophil functions including aggregation, orientation, phagocytosis and chemotaxis.

VI. NEUTROPHIL DEGRANULATION

Primary (azurophil) and secondary (specific) granules are found within human neutrophils and can be separated by density gradient centrifugation. There appear to be two distinct granule populations of azurophil granules with different densities, while specific granules have a relatively uniform density (Wright, 1982). The majority of granules in the neutrophil are secondary granules (Root and Cohen, 1981).

Degranulation is initiated by either ligand–receptor interaction or perturbation of the neutrophil membrane by stimuli, such as calcium ionophores, which do not require receptor activity. Secretion of primary and of secondary granules appear to be under separate controls since certain stimuli (e.g. phorbol myristate acetate) induce secretion of specific granules while other stimuli (e.g., N-formyl-methionyl-leucyl-phenylalanine) cause degranulation of both types of granules (Weissmann et al., 1981; Goldstein et al., 1975a). Degranulation occurs rapidly (within 15–60 seconds) after neutrophil stimulation. Specific granules are released before azurophil granules (Smolen et al., 1982).

A. Effectors of Neutrophil Degranulation

'Transmembrane signalling' is a term used to describe cellular events that occur after membrane perturbation. There are changes in electrochemical potential (Korchak and Weissmann, 1978; Seligmann and Gallin, 1980) which are followed by changes in the localisation of calcium and other ions within the cell. Intracellular calcium has a critical role in neutrophil degranulation. Increased concentrations of intracellular calcium are associated with degranulation (Weissmann et al., 1981; Korchak et al., 1980; Korchak and Weissmann, 1980; Seligmann and Gallin, 1980) and intracellular calcium antagonists inhibit the degranulation in neutrophils but degranulation can occur in the absence of extracellular calcium (Smolen et al., 1980). Calcium stores mobilised from stimulated sections of the plasma membrane are one of the main sources of intracellular calcium (Wick and Hepler, 1982; Hoffstein, 1979; Weissmann et al., 1981). Certain stimuli, such as phorbol myristate acetate, can induce neutrophil degranulation without shifts in the compartmentalisation of calcium, suggesting alternative methods of transmembrane signalling (Sha'afi et al., 1983). One such alternative mechanism may be the production of diacylglycerol in the plasma

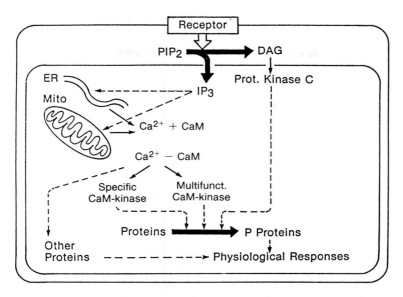

Fig. 2.2: General mechanisms by which Ca^2-mediated agonists produce their physiological responses. The scheme does not show the alterations in Ca^{2+} fluxes across the plasma membrane since their mechanisms are unknown. Examples of specific calmodulin-dependent protein kinases (CaM-kinases) are myosin light chain kinase and phosphorylase kinase. Other definitions are given in the text or in the legend to Fig. 2.1. Reproduced from Exton, J. H. (1985), Role of calcium and phosphoinositides in the actions of certain hormones and neurotransmitters, *J. Clin. Invest.* 75: 1753–7.

membrane (Exton, 1985). These intracellular messengers initiate neutrophil responses by activating protein kinases (e.g. protein kinase C) within the cytoplasm of the cell (Figure 2.2). Anions do not appear to contribute to transmembrane signalling.

Anions can alkalinise the intralysosomal pH and decrease degranulation by inhibiting the fusion of lysosomal granules with phagocytic vacuoles and the surface plasma membrane (Korchak *et al.*, 1980; Klempner and Styrt, 1983).

B. Regulation of Neutrophil Degranulation

A role for cyclic nucleotides and prostaglandins in inducing neutrophil degranulation has been postulated. Stimuli which elevate intracellular levels of cAMP decrease lysosomal secretion while agents which elevate cGMP levels augment degranulation in neutrophils (Zurier *et al.*, 1974).

This may be mediated through the effect of cyclic nucleotides on the affinity of surface receptors for ligands (Snyderman, 1985). Neutrophils can form prostaglandins by metabolising arachidonic acid. They can generate prostaglandins of the E and F series and thromboxane A2 via the cyclo-oxygenase pathway, and hydroxyeicosatetraenoic acid, hydroperoxyeicosatetraenoic acid and leukotrienes by the lipoxygenase pathway (Smolen *et al.*, 1982). Certain prostaglandins when added to neutrophils produce sustained elevations of cAMP and inhibit degranulation (Weissmann *et al.*, 1981), but a direct role for cyclic nucleotides and prostaglandins in regulating degranulation remains speculative.

Lysosomal granule contents are released into phagocytic vacuoles, or into the extracellular medium when granules fuse with the plasma membrane (Segal and Jones, 1980; Klempner and Styrt, 1983). Perturbation of neutrophil membranes is associated with assembly of microtubules (Goldstein *et al.*, 1975a, b; Hoffstein *et al.*, 1976; Oliver, 1978). The cytoskeletal apparatus appears to be important for transporting lysosomal granules to the plasma membrane. Agents which disrupt microtubule function alter the release of lysosomal enzymes (Zurier *et al.*, 1974; Hoffstein *et al.*, 1977). Additionally, neutrophils from a patient with recurrent infections had abnormal microtubule assembly, which was associated with diminished secretion of lysosomal granules in response to various stimuli (Gallin *et al.*, 1978b). While microtubules appear to be involved in granule translocation, the molecular basis for granule–membrane fusion is incompletely understood.

VII. NEUTROPHIL MICROBICIDAL FUNCTION

A. Oxygen-independent Mechanisms

Oxygen-independent mechanisms of microbial killing are important in neutrophils. Neutrophils from normal donors have bactericidal activity against a variety of micro-organisms even when the cells are placed in an anaerobic environment (Root and Cohen, 1981; Elsbach and Weiss, 1983) and patients with chronic granulomatous disease (in which the patients' phagocytic cells are unable to initiate oxidative activity) are capable of killing microbes to a limited extent. Non-oxidative microbicidal mechanisms include the following:

(1) activation of acid enzymes in phagosomes (Hirsch and Cohn, 1960; Mandell, 1970; Jensen and Bainton, 1973; Goldstein, 1976); some bacteria are killed by organic and lipophilic acids (Freese *et al.*, 1973) and acidification of phagosomes enhances the function of other oxygen-dependent and independent systems;

(2) deposition of lysozyme, elastase, collagenase and other neutral proteases in phagosomes; this is important for microbial degradation (Olsson *et al.*, 1978; Elsbach and Weiss, 1981) and in generating chemotactic and opsonic complement components (Goldstein, 1976; Root and Cohen, 1981);

(3) lactoferrin activity, which competes with bacteria for iron (Baggiolini *et al.*, 1970; Green *et al.*, 1971) and increases oxygen-dependent microbicidal activity by enhancing formation of hydroxyl radicals (Ambruso and Johnston, 1981); and

(4) deposition of cationic proteins onto bacteria, which causes loss of integrity of the bacterial outer membrane; these proteins have been labelled bactericidal/permeability-increasing proteins (BPI) (Elsbach and Weiss, 1983; Weiss *et al.*, 1982).

B. Microbial Evasion of Intracellular Killing

Some microbes can survive within the phagocytic cell by altering cellular degranulation. For example *Mycobacterium tuberculosis*[3], *Histoplasma capsulatum*[4], *Toxoplasma gondii*[5], *Neisseria gonorrhoeae* and *Chlamydia* species inhibit lysosome–phagosome fusion by secreting factors which inhibit fusion of lysosomes with phagosomes (Dumont and Robert, 1970; Jones and Hirsch, 1972; Goren *et al.*, 1976; Wyrick and Brownridge, 1978; Densen and Mandell, 1978; Wilson *et al.*, 1980). Lysosome–phagosome fusion is inhibited by *M. tuberculosis* through acidic sulfatides from this microbe which accumulate in granules (Goren *et al.*, 1976). *Salmonella typhimurium*[6] and *Mycobacterium lepraemurium*[7] can replicate within phagocytic cells despite lysosome–phagosome fusion since these organisms are resistant to the antimicrobial effects of lysosomal granules (Hart *et al.*, 1972; Carrol *et al.*, 1979). Neutrophils incubated with influenza A virus are incapable of secreting lysosomal enzymes into phagosomes which have subsequently phagocytised *Staphylococcus aureus*. Inhibition of degranulation by virus directly correlates with decreased bactericidal capacity (Abramson *et al.*, 1982). Various means by which microbes can alter the bactericidal capacity of phagocytic cells are shown in Table 2.1.

Neutrophils have been implicated in the pathogenesis of lung injury which occurs during infection, or from other causes associated with the adult respiratory distress syndrome. Secretion of neutrophil products, including lysosomal enzymes, oxygen radicals and arachidonic acid metabolites, appears to contribute to lung tissue damage. Although the

---

[3,4,5,6,7] Effective resistance to these organisms depends on macrophages, rather than neutrophils.

Table 2.1: Microbial perturbations of intraphagocytic microbicidal mechanisms

A. Inhibition of lysosome–phagosome fusion
   1. *Mycobacterium tuberculosis*[a]
   2. *Toxoplasma gondii*
   3. *Chlamydia psittaci*
   4. *Histoplasma capsulatum*
   5. *Neisseria gonorrheae*
   6. Influenza virus
   7. Sendai virus

B. Resistance to lysosomal enzymes
   1. *Mycobacterium lepraemurium*
   2. *Leishmania mexicana*
   3. *Salmonella typhimurium*

C. Exotoxin-induced cytotoxicity
   1. *Pseudomonas aeruginosa*
   2. *Staphylococcus aureus*

D. Inhibition of phagocyte oxidative response
   1. *Legionella pneumophilia*[b]
   2. *Listeria monocytogenes*
   3. *Salmonella typhi*

E. Inhibition of phagocyte function by bacterial adenylate cyclase
   1. *Bordetella pertussis*

F. Inhibition of lysosome–phagosome fusion and phagocyte oxidative response
   1. Influenza A virus

Notes:

[a] By bacterial sulfatide.
[b] By toxin.

Reproduced with permission from Quie, P. G. (1983), Perturbation of the normal mechanisms of intraleukocyte killing of bacteria, *J. Infect. Dis.* 148: 189–93.

lung matrix is rich in protease inhibitors and other inhibitors, pulmonary damage may result from excessive secretion of neutrophil lysosomal enzymes and oxygen radicals, resulting in a vicious cycle of influx of inflammatory cells and capillary leakage of fluid (Hammerschmidt, 1983).

C. Oxidative Metabolism And Microbial Killing

Neutrophils possess a potent array of microbicidal mechanisms which are effective against a broad spectrum of microbes. The products of oxidative metabolism are among the most important of these defences.

Phagocytosis of micro-organisms was first related to O_2 consumption in 1933 (Baldridge and Gerald, 1933). The role of oxygen in microbial killing was, however, not appreciated until patients with chronic granulomatous disease were found to have a defective oxidative metabolic response during phagocytosis. Since that observation, considerable effort has been directed towards determining the mechanisms by which oxygen metabolites participate in killing micro-organisms.

As noted previously, when a neutrophil responds to a chemotactic stimulus, a membrane–ligand interaction occurs resulting in chemotactic activity. The very same stimulus in higher concentrations can inhibit cell movement and lead to activation of the oxidative pathway and hexose monophosphate shunt. Depending on the nature of the stimulant, preactivation state, and maturity of the cell, the neutrophil responds by increasing fluid pinocytosis, phagocytosis, oxidative metabolism and/or degranulation (Karnovsky and Badwey, 1983).

Typically, neutrophils are activated by membrane contact with the surface of a microbe (see Figure 2.3). Avid attachment occurs when the microbes are opsonised by complement or antibody and bind to the neutrophil by C3b and Fc membrane receptors respectively. In addition to their receptor-mediated action, complement and antibody reduce bacterial hydrophilia and allow closer approximation of microbe and neutrophil (Van Oss *et al.*, 1975). Physical properties of particle–surface relationships may contribute to bacterial pathogenicity by inhibiting attachment and phagocytosis by neutrophils (Kreutzer, 1979). Thus nonpathogenic bacterial species tend to be hydrophobic, and their attachment and uptake is fairly efficient without opsonisation.

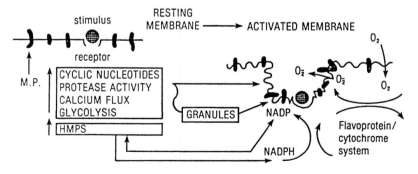

Fig. 2.3: Oxygen radical generation resulting from membrane stimulation. Stimulus–receptor interaction at the neutrophil membrane surface leads to changes in electrolyte and cyclic nucleotide flux with concurrent kinase and glycolysis activation. The membrane and membrane proteins (MP) become activated leading to increased oxygen consumption and hexose monophosphate shunt activity. See text for details.

Interaction of a ligand and a neutrophil membrane receptor is followed within seconds by changes in transmembrane potential (Weissmann *et al.*, 1978). Further alterations in the plasma membrane lead to conformational change, translocation, and activation of membrane-associated enzymes and proteins. Liberation of arachidonate and other lipid products of the phosphatidylinositol cycle, increases of cyclic nucleotides, calcium flux and glycogenolysis follow rapidly (Weisdorf *et al.*, 1982; Hallett and Campbell, 1983; Simchowitz *et al.*, 1983; Volpi *et al.*, 1983; Berridge and Irvine, 1984). As a result of some combination of these events, an oxidase enzyme system is activated, the function of which is to convert O_2 from the cellular environment to O_2^- (superoxide). Leading contenders for the mechanism by which the oxidase is activated include phosphorylation of a regulatory protein (McPhail and Snyderman, 1984) or release of membrane-bound Ca^{2+} and Mg^{2+} (Karnovsky and Badwey, 1983).

Neutrophil oxidase activity is found in the membrane of stimulated neutrophils; however, certain components of the oxidase may be transported from granules to the plasma membrane during cell stimulation (Borregaard *et al.*, 1983). It appears that all the components of the oxidase must be assembled for efficient reduction of O_2 to O_2^-. Our present understanding suggests that the oxidase system includes a flavoprotein, an ubiquinone and a cytochrome which provide a redox gradient down which single electrons can flow (Karnovsky and Badwey, 1983; Borregaard *et al.*, 1983; Gabig and Lefker, 1985). The hexose monophosphate shunt (HMPS) provides the electrons for the cascade (Booregaard *et al.*, 1984) in the form of regenerated NADPH or NADH. The oxidase activity is cyanide-resistant (non-mitochondrial) and the major substrate is felt to be NADPH (Patriarca *et al.*, 1971). Oxidase activity results in the conversion of O_2 to O_2^-. Metabolism of superoxide, by superoxide dismutase (SOD) (reaction 1 below), by spontaneous dismutation or through other reactions, results in toxic oxygen metabolites:

$$O_2^- + O_2^- + 2H^+ \xrightarrow{\text{SOD}} H_2O_2 + O_2 + ?O_2^1 \qquad (1)$$

(superoxide)   (hydrogen   (singlet
                                peroxide)   oxygen)

$$H_2O_2 \xrightarrow{\text{CATALASE}} H_2O + O_2 \qquad (2)$$

$$O_2^- + H_2O_2 \xrightarrow{\text{LACTOFERRIN?}} OH\cdot + OH^- + O_2 + ?O_2^1 \qquad (3)$$

(hydroxyl radical
and ion)

$$Cl^-(I^-) + H_2O_2 \xrightarrow{\text{MPO}} HOCl^-(HOI^-) + H_2O \qquad (4)$$

(oxyhalide)

While 90% of oxygen consumption leads to H_2O_2 production (Reiss and Roos, 1978), unstable intermediaries such as the hydroxyl radical $(OH\cdot)$ and singlet oxygen (O_2^1) may be important in microbial killing. Lactoferrin (a specific granule component) may have an important role in $OH\cdot$ generation, as shown in reaction (3) (Ambruso and Johnston, 1981). Myeloperoxidase (an azurophilic granule component) appears both to modulate the generation of O_2^- (Stendahl *et al.*, 1984) and to catalyse the generation of oxyhalides (reaction 4). Thus, degranulation is intimately involved in the regulation of the respiratory burst. (For more complete reviews of this subject see: Root and Cohen, 1981; Klebanoff, 1982; Karnovsky and Badwey, 1983; Babior, 1984).

Neutrophil microbicidal assays performed in anaerobic conditions suggest that oxidative mechanisms are important for bacterial killing. Certain organisms (e.g. *S. aureus*) are poorly killed by neutrophils under anaerobic conditions (Mandell, 1974). Bacteria with high intrinsic levels of superoxide dismutase (Johnston *et al.*, 1975) and catalase activity (Mandell, 1975) are less effectively killed by oxygen metabolites. Scavengers of H_2O_2 and of the oxygen radicals O_2^-, $OH\cdot$ and singlet oxygen (O_2^1) depress bacterial killing (Johnston *et al.*, 1975; Mandell, 1975; Repine *et al.*, 1981; Krinsky, 1974). These data support the role of oxygen metabolites as potent microbicidal agents.

D. Modulators Of Neutrophil Oxidative Metabolism

The neutrophil protects itself by releasing oxygen radicals into phagosomes or into the extracellular space (Babior,1984). It is thought that extracellular release occurs only at points of microbial contact (Ohno *et al.*, 1982)   an important observation for non-phagocytosable microorganisms such as fungi (Babior, 1984). If oxygen radicals in small amounts leak into the cytoplasm, catalase, superoxide dismutase and the glutathione reductase system prevent autolysis. However, cell death can occur after the cell is maximally stimulated. Oxidative effects on the plasma membrane are likely to contribute to this.

VIII. INTERACTION OF NEUTROPHILS WITH OTHER IMMUNE COMPONENTS

The neutrophil has a pre-eminent role in host immunity, initiating some of the earliest responses to microbes and foreign materials. It fulfils much of this activity as an independent cell, i.e. it can encounter certain foreign substances, process and destroy them without the presence of co-operating cells. In overall host immunity, however, the neutrophil is a directed, modulated cell working as a travelling mercenary, ready to intercede in 'self'-defence wherever or whenever called upon. Recently, the ways the neutrophil can interact with other arms of the immune system have been recognised to be extensive and complex.

Certain neutrophil products have been shown to affect the rest of the immune system. Myeloperoxidase and hydrogen peroxide decrease NK antitumour activity (El-Hag and Clark, 1984) and leukotriene B_4 decreases T cell mobilisation, differentiation and lymphokine generation (Goetzl, 1983 and Valone, 1984). These are examples of how neutrophils can impair cell-mediated immunity and have detrimental effects in sites of chronic inflammation. On the other hand, products of specific granules have been shown to activate the complement pathway, releasing C5a and thereby enhancing the inflammatory process (Gallin, 1984).

Several humoral products of the immune system act on neutrophils. Factors with interleukin 1 activity can, in doses insufficient to cause fever, produce leukocytosis in patients and can influence oxidative-metabolic, chemotactic and degranulation functions of neutrophils in vitro (Klempner *et al.*, 1978; Oppenheim and Gery, 1982; Luger *et al.*, 1983; Saunder *et al.*, 1984; Dinarello, 1984a, b). Interferons may have modest effects on neutrophil function in vivo and in vitro, although in one study no effect of recombinant interferon alpha was found in vitro (Jarstrand and Einhorn, 1983; Farr *et al.*, 1983; Einhorn and Jarstrand, 1984). Finally, a product of lymphocytes characterised only as a lymphokine has been isolated and shown to aggregate neutrophils (Badenoch-Jones, 1984).

Products of arachidonate metabolism, which play a major role in the inflammatory responses, have been recognised to influence neutrophil function. Exogenous arachidonate itself can initiate the respiratory burst and subsequent decreases in chemotaxis and phagocytosis (Henricks *et al.*, 1984). Prostaglandin E_1 decreases chemoattractant-induced secretion of neutrophils following in vivo infusion, while lipoxygenase products, such as LTB4 and di-HETEs, increase neutrophil responses by forming calcium channels in the plasma membrane (Serhan *et al.*, 1983; Naccache *et al.*, 1984; Valone, 1984; Palmblad *et al.*, 1984; Shak *et al.*, 1983). Other systems such as the complement cascade and the kallikrein system increase neutrophil aggregation and activate neutrophils (Craddock *et al.*, 1977; Colman, 1984). Platelet-activating factor has independent and synergistic effects with other lipid products in increasing neutrophil degranulation (O'Flaherty, 1985). The ability of complement components (C3b) and antibody to promote similar phagocytic responses is well known. Mast cells can release chemotactic factors which call forth neutrophils to sites of immediate hypersensitivity reactions. This recruitment is thought to account for neutrophil participation in the late phase reaction following mast cell degranulation (Larsen,1985).

A. Neutrophil Autoregulation

Chemotactic factors are degraded by products or the neutrophil oxidative-metabolic burst which regulates influx of these cells (Clark, 1982). By activating arachidonate metabolism, neutrophils generate prostaglandins, which decrease neutrophil chemotaxis (Kalmar and Gergely, 1983; Fantone *et al.*, 1981), or LTB4, which increases chemotaxis (Valone, 1984). By secreting specific granule contents, neutrophils can activate fibronectin and increase their own adherence to endothelial cells. Most of the products of primary granules are released at the time of neutrophil death, thus maximising their degrading influence on locally released chemoattractants (Gallin, 1984).

An indirect effect of humoral factors on neutrophils occurs through the regulation of granulopoiesis. Interferons have been shown to have both positive and negative effects on granulopoiesis in vitro (Muller *et al.*, 1984; Ball *et al.*, 1984). Interleukin 1 is thought to influence granulopoiesis (Kampschmidt and Upchurch, 1977) and complement has indirectly been demonstrated to cause neutrophilia in vivo (Mitchell *et al.*, 1982). Neutrophil colony-stimulating activity has been discussed above and ascribed to products of T cells, endothelial cells and macrophages. This can be further modulated by E-series prostaglandins and lactoferrin (Bagby *et al.*, 1983; Brennan *et al.*, 1980). Interestingly, it has been shown that a T cell product with colony-stimulating activity also has activating effects on neutrophils, resulting in increased oxidative metabolism following stimulation (Weisbart *et al.*, 1985).

The neutrophil, therefore, while possessing certain independent features, also acts in concert with other components of the immune system. Neutrophils respond to complex signals released from inflammatory sites, and these cells are also regulated by specific adaptive responses of humoral and cell-mediated immunity.

REFERENCES

Abramson, J. S., Lewis, J. C., Lyles, D. S., Heller, K. A., Mills, E. L. and Bass, D. A. (1982). Inhibition of neutrophil lysosome–phagosome fusion associated with influenza virus infection in vitro: role in depressed bactericidal activity. *J. Clin. Invest.* 69: 1393–7.

Adelstein, R. S. (1983). Regulation of contractile proteins by phosphorylation. *J. Clin. Invest.* 72: 1863–6.

Altman, A. J. and Stossel, T. P. (1974). Functional immaturity of bone marrow bands and polymorphonuclear granulocytes. *Brit. J. Haematol.* 27: 241–5.

Ambruso, D. R. and Johnston, R. B. (1981). Lactoferrin enhances hydroxyl radical production by human neutrophils, neutrophil particulate fractions, and an enzymatic generating system. *J. Clin. Invest.* 67: 352–60.

Anderson, D. C., Pickering, L. K. and Feigen, R. D. (1974). Leukocyte function in normal and infected neonates. *J. Pediatr.* 85: 420–5.

Anderson, D. C., Hughes, B. J. and Smith, C. W. (1981). Abnormal mobility of neonatal polymorphonuclear leukocytes: relationship to impaired redistribution of surface adhesion sites by chemotactic factor or colchicine. *J. Clin. Invest.* 68: 863–74.

Anderson, D. C., Hughes, B. J., Edwards, M. S., Buffone, G. J. and Baker, C. J. (1983). Impaired chemotaxigenesis by type III group B streptococci in neonatal sera: relationship to diminished concentration of specific anticapsular antibody and abnormalities of serum complement. *Pediatr. Res.* 17: 496–502.

Anderson, D. C., Schmalstieg, F. C., Arnaout, M. A., Kohl, S., Tosi, M. F., Dana, N., Buffone, G. J., Hughes, B. J., Brinkley, B. R., Dickey, W. D., Abramson, J. S., Springer, T., Boxer, L. A., Hollers, J. M. and Smith, C. W. (1984). Abnormalities of polymorphonuclear leukocyte function associated with a heritable deficiency of a high molecular weight surface glycoproteins (GP 138). *J. Clin. Invest.* 74: 536–51.

Arnaout, M. A., Pitt, J., Cohen, H. J., Melamed, J., Rosen, F. S. and Colten, H. R. (1982). Deficiency of a granulocyte-membrane glycoprotein (gp150) in a boy with recurrent bacterial infections. *N. Engl. J. Med.* 306: 693–9.

Arnold, R. R., Brewer, M. and Gauthier, J. J. (1980). Bactericidal activity of human lactoferrin: sensitivity of a variety of microorganisms. *Infect. Immun.* 28: 893–9.

Babior, B. M. (1984). Oxidants from phagocytes: agents of defense and destruction. *Blood* 64: 959–66.

Badenoch-Jones, P. (1984). Lymphokine-induced macrophage and neutrophil aggregation. In (ed.), Edgar Pick, *Lymphokines*, vol. 9. Academic Press, Orlando: 337–50.

Bagby, G. C. Jr, McCall, E. and Layman, D. L. (1983). Regulation of colony-stimulating activity production. Interactions of fibroblasts, mononuclear phagocytes, and lactoferrin. *J. Clin. Invest.* 71: 340–4.

Baggiolini, M., DeDuve, C., Masson, P. L. and Heremans, J. F. (1970). Association of lactoferrin with specific granules in rabbit heterophil leukocytes. *J. Exp. Med.* 131: 559–70.

Bainton, D. F., Ullyot, J. L. and Farquhar, M. G. (1971). The development of neutrophilic polymorphonuclear leukocytes in human bone marrow. *J. Exp. Med.* 134: 907–34.

Baldridge, C. W. and Gerard, R. W. (1933). The extra respiration of phago-cytosis. *Am. J. Physiol.* 133: 235–6.

Ball, E. D., Guyre, P. M., Shen, L., Glynn, J. M., Maliszewski, C. R., Baker, P. E. and Fanger, M. W. (1984). Gamma interferon induces monocytoid differen-tiation in the HL-60 cell line. *J. Clin. Invest.* 73: 1072–7.

Beck, W. S. (1958). The control of leukocyte glycolysis. *J. Biol. Chem.* 232: 252–70.

Berridge, M. J. and Irvine, R. F. (1984). Inositol trisphosphate, a novel second messenger in cellular signal transduction. *Nature* 312: 315–21.

Bockenstedt, L. K. and Goetzl, E. J. (1980). Constituents of human neutrophils that mediate enhanced adherence to surfaces. *J. Clin. Invest.* 65: 1372–81.

Boner, A., Zeligs, B. J. and Bellanti, J. A. (1982). Chemotactic responses of various differentiational stages of neutrophils from human cord and adult blood. *Infect. and Immun.* 35: 921–8.

Borregaard, N., Heiple, J. M., Simons, E. R. and Clark, R. A. (1983). Subcellular localization of the b-cytochrome component of the human neutrophil micro-bicidal oxidase: translocation during activation. *J. Cell. Biol.* 97: 52–61.

Borregaard, N., Schwartz, J. H. and Tauber, A. I. (1984). Protein secretion by stimulated neutrophils. *J. Clin. Invest.* 74: 455–9.

Bowen, T. J., Ochs, H. D., Altman, L. C., Price, T. H., VanEpps, D. E., Brautigan, D. L., Rosin, R. E., Perkins, W. D., Babior, B. M., Klebanoff, S. J. and Wedgwood, R. J. (1982). Severe recurrent bacterial infections associated with defective adherence and chemotaxis in two patients with neutrophils deficient in a cell-associated glycoprotein. *J. Pediatr.* 101: 932–40.

Boxer, L. A., Coates, T. D., Haak, R. A., Wolach, J. B., Hoffstein, S. and Baehner, R. L. (1982a). Lactoferrin deficiency associated with altered granulocyte func-tion. *N. Engl. J. Med.* 307: 404–10.

Boxer, L. A., Haak, R. A., Yang, H. H., Wolach, J. B., Whitcomb, J. A., Butterick, C. J. and Bachner, R. L. (1982b). Membrane-bound lactoferrin alters the surface properties of polymorphonuclear leukocytes. *J. Clin. Invest.* 70: 1049–57.

Brederoo, P., van der Meulen, J. and Mommaas-Kienhuis, A. M. (1983). Development of the granule population in neutrophil granulocytes from human bone marrow. *Cell Tissue Res.* 234: 469–96.

Brennan, J. K., Lichtman, M. A., DiPersio, J. F., and Abboud, C. N. (1980). Che-mical mediators of granulopoiesis: A review. *Exp. Hematol.* 8: 441–64.

Breton-Gorius, J., Coquin, Y. and Guichard, J. (1978). Cytochemical distinction between azurophils and catalase-containing granules in leukocytes. *Lab. Invest.* 38: 21–31.

Burgess, A. W. and Metcalf, D. (1980). The nature and action of granulo-cyte–macrophage colony stimulating factors. *Blood* 56: 947–58.

Carrol, M. E., Jackett, P. S., Aber, V. R. and Lowrie, D. B. (1979). Phagolysosome formation, cyclic adenosine 3, 5–monophosphate and the fate of *Salmonella typhimurium* within mouse peritoneal macrophages. *J. Gen. Microbiol.* 110: 421–9.

Christensen, R. D., Rothstein, G., Anstall, H. B. and Bybee, B. (1982). Granulocyte transfusions in neonates with bacterial infection, neutropenia and depletion of mature marrow neutrophils. *Pediatrics* 70: 1–6.

Clark, R. A. (1982). Chemotactic factors trigger their own oxidative inactivation by human neutrophils. *J. Immunol.* 129: 2725–8.

Cline, M. J. and Golde, D. W. (1979). Cellular interactions in hematopoieses. *Nature* 277: 177–81.

Colman, R. W. (1984). Surface-mediated defense reactions. The plasma contact activation system. *J. Clin. Invest.* 73: 1249–53.

Cotter, T. G. and Henson, P. M. (1983). A cell surface differentiation antigen involved in human neutrophil chemotaxis and degranulation. *Clin. Exp. Immunol.* 53: 249–53.

Cotton, D. J., Seligmann, B., O'Brien, W. F. and Gallin, J. I. (1983). Selective defect in human neutrophil superoxide anion generation elicited by the chemoattractant n-formyl-methionyl-leucyl-phenylalanine in pregnancy. *J. Infect. Dis.* 148: 194–9.

Craddock, P. R., Hammerschmidt, D., White, J. G., Dalmasso, A. P. and Jacob, H. S. (1977). Complement (C5a)-induced granulocyte aggregation in vitro. *J. Clin. Invest.* 60: 260–4.

Cronkite, E. P. and Vincent, P. V. (1970). Granulocytopoiesis in hemopoietic cellular proliferation. In F. Stohlman, (ed.), *Hematopoietic Cellular Proliferation.* New York: Grune and Stratton: 211–28.

Crowley, C. A., Curnutte, J. T., Rosin, R. E., Andre-Schwartz, J., Gallin, J. I., Klempner, J. R., Snyderman, R., Southwick, F. S., Stossel, T. P. and Babior, B. M. (1980). An inherited abnormality of neutrophil adhesion: its genetic transmission and its association with a missing protein. *N. Engl. J. Med.* 302: 1163–8.

Densen, P. and Mandell, G. L. (1978). Gonococcal interactions with polymorphonuclear neutrophils: Importance of the phagosome for bactericidal activity. *J. Clin. Invest.* 62: 1161–71.

Dinarello, C. A. (1984a). Interleukin-1. *Rev. Infect. Dis.* 6: 51–95.

Dinarello, C. A. (1984b). Interleukin-1 as mediator of the acute-phase response. *Surv. Immunol. Res.* 3: 29–33.

Dumont, A. and Robert, A. (1970). Electron microscopic study of phagocytosis of *Histoplasma capsulatum* by hamster peritoneal macrophages. *Lab. Invest.* 23: 278–86.

Einhorn, S. and Jarstrand, C. (1984). Functions of human neutrophilic granulocytes after *in vivo* exposure to interferon alpha. *Infect. Immun.* 43: 1054–7.

El-Hag, A. and Clark, R. A. (1984). Down-regulation of human natural killer activity against tumors by the neutrophil myeloperoxidase system and hydrogen peroxide. *J. Immunol.* 133: 3291–7.

Elsbach, P. and Weiss, J. (1981). Oxygen-independent bactericidal systems of polymorphonuclear leukocytes. *Inflammation Res.* 2: 95–113.

Elsbach, P. and Weiss, J. (1983). A reevaluation of the roles of the oxygen-dependent and oxygen-independent microbicidal systems of phagocytes. *Rev. Infect. Dis.* 5: 843–53.

Erdman, S. H. Christensen, R. D., Bradley, P. P. and Rothstein, G. (1982). Supply and release of storage neutrophils. *Biol. Neonate* 41: 132–7.

Exton, J. H. (1985). Role of calcium and phosphoinositides in the actions of certain hormones and neurotransmitters. *J. Clin. Invest.* 75: 1753–7.

Fantone, J. C., Kunkel, S. L. and Ward, P. A. (1981). Suppression of human polymorphonuclear function after intravenous infusion of prostaglandin E1. *Prostaglandins Leukotrienes Med.* 7: 195–8.

Fantone, J. C., Marasco, W. A., Elgas, L. J. and Ward, P. A. (1983). Anti-inflammatory effects of prostaglandin E_1: *In vivo* modulation of the formyl peptide chemotactic receptor on the rat neutrophil. *J. Immunol.* 130: 1495–7.

Farr, B., Gwaltney Jr., J. M., Hayden, F. G. and Mandell, G. L. (1983). Human polymorphonuclear neutrophil functions are unaffected by human interferon-alpha$_2$. *Infect. Immun.* 42: 1195–7.

Fleit, H. B., Wright, S. D., Durie, C. J., Valinsky, J. E. and Unkeless J. C. (1984). Ontogeny of Fc receptors and complement receptor (CR3) during human myeloid differentiation. *J. Clin. Invest.* 73: 516–25.

Fletcher, M. P. and Gallin J. I. (1983). Human neutrophils contain an intracellular pool of putative receptors for the chemoattractant N-formyl-methionyl-leucyl-phenylalanine. *Blood* 62: 792–9.

Fliedner, T. M., Cronkite, E. P. and Robertson, J. S. (1964a). Granulopoiesis: I: Senescence and random loss of neutrophilic granulocytes in human beings. *Blood* 24: 402–14.

Fliedner, T. M., Cronkite, E. P., Killmann, S. A. and Bond, VP. (1964b). Granulopoiesis: II: Emergence and pattern of labeling of neutrophilic granulocytes in humans. *Blood* 24: 683–700.

Fontan, G., Lorente, F., Garcia Rodriguez, M. C. and Ojeda, J. A. (1981). *In vitro* human neutrophil movement in umbilical cord blood. *Clin. Immunol. and Immunopath.* 20: 224–30.

Fontana, J. A., Wright, D. G., Schiffman, E., Corcoran, B. A. and Deisseroth, A. B. (1980). Development of chemotactic responsiveness in myeloid precursor cells: studies with a human leukemia cell line. *Proc. Natl. Acad. Sci. USA* 77: 3364–8.

Frazier, J. P., Cleary, T. G., Pickering, L. K., Kohl, S. and Ross, P. J. (1982). Leukocyte function in healthy neonates following vaginal and cesarean section deliveries. *J. Pediatr.* 101: 269–72.

Freese, E., Sheu, C. W. and Galliers, E. (1973). Function of lipophilic acids as antimicrobial food additives. *Nature* 241: 321–5.

Gabig, T. G. and Lefker, B. A. (1985). Activation of the human neutrophil NADPH oxidase results in coupling of electron carrier function between ubiquinone-10 and cytochrome b559. *J. Biol. Chem.* 260: 3991–5.

Gallin, J. I. (1982). Role of neutrophil lysosomal granules in the evolution of the inflammatory response. In M. L. Karnovsky and L. Bolis (eds.), *Phagocytosis–Past and Future.* New York: Academic Press: 519–41.

Gallin, J. I. (1984). Neutrophil specific granules: A fuse that ignites the inflammatory response. *Clin. Res.* 32: 320–8.

Gallin, J. I. and Seligmann, B. E. (1984). Mobilization and adaption of human neutrophil chemoattract f-Met-Leu-Phe receptors. *Fed. Proc.* 43: 2732–6.

Gallin, J. I., Wright, D. G. and Schiffmann, E. (1978a). Role of secretory events in modulating human neutrophil chemotaxis. *J. Clin. Invest.* 62: 1364–74.

Gallin, J. I., Malech, H. L., Wright D. G., Whisnant, J. K. and Kirkpatrick, C. H. (1978b). Recurrent severe infections in a child with abnormal leukocyte function: possible relationship to increased microtubule assembly. *Blood* 51: 919–33.

Gallin, J. I., Wright, D. G., Malech, H. L., Davis, J. M., Klempner, M. S. and Kirkpatrick, C. H. (1980). Disorders of phagocyte chemotaxis. *Ann. Intern. Med.* 92: 520–38.

Gallin, J. I., Fletcher, M. P., Seligmann, B. E., Hoffstein, S., Cehrs, K. and Mounessa, N. (1982). Human neutrophil-specific granule deficiency: A model to assess the role of neutrophil-specific granules in the evolution of the inflammatory response. *Blood* 59: 1317–29.

Goetzl, E. J. (1983). Leukocyte recognition and metabolism of leukotrienes. *Fed. Proc.* 42: 3128–31.

Golde, D. W. (1983). Production, distribution and fate of neutrophils. In W. J. Williams, E. Beutler, A. J. Erslev and M. A. Lichtman (eds), *Hematology,* 3rd edn. New York: McGraw-Hill: 759–65.

Goldstein, I. M. (1976). Polymorphonuclear leukocyte lysosomes and immune tissue injury. *Prog. Allergy* 20: 301–40.

Goldstein, I. M., Hoffstein, S. T. and Weissmann, G. (1975a). Mechanisms of lysosomal enzyme release from human polymorphonuclear leukocytes: Effects of phorbol myristate acetate. *J. Cell Biol.* 66: 647–52.

Goldstein, I. M., Roos, D., Weissmann, G. and Kaplan, H. (1975b). Complement and immunoglobulin stimulate superoxide production by human leukocytes independently of phagocytosis. *J. Clin. Invest.* 56: 1155–63.

Gordon, L. I., Douglas, S. D., Kay, N. E., Yamada, O., Osserman, E. F. and Jacob, H. S. (1979). Modulation of neutrophil function by lysozyme. *J. Clin Invest.* 64: 226–32.

Goren, M. B., D'Arcy Hart, P., Young, M. R. and Armstrong, J. A. (1976). Prevention of phagosomelysosome fusion in cultured macrophages by sulfatides of *Mycobacterium tuberculosis. Proc. Natl. Acad. Sci. USA* 73: 2510–14.

Green, I., Kirkpatrick, C. H. and Dale, D. C. (1971). Lactoferrin-specific localization in the nuclei of human polymorphonuclear neutrophilic leukocytes. *Proc. Soc. Exp. Biol. Med.* 137: 1311–17.

Hallett, M. B. and Campbell, A. K. (1983). Two distinct mechanisms for stimulation of oxygen-radical production by polymorphonuclear leukocytes. *Biochem. J.* 216: 459–65.

Hammerschmidt, D. E. (1983). Leukocytes in lung injury. *Chest* 83: 16S–20S.

Harris, M. C., Stroobant, J., Cody, C. S., Douglas, S. D. and Polin, R. A. (1983). Phagocytosis of group B streptococcus by neutrophils from newborn infants. *Pediatr. Res.* 17: 358–61.

Hart, P. D., Armstrong, J. A., Brown, C. A. and Draper, P. (1972). Ultrastructural study of the behavior of macrophages toward parasitic mycobacteria. *Infect. Immun.* 5: 803–7.

Harvath, L. and Leonard, E. J. (1982). Two neutrophil populations in human blood with different chemotactic activities: separation and chemoattractant binding. *Infect. Immun.* 36: 443–9.

Harvath, L., Falk, W. and Leonard, E. J. (1980). Rapid quantitation of neutrophil chemotaxis: Use of a polyvinyl—pyrrolidone-free polycarbonate membrane in a multiwell assembly. *J. Immunol. Methods* 37: 39–45.

Henricks, P. A. J., Van Der Tol, M. E., Kats-Renaud, J. H. V., Nijkamp, F. P. and Verhoef, J. (1984). Differences in the effect of arachidonic acid on polymorphonuclear and mononuclear leukocyte function. *Biochim. Biophys. Acta* 801: 206–14.

Hirsch, J. G. and Cohn, Z. A. (1960). Degranulation of polymorphonuclear leukocytes following phagocytosis of microorganisms. *J. Exp. Med.* 112: 1005–14.

Hoffstein, S. T. (1979). Ultrastructural demonstration of calcium loss from local regions of the plasma membrane of surface-stimulated human granulocytes. *J. Immunol.* 123: 1395–1402.

Hoffstein, S., Soberman, R., Goldstein, I. and Weissmann, G. (1976). Concanavalin A induces microtubule assembly and specific granule discharge in human polymorphonuclear leukocytes. *J. Cell Biol.* 68: 781–7.

Hoffstein, S., Goldstein, I. M. and Weissmann, G. (1977). Role of microtubule assembly in lysosomal enzyme secretion from human polymorphonuclear leukocytes. *J. Cell Biol.* 73: 242–56.

Jarstrand, C. and Einhorn, S. (1983). Effect of interferon on human neutrophilic granulocytes. *Cancer Immunol. Immunother.* 16: 123–6.

Jensen, M. S. and Bainton, D. F. (1973). Temporal changes in pH within the phagocytic vacuole of the polymorphonuclear neutrophilic leukocyte. *J. Cell Biol.* 56: 379–88.

Johnston, R. B. Jr, Keele, B. B. Jr, Misra, H. P., Lehmeyer, J. E., Webb, L. S., Baehner, R. L. and Rajagopalan, K. V. (1975). The role of superoxide anion generation in the phagocytic bactericidal activity. Studies with normal and chronic granulomatious disease leukocytes. *J. Clin. Invest.* 55: 1357–72.

Jones, T. C. and Hirsch, J. G. (1972). The interaction between *Toxoplasma gondii* and mammalian cells. *J. Exp. Med.* 136: 1173–94.

Kalmar, L. and Gergely, P. (1983). Effect of prostaglandins on polymorphonuclear leukocyte motility. *Immunopharmacology* 6: 167–75.

Kampschmidt, R. F. and Upchurch, H. F. (1977). Possible involvement of leukocytic endogenous mediator in granulopoiesis. *Proc. Soc. Exp. Biol. Med.* 155: 89–93.

Karnovsky, M. L. and Badwey, J. A. (1983). Determinants of the production of active oxygen species by granulocytes and macrophages. *J. Clin. Chem. Clin. Biochem.* 21: 545–53.

Klebanoff, S. J. (1982). Oxygen-dependent cytotoxic mechanisms of phagocytes. In J. I. Gallin and A. S. Fauci (eds), *Advances in Host Defence Mechanisms*, vol. 1, New York: Raven: 111–62.

Klein, R. B., Fischer, T. J., Gard, S. E., Biberstein, M., Rich, K. C. and Stiehm, E. R. (1977). Decreased mononuclear and polymorphonuclear chemotaxis in human newborns, infants and young children. *Pediatrics* 60: 467–72.

Klempner, M. S. and Styrt, B. (1983). Alkalinizing the intralysosomal pH inhibits degranulation of human neutrophils. *J. Clin. Invest.* 72: 1793–1800.

Klempner, M. S., Dinarello, C. A. and Gallin, J. I. (1978). Human leukocytic pyrogen induces release of specific granule contents from human neutrophils. *J. Clin. Invest.* 61: 1330–6.

Kobayashi, K., Fujita, K., Okino, F., Kajii, T. (1984). An abnormality of neutrophil adhesion: autosomal recessive inheritance associated with missing neutrophil glycoproteins. *Pediatrics* 73: 606–10.

Korchak, H. M. and Weissmann, G. (1978). Changes in membrane potential of human granulocytes antecede the metabolic responses to surface stimulation. *Proc. Natl. Acad. Sci. USA* 75: 3818–22.

Korchak, H. M. and Weissmann, G. (1980). Stimulus–response coupling in the human neutrophil: Transmembrane potential and the role of extracellular Na+. *Biochim. Biophys. Acta.* 601: 180–94.

Korchak, H. M., Eisenstat, B. A., Hoffstein, S. T., Dunham, P. B. and Weissmann, G. (1980). Anion channel blockers inhibit lysosomal enzyme secretion from human neutrophils without affecting generation of superoxide anion. *Proc. Natl. Acad. Sci. USA* 77: 2721–5.

Krause, P. J., Maderazo, E. G. and Scroggs, M. (1982). Abnormalities of neutrophil adherence in newborns. *Pediatrics* 69: 184–7.

Kreutzer, D. L., Dreyfus, L. A. and Robertson, D. C. (1979). Interaction of polymorphonuclear leukocytes with smooth and rough strains of *Brucella abortus. Infect. Immun.* 23: 737–42.

Krinsky, N. I. (1974). Singlet excited oxygen as a mediator of the antibacterial action of leukocytes. *Science* 186: 363–5.

Larsen, G. L. (1985). Late-phase reactions: observations on the pathogenesis and prevention. *J. Allergy Clin. Immunol.* 76: 665–9.

Lichtman, M. A. and Weed, R. I. (1972). Alteration of the cell periphery during granulocyte maturation: relationship to cell function. *Blood* 39: 301–16.

Lippa, S., DeSole, P., Meucci, E., Littarru, G. P., DeFrancisci, G. and Magalini, S. I. (1983). Effect of general anesthetics on human granulocyte chemiluminescence. *Experientia* 39: 1386–7.

Luger, T. A., Charon, J. A., Colot, M., Micksche, M. and Oppenheim, J. J. (1983). Chemotactic properties of partially purified human epidermal cell-derived thymocyte-activating factor (ETAF) for polymorphonuclear and mononuclear cells. *J. Immunol.* 131: 816–20.

McCullough, J., Yunis, E. J., Benson, S. J. and Quie, P. G. (1969). Effect of blood-bank storage on leukocyte function. *Lancet* 2: 1333–7.

McPhail, L. C. and Snyderman, R. (1984). Mechanisms of regulating the respiratory burst in leukocytes. In R. Snydermann, (ed.), *Contemporary Topics in Immunobiology 14.* New York: Plenum Press: 247–81.

Malech, H. L., Root, K. R. and Gallin, J. I. (1977). Structural analysis of human neutrophil migration: centriole, microtubule and microfilament orientation and function during chemotaxis. *J. Cell Biol.* 75: 666–93.

Mandell, G. L. (1970). Intraphagosomal pH of human polymorphonuclear neutrophils. *Proc. Soc. Exp. Biol. Med.* 134: 447–9.

Mandell, G. L. (1974). Bactericidal activity of aerobic and anaerobic polymorphonuclear neutrophils. *Infect. Immun.* 9: 337–41.

Mandell, G. L. (1975). Catalase, superoxide dismutase, and virulence of *Staphylococcus aureus. J. Clin. Invest.* 55: 561–6.

Mauer, A. M., Athens, J. W., Ashenbrucker, H., Cartwright, G. E. and Wintrobe, M. M. (1960). Leukokinetic studies: II A method for labeling granulocytes *in vitro* with radioactive di-isopropylfluorophosphate (DFP32). *J. Clin. Invest.* 39: 1482–6.

Mease, A. D., Burgess, D. P. and Thomas, P. J. (1981). Irreversible neutrophil aggregation: a mechanism of decreased newborn neutrophil chemotactic response. *Am. J. Path.* 104: 98–102.

Miller, M. E. (1979). Phagocyte function in the neonate: selected aspects. *Pediatrics* 64 (suppl.): 709–12.

Mills, E. L., Thompson, T., Bjorksten, B., Filipovich, D. and Quie, P. G. (1979). The chemiluminescence response and bactericidal activity of polymorphonuclear neutrophils from newborns and their mothers. *Pediatrics* 63: 429–34.

Mitchell, R. H., McClelland, R. M. and Kampschmidt, R. F. (1982). Comparison of neutrophilia induced by leukocytic endogenous mediator and by cobra venom factor. *Proc. Soc. Exp. Biol. Med.* 169: 309–15.

Mohandes, A. E., Touraine, J. L., Osman, M. and Salle, B, (1982). Neutrophil chemotaxis in infants of diabetic mothers in preterms at birth. *J. Clin. Lab. Immunol.* 8: 117–20.

Muller, M. R., Hofmann, V., Cogoli, M., Erni, J. and Arrenbrecht, S. (1984). The effects of interferon on granulopoiesis *in vitro. Hematol. Oncol.* 2: 199–208.

Naccache, P. H., Molski, T. F. P., Borgeat, P. and Sha'afi, R. I. (1984). Mechanism of action of leukotriene B_4: intracellular calcium redistribution in rabbit neutrophils. *J. Cell. Physiol.* 118: 13–18.

O'Flaherty, J. T. (1985). Neutrophil degranulation: evidence pertaining to its mediation by the combined effects of leukotriene B_4, platelet-activating factor, and 5-HETE. *J. Cell. Physiol.* 122: 229–39.

Ohno, Y., Hirai, K., Kanoch, T., Uchino, H. and Ogawa, K. (1982). Subcellular localization of H_2O_2 production in human neutrophils stimulated with particles and an effect of cytochalasin-B on the cells. *Blood* 60: 253–60.

Oliver, J. M. (1978). Cell biology of leukocyte abnormalities: membrane and cytoskeletal function in normal and defective cells. *Am. J. Pathol.* 93: 221–70.

Olson, T. A., Ruymann, F. B., Cook, B. A., Burgess, D. P., Henson, S. A. and Thomas, P. J. (1983). Newborn polymorphonuclear leukocyte aggregation: a study of physical properties and ultrastructure using chemotactic peptides. *Pediatr. Res.* 17: 993–7.

Olsson, I., Odeberg, H., Weiss, J. and Elsbach, P. (1978). Bactericidal cationic proteins of human granulocytes. In K. Havemann, and A., Janoff, (eds), *Neutral Proteases of Human Polymorphonuclear Leukocytes: Biochemistry, Physiology and Clinical Significance.* Baltimore: Urban and Schwarzenberg: 18–32.

Oppenheim, J. J. and Gery, I. (1982). Interleukin-1 is more than an interleukin. *Immunol. Today* 3: 113–19.

Oseas, R., Yang, H. H., Baehner, R. L. and Boxer, L. A. (1981). Lactoferrin: a promoter of polymorphonuclear leukocyte adhesiveness. *Blood* 57: 939–45.

Palmblad, J., Gyllenhammar, H., Lindgren, J. A. and Malmsten, C. L. (1984). Effects of leukotrienes and F-Met-Leu-Phe on oxidative metabolism of neutrophils and eosinophils. *J. Immunol.* 132: 3041–5.

Patriarca, P., Cramer, R., Moncalvo, S., Rossi, F. and Romeo, D. (1971). Enzymatic basis of metabolic stimulation in leucocytes during phagocytosis: the role of activated NADPH oxidase. *Arch. Biochem. Biophys.* 145: 255–62.

Playfair, J. H. L., Wolfendale, M. R. and Kay, H. E. M. (1963). The leukocytes of peripheral blood in the human foetus. *Brit. J. Haematol.* 9: 336–44.

Quesensberry, P. and Levitt, L. (1979). Hematopoietic stem cells. *N. Engl. J. Med.* 301: 755–60, 819–22, 868–72.

Reiss, M. and Roos, D. (1978). Differences in oxygen metabolism of phagocytosing monocytes and neutrophils. *J. Clin. Invest.* 61: 480–8.

Repine, J. E., Fox, R. B. and Berger, E. M. (1981). Dimethyl sulfoxide inhibits killing of *Staphylococcus aureus* by polymorphonuclear leukocytes. *Infect. Immun.* 31: 510–13.

Root, R. K. and Cohen, M. S. (1981). The microbicidal mechanisms of human neutrophils and eosinophils. *Rev. Infect. Dis.* 3: 565–98.

Sacchi, F., Rondini, G., Mingrat, G., Stronati, M., Gancia, B. P., Marseglia, G. L. and Siccardi, A. G. (1982). Different maturation of neutrophil chemotaxis in term and preterm newborn infants. *J. Pediatr.* 101: 273–4.

Saunder, D. N., Mounessa, N. L., Katz, S. I., Dinarello, C. A. and Gallin, J. I. (1984). Chemotactic cytokines: The role of leukocytic pyrogen and epidermal cell thymocyte-activating factor in neutrophil chemotaxis. *J. Immunol.* 132: 828–32.

Scott, R. E. and Horn, R. G. (1970). Ultrastructural aspects of neutrophil granulocyte development in humans. *Lab. Invest.* 23: 202–15.

Segal, A. W., and Jones, O. T. G. (1980). Absence of cytochrome b reduction in stimulated neutrophils from both female and male patients with chronic granulomatous disease. *FEBS Lett.* 110: 111–14.

Seligmann, B. E. and Gallin. J. I. (1980). Use of lipophilic probes of membrane potential to assess human neutrophil activation. *J. Clin;. Invest.* 66: 493–503.

Serhan, C. N., Smolen, J. E., Korchak, H. M. and Weissmann, G. (1983). Leukotriene B_4 is a complete secretagogue in human neutrophils: Ca^{2+} translocation in liposomes and kinetics of neutrophil activation. *Adv. Prostag. Throm. Leuko. Res.* 11: 53–63.

Sha'afi, R. I., White, J. R., Molski, T. F., Shefcyk, J., Volpi, M., Naccache, P. H. and Feinstein, M. B. (1983). Phorbol 12-myristate 13-acetate activates rabbit neutrophils without an apparent rise in the level of intracellular free calcium. *Biochem. Biophys. Res. Commun.* 114: 638–45.

Shak, S., Perex, H. D. and Goldstein, I. M. (1983). A novel dioxygenation product of arachidonic acid possesses potent chemotactic activity for human polymorphonuclear leukocytes. *J. Clin. Chem.* 258: 14948–53.

Shigeoka, A. O., Santos, J. I. and Hill, H. R. (1979). Functional analysis of neutrophil granulocytes from healthy, infected, and stressed neonates. *J. Pediatr.* 95: 454–60.

Simchowitz, L., Spilberg, I. and Atkinson, J. P. (1983). Evidence that the functional responses of human neutrophils occur independently of transient elevations in cyclic AMP levels. *J. Cyclic Nucleotide Protein Phosphor. Res.* 9: 35–47.

Smith, C. W. and Hollers, J. C. (1980). Motility and adhesiveness in human neutrophils: Redistribution of chemotactic factor-induced adhesion sites. *J. Clin. Invest.* 65: 804–12.

Smith, C. W., Hollers, J. C., Patrick, R. A. and Hassett, C. (1979). Motility and adhesiveness in human neutrophils: Effects of chemotactic factors. *J. Clin. Invest.* 63: 221–9.

Smolen, J. E., Korchak, H. M. and Weissmann, G. (1980). Increased levels of cyclic adenosine-3',5'-monophosphate in human polymorphonuclear leukocytes after surface stimulation. *J. Clin. Invest.* 65: 1077–85.

Smolen, J. E., Korchak, H. M. and Weissmann, G. (1982). Stimulus–response coupling in neutrophils. *Trends Pharmacol. Sci.* 3: 483–7.

Snyderman, R. (1985). Regulatory mechanisms of a chemoattractant receptor on human polymorphonuclear leukocytes. *Rev. Infect. Dis.* 7: 390–4.

Spitznagel, J. K. (1983). Microbial interactivities with neutrophils. *Rev. Infect. Dis.* 5: 5806–21.

Stendahl, O., Coble, B. I., Dahlgren, Hed, J. and Molin, L. (1984). Myeloperoxidase modulates the phagocytic activity of polymorphonuclear leukocytes: Studies with cells from a myeloperoxidase deficient patient. *J. Clin. Invest.* 73: 366–73.

Suzuki, K., Swenson, C., Sasagawa, S., Sakatani, T., Watanabe, M., Kobayashi, M. and Fujikura, T. (1983). Age-related decline in lysosomal enzyme release from polymorphonuclear leukoctes after n-formyl-methionyl-leucyl-phenylalanine stimulation. *Exp. Hematol.* 11: 1005–13.

Valone, F. H. (1984). Regulation of human leukocyte function by lipoxygenase products of arachidonic acid. In R. Snyderman(ed.), *Contemporary Topics in Immunobiology 14.* New York: Plenum: 155–70.

Van Oss C. J., Gillman. C. F. and Neuman, A. W. (1975). Phagocytic engulfment and cell adhesiveness as cellular surface phenomena. In Henry D. Isenberg (ed.), *Microorganisms and Infectious Diseases,* vol. 2 New York: Marcel Dekker.

Venge, P. and Olsson, I. (1975). Cationic proteins of human granulocytes: VI: Effects on the complement system and mediation of chemotactic activity. *J. Immunol.* 115: 1505–8.

Vercellotti, G. M., McCarthy, J., Furcht, L. T., Jacob, H. S., and Moldow, C. F. (1983). Inflamed fibronectin: an altered fibronectin enhances neutrophil adhesion. *Blood* 62: 1063–9.

Volpi, M., Yassin, R., Naccache, P. H. and Sha'afi, R. I. (1983). Chemotactic factor causes rapid decreases in phosphatidylinositol 4,5,-bisphosphate and phosphatidylinositol 4-monophosphate in rabbit neutrophils. *Biochem. Biophys. Res. Comm.* 112: 957–64.

Ward, P. A. and Hill, J. H. (1970). C5 chemotactic fragments produced by an enzyme in lysosomal granules of neutrophils. *J. Immunol.* 104: 535–43.

Weisbart, R. H., Golde, D. W., Clark, S. C., Wong, G. G. and Gasson, J. C. (1985). Human granulocyte-macrophage colony stimulating factor is a neutrophil activator. *Nature* 34: 361–3.

Weisdorf, D. J., Craddock, P. R. and Jacob, H. S. (1982). Glycogenolysis versus glucose transport in human granulocytes: differential activation in phagocytosis and chemotaxis. *Blood* 60: 888–93.

Weiss, J., Elsbach, P., Olsson, I. and Odelberg, H. (1978). Purification and characterization of a potent bactericidal and membrane active protein from the granules of human polymorphonuclear leukocytes. *J. Biol. Chem.* 253: 2664–72.

Weiss, J., Victor, M., Stendhal, O. and Elsbach, P. (1982). Killing of gram-negative bacteria by polymorphonuclear leukocytes. *J. Clin. Invest.* 69: 959–70.

Weissmann, G., Hoffstein, S., Korchak, H. and Smolen, J. E. (1978). The earliest membrane responses to phagocytosis: Membrane potential changes and Ca^{++} loss in human granulocytes. *Trans. Assoc. Am. Physicians* 91: 90–103.

Weissmann, G., Smolen, J., Korchak, H. and Hoffstein, S. (1981). The secretory code of the neutrophil. In J. T. Dingle and J. L. Gordon (eds), *Cellular Interactions* North-Holland, New York: Elsevier: 15–31.

Wheeler, J. G., Chauvenet, A. R., Johnson, C. A., Dillard, R., Block, S. M., Boyle, R. and Abramson, J. S. (1984a). Neutrophil storage pool depletion in septic, neutropenic neonates. *Pediatr. Inf. Dis.* 3: 407–9.

Wheeler, J. G., Abramson, J. S. and Ekstrand, K. (1984b). Function of irradiated polymorphonuclear leukocytes obtained by buffy-coat centrifugation. *Transfusion* 24: 238–9.

White, I. W. C., Gelb, A. W., Wexler, H. R., Stiller, C. R. and Keown, P. A. (1983). The effects of intravenous anaesthetic agents on human neutrophil chemiluminescence. *Can. Anesth. J.* 30: 506–11.

Wick, S. M. and Hepler, P. K. (1982). Selective localization of intracellular Ca^{2+} with potassium antimonate. *J. Histochem. Cytochem.* 30: 1190–1204.

Williams, L. T., Snyderman R., Pike, M. C. and Lefkowitz, R. J. (1977). Specific receptor sites for chemotactic peptides on polymorphonuclear leukocytes. *Proc. Natl. Acad. Sci. USA* 74: 1204–8.

Wilson, C. B., Tsai, V. and Remington, J S. (1980). Failure to trigger the oxidative metabolic burst by normal macrophages: possible mechanism for survival of intracellular pathogens. *J. Exp. Med.* 151: 328–46.

Wright, D. G. (1982). The neutrophil as a secretory organ of host defense. In J. I. Gallin and A. S. Fauci (eds), *Advances in Host Defence Mechanisms* vol. 1. New York: Raven Press: 75–110.

Wright, D. G. and Gallin, J. I. (1975). Modulation of the inflammatory response by products released from human polymorphonuclear leukocytes during phagocytosis: generation and inactivation of the chemotactic factor C5a. *Inflammation* 1: 23–39.

Wright, D. G., Gallin J. I. (1977). A functional differentiation of human neutrophil granules: generation of C5a by a specific (secondary) granule product and inactivation of C5a by azurophil (primary) granule products. *J. Immunol.* 119: 1068–76.

Wright, D. G. and Klock, J. C. (1979). Functional changes in neutrophils collected by filtration leukapheresis and their relationship to cellular events that occur during adherence of neutrophils to nylon fibers. *Exp. Hematol.* 7 (suppl. 4): 11–23.

Wright, W. C., Ank, B. J., Herbert, J. and Stiehm, R. (1975). Decreased bactericidal activity of leukocytes of stressed newborn infants. *Pediatrics* 56: 579–84.

Wyrick, P. B. and Brownridge, E. A. (1978). Growth of *Chlamydia psittaci* in macrophages. *Infect. Immun.* 19: 1054–60.

Zigmond, S. H. (1974). Mechanisms of sensing chemical gradients by polymorphonuclear leukocytes. *Nature* 249: 450–2.

Zigmond, S. H. (1977). Ability of polymorphonuclear leukocytes to orient in gradients of chemotactic factors. *J. Cell. Biol.* 75: 606–16.

Zurier, R. B., Weismann, G., Hoffstein, S., Kammerman, S. K. and Tai, H. H. (1974). Mechanisms of lysosomal enzyme release from human leukocytes. *J. Clin. Invest.* 53: 297–309.

3

Natural Killer Cells

RONALD B. HERBERMAN

*Pittsburgh Cancer Institute and Departments of Medicine and Pathology,
University of Pittsburgh, School of Medicine, Pittsburgh, PA 15213–2592, USA*

I. INTRODUCTION
II. PHENOTYPIC CHARACTERISTICS OF NK CELLS
III. PHYLOGENY AND ONTOGENY OF NK CELLS
IV. REGULATION OF NK ACTIVITY
    A. Augmentation of NK activity
    B. Factors inhibiting NK activity
V. MECHANISM OF CYTOTOXICITY BY NK CELLS
    A. Recognition of target cells by effector cells
    B. Post-recognition steps leading to lysis of target cells
REFERENCES

I. INTRODUCTION

Natural killer cells were discovered about 15 years ago during studies of cell-mediated cytotoxicity (Rosenberg *et al.*, 1972; McCoy *et al.*, 1973; Herberman *et al.*, 1975; Kiessling *et al.*, 1975a; Kiessling *et al.*, 1975b; Kiessling *et al.*, 1976). Although investigators expected to find specific cytotoxic activity of tumour-bearing individuals against autologous tumour cells or against allogeneic tumours of similar or the same histologic type, appreciable cytotoxic activity was observed with lymphocytes from normal individuals. Since this time, the studies of natural killer cells have expanded into a broad and multifaceted research area, stimulated by the increasing indications that these cells may play

NATURAL IMMUNITY
ISBN 0 12 5145551

important roles in natural host resistance against cancer and infectious diseases (Baldwin, 1976; Oldham *et al.*, 1973; Cudkowicz and Hochman, 1979; Haller *et al.*, 1977a and b; Hanna and Burton, 1981; Hanna and Fidler, 1980; Herberman, 1974; Herberman, 1980; Herberman and Holden, 1978; Herberman, 1982; Herberman *et al.*, 1982a; Herberman and Ortaldo, 1981; Nunn, *et al.*, 1977; Ojo and Wigzell, 1978; Ortaldo *et al.*, 1977; Petranyi *et al.*, 1976; Pollack *et al.*, 1972; Herberman *et al.*, 1975; Herberman *et al.*, 1979a). With the wide array of recent studies related to natural cell-mediated cytotoxicity, there has been considerable diversity in the terminology related to the effector cells and consequently some confusion in the literature. However, at a workshop devoted to the study of natural killer cells, a consensus definition for these effector cells was developed (Koren and Herberman, 1983). Natural killer (NK) cells were defined as effector cells with spontaneous cytotoxicity against various target cells; these effector cells lack the phenotypic characteristics of classical macrophages, granulocytes, or cytotoxic T lymphocytes (CTLs); and, in contrast to specifically immune CTL, the observed cytotoxicity does not show restriction related to the major histocompatibility complex (MHC). This definition is sufficiently broad to include not only 'classical' NK cells but also other natural effector cells such as natural cytotoxic (NC) cells (see Chapters 4 and 5), but differentiates NK cells from T cells with MHC unrestricted cytotoxic activity and hence 'NK-like' activity. As will be discussed below in Section II, on the basis of very extensive studies on phenotypic characteristics, a more precise definition of NK cells can now be formulated.

NK cells are not the sole effectors of natural immunity but rather have been recognised to be one of several cell types that play important roles in natural resistance. In addition to NK cells, macrophages, natural antibodies, and polymorphonuclear leukocytes are major effector mechanisms involved in natural resistance (see Chapters 1, 2 and 6). Detailed reviews and comparisons of these effectors and their characteristics have been published (Herberman, 1980; Herberman, 1982; Herberman and Ortaldo, 1981).

II. PHENOTYPIC CHARACTERISTICS OF NK CELLS

Until recently, the cells responsible for NK activity could be defined only in a negative way i.e. by distinguishing them from typical T cells, B cells, or macrophages. However, it is now possible to isolate highly enriched populations and show that the NK activity is closely associated with a subpopulation of lymphocytes, morphologically identified as large granular lymphocytes (LGLs), that comprise about 5 per cent of peripheral blood lymphocytes and 1–3 per cent of total mononuclear cells (Timonen and Saksela, 1980; Timonen *et al.*, 1981, 1982a, b, c; Reynolds *et al.*, 1981a and b; Reynolds *et al.*, 1982; Tagliabue *et al.*, 1981; Kumugai *et al.*, 1982). LGLs, which contain azurophilic cytoplasmic granules, can be isolated by discontinuous density gradient centrifugation on Percoll. LGLs are non-phagocytic, non-adherent cells that lack surface immunoglobulin.

Although LGLs appear to account for most NK activity in humans, other primates, and rodents, not all LGLs possess measurable NK activity (Herberman, 1980; Herberman, 1982; Herberman and Ortaldo, 1981; Timonen and Saksela, 1980; Timonen *et al.*, 1981; 1982a, b, c; Reynolds *et al.*, 1981a and b; Tagliabue *et al.*, 1981). One possible explanation for the lack of detectable cytotoxic activity in some LGLs is that the array of target cells tested has not been sufficient to reflect the entire repertoire and that some LGLs may recognise and lyse only a limited variety of target cells. Despite this potential limitation, tests of human LGLs against several NK susceptible target cell lines in a single-cell cytotoxicity assay allow the estimate that in most normal individuals, after activation of the cells with interferon, 75–85 per cent (Timonen *et al.*, 1982a) of the LGLs are capable of killing at least one NK-susceptible target cell line. The nature of the other 15 or 20 per cent of the LGLs, with no detectable cytolytic activity, is unclear. They may represent a distinct subset of cells that inherently lack this functional capability or they may simply be at a non-cytolytic stage of differentiation or activation. On the basis of available information this latter possibility seems more likely. The concept that LGLs may vary in their levels of activation is consistent with a variety of reports of cells that lack spontaneous NK activity but can be activated by agents such as interferon or interleukin 2 (IL-2) to develop the ability to bind to NK-susceptible target cells or to lyse bound target cells (Herberman, 1980; Herberman, 1982; Herberman and Ortaldo, 1981; Timonen *et al.*, 1982a; Tagliabue *et al.*, 1981; Landazuri *et al.*, 1981; Mantovani *et al.*, 1981; Brunda *et al.*, 1980b; Zarling *et al.*, 1979). Thus it is currently unclear whether all LGLs have the capacity to mediate NK activity when sufficiently activated and presented with the appropriate target cells or whether a small proportion of LGLs are not NK cells. There have been recent indications that immune cytolytic T cells can have LGL morphology, particularly at certain times after in vivo immunisation (Biron and Welch, 1982).

Most LGLs have surface receptors for the Fc portion of IgG, and both killer-cell-mediated antibody-dependent cellular cytotoxicity (ADCC) and NK activity have been closely associated with LGLs (Herberman,

1980; Herberman, 1982; Herberman and Ortaldo, 1981; Timonen *et al.*, 1981; Reynolds *et al.*, 1981b; Hattori *et al.*, 1983; Breard *et al.*, 1981; Kay and Horwitz, 1980). Approximately one-half of human NK cells and LGLs express detectable receptors for sheep erythrocytes, as measured by rosette formation at 4°C (Herberman, 1980; Herberman, 1982; Herberman and Ortaldo, 1981; West *et al.*, 1977; Ortaldo *et al.*, 1981). However, some monoclonal antibodies to the sheep erythrocyte receptor (CD2) react with a considerably higher proportion of LGLs and NK cells (Scala *et al.*, 1986; Ortaldo *et al.*, 1981). Analogously, a proportion of mouse NK cells express Thy 1 antigens, and most rat NK cells express OX-8 and some other T-cell-associated markers (Reynolds *et al.*, 1981b). Thus, NK cells share many characteristics associated with T cells, although they are clearly not thymus-dependent, since high levels of activity have been detected in athymic nude mice or in neonatally thymectomised mice (Herberman, 1980; Herberman, 1982; Herberman and Ortaldo, 1981; Axberg *et al.*, 1980; Cantor *et al.*, 1979; Hanna, 1980; Hanna and Fidler, 1981; Law, 1965; Law, 1966; Maguire Jr. *et al.*, 1976; Schmidt and Good, 1976; Shin *et al.*, 1975; Yunis *et al.*, 1969).

Overall, the results to date indicate that a discrete, small subpopulation of lymphoid cells i.e. LGLs, are responsible for most NK activity (at least 90 per cent). These findings seem to rule out the possibility that diverse cell types share the NK function.

Some cell-surface antigens, particularly those detected by monoclonal antibodies, have been found on virtually all NK cells. They therefore help to characterise the phenotype of these effector cells. For example, most human NK cells react with the following antibodies: (a) several monoclonal antibodies (B73.1, 3G8, Leu 11) (Perussia *et al.*, 1983; Lanier *et al.*, 1983; Fleit *et al.*, 1982) are reactive with the CD16 Fc receptors for IgG on LGLs, and in addition 3G8 and Leu 11 are strongly expressed on granulocytes (PMN); (b) monoclonal antibodies to NKH1 or Leu 19, which is also expressed on a small subpopulation of CD3$^+$ T cells that can also display non-MHC-restricted cytotoxic reactivity (Hercend *et al.*, 1985; Schmidt *et al.*, 1985 and 1987; Lanier and Phillips, 1986; van de Griend *et al.*, 1984); (c) rabbit antisera to the glycolipid asialo GM1 which also reacts with monocytes and granulocytes; (d) OKT10, which also reacts with most thymocytes and activated lymphocytes (Ortaldo *et al.*, 1981; Reinherz *et al.*, 1980a and b); and (e) OKM1, which also reacts with monocytes/macrophages, polymorphonuclear leukocytes, and platelets (Herberman, 1980; Herberman, 1982; Breard *et al.*, 1981; Kay and Horwitz, 1980; Ortaldo *et al.*, 1981; Reinherz *et al.*, 1980a; Zarling and Kung, 1980). Removal of cells bearing any of these markers, either by treatment with antibody plus complement or by negative selection immunoaffinity procedures, results in a depletion of most or all detectable NK activity.

In the rat, a monoclonal antibody, OX-8, which also reacts with the subpopulation of T cells with suppressor activity (similar to the human T8 subpopulation of T cells with cytotoxic and suppressor activities [Herberman, 1980; Herberman, 1982; Reynolds *et al.*, 1981b; Reynolds *et al.*, 1982; Ward *et al.*, 1983]), reacts with most NK cells and LGLs. In the mouse, antibodies to the alloantigen NK1.1 react with most if not all NK cells (Tam *et al.*, 1980). Laminin, as detected by polyclonal antisera or by monoclonal antibodies to the B2 chain, also is selectively expressed on most mouse and rat NK cells and LGLs (Hiserodt and Reynolds, 1987). Antisera to asialo GM1 also react with virtually all rat and mouse NK cells (Herberman, 1982; Reynolds *et al.*, 1981b; Kumugai *et al.*, 1982).

NK cells can also be characterised by a lack of expression of certain cell-surface markers. For example, human NK cells have no detectable surface reactivity with monoclonal antibodies to pan-T-cell antigens such as CD3 or CD5, or to the CD4 T-helper antigen (Herberman, 1980; Herberman, 1982; Breard *et al.*, 1981; Kay and Horwitz, 1980; Ortaldo *et al.*, 1981; Fleit *et al.*, 1982). Human NK cells also do not express surface antigens detected by a number of monocyte-specific reagents such as MO2 and Leu-M1 (Herberman, 1980; Herberman, 1982; Ortaldo *et al.*, 1981).

In contrast to a pattern of some phenotypic features common to most or all NK cells, these effector cells, and LGLs in general, are rather heterogeneous with respect to other monoclonal-antibody-defined markers. Human NK cells react to a variable extent with monoclonal antibodies (MoAb) directed against the CD2 sheep erythrocyte receptors (Lyt3, OKT11, Leu5) (Ferrarini *et al.*, 1980; Ortaldo *et al.*, 1981), with only about half of the NK cells in some experiments giving positive results. Only a portion of human NK cells have been shown to react with a variety of other monoclonals, including 3A1 (on most T cells and 50–60 per cent of LGLs) (Ortaldo *et al.*, 1981), OKT8 (CD8, on the suppressor/ cytotoxic T lymphocytes and 10–30 per cent of LGLs) (Ortaldo *et al.*, 1981; Reinherz *et al.*, 1980a), and about 25 per cent of the LGLs react with some MoAb against Ia framework (HLA-DR) determinants (Ortaldo *et al.*, 1981). HNK1 or Leu7, a marker initially thought to be selective for most or all human NK cells, has more recently been shown to be expressed on only about 50 per cent of NK cells or LGLs and also on a subset of T cells (Lanier *et al.*, 1983).

Similarly in the mouse, only about half of the NK cells (as detected by abrogation of cytolytic function) express Thy 1, and only 20 per cent express readily detectable Lyt 1 (Herberman, 1980; Herberman, 1982; Koo and Hatzfeld, 1980; Tai and Warner, 1980).

Although most NK cells and LGLs are non-adherent to plastic or nylon wool, a subset of these cells shows some adherence. For instance, when human myelomonocytic cells are isolated by means of their adherence to plastic, the small percentage of contaminating cells include a disproportionate number of LGLs (Chang *et al.*, 1983). In addition, after in vivo stimulation of NK cells with microbial agents such as *Corynebacterium parvum* or with interferon after in vitro stimulation with allogeneic cells or lectins, a substantial proportion of NK cells adhere either to plastic or to nylon wool columns (Herberman, 1980; Schmidt *et al.*, 1984; Ortaldo and Timonen, 1981). Although this subpopulation of cells shares the adherence property with myelomonocytic cells, it retains the morphology and cell-surface characteristics of LGLs. The phenotype of human adherent NK cells has been shown to be OKT3$^-$ OKT10$^+$ CD2$^+$ OKM1$^+$ Leu-M1$^-$ CD16$^+$ (Chang *et al.*, 1983). Such cells thus contrast with typical adherent monocytes, which only react with OKM1 and Leu M1. On the basis of recent findings that activation of NK cells with IL-2 induces the ability to adhere to plastic (see Section IV below), the adherent properties of a subpopulation of NK cells probably reflect the activated state of these cells.

The proportions of LGLs in various lymphoid and other tissues vary; in general, the levels of NK activity follow a similar distribution. Generally, the highest reactivity is in the peripheral blood, and spleen cells have intermediate levels of activity (Kiessling *et al.*, 1975a; Kiessling *et al.*, 1976; Nunn *et al.*, 1977; Herberman *et al.*, 1975). Low levels of activity are found in other sites (Haller *et al.*, 1977a, b; Herberman *et al.*, 1975; Reynolds *et al.*, 1981a), including lymph nodes, bone marrow, lung, and gut epithelium. However, it is as yet unclear whether human or rat NK cells at various sites differ substantially in other characteristics. Further, it has been suggested that the NK cells in bone marrow may represent a particular subset, NK$_{(M)}$ (Minato and Bloom, 1982).

In summary, NK cells have a characteristic phenotype. For example, most human NK cells and LGL can be described as CD3$^-$ CD16$^+$ NKH1 (Leu19)$^+$ CD4$^-$ OKM1$^+$ LeuM1$^-$. Thus, these cells have a readily definable and general phenotype, which sets them apart from all other lymphoid cell types. The heterogeneity in cell-surface phenotype extends to only a few markers e.g. with human NK cells: CD8, CD2, HNK1 (Leu 7), Ia.

Until recently, a precise definition of NK cells has been difficult and this has led to considerable confusion in the literature related to natural cell-mediated cytotoxicity. It does not seen satisfactory to refer to all effector cells that mediate non-MHC-restricted cytotoxicity against NK-sensitive target cells or other target cells, as NK cells, since, as pointed out recently by Lanier *et al.* (1986), a subset of T cells as well as macrophages and neutrophils can also mediate non-MHC-restricted cytotoxic activity. Rather, with the extensive phenotypic information now available, it is possible to define NK cells rather precisely as having LGL morphology and non-MHC-restricted cytotoxic activity. In addition, the cell-surface phenotype can be defined to an extent which sets these effector cells apart from all other lymphoid cell types. Just as human NK cells have a typical surface phenotype (see above), mouse NK cells can be defined as $L3T4^-$, $Lyt2^-$, asialo $GM1^+$, $NK\text{-}1.1^+$, laminin$^+$, and rat NK cells have the following phenotype: $CD5^-$, $CD8^+$, asialo $GM1^+$, laminin$^+$. According to this definition, NK cells represent a quite particular subpopulation of lymphocytes with a very characteristic functional activity, i.e. their non-MHC-restricted cytotoxicity. Reynolds and Ortaldo (1987) have recently objected to such a definition for NK cells, pointing out that these cells also exhibit a variety of non-cytotoxic functions, including cytokine production, immune regulation, and antimicrobial activities. Although NK cells do indeed have a wide range of functional activities, this does not seem to be a basis to avoid linking the cell type with its predominant function. The macrophage provides a good precedent for such nomenclature. Although it is quite clear that macrophages exhibit an extraordinarily wide range of functional activities besides phagocytic activity, it has been satisfactory to retain the original name for these cells. In fact, in some situations, macrophages may lack detectable phagocytic activity. Since macrophages can be described extensively in terms of a variety of other phenotypic and functional characteristics, it seems satisfactory to call such cells macrophages without detectable phagocytic activity since these cells have an unexpressed potential for this key function. Similarly, there may be non-cytotoxic NK cells, with their cytotoxic activity being inhibited or not yet activated. In addition, as discussed below in Section III, cells in the same lineage, but lacking some of the phenotypic characteristics of NK cells as well as cytotoxic activity, may be referred to as pre-NK cells. Ultimately, NK cells will probably be defined best in terms of their expression of characteristic NK recognition receptors for target cells. Unfortunately, however, the recognition receptors on NK cells have not yet been defined and until they are, we must rely on the constellation of other phenotypic characteristics.

III. PHYLOGENY AND ONTOGENY OF NK CELLS

Although most studies on NK cells have been performed with mammalian lymphocytes, there have been several studies of the phylogeny of these effector cells. There is now considerable suggestive evidence for NK activity in more primitive species, including various invertebrates (see Savary and Lotzova, 1986, for detailed review). Cells from the coelomic cavity of sipunculid and annelid worms have been shown to have rapid cytotoxic activity against allogeneic and xenogeneic erythrocytes (Valembois *et al.*, 1980; Decker *et al.*, 1981). Natural cytotoxic reactivity against erythrocytes or normal mononuclear cells has also been observed in other invertebrate species, including starfish and molluscs. In addition to spontaneous cytotoxic reactivity against normal cells, coelomocytes of invertebrates have also been found to have cytotoxic reactivity against malignant cells (Valembois *et al.*, 1980; Decker *et al.*, 1981; Tyson and Jenkin, 1974; Luquet and Leclerc, 1983). The effector cells responsible for the cytotoxic reactivity of invertebrates appear to be functionally and morphologically similar to mammalian NK cells. The cytolytic coelomocytes have been found to be nylon wool non-adherent (Valembois *et al.*, 1980) and negative for non-specific esterase, and their cytotoxic activity has been inhibited by monosaccharides (Decker *et al.*, 1981), similiar to the inhibitory effect of sugars on mammalian NK activity (see Section V). The most striking analogy between mammalian NK cells and the cytolytic coelomocytes of invertebrates has come from the observation that the coelomocytes of the earthworm, which are involved in rejection of xenogeneic skin grafts, have the morphology of LGLs (Hostetter and Cooper, 1972; Linthicum *et al.*, 1977). The major, continuing limitations in conclusive interpretation of these results with invertebrate effector cells are the lack of adequate markers to characterise the cells fully, and the lack of tumour target cells within the same species that would be sufficiently analogous to the usual target cells used for studies of mammalian NK activity. However, the above results are quite intriguing and at least suggest strongly that NK cells as well as macrophages are phylogenetically rather ancient. This would support the conclusion that NK cells seem to be quite important for normal functioning and/or critical host defences of a very wide range of species.

Cells from primitive vertebrates, including fish and amphibians, have also been found to have spontaneous cytotoxic activity against a variety of normal and malignant mammalian cell lines (Hinuma *et al.*, 1980). It is of interest that the cytotoxic reactivity in fish was found mainly in the kidney, which is a haemopoietic organ in fish, with lower and more variable activity in the blood or spleen. In amphibia, splenocytes were most active, whereas bone marrow or thymus cells had quite low activity (Roder *et al.*, 1981). Fish effector cells resembled mammalian NK cells in terms of their rapid cytolytic activity, with lysis detectable in a six hour assay, and the lack of species restriction for targets. However, as with the invertebrate studies, the lack of adequate markers for characterisation of the effector cells makes conclusions about the relationship to NK cells difficult.

Various avian species, particularly chicken and quail, have been shown to have spontaneous cytotoxic activity against various normal and malignant target cells (Sharma and Coulson, 1979; Yamada *et al.*, 1980; Leibold *et al.*, 1980; Fleischer, 1980). The characterisation of the cells involved has indicated fairly close analogies to the characteristics of mammalian NK cells. The effector cells were found mainly in the spleen and blood, but not in the thymus. Cells with typical LGL morphology have been observed in the blood of chickens as well as in a wide variety of mammalian species (Herberman *et al.*, 1980), although these studies did not include a demonstration of a direct relationship between LGLs and the observed cytotoxic reactivity.

Clearly, NK cells have been most extensively studied in mammalian species, particularly rodents and humans. The phenotypic characteristics of mouse and rat NK cells have been summarised above in Section II. Cytotoxic activity with similar properties has also been observed in hamsters and guinea pigs (Tatta *et al.*, 1979; Tsang *et al.*, 1981; Teale *et al.*, 1983; Altman and Rapp, 1978; Arnaud-Battandier *et al.*, 1978). Hamster LGLs have been reported to be of relatively high density, in contrast to the low density LGLs found in other rodents or in humans (Teale *et al.*, 1983). The NK activity of guinea pigs may be associated with their Kurloff cells (Eremin *et al.*, 1980), which have intracytoplasmic inclusion bodies with staining characteristics similar to the azurophilic granules of LGLs. Aside from some difference in morphology, Kurloff cells have other characteristics that are quite analogous to typical LGLs and NK cells (Eremin *et al.*, 1977; Revell, 1977).

Another mammalian species that has been extensively studied in regard to NK activity is the miniature swine (Koren *et al.*, 1978; Kim *et al.*, 1980). In this species, reactivity has been limited mainly to the peripheral blood, with little or no reactivity detectable in the spleen, bone marrow, lymph nodes or other lymphoid organs (Kim *et al.*, 1980). The effector cells have been found to be non-adherent and distinguishable from T cells (Koren *et al.*, 1978). Although LGLs have been detected in the peripheral blood of pigs (Herberman *et al.*, 1980), LGLs have not yet been shown to be responsible for swine NK activity.

NK cells have also been studied to a limited extent in non-human primates. NK activity is detectable in both Old and New World monkeys (Clark and Sturge, 1981). It has been possible to isolate LGLs from non-adherent mononuclear blood cells of rhesus and other monkeys and to demonstrate that they are responsible for the NK activity (Savary and Lotzova, 1986; Ortaldo and Herberman, unpublished observations).

From the suggestive evidence in the phylogenetic studies of NK activity in quite primitive forms of life, one might expect to find NK activity developing very early also in ontogeny. However, there are as yet few data to support this expectation. There has been some suggestion of NK activity in fetal mice, with cytotoxic activity detected in cells from the yolk sac of 10-day-old mouse embryos (Dahl, 1980). However, these findings are difficult to interpret, since newborn mice have undetectable NK activity (Herberman *et al.*, 1975) and the effector cells from the embryonic yolk sac lacked most of the markers characteristic of mature mouse NK cells (Dahl, 1983).

It is of interest that the human has been the mammalian species with the most consistent evidence for early development of NK activity. Low but significant NK activity has been reported in fetal liver at 9–19 weeks of gestation and also in fetal spleen at 19 weeks (a low percentage of HNK-1[+] cells has also been detected in 13–17-week-old fetal liver cells and in fetal spleen cells (Abo *et al.*, 1983). Quite variable levels of NK activity have been reported at birth in the cord blood along with low levels of HNK-1[+] lymphocytes (Abo *et al.*, 1983; Antonelli *et al.*, 1981; Kaplan *et al.*, 1982). Abo *et al.* (1983) have proposed a differentiation pathway of NK cells from small aḡanular HNK-1[+] T3[−] M1[−] cells in the fetus to poorly granulated, HNK1[+] T3[+] M1[−] cells in the bone marrow, and then highly granular HNK1[+] T3[−] M1[+] cells in peripheral lymphoid tissues. However, this model was based largely on the use of the HNK1 marker and as discussed above, in Section II, this marker is expressed on a subset of T cells as well as NK cells and the developmental observations may reflect a mixture of effector cells and unrelated non-effector cells.

In rodents, avians, and swine, NK activity has been undetectable at birth, but has risen rather promptly at about three weeks of age (Herberman *et al.*, 1975; Reynolds *et al.*, 1981a; Sharma and Coulson, 1979; Huh *et al.*, 1981).

The developmental pathway for NK cells has been most extensively studied in mice. Considerable evidence has indicated that the stem cells for NK cells reside mainly in the bone marrow. The NK activity of congenitally NK-deficient mice, or of mice with NK activity experimentally depressed, could be fully reconstituted for NK reactivity by adoptive transfer of bone marrow cells from high-NK donor strains of mice (Haller *et al.*, 1977b). In addition to serving as a source for NK stem cells, the bone marrow appears to provide an important microenvironment for differentiation of NK cells. Damage of the bone marrow microenvironment with ^{89}Sr resulted in prolonged deficiency in NK activity, and such mice could not be reconstituted with bone marrow cells from NK-reactive donors (Bennett *et al.*, 1976; Haller and Wigzell, 1977; Kumar *et al.*, 1982).

Recent detailed studies have begun to dissect some of the stages of differentiation of NK cells from bone-marrow stem cells and to elucidate the factors regulating the differentiation of mature effector cells. The main experimental approach has been to lethally irradiate normal mice and then determine the cells and other treatments needed to reconstitute NK activity. Lethal irradiation of normal mice produces a profound suppression of normal NK activity (Hackett *et al.*, 1985). Untreated mice begin to die of bone-marrow failure at approximately 14–16 days after irradiation. NK activity at this time is low and reconstitution with syngeneic marrow demonstrates a dose-dependent relationship between the number of donor bone-marrow cells and the generation of NK activity. When bone marrow from a mouse strain (C.B-17 *scid*) with severe combined immunodeficiency was used for reconstitution, the rate of development of NK activity was normal. This strain has an early defect in the differentiation of T and B lymphocytes and these results led the authors to conclude that the early transplantable precursors of NK cells are distinct from those of the T and B lineages (Hackett *et al.*, 1986a). However, it is not possible to eliminate the possibility that a common precursor cell in *scid* mice is selectively blocked from differentiation into T or B lymphocytes while not blocked from differentiation into NK cells.

In collaborative studies with Dr Carlo Riccardi's group in Italy, this author has found that the development of bone-marrow NK precursors in irradiated, reconstituted animals can be accelerated by the in vivo treatment of the recipients with soluble growth factors (Riccardi *et al.*, 1986a; Riccardi *et al.*, 1986b). Treatment with IL-1, IL-2, IFN-α or IFN-β stimulated growth and/or differentiation of NK precursor cells such that NK activity levels returned to normal significantly faster than in untreated controls. Treatment with CSF-1 and IL-3, factors that stimulate early haemopoietic development, did not accelerate NK functional development.

In attempts to more specifically examine the characteristics of NK precursor cells, studies have been conducted on the effect of NK depletion of bone marrow using antibodies against a rather selective mouse phenotypic NK marker (NK-1.1). Weekly injections of the monoclonal anti-NK-1.1 antibody from birth to adulthood depleted NK cells in vivo and resulted in an NK-1.1$^-$ mouse (Koo *et al.*, 1986). These NK-1.1$^-$ mice had marked reductions in the number of NK-1.1$^+$ cells in their spleens and a decrease in NK lytic activity. The bone-marrow precursors of NK cells, however, were present in normal numbers. NK activity could be restored by culturing NK-1.1⁻ bone-marrow cells in IL-2 for 5-6 days. NK activity was not enhanced by treatment with IFN-α or IFN-β, suggesting that the stimulating effects of IL-2 and IFN occur relatively early and late, respectively, in the functional development of NK precursor cells. These data indicate that although NK-1.1 is expressed on mature NK cells and is expressed in a substantial proportion of bone-marrow cells (Koo *et al.*, 1984), it does not seem to be a marker for NK precursors in the bone marrow.

The relationship between early NK precursors and other bone-marrow progenitor cells has been examined by treating animals with drugs, such as 5-fluorouracil (5-FU), that eliminate proliferating cells and spare the quiescent, non-dividing stem cells (Hodgson and Bradley, 1979). In normal bone marrow, pluripotent stem cells exist in a G_0 resting phase. They are recruited into an active cell cycle on demand, perhaps through stimulation by soluble growth factors (Lord *et al.*, 1977; Williams *et al.*, 1985). Treatment of the bone marrow with 5-FU eliminates the more mature, rapidly dividing cells, stimulating the cell-cycling activity of the stem cells. The stem cells present in the marrow of treated mice have been shown to express the Thy-1 antigen at levels that are directly related to their regenerative potential (Hodgson and Bradley, 1979; Boswell *et al.*, 1984).

In collaboration with Dr Riccardi's group, this author has found that the incubation of mouse bone marrow with IL-2 leads to the generation of NK activity. The treatment of animals with 5-FU results in the enrichment of very primitive stem cells early (1–2 days) followed by progressive maturation of the cells for approximately two weeks (Migliorati *et al.*, 1987). The bone-marrow cells from 5-FU treated mice did not respond to incubation with IL-2 until approximately four days after treatment. The number of precursors that responded at four days was augmented and enriched 20–30 times over the levels found in non-5-FU-treated mice. Incubation of bone marrow cells from 5-FU-treated mice with IL-3 or CSF-1 did not influence the generation of NK activity. Pretreatment of the bone-marrow cells with anti-asialo GM1, anti-Lyt.2 or anti-Lyt.1 plus complement did not influence the generation of cytotoxic cells after culture with IL-2, indicating that the IL-2-responsive bone-marrow precursor cells lacked these markers. Treatment with anti-Thy.1, however, resulted in a significant reduction in total cell recovery and in the potential to generate cytotoxic NK cells. The addition of the growth factor haemopoietin-1 (H-1) (Migliorati *et al.*, 1987) or of interleukin 1 (IL-1) (Migliorati *et al.*, submitted for publication) to one- and two-day 5-FU-treated marrow significantly increased the cell recovery and the yield of cytotoxic cells after incubation with IL-2. The cells involved express high levels of Thy.1 and have been stimulated to express receptors for IL-2, as detected by a monoclonal antibody to the IL-2 receptor.

The results of these recent experiments indicate that the NK precursor in the bone marrow of mice is a bone-marrow stem cell that expresses the Thy.1 antigen, is not susceptible to the action of 5-FU, and responds to sequential stimulation with H-1 or IL-1 and then IL-2, to develop into a mature active NK cell. It is clear that the correlation between the growth factors and cell-surface markers involved in regulating bone-marrow and NK differentiation indicates a close developmental relationship at an early stage in the marrow. Little information is currently available as to the stage of expression of various NK-cell-associated surface molecules, and the time when the bone-marrow progenitor cells develop the ability to first bind to target cells and then kill them.

It has also been of considerable interest to determine the developmental correlations between these functions and the appearance of the characteristic cytoplasmic granules that provide the link between the morphological identification of LGLs and NK function. Cells with morphology quite similar to large granular lymphocytes but lacking visible azurophilic granules have been observed particularly in the spleens of rats and other species, and in peripheral blood (Saksela *et al.*, 1979, Itoh *et al.*, 1982, Hackett *et al.*, 1986b, Koo *et al.*, 1986, and Hackett *et al.*, 1985). These large agranular lymphocytes (LALs) have very similar density and cell-surface markers and it has therefore been quite difficult to separate LALs from LGLs. Although LALs have been suggested to be less mature cells and immediate precursors of LGLs with NK activity, the lack of purified populations of LALs devoid of LGLs, has interfered with a direct evaluation of this hypothesis. The finding that L-leucine methyl ester (LME) is selectively cytotoxic for LGLs (Shau and Golub, 1985) has recently allowed us to prepare the needed purified populations of rat LALs and examine their developmental relationship to LGLs and NK cells (Maghazachi *et al.*, 1988). LALs were found to have undetectable NK activity but upon culture with even a low concentration of IL-2, for 24 hours or longer, a considerable proportion of cells developed LGL morphology and the cultured population had substantial NK activity. This cytotoxic activity could be attributed to newly granulated cells, since a second course of treatment with LME, after the in vitro incubation with IL-2, selectively removed both LGLs and NK activity. Thus, it appears that LALs represent functionally inactive precursors of NK cells and that IL-2-induced maturation of LALs in the spleen and other peripheral sites, with the development of visible azurophilic cytoplasmic granules, is an important step for their development of NK activity. Consistent with this interpretation has been the observation that although LALs and LGLs have similar cell surface phenotypes, rat LALs have no detectable laminin and have low levels of OX8 (Maghazachi *et al.*, 1988), markers that are highly associated with LGLs and NK cells.

IV. REGULATION OF NK ACTIVITY

A. Augmentation of NK Activity

In addition to variations in levels of NK activity with age, as discussed in Section III, there are also considerable differences in levels of activity among various strains of mice or rats (Herberman and Holden, 1978). Similarly, normal human donors vary considerably in their levels of reactivity, and some of this variability has been shown to be influenced by the HLA phenotype (Santoli *et al.*, 1976). It should be noted that some of the apparent differences in age-related regulation of NK activity appear to be due to the sources of NK cells used for such studies. In the peripheral blood of rats (Reynolds *et al.*, 1981a) and mice (Lanza and Djeu, 1982), NK activity has been found to decline much more slowly than in the spleen.

It has been of considerable interest to determine the mechanisms responsible for the age-related, genetic, and organ-associated differences and whether environmental factors may influence these activities. Some clues were initially obtained by observations that inoculation of mice with a variety of viruses, immune adjuvants such as Bacillus Calmette-Guérin (BCG) or *Corynebacterium parvum*, or tumour cells susceptible to NK activity could induce a rapid and strong augmentation of reactivity (Herberman *et al.*, 1977b; Wolfe *et al.*, 1976; Djeu *et al.*, 1980). Rat NK activity was also found to be strongly boosted by poly I:C (Oehler *et al.*, 1978), a potent IFN-inducer, suggesting that IFN might play a major role in activating NK cells. Indeed, a variety of IFN-inducers have been found to augment NK activity in mice, and inoculation with IFN itself led to boosting of activity within three hours (Gidlund *et al.*, 1978; Djeu *et al.*, 1979).

1. In vitro augmentation of NK activity

Incubation of mouse spleen cells with poly I:C or with IFN has also resulted in appreciable increases in NK activity (Djeu *et al.*, 1979). Similar observations have been made with human and rat NK and K cells

(Herberman *et al.*, 1979b; Reynolds and Herberman, 1981). Administration of poly I:C to some patients resulted in increased levels of cytotoxicity after two days. Incubation of human peripheral blood lymphocytes (PBLs) with three different IFN preparations (leukocyte, lymphoblastoid, and fibroblast) for one hour or 18 hours caused increased NK- and K-cell activities with most donors. In fact, all of the proteins with antiviral activity that have been studied, including various species of natural or recombinant IFN-α, IFN-β and IFN-γ, have all had the ability to increase NK activity significantly (Herberman *et al.*, 1981, 1982b; Ortaldo *et al.*, 1983). However, there have been considerable quantitative differences in the efficacy of boosting by the various species. Some species have been shown to be high-level boosters, with greater than 50 per cent increase in NK activity by less than 50 units of natural or recombinant (r) IFN-α (IFN-α: β2, β3, rA, rC), IFN-β or IFN-γ, whereas other species of IFN-α have been found to have low-level boosting activity, with an increase in NK activity by 50 per cent being seen only with 500 units or more of IFN (IFN-α: α1, γ1, γ2, γ3, γ4, γ5, rB, rD, rG).

Our laboratory and several others have been interested in determining the mechanisms by which interferon augments NK activity. Such studies were considerably facilitated by the ability to identify morphologically and purify human and rat NK cells. We have analysed whether purified LGLs, after pretreatment with IFN, acquire an increased ability to recognise and bind to NK-susceptible target cells (Timonen *et al.*, 1982b). When such studies were done with K562 or other suspension target cells, pre-treatment with IFN was not found to result in an increased percentage of LGLs forming conjugates. In contrast, when various monolayer target cells were studied, IFN pretreatment of LGLs resulted in an increased proportion of binding cells. Thus, with some target cells but not with others, one action of IFN is to convert pre-NK cells into cells able to recognise and bind to the targets. To determine the possible effects of IFN on post-binding interactions with target cells, we have utilised a single-cell agarose cytotoxicity assay, as described by Grimm and Bonavida (1979). With K562 targets, pretreatment of LGLs with IFN was shown to result primarily in an accelerated rate of lysis of bound target cells. In contrast, with G-11 monolayer target cells, IFN pretreatment of LGLs resulted in a substantial increase in the proportion of bound targets that were lysed, as well as accelerating the kinetics of lysis. IFN has also been shown to increase interactions with target cells by increasing the degree of recycling, i.e. facilitating the interaction with, and lysis of, multiple target cells during the cytotoxicity assay. We have been able to demonstrate directly IFN-induced augmentation of recycling by observing the dissociation of LGLs from bound targets and their subsequent rebinding (Timonen *et al.*, 1982b). When LGLs were pretreated with IFN, the dissociation was decreased and rebinding occurred considerably more rapidly. Yet another aspect of the effect of IFN on the interactions between NK cells and targets has been the demonstration of the ability of IFN to protect certain target cells from lysis by NK cells (Trinchieri and Santoli, 1978). Thus, IFN can have opposite effects on effector cell–target cell interactions, depending on the cells exposed to the IFN.

Overall it has become clear that the effects of IFN on NK cells are quite complex, with the possibility of affecting NK activity at several different levels or phases of differentiation of interaction with target cells. Such complex interactions may have considerable impact on the strategies and results related to in vivo administration of IFN.

It should be noted that IFN or IFN-inducers may not be able to augment all forms of natural cell-mediated cytotoxicity. Lattime *et al.* (1982) have recently reported that IFN treatment in vitro or various IFN-inducers (poly I:C, tilorone, *C. parvum*) in vivo failed to induce detectable augmentation of mouse NC activity, under conditions in which NK activity was boosted well. It appears that NC cells and NK cells are regulated by different cytokines, with the growth and activation of NC cells being influenced primarily by interleukin 3 (Djeu *et al.*, 1982).

Since the discovery by Morgan *et al.* (1976) that human T cells could be maintained in continuous culture in the presence of T cell growth factor (TCGF), much research has been performed on the role of this factor in the growth and regulation of T cells. TCGF, now known as interleukin 2(IL-2), is a key intermediary for the proliferative responses of T cells (Bonnard *et al.*, 1979) and for the generation of cytotoxic T lymphocytes (CTLs) (Farrar *et al.*, 1981). The response of T cells to IL-2 has been shown to be dependent on the activation of the cells to express cell surface receptors for IL-2 (Bonnard *et al.*, 1979) and the human IL-2 receptor on T cells has been found to react with a monoclonal antibody, anti-Tac (Robb and Greene, 1983). The anti-Tac antibody has been found to inhibit the binding of radiolabelled IL-2 to T cell lines or to activated T cells expressing Tac (Robb and Greene, 1983) and it thereby strongly inhibits the proliferative responses to IL-2.

IL-2 also has been shown to have two types of effects on NK cells: it stimulates proliferation and increases cytotoxicity. In parallel with its potent activity as a growth factor for T cells, IL-2 has also been shown to promote the growth of NK cells (Timonen *et al.*, 1982c). As with T cells, this proliferative effect of IL-2 on NK cells has been shown to be dependent on an interaction of the lymphokine with receptors for IL-2, as detected by anti-Tac monoclonal antibodies (Yamada *et al.*, 1987). Proliferating LGLs have been shown to express Tac, and anti-Tac completely interfered with the growth of the cells and their maintenance of cytotoxic activity. However, as a major divergence from the data obtained with T cells, in which IL-2 receptors had to be induced by stimulation with mitogens or antigens in order for the cells to become responsive to IL-2 (Bonnard *et al.*, 1979), IL-2 alone has been shown to promote the growth of human or murine NK cells (Talmadge *et al.*, 1986; Yamada *et al.*, 1987). Quite unexpectedly, fresh IL-2-responsive human LGLs have been found to have no detectable IL-2 receptors, as measured either by flow cytometry with anti-Tac or by binding studies with radiolabelled anti-Tac (Yamada *et al.*, 1987). In addition, messenger RNA for IL-2 receptors was not detectable in fresh human LGLs (Yamada *et al.*, 1987). However, upon exposure of such LGLs to IL-2 alone, message for the Tac receptor became detectable within two days of culture and this was accompanied by detectable expression of Tac receptors on the cells and the onset of proliferation. Thus, it appears that IL-2 alone can induce the up-regulation of Tac receptors at the transcriptional level (Yamada *et al.*, 1987) and this appears to account for the ability of this lymphokine by itself to promote the growth of NK cells.

In contrast to the dependence of NK cell proliferation on the expression of detectable levels of IL-2 receptors, the ability of IL-2 to rapidly induce augmented levels of cytolytic activity has been found to be independent of entry into the cell cycle or the detectable expression of Tac (Ortaldo *et al.*, 1984a). Overnight incubation of LGLs with IL-2 could strongly stimulate NK activity, despite the presence in the culture medium of high concentrations of antibodies to Tac. Thus, it appears that LGLs express some non-Tac receptors for IL-2, which allow their cytotoxic reactivity to be stimulated. In addition, such interaction of IL-2 with Tac-independent receptors for IL-2 may provide the signal for induction of expression of Tac and the consequent proliferative response to IL-2. Recently, Hiserodt, DeLeo and colleagues in the Pittsburgh Cancer Institute (unpublished observation) have produced monoclonal antibodies against purified, IL-2-activated rat NK cells and demonstrated that one of these antibodies detects a non-Tac-related receptor for IL-2 on rat NK cells.

Lymphokine-activated killer (LAK) cells have been described (Grimm *et al.*, 1982) that share many of the characteristics of NK cells. LAK cells have been activated after a short period of culture in vitro with highly purified IL-2 and display cytotoxic activity against a variety of autologous, allogeneic, and xenogeneic tumours. These cells were initially thought to lack markers typical of fresh NK cells, to be devoid of cytolytic activity prior to culture, and to develop T cell markers upon activation (Grimm *et al.*, 1983). However, more recent studies in several laboratories have indicated that most LAK activity developing from blood or splenic lymphocytes is attributable to IL-2-stimulated NK cells and in fact, most LAK cells and their progenitors have a phenotype characteristic of NK cells but not of T cells (Herberman *et al.*, 1987).

In the initial descriptions of LAK cells, much emphasis was placed on the observation that fresh solid tumour target cells appeared to be resistant to lysis by NK cells (Grimm *et al.*, 1982). However, susceptibility or resistance of target cells to lysis by NK cells appears to be a relative rather than an absolute distinction. Under some circumstances, 'NK-resistant' targets can be lysed to a significant extent by unstimulated NK cells. Regarding the possibility of NK activity against fresh non-cultured tumour cells, low but significant levels of cytotoxic activity against fresh human leukaemia cells were observed in the earliest studies of human NK cells (Rosenberg *et al.*, 1972). Similarly, some of the 'NK-resistant' culture cell lines that are being used as good targets for assessing LAK activity, particularly the Raji cell line, were used in early studies of NK activity (McCoy *et al.*, 1973; Rosenberg *et al.*, 1974), before the discovery of more sensitive targets such as K562. Clearly, the increase of NK activity by various agents, including IFN as well as IL-2, not only can increase the levels of reactivity against NK-sensitive target cells but also can induce detectable levels of lysis of targets that seemed refractory to unstimulated NK cells. The artificiality of the distinction between NK-sensitive and NK-resistant target cells has been emphasised by a series of in vivo studies of the role of NK cells in resistance to metastatic spread of tumours. Much of the strong evidence for the potent ability of NK cells in vivo to rapidly eliminate tumour cells from the circulation and to prevent the subsequent development of metastases in the lungs and other organs has come from studies with tumour cell lines which appear to be highly resistant to NK activity in vitro (Barlozzari *et al.*, 1985; Barlozzari *et al.*, 1983; Gorelik *et al.*, 1982).

Even when it has not been possible to detect lysis of fresh leukaemia or solid tumour target cells by unseparated blood or splenic lymphocytes, significant levels of NK activity have been detected simply after purification of the effector cells. Human LGLs, purified by Percoll density gradient centrifugation, have been shown to have significant cytotoxic activity against the majority of fresh solid tumour cells or fresh leukaemia cells tested. The effector cells for solid tumour targets appeared to be a subset of LGLs (Uchida and Micksche, 1983), but in conjugate assays with two target cells it was shown that the effector cells lysing autologous tumour cells could also lyse the NK-sensitive K562 cell line (Uchida and Yanagawa, 1984). The effector cells reactive against human leukaemia targets were further shown to be CD16$^+$ and NKH1$^+$ (Leu 19$^+$) (Lotzova *et al.*, 1987; Lotzova *et al.*, 1986). In contrast to such lytic activity of LGLs against fresh human 'NK-resistant' targets, LGL-depleted populations of small T cells were without detectable activity.

In addition to the above evidence that unstimulated NK cells as well as LAK cells can have cytotoxic activity against fresh tumour cells and other 'NK-resistant' targets, there are some indications that NK cells and LAK cells may recognise the same target structures. In cold target inhibition experiments, NK-susceptible targets such as K562 could efficiently inhibit human LAK activity against an NK-resistant target. Similarly, NK-sensitive target cells were found to adsorb LAK cells more efficiently in monolayer depletion experiments than did NK-resistant cells. Further, after exposure of NK-susceptible target cells to LAK cells, the surviving target cells were found to be transiently resistant to both NK cells and cells with LAK activity (DeVries and Golub, 1986). One might explain such data by postulating that NK-sensitive target cells simply express NK target structures better or in higher concentration than NK-resistant targets. However, to settle this question, it will be necessary to directly characterise the target structures recognised by NK cells and LAK cells and, in a complementary way, characterise the recognition structures on each type of effector cell.

Extensive studies have now been made of the phenotype of both lymphocytes which develop LAK activity after culture with IL-2 (i.e. progenitors of cells with LAK activity) and the effector cells themselves, after culture in the presence of IL-2. Although the initial studies on LAK activity suggested a shift in phenotype, from progenitors lacking T cell as well as NK cell markers (Grimm *et al.*, 1983) to effector cells with T cell markers, subsequent studies have indicated the expression of a very similar pattern of markers on both the progenitors and effector cells. Data on the phenotype of LAK cells have now been obtained in three species (mouse and rat as well as human), and these are summarised below.

In regard to the characteristics which have been associated with the blood or splenic lymphocytes which developed LAK activity after culture in the presence of IL-2, the most extensive studies have been performed with human lymphocytes. It seems clear that most of the LAK activity from blood lymphocytes is generated from cells with the same characteristics as NK cells. The progenitors of LAK activity in human peripheral blood have been shown to be mainly LGLs with the CD3$^-$ CD16$^+$ NKH1$^+$ phenotype. Some of the progenitors appear to be low-density lymphocytes which lack the characteristic granules of LGLs and thereby are resistant to the lysosomotropic agent, L-leucine methyl ester (Shau and Golub, 1985). Somewhat divergent data have been the finding of low levels of LAK activity generated from $CD3^+$ blood lymphocytes. $CD3^+$ $NKH1^+$ lymphocytes have been detected in low concentrations in peripheral blood, have been associated with some MHC-unrestricted cytotoxcity, and have been shown to give rise to some clones with 'NK-like' activity (Hercend *et al.*, 1983a; Schmidt, *et al.*, 1985). More strongly divergent results have come from a recent study (Damle *et al.*, 1986), indicating that appreciable LAK activity could be generated from a wide variety of lymphocyte subpopulations, including $CD4^+$ and $CD8^+$ T cells and also B cells. The explanation for these divergent results is not clear, but may be attributable to some technical limitations of the panning technique used for separating cells.

The LAK activity generated from mouse or rat spleen cells or bone-marrow cells has been associated with progenitors with characteristics virtually identical to those associated with NK cells. For example, rat NK cells have been closely associated with LGLs and the asialo GM_1 and CD8 cell surface antigens (Reynolds *et al.*, 1981b). In addition, cell-surface molecules reactive with polyclonal and monoclonal antibodies to laminin have been found to be selectively expressed on rat NK cells (Hiserodt *et al.*, 1985). These same markers are also expressed on the progenitors of rat LAK cells. Furthermore, high levels of LAK activity were generated from highly purified populations of blood or splenic LGLs, while little or no activity was generated from purified populations of T cells. Most studies with mouse lymphocytes have also indicated that the splenic progenitors of LAK activity have a phenotype compatible with NK cells, with expression of asialo GM1, some positivity for Thy 1, and absence of L3T4 or Lyt2. However, Shortman *et al.* (1984) have depicted the generation, from $Lyt2^+$ cells of some mouse strains by a limiting dilution technique, of cells with lytic activity against NK-resistant targets. However, these cultures have been performed in the presence of concanavalin A and irradiated killer cells and those conditions may account for the divergent results.

In regard to characteristics of cells with LAK activity, generated from blood or splenic lymphocytes upon culture in the presence of IL-2, the phenotype of most of the progenitor cells and of most of the effectors for LAK activity is very similar, each quite compatible with the phenotype of NK cells but divergent from that of typical T cells. As with the progenitors of LAK activity, some effectors cells with LAK activity have been shown to have T cell markers. However, under the usual conditions of generating LAK activity from blood or splenic lymphocytes, such effector cells appear to be very infrequent. Also, such T cells with LAK activity appear to have been derived from T cell progenitors. It is of interest that the CD3$^+$ human lymphocytes with LAK activity appear to be, at least in part, atypical T cells expressing NKH1 (Hercend *et al.*, 1983b; Schmidt *et al.*, 1985) but lacking expression of either CD4 or CD8 (van de Griend *et al.*, 1987).

Thus, LAK should be considered a phenomenon rather than a new or distinct effector cell, with most of the blood or splenic activity attributable to NK cells. The LAK phenomenon appears to be of particular interest because of the potent ability of IL-2 both to stimulate cytotoxic activity and to promote the expansion of the effector cell population. In regard to the major therapeutic effects of LAK cells, this should now be viewed as an outgrowth of the extensive studies over the last several years on the role of natural effector cells in host resistance against tumours. Most of the results in animal models have indicated a predominant involvement of NK cells in prevention of metastases (Wiltrout *et al.*, 1987) and there have been fewer data supporting a role for these effector cells in therapy. However, the recent experience with the LAK phenomenon suggests that this distinction is not complete, and that highly activated NK cells, when given in sufficient numbers, can have therapeutic as well as prophylactic antitumour effects.

Recently, a new and simple procedure for the purification and rapid expansion of LAK cells from peripheral blood and splenic LGLs has been developed (Vujanovic *et al.*, 1988). This procedure exploits the observation made in our laboratory that rat LGL/NK cells initially respond to IL-2 by adhering to plastic surfaces. As soon as two hours after the addition of IL-2, LGLs adhere to plastic. This adherence is maximal at 24 to 48 hours in culture. These adherent cells are 94–97 per cent LGLs and express surface markers characteristic of rat NK cells, including OX8, asialo GM1 and laminin. The cells do not express pan T cell (CD5), helper T cell (CD4) or B cell (Ig) markers, nor do they express the rat T-cell-associated IL-2 receptor, OX39. While two-hour adherent cells show high levels of cytotoxic activity against YAC-1 targets only (NK activity), 48-hour adherent cells already demonstrate the development of high levels of LAK activity. The adherent LGL cells exhibiting LAK activity have been designated A-LAK cells.

When 48-hour A-LAK cells were separated from the non-adherent cells, washed and refed with conditioned medium, they rapidly expanded over the next 3–4 days, with expansion indices often reaching 90-fold in this time period. These expanding cells generated very high levels of LAK cytotoxic activity. When compared to the levels of cytotoxic LAK activity generated in standard bulk cultures, the adherent cultures generated between 20 and 50 times more total lytic units per culture.

Studies of the phenotype of the rat A-LAK cells after expansion for five days or more in culture, indicated that these cells are LGLs and express surface markers (CD5) or helper T cell (CD4) markers and do not express significant levels of rat IL-2 receptor (Tac type), as detected by the OX 39 MoAb. These activated lymphocytes display cytolytic activity against neoplastic cells from a wide variety of tumours. Cytolytic activity could be demonstrated against tumour lines from different tissues and cell preparations, including ascites tumours, solid tumours, or neoplastic cell lines grown in vitro or in vivo.

In some situations, interleukin 1 (IL-1), a cytokine produced mainly by monocytes and macrophages, may also stimulate NK activity. DeVries *et al.* (1982) reported that the natural cytotoxicity of human lymphocytes against adherent tumour target cells was dependent on the presence of a subpopulation of monoctyes and that this requirement could be replaced by IL-1.

2. In vivo augmentation of NK activity

In order to apply the detailed knowledge about in vitro augmentation of NK activity to the therapy of cancer, it is necessary to determine how to extend such information to the in vivo boosting of NK activity. As noted above, some of the initial observations on augmentation of NK activity were made by injection of various IFN-inducers into mice and rats. Since then, a wide variety of viruses, adjuvants and immunomodulators have been found to augment NK activity, most of them acting by induction of IFN. However, some of the NK-boosting agents appear to be stimulatory via other, IFN-independent mechanisms. For example, augmentation of NK activity by diethylthiocarbamate (Renoux *et al.*, 1982), OK 432 (Uchida and Micksche, 1982b), or ethanol (Saxena *et al.*, 1982) has not been accompanied by detectable production of IFN.

As shown in the in vitro studies on positive regulation of NK activity, the in vivo administration of IFN or other agents may affect the growth and differentiation of NK cells as well as stimulate the effector phase of their activity. Biron and Welsh (1982) have shown that stimulation of NK activity by in vivo administration of various viruses or poly I:C is associated with some proliferation of NK and the appearance of blast cells with NK activity. Similarly, we have found that, after administration of *C. parvum*, MVE-2, or poly I:C, there was a significant increase in LGLs in the spleens of nude as well as euthymic mice, and that a substantial proportion of the augmented NK activity was associated with LGLs that were of lower density and were larger and more vacuolated than the LGLs of unstimulated mice (Santoni *et al.*, 1985). Although these observations indicate that expansion of the pool of NK cells as well as activation may contribute to the augementation of NK activity, proliferation has been shown not to be required for boosting (Herberman and Holden, 1978; Biron and Welsh, 1982).

In vivo administration to mice of human recombinant IL-2 has also been shown to induce both an expansion of lymphocytes and an augmentation of cytotoxic activity (Mulé *et al.*, 1985; Talmadge, 1985; Talmadge *et al.*, 1985; Ettinghausen *et al.*, 1985a). Recent clinical studies with IL-2 have also indicated an induction of LAK activity in cancer patients (e.g. Lotze *et al.*, 1984; Hank *et al.*, 1987). However, since the cellular composition of the proliferating lymphocytes was not studied in detail, it remains unclear whether the augmented levels of cytotoxic reactivity against NK-resistant as well as NK-sensitive target cells were the result of parallel stimulation of proliferation as well as effector activity of LAK/NK cells. The observation that administration of IL-2 was needed for effective therapy of tumours by adoptively transferred LAK cells (Mulé *et al.*, 1985) has led to an approach to resolve this issue. The combination of both IL-2 and LAK cells gave higher levels of proliferation in some organs, even in preirradiated recipients, and it was assumed that the IL-2 was instrumental in maintaining the viability and promoting the expansion of the transferred effector cells (Ettinghausen *et al.*, 1985b). However, since the transferred cells were actually unpurified populations of IL-2-cultured spleen cells, the proliferation and the effector cells could not be conclusively related. The recent ability in our laboratory to purify LAK cells by plastic adherence has allowed a closer examination of this question (Maghazachi *et al.*, 1987). Somewhat unexpectedly, it was found that administration of IL-2 along with radiolabelled A-LAK cells was needed to maintain the cytotoxic activity of the transferred cells, but did not detectably affect their viability or numbers.

Most of the studies on in vivo augmentation of NK activity have been performed with single inoculations of an agent, administered by only one route of inoculation. There is therefore a very limited experimental base for deciding on appropriate protocols for attempts at cancer therapy based on augmentation of NK activity.

There are, however, some indications that considerations as to route, dose, and frequency of administration of an NK-augmenting agent may have profound effects on the results. The many clinical trials with IFN appear to provide a good example of this point. In contrast to the consistent ability of IFN treatment in vitro to boost the NK activity of most cancer patients as well as normal donors, there have been major differences in the results obtained among the various studies. In a trial with Cantell IFN-α, with 1.5–6 million units given intramuscularly on a daily basis (Einhorn *et al.*, 1982), NK activity was increased in most patients at 24 hours after the first inoculation and this increase appeared to be sustained in most patients for up to 12 months. It is of interest that even in this study the lowest dose used was associated with the highest boost in NK activity and that the highest dose gave the lowest increase. Golub (1982) evaluated the effects of a similar preparation of IFN-α, 1–9 million units being given intramuscularly daily for 42 days to patients with melanoma. In contrast to the findings of Einhorn *et al.*, (1982), a depression of NK activity was usually seen after one day, boosting was seen primarily at seven days, and the reactivity tended to return to baseline levels thereafter. Even more divergent results were obtained by Maluish *et al.*, (1982), who studied advanced cancer patients receiving highly purified recombinant clone A IFN-α intramuscularly, either twice daily or three times per week, at dose levels varying from 1 million to over 100 million units. Very few of the patients showed a significant increase in NK activity, and a considerable proportion actually showed a significant decrease (see Section IV.B for more detailed discussion). As yet, there are no clear indications as to the main variable contributing to the disparate results among such clinical studies. It will probably be necessary to perform more systematic studies, with the same preparation of IFN, of the effects of such parameters as dose and frequency of administration. It is to be hoped that studies along these lines in rodents will provide insights which will be translatable into clinical protocols that are more consistently effective for boosting of NK activity.

Studies involving frequently repeated administration of IFN inducers might be expected to show only transient augmentation of NK activity because of the known development of refractoriness to induction of IFN release (Stringfellow, 1978). Results along these lines have been obtained in cancer patients receiving high doses of poly I:C poly-L-lysine-carboxymethyl cellulose complex (poly ICLC) frequently by the intravenous route (J. Jett, A. Levine, and R. B. Herberman, unpublished observations). After the first few doses of poly ICLC, substantial augmentation of NK activity was seen. Subsequently, the NK activity of the patients tended to return to pretreatment levels, and this decline coincided with diminished or undetectable levels of serum IFN. When patients were given poly ICLC intramuscularly on a three times per week schedule, a low dose gave more consistent and prolonged augmentation of NK activity (A. Maluish, J. Reid and R. B. Herberman, unpublished observations). We have performed experiments (in collaboration with M. Piccoli and M. A. Chirigos) in mice with poly I:C or poly ICLC, to gain a better understanding of the schedule of administration that might give sustained augmentation of NK activity without development of refractoriness. Twice-weekly intraperitoneal administration of these agents has been found to continue giving significant boosting of NK activity for up to eight weeks. Thus, it seems likely that the objective of producing sustained augmentation of NK activity can be achieved, once the optimal schedule has been worked out.

Dose, route and schedule of administration of IL-2 have also been shown to be important factors in determining the kinetics and magnitude of augmentation of NK/LAK activity. Low, sustained levels of IL-2 induced by intraperitoneal administration of IL-2 was found to augment cytotoxic reactivity more effectively, especially in the peritoneal cavity, than much higher doses of IL-2 administered by intravenous injections (Talmadge, 1985; Talmadge *et al.*, 1985; Ettinghausen and Rosenberg, 1986).

B. Factors Inhibiting NK Activity

There are increasing indications that NK is a well-regulated system, subject to inhibitory controls as well as to activating or augmenting signals. In contrast to the situation with augmentation of NK activity, where two mediators, IFN and IL-2, appear to play a predominant role, inhibition of NK activity may result from a variety of mechanism. Three main categories of mechanisms for negative regulation of the function of NK cells may be considered: (1) direct inhibition of the development or the function of NK cells, (2) inhibition by suppressor cells, and (3) inhibition of the function of accessory cells. The last possibility remains basically a theoretical one, since there is little evidence for this mechanism being responsible for known situations with depressed NK activity.

Prostaglandins (PG) have been shown to be inhibitors of both spontaneous and IFN-boosted human and mouse NK activity in vitro (Droller *et al.*, 1978; Brunda *et al.*, 1980a; Lang *et al.*, 1982; Koren *et al.*, 1981; Kendall and Targan, 1980). The addition of 10^{-6} molar PGE_1, PGE_2, PGA_1, or PGA_2 to the cytolytic assay inhibited NK activity. On the other hand, PGB_1, PGB_2, PGF_1, or PGF_2 had no inhibitory effects. Interestingly, the administration of inhibitors of PG synthesis (i.e. aspirin or indomethacin) to mice bearing murine sarcoma virus-induced tumours led to partial restoration of their depressed NK activity (Brunda *et al.*, 1980a).

The mechanism for the inhibition of NK activity remains to be fully defined, but several pieces of evidence are available. The inhibition is reversible, with less or no inhibition seen after preincubation of effector cells or target cells with prostaglandins and then washing prior to assay

(Brunda *et al.*, 1980a; Lang *et al.*, 1982; Goto *et al.*, 1983). However, it has been possible to demonstrate that inhibition was at the level of the effector cells, since mouse spleen cells that had been incubated in vitro overnight were no longer susceptible to inhibiton (Brunda *et al.*, 1980a).

Similarly, it has been reported that activation of human or mouse NK cells by IFN or poly I:C resulted in a partial loss of sensitivity of these cells to suppression by PGE_2 (Leung and Koren, 1982). Furthermore, Goto *et al.* (1983) detected some residual inhibition of NK activity after pretreatment of purified human LGLs with PGE_2. In other studies with human peripheral blood mononuclear cells (Kendall and Targan, 1980) or with purified LGLs (Ortaldo *et al.*, 1984b), the presence of PGE was found not to inhibit conjugate formation with susceptible target cells, but rather to inhibit the subsequent lysis in ^{51}Cr release or single-cell agarose cytotoxicity assays. These results indicate that the inhibition of NK activity by PGE is not at the level of recognition of target cells, but rather at some post-binding metabolic step required for lysis. Hiserodt *et al.* (1982) reported that at least one of the sites of PGE_2 inhibition was at the phase of killer-cell-independent lysis.

It has been generally assumed that PGE inhibits cellular cytotoxicity by the induction of intracellular cyclic AMP (cAMP) (Henney *et al.*, 1978). This possibility is supported by observations that addition to NK assays of dibutyryl cAMP also strongly inhibited cytotoxicity (Lang *et al.*, 1982). Goto *et al.* (1983) have examined in detail the association between PGE-mediated inhibition of NK activity and elevation of intracellular levels of cAMP. Treatment of human LGLs with PGE_2 was shown to cause considerable increases in cAMP, whereas similar treatment of typical T cells had a much less pronounced effect. NK activity could also be inhibited by inhibitors of phosphodiesterase, which also elevate cAMP by a different mechanism. The presence of both PGE_2 and a phosphodiesterase inhibitor resulted in higher levels of cAMP and in more marked inhibition of NK activity than was seen with either agent alone. Thus, it appears that elevation of intracellular levels of cAMP within NK cells provides a strong negative signal for reactivity. It will now be important to analyse the subsequent metabolic events triggered by this signal.

It should be noted that exposure of NK cells to PGE has not invariably led to inhibition of their reactivity. Kendall and Targan (1980) reported that whereas the presence of PGE_2 during the assay produced inhibition, preincubation of human peripheral blood lymphocytes (PBLs) with PGE for an hour or more and then removal prior to the assay caused augmented reactivity. However similar experiments with purified human LGLs by Goto *et al.* (1983) failed to show any augmentation, but rather resulted in some inhibition of reactivity. The reasons for the divergent results are not clear, but they are probably attributable to some important differences in the technical details of the experiments or in the PGE preparations that were used.

Another type of negative regulation of NK activity was found in studies of short-term incubation of human peripheral blood mono-nuclear cells (Sulica *et al.*, 1982). After incubation for 1–2 hours in medium lacking human serum, increased NK activity was seen. This seemed to be due to release from inhibition by human serum factors, since incubation in 20 per cent autologous serum prevented the augmentation. The serum-mediated effect appeared to be attributable to the degree of binding of labile IgG to the cells and could be reduced by selective depletion of IgG from the serum. Human or rabbit monomeric IgG was found to inhibit efficiently the culture-induced augmentation of NK activity, and the inhibitory IgG had properties consistent with those previously described for cytophilic IgG. The overall pattern of results suggested that this mechanism may be involved in negative regulation of NK activity in vivo. Recent studies along the same lines as those performed by Goto *et al.*, (1983) with PGE, have indicated that the mechanism for inhibition of NK activity by cytophilic IgG is also related to elevation of cAMP levels within the effector cells (Bancu *et al.*, 1987).

1. Inhibition by suppressor cells

Many of the inhibitory effects on NK activity appear to be mediated by suppressor cells. Cells capable of inhibiting the lytic activity of mouse NK cells have been generated after treatment with immunoaduvants, such as *C. parvum* (Lotzova, 1980; Santoni, *et al.*, 1982a), pyran copolymer (Santoni *et al.*, 1980a), glucan (Lotzova and Gutterman, 1979), and BCG (Ito *et al.*, 1980), or with various therapeutic modalities, such as irradiation (Hochman *et al.*, 1978; Cudkowicz and Hochman, 1979), corticosteroids (Hochman and Cudkowicz, 1979), and adriamycin (Santoni *et al.*, 1980b). In most instances, the suppressor cells have been shown to be active at the effector phase, being measured by their effects when present during the cytotoxicity assay. In most cases, detection of such suppressor cells has required rather large numbers of cells, usually at suppressor:effector cell ratios of at least 1:1. There is as yet no clear indication whether they exert their inhibitory activity at the initial target recognition phase or at some post-binding metabolic step.

With regard to the nature of suppressor cells, two main categories of suppressor cells have been defined: macrophage-like suppressor cells with adherent and phagocytic properties, and null cells, i.e., nylon- and plastic-non-adherent cells lacking detectable cell-surface markers.

Macrophage-like suppressor cells have been found in the spleens of mice treated with pyran copolymer (Santoni *et al.*, 1980a), *C. parvum* (Santoni *et al.*, 1982a), carrageenan (Hochman *et al.*, 1981), or corticosteroids (Hochman and Cudkowicz, 1979). Non-adherent suppressor cells lacking easily detectable markers have been described in the spleens of mice exposed to ^{89}Sr or gamma radiation (Cudkowicz and Hochman, 1979) or treated with BCG (Ito *et al.*, 1980) or *C. parvum* (Santoni *et al.*, 1982a).

In addition to induction of suppressor cells by various treatments, suppressor cells for NK activity have been detected in some natural situations. The low NK activity in newborn mice may be attributable at least in part to the presence of non-adherent suppressor cells (Cudkowicz and Hochman, 1979; Santoni *et al.*, 1982b). Furthermore, some strains of mice with genetically determined low NK activity have been found to have suppressors for NK activity. Adherent spleen cells of normal SJL mice have been found to inhibit the NK activity of spleen cells of high-NK strains (Riccardi *et al.*, 1981). In studies of adoptive transfer of NK activity, SJL recipients have also been found to inhibit the full expression of the reactivity of donor NK cells (Riccardi *et al.*, 1982). Suppressor cells for the lytic function of NK or K cells have also been found in organs exhibiting low levels of cytotoxic activity, such as the thymus (Nair *et al.*, 1981) or lymph nodes (Pollack and Emmons, 1981). Similarly, in the peritoneal cavity of high as well as low NK-reactive mice and also of athymic nude mice, adherent cells with the characteristics of macrophages have been found to be able to suppress NK activity (Santoni *et al.*, 1982b), suggesting that their presence could, in part, account for the low NK activity at this site.

Most evidence for suppression of NK activity has come from studies in mice. However, evidence has now accumulated for the presence of human suppressor cells for NK activity. Bordignon *et al.* (1982) have reported that alveolar macrophages, unlike other mononuclear phagocyte populations such as blood monocytes and peritoneal or milk macrophages, caused a marked dose-dependent inhibiton of spontaneous or IFN-augmented human NK activity. Furthermore, it has been shown that a major portion of the suppression of natural killing by phorbol ester (PMA) or by opsonised zymosan is mediated by monocytes or polymorphonuclear leukocytes (Seaman *et al.*, 1982). Moreover, Fc-receptor-positive small to medium-sized T cells in human umbilical cord blood have been reported to suppress strongly the cytotoxic activity of NK cells (Tarkkanen and Saksela, 1982).

Suppressor cells for NK activity have also been found in some tumour-bearing individuals with low NK activity. Mice bearing progressively growing primary tumours induced by murine sarcoma virus had low or undetectable NK activity in situ but removal of adherent or phagocytic cells led to a marked increase in activity (Gerson *et al.*, 1981). A role for suppressor macrophages within the tumour was supported by mixing experiments, in which cells from the tumour inhibited the activity of normal spleen cells. Similar evidence for the in situ presence of suppressor cells has been obtained with some human tumours (Gerson, 1980; Vose and Moore, 1979; Eremin, 1980; Allavena *et al.*, 1981).

Although little information is available about the factors that activate or stimulate suppressor cells, some situations have been found in which suppressor activity is modulated. Normal peritoneal macrophages, after in vitro activation by IFN or poly I:C, or in vivo activation by *C. parvum*, showed a reduced capacity to inhibit the lytic activity (Santoni *et al.*, 1982a). However, no changes in suppressor capacity of peritoneal macrophages could be observed following in vitro activation with supernatants containing macrophage-activating factor. Similarly, abrogation of the suppressor activity by human cord blood T cells was obtained following in vitro pretreatment with IFN (Tarkkanen and Saksela, 1982). These results indicate that the augmentation of NK activity by IFN could be the result not only of activation of NK cells, but also of a decrease in the activity of suppressor cells. Uchida and Micksche (1982b) have reported that exposure of human adherent suppressor cells to the bacterial adjuvant OK-432 caused a decrease in or loss of their ability to inhibit the activity of human cells. However, the mechanism of this effect and its possible relationship to production of IFN have not been determined. The mechanisms by which these suppressor cells inhibit NK activity have not been defined, but soluble mediators seem to be involved in many situations (Santoni *et al.*, 1980a; Riccardi *et al.*, 1981; Hochman *et al.*, 1981; Santoni *et al.*, 1982a; Tarkkanen and Saksela, 1982). The nature of the inhibitory soluble factors remains to be defined. In view of the known inhibitory effects of prostaglandins and their production by macrophages, these mediators are good candidates for careful consideration. However, in vitro treatment with indomethacin did not reverse the inhibition of NK activity mediated by *C. parvum*-induced suppressor cells (Santoni *et al.*, 1982a) or by alveolar macrophages in humans (A. Mantovani, personal communication).

Reactive oxygen species, previously shown to be involved in the suppression of mitogen-induced proliferation (Metzger *et al.*, 1980), have been implicated in the inhibition of NK activity. For example, the monocyte- or granulocyte-dependent inhibition of natural killing by PMA appearted to be linked closely to the generation of reactive forms of molecular oxygen and in particular hydrogen peroxide (Seaman *et al.*, 1982). PMA-induced suppressor activity was reduced in glucose-free medium, was inhibited by catalase, and was not exerted by monocytes or granulocytes from a patient with chronic granulomatous disease. Moreover, Mantovani and his colleagues have reported a correlation between the capacity of different populations of macrophages to inhibit NK activity and their ability to produce oxygen metabolites, with alveolar macrophages appearing to be unique in their capacity to inhibit effectively the expression of NK activity and to produce high amounts of superoxide (Biondi *et al.*, 1983).

With regard to the mechanisms of inhibition of NK activity mediated by non-adherent suppressor cells, it has been suggested (Cudkowicz and Hochman, 1979) that these cells might be pre-NK cells, with the ability to bind but not to lyse the NK target cells, thus acting as competitive inhibitors of lytically active NK cells. However, fractionation of spleen cells from *C. parvum*-treated mice on a seven-step discontinuous Percoll gradient resulted in physical separation of NK cells from suppressor cells, with the NK activity recovered in the low-density fractions and the suppressor activity in the high-density fractions (Santoni and Herberman, unpublished observations). The suppressor cells in this system also lacked the expression of other markers of NK cells, e.g. any detectable Thy 1 antigen or asialo GM_1 antigen on their surface. Moreover, Pollack and Emmons (1981) reported that non-adherent suppressor cells present in the lymph nodes of normal mice did not bind target cells and therefore did not appear to act by competing with spleen cells for binding sites. Taken together, these results make unlikely the hypothesis that non-adherent suppressor cells are pre-NK cells which exert a competitive inhibition. However, the nature of these non-adherent suppressor cells in mice and the mechanism for their suppressor activity remain to be determined.

Suppressor cells for NK activity have been found to affect not only the effector phase of NK activity, but also the maintenance of the activity of NK cells. In studies on the maintenance of mouse NK activity upon overnight incubation at 37°C , a role for suppressor cells from normal mice has been detected (Brunda *et al.*, 1982). Peritoneal macrophages from normal mice, i.e. resident cells obtained without any stimuli or elicited by various sterile irritants, markedly suppressed the NK activity of effector cells incubated alone or with IFN. This suppressor activity appeared restricted to peritoneal macrophages because splenic adherent cells were inactive. The peritoneal macrophages of several strains had suppressor activity, including those from high-NK strains and from nude mice. It was of interest that peritoneal macrophages from *C. parvum*-injected mice had a reduced ability to suppress NK activity, and this was parallelled by the high levels of peritoneal NK activity in these mice.

Uchida and Micksche (1982a) have obtained similar results with macrophages of patients with cancer. These cells caused no detectable inhibition of NK activity when present during the cytotoxicity assay, but were strongly suppressive when co-cultured overnight with NK cells prior to assay.

It is not known whether the suppression of the maintenance of IFN augmentation of NK activity and the suppression of the cytolytic effector phase work through common pathways. However, the limited available data suggest some divergence between these two forms of inhibition of NK activity. The suppression by mouse peritoneal macrophages or by human macrophages of spontaneously maintained or IFN-augmented in vitro activity occurred at considerably lower suppressor:effector cell ratios than in other studies showing suppression at the effector phase. As a further contrast between the two types of suppression systems, splenic suppressor cells from low-NK-reactive mice or induced by *C. parvum* were not capable of suppressing the maintenance of NK activity.

V. MECHANISM OF CYTOTOXICITY BY NK CELLS

As a result of efforts to dissect the mechanisms involved in the interactions between cytotoxic effector cells and target cells, it has been possible to define a sequence of events which appear to be required for the lytic process. These steps were first described for CTLs (Berke, 1980), and subsequently a similar sequence has been shown to be involved in NK activity (Herberman, 1982). The main stages can be identified as: (1) recognition of target cells by effector cells; (2) binding of effectors to targets: (3) activation of lytic machinery of effector cells: (4) lytic effects on target cells, often referred to as the 'lytic hit'; and (5) effector-cell-in-dependent dissolution of the targets. In the following discussion, some of the main features of each of these stages will be summarised, with particular emphasis on the similarities and differences between CTLs and NK cells.

A. Recognition of Target Cells by Effector Cells

The recognition event appears to be dependent on two types of structures, the cell surface recognition receptors on the effector cells, and the 'antigens' or other structures on the target cells which need to be recognised.

1. Recognition structures on effector cells

Much attention has been devoted to the nature of the T cell receptor and there have been some recent exciting advances in our understanding of the biochemical and molecular biological features of this receptor (Williams, 1984). In contrast, there has as yet been little documentation of the nature of the recognition receptors on NK cells. The binding of NK cells to target cells is clearly required to activate the lytic process of these cells. Most of the data regarding the NK-recognition receptor only serve to show what it is not. For instance, although NK and antibody-dependent cellular cytotoxic (ADCC) activities may be mediated by the same effector cell, blocking of the receptor for the Fc portion of IgG (FcγR) inhibits only ADCC activity and has little or no effect on NK activity (Perussia *et al.*, 1983). This demonstrates that the NK receptor is not simply the FcγR binding to cell-bound antibody on the target. Similarly, the NK-recognition receptor is unlikely to be immunoglobulin (Ig) since Ig-like molecules are absent from the surface membrane of LGLs (Ortaldo *et al.*, 1981; Reynolds *et al.*, 1981b), and treatment of lymphocytes with anti-Ig and complement has no effect on their NK activity (Kiessling *et al.*, 1975a).

It has been suggested that the recognition of NK-susceptible target cells by NK cells is via a laminin-like structure (Hiserodt *et al.*, 1985; Hiserodt *et al.*, 1987). NK cells and LAK cells selectively express surface structures which react with polyclonal and some monoclonal antibodies to laminin. Such antibodies have been found to inhibit NK activity. However, it is as yet unclear whether the laminin-like molecules on NK cells represent primary recognition structures or are needed for secondary binding interactions with target cells.

It has also been suggested that murine NK cells and cytotoxic T lymphocyte (CTL) and other clones with NK-like activity express mRNA as well as rearrangements of the genes coding for the β-chain of the T cell receptor (Yanagi *et al.*, 1985). Experiments with human cells using $CD3^+$, but not $CD3^-$, lymphocyte clones with NK-like activity have produced similar data (Ritz *et al.*, 1985). The authors suggest that the T cell receptor on such cells acts as the recognition receptor for NK-like activity, since antibodies to the idiotypic determinants of the T cell receptor blocked cytotoxic activity against K562 (Hercend *et al.*, 1983a). However, even in those studies, some clones with NK-like activity had no detectable expression of T cell receptors, indicating that other structures can recognise NK-susceptible targets. In addition, abundant data now indicate that the NK-recognition receptor is different from the T cell receptor. First, in the rat, LGL tumour lines with high NK activity have no genomic rearrangement of the T cell receptor β-chain and no detectable complete 1.3-kb mRNA for this structure (Reynolds *et al.*, 1985). Second, freshly isolated, highly purified populations of rat, mouse, and human LGLs have no detectable 1.3-kb mRNA or β-chain gene rearrangement, in spite of very high NK activity (Young *et al.*, 1986). Third, the addition of anti-CD3 antibody, which recognises a portion of the human T cell receptor complex, has no effect on the NK activity of freshly isolated human LGL or CD3[+] cytotoxic clones with NK-like activity (Herberman *et al.*, 1986). Finally, Binz, Wigzell and associates (Binz *et al.*, 1983) have reported that addition of anti-idiotype antibodies to CTL lines with both antigen-specific and NK-like activity inhibited only the antigen-specific cytotoxicity but did not affect the NK-like activity of these clones.

The likely reason for divergent results regarding fresh mouse NK cells (Yanagi *et al.*, 1985; Young *et al.*, 1986) is related to the difficulty in obtaining highly purified NK cells without appreciable contamination by T cells (i.e. less than 5 per cent T cells) from mouse spleen, and the previous positive report (Yanagi *et al.*, 1985) is probably due to insufficient purification of the effector cell population. The detection of T cell receptor gene rearragement and/or expression in cells in vitro is more likely the development of NK-like activity in typical T cells when cultured in IL-2 (Brooks, 1983). However, the expression of the T cell receptor is unlikely to be related to the expression of NK-like receptors on these cells.

Taken together, these results indicate that the NK-cell recognition receptor is not identical to the previously described T cell receptor complex and its molecular nature remains elusive. Perhaps use of a molecular biological approach similar to that successfully used for the T cell receptor will lead to elucidation of the structure(s) by which NK cells recognise target cells.

2. Target structures recognised by effector cells

In most instances, the recognition of target cells by CTLs is restricted by the major histocompatibility complex (MHC) and the target structures themselves seem to be closely associated with the MHC (Berke, 1980). It has been proposed that MHC proteins on target cells are critical molecular mediators by which the CTL receptors transmit signals required for the subsequent lysis of the target cells (Berke, 1980).

In contrast to the extensive studies on the target structures recognised by CTLs, little definitive information exists about the nature of the target structures recognised by NK cells.

A central issue in the study of the specificity of NK cells is whether one common target structure is recognised by all NK cells or whether subsets of NK cells recognise a variety of target-cell structures. If multiple structures exist, attention must be focused on the extent or size of the repertoire and on whether discrete subpopulations of NK cells each have restricted reactivity against one or a few of these target structures.

From studies using adsorption procedures (Jensen and Koren, 1979; Phillips *et al.*, 1980) or cloning of effector cells (Allavena and Ortaldo, 1983; Bolhuis *et al.*, 1983; Hercend *et al.*, 1982), the evidence favours the existence of at least several subsets of NK cells, some with broad reactivity and others with narrower patterns of cytotoxic effects.

Insight into the nature of the NK target structure and its heterogeneity would be much increased by determination of the biochemical nature of the target cell determinant. However, to date very few studies have directly addressed this question. The paucity of biochemical studies on the NK target structure can be attributed (a) to limitations, at least until recently, in the methodology to isolate and purify large numbers of NK cells, and (b) to unavailability of a rapid quantitative method to assess the interaction of NK cells with soluble membrane-derived materials.

A number of indirect approaches have been used to investigate NK target structure(s). Treatment of targets with various enzymes (e.g. proteases, lipases) and agents like tunicamycin have led to the suggestion of a role for a glycoprotein or glycolipid structure (Ortaldo *et al.*, 1985). A second, more indirect, approach used specific reagents such as antitransferrin receptor (Alarcon and Fresno, 1985; Newman *et al.*, 1984; Schuurman *et al.*, 1985; Vodinelich *et al.*, 1983), anti-laminin (Hiserodt *et al.*, 1985, or antitarget antibodies (Werkmeister *et al.*, 1984). However, none of these studies yielded information that accounts for NK activity against an array of susceptible target cells; of more concern, most such inhibitory agents block NK activity at step(s) subsequent to binding of the effector cells to target cells. However, digestion of target cells with proteases can result in the loss of recognition by NK cells (Decker *et al.*, 1984), implying that surface proteins are a part of the target structure that is recognised.

A more direct approach would be to isolate membrane components from NK-susceptible targets and to measure their effects on the binding of NK cells to targets. Roder *et al.* 1979a and b reported that high molecular weight (140–200 kD) glycoproteins can inhibit conjugate formation of normal mouse spleen cells with NK-susceptible targets, but a more detailed characterisation of the target-cell molecules and the determinants recognised by mouse NK cells has not been reported. The ability to isolate highly purified NK cells, using discontinuous Percoll gradients, prompted a biochemical characterisation of NK target-cell molecules involved in binding of human NK cells to the highly NK-susceptible target K562 (Ortaldo *et al.*, 1982). Solubilised membrane proteins from K562 target cells, purified by various chromatographic procedures and reconstituted with exogenous lipid, were shown to be able to inhibit the formation of conjugates of LGLs and target cells. The size of the inhibitory molecules appeared to cover a broad range of molecular weights, from 30 to 165 kD.

B. Post-recognition Steps Leading to Lysis of Target Cells

After the requisite recognition of target cells by effectors and their binding together to form conjugates, a complex series of events is initiated which lead to the lysis of the target cells. Many of the early bio-chemical changes in the effector cells and the clear definition of a Ca^{2+}-dependent step have been found to be similar for CTLs and NK cells (Berke, 1980; Carpen *et al.*, 1982). However, the actual mechanism underlying the lethal hit has been difficult to identify. There have been some suggestions that both CTL activity and NK activity are dependent on the generation of reactive oxygen intermediates (Roder *et al.*, 1982). However, subsequent studies have essentially ruled out an involvement of this mechanism (Kay *et al.*, 1985).

Recently, an appreciable amount of experimental evidence has accumulated for a mechanism of NK activity involving secretion of cytolytic molecules. This evidence includes (1) rearrangement of cyto-plasmic organelles and release of granules from NK cells following their binding to target cells (Carpen *et al.*, 1982; Henkart and Henkart, 1982); (2) decreased NK activity in Chediak-Higashi patients (Abo *et al.*, 1982; Haliotis *et al.*, 1980; Katz *et al.*, 1982) and beige (*bg/bg*) mice (Roder and Duwe, 1979) that bear mutations leading to abnormal formation of lysosomal granules; (3) the reported inability of agranular lymphocytes to kill after they contact tumour cells (Itoh *et al.*, 1982); (4) a reduction in NK activity by strontium (Neighbour and Huberman, 1982), which promotes leukocyte degranulation (Foreman, 1977); (5) a requirement for lipid metabolism (transmethylation and phospholipase A_2 activity) for both secretion of lysosomal enzymes and NK-cell activity (Hattori *et al.*, 1983; Hoffman *et al.*, 1981); and (6) the inhibition of NK activity by lysosomotropic amines that interfere with lysosomal function (Verhoef and Sharma, 1983). Demonstrations that NK cells release soluble cytolytic factors (NKCF) upon incubation with NK-susceptible target cells or lectins (Wright and Bonavida, 1981; Wright and Bonavida, 1982) provide further evidence that a secretory process is involved.

1. LGL granule cytolysin

To evaluate the role of LGL granules in the lysis of tumour cells, the cyto-plasmic granules from rat LGL tumours have been purified (Henkart *et al.*, 1984; Millard *et al.*, 1984). These cells provide a convenient and uniform source of highly active cytolytic cells with NK specificity (Reynolds *et al.*, 1984). The granules contain a potent, calcium-dependent cytolytic material, termed LGL granule cytolysin, not present in the cytoplasmic granules of other noncytolytic leukocytes (Henkart *et al.*, 1984). LGL-cytolysin is a protein of approximately 60 kD that lyses a wide range of target cells in a rapid and Ca^{2+}-dependent manner. When tested on liposomes, LGL-cytolysin induced a rapid release of internalised carboxyfluorescein. As previously seen on lysed NK or ADCC targets, characteristic ring-like structures appeared, inserted into the lipid membrane. Penetration of negative stain into the liposomes correlated well with the presence of these pore structures. Together these data provide strong support for the model that assumes LGL granule-derived pore insertion into the lipid layer as a mechanism of cytolysin activity.

The activity of LGL-cytolysin clearly supports the model for lymphocyte cytotoxicity involving granule exocytosis after target-cell recognition. However, it is not easy to design definitive experiments to test whether granule cytolysins are responsible for the lethal damage inflicted by cytotoxic lymphocytes. One approach has been to use rabbit antibodies against the purified LGL tumour granules. Fluorescence microscopy has shown that such rabbit antibodies stain cytoplasmic granules in LGL tumour cells, LGLs and CTLs, but not in normal splenocytes, thymocytes, or peripheral T cells (Reynolds *et al.*, 1987). The antibodies did not stain the plasma membranes of LGLs and granule staining could be detected only after permeabilisation of the membrane. By Western blots, antigranule antibodies reacted with four of the five major granule proteins and IgG from the antigranule sera specifically blocked granule cytolysin activity (Reynolds *et al.*, 1987). Importantly, $F(ab')_2$ fragments of these antibodies specifically blocked the lytic activity of purified rat LGLs in NK and ADCC assays in addition to the cytolysin activity. The antibodies did not interfere with binding of LGLs to target cells, an expected result for antibodies to cytoplasmic granules. Presumably the antibodies gained access to the granule cytolysin upon its release from the NK cells and prior to its effective interaction with target cells bound to the effector cells.

The LGL granule cytolysin has much broader specificity for target cells than that seen with NK cells. NK-resistant tumour cell lines and even LGLs themselves have been lysed by the cytolysin; and sheep erythrocytes — not susceptible to NK activity — have been particularly sensitive indicators of cytolysin activity (Henkart *et al.*, 1984). This major difference in specificity of NK cells and cytolysin, and the lack of NK-resistant third-party cells during an NK assay, need to be explained to postulate a central role for LGL granule cytolysin in the lytic process of

NK cells. It is likely that during the interaction between NK cells and targets, the granule cytolysin is released mainly in the small intercellular space at the point of conjugate formation. Extracellular Ca^{2+} should rapidly inactivate the cytolysin that escapes into the surrounding medium before it reaches other target cells. Thus, the specificity of the NK reaction would be defined mainly by the initial recognition of susceptible targets, with cytolysin being released only upon an effective interaction. According to this model, it would not be necessary to have specificity at the lytic molecule phase as well.

Essentially the same cytolytic molelcule, termed perforin, has been isolated from some murine cloned CTL lines (Dennert and Podack, 1983; Podack *et al.*, 1985). Thus, it has been proposed that granule cytolysin or perforin is responsible for the lytic damage by both NK cells and CTLs (Podack, 1985). However, as noted above, in many instances azurophilic granules have not been detected in CTLs and some recent studies have failed to detect any involvement of a granule-dependent lytic molecule in the potent cytolysis produced by some preparations of CTLs (Berke and Rosen, 1987a and b). These studies have included attempts to block cytotoxicity by anti-cytolysin antibodies, and under conditions in which inhibition of NK activity had been observed, no inhibition of lysis by CTLs was seen. Thus, it seems quite possible that these molecules contribute to the lytic process but may not be essential for cytotoxicity.

2. NK cytotoxic factor (NKCF)

Another somewhat similar pathway for the mechanism of cytotoxicity by NK cells has been described involving the release of a soluble cytotoxic factor, termed NK cytotoxic factor (NKCF), from NK cells upon stimulation by NK-susceptible target cells or lectins (Herberman and Callewaert, 1985). NKCF has been shown to bind selectively to NK-susceptible target cells and then cause their lysis, but with kinetics considerably slower than those observed with intact NK cells or the LGL granule cytolysin. Although the difference in kinetics stands out as a major divergent point, most other characteristics related to NKCF have been very similar to those associated with NK activity. For example, a variety of inhibitors which were previously demonstrated to inhibit NK activity were also shown to inhibit the activity of NKCF. Initial attempts at purification have indicated that NKCF has apparent molecular weights of 18 000 and 36 000. The possible relationship between NKCF and the granule cytolysin is currently unclear. However, they may represent alternative pathways of a common mediator, since the anti-LGL granule antibodies have been found to interfere with the cytotoxic activity of human NKCF. It is possible that NKCF represents an altered or considerably more diluted version of the cytolysin in granules; direct studies on the possible relationship between their physicochemical properties and amino acid sequences will be needed to settle this question.

Recently, studies have been performed to determine the possible relationship of NKCF to other, known cytotoxic molecules. It has been possible to demonstrate that NKCF is distinct from tumour necrosis factor, lymphotoxin or leukoregulin (Herberman *et al.*, 1986; Ortaldo *et al.*, 1986b) and thus appears to be a quite novel cytotoxic molecule. In contrast, mouse NC activity has been found to be dependent on the release of tumour necrosis factor upon interaction of NC cells with their target cells (Ortaldo *et al.*, 1986b).

REFERENCES

Abo, T., Cooper, M. and Balch, C. (1982). *J. Clin. Invest.* 70: 193–200.

Abo, T., Miller, C. A., Gartland, G. L. and Balch, C. M. (1983). *J. Exp. Med.* 157: 273.

Alarcon, B. and Fresno, M. (1985). *J. Immunol.* 134: 1286–91.

Allavena, P. and Ortaldo, J. R. (1983). *Diagnostic Immunol.* 1: 162–7.

Allavena, P., Introna, M., Mangioni, C. and Mantovani, A. (1981). *J. Natl. Cancer Inst.* 67: 319–25.

Altman, A. and Rapp, H. J. (1978). *J. Immunol.* 121: 2244.

Antonelli, P., Stewart, W., II, and Dupont, B. (1981). *Clin. Immunol. Immunopathol.* 19: 161.

Arnaud-Battandier, F., Bundy, B. M. and Nelson, D. L. (1978). *Eur. J. Immunol.* 8: 400.

Axberg, I., Gidlund, M., Orn, A., Pattengale, P., Riesenfeld, I., Stern, P. and Wigzell, H. (1980). In F. Aiuti (ed.), *Thymus, Thymic Hormones and T Lymphocytes.* New York: Plenum: 181–96.

Baldwin, R. W. (1976). *Transplant Rev.* 28: 62.

Bancu, A.C., Gherman, M., Sulica, A. I., Goto, T., Farrar, W. and Herberman, R. B. (1987). *Cellular Immunology.* Submitted for publication.

Barlozzari, T., Reynolds, C. W. and Herberman, R. B. (1983). *J. Immunol.* 131:1024–7.

Barlozzari, T., Leonhardt, J., Wiltrout, R., Herberman, R. and Reynolds, C. (1985). *J. Immunol.* 134: 2783–9.

Bennett, M., Baker, E. E., Eastcott, J. W., Kumar, V. and Yonkosky, D. (1976). *J. Reticuloendothel. Soc.* 20: 71.

Berke, G. (1980). *Progr. Allergy* 27: 69–95.

Berke, G. and Rosen, D. (1987a). In *Membrane Mediated Cytotoxicity*, UCLA Symposia. In press.

Berke, G. and Rosen, D. (1987b). *Transpl. Proc.* 19: 412–16.

Binz, H., Fenner, M., Frei, D., and Wigzell, H. (1983). *J. Exp. Med.* 157: 1252–60.

Biondi, A., Bordignon, C., Peri, G., Donati, M. B., Vicenzi, E., Ghezzi, P., Salmona, M. and Mantovani, A. (1983). In J. W. Hadden, L. Chedid, P. Dukor, F. Spreafico and D. Willoughby (eds), *Advances in Immunopharmacology 2*. Oxford: Pergamon Press: 251–6.

Biron, C. A. and Welsh, R. M. (1982). In R. B. Herberman (ed.), *NK Cells and Other Natural Effector Cells*. New York: Academic Press: 493–8.

Bolhuis, R. L., van de Griend, R. J. and Ronteltap, C. P. (1983). *Natural Immunity Cell Growth Regul.* 3: 61–72.

Bonnard, G. D., Yasaka, K. and Jacobson, D. (1979). *J. Immunol.* 123: 2704–8.

Bordignon, C., Villa, F., Allavena, P., Introna, M., Biondi, A., Avallone, R. and Mantovani, A. (1982). *J. Immunol.* 129: 587–91.

Boswell, H. S., Wade, P. M. Jr., and Quesenberry, P. J. (1984). *J. Immunol.* 133: 2940.

Breard, J., Reinherz, E. L., O'Brien, C., and Schlossman, S. F. (1981). *Clin. Immunol. Immunopathol.*, 18: 145.

Brooks, C. G. (1983). *Nature* 305: 155–8.

Brunda, M. J., Holden, H. T. and Herberman, R. B. (1980a). In R. B. Herberman (ed.), *Natural Cell-Mediated Immunity Against Tumours*. New York: Academic, Press.

Brunda, M. J., Herberman, R. B. and Holden, H. T. (1980b). *J. Immunol.* 124: 2682–7.

Brunda, M. J., Taramelli, D., Holden, H. T. and Varesio, L. (1982). In R. B. Herberman (ed.), *NK Cells and Other Natural Effector Cells*. New York: Academic Press: 535–40.

Cantor, H., Kasai, M., Shen, H. W., LeClerc, J. C. and Glimcher, L. (1979). *Immunol. Rev.* 44: 1.

Carpen, O. Virtanen, I., and Saksela, E. (1982). *J. Immunol.* 128: 2691–7.

Chang, Z. -L., Hoffman, T., Bonvini, E., Stevenson, H. C., and Herberman, R. B. (1983). *Scand. J. Immunol.* 18: 439–49.

Clark, E. A. and Sturge, J. C. (1981). *J. Immunol.* 126: 969–74.

Cudkowicz, G. and Hochman, P. S. (1979). *Immunol. Rev.* 44: 13.

Dahl, C. A (1980). *J. Immunol.* 125: 1924.

Dahl, C. A (1983). *Eur. J. Immunol.* 13: 747.

Damle, N. K., Doyle, L. V. and Bradley, E. C. (1986). *J. Immunol.* 137: 2814–22.

Decker, J. M., Elmholt, A., and Muchmore, A. V. (1981). *Cell. Immunol.* 59: 161.

Decker, J. M., Hinson, A., and Ades, E. W. (1984). *J. Clin. Lab. Immunol.* 15: 137–43.

Dennert, G. and Podack, E. R. (1983). *J. Exp. Med.* 157: 1483–95.

DeVries, J. E., Figdor, C. G. and Spits, H. (1982). In R. B. Herberman (ed.), *NK Cells and Other Natural Effector Cells*, New York: Academic Press: 657–68.

DeVries, R. and Golub, S. (1986). *Feder. Proc.* 45: a2760.

Djeu, J. Y., Heinbaugh, J. A., Holden, H. T. and Herberman, R. B. (1979). *J. Immunol.* 122: 175–81.

Djeu, J. Y., Huang, K. -Y. and Herberman, R. B. (1980). *J. Exp. Med.* 151: 781–9.

Djeu, J. Y., Hapel, A. J. and Ihle, J. N. (1982). In R. B. Herberman (ed.), *NK Cells and Other Natural Effector Cells*. New York: Academic Press: 917–21.

Droller, M. J., Schneider, M. V. and Perlmann, P. (1978). *Cell. Immunol.* 39: 165–72.

Einhorn, S., Ahre, A., Blomgren, H., Johansson, B., Mellstedt, H. and Strander, H. (1982). In R. B. Herberman (ed.), *NK Cells and Other Natural Effector Cells*. New York: Academic Press: 1259–63.

Eremin, O. (1980). In R. B. Herberman (ed.) *Natural Cell-Mediated Immunity Against Tumours*. New York: Academic Press: 1011–27.

Eremin, O., Kraft, D., Coombs, R. R., Franks, D., Ashby, J. and Plumb, D. (1977). *Int. Arch. Allergy Appl. Immunol.* 55: 112–25.

Eremin, O., Wilson, A. B., Coombs, R. R. A., Ashby, J. and Plumb, D. (1980). *Cell. Immunol.* 55: 312.

Ettinghausen, S. E. and Rosenberg, S. A. (1986). *Cancer Research* 46: 1784.

Ettinghausen, S. E., Lipford, E. H., Mulé, J. J. *et al.* (1985a). *J. Immunol.* 135: 1488–97.

Ettinghausen, S. E., Lipford, E. N., Mulé, J. J. *et al.* (1985b). *J. Immunol.* 135: 3623–35.

Farrar, W. L., Johnson, H. M. and Farrar, J. J. (1981). *J. Immunol.* 126: 1120–5.

Ferrarini, M., Cadoni, A., Franzi, T., Ghigliotti, C., Leprini, A., Zicca, A. and Grossi, C. E. (1980). In F. Aiuti (ed.), *Thymus, Thymic Hormones and T Lymphocytes*. New York: Plenum : 39–47.

Fleischer, B. (1980). *J. Immunol.* 125: 1161.

Fleit, H. B., Wright, S. D., and Unkeless, J. C. (1982). *Proc. Natl. Acad. Sci. USA* 79: 3275.

Foreman, J. C. (1977). *J. Physiol.* 271: 215–32.

Gerson, J. M. (1980). In R. B. Herberman (ed.), *Natural Cell-Mediated Immunity Against Tumors* New York: Academic Press: 1047–62.

Gerson, J. M., Varesio, L. and Herberman, R. B. (1981). *Int. J. Cancer* 27: 243–8.

Gidlund, M., Orn, A., Wigzell, H., Senik, A. and Gresser, I. (1978). *Nature* 223:259–61.

Golub, S. H. (1982). In R. B. Herberman (ed.), *NK Cells and Other Natural Effector Cells.* New York: Academic Press: 1265–71.

Gorelik, E., Wiltrout, R. H., Okomura, K., Habu, S. and Herberman, R. B. (1982). *Int. J. Cancer* 30: 107–12.

Goto, S. H., Herberman, R. B., Maluish, A. and Strong, D. M. (1983). *J. Immunol.* 130: 1350–5.

Grimm, E. and Bonavida, B. (1979). *J. Immunol.* 123: 2861–9.

Grimm, E. A., Mazumder, A., Zhang, H. Z. and Rosenberg, S. A. (1982). *J. Exp. Med.* 155: 823–30.

Grimm, E. A., Ramsey, K. M., Mazumder, A., Wilson, D. J., Djeu, J. Y. and Rosenberg, S. A. (1983). *J. Exp. Med.* 157: 884–97.

Hackett, J. Jr., Bennett, M. and Kumar, V. (1985). *J. Immunol.* 134: 3731.

Hackett, J. Jr., Bosma, G. C., Bosma, M. J., Bennett, M. and Kumar, V. (1986a). *Proc. Natl. Acad. Sci. U.S.A.* 83: 3427.

Hackett, J., Tutt, M., Lipscomb, M., Bennett, M., Koo, G. C. and Kumar, V. (1986b). *J. Immunol.* 136: 3124.

Haliotis, R., Roder, J., Klein, M., Ortaldo, J. R., Fauci, A. S. and Herberman, R. B. (1980). *J. Exp. Med.* 151: 1039–48.

Haller, O. and Wigzell, H. (1977). *J. Immunol.* 118: 1503.

Haller, O., Kiessling, R., Orn, A., Karre, K., Nilsson, K., and Wigzell, H. (1977a). *Int. J. Cancer* 20: 93.

Haller, O., Kiessling, R., Orn, A., and Wigzell, H. (1977b). *J. Exp. Med.* 145: 1411.

Hank, J., Rosenthal, N., Kohler, P., Storer, B. and Sondel, P. (1987). *Fed. Proc.* 46: 1509.

Hanna, N. (1980). *Int. J. Cancer.* 26: 675.

Hanna, N. and Burton, R. (1981). *J. Immunol.* 127: 1754.

Hanna, N. and Fidler, I. J. (1980). *J. Natl. Cancer Inst.* 65: 801.

Hanna, N. and Fidler, I. J. (1981). *Cancer Res.* 41: 438.

Hattori, T., Hirata, F., Hoffman, T., Hizuta, A. and Herberman, R. B. (1983). *J. Immunol.* 131: 662–5.

Henkart, M. P. and Henkart, P. A. (1982). In W. R. Clark and P. Goldstein (eds), *Mechanisms of Cell Mediated Cytotoxicity.* New York: Plenum Press: 227.

Henkart, P. A., Millard, P. J., Reynolds, C. W. and Henkart, M. P. (1984). *J. Exp. Med.* 160: 75–93.

Henney, C. S., Tracey, D., Durdik, J. M. and Klimpel, G. (1978). *Am. J. Pathol.* 93: 459.

Herberman, R. B. (1974). *Adv. Cancer Res.* 19: 206–63.

Herberman, R. B. (ed.) (1980). *Natural Cell-Mediated Immunity against Tumors.* New York: Academic Press.

Herberman, R. B. (ed.) (1982). *NK Cells and other Natural Effector Cells.* New York: Academic Press.

Herberman, R. B. and Callewaert, D. (eds) (1985). *Mechanisms of Cytotoxicity by NK Cells*: Orlando: Academic Press.

Herberman, R. B. and Holden, H. T. (1978). *Adv. Cancer Res.* 27: 305–77.

Herberman, R. B. and Ortaldo, J. R. (1981). *Science* 214: 24.

Herberman, R. B., Nunn, M. E., and Lavrin, D. H. (1975). *Int. J. Cancer* 16: 216.

Herberman, R. B., Nunn, M. E., Holden, H. T., Staal, S. and Djeu, J. Y. (1977). *Int. J. Cancer* 19: 555–64.

Herberman, R. B., Djeu, J. Y., Kay, H. D., Ortaldo, J. R., Riccardi, C., Bonnard, G. D., Holden, H. T., Fagnani, R., Santoni, A. and Puccetti, P. (1979a). *Immunol. Rev.* 44: 43.

Herberman, R. B., Ortaldo, J. R. and Bonnard, G. D. (1979b). *Nature* 277: 221–3.

Herberman, R. B., Brunda M. J., Domzig, W., Fagnani, R., Goldfarb, R. H., Holden, H. T., Ortaldo, J. R., Reynolds, C. W., Riccardi, C., Santoni, A., Stadler, B. M., Taramelli, D., Timonen, T. and Varesio, L. (1980). In L. N. Ruben and M. E. Gershwin (eds), *Immune Regulation: Evolutionary and Biological Significance.* New York: Marcel Dekker: 139.

Herberman, R. B., Ortaldo, J. R., Rubinstein, M. and Pestka, S. (1981). *J. Clin. Immunol.* 1: 149–53.

Herberman, R. B., Brunda, M. J., Djeu, J. Y., Domzig, W., Goldfarb, R. H., Holden, H. T., Ortaldo, J. R., Reynolds, C. W., Riccardi, C., Santoni, A., Stadler, B. M. and Timonen, T. (1982a). In B. Serrou, C. Rosenfeld and R. B. Herberman (eds), *Natural Killer Cells: Human Cancer Immunology.* Amsterdam: Elsevier.

Herberman, R. B., Ortaldo, J. R., Mantovani, A., Hobbs, D. S., Kung, H. F. and Pestka, S. (1982b). *Cell. Immunol.* 67: 160–7.

Herberman, R. B., Reynolds, C. W. and Ortaldo, J. R. (1986). *Annual Review of Immunology.* 4: 651–80.

Herberman, R. B., Balch, C., Bolhius, R., Golub, S., Hiserodt, J., Lanier, L., Lotzova, E., Phillips, J., Riccardi, C., Ritz, J., Santoni, A., Schmidt, R., Uchida, A. and Vujanovic, N. (1987). *Immunol. Today* 8: 178–81.

Hercend, T., Meuer, S., Reinherz, E. L., Schlossman, S. F., and Ritz, J. (1982). *J. Immunol.* 129: 1299–1305.

Hercend, T., Meuer, S. C., Brennan, A., Edson, M. A., Acuto, O., Reinherz, E. L., Schlossman, S. F., and Ritz, J. (1983a). *J. Exp. Med.* 158: 1547–60.

Hercend, T., Reinherz, E. L., Meuer, S. C., Schlossman, S. F. and Ritz, J. (1983b). *Nature* 30: 158–60.

Hercend, T., Bensussan, A., Schmidt, R. E., Edson, M. A., Brenna, A., Murray, C., Daley, J. F., Schlossman, S. F. and Ritz, J. (1985). *J. Clin. Invest.* 75: 932–43.

Hinuma, S., Abo, T., Kumagai, K., and Hata, M. (1980). *Dev. Comp. Immunol.* 4: 653.

Hiserodt, J. C. and Reynolds, C. W. (1987). In B. Bonivida and R. Collier (eds), *Membrane Mediated Cytotoxicity.* New York: Alan R. Liss, Inc: 515–23.

Hiserodt, J. C., Britvan, L. F. and Targan, S. R. (1982). *J. Immunol.* 129: 1782–7.

Hiserodt, J. C., Laybourn, K. A., and Varani, J. (1985). *J. Immunol.* 135: 1481.

Hiserodt, J. C., Vujanovic, N. L., Reynolds, C. V. Herberman, R. B. and Cramer, D. V. (1987). In R. L. Truitt, R. P. Gale and M. M. Bortin (eds), *Cellular Immunotherapy of Cancer.* New York: Alan R. Liss, Inc: 137–46.

Hochman, P. S. and Cudkowicz, G. (1979). *J. Immunol.* 123: 968–76.

Hochman, P. S., Cudkowicz, G. and Dausset, J. (1978). *J. Natl. Cancer Inst.* 61: 265–8.

Hochman, P. S., Cudkowicz, G. and Evans, P. D. (1981). *Cell. Immunol.* 61: 200–12.

Hodgson, G. S. and Bradley, T. R. (1979). *Nature* 281: 381.

Hoffman, T., Hirata, F., Bougnoux, P., Fraser, B. A., Goldfarb, R. H., Herberman, R. B. and Axelrod, J. (1981). *Proc. Natl. Acad. Sci. (USA)* 78: 3839–43.

Hostetter, R. K. and Cooper, E. L. (1972). *Immunolog. Commun.* 1: 155.

Huh, N. D., Kim, Y. B., Koren, H. S. and Amos, D. B. (1981). *Int. J. Cancer* 28: 175.

Ito, M., Ralph, P. and Moore, M. A. S. (1980). *Clin. Immunol. Immunopathol.* 16: 30–8.

Itoh, K., Suzuki, R., Umezu, Y., Hanaumi, K., and Kumagai, K. (1982). *J. Immunol.* 129: 395–405.

Jensen, P. J. and Koren, H. S. (1979). *J. Immunol.* 123: 1127–32.

Kaplan, J., Shope, T. C., Bollinger, R. O. and Smith, J. (1982). *J. Clin. Immunol.* 2: 350.

Katz, P., Zaytoun, A. M., and Fauci, A. S. (1982). *J. Clin. Invest.* 69: 1231–8.

Kay, H. D. and Horwitz, D. A. (1980). *J. Clin. Invest.* 66: 847.

Kay, H. D., Goldfarb, R. H., Wayner, E. A. and Brooks, C. G. (1985). In R. B. Herberman and D. M. Callewaert (eds), *Mechanisms of Cytotoxicity by NK Cells.* Orlando: Academic Press: 263–86.

Kendall, R. A. and Targan, S. (1980). *J. Immunol.* 125: 2770–7.

Kiessling, R., Klein, E., and Wigzell, H. (1975a). *Eur. J. Immunol.* 5: 112.

Kiessling, R., Petranyi, G., Klein, G. and Wigzell, H. (1975b). *Int. J. Cancer* 15: 933.

Kiessling, R., Petranyi, G., Klein, G. and Wigzell, H. (1976). *Int. J. Cancer* 17: 275.

Kim, Y. B., Huh, N. D., Koren, H. S. and Amos, D. B. (1980). *J. Immunol.* 125: 755.

Koo, G. C. and Hatzfeld, A. (1980). In R. B. Herberman (ed.), *Natural Cell-Mediated Immunity Against Tumors.* New York: Academic Press.

Koo, G. C., Peppard, J. R., and Mark, W. H. (1984). *J. Immunol.* 132: 2300.

Koo, G. C., Dumont, F. J., Tutt, M., Hackett, J. Jr., and Kumar, V. (1986). *J. Immunol.* 137: 3742.

Koren, H. S. and Herberman, R. B. (1983). *J. Natl. Cancer Inst.* 70: 785.

Koren, H. S., Amos, D. B., and Kim, Y. B. (1978). *Proc. Natl. Acad. Sci. U.S.A.* 75: 5127.

Koren, H. S., Anderson, S. J., Fischer, D. G., Copeland, C. S. and Jensen, P. J. (1981). *J. Immunol.* 127: 2007–12.

Kumar, V., Mellen, P. F., and Bennett, M. (1982). In R. B. Herberman (ed.), *NK Cells and Other Natural Effector Cells.* New York: Academic Press: 329.

Kumugai, K., Itoh, K., Suzuki, R., Hinuma, S. and Saitoh, F. (1982). *J. Immunol.* 127: 282.

Landazuri, M. O., Lopez-Botet, M., Timonen, T., Ortaldo, J. R. and Herberman, R. B. (1981). *J. Immunol.* 127: 1380.

Lang, N. P., Ortaldo, J. R., Bonnard, G. D. and Herberman, R. B. (1982). *J. Natl. Cancer Inst.* 69: 339–43.

Lanier, L. L. and Phillips, J. H. (1986). *Med. Oncol. Tumor Pharmacother.* 3: 247–54.

Lanier, L. L., Le, A. M., Phillips, J. H., Warner, W. L. and Babcock, G. F. (1983). *J. Immunol.* 131: 1789.

Lanier, L. L., Phillips, J. H. and Hackett, J. (1986). *J. Immunol.* 137: 2735–9.

Lanza, E. and Djeu, J. Y. (1982). In R. B. Herberman (ed.) *NK Cells and Other Natural Effector Cells.* New York: Academic Press: 335–40.

Lattime, E. C., Pecoraro, G. A., Cuttito, M. and Stutman, O. (1982). In R. B. Herberman (ed.), *NK Cells and Other Natural Effector Cells.* New York: Academic Press: 179–86.

Law, L. W. (1965). *Nature* 205: 672.

Law, L. W. (1966). *Cancer Res.* 26: 551.

Leibold, W., Janotte, G., and Peter, H. H. (1980). *Scand. J. Immunol.* 11: 203.

Leung, K. H. and Koren, H. S. (1982). *J. Immunol.* 129: 1742–7.

Linthicum, D. S., Stein, E. A., Marks, D. H. and Cooper, E. L. (1977). *Cell. Tiss. Res.* 185: 315.

Lord, B. I., Mori, K. J. and Wright, E. G. (1977). *Biomedicine* 27: 223.

Lotze, M. T., Robb, R. J., Sharron, S. W., Frana, L. W. and Rosenberg, S. A. (1984). *J. Biol. Resp. Modif.* 3: 475.

Lotzova, E. (1980). In R. B. Herberman (ed.), *Natural Cell-Mediated Immunity Against Tumors.* New York: Academic Press: 735–53.

Lotzova, E. and Gutterman, J. V. (1979). *J. Immunol.* 123: 607–12.

Lotzova, E., Savary, C. A., Herberman, R. B. and Dicke, K. A. (1986). *Natural Immunity and Cell Growth Regulation* 5: 61–3.

Lotzova, E., Savary, C. A. and Herberman, R. B. (1987). *J. Immunol.* 138: 2718–27.

Luquet, G. and Leclerc, M. (1983). *Immunol. Lett.* 6: 339.

McCoy, J. L., Herberman, R. B., Rosenberg, E. B., Donnelly, F. C., Levine, P. H. and Alford, C. (1973). *Natl. Cancer Inst. Monogr.* 37: 59–67.

Maghazachi, A. A., Vujanovic, N. L., Hiserodt, J. C. and Herberman, R. B. (1988). *J. Immunol.* 140: 2846–52.

Maguire, H. Jr., Outzen, H. C., Custer, R. P. and Prehn, R. T. (1976). *J. Natl. Cancer Inst.* 57: 439.

Maluish, A. E., Ortaldo, J. R. and Herberman, R. B. (1982). In R. B. Herberman (ed.), *NK Cells and Other Natural Effector Cells.* New York: Academic Press: 1279–83.

Mantovani, A., Allavena, P., Biondi, A., Sessa, C. and Introna, M. (1981). In B. Serrou and R. B. Herberman (eds), *NK Cells: Fundamental Aspects and Role in Cancer.* Amsterdam: Elsevier.

Metzger, Z., Hoffeld, J. T. and Oppenheim, J. J. (1980). *J. Immunol.* 124: 983–8.

Migliorati, G., Cannarile, L., Herberman, R. B., Bartocci, A., Stanley, E. R. and Riccardi, C. (1987). *J. Immunol.* 138: 3618.

Millard, P., Henkart, P., Reynolds, C. W. and Henkart, P. A. (1984). *J. Immunol.* 132: 3197–3204.

Minato, N. and Bloom, B. R. (1982). In R. B. Herberman (ed.), *NK Cells and Other Natural Effector Cells.* New York: Academic Press.

Morgan, D. A., Ruscetti, F. W. and Gallo, R. (1976). *Science* 193: 1007–8.

Mulé, J. J., Shu, S. and Rosenberg, S. A. (1985). *J. Immunol.* 135: 646–52.

Nair, M. P. N., Schwartz, S. A., Fernandes, G., Pahwa, R., Ikehara, S. and Good, R. A. (1981). *Cell. Immunol.* 58: 9–18.

Neighbour, P. A. and Huberman, H. S. (1982). *J. Immunol.* 128: 1236–40.

Newman, R. A., Warner, J. F. and Dennert, G. (1984). *J. Immunol.* 133: 1841–5.

Nunn, M. E., Herberman, R. B., and Holden, H. T. (1977). *Int. J. Cancer* 20: 381.

Oehler, J. R., Lindsay, L. R., Nunn, M. E., Holden, H. T. and Herberman, R. B. (1978). *Int. J. Cancer* 21: 210–20.

Ojo, E. and Wigzell, H. (1978). *Scand. J. Immunol.* 7: 297.

Oldham, R. K., Siwarski, D., McCoy, J. L., Plata, E. J. and Herberman, R. B. (1973). *Natl. Cancer Inst. Monogr.* 37: 49.

Ortaldo, J. R. and Timonen, T. T. (1981). *Proceedings of the 14th International Leukocyte Culture Conference.* New York: Elsevier-North Holland.

Ortaldo, J. R., Oldham, R. K., Cannon, G. C. and Herberman, R. B. (1977). *J. Natl. Cancer Inst.* 59: 77.

Ortaldo, J. R., Sharrow, S. O., Timonen, T., and Herberman, R. B. (1981). *J. Immunol.* 127: 2401–9.

Ortaldo, J. R., Lewis, J. T., Braatz, J., Mason, A. and Henkart, P. (1982). In J. W. Parker and R. L. O'Brien (eds), *Intracellular Communication in Leukocyte Functions.* New York: Wiley.

Ortaldo, J. R., Mantovani, A., Hobbs, D., Rubinstein, M., Pestka, S. and Herberman, R. B. (1983). *Int. J. Cancer* 31: 285–9.

Ortaldo, J. R., Timonen, T. T. and Herberman, R. B. (1984a). *Clin. Immunol. Immunopathol.* 31: 439–43.

Ortaldo, J. R., Mason, A. T., Gerard, J. P., Henderson, L. E., Farrar, W., Hopkins, R. F. III, Herberman, R. B. and Rabin, H. (1984b) *J. Immunol.* 133: 779–83.

Ortaldo, J. R., Blanca, I., and Herberman, R. B. (1985). In P. Henkart and E. Martz (eds), *Mechanisms of Cell-Mediated Cytotoxicity.* New York: Plenum Press: 203–20.

Ortaldo, J. R., Ransom, J. R., Sayers, T. J. and Herberman, R. B. (1986a). *J. Immunol.* 137: 2857–63.

Ortaldo, J. R., Mason, L. H., Mathieson, B. J., Liang, S. M., Flick, D. A. and Herberman, R. B. (1986b). *Nature* 321: 700–2.

Perussia, D., Acuto, D., Terhorst, C., Faust, J., Lazarus, R., Fanning, V. and Trinchieri, G. (1983). *J. Immunol.* 130: 2142–8.

Petranyi, G., Kiessling, R., Povey, S., Klein, G., Herzenberg, E. and Wigzell, H. (1976). *Immunogenetics* 3: 15.

Phillips, W. H., Ortaldo, J. R. and Herberman, R. B. (1980). *J. Immunol.* 125: 2322–7.

Podack, E. R. (1985). *Immunol. Today* 6: 21–7.

Podack, E. R., Young, J. D. E. and Cohn, Z. A. (1985). *Proc. Natl. Acad. Sci. (USA)* 82: 8629–33.

Pollack, S. B. and Emmons, S. L. (1981). In M. A. Chirigos, M. Mitchell, M. J. Mastrangelo and M. Krim (eds), *Mediation of Cellular Immunity in Cancer by Immune Modifiers.* New York: Raven Press: 225–35.

Pollack, S., Heppner, S., Brawn, R. J. and Nelson, K. (1972). *Int. J. Cancer* 9: 316.

Reinherz, E. L., Kung, P. C., Goldstein, G., Levey, R. H. and Schlossman, S. F. (1980a). *Proc. Natl. Acad. Sci. USA* 71: 1588.

Reinherz, E. L., Moretta, L., Roper, M., Breard, J. M., Mingari, M. C., Cooper, M. D. and Schlossman, S. F. (1980b). *J. Exp. Med.* 151: 969.

Renoux, G., Bardos, P. and Degenne, D. (1982). In R. B. Herberman (ed.), *NK Cells and Other Natural Effector Cells.* New York: Academic Press: 443–8.

Revell, P. A. (1977). *Int. Rev. Cytol.* 51: 275.

Reynolds, C. W. and Herberman, R. B. (1981). *J. Immunol.* 126: 1581–5.

Reynolds, C. W. and Ortaldo, J. R. (1987). *Immunol. Today* 8: 172.

Reynolds, C. W., Timonen, T. and Herberman, R. B. (1981a). *J. Immunol.* 127: 282.

Reynolds, C. W., Sharrow, S. O., Ortaldo, J. R., and Herberman, R. B. (1981b). *J. Immunol.* 127: 2204.

Reynolds, C. W., Timonen, T., Holden, H. T., Hansen, C. T. and Herberman, R. B. (1982). *Eur. J. Immunol.* 12: 577.

Reynolds, C. W., Bere, E. W. and Ward, J. M. (1984). *J. Immunol.* 132: 534–40.

Reynolds, C. W., Bonyhadi, M., Herberman, R. B., Young, H. A. and Hedrick, S. M. (1985). *J. Exp. Med.* 161: 1249–54.

Reynolds, C. W., Reichardt, D., Henkart, M., Millard, P. and Henkart, P. (1987). *J. Leukocyte Biol.* 42: 642–52.

Riccardi, C., Santoni, A., Barlozzari, T., Cesarini, C. and Herberman, R. B. (1981). *Int. J. Cancer* 28: 811–18.

Riccardi, C., (1982). In R. B. Herberman (ed.), *Natural Killer Cells and Other Natural Effector Cells.* New York: Academic Press: 549–56.

Riccardi, C., Giampietri, A., Migliorati, G., Cannarile, L., D'Adamio, L., and Herberman, R. B. (1986a). *Int. J. Cancer* 38: 553.

Riccardi, C., Migliorati, G., Giampietri, A., Ayroldi, E., Cannarile, L., D'Adamio, L. and Herberman, R. B. (1986b). In E. Lotzova and R. B. Herberman (eds), *Natural Immunity, Cancer and Biological Response Modification.* Basel: S. Karger: 34.

Ritz, J., Campen, T.J., Schmidt, R. E., Royer, H. D., Hercend, T., Hussey, R. E. and Reinherz, E. L. (1985). *Science* 228: 1540–3.

Robb, R. J. and Greene, W. C. (1983). *J. Exp. Med.* 158: 1332–40.

Roder, J. C. and Duwe, A. K. (1979). *Nature* 278: 451–81.

Roder, J. C., Ahrlund-Richter, L. and Jondal, M. (1979a). *J. Exp. Med.* 150: 471–81.

Roder, J. C., Rosen, A., Fenyo, E. and Troy, F. (1979b). *Proc. Natl. Acad. Sci. USA* 3: 1405–9.

Roder, J. C., Karre, K. and Kiessling, R. (1981). *Prog. Allerg.* 28: 66.

Roder, J. C., Helfand, S. L., Werkmeister, J. McGarry, R., Beumont, T. J. and Duwe, A. (1982). *Nature* 298: 569–71.

Rosenberg, E. B., Herberman, R. B., Levine, P. H., Halteman, R. H., McCoy, J. L., and Wunderlich, J. R. (1972). *Int. J. Cancer* 9: 648–58.

Rosenberg, E. B., McCoy, J. L., Green, S. S., Donnelly, F. C., Siwarski, D. F., Levine, P. H. and Herberman, R. B. (1974). *J. Natl. Cancer Inst.* 52: 345–52.

Saksela, E., Timonen, T., Ranki, A. and Hayry, P. (1979). *Immunol. Rev.* 44: 71.

Santoli, D., Trinchieri, G., Zmijewski, C. M. and Koprowski, H. (1976). *J. Immunol.* 117: 765–70.

Santoni, A., Riccardi, C., Barlozzari, T. and Herberman, R. B. (1980a). *Int. J. Cancer.* 26: 837–43.

Santoni, A., Riccardi, C., Sorci, V. and Herberman, R. B. (1980b). *J. Immunol.* 124: 2329–35.

Santoni, A., Riccardi, C., Barlozzari, T. and Herberman, R. B. (1982a). In R. B. Herberman (ed.), *NK Cells and Other Natural Effector Cells.* New York: Academic Press: 519–26.

Santoni, A., Riccardi, C., Barlozzari, T. and Herberman, R. B. (1982b). In R. B. Herberman (ed.), *NK Cells and Other Natural Effector Cells.* New York: Academic Press: 527–33.

Santoni, A., Piccoli, M., Ortaldo, J. R., Mason, L., Wiltrout, R. H. and Herberman, R. B. (1985). *J. Immunol.* 134: 2799–2810.

Savary, C. A. and Lotzova, E. (1986). In E. Lotzova and R. B. Herberman (eds), *Immunobiology of Natural Killer Cells,* vol. I. Boca Raton: CRC Press.

Saxena, Q. B., Sazena, R. K. and Adler, W. H. (1982). In R. B. Herberman (ed.), *NK Cells and Other Natural Effector Cells.* New York: Academic Press: 651–6.

Scala, G., Djeu, J., Allavena, P., Herberman, R. B. and Ortaldo, J. R. (1986). In E. Lotzova and R. B. Herberman (eds), *Immunobiology of Natural Killer Cells,* vol. II. Boca Raton: CRC Press: 134–44.

Schmidt, M. and Good, R. A. (1976). *Lancet* 1: 39.

Schmidt, A., Ortaldo, J. R., and Herberman, R. B. (1984). *J. Immunol.* 132: 146–51.

Schmidt, R. E., Hercend, T., Fox, D. A., Bewnsussan, A., Bartley, G., Daley, J. F., Schlossman, S. F., Reinherz, E. L. and Ritz, J. (1985). *J. Immunol.* 135: 672–8.

Schmidt, R. E., Michon, J. M., Woronicz, J., Schlossman, S. F., Reinherz, E. L. and Ritz, J. (1987). *J. Clin. Invest.* 79: 305–8.

Schuurman, H. J., Kluin, P. M., deGast, R. and Kater, L. (1985). *Br. J. Cancer* 51: 171–7.

Seaman, W. E., Gindhart, T. D., Blackman, M. A., Dalal, B., Talel, N. and Werb, Z. (1982). *J. Clin. Invest.* 69: 876–88.

Sharma, J. M. and Coulson, B. D. (1979). *J. Natl. Cancer Inst.* 63: 527.

Shau, H. and Golub, S. H. (1985). *J. Immunol.* 134: 1136–41.

Shin, H. S., Hayden, M. L., Langley, S., Kaliss, N. and Smith, M. R. (1975). *J. Immunol.* 114: 1255.

Shortman, K., Wilson, A. and Scollay, R. (1984). *J. Immunol.* 132: 584–93.

Stringfellow, D. A. (1978). *Science* 201: 376–8.

Sulica, A., Gherman, M., Galatiuc, C., Manciulea, M. and Herberman, R. B. (1982). *J. Immunol.* 128: 1031–6.

Tagliabue, A., Luini, W., Soldaleschi, D., and Boraschi, B. (1981). *Eur. J. Immunol.* 11: 919.

Tai, A. and Warner, N. L. (1980). In R. B. Herberman (ed.), *Natural Cell-Mediated Immunity Against Tumors.* New York: Academic Press.

Talmadge, J. E. (1985). *J. Biol. Resp. Modif.* 4: 18.

Talmadge, J. E., Dennis-Tait, S., Schneider, M. A., Meeker, A. K. and Adams, J. S. (1985). In A. E. Reif and M. S. Mitchell (eds), *Immunity to cancer.* New York : Academic Press: 215.

Talmadge, J. E., Wiltrout, R. H., Counts, D. F., Herberman, R. B., McDonald, T. and Ortaldo, J. R. (1986). *Cell. Immunol.* 102: 261–72.

Tam, M. R., Emmon, S. S. 1. and Pollack, S. B. (1980). *J. Immunol.* 124: 650.

Tarkkanen, J. and Saksela, E. (1982). *Scand. J. Immunol.* 15: 149–57.

Tatta, S. K., Gallagher, M. T., and Trentin, J. J. (1979). Prog. Exp. Tumor Res. 23:180.

Teale, D. M., Rees, R. C., Clark, A. and Potter, C. W. (1983). *Eur. J. Cancer Clin. Oncol.* 19: 537.

Timonen, T. and Saksela, E. (1980). *J. Immunol. Meth.* 36: 285.

Timonen, T., Ortaldo, J. R. and Herberman, R. B. (1981). *J. Exp. Med.* 153: 569.

Timonen, T., Reynolds, C. W., Ortaldo, J. R. and Herberman, R. B. (1982a). *J. Immunol. Meth.* 41: 269.

Timonen, T., Ortaldo, J. R. and Herberman, R. B. (1982b). *J. Immunol.* 128: 2514–21.

Timonen, T., Ortaldo, J. R., Stadler, B. M., Bonnard, G. D., Sharrow, S. O. and Herberman, R. B. (1982c). *Cell Immunol.* 72: 178–85.

Trinchieri, G. and Santoli, D. (1978). *J. Exp. Med.* 147: 1314–33.

Tsang, K. Y., Gnagy, M. J., Yamamauri, Y. and Fudenberg, H. H. (1981). *Clin. Immunol. Immunopathol.* 21: 332.

Tyson, C. J. and Jenkin, C. R. (1974). *Aust. J. Exp. Biol. Med. Sci.* 52: 915.

Uchida, A. and Micksche, M. (1982a). In R. B. Herberman (ed.), *NK Cells and Other Natural Effector Cells.* New York : Academic Press: 1303–8.

Uchida, A. and Micksche, M. (1982b). In R. B. Herberman (ed.), *NK Cells and Other Natural Effector Cells.* New York: Academic Press: 589–94.

Uchida, A. and Micksche, M. (1983). *J. Natl. Cancer Inst.* 71: 673–80.

Uchida, A. and Yanagawa, E. (1984). *J. Natl. Cancer Inst.* 73: 1093–1100.

Valembois, P., Roch, P. and Boiledieu, D. (1980). In M. J. Manning (ed.), *Phylogeny of Immunological Memory.* Elsevier: North Holland: 47.

Van de Griend, R. J., Giphart, M. J., Van Krimpen, B. A. and Bolhius, R. L. (1984). *J. Immunol.* 133: 1222–9.

Van de Griend, R. J., Tax, W. J. M., Krimpen, B. A., Vreugdenhil, R. J., Runteltap, C. P. M. and Bolhuis, R. L. H. (1987). *J. Immunol.* 138: 1627–33.

Verhoef, J. and Sharma, S. D. (1983). *J. Immunol.* 131: 125–31.

Vodinelich, L., Sutherland, R., Schneider, C., Newman, R. and Greaves, M. (1983). *Proc. Natl. Acad. Sci. USA* 80: 835–9.

Vose, B. M. and Moore, M. (1979). *Int. J. Cancer* 24: 579–85.

Vujanovic, N. L., Herberman, R. B., Al Maghazachi, A. and Hiserodt, J. C. (1988). *J. Exp. Med.* 167: 15–29.

Ward, J. M., Argilan, F. and Reynolds, C. W. (1983). *J. Immunol.* 131: 132–9.

Werkmeister, J. A., Burns, G. F. and Triglia, T. (1984). *J. Immunol.* 133: 1385–91.

West, W. H., Cannon, G. B., Kay, H. D., Bonnard, G. D. and Herberman, R. B. (1977). *J. Immunol.* 118: 355.

Williams, A. F. (1984). *Nature* 308: 108.

Williams, A. F., Barclay, A. N., Clark, M. J. and Gagnon, J. (1985). *Ann. Inst. Pasteur Immunol.* 136C(2): 283–94.

Wiltrout, R. H., Talmadge, J. E. and Herberman, R. B. (1987). In R. B. Herberman, R. H. Wiltrout and E. Gorelik (eds), *Immune Responses to Metastases*, vol. II. Boca Raton: CRC Press: 25–41.

Wolfe, S. A., Tracey, D. E. and Henney, C. S. (1976). *Nature* 262: 584–6.

Wright, S. C. and Bonavida, B. (1981). *J. Immunol.* 125: 1516–21.

Wright, S. C. and Bonavida, B. (1982). *J. Immunol.* 129: 433–9.

Yamada, A., Hayami, M., Yamanouchi, K. and Fujiwara, K. (1980). *Int. J. Cancer* 26: 381.

Yamada, S., Ruscetti, F. W., Overton, W. R., Birchenall-Sparks, M. C. Herberman, R. B. and Ortaldo, J. R. (1987). *J. Leukocyte Biol.* 41: 505–17.

Yanagi, Y., Caccia, N., Kronenberg, M., Chin, B., Roder, J., Rohel, D., Koyohara, T., Lauzon, R., Toyanaga, B., Rosenthal, O. K., Dennert, G., Acha-Orbea, H., Hengartner, H., Hood, L. and Mak, T. W. (1985). *Nature* 314: 631.

Young, H. A., Ortaldo, J. R., Herberman, R. B. and Reynolds, C. W. (1986). *J. Immunol.* 136: 2701–4.

Yunis, E. J., Martinez, C., Smith, J. Stutman, O. and Good, R. A. (1969). *Cancer Res.* 29: 174.

Zarling, J. M. and Kung, P. C. (1980). *Nature* 288: 394.

Zarling, J. M., Eskra. L., Borden, E. C., Horoszewicz, J. and Carter, W. A. (1979). *J. Immunol.* 123: 63.

Non-MHC-Restricted Cytotoxic T Lymphocytes

PETER HERSEY

Immunology and Oncology Unit of the Mater Misericordiae Hospital,
Royal Newcastle Hospital, Newcastle, NSW 2300, Australia

I. INTRODUCTION

As outlined in Chapter 3 of this volume and in other publications (Lanier and Phillips, 1986; Lanier *et al.*, 1986b) there is increasing consensus that natural killer (NK) cells in blood of normal subjects which mediate cytotoxic activity against certain cultured tumour cells may belong to a

NATURAL IMMUNITY
ISBN 0 12 5145551

cell lineage separate from those of T cells or macrophages. There are three main lines of evidence for this. The first is the absence of rearranged α and β genes of the T cell receptor (TCR) or of functional transcripts of $\alpha\beta$ or γ genes in NK cells. Second, progenitors of NK cells could be identified in bone marrow from certain mouse strains that were either deficient in multipotent myeloid stem cells (*W/W* mutant mice) or had abnormalities in differentiation of B and T lymphocytes (C.B-17 *scid* mutant mice). Third, the phenotype of NK cells could be distinguished from those of T cells and monocytes, e.g. in humans NK cells could be defined as $CD3^-$ $CD16^+$ $NKH1^+$ $OKM1^+$ $LeuM1^-$, i.e. as cells which lack the CD3 marker of T cells and the LeuM1 (CD15) marker of macrophages.

Much of the debate concerning the nature of NK cells centred on whether or not they were T cells which acquired non-MHC-restricted cytotoxic activity at certain stages in their activation (Hersey *et al.*, 1975; Klein, 1980) or differentiation (Kaplan, 1986; Grossman and Herberman, 1986). These views have been, to some extent, reconciled by the recognition that the main functional property of NK cells, i.e. mediation of non-MHC-restricted cytotoxic activity, is shared by certain activated T cells. These were referred to as non-MHC-restricted cytotoxic T lymphocytes (CTL) (Lanier and Phillips, 1986) and as Type 2 CTLs (Hersey *et al.*, 1986a, b) to distinguish them from Type 1 antigen-specific MHC-restricted CTLs. These and other studies showed that Type 2 CTLs shared not only functional properties with NK cells but also expression of the NK-associated phenotypic markers CD16 and NKH1. T cells expressing CD16 were reported to constitute approximately 2 per cent of the mononuclear cells compared with 10–12 per cent of cells with the NK phenotype (Lanier *et al.*, 1985). Although Type 2 CTLs are numerically less important than NK cells in blood of normal subjects, there is as yet no information about the relative proportions of the two cell types in pathological states. Given that T cells, but not NK cells, proliferate in response to antigenic stimuli, it is conceivable that Type 2 CTLs may become the major cell type mediating non-MHC-restricted cytotoxic activity during immune responses, e.g., to tumours following treatment with IL 2 or other agents administered to patients with cancer. Type 2 CTLs may have an even more important role in tissues around tumours or in lymph nodes where NK cells appear sparse or absent (Vose and Moore, 1985; Hersey *et al.*, 1985). In view of the importance of these cells in these contexts, the present chapter reviews the conditions resulting in generation of this cell type, their relation to other cytotoxic lymphocytes, and the receptors that may be involved in their cytotoxic activity.

II. GENERATION OF TYPE 2 CYTOTOXIC T LYMPHOCYTES

A. Mixed Lymphocyte Cultures

Unlike NK cells, which by definition can mediate spontaneous cytotoxic activity, that of Type 2 CTLs becomes apparent only after stimulation by various means. The earlier descriptions of their activity were made during studies on 'anomalous' killer (AK) cells generated during mixed lymphocyte cultures (MLC) (Seeley and Golub, 1978; Poros and Klein, 1979; Seeley *et al.*, 1979). AK cells and specific CTLs against alloantigens were generated from E-rosette positive (E^+) cells but could be distinguished from specific CTLs by several criteria, e.g.: (1) AK activity could be detected much earlier in the cultures than specific CTL activity; (2) AK activity did not show a memory response to antigens; (3) target cells (TCs) sensitive to lysis by AK cells did not cross-compete with specific TCs for CTLs in cold target inhibition studies; (4) AK cells but not CTLs adhered to immune complexes (ICs) immobilised on plastic; and (5) hydrocortisone suppressed generation of AK cells, but not specific CTL activity (Muul and Gately, 1984).

Differences were also demonstrated between AK and NK activity, e.g.: (1) AK activity was as effective against certain TCs resistant to lysis by NK cells (Masucci *et al.*, 1980; Carroll and De Wolf, 1983) as against those sensitive to NK cells; (2) AK activity was low or absent in resting T cell populations, but increased in parallel with the degree of blastogenesis in cultures (Masucci *et al.*, 1980; Rimm *et al.*, 1984). NK activity decreased during long-term culture of blood lymphocytes, but on stimulation the cultured lymphocytes exhibited cytotoxic activity, against both NK-sensitive and NK-resistant TCs, consistent with that of AK cells. AK cells, unlike most NK cells, did not express the OKM1 marker for the C3d component of complement (Rimm *et al.*, 1984) but did express CD3 and CD8. Precursor cells for AK cells could be separated from NK cells on Percoll gradients and could be generated from thoracic duct lymphocytes devoid of NK activity (Mazumder *et al.*, 1983a). Conflicting results were produced in several studies, e.g. elimination of Fc receptor (FcR) positive cells from peripheral blood lymphocytes (PBLs) reduced AK activity, which led the authors to suggest that NK cells might have been precursor cells for the AK activity. The latter studies did not, however, exclude the possibility that the results reflected removal of T cells expressing FcR in blood (Phillips *et al.*, 1984).

Clonal analysis of cytotoxic T cells confirmed that CTLs with non-MHC-restricted cytotoxic activity against a wide range of TCs were generated in MLCs. These clones accounted for a third of the clones isolated from MLCs with PBLs from melanoma patients as responders (Hersey *et al.*, 1986a). Similar results were reported in studies by Van de Griend *et al.* (1984b, 1985), DeVries and Spits (1984), Burns *et al.* (1984) and Pawelec *et al.* (1985). The panel of monoclonal antibodies (MAbs) used for phenotyping the various T cell clones described in the studies did not always include those against CD16, so that extensive comparisons between the studies are not possible. In our work all CTL clones mediating broad cytolytic activity expressed CD16 and NKH-1, whereas Van de Griend *et al.* (1984a, b) found a reciprocal relationship between expression of CD16 and CD3 on both specific and non-MHC-restricted clones of CTLs. There appears to be general consensus, however, from the clonal analysis studies that non-MHC-restricted cytotoxicity was mediated by $CD3^+$ CTLs.

B. Mixed Lymphocyte and Tumour Cell Cultures (MLTCs)

Studies on cytotoxic lymphocytes generated in cultures of autologous lymphocytes and tumour cells have received much attention because of their possible relevance to in vivo responses by patients against tumour cells. Clonal analysis of the responding cells suggested, in most instances, that they were $CD3^+$ lymphocytes with cytotoxic activity directed predominantly against autologous tumour cells, i.e. their cytotoxic specificity was directed to a narrower range of TCs than that of CTLs generated from MLCs (Vose and White, 1983; DeVries and Spits, 1984; Knuth *et al.*, 1981; Hersey *et al.*, 1986a). This restricted pattern of cytotoxicity was not due to differences in PBLs from the patients as, when stimulated in MLCs, they generated CTL clones with broad cytotoxic activity (Vose and White, 1983). No Type 2 CTLs were detected among thirteen clones of CTLs isolated from MLTCs from two patients and only three of sixteen clones from a third MLTC exhibited non-MHC-restricted cytotoxicity (Hersey *et al.*, 1986a and unreported).

Anichini *et al.* (1985) found that CTL clones obtained from MLTCs with melanoma cells had a wide range of cytotoxic activity: 13 out of 55 clones lysed only autologous melanoma cells, whereas the other clones killed K562 and a variety of allogeneic melanoma cells. Killing of some allogeneic TCs appeared non-MHC-restricted, as judged by failure to inhibit lysis by MAbs to class 1 MHC antigens. Roberts *et al.* (1987) in studies on blood lymphocytes from patients with a variety of carcinomas and using a protocol similar to that used by us also found a much higher proportion of non-MHC-restricted T cell clones than that reported in our studies. It was noticeable, however, that the proportion of clones with

Type 2 CTL activity varied widely between patients, suggesting that some individual autologous tumour lymphocyte reactions generated more Type 2 CTL activity than others. Expression of CD16 on the T cell clones was not examined in the latter studies.

Extrapolation of these in vitro studies to the in vivo response to tumours would predict that there would be few, if any, $CD3^-$ $CD16^+$ cells around tumour cells and that there would be variable proportions of CTLs with non-MHC-restricted cytotoxic activity. This prediction is consistent with results from immunohistological studies showing that more than 90 per cent of infiltrating lymphocytes were $CD3^+$ and that fewer than 2 per cent of lymphocytes expressed markers of NK cells, such as C3d receptors detected by OKM1 or CD16 detected by MAb B73.1 (Hersey *et al.*, 1985; Vose and Moore, 1985; Kornstein *et al.*, 1987). Functional studies on lymphocytes infiltrating melanoma revealed that co-culture in interleukin 2 for 8–10 days induced cytotoxic activity which, in most patients, was specific for autologous tumour cells, but in four of nine specimens the T cells had cytotoxic activity against allogeneic melanoma and K562 TCs consistent with that of Type 2 CTLs (Itoh *et al.*, 1986).

C. Stimulation with Interleukin 2 (IL-2)

Lysis of freshly isolated tumour cells by autologous PBLs is usually slight or undetectable. Studies on the stimulation by IL-2 of autologous lymphocyte killing followed from those studies showing that IL-2 was a cofactor for the induction of CTLs against allogeneic TCs (Lafferty *et al.*, 1980; Wagner *et al.*, 1980). Addition of IL-2 to co-cultures of tumour cells and lymphocytes was also shown to increase the induction of cytotoxic activity against a variety of experimental tumours (Mills and Paetkau, 1980; Gillis and Watson, 1981). Similar results were reported in studies on human tumours, except that it was found that co-culture of lymphocytes with IL-2 alone in the absence of tumour cells was sufficient to generate cytotoxic activity against autologous tumours (Hersey *et al.*, 1981; Vose and Moore, 1981; Lotze *et al.*, 1980). We suggested these results indicated activation of memory T cells in the circulation of patients and that the 'non-specific' cytotoxic activity was due to activated T cells. This interpretation was called into question by the studies of Grimm *et al.* (1982, 1983b). These authors suggested that IL-2-induced autologous killing of tumour cells was mediated by a particular population of T cells referred to as lymphokine-activated killer (LAK) cells that were induced from $CD3^-$ precursors in blood of both normal and tumour-bearing subjects.

The effector cells induced by IL-2 have since been the subject of considerable dissent which has centred on whether they are CTLs or NK cells. Arguments in favour of their T cell nature reported by Grimm *et al.* (1982) were the expression of T cell markers CD3 and CD5 but not the NK marker OKM1 on LAK cells, and the finding that LAK activity could be generated from thoracic duct or thymus lymphocytes devoid of NK activity (Grimm *et al.*, 1983a). The view that LAK precursor cells in blood were T cells was disputed in a number of subsequent studies. Phillips and Lanier (1986) reported that LAK activity generated from PBLs was largely attributable to cells with the NK phenotype. Similar results were reported by Tilden *et al.* (1987). Ortaldo *et al.* (1986) estimated the frequency of LAK cells from NK cells to be 10–50 times greater than that of LAK cells from T cells. Moretta *et al.* (1986a) estimated that one in 25 T cells were LAK precursors. In the studies by Tilden *et al.* (1987) a higher proportion of T cells with LAK activity was found when cell sorting was carried out at the end of the culture period than when IL-2 was added to lymphoid cells separated before culture. This suggested that cofactors released from other lymphocytes might have contributed to induction of T cells with LAK activity. CD16 appeared to be expressed exclusively on the CD3$^-$ population.

On balance, the evidence from these studies therefore suggested that NK cells, and not CD3$^+$ CTLs, were the predominant blood cell type mediating LAK activity. Most of the authors, however, conceded that certain T cells in blood mediated LAK activity and that this cell type was responsible for LAK activity generated from lymphoid tissue with few or no NK cell precursors.

Factors determining the nature of cells mediating LAK activity

As reviewed elsewhere (Hersey and Bolhuis, 1987), one of the variables which determine the cell type mediating IL-2-induced non-MHC-restricted cytotoxicity is whether stimuli additional to IL-2 are present in the cultures. IL-2 is known to act only on cells that have been activated and, in blood, NK cells appear to constitute a population of activated cells that respond to high concentrations of IL-2 by increased proliferative and cytotoxic activity (Talmadge *et al.*, 1986). This was shown by studies on the precursor frequency of cells responding to IL-2, which was estimated at one in 200 in the large granular lymphocyte (LGL) fraction compared with one in 5000 among resting T cells (Vose and Bonnard, 1983). These studies indicate that in non-pathological states very few T cells in blood express IL-2R or respond to IL-2. However, in the presence of other stimuli such as lectins and fetal calf serum, T cell populations as well as NK cells respond to IL-2 (Talmadge *et al.*, 1986). T cells proliferate more rapidly than NK cells in response to IL-2 (Van de Griend *et al.*, 1984a; Phillips and Lanier, 1986), so that prolonged culture could also be expected to yield predominantly non-MHC-restricted CTLs rather than NK cells.

A second variable is the nature of the cells in the starting population. Should these have few or no NK cell precursors or be depleted of such precursors, it could be expected that the resulting non-MHC-restricted cytotoxic cells would be predominantly T cells. The frequency of precursor cells for 'NK' and 'T' cell LAK activity in different organs has as yet received little attention. In mice it was shown that the frequency of NK LAK precursors in blood was 2.5 times that in the spleen and the frequency of T cell LAK precursors was 1.6 times higher in blood than in the spleen (Kalland *et al.*, 1987). Given the low NK activity of lymph nodes and thymus, it could be predicted that the precursor frequency for T cell LAK activity would be much higher than that for NK LAK activity in these tissues.

Another variable that may determine the type of cytotoxic cell responding to IL-2 is the concentration of IL-2. NK cells require high levels of IL-2 to develop optimal LAK activity, estimated as 500 U/mL in one study (Phillips and Lanier, 1986). T cells, on the other hand, respond to amounts of IL-2 as low as 1–2 U/mL. Hence the presence of high concentrations of IL-2, as used for LAK cell production in clinical studies, would favour the production of NK cells over T cells. The relatively low concentrations of IL-2 generated during MLC may, on the other hand, favour the production of Type 2 CTLs over NK cells as mediators of non-MHC-restricted cytotoxicity. The same explanation may account for the relatively low frequency of cells with non-MHC-restricted cytotoxic activity from MLTCs, compared with MLCs. IL-2 production in such cultures may be at low levels because of the low frequency of lymphocytes responding to autologous tumours and be insufficient to stimulate lymphocytes near responding cells or with low-affinity receptors for the tumour cells.

The therapeutic implications of these considerations were shown by animal studies which suggested that different cell populations were activated in vivo at different dose levels of IL-2 (Talmadge *et al.*, 1987). Optimal therapeutic responses against tumours were seen at both low and high doses of IL-2 (10 – 1000 U/animal, or > 100 000 U/animal). Therapeutic activity was only apparent at high and not low dose levels in nude mice, suggesting that NK cells were activated at the high but not the low dose levels. IL-2 was also shown to act as an adjuvant to vaccines for development of CTLs against tumours when given in low doses but not at high doses, indicating selective effects of low doses of IL-2 on T cells in vivo (Talmadge *et al.*, 1986; O'Donnell *et al.*, 1986). High doses of IL-2 actually inhibited induction of CTL responses, possibly as a result of induction of suppressor cells at high IL-2 dose levels. Whether the latter are NK cells, as suggested in studies on self-reactive CTLs, is not known (Kornbluth, 1986).

D. Induction of Type 2 CTL activity by monoclonal antibodies and lectins

MAbs against CD3 were shown to induce non-MHC lytic activity by CTLs in a number of studies (Suthanthiran *et al.*, 1984; Leeuwenberg *et al.*, 1985; Schwab *et al.*, 1985; Van de Griend *et al.*, 1987a, b). This was shown to be dependent on interaction of the Fc portion of the MAb with Fc receptors (FcRs) on the TCs (Leeuwenberg *et al.*, 1985; Schwab *et al.*, 1985; Van de Griend *et al.*, 1987b), suggesting that cross-linking of CD3 was necessary to trigger lysis and to form a conjugate with the TCs. In the absence of such interactions MAb to CD3 inhibited lysis by T cells at a post-recognition step (Leeuwenberg *et al.*, 1985). Specific lysis by CTLs was frequently inhibited by MAb to T3, concomitant with the increase in non-MHC-restricted lysis. This suggested that the latter was not mediated via the $\alpha\beta$ TCR linked to CD3 but by other receptors (as discussed below), analogous to the mechanism of 'backward killing' described by Lanzavecchia (1986). MAbs to clonotypic determinants on CTLs (Henkel *et al.*, 1987) and to a common determinant on the $\alpha\beta$ TCR (Leeuwenberg *et al.*, 1985) may also induce non-MHC-restricted lysis by similar mechanisms. The potential therapeutic importance of these findings has received attention from several groups who have used heteroaggregates formed between MAbs to CD3 and tumour antigens to target CTLs to tumour cells in vitro (Perez *et al.*, 1986; Jung *et al.*, 1986).

As discussed below, MAbs against CD16 and CD2 may also induce non-MHC-restricted CTL activity against TCs with FcRs for the Fc part of MAb by similar mechanisms to that described for MAb against CD3 (Van de Griend, 1987a, b). The common feature of these MAbs is that they interact with activation sites on CTLs. There is some evidence, however, that the activation signal from CD2 may be transmitted by CD3 (Moretta *et al.*, 1986b).

Similar mechanisms may explain induction of Type 2 CTL activity by phytohaemagglutinin (PHA). Bolhuis and Van de Griend (1985) reported that PHA increased the lytic activity of CD3$^+$ but not CD3$^-$ clones, which implied that PHA induced CTL activity via the CD3 $\alpha\beta$ TCR complex. As shown in the studies of Thiele and Lipsky (1986), CD3$^+$ Type 2 CTLs activated by PHA constitute a separate population from Type 1 CTLs. However, if PHA is present in the culture it may act as a ligand between effector and TCs, with resulting lysis of the TC by Type 1 and 2 CTLs.

III. RELATION OF CD3$^+$ NON-MHC-RESTRICTED CTLs TO OTHER CYTOTOXIC T CELLS

The presence of the NK markers, NKH1 and CD16, on Type 2 CTLs raises the question of whether they have a different lineage from Type 1 CTLs. NKH1 is a 220 kD glycoprotein, expressed on approximately 15 per cent of PBLs, including practically all cells with non-MHC-restricted cytotoxic activity (Hercend *et al.*, 1985). From 66 to 76 per cent of the cells are CD3$^-$ and the remainder are CD3$^+$ CD8$^+$ or CD3$^+$ CD4$^-$ CD8$^-$ (Schmidt *et al.*, 1986; Lanier *et al.*, 1986a). The question of the lineage of CD3$^+$ NKH1$^+$ lymphocytes in blood was investigated in studies on thymocytes, which showed that incubation with recombinant interleukin 2 (rIL-2) for seven days induced non-MHC-restricted cytotoxic activity (Phillips and Lanier, 1987). The presursor cells were NKH1$^-$ but during culture they became NKH1$^+$. Sequential analysis during culture demonstrated that thymocytes with an immature phenotype (CD1$^+$ CD4$^+$ CD8$^+$) acquired cytolytic activity concomitant with acquisition of the NKH1 antigen. After two weeks' incubation in rIL-2 their phenotype was largely CD3$^+$ CD4$^-$ CD8$^-$ NKH1$^+$. Interestingly, all were CD16$^-$. (The presence of CD3 on the cells also suggested they were different from the CD3$^-$ CD2$^+$ 'NK - like' cells generated from thymus and blood by co-culture with both IL-2 and lymphoblasts [Torten *et al.*, 1982; Warren, 1984].) These studies suggested that the CD3$^+$ CD8$^+$ NKH1$^+$ and CD3$^+$ CD4$^-$ CD8$^-$ NKH1$^+$ cells in blood were derived from a subpopulation in the thymus that differentiated into NKH1$^+$ T cells under the influence of IL-2.

A second question is whether CD16$^+$ CD3$^+$ cells represent a separate lineage from CD3$^+$ CD16$^-$ CTLs. The absence of CD16 on the CD3$^+$ NKH1$^+$ cells in the thymus may indicate that CD3$^+$ CD16$^+$ cells are of a different lineage. Another alternative is that CD16 is acquired as an activation marker on CD3$^+$ NKH1$^+$ cells. CD16 was reported to encompass practically all cells with non-MHC-restricted cytotoxicity in blood (Lanier *et al.*, 1983) and to be present on approximately 2 per cent of CD3$^+$ lymphocytes in normal subjects. Higher levels (up to 23 per cent) were present in some individuals. CD16 was also expressed at lower levels on CD3$^+$ cells than on CD3$^-$ cells (Lanier *et al.*, 1985). In view of these reports it appears surprising that CD16 was not detected on CD3$^+$ NKH1$^+$ (Lanier *et al.*, 1986a) or on CD3$^+$ CD4$^-$ CD8$^-$ non-MHC-restricted cytotoxic cells in blood (Lanier *et al.*, 1986c). These reports were also at variance with those describing the expression of

CD16 on the $\gamma\delta$ TCR CD3$^+$ CD4$^-$ CD8$^-$ WT31$^-$ non-MHC-restricted CTLs (Borst *et al.*, 1987; Van de Griend *et al.*, 1987a). All clones of Type 2 CTLs described in our studies (Hersey *et al.*, 1986a) expressed both CD16 and NKH1 markers, whereas Type 1 CTLs did not express NKH1 or CD16. Both Type 1 and Type 2 clones were maintained in culture for similar time periods so that it is unlikely that the presence of NKH1 on the Type 2, but not Type 1, CTLs was acquired as a result of culture, as suggested in other studies (Lanier *et al.*, 1987).

Although in our studies CD16 was present on all clones of Type 2 CTLs, it was not detected on CTLs with these properties by others (Van de Griend *et al.*, 1984a). The reason for these differences is not clear, but may depend on the type of stimulus used to generate CTLs, e.g., Thiele and Lipsky (1986) reported that PHA-induced non-MHC-restricted CTLs were CD3$^+$ CD16$^-$ and not CD3$^+$ CD16$^+$. PHA was also the stimulus used in studies by Van de Griend *et al.* (1984a), whereas our clones were generated from MLC or MLTC reactions. Our guess at this stage is that the CD3$^+$ CD8$^+$ CD16$^+$ and the CD3$^+$ CD4$^-$ CD8$^-$ WT31$^-$ CD16$^+$ Type 2 CTLs are of the same lineage as the corresponding CD16$^-$ Type 2 CTLs, and that the difference lies in the activation stimulus for induction of cytotoxic activity.

Are Type 2 CTLs merely activated Type 1 CTLs that kill by receptors other than $\alpha\beta$ TCR? The evidence reviewed above in studies on CTLs from MLCs suggests this is most unlikely. Some studies however, particularly with MAbs against CD3 (Leeuwenberg *el al.*, 1985) or TCR idiotypes (Henkel *et al.*, 1987) as the stimulus, suggest that specific CTLs may become non-MHC-restricted effectors. This may, however, represent cross-linking of Type 1 CTLs and TCs via anti-CD3 bound to FcRs on the TCs, which not only acts as an activation stimulus but also binds TC and CTL in close apposition (Leeuwenberg *el al.*, 1985; Van de Griend *et al.*, 1987b). A similar explanation may apply to the induction of non-MHC-restricted cytotoxicity by PHA, which appears to bind to both the CD3 $\alpha\beta$ TCR complex and the TC (Bolhuis and Van de Griend, 1985). When PHA is present in the cultures, binding of TC and effectors may occur non-specifically, and Type 1 CTLs then appear to mediate 'non-MHC-restricted' CTL activity. If however, the CTLs are activated by PHA, and PHA is then removed by washing, Type 1 CTLs do not mediate non-MHC-restricted cytotoxicity (Thiele and Lipsky, 1986).

The evidence at present therefore suggests that Type 1 antigen-specific MHC-restricted CTLs and Type 2 CTLs are discrete T cell lineages. Among the latter at least two lineages can be recognised depending on whether they express $\alpha\beta$ or $\gamma\delta$ TCR. Whether the presence of CD16 on Type 2 represents a third lineage, or a state of activation of Type 2 CTLs, remains uncertain.

IV. RECEPTORS ON TYPE 2 CYTOTOXIC T LYMPHOCYTES

A. Receptors Activating Non-MHC-restricted Lytic Activity

In the case of Type 1 CTLs it is now accepted that lytic activity is induced by interaction of antigens plus MHC structures with receptors coded for by the $\alpha\beta$ genes of the TCR. As in the case of B lymphocytes, the different specificity of T cells results from polymorphic TCRs resulting from recombination of variable (V), joining (J) and diversity (D) genes in the T cell during its development (Marrack and Kappler, 1986; Raulet *et al.*, 1985). Signals resulting from interactions with the TCR cause activation of T cell function via the T3 structures in the cell membrane (Reinherz *et al.*, 1982). Several studies based on blocking of killing with MAb to CD3 suggested that in some instances the $\alpha\beta$ TCR-CD3 complex was also involved in non-MHC-restricted cytotoxicity (Hercend *et al.*, 1983a, b; Pawelec *et al.*, 1985). These could be interpreted, however, as specific killing by CTLs which recognised a determinant expressed on a wide range of target cell (perhaps in association with other as yet undefined restricting elements — see below). More commonly, the $\alpha\beta$ TCR-CD3 receptors did not appear to mediate non-MHC-restricted cytotoxic activity (Hersey *et al.*, 1986a; Burns *et al.*, 1984; De Vries and Spits, 1984). This was not the result of abnormalities in the $\alpha\beta$ TCR-CD3 complex, as in some studies (Burns *et al.*, 1984; De Vries and Spits, 1984) cloned CTLs killed specific targets through an MHC-restricted pathway involving CD3 $\alpha\beta$ TCR but MHC-unrelated tumour TCs were killed via other receptors. Gene probe studies also suggested that the α and β genes were rearranged normally in Type 2 CTL cells (Kornbluth *et al.*, 1986). MAb against CD3 did not in some instances inhibit killing of allogeneic targets but it was uncertain whether this indicated that killing was mediated via non-$\alpha\beta$ TCRs or was due to different affinities of the TCR for antigen (Moretta *et al.*, 1984; Leontsini *et al.*, 1986).

Any discussion of the receptors involved in non-MHC-restricted CTL activity has to account not only for the non-MHC and broad cytolytic activity of Type 2 CTLs but also the differences in specificity shown in a number of studies on clones of CTLs (Pawelec *et al.*, 1985; Van de Griend *et al.*, 1984b; Hersey *et al.*, 1986a; Anichini *et al.*, 1985; Roberts *et al.*, 1986, 1987). As summarised in Table 4.1, the theoretical explanations that could be considered are as follows.

1. As suggested above, the $\alpha\beta$ TCR on the CTL could recognise a common determinant on all the TCs and be restricted by non-polymorphic areas of the MHC antigens, such as the Ig-like determinants at the proximal region of Class 1 MHC antigens (Bjorkman *et al.*,

Table 4.1: Receptors involved in activation of killing by Type 2 non-MHC-restricted cytotoxic T lymphocytes

Receptors	Phenotype	Activating signals
(a) $\alpha\beta$ TCR	CD3$^+$ CD4$^\pm$ CD8$^\pm$ CD16$^\pm$ NKH-1$^+$	Antigen $\pm$ non-polymorphic regions, PHA, MLC, MLTC, MAb to CD3 and IL2
(b) $\gamma\delta$ TCR	CD3$^+$ CD4$^-$ CD8$^-$ CD16$^+$ WT31$^-$ NKH-1$^+$	?Antigen, PHA, IL2, MAb to CD3 and CD16
?$\beta\beta$ TCR		Unknown
?$\alpha\beta$ TCR		Unknown
(c) FcR1o (CD16)	CD3$^+$ CD4$^-$ CD8$^\pm$ CD16$^+$ NKH-1$^+$	MLC, MAb to CD16, ?Ig-like determinants on TCs
(d) CD2	CD3$^+$ CD8$^+$	LFA-3 on TCs, MAbs to CD2, ?PHA.

1987). This appears unlikely to explain killing of TCs that do not appear to express MHC antigens at all, such as the K562 TCs or a melanoma TC described in previous studies (Hersey *et al.*, 1986a).

2. There may be an additional receptor perhaps linked to T3 which has limited polymorphism. One possibility is the TCR coded for by $\gamma(\delta)$ genes. These undergo similar rearrangement to $\alpha\beta$ genes in T cell development but appear to have limited diversity (Kranz *et al.*, 1985). Lymphocytes expressing $\gamma\delta$ TCR were first identified in patients with immunodeficiency by negative selection with MAb WT31, thought to be against a common determinant on $\alpha\beta$ TCR (Spits *et al.*, 1985b; Brenner *et al.*, 1986). Expression of $\gamma\delta$ TCR was subsequently detected on CD4$^-$ CD8$^-$ thymocytes and CD3$^+$ CD4$^-$ CD8$^-$ WT31$^-$ blood lymphocytes. The latter accounted for approximately 2 per cent of all CD3$^+$ PBLs and mediated both non-MHC-restricted and antibody-dependent cell-mediated cytotoxic activity (Borst *et al.*, 1987; Brenner *et al.*, 1987). While it is clear from these studies that this cell type may account for some non−MHC−restricted CTL activity, the majority of cells with Type 2 CTL activity express $\alpha\beta$ TCR and CD8 and hence use receptors other than $\gamma\delta$ TCR.

Some studies have suggested the presence of other types of TCR, e.g. some double negative (CD4$^-$ CD8$^-$) thymocytes were reported to have $\alpha\beta$ TCR with limited diversity of the β chain (Fowlkes *et al.*, 1987) but whether this may also apply to CD4$^-$ CD8$^-$ PBLs is unknown. Moingeon *et al.* (1986) reported that a third receptor, perhaps composed of two β chains, may be a receptor on Type 2 CTLs. This suggestion came from studies on CD3$^+$ CD8$^+$ WT31$^-$ CTL clones isolated from a 25-week-old fetus which expressed a clonotypic 85 kD TCR coded for by β but not α genes.

3. The requirement for different specificity but broad non-MHC-restricted cytolytic activity could also be satisfied by the postulate that several different non-polymorphic receptors can activate Type 2 CTLs when they interact with ligands on different TCs. One of the most likely candidates is the labile FcR present on the majority of Type 2 CTLs. FcRs are known to be capable of activating lytic activity, referred to as antibody-dependent cell-mediated cytotoxicity (ADCC), by interaction with IgG complexed to TCs. Interaction of MAb with CD16 may also induce cytotoxic activity in Type 2 CTLs (Karpovsky *et al.*, 1984; Van de Griend *et al.*, 1987a, b). Additional evidence for the role of these receptors in non-MHC-restricted killing from our studies is as follows:

(i) Blocking the FcR with MAb to CD16, aggregated IgG (see also Kristensen and Langvad, 1978) or TCs complexed with IgG, inhibited lysis by Type 2 CTLs.

(ii) Modulation of FcR from the cell surface with sensitised red cells (see also studies by Kay *et al.*, 1979) or MAb to CD16, or by incubation in phorbol esters (Perussia *et al.*, 1984), resulted in loss of cytotoxic activity by Type 2 but not Type 1 CTLs. The latter experiments showed that modulation of FcR by non-IgG interactions also resulted in loss of cytotoxic activity. This is an important point as a number of studies have shown that FcR interactions with IgG may have inhibitory effects (at post-recognition steps) on cell function (Moretta *et al.*, 1978; Sulica *et al.*, 1982, 1986; Perussia *et al.*, 1983b, 1984), perhaps by elevation of cAMP (Ziegler and Henney, 1977).

Evidence that there may be Fc-like determinants on TCs recognised by Type 2 CTLs was shown by capping of FcRs from the effector cells by overnight incubation on TCs sensitive to lysis, but not on those insensitive to lysis (MacDonald and Hersey, submitted for publication). The nature of the determinants recognised on the TCs is at present unknown but they could conceivably be determinants on members of the immunoglobulin superfamily distributed on many cells (Hunkapiller and Hood, 1986; Bjorkman *et al.*, 1987). Previous studies have shown that interaction with both CH2 and CH3 domains of IgG was necessary to induce ADCC (Sarmay *et al.*, 1985). Studies in progress have shown that MAbs used in the latter study interacted with determinants on TCs sensitive to killing by Type 2 CTLs. In sum, these experiments suggest that FcRs are receptors on Type 2 CTLs which interact with determinants on TCs and activate their lytic activity. Reports by others suggest, however, that not all Type 2 CTLs have FcR (Van de Griend *et al.*, 1984a), so that receptors other than FcR are clearly involved.

A second non-polymorphic receptor which is distributed widely on both NK cells and Type 2 CTLs is the sheep red cell receptor (CD2). Activation of T cells by MAb to CD2 may, like MAb to CD3, induce non-MHC-restricted lytic activity, provided that a combination of MAbs to different epitopes on CD2 is used and/or accessory cells with FcR are present (Siliciano *et al.*, 1985; Huet *et al.*, 1986; Bolhuis *et al.*, 1986; Van de Griend *et al.*, 1987b). LFA-3 (a 40–80 kD membrane glycoprotein) appears to be a ligand for this receptor (Krensky *et al.*, 1983; Takai *et al.*, 1986; Dustin *et al.*, 1986) and it is conceivable that cells expressing LFA-3 may activate Type 2 CTLs. The main problem in accepting this role for CD2 on CTLs is the wide distribution of CD2 on Type 1 CTLs, which do not exhibit non-MHC-restricted cytotoxic activity. MAbs against CD2 were shown to inhibit T cell functions (Palacios and Martinez-Maza, 1982; Reed *et al.*, 1985) so that it is equally plausible that the physiological role for CD2 is to inhibit CTL activation. Absence of LFA-3 on TCs would therefore allow activation of CTLs and lysis of the TC (see discussion below for role of CD4 and CD8). Another possibility is that CD2–LFA-3 interactions serve to form stable conjugates between effector and TC, as discussed below (Shaw *et al.*, 1986; Shaw and Luce, 1987).

B. Receptors Regulating Type 2 Cytotoxic T Lymphocyte Function

In addition to the receptors described above which may directly activate CTLs, a number of structures on T cells (as summarised in Table 4.2) have been identified which either enhance or inhibit their lytic activity. Among those inhibiting CTL activity are MAbs against CD2, referred to

Table 4.2: Receptors involved in regulation of Type 2 cytotoxic T lymphocyte activity

Receptors decreasing lytic activity	*Possible ligands*
CD4	Class II MHC[a]
CD8	Class I MHC[a]
CD2	LFA-3, MAbs to CD2
TL1SA1, L24, L25	Unknown
Receptors increasing lytic activity	
Tp44	Unknown
CD5	Unknown
T200 (p220)	Unknown
p103 kD	Unknown
GD2, GD3	?IL2 ?Ca^{2+}

[a] Non-polymorphic regions.

above, and those against CD8 (Van Seventer *et al.*, 1986), CD4 (Saizawa *et al.*, 1987) and TLISAI (Burns *et al.*, 1985). MAbs against the latter structure and those referred to as L24 and L25 (Clayberger *et al.*, 1987) appear to specifically inhibit CTL functions. In some instances these inhibitory effects may mimic physiological interactions between the receptor and its ligand, e.g. it was suggested that the interaction of CD4 and CD8 with Class II or Class I MHC antigens provided an inhibitory signal to cytotoxic cells which could be overruled by interaction of antigens with the TCR or other receptors (Fleischer *et al.*, 1986a). This model explains the inverse relationship shown between the expression of Class I antigens on TCs and their susceptibility to non-MHC-restricted cytotoxicity (Ljunggren and Karre, 1985; Storkus *et al.*, 1987) and the frequency with which $CD3^+ CD4^- CD8^-$ CTLs exhibit spontaneous non-MHC-restricted cytotoxic activity.

Enhancement of CTL function was shown by MAbs against Tp44, CD5 (Ledbetter *et al.*, 1985a), 103 kD proteins on CTLs (Fleischer *et al.*, 1986b) the p220 form of T200 (Ledbetter *et al.*, 1985b) and T10. The mechanisms underlying this enhancement of cytolytic function include increased expression of IL-2 receptors and IL-2 production (Clark and Ledbetter, 1986). MAbs against the gangliosides GD2 and GD3 were also shown to increase non-MHC-restricted CTL activity (Hersey *et al.*, 1986c, d). The mechanism involved in enhancement by the latter MAb appears to be both enhanced IL-2 production (Schibeci *et al.*, submitted) and, more importantly, a post-binding step following interaction of IL-2 with its receptor (work in progress). The gangliosides are expressed on activated T cells in vivo (Hersey *et al.*, 1988) so that administration of MAb may have similar effects in vivo to those demonstrated in vitro.

C. Receptors Involved in Conjugate Formation

A third class of receptors do not appear to have activating or regulatory roles but appear to stabilise conjugate formation between effector and TCs. The best example may be that of leukocyte function antigen 1 (LFA-1) which belongs to the family of high molecular weight glycoproteins with identical 95 kD subunits on leukocyte cell surfaces (Springer, 1985). Other members of this family include complement receptor 3 (CR3) and p150,95 on CTLs (Keizer *et al.*, 1987). MAbs against LFA-1 were shown to block cytolysis by both non-MHC- and MHC-restricted CTLs (Krensky *et al.*, 1983; Shaw and Luce, 1987; Kaufmann *et al.*, 1982; Schmidt *et al.*, 1985; Shaw *et al.*, 1986) but interaction with LFA-1 and other similar cell adhesion molecules did not appear to activate cell function (Patarroyo *et al.*, 1985). The ligand for LFA-1 is not well established but may be a 90 kD molecule referred to as ICAM-1 (Rothlein *et al.*, 1986). LFA-1 was not modulated from the cell surface by interaction with MAbs (Schmidt *et al.*, 1985), which may be an important property necessary to stabilise conjugate formation (Carpen *et al.*, 1986).

Other structures which may be involved in conjugate formation rather than cell activation are laminin, C3d and the T200 common leukocyte antigen. Laminin has been detected on NK cells (but not CTLs) and MAbs to laminin inhibited conjugate formation between NK cells and TCs (Hiserodt *et al.*, 1985). Subsets of thymocytes were also shown to bind to fibronectin (Cardarelli and Pierschbacher, 1986) and sulfated polysaccharides (Parish and Snowden, 1985), but whether receptors for these structures are present on human CTLs is unknown. Selected MAbs to T200 were shown to block non-MHC-restricted cytotoxicity against only certain TCs (Van de Griend *et al.*, 1984b; Pawelec *et al.*, 1985), suggesting that the ligand for T200 may be present only on certain TCs. C3b breakdown products on the surface of TCs were also shown to increase conjugate formation with effector lymphocytes (Klein *et al.*, 1986).

V. CONCLUSION

Type 2 (non-MHC-restricted) CTLs appear to represent a discrete lineage of T cells that can be recognised in thymus, blood and all lymphoid tissues. They consist of at least two phenotypes depending on whether they express $\alpha\beta$ TCR with the phenotype CD3$^+$ CD8$^+$ or $\gamma\delta$ TCR with the phenotype CD3$^+$ CD4$^-$ CD8$^-$ WT31$^-$. Low affinity FcRs for IgG on Type 2 CTLs may indicate further subtypes of the cells or represent a different state of activation. Type 2 CTLs appear to represent a component of the normal immune responses to cell-associated antigens but may be induced by other artificial stimuli such as IL-2, alloantigens, lectins and MAbs against activation structures (CD8, CD3, CD16) on CTLs.

At least three groups of receptors are present on the surface of these cells. These include: the activation sites represented by the CD3 $\alpha\beta$ or $\gamma\delta$ TCR complex; CD2; and CD16. It is not yet clear whether a third type of TCR with restricted polymorphism may exist on some Type 2 CTLs. CD3 may be involved in signal transduction but the signal is not necessarily from interaction with normal $\alpha\beta$ TCR. In some instances FcR may be the normal activation site, perhaps by interaction with Ig-like determinants on TCs. A second set of receptors act to regulate cell activity. Those acting to inhibit cytotoxic activity, represented by CD8, may maintain CTLs in a quiescent state which is overriden in the absence of Class I MHC on the TCs, on interaction of ligands on TCs with activation receptors on Type 2 CTLs. Receptors which increase cytolytic activity include the gangliosides GD2 and GD3. A third set of receptors appear to be involved in conjugate formation between TC and CTL.

Existing knowledge appears to provide a number of possibilities for therapeutic exploitation of Type 2 CTLs. One is the use of MAb conjugates to activate and direct the Type 2 CTLs to tumour cells. The other is the use of MAbs to gangliosides to enhance their activity in situ about tumours. Administration of low doses of IL-2 in conjunction with these activating agents could be expected to favour the expansion and activation of Type 2 (and Type 1) CTLs at sites near tumours but to have little effect on NK cells.

ACKNOWLEDGMENTS

Work of the author referred to was supported by grants from the National Health and Medical Research Council, New South Wales State Cancer Council and Hunter Valley Cancer Appeal. I wish to thank Christine Cook for expert secretarial assistance.

REFERENCES

Anichini, A., Fossati, G. and Parmiani, G. (1985). *Int. J. Cancer.* 35: 683–9.

Bjorkman, P. J., Saper, M. A., Samraoui, B., Bennett, W. S., Strominger, J. L., and Wiley, D. C. (1987) *Nature* 506: 512.

Bolhuis, R. L. H. and Van de Griend, R. J. (1985). *Cellular Immunol.* 93: 46–57.

Bolhuis, R. L. H., Roozemond, R. C. and Van de Griend, R. J. (1986). *J. Immunol.* 136: 3939–44.

Borst, J., Van de Griend, R. J., Van Oostveen, J. W., Ang, S. L., Melief, C. J., Seidman, J. G. and Bolhuis, R. (1987). *Nature* 325: 683–8.

Brenner, M. B., McLean, J., Dialynas, D. P., Strominger, J. L., Smith, J. A., Owen, F. L., Seidman, J. G., Ip, S., Rosen, F. and Krangel, M. S. (1986). *Nature* 322: 145–9.

Brenner, M. B., McLean, J., Scheft, H., Riberdy, J., Ang, S. L., Seidman, J. G., Devlin, P. and Krangel, M. S. (1987). *Nature* 325: 689–94.

Burns, G. F., Triglia, T. and Werkmeister, J. A. (1984). *J. Immunol.* 133: 1656–63.

Burns, G. F., Triglia, T., Werkmeister, J. A., Begley, C. G. and Boyd, A. W. (1985). *J. Exp. Med.* 161: 1063–78.

Cardarelli, P. M. and Pierschbacher, M. D. (1986). *Proc. Natl. Acad. Sci. USA* 83: 2647–51.

Carpen, O., Keiser, G. and Saksela, E. (1986). *Nat. Imm. Cell Growth Reg.* 133: Abstract 17.

Carroll, P. G. and Dewolf, W. C. (1983). *J. Immunol.* 131: 1007.

Clark, E. A. and Ledbetter, J. A. (1986). *Immunol. Today* 7: 267–70.

Clayberger, C., Krensky, A. M., McIntyre, B. W., Koller, T. D., Parham, P., Broosky, F., Linn, D. J. and Evans, E. L. (1987). *J. Immunol.* 138: 1510–14.

DeVries, J. E. and Spits, H. (1984). *J. Immunol.* 132: 510–19.

Dustin, M., Sanders, M., Shaw, S. and Springer, T. (1986). *A. A. I.* Abstract 6893.

Ferrini, S., Miescher, S., Zocchi, M. R., Von Fliedner, V. and Moretta, A. (1987). *J. Immunol.* 138: 1297–1302.

Fleischer, B., Schendel, D. J. and Von Steldern, D. (1986a). *Eur. J. Immunol.* 16: 741–6.

Fleischer, B., Schrezenmeier, H. and Wagner, H. (1986b). *J. Immunol.* 136: 1625.

Fowlkes, B. J., Kruisbeek, A. M., Ton-That, H., Weston, M. A., Coligan, J. E., Schwartz, R. H. and Pardoll, D. M. (1987). *Nature* 329: 251–4.

Gillis, S. and Watson, J. (1981). *Immunol. Rev.* 54: 81–110.

Grimm, E. A., Mazumder, A., Zhang, H. Z. and Rosenberg, S. A. (1982). *J. Exp. Med.* 155: 1823–41.

Grimm, E. A., Ramsey, K. M., Mazumder, A., Wilson, D. J., Djeu, J. Y. and Rosenberg, S. A. (1983a). *J. Exp. Med.* 157: 884–97.

Grimm, E. A., Robb, R. J., Roth, J. A., Weckers, L. M., Lachman, L. B., Wilson, D. J. and Rosenberg, S. A. (1983b). *J. Exp. Med.* 158: 1356–61.

Grossman, Z. and Herberman, R. B. (1986). *Canc. Res.* 46: 2651–8.

Henkel, T. J., Braciale, V. L. and Braciale, T. J. (1987). *J. Immunol.* 138: 1221–8.

Hercend, T., Reinherz, E. L., Meuer, S., Schlossman, S. F. and Ritz, J. (1983a). *Nature* 301: 158–60.

Hercend, T., Meuer, S., Brennan, A., Edson, M. A., Acuto, O., Reinherz, E. L., Schlossman, S. F. and Ritz, J. (1983b). *J. Exp. Med.* 158: 157–60.

Hercend, T., Griffin, J. D., Bensussan, A., Schmidt, R. E., Brennan, E. A., Murray, C., Daley, J. F., Schlossman, S. F. and Ritz, J. (1985). *J. Clin. Invest.* 75: 932–43.

Hersey, P. and Bolhuis, R. L. (1987). *Immunol. Today.* 8: 233–9.

Hersey, P., Edwards, A. E., Edwards, J., Adams, E., Milton, G. W. and Nelson, D. S. (1975). *Int. J. Cancer.* 16: 173–83.

Hersey, P., Bindon, C., Edwards, A., Murray, E., Phillips, G. and McCarthy, W. H. (1981). *Int. J. Cancer.* 28: 695–703.

Hersey, P., Murray, E., Grace, J. and McCarthy, W. H. (1985). *Pathology* 17: 385–91.

Hersey, P., MacDonald, M. J., Schibeci, S. D. and Burns, C. (1986a). *Cancer Immunol. Immunother.* 22: 15–23.

Hersey, P., MacDonald, M. and Schibeci, S. (1986b). In U. Veronesi, N. Cascinelli and M. Santinami (eds) *Cutaneous Melanoma.* New York: Academic Press: 421–32.

Hersey, P., Schibeci, S., Townsend, P., Burns, C. and Cheresh, D. A. (1986c). *Canc. Res.* 46: 6083–90.

Hersey, P., MacDonald, M., Burns, C. and Cheresh, D. A. (1986d). *Canc. Immunol. Immunotherap.* 15: 22–8.

Hersey, P., Jamal, O., Henderson, C., Zardawi, I. and D'Alessandro, G. (1988). *Int. J. Cancer.* 41: 336–43.

Hiserodt, J. C., Laybourn, K. A. and Varani, J. (1985). *J. Immunol.* 135: 1484–7.

Huet, S., Wakasugi, H., Sterkers, G., Gilmour, J., Tursz, T., Boumsell, L. and Bernard, A. (1986). *J. Immunol.* 137: 1420–8.

Hunkapiller, T. and Hood, L. (1986). *Nature* 323: 15–16.

Itoh, K., Tilden, A. B. and Balch, C. M. (1986). *Canc. Res.* 46: 3011–17.

Jung, G., Honsik, C. J., Reisfeld, R. A. and Muller-Eberhard, H. J. (1986). *Proc. Natl. Acad. Sci. USA* 83: 4479–83.

Kalland, T., Belfrage, H., Bhilaovala, P. and Hedlund, G. (1987). *J. Immunol.* 138: 3640–5.

Kaplan, J. (1986). *Immunol. Today* 7: 10–13.

Karpovsky, B., Titus, J. A., Stephany, D. A., and Segal, D. M. (1984). *J. Exp. Med.* 160: 1686–94.

Kaufmann, Y., Golstein, P., Pierres, M., Springer, T. A. and Eshhar, Z. (1982). *Nature.* 300: 357–9.

Kay, D. H., Fagnani, R. and Bonnard, G. D. (1979). *Int. J. Cancer* 24: 141–50.

Keizer, G. D., Borst, J., Visser, W., Schwarting, R., DeVries, J. E. and Figdor, C. G. (1987). *J. Immunol.* 138: 3130–6.

Klein, E. (1980). *Immunol. Today.* 1: IV.

Klein, E., Kai, C., Sarmay, G., Yefenof, E. and Gergely, J. (1986). *6th Internat. Congress of Immunol.* : 2.51.26.

Knuth, H., Danowski, B., Oettgen, H. F. and Old, L. J. (1981). *Proc. Natl. Acad. Sci. USA* 81: 3511–15.

Kornbluth, J. (1986). *Nat. Imm. Cell Growth Reg.* 5: 143, Abstract 42.

Kornbluth, J., Leiden, J., Quertermous, L., Coury, J., Seidman, J., and Strominger, J. (1986). *Nat. Imm. Cell Growth Reg.* 5: 143, Abstract 41.

Kornstein, M. J., Stewart, R., and Elder, D. E. (1987). *Canc. Res.* 47: 1411–12.

Kranz, D. M., Saito, H., Heller, M., Takagaki, Y., Haas, W., Eisen, H. N. and Tonegawa, S. (1985). *Nature* 313: 752–5.

Krensky, A. M., Sanchez-Madrid, F., Robbins, E., Nagy, J. A., Springer, J. A. and Burakoff, S. J. (1983). *J. Immunol.* 131: 611–16.

Kristensen, E. and Langvad, E. (1978). *Cancer Immunol. Immunother.* 5: 71–6.

Lafferty, K. J., Andrus, L. and Prowse, S. J. (1980). *Immunol. Rev.* 51: 279–314.

Lanier, L. L. and Phillips, J. H. (1986). *Immunol. Today.* 7: 132–4.

Lanier, L. L., Myle, A., Phillips, J. H., Warner, N. L. and Babcock, G. F. (1983). *J. Immunol.* 131: 1789–96.

Lanier, L. L., Kipps, T. J. and Phillips, J. H. (1985). *J. Exp. Med.* 162: 2089–2106.

Lanier, L. L., My Le, A., Civin, C. I., Loken, M. R. and Phillips, J. H. (1986a). *J. Immunol.* 136: 4480–6.

Lanier, L. L., Phillips, J. H., Hackett, J., Tutt, M. and Kumar, V. (1986b). *J. Immunol.* 137: 2735–9.

Lanier, L. L., Ruitenberg, J. J. and Phillips, J. H. (1986c). *J. Exp. Med.* 164: 339–44.

Lanier, L. L., My Le, A., Ding, A., Evans, E. L., Krensky, A. M., Clayberger, C. and Phillips, J. H. (1987). *J. Immunol.* 138: 2019–23.

Lanzavecchia, A. (1986). *Nature.* 319: 778–80.

Ledbetter, J. A., Martin, P. J., Spooner, C. E., Wofsky, D., Tsu, T. T., Beatty, P. G. and Gladstone, P. (1985a). *J. Immunol.* 135: 2331–8.

Ledbetter, J. A., Rose, L. M., Spooner, C. E., Beatty, P. G., Martin, P. J. and Clark, E. A. (1985b). *J. Immunol.* 135: 1819–25.

Leeuwenberg, J. F. M., Spits, H., Tax, W. J. M. and Capel, P. J. A. (1985). *J. Immunol.* 134: 3770–5.

Leontsini, E., Brown, T. and Biddison, W. E. (1986). *Cell. Immunol.* 102: 21–32.

Ljunggren, H. G. and Karre, K. (1985). *J. Exp. Med.* 162: 1745–59.

Lotze, M. T. and Matory, Y. L. (1985). *J. Immunol.* 135: 2865–75.

Lotze, M. T., Strausser, J. L. and Rosenberg, S. A. (1980) *J. Immunol.* 124: 2972–8.

Marrack, P. and Kappler, J. (1986). *Scientific American* 28–37.

Masucci, M. G., Klein, E. and Argov, S. (1980). *J. Immunol.* 124: 2458–63.

Mazumder, A., Grimm, E. A. and Rosenberg, S. A. (1983a) *Cancer Immunol. Immunother.* 15: 1–10.

Mazumder, A., Grimm, E. A. and Rosenberg, S. A. (1983b). *J. Immunol.* 130: 958–63.

Meuer, S. C., Hussey, R. E., Cantrell, D. A., Hodgdon, J. C., Schlossman, S. F., Smith, K. A. and Reinherz, E. L. (1984). *Proc. Natl. Acad. Sci. USA* 81: 1509.

Mills, G. B. and Paetkau, V. (1980). *J. Immunol.* 125: 1897–1901.

Moingeon, P., Ythier, A., Goubin, G., Faure, F., Nowill, A., Delmon, L., Rainaud, M., Forestier, F., Daffos, F., Bohuon, C. and Hercend, T. (1986). *Nature* 323: 638–40.

Moretta, A., Pantaleo, G., Mingari, M. C., Moretta, L. and Cerottini, J. C. (1984). *J. Exp. Med.* 159: 921–34.

Moretta, A., Olive, D., Poggi, A., Pantaleo, G., Mawas, C. and Moretta, L. (1986b). *Eur. J. Immunol.* 16: 1427–32.

Moretta, L., Mingari, M. C. and Romanzi, C. A. (1978). *Nature.* 272: 618–20.

Moretta, L., Pende, D., Cozzani, R. *et al.* (1986a). *Eur. J. Immunol.* 16: 1623–1625.

Mukherji, B. and Macalister, T. J. (1983). *J. Exp. Med.* 158: 240–5.

Muul, L. M. and Gately, M. K. (1984). *J. Immunol.* 132: 1202.

O'Donnell, R. W., Marquis, D. M., Muoholkar, G. S. and McCune, C. S. (1986). *Canc. Res.* 46: 3273–8.

Ortaldo, J. R., Mason, A. and Overton, R. (1986). *J. Exp. Med.* 164: 1193–1205.

Palacios, R. and Martinez-Maza, O. (1982). *J. Immunol.* 129: 2479–85.

Parish, C. R. and Snowden, J. M. (1985). *Cell Immunol.* 91: 201–14.

Patarroyo, M., Beatty, P. G., Fabre, J. W. and Gahmberg, C. G. (1985). *Scand. J. Immunol.* 22: 171–82.

Pawelec, G., Newman, W., Schwulera, U. and Wernet, P. (1985). *Cell. Immunol.* 92: 31–40.

Perez, P., Titus, J. A., Lotze, M. A., Cuttitta, F., Longo, D. L., Groues, E. S., Rabin, H., Durda, P. J. and Segal, D. M. (1986). *J. Immunol.* 137: 2069–72.

Perussia, B., Starr, S., Abraham, S., Fanning, V. and Trinchieri, G. (1983a). *J. Immunol.* 130: 2133–41.

Perussia, B., Acuto, O., Terhorst, C., Faust, J., Lazarus, R., Fanning, V. and Trinchieri, G. (1983b). *J. Immunol.* 130: 2142–8.

Perussia, B., Trinchieri, G., Jackson, A., Warner, N. L., Faust, J., Rumpold, H., Kraft, D. and Lanier, L. (1984). *J. Immunol.* 133: 180–9.

Phillips, J. H. and Lanier, L. L. (1986). *J. Exp. Med.* 164: 814–25.

Phillips, J. H. and Lanier, L. L. (1987). *J. Immunol.* 139: 683–7.

Phillips, J. H. My Le, A., and Lanier, L. L. (1984). *J. Exp. Med.* 159: 993–1008.

Poros, A. and Klein, E. (1979). *Cell. Immunol.* 46: 57.

Raulet, D. H., Garman, R. D., Saito, H. and Tonegawa, S. (1985). *Nature* 314: 103–7.

Reed, J. C., Tadmori, W., Kamoun, M., Koretzky, G. and Nowell, P. C. (1985). *J. Immunol.* 134: 1631–9.

Reinherz, E. L., Meuer, S., Fitzgerald, K. A., Hussey, R. E., Levine, H. and Schlossman, S. F. (1982). *Cell* 30: 735–43.

Rimm, I., Schlossman, S. F. and Reinherz, E. L. (1984). *Cell Immunol.* 87: 327–39.

Roberts, T. E., Shipton, U. and Moore, M. (1986). *Cancer Immunol. Immunother.* 22: 107–13.

Roberts, T. E., Shipton, U. and Moore, M. (1987). *Int. J. Cancer* 39: 436–41.

Rothlein, R., Dustin, M. L., Marlin, S. D. and Springer, T. A. (1986). *J. Immunol.* 37: 1270–4.

Saizawa, K., Rojo, J. and Janeway, C. A. (1987) *Nature* 328: 260–3.

Sarmay, G., Jefferis, R., Klein, E., Benczur, M. and Gergely, J. (1985). *Eur. J. Immunol.* 15: 1037–42.

Schmidt, R. E., Bartley, G., Levine, H., Schlossman, S. F. and Ritz, J. (1985). *J. Immunol.* 135: 1020–4.

Schmidt, R. E., Murray, C., Daley, J. F., Schlossman, S. F. and Ritz, J. (1986). *J. Exp. Med.* 164: 351–6.

Schwab, R., Crow, M. K., Russo, C. and Weksler, M. E. (1985). *J. Immunol.* 135: 1714–8.

Seeley, J. K. and Golub, S. H. (1978). *J. Immunol.* 120: 1415.

Seeley, J. K., Masucci, G., Poros, A., Klein, E. and Golub, S. H. (1979). *J. Immunol.* 123: 1303–11.

Shaw, S. and Luce, G. E. G. (1987). *J. Immunol.* 139: 1037–45.

Shaw, S., Ginther Luce, G. E., Quinones, R., Gress, R. E., Springer, T. A. and Sanders, M. E. (1986). *Nature* 323: 262–4.

Siliciano, R. F., Pratt, J. C., Schmidt, R. E., Ritz, J. and Reinherz, E. L. (1985). *Nature* 317: 428–30.

Spits, H., Yssel, H., Leeuwenberg, J. and De Vries, J. E. (1985a). *Eur. J. Immunol.* 15: 88–91.

Spits, H., Borst, J., Tax, W., Capel, P. J. A., Terhorst, C. and De Vries, J. E. (1985b). *J. Immunol.* 135: 1922–8.

Springer, T. A. (1985). *Fed. Proc.* 44: 2660–3.

Storkus, W. J., Howell, D. N., Salter, R. D., Dawson, J. R. and Cresswell, P. (1987). *J. Immunol.* 138: 1657–9.

Sulica, A., Gherman, M., Galatiuc, C., Manciulea, M. and Herberman, R. B. (1982). *J. Immunol.* 128: 1031–6.

Sulica, A., Bancu, A., Gherman, M., Stanworth, D. and Herberman, R. (1986). *6th International Congress of Immunology:* 4.25.27.

Suthanthiran, M., Williams, P. S., Solomon, S. D., Rubin, A. L. and Stenzel, K. H. (1984). *J. Clin. Invest.* 74: 2263–71.

Takai, Y., Rosenstein, Y., Reed, M. L., Burakoff, S. J. and Herrmann, S. H. (1986). *A. A. I.,* Abstract 4288.

Talmadge, J. E., Wiltrout, R. H., Counts, D. F., Herbermann, R. B., McDonald, T. and Ortaldo, J. R. (1986). *Cell Immunol.* 102: 261–72.

Talmadge, J. E., Phillips, H., Schindler, J., Tribble, H. and Pennington, R. (1987). *Canc. Res.* 47: 5725–32.

Thiele, D. L. and Lipsky, P. E. (1986). *J. Immunol.* 137: 1399–1406.

Tilden, A. B., Itoh, K. and Balch, C. M. (1987). *J. Immunol.* 138: 1068–73.

Torten, M., Sidell, N. and Golub, S. H. (1982). *J. Exp. Med.* 156: 1545–50.

Trinchieri, G., O'Brien, T., Shade, M. and Perussia, B. (1984). *J. Immunol.* 133: 1869–77.

Van de Griend, R., Van Krimpen, B. A., Ronteltap, C. P. M. and Bolhuis, R. L. H. (1984a). *J. Immunol.* 132: 3185–91.

Van de Griend, R. J., Giphart, M. J., Van Krimpen, B. A. and Bolhuis, R. L. H. (1984b). *J. Immunol.* 133: 1222–8.

Van de Griend, R. J., Tax, W. J. M., Van Krimpen, B. A., Vreugdenhill, R. J., Ronteltap, C. P. M. and Bolhuis, R. L. H. (1987a). *J. Immunol.* 138: 1627–32.

Van de Griend, R. J., Bolhuis, R. L. H., Stoter, G. and Rouzemond, R. C. (1987b). *J. Immunol.* 138: 3137–44.

Van Seventer, G., Van Lier, R. A. W., Spits, H., Ivanyi, P. and Melief, C. J. M. (1986). *Eur. J. Immunol.* 16: 1363–71.

Vose, B. M. and Bonnard, G. D. (1983). *J. Immunol.* 130: 687–93.

Vose, B. M. and Moore, M. (1981). *Immunology Letters.* 3: 237–41.

Vose, B. M. and Moore, M. (1985). *Seminars in Hematol.* 22: 27–40.

Vose, B. M. and White, W. (1983). *Cancer Immunol. Immunother.* 15: 227–36.

Wagner, H. Hardi, C., Heeg, K., Pfizenmaier, K., Solbach, W., Bartlett, R., Stockinger, H. and Rollinghof, M. (1980). *Immunol. Rev.* 51: 215–55.

Warren, H. S. (1984). *J. Immunol.* 132: 2888–2893.

Ziegler, H. K. and Henney, C. S. (1977). *J. Immunol.* 119: 1010–7.

5

Natural Cytotoxic (NC) Activity

PAUL Q. PATEK[1]
JOHN LESLIE COLLINS[2]

Salk Institute
P.O. Box 85800
San Diego, CA 92138–9216, USA

> The most savage
> controversies are those
> about matters to which
> there is no good
> evidence either way.
>
> Bertrand Russell

[1]Present address: Department of Microbiology, University of Hawaii, Honolulu, HI 96822, USA
[2]Present address: Department of Obstetrics and Gynecology, Division of Oncology, Washington University School of Medicine, St Louis, MO 63110, USA

NATURAL IMMUNITY
ISBN 0 12 5145551

I. INTRODUCTION

Natural cell-mediated cytotoxicity (NCMC) is the cell-mediated cytotoxic activity found in normal, untreated mice, humans, and other
species. NCMC differs from classical immune reactivity mediated by B
and T cells in the following ways: (1) NCMC is present in non-immunised
individuals; (2) it is not directly inducible by antigen; (3) it has no
'immune memory'; and (4) it has a small antigenic recognition repertoire.
In spite of these limitations NCMC acts in a 'specific' way to kill target
cells in vivo and in vitro.

Although NCMC is a generic term which can encompass many cell
types, it has come to refer mainly to the activity mediated by natural
cytotoxic (NC) and natural killer (NK) cells. While the distinction
between NC and NK cells is clear (Table 5.1), many of the early

Table 5.1 Some differences between natural cytotoxic cell activity and natural
killer cell activity.[a]

Features	NC	NK
Mouse strain distribution	different from NK	different from NC
nude, CBA/HN, C3H/HeJ	yes	yes
beige, SJL	yes	no
Age of appearance	birth to 4 weeks	4 weeks or more
Age-related decline	none	6 months
Present in tumour-bearing mice	yes	low
In vivo effect of:		
[89]Sr	none	decreases activity
Oestrogen	none	decreases activity
Cyclophosphamide	none	decreases activity
Silica	none	decreases activity
Carrageenan	none	decreases activity
In vitro effect of:		
Glucocorticosteroids	decreases activity	none
Protein synthesis		
inhibition	increases activity	none
Preincubation	none or increases activity	decreases activity
In vitro kinetics of lysis	4–8 h lag then linear	linear for t = 0

[a] Modification of a table from O. Stutman and E. Lattime (1981), *Transplantation
Proceedings* 13: 752.

experiments or experimenters failed to distinguish these effector cells; to a lesser extent this continues. The result of not distinguishing NC from NK cells has been that NC activity is often referred to in the literature as NK activity (we too have been guilty of this — Collins *et al.*, 1981).

Although the intent of this chapter is to focus on the interactions between NC effectors and targets, it is useful to relate much of what is known about NC cells to what is known about NK cells (NK cells are discussed in detail in Chapter 3). Such a comparison serves further to delineate NC and NK activity, and thereby enhances our understanding of NCMC. In this chapter we refer only briefly to material already reviewed by others (see Stutman and Lattime, 1985) and focus our attention on questions about NC activity which remain unanswered or have not been raised by others. Since most the studies of NC and NK activity have used mouse model systems, when we refer to NC or NK activities we mean mouse NC or NK activity, unless otherwise stated.

II. SURFACE ANTIGENS OF NC CELLS

Within the past few years, studies designed to discern the markers of cells with NC activity have resulted in a major advance in our understanding of the origin of the NC effectors. The surface phenotype of NC cells has been surveyed by several groups utilising antibodies plus complement in an attempt to deplete various cell populations of NC activity; it appeared that determinants common to cells of the immune system were absent from NC cells; this, in spite of the fact that NC activity seemed to be mediated by bone-marrow-derived lymphocytes or monocytes. The lack of surface markers on NC effectors made difficult their assignment to a particular cell lineage. It also made impossible the selective depletion of NC cells from mixed lymphoid populations, thus eliminating an often revealing class of experiments.

Employing antibodies and complement, NC activity was found to be in a population of cells that did not express Thy-1, Qa-2, 3, Qa-5, Lyt-1, Lyt-2, Lyt-11, NK-1, Ala-1, Mph-1, sIg, FcR and expressed low levels of asialo-GM1 and H-2; there was no antibody that depleted a majority of the NC activity. It was concluded that NC activity was mediated by null cells.

More recent studies have lead to just the opposite conclusion; that is, NC activity is mediated by cells expressing surface markers generally associated with a variety of cell types. Using a fluorescence-activated cell sorter and monoclonal antibodies, Bykowsky and Stutman (1986) have been able to positively select for cells expressing both NC activity and a number of surface determinants previously thought absent from NC cells. They found that NC activity sorts into the cell populations expressing H-2, Qa-5 and Thy-1, and a small but significant proportion of the cells with NC activity express Lyt-2 and sIg. Thus, the antibody plus complement experiments suggesting that null cells mediate NC activity were most likely misinterpreted. It now appears likely that NC activity belongs to a heterogenous family of effectors which include B cells, T cells, NK cells and cells in the myeloid lineage (reviewed by Lattime, 1986). The failure to deplete NC activity with antibody and complement was probably due to the multilineage origin of NC activity; depletion of any one population always leaving significant activity in the remaining cells.

III. GENETICS OF NC ACTIVITY

Mice with genetic defects which affect B or T cell function (e.g. nude, C3H/HEJ or NZB) appear to have normal levels of NC activity.

Genetic influences on the NC activity of mice have been studied by Stutman and Cuttito (1980, 1982). Briefly, they have shown that various strains of mice have different levels of NC activity. In addition, the classification of mice as having high, intermediate or low NC activity is dependent upon the target cell, such that the rank order of strains for their level of expression of NC activity can change with different targets. For example, A/J mice have high NC activity to the fibrosarcomas Meth-A, Meth-113 and Meth-E4 and intermediate activity to Meth-X; the NC activity of I/St mice to the same tumours is high, intermediate, high, and intermediate, respectively, while the NC activity of BALB/c mice is high, low, intermediate, and low, respectively. While these results indicate a heterogeneity among NC effectors, it is not clear if the heterogeneity results from differences in the way the NC effectors of different strains recognise these targets, from differences in the NC lytic signals (see Section VIII) sent by the effectors of different strains of mice, or if other factors are involved.

The studies of Stutman and Cuttito (1980, 1982) have also provided evidence that NC activity (to the fibrosarcoma target Meth-113) is under the control of several genes. Using congenic mouse strains, they have found evidence that NC activity is controlled by three 'NC genes', expression of any two being sufficient for high NC activity against Meth-113. All three genes are located on chromosome 17. One gene maps to a locus near the Tla marker; the a, c and d alleles of Tla are associated with high NC activity while the b allele (which results in no Tla surface expression) is associated with low NC activity. Another gene maps to a locus near Qa-2,3. For this gene high NC activity is associated with the b allele of Qa-2,3 (which results in no Qa-2,3 expression). The existence of the third gene has been surmised from differences in NC activity of the congenic mice, but it cannot be mapped to any known locus; it is referred to as the 'A-AKR' gene (because it is expressed by mice with the A or AKR genetic background). Gene complementation in F_1 hybrids also supports the hypothesis that the expression of any two of these three genes results in high NC activity.

IV. AUGMENTATION OF NC ACTIVITY

Augmentation of NC activity by BCG or *Corynebacterium parvum* has been reported (Stutman *et al.*, 1978; Lattime *et al.*, 1982b). Intraperitoneal injection of either BCG or *C. parvum* resulted in a substantial increase in peritoneal NC activity against the targets Meth-A and Meth-113. While higher intraperitoneal doses of *C. parvum* were required to increase splenic NC activity, higher intraperitoneal doses of BCG had little effect on splenic NC activity. Since macrophages can use TNF as a lytic signal (Decker *et al.*, 1987) and it appears that TNF is also part of the NC lytic mechanism (see Section VIII) it is conceivable that the activity described here is mediated by macrophages.

Lattime and Stutman (1984a) have examined the augmentation of NC activity by poly I:C and interferon. Using antibody plus complement, they found that only the NCMC activity mediated by $Qa-5^+$ cells is augmented by poly I:C while $Qa-5^-$ cells are not affected. The definition used by Stutman and co-workers that NC activity is mediated by NCMC effectors that do not express Qa-5, and that NK activity is mediated by NCMC effectors that express Qa-5, is valid for naive spleen cell populations. However, these definitions may not be applicable to populations of effector cells that have been augmented by various agents. Since effector cells other than NK cells also express Qa-5 (e.g., T cells) the augmented activity might be due to effector cells which are not NK cells. However, because the $Qa-5^-$ cells are not affected by poly I:C the conclusion that NC activity is not augmented by poly I:C is no doubt correct. In other studies with poly I:C either in vivo or in vitro, or other interferon-inducing agents (Tilorone or *C. parvum*) there was no augmentation of NC activity (Lattime *et al.*, 1982a; Lattime and Stutman, 1984a).

Interleukin 2 (IL-2) and interleukin 3 (IL-3) are lymphokines known to affect T cell differentiation. A 24-hour pre-treatment of spleen cells with either IL-2 or IL-3 caused a marked increase in lytic activity when assayed on the fibroblast target WEHI-164 (Lattime and Stutman, 1984a). All of the lysis of WEHI-164 (i.e. constitutive plus induced) was due to Qa-5$^-$ cells (i.e. NC cells). It has been shown that NK activity is augmented by IL-2 but not affected by IL-3 (Ihle *et al.*, 1982). Consistent with this is the observation that all of the IL-2-augmented lytic activity against the lymphoma YAC-1 was due to a Qa-5$^+$ (i.e. NK) cell population (Lattime and Stutman 1984a). To determine whether the IL-2- or IL-3-stimulated NC or NK precursor cells were different, Lattime and Stutman (1984a) treated spleen cells with anti-Qa-5 antibody plus C before the 24 hour IL-2 or IL-3 stimulation. This treatment eliminated all NK activity but did not effect NC augmentation. Thus for NK cells, the IL-2-stimulated precursor cells, as well as the effectors, are Qa-5$^+$, while for NC cells, the IL-2 and IL-3-stimulated cells, as well as the effectors, are Qa-5$^-$. Again, although it is reasonable, we remain cautious of the interpretation, based solely on the Qa-5 phenotype, that the augmented lytic activity is mediated by NC or NK effectors.

We have found that maintaining spleen cells in culture for five days in medium containing fetal bovine serum also results in a significant increase in NC lytic activity over that of non-cultured spleen cells, when assayed on the fibroblast target 10ME (Patek *et al.*, 1982). This is unlike the results of Paige *et al.*, (1978), who found no change in the level of splenic NC activity on Meth-A after six hours to six days of spleen cell culture. However, both of these findings distinguish NC from NK activity, in that NK activity diminishes after a few hours of culture (Herberman *et al.*, 1975), whereas NC activity persists under the same conditions. In addition to the augmentation of NC activity as a result of culture we found that freshly prepared spleen cells treated for 10 hours with the conditioned medium from five-day cultured spleen cells, had significantly more NC lytic activity than spleen cells treated with medium alone. We do not know what factor is responsible for this NC augmentation, but it could be IL-2 or IL-3.

V. INHIBITION OF NC ACTIVITY

NC cells are neither adherent to plastic nor phagocytic (i.e. they cannot be removed from a spleen cell population by carbonyl iron and magnetism [Paige *et al.*, 1978]). Twenty per cent of splenic NC activity adheres to nylon wool columns and full NC activity can be restored by mixing the nylon-adherent and non-adherent fractions (Paige *et al.*, 1978). Similarly, approximately 30 per cent of NC activity is retained by G10 Sephadex filtration. A comparison of the NC activity of unfractionated spleen cells and G10 effluent cells reveals that at a high concentration of effector cells these populations have roughly equivalent NC activity when assayed on WEHI-164, but at low effector cell concentrations the effluent cells have far less NC activity that the unfractionated spleen cells. This suggests that the low NC activity of dilute G10 effluent cells is not due to the lack of NC cells *per se*, but results from a reduction in the number of adherent accessory cells which play a role in the induction or regulation of NC activity. The adherence properties of NC activity are distinct from those of NK cells or macrophages, in that NK activity is not retained on G10 Sephadex or nylon wool, while most macrophage activity is retained.

NC activity is relatively radio-resistant. One day following a single dose of 5000 R whole body irradiation there was only a 20 per cent decrease in splenic NC activity (Stutman *et al.*, 1980a). Doses of irradiation less than 2500 R had little or no effect on splenic NC activity in one day. Unlike splenic NC activity, bone marrow NC activity was reduced by 90 per cent 24 hours after only 1100 R, or seven days after 700 R. Stutman *et al.*, (1980a) also found that 700 R caused a 40 per cent reduction in splenic NC activity 16 days later followed by a slow recovery of the activity to almost normal levels by 30 days.

Several drugs which inhibit immune or non-immune reactivity have been tested for their inhibitory effect on NC cells. Five mg of hydrocortisone (HC), injected intraperitoneally, had no effect on murine splenic NC activity in 24 hours, but after 48 hours there was approximately a 60 per cent reduction in lytic activity on Meth-A targets. By 72 hours the NC activity had returned to near normal levels (Stutman *et al.*, 1980a). Mice had low NC activity 48 hours after 10 mg HC, but significantly elevated levels after 72 hours. Although we did not find elevated levels of NC activity, we found that repeated injections of HC every two days did not inhibit the NC activity beyond 72 hours (i.e., chronic HC treatment did not produce an NC-low mouse) (unpublished observations). We have also shown that dexamethasone (DEX), a water-soluble synthetic glucocorticosteroid, is a potent inhibitor of NC activity when added directly to the NC assay (Patek *et al.*, 1982) or when effectors, but not targets, are pretreated in vitro with DEX for as little as 30 minutes before the NC assay (Patek *et al.*, 1982). DEX does not inhibit murine or human NK activity if added to a four-hour assay (Holbrook *et al.*, 1983) and, although it does inhibit some murine NK activity on YAC-1 in an 18-hour assay, the effect is never as marked as it is on the NC activity against 10ME.

As mentioned, NC activity is increased when spleen cells are cultured in serum-containing medium for five days, or treated for 10 hours with the conditioned medium from five-day cultured spleen cells. These treatments also change the NC activity so that, unlike fresh spleen cells which are markedly inhibited by DEX, the NC activity of cultured spleen cells or spleen cells treated with conditioned medium is only slightly (about 20 per cent) inhibited by the addition of DEX (Patek *et al.*, 1982). In the NK system there is evidence that HC in vivo induces NK suppressor cells (Hochman and Cudkowicz, 1979); whether such suppressor cells are involved in the inhibition of NC activity by DEX is unknown. DEX could be acting directly on NC cells, on NC precursors, or via a regulatory cell. These findings are, however, consistent with the hypotheses that DEX is acting on the NC effector cell, in that tumour necrosis factor (TNF) is the NC lytic signal (see Section VIII), and DEX has been shown to be a potent inhibitor of TNF synthesis (Beutler *et al.*, 1985; Beutler and Cerami, 1986).

Other agents which, at various doses and treatment schedules, inhibit NK, macrophage or B and T cell responsiveness, have been tested for their effect on NC lytic activity (using BALB/c spleen cells, Meth-A targets and a 24-hour ^{3}H-proline release assay). These agents include ^{89}Sr, beta-estradiol, carrageenan, vinblastine, silica, trypan blue, and 3-methylcholanthrene; none had inhibitory effects on NC activity and some caused slight augmentation of NC activity (Stutman *et al.*, 1980a; Lust *et al.*, 1981).

VI. TARGET RECOGNITION

NCMC requires, as an initial event in target lysis, contact between effector cells and target cells. This cell–cell contact is envisaged to occur via a receptor on the effector cell that recognises a determinant expressed on the surface of the target cell (referred to here as the recognition determinant). In addition to the receptors on effector cells that recognise this determinant, it has been suggested that effector cells may also have receptors that recognise other determinants necessary to the delivery of lytic signals from the effector to the target (Bonavida *et al.*, 1984). These latter receptors are thought to act as 'triggers' that provide a signal to the effector cell to lyse the target it has recognised (referred to here as the triggering determinant). Experimentally, targets which are thought to be NCMC-resistant because they do not express the triggering determinant compete for the lysis of sensitive targets (Targan and Newman, 1984; Wright *et al.*, 1984). This indicates that binding of this hypothetical triggering determinant does not contribute significantly to the recognition of targets. For this reason we will confine our discussion of recognition to recognition which results in lysis or recognition which is competitive with lysis.

The majority of studies of NCMC target recognition deal with NK effectors but, as discussed below, many of these studies are also relevant to the analysis of the recognition of targets by NC effectors. Shortly after the identification of NK cells as a unique class of cytotoxic effector cells, there were several studies of the specificity of NK cells for determinants on the surface of sensitive target cells (Santoli *et al.*, 1978; Ault and Weiner, 1979). At the time these determinants were thought to be of viral origin or associated with transformation and tumorigenicity. It is now clear that NK and NC effectors recognise, not viral or transformation-specific determinants, but rather determinants that are expressed by many cells including those which are virally infected, malignantly transformed, or even uninfected normal cells. Efforts to identify the NK and NC recognition determinant have focused on the transferrin receptor (Vodinelich *et al.*, 1983) and other, as yet, unidentified proteins (Roder *et al.*, 1979; Hercend *et al.*, 1984). While there is conflicting evidence about the recognition determinant, it is clear that it must be expressed by many types of normal cells.

Some problems with early studies might be related to the way target recognition was assayed. In those studies the specificity of NK effectors was based, not only on the ability of NK effectors to recognise targets, but also on their ability to lyse the targets that they recognised. It was presumed (and still is by some) that failure to express the recognition determinant was the only NK resistance mechanism; post-recognition resistance mechanisms were rarely considered. Although lysis obviously requires recognition, recognition is not necessarily sufficient for lysis; there are many targets which, while being recognised by NK and NC effectors, are resistant to lysis at some post-recognition step (Collins *et al.*, 1981; Roder *et al.*, 1981; Lin *et al.*, 1983). Thus, while viral infection or chemical transformation of cells may result in sensitivity to NCMC, the sensitivity is not necessarily the result of *de novo* expression of recognition determinants. We first realised this when we found that some chemically transformed fibroblasts, isolated after exposure of a non-transformed cell line, B/C-N, to chemical carcinogens, were sensitive to NC lysis and that the nontransformed NC-resistant parental cell line was able to compete for the NC lysis of the tumorigenic transformants derived from it. In these studies, a comparison of the number of resistant or sensitive cells required to compete for the lysis of the sensitive cells showed that the level of determinants expressed by sensitive and resistant cells was equivalent. Further analysis of the ability of unlabelled targets to compete for the lysis of the labelled NC-sensitive chemically transformed cells revealed that other fibroblast cell lines (such as the C3H10T1/2 clone 8 cell line) that were resistant to NCMC, also competed, as did freshly explanted adult and fetal fibroblasts (Collins *et al.*, 1981; Table 5.2) (there is a report that normal fibroblasts do not compete for NC lysis [Lattime and Stutman, 1984b]).

Competition for the NC-mediated lysis of chemically transformed cell lines is not limited to fibroblasts; transformed neuronal and lymphoid cells also compete (Table 5.2). Among the transformed lymphoid cells that act as competitors is the NK-sensitive cell line YAC-1 (Collins *et al.*, 1981; Lattime and Stutman, 1984b). The ability of YAC-1 cells to

Table 5.2 The NC and NK sensitivity of cells that are competitors or non-competitors for the NC lysis of 10ME or YAC-1

10ME competitors	Sensitivity[a] to:		10ME non-competitors	Sensitivity to:	
	NC	NK		NC	NK
Primary adult fibroblasts	R	R	Normal thymocytes	?	S/R
Primary fetal fibroblasts	R	R	WEHI-7[c]	R	R
10ME[b]	S	R	P-815[e]	R	R
B/C-N[b]	R	R	C1300 N18[f]	?	?
C3H 10T1/2[b]	R	R			
YAC-1[c]	R	S			
et R7[d]	?	?			
YAC-1 competitors			YAC-1 non-competitors		
YAC-1	R	S	P-815	R	R
10ME	S	R	WEHI-7	R	R
METH-A[b]	S	R			
B/C-N	R	R			

[a] S = sensitive; R = resistant.
[b] Fibroblast cell line.
[c] T cell lymphoma cell line.
[d] Neuronal cell line.
[e] Mastocytoma cell line.
[f] Neuroblastoma cell line.

compete for the lysis of NC-sensitive fibroblasts is interesting because these fibroblasts are NK-resistant, and YAC-1 is NC-resistant. These competition experiments indicate that NC effectors are able to recognise the NK-sensitive YAC-1 cells and that YAC-1 must be resistant at some post-recognitive step in the NC lytic process.

The question of the recognition specificity of NK and NC effectors was further investigated using NC-sensitive and resistant fibroblasts to complete for the NK-mediated lysis of YAC-1 labelled targets. These experiments demonstrated that fibroblasts express determinants recognised by NK effectors such that they compete for the lysis of YAC-1 targets (Collins *et al.*, 1981). Thus not only are targets which are lysed by NK effectors recognised by both NK and NC effectors, but targets that are lysed by NC effectors are recognised by both NK and NC effectors. The similarity of the recognition specificity of NK and NC effectors is further shown by the fact that when NK- and NC-resistant targets do not compete for the lysis of the NC-sensitive target 10ME, they also do not compete for the lysis of the NK-sensitive target YAC-1 (Collins *et al.*, 1981; Table 5.2). It is possible to envisage NK effectors recognising a determinant distinct from that recognised by NC effectors, and the expression of both by all cells that compete for NK- and NC-mediated lysis. Nevertheless, the co-ordinated expression, or lack of expression, of these recognition determinants indicates that NK and NC effectors probably recognise the same determinant. We will refer to this as the NK/NC recognition determinant.

Although many cells express NK/NC recognition determinants, some do not. Most lymphoid cells are of this type. Normal splenic, thymic, and peripheral blood lymphocytes do not compete for the lysis of either NK- or NC-sensitive targets, nor do a variety of transformed cells of bone-marrow origin (e.g. P815 and WEHI-7). Since a surveillance role for NK and NC cells in the elimination of *de novo* transformed cells has been repeatedly suggested, the question of how NK or NC effectors recognise and eliminate *de novo* transformants becomes a problem, given that many normal cells also express the NK/NC recognition determinant.

Models of NK-mediated tumour surveillance emphasise the expression of the NK/NC recognition determinants by the NK-sensitive YAC-1 cell line and the absence of this determinant on normal lymphocytes and a variety of transformed cell lines, such as the NK-resistant mastocytoma cell line P815. According to these models transformation results in the expression of the NK/NC recognition determinant by the transformed cells. It is assumed that normal lymphoid cells (and the transformants derived from them) would be sensitive to NK-mediated lysis if they were recognised by NK effectors. Further, it has been assumed by many that NK lysis of the transformants which express the NK/NC recognition determinant results in either elimination of the transformants, or selection for variants of the transformants that no longer express the NK/NC recognition determinant. In fact, there are few data which compel one to accept these assumptions. Another important problem associated with these models is that they fail to consider the effect of the expression of the NK/NC recognition determinant by non-lymphoid normal cells. The expression of this determinant by non-transformed cells limits the ability of NK (or NC) effectors to recognise transformed cells in a sea of normal cells expressing the same determinant, i.e., NK effectors would be unable to distinguish transformed lymphoid cells from many normal non-lymphoid cells.

It has also been suggested that NC cells are involved in tumour surveillance. However, the expression of NK/NC determinants by normal cells would present the same problem to NC-mediated surveillance as it does to NK-mediated surveillance, that is, normal cells would limit the ability of NC effectors to recognise specifically and to eliminate transformants arising *de novo*. The problem of normal cells expressing the NK/NC recognition determinant and thus inhibiting anti-tumour activity of NC cells is discussed in detail in Section IX.

VII. TARGET RESISTANCE

One mechanism by which targets could be resistant to NC-mediated lysis is failure to express the determinant recognised by the effectors. There are many examples of normal and transformed 'lymphoid' cells (P815, WEHI-7, YAC-8, etc.) which are resistant to NC-mediated lysis because they are not effectively recognised by NC effectors (Table 5.2). Since the determinant recognised by NK effectors is indistinguishable from that recognised by NC effectors (see Section VI), targets which are resistant to NK-mediated lysis because they are not recognised are also resistant to NC-mediated lysis for the same reason. If targets are not recognised, there is no assay of their sensitivity to post-recognition NK or NC lytic mechanisms. It is a common assumption that a cell expressing recognition determinants should be NC- or NK-sensitive; this assumption is without basis. As discussed in Section VI, there are many normal cell types which express the NK/NC recognition determinant and, despite their recognition by NK or NC effectors, are resistant to lysis at some post-recognition step in the lytic pathway (Collins *et al.*, 1981; Roder *et al.*, 1981). We have shown that there are at least two such post-recognition NC-resistance mechanisms and at least one post-recognition NK-resistance mechanism expressed by target cells that also express NK/NC recognition determinants (Lin *et al.*, 1983).

The two post-recognition NC-resistance mechanisms can be distinguished by their requirements for protein synthesis. Some normal, non-transformed fibroblasts express a protein synthesis-dependent NC-resistance mechanism: if protein synthesis by the targets is blocked they become NC-sensitive (Collins *et al.*, 1981). The fact that these non-transformed cells become sensitive to NC-mediated lysis when protein synthesis is inhibited confirms the competition experiments showing that the cells express NK/NC recognition determinants. It also shows that the recognition of these determinants by NC effectors results in the delivery of NC lytic signals to the targets. When protein synthesis proceeds normally these cells are unaffected by the delivery of the NC lytic signals. The loss of this resistance mechanism is associated with malignant transformation of fibroblasts, in that cells derived from anchorage-dependent, non-tumorigenic, NC-resistant cells treated with carcinogens and selected for anchorage-independence, are sometimes NC-sensitive (see Section IX). The anchorage-independent transformants that are NC-sensitive are unable to prevent NC-mediated lysis once they have received the NC lytic signal because of low levels of the protein synthesis-dependent NC-resistance mechanism. It is the loss of this mechanism which probably accounts for the NC-sensitivity of many transformed fibroblasts. Although transformed fibroblasts that lose this mechanism become sensitive to NC effectors, they do not become sensitive to NK effectors. This emphasises the point that, although NC and NK cells recognise a common determinant, their lytic mechanisms must be different.

While NC-sensitive transformants do not express an NC-resistance mechanism, we have shown that many NC-resistant variants derived from them are resistant because they express a protein synthesis-dependent NC-resistance mechanism that is indistinguishable from the one expressed by the non-transformed parental cell line (Patek *et al.*, 1986). We do not know if the variants are re-expressing the resistance mechanism expressed by the parental non-transformed cells, which was lost upon transformation, or if they express a different NC-resistance mechanism which is also dependent on protein synthesis. Whatever the case, the NC-resistant variants selected in vitro or in vivo always maintain the transformed phenotype, never reverting to non-tumorigenic. We do not know how either of these NC-resistance mechanisms functions, except that they function after targets have been recognised and have received lytic signals from NC effectors. These resistance mechanisms could inactivate the lytic signals, block some intermediate step in the lytic pathway, or even repair the damage which ultimately occurs. If the resistance mechanisms are normal membrane repair or replacement mechanisms, or are involved in some essential cell metabolic process, the loss of the resistance mechanism has no apparent effect on the ability of these transformed cells to grow either in vitro, or in immune and NCMC-compromised mice (see Section IX).

Normal fibroblasts express not only a protein synthesis-dependent NC-resistance mechanism, but also an NK-resistance mechanism which does not require protein synthesis. Besides the differences in 'specificity' of the resistance mechanisms (NK *vs.* NC), and the requirement for protein synthesis, the NK-resistance mechanism, unlike the NC-resistance mechanism, is not lost when fibroblasts are transformed. Thus, transformed fibroblasts are generally NK-resistant.

In addition to the protein synthesis-dependent NC-resistance mechanism expressed by many fibroblasts, the cell line YAC-1 expresses an NC-resistance mechanism which does not require protein synthesis. YAC-1 cells are recognised by both NK effectors and NC effectors (see Section VI), yet are resistant to NC-mediated lysis. Normal fibroblasts do not express this protein synthesis-independent NC-resistance mechanism, since they become NC-sensitive when protein synthesis is inhibited. Like the protein synthesis-dependent NC-resistance mechanism, the protein synthesis-independent NC-resistance mechanism is 'specific' for NC-mediated lysis, in that it provides resistance to NC-mediated lysis, but not to lysis by NK cells or allo-immune cytotoxic lymphocytes (CTL) (i.e., YAC-1 is sensitive to both NK and CTL lysis).

It is possible that the post-recognition protein synthesis-independent NK- and NC-resistance mechanisms, unlike the protein synthesis-dependent NC-resistance mechanism, operate before lytic signals are sent from NK or NC effectors. If triggering determinants, in addition to the NK/NC recognition determinant, must be recognised by NK and NC effectors before lytic signals are sent, the resistance might be a result of not expressing these determinants (see Section III). While this hypothesis is a possible explanation of why targets that compete for the lysis of NK- and NC-sensitive targets are not themselves sensitive to lysis, it is not tenable for targets that become sensitive to NC-mediated lysis when protein synthesis is inhibited within the target; these targets must express a resistance mechanism which operates after lytic signals are received by the targets.

YAC-1 cells express a protein synthesis-independent NC-resistance mechanism, and we know of no derivatives of YAC-1 or other lymphoid cells that have lost this NC-resistance mechanism (recall that such a loss can only be assayed in lymphoid cells that express NK/NC recognition determinants). The loss of these protein synthesis-independent NC- or NK-resistance mechanisms is not associated with transformations (as is the protein synthesis-dependent NC-resistance mechanism); this may be because loss of this resistance mechanism does not provide a selective growth advantage, or the loss may inhibit normal cell function, and is therefore never observed. Given that tumour necrosis factor(TNF) is the NC lytic signal (see Section VIII) then YAC-1 may be NC-resistant simply because it does not express TNF receptors.

Both normal and transformed fibroblasts express a protein synthesis-independent NK-resistance mechanism such that only a small amount of lysis of fibroblasts by spleen cells from *untreated* mice can be attributed to NK cells. We know of no fibroblast cell line which has lost this NK-resistance mechanism and therefore is highly susceptible to the NK activity of normal, untreated mice. Thus, although the proportion of the total Qa-5$^+$ NCMC against some fibroblast targets (i.e. NK activity) can be high, because the lysis of these targets is low, the absolute amount of Qa-5$^+$ activity is low — rarely more than 10 per cent specific[51] Cr or ^{3}H-proline release (Lattime *et al.*, 1983). Some fibroblasts are sensitive to the Qa-5$^+$ cell-mediated lytic activity found in spleens of interferon or poly I:C treated mice. Because interferon and interferon-inducers are known to augment NK activity, and because the anti-fibroblast activity found in interferon-treated mice is Qa-5$^+$, it has been assumed that the induced activity against fibroblast targets is NK. Although this is a reasonable assumption, there is no proof that the interferon is not inducing another Qa-5$^+$ lytic activity (i.e. an activity which is not found in untreated mice, similar to lymphokine-activated killer activity). Moreover, the in vivo significance of induced 'natural' immunity is unknown.

Assuming the activity assayed in vitro reflects an in vivo function for NC or NK cells, then the differences between fibroblasts and lymphocytes in their expression of post-recognition NK- and NC-resistance mechanisms suggests that these effectors have different functional roles. Because a significant loss of the protein synthesis-independent NK-resistance mechanism is not associated with the transformation of fibroblasts, fibroblasts do not become highly sensitive to the NK effectors found in normal mice (although they may be quite sensitive to induced NK activity); this limits NCMC interactions with most fibroblasts to those involving NC effectors. Further, while the transformation of lymphocytes is, on occasion, accompanied by the expression of NK/NC recognition determinants, it is not associated with the loss of the protein synthesis-dependent NC-resistance mechanism. This limits effective NCMC interactions with lymphocytes to interactions involving NK effectors.

VIII. LYTIC MECHANISM

The lysis of targets by the effectors that mediate NCMC can be divided into at least three sequential steps: (1) recognition of the targets by the effectors, (2) delivery of lytic signals from the effectors to the targets, and (3) target lysis. Recognition is required, but by itself is insufficient, for target lysis. There are targets which are recognised by both NK and NC effectors but are not lysed by either; in addition, there are targets which are recognised by both NC and NK effectors but are sensitive only to NC-mediated lysis or only to NK-mediated lysis (see Section VII). This differential sensitivity to NK- and NC-mediated lysis indicates that the NC lytic mechanism is different from the NK lytic mechanism. Given that NK and NC effectors recognise the same determinant (Section VI) and that the recognition of this determinant accounts for the binding of NK and NC effectors to targets, the difference in the NK and NC lytic mechanisms must be due to differences in the delivery or interpretation of lytic signals or differences in the kind of lytic signal sent to the targets. If the difference between the NK and NC lytic mechanisms results from the delivery of different lytic signals, then the simplest models of NC or NK lysis would have NK effectors recognise the NK/NC recognition determinant and, as a consequence, send NK lytic signals, while NC effectors, recognising the same determinant, would send NC lytic signals. The lytic signals sent by NK and NC effectors might be able to cause lysis directly (i.e. complement-like lysis), or they might signal events within the target that ultimately result in autolysis. Targets which are NCMC-resistant could negate lytic signals at any point after their delivery from effectors, including repair of the lytic damage. With this model it is not necessary to postulate the existence of a triggering mechanism that is independent of the recognition of the NK/NC recognition determinant.

It is also possible that the difference between the NK and NC lytic mechanisms might be due to differences in the triggering requirements for the release of lytic signals; NK and NC lytic signals could then be identical. NK effectors would recognise the NK/NC recognition determinant, and in addition recognise a triggering determinant. NC effectors would also recognise the NK/NC recognition determinant and a triggering determinant distinct from the one required by NK effectors. Targets that are resistant could express the NK/NC recognition determinant, but not express the determinant or mechanism that triggers the release of lytic signals. Obviously, these two models can be combined so that NK and NC effectors send different lytic signals as well as requiring different mechanisms to trigger the release of lytic signals.

A third possibility is that target recognition results in the release of the lytic signal and only cells with receptors for the lytic signals can be lysed, NK-sensitive cells expressing NK signal receptors and NC-sensitive targets expressing NC signal receptors. This model also requires that the NK lytic signal is distinct from the NC lytic signal.

As mentioned above, lytic signals sent by NK and NC effectors could themselves cause target damage (i.e., the target is passively involved in lysis) or they could be signals that once received initiate a series of events within the target that ultimately results in lysis (i.e. autolysis). Two lytic signals have been described for NK effectors. One involves the release of cytolytic precursor molecules (perforins) from granules contained within NK effectors, that, upon release and polymerisation (to polyperforins), form membrane lesions in sensitive targets (Dourmashkin *et al.*, 1980; Podack and Dennert, 1983; Dennert and Podack, 1983). Lysis occurs via channels formed by the polyperforins inserted through the membrane. This is an example of a lytic signal which is able to cause lysis directly, the target having a passive role.

The other proposed mechanism of lysis by NK effectors is via the release of a soluble mediator, referred to as NK cytotoxic factor (NKCF). In contrast to the rapid lysis of targets by isolated perforin, perforin-containing granules, or NK effectors, the lysis of targets by soluble NKCF is very slow, requiring up to 48 hours with initial lags of up to 12 to 14 hours (Wright *et al.*, 1983). Since the NK lytic process mediated by spleen cells takes only 4–6 hours, it is clear that NK effectors do not recognise a target and secrete NKCF into the medium which binds to targets eventually resulting in their lysis. In order to account for the difference in the kinetics of lysis of NKCF-mediated lysis and NK effector cell mediated lysis, it is necessary to postulate that NKCF requires something to potentiate its activity, and that this something be associated with the NK effector cell. This could be an activation step which occurs rapidly when NK cells and target cells are associated, but slowly in solution. If NKCF is involved, the way in which it is delivered by the NK effector cell to the target must be an important part of the lytic signal. Because of the different kinetics of lysis by perforins and by NKCF it seems more likely that NK effectors act by the release of perforins, rather than by the release of soluble NKCF. The fact that cells which are NK-resistant are not killed when present during the NK lysis of NK-sensitive targets (i.e. lack of bystander killing) has been used to argue against soluble factors being involved in the NK-mediated lysis. For this argument to be valid it is necessary to show that the bystander cells are in fact sensitive to the lytic mechanism, be it soluble or cell-mediated. Often bystanders are cells which are not recognised by NK effectors and it is presumed that if they were recognised they would be sensitive to the NK lytic mechanism. This is an assumption that may not be valid, as there are NK-resistance mechanisms which operate after target recognition (see Section VI).

The kinetics of NC-mediated lysis (i.e. a 4–6 hour lag, followed by a linear release of ^{51}Cr for 6–10 hours) suggest that perforins are not involved in NC target lysis. We have shown that there is more lysis of NC-sensitive target when protein synthesis is blocked two hours after mixing targets and effectors than if it is blocked at the start of the assay (Collins *et al.*, 1981). This result implies that NC-mediated lysis is, in part, dependent upon protein synthesis within the target, again suggesting that NC lysis involves target cell autolysis and that perforins, or other mechanisms where targets are passively lysed, are not involved.

Considerable evidence suggests that tumour necrosis factor (TNF)[1] is the NC lytic signal. It has been shown that anti-TNF antibody blocks NC activity directed against WEHI-164 targets (Ortaldo *et al.*, 1986). Using a variety of targets we have shown that there is a remarkable similarity between TNF-mediated lysis and NC-mediated lysis. TNF lyses NC-sensitive, but not NC-resistant targets. The kinetics of NC-mediated lysis of ^{51}Cr-labelled targets is similar to that of TNF-mediated lysis of the same targets, both requiring an initial lag of 4–6 hours followed by a linear release of ^{51}Cr. Targets selected in vivo or in vitro for resistance to NC-mediated lysis are resistant to TNF-mediated lysis. Conversely, targets selected for TNF resistance are resistant to NC lysis. And finally, those targets that become sensitive to NC-mediated lysis when protein synthesis is inhibited also become sensitive to TNF when protein synthesis is inhibited. Together these experiments indicate that TNF is the lytic signal sent by NC effectors.

We favour a model in which NC effectors express a cell-associated TNF similar to that described for some macrophage-mediated cytolisis; we do not find that the release of TNF is a necessary process for NC me-

[1] The biological and biochemical properties of TNF, also known as cachectin, have been reviewed by Beutler and Cerami, 1986; see also Chapter 8.

diated lysis. Others (Ortaldo *et al.*, 1986) do find release of a significant amount of TNF during an in vitro NC assay. In either case, the TNF binds to targets and thereby initiates the events which can result in autolysis. TNF-sensitive targets are those that express a TNF receptor and have lost the protein synthesis-dependent NC-(TNF)-resistance mechanism, while TNF-resistant targets are those that express either the protein synthesis dependent NC-(TNF)-resistance mechanism or the protein synthesis independent NC-(TNF)-resistance mechanism (e.g. no TNF receptor) (see Section VII).

IX. EVIDENCE THAT NC ACTIVITY PROTECTS AGAINST CANCER[2]

The hypothesis that NC activity can function as a protective mechanism against incipient tumours is derived from the observations that some tumour cells are lysed, in vitro, by NC cells while normal cells are not lysed (Stutman *et al.*, 1978; Collins *et al.*, 1981). If NC cells act as an anti-tumour surveillance mechanism then several predictions about the growth of tumours *in vivo* can be made. For example, the frequency of *de novo* transformants that are NC-sensitive should be high; NC cells should interact with tumours *in vivo*; individuals with low NC activity should have a higher incidence of tumours, or require inoculation of fewer NC-sensitive cells to form tumours, than normal individuals; and tumours which arise in individuals with normal levels of NC activity, whether the tumours are induced by carcinogens or by the inoculation of tumorigenic cells, should escape NC-mediated surveillance. Experimentally, this implies that the passage of NC-sensitive tumour cells in vivo will result in a decrease in the NC-sensitivity of the resultant tumour cells (i.e., selection for increased tumorigenicity should select for decreased NC-sensitivity, although escape mechanisms other than a reduction in sensitivity to in vitro NC lysis are possible). Conversely, selection for NC-resistance should select for increased tumorigenicity.

One of the most important facts of NC activity is the basic observation that malignant transformation sometimes results in the expression of NC-sensitivity (Stutman *et al.*, 1980a; Collins *et al.*, 1981). If NC activity is involved in host protection against cancer then it is important to know the frequency with which malignant transformation results in potentially tumorigenic cells that are NC-sensitive. If the

[2] See also Chapter 25

frequency is very low, then NC activity cannot be a major protective mechanism against cancer no matter how effective it is in ridding individuals of the rare NC-sensitive transformant. Presently, screening existing transformed cell lines for NC-sensitivity would indicate that the proportion of cell lines that are NC-sensitive is low; however, because most of the cell lines available today were derived from tumours that arose in animals with normal levels of NC activity, the tumours may have been selected in vivo for NC resistance. Selection for NC resistance has been well documented by us (Collins *et al.*, 1981) and others (Stutman *et al.*, 1980a). The frequency of transformed cells 'born' NC-sensitive is surely higher then the proportion of existing cell lines which are NC-sensitive. Experiments designed expressly to determine the frequency of *de novo* transformants which are NC-sensitive show that a high proportion of fibroblasts transformed in vitro are NC-sensitive. Stutman *et al.*, (1980a) showed that six cell lines, independently transformed in vitro, were all NC-sensitive. In a similar experiment we found that only two of 21 fibroblasts transformed in vitro were NC-sensitive (Patek *et al.*, 1978; Collins *et al.*, 1981). This discrepancy between our results and those of Stutman might be due to a number of factors, including differences in the cell types transformed, the carcinogenesis procedure, or the method of selecting for transformants. Regardless of these differences, both experiments demonstrate a positive correlation between transformation and NC-sensitivity.

It is important to note that in our experiments neither of the NC-sensitive cell lines formed tumours in normal syngeneic mice, though they are tumorigenic in ATXFL[3] mice (Patek *et al.*, 1978; Collins *et al.*, 1981). ATXFL mice are transiently low in NC activity as a result of high dose irradiation; they are also T-cell-deficient. We have evidence that both the NC and T cell deficiencies contribute to the inability of ATXFL mice to reject these NC-sensitive cell lines (see Discussion below and Collins *et al.*, 1981; Lin *et al.*, 1985; Patek *et al.*, 1986).

Stutman and associates have shown that NC effectors infiltrate tumours in vivo (Stutman *et al.*, 1980b). In addition, they have shown that more NC-sensitive tumour cells than NC-resistant tumour cells are required to form tumours in mice which have high levels of NC activity. Cells of intermediate NC-sensitivity are tumorigenic at a dose which is intermediate between those required for NC-sensitive and for NC-resistant cells (Stutman *et al.*, 1980a).

---

[3] Adult thymectomised, X-irradiated, fetal liver cell treated mice.

If NC activity functions in vivo as a tumour surveillance mechanism, then a prediction is that cells grown as tumours in animals with a normal level of NC activity would be less sensitive to NC lysis and more tumorigenic than the inoculated cells because of selection for NC resistance. This has been confirmed both by Stutman *et al.*, (1978) and by ourselves (Collins *et al.*, 1981). In particular, we isolated NC-sensitive cell lines (10ME and 10CR) that do not form tumours in normal mice but will grow as tumours in NC-deficient animals (i.e. ATXFL mice). Selecting from these NC-sensitive cells for variants that grow in normal mice always selects for NC-resistant cells (Collins *et al.*, 1981). We have also selected from NC-sensitive cell lines (10ME and 10CR), both in vivo and in vitro, for NC-resistant variants. The tumorigenicity of cloned NC-resistant variants was compared with that of the parental cell lines and of cell lines that remained NC-sensitive when cloned after the selection procedure. Cloned NC-resistant cell lines derived from tumours that developed in irradiated nude mice after the injection of an NC-sensitive cell line were tumorigenic in normal mice, whereas cloned NC-sensitive cell lines derived from the same tumours were unable to grow as tumours in normal mice. Similarly, six of seven NC-resistant cloned cell lines independently isolated after selection in vitro for NC-resistance were tumorigenic in normal mice, whereas cloned NC-sensitive cell lines isolated from the same in vitro selected populations were not tumorigenic in normal mice. Thus, not only does selection for cells tumorigenic in normal mice select for NC-resistant cells, but in vivo or in vitro selection for NC-resistant cells selects for cells tumorigenic in normal mice (Patek *et al.*, 1986).

Taken together, these observations concerning the relationship between NC activity and tumorigenesis provide compelling evidence that NC activity is protective against some experimentally induced tumours, and furnishes strong, albeit circumstantial, evidence that NC activity is normally involved in anti-tumour surveillance.

However, there is a dilemma. Without a mechanism for locally concentrating NC effectors at the site of incipient tumours, and thereby reducing the competitive effects of the expression of the NK/NC recognition determinant by normal cells, it is difficult to envisage how NC (or NK) cells could function outside the vascular or lymphatic systems as an effective in vivo tumour surveillance mechanism. A possible mechanism by which NK or NC effectors could be concentrated in extravascular compartments at the site of incipient tumours (where many normal cells express the NK/NC recognition determinant) would be to have effector cells other than NC or NK cells (e.g. B or T cells) recognise transformants arising *de novo* and release antibodies or lympho-kines which would attract or immobilise NK or NC effectors at the site, thus increasing their effectiveness as 'tumour-specific' killer cells. In this regard, there is evidence that the immune system and NC effectors are cooperatively involved in the elimination in vivo of NC-sensitive chemically transformed fibroblasts (Lin *et al.*, 1985) and that NK cells can be armed by antibody to mediate antibody-dependent cell-mediated cytotoxicity (Jensen and Koren, 1980; Hamilton *et al.*, 1981).

Because normal lymphocytes and other blood-borne cells do not express NK/NC recognition determinants, it is possible that NK- or NC-mediated surveillance could function autonomously within the vascular and lymphatic systems. This may be why NK effectors are able to eliminate some tumour cells that are injected intravenously as exper-imental models of metastases (Talmadge *et al.*, 1980; Hanna and Burton, 1981; Hanna and Fidler, 1981).

X. CONCLUSION

Despite all that is known about NC cells and NC activity, there remains one overriding issue: What is the actual function(s) of NC cells in vivo? Data are presented which suggest that NC cells could be involved in the lysis of certain tumour cells in vivo. While this is the only known function for NC effectors, in these model systems NC-mediated surveillance would be limited in its capacity as an anti-tumour surveillance mechan-ism (see Section IX). Accordingly, it seems rather unlikely that effectors such as NC cells are, by themselves, efficient enough in eliminating tumours arising *de novo* to be maintained by evolution solely for that purpose. Since mice have high levels of NC activity in spleen and other tissue, it is presumed that NC cells do have a significant function(s) in vivo. Because NC lysis is likely to be mediated by TNF, and since TNF mediates biological effects other than tumour cell lysis (e.g. cachexia, shock, neutrophil and eosinophil activation, and growth stimulation of some cultured cells [Beutler and Cerami, 1986]), likewise NC cells may be capable of mediating other effects. Thus it could be that the production and controlled distribution of TNF by NC cells is what was selected for, and what maintains NC activity.

ACKNOWLEDGEMENTS

This work was supported by US Public Health Service Grant CA 34805 and CA 19754 awarded by the National Institutes of Health, Department of Health Services.

REFERENCES

Ault, K. A. and Weiner, H. L. (1979). *J. Immunol.* 122: 2611.

Beutler, B. and Cerami, A. (1986). *Nature* 320: 584.

Beutler, B., Milsark, I. W., Krochin, N. and Cerami, A. (1985). *Blood* 66: 83.

Bonavida, B., Lebow, L. T. and Bradley, T. P. (1984). In T. Hoshino, H. S. Koren and A. Uchida (eds), *Natural Killer Activity and Its Regulation*. Amsterdam: Excerpta Medica: 121–6.

Bykowsky, M. J. and Stutman, O. (1986). *J. Immunol.* 137: 1120.

Collins, J. L., Patek, P. Q. and Cohn, M. (1981). *J. Exp. Med.* 153: 89.

Decker, T., Johmann-Matthes, M. L. and Gifford, G. E. (1987), *J. Immunol.* 138: 957.

Dennert, G. and Podack, E. R. (1983). *J. Exp. Med.* 157: 1483.

Dourmashkin, R. R., Detrix, P., Simone, C. B. and Henkart, P. A. (1980). *Clin. Exp. Immunol.* 42: 554.

Hamilton, M. S., Burton, R. C. and Winn, H. J. (1981). *Transplantation Proc.* 13: 787.

Hammerling, G. J., Hammerling, U. and Flaherty, L. (1979). *J. Exp. Med.* 150: 108.

Hanna, N. and Burton, R. C. (1981). *J. Immunol.* 127: 1754.

Hanna, N. and Fidler, I. J. (1981). *Cancer Res.* 41: 438.

Herberman, R. B., Nunn, M. E., Holden, H. T. and Lavrin, D. H. (1975). *Int. J. Cancer* 16: 230.

Herberman, R. B., Nunn, M. E. and Holden, H. T. (1978). *J. Immunol.* 121: 304.

Hercend, T., Schmidt, R., Brennan, A., Edson, M. A., Reinherz, E. L., Schlossman, S. F. and Ritz, J. (1984). *Eur. J. Immunol.* 14: 844.

Hochman, P. S. and Cudkowicz, G. (1979). *J. Immunol.* 123: 968.

Holbrook, N. J., Cox, W. I. and Horner, H. C. (1983). *Cancer Res.* 43: 4019.

Ihle, J. N., Rebar, L., Keller, J., Lee, J. C. and Hopel, A. (1982). *Immunol. Rev.* 63: 1.

Jensen, P. J. and Koren, H. S. (1980). *J. Immunol.* 124: 395.

Koo, G. C. (1980). *J. Immunol.* 125: 1003.

Lattime, E. C. (1987). *Concepts Immunopathol.* 4: 77.

Lattime, E. C. and Stutman, O. (1983). *Surv. Synth. Pathol. Res.* 2: 57.

Lattime, E. C. and Stutman, O. (1984a). In T. Hoshino, H. S. Koren and A. Uchida (eds), *Natural Killer Activity and Its Regulation.* Amsterdam: Excerpta Medica: 193–8.

Lattime, E. C. and Stutman, O. (1984b). In T. Hoshino, H. S. Koren and A. Uchida (eds), *Natural Killer Activity and Its Regulation.* Amsterdam: Excerpta Medica: 314–9.

Lattime, E. C., Pecoraro, G. A. and Stutman, O. (1981). *J. Immunol.* 126: 2011.

Lattime, E. C., Pecoraro, G. A., Cuttito, M. and Stutman, O. (1982a). In R. B. Herberman (ed.), *NK Cells and Other Natural Effector Cells.* New York: Academic Press: 179–86.

Lattime, E. C., Ishizaka, S. T., Pecoraro, G. A., Koo, G. and Stutman, O. (1982b). In R. B. Herberman (ed.), *NK Cells and Other Natural Effector Cells.* New York: Academic Press: 187–92.

Lattime, E. C., Pecoraro, G. A., Cuttito, M. J. and Stutman, O. (1983). *Int. J. Cancer* 32: 523.

Lin, Y., Collins, J. L., Patek, P. Q. and Cohn, M. (1983). *J. Immunol.* 131: 1154.

Lin, Y., Patek, P.Q., Collins, J. L. and Cohn, M. (1985). *J. Natl. Cancer Inst.* 74: 1025.

Ortaldo, J. R., Mason, L. H., Mathieson, B. J., Liang, S. M., Flick, D. A. and Herberman, R. B. (1986). *Nature* 321: 700.

Paige, C. J., Feo Figarella, E., Cuttito, M. J., Cahan, A. and Stutman, O. (1978). *J. Immunol.* 121: 1827.

Patek, P. Q., Collins, J. L. and Cohn, M. (1978). *Nature* 276: 510.

Patek, P. Q., Collins, J. L. and Cohn, M. (1982). *Cellular Immunol.* 72: 113.

Patek, P. Q., Lin, Y., Collins, J. L. and Cohn, M. (1986). *J. Immunol.* 136: 741.

Podack, E. R. and Dennert, G. (1983). *Nature* 302: 442.

Roder, J. C., Rosen, A., Fenyo, E. M. and Troy, F. A. (1979). *Proc. Natl. Acad. Sci. USA* 76: 1405.

Roder, J. C., Beaumont, T. J., Kerbel, R. S., Halitotis, T. and Kozbor, D. (1981). *Proc. Natl. Acad. Sci. USA* 78: 6396.

Santoli, D., Trinchieri, G. and Lief, F. S. (1978). *J. Immunol.* 121: 526.

Stutman, O. and Cuttito, M. J. (1980). In R. B. Herberman (ed.), *Natural Cell-mediated Immunity Against Tumors.* New York: Academic Press: 431–42.

Stutman, O. and Cuttito, M. J. (1982). In R. B. Herberman (ed.), *NK Cells and Other Natural Effector Cells.* New York: Academic Press: 281–1080.

Stutman, O. and Lattime, E. C. (1985). In E. Pick and M. Landy (eds), *Lymphokines*. Orlando: Academic Press: 107–59.

Stutman, O., Paige, C. J. and Feo Figarella, E. (1978). *J. Immunol.* 121: 1819.

Stutman, O., Feo Figarella, E., Paige, C. J. and Lattime, E. C. (1980a). In R. B. Herberman (ed.), *Natural Cell-mediated Immunity Against Tumors*. New York: Academic Press: 187–230.

Stutman, O., Feo Figarella, E. and Wisun, R. (1980b). In R. B. Herberman (ed.), *Natural Cell-mediated Immunity Against Tumors*. New York: Academic Press: 1073–80.

Talmadge, J. E., Meyers, K. M., Prieur, D. J. and Starkey, J. R. (1980). *Nature* 284: 622.

Targan, S. R. and Newman, W. (1984). In T. Hoshino, H. S. Koren and A. Uchida (eds), *Natural Killer Activity and Its Regulation*. Amsterdam: Excerpta Medica: 135.

Vodinelich, L., Sutherland, R., Scheider, C., Newman, R. and Greaves, M. (1983). *Proc. Natl. Acad. Sci. USA* 80: 835.

Wright, S. C., Weitzen, M. L., Kahle, R., Granger, G. A. and Bonavida, B. (1983). *J. Immunol.* 130: 2479.

Wright, S. C., Roder, J. C. and Bonavida, B. (1984). In T. Hoshino, H. S. Koren and A. Uchida (eds), *Natural Killer Activity and Its Regulation*. Amsterdam: Excerpta Medica: 305.

6

Natural Antibodies

VERONICA MILLER[1]
DONNA CHOW
ARNOLD GREENBERG

Manitoba Institute of Cell Biology
University of Manitoba,
Winnipeg, Manitoba, Canada

[1] Present address: Department of Microbiology and Immunology, UCLA School of Medicine, Los Angeles, CA 90024, USA.

NATURAL IMMUNITY
ISBN 0 12 5145551

I. DISTRIBUTION OF NATURAL ANTIBODIES

The definition most commonly used for natural antibodies (NAbs) is that they are antibodies in the serum of animals which have not been intentionally immunised. Several theories to account for their origin have been presented, including environmental stimulation, endogenous bacterial and viral stimulation, and stimulation by autologous antigen, as well as the theory that they represent original germ-line sequences, before alteration of specificities due to variable region DNA rearrangement has taken place. These theories will be discussed in Section III. Although the concept of 'immunisation' cannot be excluded in some of these theories, the definition stated above will be used, stressing the fact that the animals used for the study of NAb have not been intentionally immunised. Two other points should be noted in a discussion of the definition of NAbs: (1) although they are true antibodies, their binding affinity to their respective antigens may be lower than that of induced antibodies (Guilbert *et al.*, 1982); and (2) the genetics of production of NAb to a defined antigen is not necessarily the same as that of induced antibodies to the same antigen. This latter point will be discussed in more detail in Section V.

NAbs have been detected in the serum of many vertebrate species, including mammals such as mice, rats, rabbits, guinea pigs, dogs, cows and humans (Guilbert *et al.*, 1982; Mittal *et al.*, 1973; Hughes *et al.*, 1973; Grönberg *et al.*, 1980; Longenecker and Mosmann, 1980; Jones, 1984), avian species such as chicken and ducks (Mittal *et al.*, 1973; Longenecker and Mosmann, 1980; Springer and Tegtmeyer, 1981), and reptiles such as alligators (Longenecker and Mosmann, 1980). In addition, in a study which characterised the primary immunoglobulin response of lampreys (Agnatha), the most primitive vertebrates (Marchalonis and Edelman, 1968), low levels of bacteriophage-neutralising activity were found in sera from unimmunised lampreys. The most common example of NAbs in humans is the anti-blood-group antibodies (Kabat, 1976; Watkins, 1966). In mice, NAbs have been detected in most of the strains examined

(Cunningham, 1974; Lord and Dutton, 1975; Martin and Martin, 1975b; Pierroti and Colnaghi, 1976). The variation in the levels of NAbs was found to be considerable within the different strains (Martin and Martin, 1975b; Pierroti and Colnaghi, 1976; Aoki *et al.*, 1966; Wolosin and Greenberg, 1981), and genetic studies have revealed that the production of NAb is under genetic control, although differences exist in the various systems used for these studies (see Section V).

A common method used for the detection of NAb is the complement-dependent cytotoxicity assay (Martin and Martin, 1975b; Herberman and Aoki, 1972; Pierotti and Colnaghi, 1975; Ferrone *et al.*, 1976; Ménard *et al.*, 1977; Chow *et al.*, 1981a). In addition, agglutination assays (Galili *et al.*, 1984), enzyme-linked immunoassays (ELISA) (Guilbert *et al.*, 1982; Dwyer *et al.*, 1983), radioimmunoassays (RIA) (Hamilton and Adkinson, 1985; Challacombe *et al.*, 1984) and immuno-fluorescence (Underwood *et al.*, 1985) have been used. Most NAbs are of the IgM class (Martin and Martin, 1975a; Schoolnik *et al.*, 1979; Houghton *et al.*, 1980; Colnaghi *et al.*, 1982; Springer, 1984), and therefore easily detected by complement-dependent assays, if cellular target antigens are being examined. Other classes of NAb that have been detected using non-complement-dependent assays include IgG (various subclasses) (Guilbert *et al.*, 1982; Galili *et al.*, 1984; Hamilton and Adkinson, 1985; Challacombe *et al.*, 1984; Underwood *et al.*, 1985; Houghton *et al.*, 1980; Colnaghi *et al.*, 1982; Pearson and Steigbigel, 1980; Lutz *et al.*, 1984) and IgA (Guilbert *et al.*, 1982; Challacombe *et al.*, 1984).

II. SPECIFICITY OF NATURAL ANTIBODIES

Some of the antigens recognised by NAbs have been identified and characterised in detail; others, such as some cell-surface membrane antigens, have not been characterised at all. A general statement that can be made regarding NAb specificities is that they are to a large extent car-bohydrate-reactive (Jones, 1984; Hamilton and Adkinson, 1985; Snyder and Fleissner, 1980; Galili *et al.*, 1985; Rogentin and Plocinik, 1974; Grönberg *et al.*, 1985). Although the sugars found in mammalian cell glycoprotein and glycolipid structures are relatively restricted, they have the potential of forming a wide array of antigenic determinants, based on the degree of complexity of the sugar components as well as the amount of branching (Hubbard and Ivatt, 1981). Carbohydrate-reactive NAbs can sometimes distinguish between structural differences of carbohy-drate sequences, such as between $\alpha(1 \to 3)$- and $\alpha(1 \to 4)$-linked galactose residues (Galili *et al.*, 1985) and between α- and β-linked galactosides

(Imai *et al.*, 1980). Other specificities include common conformational structures, such as α-helices (Dighiero *et al.*, 1983) and phosphodiester groups (Carroll *et al.*, 1985). It has also been found that NAbs are highly cross-reactive (Guilbert *et al.*, 1982; Dighiero *et al.*, 1983; Carroll *et al.*, 1985; Faaber *et al.*, 1984; Sela *et al.*, 1975), although in some cases it has been possible to define particular antigens and differentiate these from other closely related antigens using NAbs (Obata *et al.*, 1981).

In the following sections, some of the more prominent NAb-reactive antigens will be discussed. As interest in the study of NAbs, their origin and their specificities has increased in the recent years, the literature has become extensive. Therefore only representative examples will be listed in each category.

A. Cell-surface Antigens

NAbs to cell-surface antigens are present in most species examined and include NAbs to cryptic antigens, differentiation antigens, major histocompatibility antigens, thymocyte antigens, and tumour-related antigens. These antigens have been detected using syngeneic (Cunningham, 1974; Martin and Martin, 1975b; Herberman and Aoki, 1972; Ménard *et al.*, 1977), allogeneic (Martin and Martin, 1975b; Wolosin and Greenberg, 1981; Ménard *et al.*, 1977) and xenogeneic (Mittal *et al.*, 1973; Hughes *et al.*, 1973; Ferrone *et al.*, 1976; Mosmann and Longenecker, 1982) sera.

1. Blood group antigens

NAbs to human blood group antigens include those to the ABO blood groups, as well as to precursor structures such as the T and Tn antigens (Kabat, 1976; Watkins, 1966; Springer, 1984). For example, anti-T antibodies are found in all humans, but not in mice (Springer, 1984; Bray *et al.*, 1981). These are predominantly of the IgM class (Springer, 1984). The levels of these antibodies remain constant throughout adult life, although changes have been observed in patients with certain carcinomas. The T antigen, βGal ($1 \rightarrow 3$) $\alpha GalNac$, is a precursor of the MN blood group antigens and can be detected easily on enzyme-treated erythrocytes. It has also been found on several carcinomas (Springer *et al.*, 1975), as well as fetal tissue (Springer, 1984). ABO blood group antigens have also been found on tumour cells originating from tissue not usually expressing these antigens, and can be detected by NAbs (Knuth *et al.*, 1983).

2. Cryptic antigens

It has been shown by several laboratories that enzyme treatment of cells such as lymphocytes and erythrocytes reveals NAb-reactive determinants which are not detectable on normal cells (Hughes *et al.*, 1973; Cunningham, 1974; Lord and Dutton, 1975; Rogentine and Plocinik, 1974; Rosenberg and Schwarz, 1974; Rogentine, 1975; Rogentine *et al.*, 1977). The anti-T antibody system described above is one example of NAb recognition of cryptic antigens on erythrocytes. Although other specificities have not been examined in such detail, one can infer that these antibodies have carbohydrate reactivities, because their detection is dependent on neuraminidase treatment. In addition, Rogentine and Plocinik (1974) have shown that NAb reactivity with neuraminidase-treated lymphocytes can be inhibited by some carbohydrates. Another study revealing the carbohydrate specificities of NAbs reactive with neuraminidase-treated cells is that of Imai *et al.*, (1980), who found that sugars such as phenyl-β-galactoside, lactose and melibiose could inhibit this interaction.

Human NAb reactivity with a non-carbohydrate cryptic antigen was described recently (Lutz *et al.*, 1984). This IgG antibody reacted with cryptic regions of the band 3 protein of human erythrocytes.

3. Thymocyte antigens

The thymocyte reactivity of NAbs has been studied mainly in mice. It was found that all strains examined had natural thymocytotoxic antibodies (NTAs), although the levels showed considerable variation between strains (Martin and Martin, 1975b; Klassen *et al.*, 1977; Eisenberg *et al.*, 1979). NTAs do not display alloreactivity (Martin and Martin, 1975d; Parker *et al.*, 1974). Imai *et al.*, (1980) showed that the NTA population of NZB mice was heterogenous, and that it could be divided into two major subpopulations: those reacting with normal thymocytes, and those reacting with neuraminidase-treated thymocytes and lymphocytes. This latter population was inhibitable by several sugars, and was reactive with a subpopulation of peripheral T cells.

In our own studies of NAbs we found that a large proportion of tumour-reactive NAbs could be absorbed by thymocytes (either Thy 1.1 or Thy 1.2). We confirmed our serum studies with monoclonal NAb, raised by fusing lipopolysaccharide-stimulated spleen cells with a non-secreting myeloma. The majority of the monoclonal NAbs (selected on the basis of tumour reactivity) were also positive for thymocytes (see

Table 6.1: Reactivity of monoclonal natural antibodies with thymocytes and tumours

Monoclonal NAb hybridoma	Strain of origin	Monoclonal NAb reactivity Optical density ± s.e.		
A)		Thymocytes	SL2 (H-2^d)	L5178Y (H-2^d)
20N.2	CBA/J (H-2^k)	0.550 ± 0.06	0.340 ± 0.05	0.420 ± 0.06
20N.4	CBA/J	0.520 ± 0.03	0.430 ± 0.08	0.416 ± 0.07
40N.1	CBA/J	0.600 ± 0.01	0.030 ± 0.01	0.061 ± 0.02
40N.2	CBA/J	0.755 ± 0.07	0.032 ± 0.02	0.095 ± 0.01
40N.3	CBA/J	0.711 ± 0.06	0.044 ± 0.02	0.100 ± 0.05
37N.1	BALB/c (H-2^d)	0.560 ± 0.04	0.112 ± 0.02	0.200 ± 0.05
37N.4	BALB/c	0.412 ± 0.06	0.125 ± 0.05	0.075 ± 0.05
37N.5	BALB/c	0.870 ± 0.06	0.560 ± 0.06	0.370 ± 0.03
B)		CBA/J (H-2^k) Thymocytes	C57B1/6 (H2^b) Thymocytes	DBA/2 (H-2^b) Thymocytes
10M.1	CBA/J (H-2^k)	0.157 ± 0.01	0.045 ± 0.07	0.125 ± 0.01
10M.2	CBA/J	0.155 ± 0.02	0.252 ± 0.01	0.155 ± 0.01
10M.3	CBA/J	0.262 ± 0.02	0.216 ± 0.02	0.168 ± 0.01
10M.4	CBA/J	0.194 ± 0.01	0.214 ± 0.02	0.156 ± 0.02
C)		Thymocytes (H-2^d)		L5178Y (H-2^d)
PEC.1	BALB/c (H-2^d)	0.152 ± 0.01		0.133 ± 0.02
PEC.2	BALB/c	0.242 ± 0.03		0.145 ± 0.02
PEC.3	BALB/c	0.044 ± 0.01		0.362 ± 0.04

Cells were glutaraldehyde-fixed to poly-L-lysine-treated plates, then incubated with supernatants from cloned hybridomas in culture. Antibody binding was determined by ELISA screening and optical density read on a Titertek ELISA plate reader. In experiment A, we show that all of the tumour-reactive mNAbs were also thymocyte-reactive. The thymocytes used in these screenings were syngeneic to the strain of the spleen (A and B) or peritoneal cell (C) donors for fusion. When we tested some of the mNAbs against thymocytes of different strains, we found that most of them reacted with thymocytes regardless of the strain of origin (experiments B and C) confirming previous reports with serum NTA.

Table 6.1). We have not yet determined the nature of the cell-surface antigen(s) reactive with the monoclonal NAbs.

In examining the cell-surface determinants recognised by NTAs, Parker *et al.*, (1974) found that the NTA-reactive antigen co-capped with the Thy-1 glycoprotein, and concluded that NTAs are reactive with this major glycoprotein on the thymocyte surface, or with a closely related molecule. The Thy-1 antigen is heavily glycosylated, and the carbohydrate structure changes during differentiation (Morrison *et al.*, 1984).

Thus, it is possible that NTAs are reactive with one or more carbohydrate determinants on the Thy-1 glycoprotein that are absent on peripheral T cells.

Other antigens present on murine thymocytes which are recognised by NAb are antigens related to endogenous murine leukaemia viruses (MuLV) (Obata *et al.*, 1981; Obata *et al.*, 1976; Obata *et al.*, 1979; Stockert *et al.*, 1979). In fact, NAbs have been used to define some of these antigens (Obata *et al.*, 1981). Mouse thymocytes express on their surface a glycoprotein (gp70) related to the *env* gene product of MuLV. Four antigenic systems have been described: G_{IX}, G_{RADA1}, G_{AKSL2}, and G_{ERLD} (the G stands for Ludwig Gross, the discoverer of the class of virus; it is followed by the designation of the prototype leukemia cell line used for defining the antigen). These antigens are expressed in varying amounts on thymocytes of different mouse strains (Obata *et al.*, 1981) and are not always associated with the production of complete viral particles. Some strains of mice (e.g. AKR), express all four antigens, and other strains (e.g. BALB/c), express none of these, although they may appear on tumours of BALB/c origin (Obata *et al.*, 1981). These antigens are accessible on the thymocyte surface, rendering the thymocytes susceptible to NAb and complement lysis, in contrast to the group-specific antigen also present on the gp70 molecule, which is detectable only after membrane disruption (Tung *et al.*, 1975).

4. Major histocompatibility antigens

NAbs to major histocompatibility complex (MHC) or MHC-linked antigens have been described by three laboratories. In previous studies from our own laboratory (Wolosin and Greenberg, 1981), using congenic mouse strains we had shown that NAbs from H-2^b mice reactive with an H-2^d tumour could be absorbed with splenocytes from H-2^d mice, but not other congenic strains. Longenecker and Mosmann (1980) have shown that sera from a variety of other species contain NAbs reactive against chicken MHC antigens. This was confirmed further by the production of murine monoclonal NAbs, which revealed that the determinants recognised by the chicken red blood cell reactive NAb were predominantly of the polymorphic type, including MHC antigens rather than species-specific antigens (Mosmann and Longenecker, 1982). Ivanyi and co-workers have also identified anti-MHC NAbs (Ivanyi *et al.*, 1982; Cerny-Provasnik *et al.*, 1985a, b, c). They have detected anti-MHC antibodies in the serum of aged normal mice, and have also been able to confirm their findings by producing monoclonal NAb with MHC specificity from spleens of non-immunised mice. These antibodies recognized public Class I determinants, and one was reactive with determinants on syngeneic K and D antigens. The presence of anti-self MHC-reactive antibody-producing B cell clones was also established by Risser and Grunwald (1981). They immunised H-2$^{b/k}$ hybrid mice with a parental Abelson virus induced lymphoma (H-2$^{b/b}$) and found that some of the mice produced antibodies reactive with private specificities on the H-2D^b and H-2K^b glycoproteins. Whether any of these MHC-reactive antibodies have carbohydrate specificities has not been reported, but since MHC antigens are glycosylated and immunisation may lead to anti-MHC antibodies which are carbohydrate-reactive (Swiedler *et al.*, 1983), it is possible that the anti-MHC NAbs are also carbohydrate-reactive.

5. *Viral antigens*

Some of the antigens related to murine oncornaviruses have already been described (Section II.A.3) since they can also be considered to be thymocyte antigens, in some cases being expressed as differentiation antigens (Obata *et al.*, 1981). In addition to antibodies to the gp70 glycoprotein, normal murine serum contains NAbs to the gp45 and p15 viral determinants (Nowinski *et al.*, 1976; Ihle and Hanna, 1977). In a survey of murine monoclonal NAbs, Colnaghi *et al.*, (1982) also demonstrated that some of these antibodies had antiviral activity, reacting with structures related to murine ecotropic virus.

Human NAbs to gp70 glycoprotein have also been described (Snyder and Fleissner, 1980; Barbacid *et al.*, 1980). One study has demonstrated the carbohydrate nature of these antigenic determinants (Snyder and Fleissner, 1980), which has not yet been established in the murine system. Barbacid *et al.*, (1980) have presented evidence that the antigens recognised by the antiviral gp70 NAbs in human sera are actually cell-surface antigens of the cell line used to grow the viruses, but this has not been substantiated by others. Human antibodies to viral antigens have also been found when endemic populations were screened for the presence of human T-cell leukaemia virus (HTLV-I) (Sugamura and Hinuma, 1985). These anti-HTLV antibodies were found in patients with adult T cell leukaemia, as well as in 10–37 per cent of non-tumour-bearing residents of endemic areas in Japan. The antibodies reacted with the p24 and p19 proteins, both of which are specific to this virus (Gallo and Reitz, 1982).

6. *Tumour-cell-associated antigens*

Many laboratories have reported the presence of tumour-reactive NAbs in normal serum (Martin and Martin, 1975b; Pierroti and Colnaghi,

1976; Herbermann and Aoki, 1972; Ménard *et al.*, 1977; Colnaghi *et al.*, 1982; Chow *et al.*, 1981a). From the above discussion of cell-surface antigens recognised by NAbs, it is evident that many of these are also present on tumour cells as is the case for the MuLV and HTLV related antigens in mice and humans respectively, and the T/Tn antigens in humans. Other normal cellular antigens, such as the MHC and blood group antigens, may also be present on tumour cells. For example, in an analysis of tumour-reactive NAbs, our laboratory, using congenic strains of mice, has shown that a population of tumour-reactive NAbs can be absorbed by spleen cells of certain haplotypes but not others (Wolosin and Greenberg, 1981), as discussed in Section II.A.4. It is also possible, as proposed by Rogentine (1975) that some of the NAb-reactive antigens that are normally cryptic and require neuraminidase treatment for their detection on normal cells, or are exposed on aged cells due to desialylation, are expressed in unsubstituted form on tumour cells owing to alterations in the glycosylation of cell-surface glycoproteins and glycolipids, or to increased enzymatic cleavage of the terminal sialic acid molecules.

Grönberg *et al.*, (1985) have shown the binding of NAb to the YAC lymphoma can be inhibited by purified C-type virus particles and gp70 molecules, as well as by bacterial sonicates. They also found that NAb bound less to tunicamycin-treated tumours, a treatment which prevents N-linked glycosylation of cell-surface proteins.

Another general group of tumour-associated antigens recognised by NAbs are differentiation antigens, such as the Mel 1 and AH antigens on melanomas detected by human IgG and IgM NAbs respectively (Houghton *et al.*, 1980). The Mel 1 antigen is expressed by fetal, but not adult, fibroblasts, and by several epithelial cancer cell lines. It is absent from glioma and B cell lines, and melanomas can be classified into Mel 1^+ and Mel 1^- subsets. In contrast, the AH antigen is found on a large proportion of melanomas, all astrocytomas, and some sarcomas, but is absent from epithelial cancers. This antigen has not yet been detected on normal cultured cells, and Houghton *et al.*, (1980) have classified it as a Class 2 antigen, that is, antigens expressed on various tumours of similar origin, but not on normal tissue. Their absence from normal tissue would, however, be difficult to confirm.

In conclusion, it is unlikely that tumour-reactive NAbs recognise antigens that are truly tumour-specific; rather, they probably react with antigens present on some normal tissue, such as thymocytes or aged erythrocytes. Their detection on tumour cells could be due to a higher degree of expression.

B. Bacterial and Parasitic Antigens

NAbs to bacterial antigens have been frequently described (Springer and Tegtmeyer, 1981; Challacombe *et al.*, 1984; Schoolnik *et al.*, 1979; Carroll *et al.*, 1985; Lieberman *et al.*, 1974). For example, a common antibody in the serum of BALB/c mice is the T15 idiotype bearing antibody reactive with phosphorylcholine (PC), a component of *Streptococcus pneumoniae* (Lieberman *et al.*, 1974). Other determinants are those of certain strains of *Escherichia coli*, which are cross-reactive with the carbohydrate sequences responsible for the human ABO blood group determinants (Kabat, 1976; Springer, 1971; Hoskins and Boulding, 1976). The anti-T antibodies in human serum have also been shown to react with *E. coli*, strain O86 (Springer and Tegtmeyer, 1981). In addition, it has been shown that anti-DNA antibodies derived in monoclonal form from MRL-lpr/lpr mice bind to bacteria common in the murine intestinal flora, such as *Streptococcus faecalis*, *Staphylococcus aureus* and *E. coli* (Carroll *et al.*, 1985).

Another series of interesting human NAbs are those reactive with *Streptococcus mutans*, an organism thought to play an important role in the development of dental caries (McGhee and Michalek, 1981). NAbs to *S. mutans* have been detected in serum and in saliva (Arnold *et al.*, 1976; Challacombe, 1980; Lehner *et al.*, 1970). Challacombe *et al.*, (1984) analysed the determinants recognised by serum NAbs reactive with *S. mutans*. They found that the binding of antibodies to whole bacterial cells could be inhibited by a purified protein antigen (SA I/II), glucosyltransferase, C polysaccharide and lipoteichoic acid. Thus, in this system, the antigens being recognised by human NAbs include those that are specific to this bacterium, as well as some which are shared with other Gram-positive bacterial species.

NAbs to pathogenic Gram-negative bacteria are also present in human serum, as exemplified by the natural bactericidal activity of normal human serum for *Neisseria gonorrhoeae* (Schoolnik *et al.*, 1976). This bactericidal activity has been ascribed to IgM antibodies, but the nature of the bacterial determinants recognised has not been determined (Schoolnik *et al.*, 1979).

Human NAbs reactive with *Leishmania donovani* have also been described, and are present in individuals from endemic areas as well as in donors with no history of exposure to leishmania. The antigens recognised by these antibodies have not been characterised, but they are present on promastigotes and not on amastigotes (Pearson and Steigbigel, 1980).

C. Cellular and Serum Protein Antigens

The fact that much of the antibody activity found in normal serum is directed at autoantigens has already been discussed in Section II.A in relation to cell-surface antigens. Another group of autoantibodies not uncommonly found at low titres in 'normal' serum, is reactive against sub-cellular structures and serum proteins. These include the anti-DNA antibodies which are prominent in patients with systemic lupus erythematosus (SLE) (Schwartz and Stollar, 1985; Tan, 1982). To this category also belong the anti-immunoglobulin or rheumatoid factors (RF) (Kunkel *et al.*, 1961). These types of antibody, although prominent in autoimmune diseases, are not necessarily always associated with them (Kissick, 1961; Carson *et al.*, 1981; Slaughter *et al.*, 1978). Anti-DNA as well as RF NAbs have also been frequently described in mice, again not in strict association with autoimmune disease (Dighiero *et al.*, 1983; Van Snick *et al.*, 1983).

In a systematic study of normal human sera Guilbert *et al.*, (1982) examined human NAb reactivity against nine common antigens. NAbs to tubulin, actin, thyroglobulin, myoglobin, fetuin, transferrin, albumin, cytochrome c, and collagen were commonly present. Although binding of these antibodies to their respective antigens could be inhibited most efficiently by the same antigen, some cross-reactivity was observed, which differentiated the NAbs from induced antibodies. In addition, they confirmed the auto-reactivity of these antibodies by staining cultured human hepatocytes.

In a further study, this group was able to produce monoclonal NAbs from normal, non-immunised BALB/c splenocytes, which reacted with thyroglobulin, myosin, actin, tubulin, spectrin and dsDNA (Dighiero *et al.*, 1983; Dighiero *et al.*, 1986). Some cross-reactivity was observed in this study as well. Analysing one of their monoclonal NAbs in more detail, they found that it reacted predominantly with the light meromyosin sub-fragment of myosin, which is rich in alpha helices. Thus, they postulated that NAbs recognise common structural determinants present on several molecules found in nature. Other evidence for this concept includes the demonstration that phosphodiester groups were responsible for the cross-reactivity of human anti-DNA antibodies with phospholipids (Lafer *et al.*, 1981). In this context, it is worth pointing out again the study by Carroll *et al.*, (1985), which demonstrated that murine monoclonal anti-DNA antibodies bind to endogenous bacteria containing phosphate esters such as teichoic and lipoteichoic acids, lipopolysaccharides, and phospholipids. The antibodies bound to bacterial preparations that had been pre-treated with DNase, thus ruling out the possibility that the binding was due to the presence of DNA on the cell surface. In addition, these antibodies were able to bind to phospholipid extracted from the bacterial cell walls.

The analysis of NAbs reactive with normal immunoglobulins (RFs) has also been carried out at the level of serum antibodies as well as monoclonal antibodies (Van Snick *et al.*, 1983; Stassin *et al.*, 1983). It was found that these RF antibodies could be separated into groups defined by their isotypic and allotypic specificities, and that both allotypic and isotypic determinants recognised by mouse RFs are located in the CH3 domain of IgG1, and IgG2a and IgG2b-immunoglobulins (Stassin *et al.*, 1983).

Natural anti-idiotypic antibodies have also been described. These have been detected after immunisation with exogenous antigen (Schrater *et al.*, 1979; Geha, 1982; Cleveland *et al.*, 1983) and in autoimmune diseases (Dwyer *et al.*, 1983), and have been obtained in monoclonal form from neonatal mice (Holmberg *et al.*, 1984).

A recent report describes the presence and increase with advancing age of naturally occurring anti-interferon antibodies in the serum of rats bred for their high incidence of spontaneous melanomas (De Maeyer-Guignard *et al.*, 1984). Although the appearance of easily detectable amounts of these antibodies may be due to their association with the disease state, they may be representative of the specificities present in lower concentrations in normal animals. This has been suggested for other auto-antibodies (thymocyte antibodies).

D. Synthetic Haptens

Another interesting group of NAbs are those reactive with synthetic haptens, such as oxazalone, 2,4-dinitrophenol (DNP), and 4-hydroxy-3-nitrophenol (NP) (Jormalainen and Makela, 1971; Makela and Imanishi, 1975; Ando *et al.*, 1978). These have also been found in a wide variety of species. They are important in that they provide a system in which studies of the origin, genetics, and regulation of NAbs can be carried out without the complicating factors of unintentional exposure to environmental antigens.

E. Heterogeneity and Cross-reactivity

A survey of the antigenic determinants recognised by NAbs, as described in this section, would indicate that NAbs are a rather heterogeneous population, their specificities ranging from natural determinants found on bacteria and autologous cells, to synthetic haptens which would normally not have been encountered by the individual under study. In spite of the large number of antigens that have been identified as being NAb-reactive, there are some striking examples of rather selective recognition. An example of this is the polymorphic versus species-specific antigens on chicken red blood cells that are recognised by murine NAbs (Mosmann and Longenecker, 1982).

When discussing the heterogeneity of NAbs, it is important to point out that each laboratory may have used different systems for their identification, and in this way, some cross-reactivities may not have been detected. The cross-reactivity between DNA and phospholipids has already been stressed (Carroll *et al.*, 1985; Lafer *et al.*, 1981). More recently, anti-DNA antibodies have also been shown to react with proteoglycans, such as hyaluronic acid and chondroitin sulfates (Faaber *et al.*, 1984). Another striking example of cross-reactivity is the binding to DNA of *Klebsiella pneumoniae* polysaccharide K30-specific mono-clonal antibodies; the binding being inhibited by the K30 polysaccharide (Naparstek *et al.*, 1985). These authors also established that the anti-*Klebsiella* and anti-DNA antibodies shared idiotypic determinants.

In a study of monoclonal auto-antibodies, Haspel *et al.*, (1983) detected multiple organ-reactive antibodies, which appeared frequently after immunisation, as well as in normal animals (Haspel *et al.*, 1983; Prabhakar *et al.*, 1984). These antibodies reacted with organ sites such as the anterior (but not posterior) pituitary, pancreatic islets (but not pancreatic acinar tissue), small intestine and stomach. Garzelli *et al.*, (1986) have also described monoclonal auto-antibodies reacting with pancreatic islet and thyroid cells.

It has also been reported that RF antibodies cross-react with nuclear protein antigens (Hannestad and Stollar, 1978; Johnson, 1979; Agnello *et al.*, 1980).

It is possible that some of the NAb populations, distinguished on the basis of antigenic specificity, may be overlapping. The relatively high concentration of anti-DNP antibodies in normal human sera has been used as an argument in favour of the idea that natural antibody is multi-specific (Ortega *et al.*, 1984); A systematic study of NAbs in monoclonal form, many specificities of which are now becoming available, would be useful in resolving this question.

III. ORIGIN OF NATURAL ANTIBODIES

Theories about the origin of NAbs often reflect the particular system used by the proponents in their own studies. As is evident from the discussion in Section II, it may be difficult to classify all NAbs as one group in terms of origin and regulation.

A. Environmental Stimulation

Environmental stimulation has been the most common model proposed to account for the prevalence of NAbs in normal serum. If one assumes that NAbs arise from 'natural immunisation', then the difference between NAb and induced antibody lies only in the method of immunisation. Whether some of the differences in affinity and genetic control seen in the production of NAbs versus immune antibodies can be ascribed to 'natural' versus 'intentional' immunisation is not clear at present, and would be difficult to test in the cases where the antigens involved are a part of the individual's internal and external environment. In this context it should be pointed out that there are well-characterised differences between the mucosal and gut-associated lymphoid systems and the systemic immune system (Wade and Szewczuk, 1984). For example, it has been reported that there are differences in B cell repertoire directed against phosphorylcholine (PC) (Gearhart and Cebra, 1979), and that the B cell subpopulation missing in spleens of CBA/N mice, which are unable to respond to TI-2 antigens (see Section IV.B.1), is not lacking in CBA/N mucosal tissues (Eldridge *et al.*, 1983). Cooperation between the two systems, which occurs when antigen is introduced via the two routes, may affect the anti-idiotypic regulatory circuits (Jackson and Mestecky, 1981). The immune response to antigen may be quite different, depending on the route of immunisation (Pierce and Gowans, 1975; Challacombe and Tomasi, 1980). These considerations are important in view of the fact that the environmental antigens responsible for the production of NAbs, according to this model, would be introduced to the host via the mucosal system. Yet, comparisons between NAb and induced antibody have generally used the systemic route of induction (Guilbert *et al.*, 1982; Ando *et al.*, 1978).

A considerable amount of evidence has been accumulated in support of the environmental stimulation model. Galili *et al.*, (1985) found that the structure recognised by their NAb ($\alpha(1 \rightarrow 3)$Gal) was also present on bacteria present in the environment. Numerous other examples of this type exist, such as the ABO blood group determinants (Kabat, 1976; Springer, 1971; Hoskins and Boulding, 1976), the T antigen (Springer and Tegtmeyer, 1981), and the fact that even anti-DNA NAb can bind to endogenous bacteria (Carroll *et al.*, 1985). In a more direct approach to this question, Springer and Tegtmeyer (1981) established that the production of anti-T antibodies in normal serum was dependent on the presence of certain strains of *E. coli* in the gut of the individual under study. Others have shown that certain NAb specificities are absent in the sera of animals raised under germ-free conditions, for example, RF NAb (Van Snick and Masson, 1980) and anti-PC NAb (Lieberman *et al.*,

1974). In the latter case, it was shown that this specificity of NAb was produced if the mice were exposed to a normal environment (Lieberman *et al.*, 1974). A more recent study indicated that although anti-PC antibody levels were lower in germ-free mice, they were nevertheless detectable (Gearhart and Cebra, 1979).

Genetic studies of anti-MuLV NAb production in mice have indicated that the presence of these antibodies in backcrosses correlated with the presence of viral particles (Nowinski *et al.*, 1976). In this system, however, there are also exceptions where mice do produce anti-MuLV NAb in the absence of viral particles. Anti-HTLV NAb has been found in people without leukaemia, but as they were residing in the environment were this virus is prevalent, exposure cannot be ruled out (Gallo and Reitz, 1982).

Although the evidence listed above argues strongly in favour of some NAb specificities being the result of environmental stimulation, this model cannot account for all NAb populations. In addition to the exceptions cited in the anti-MuLV system, results from other studies indicate that additional mechanisms must be operative. For example, it has been shown that mice raised under germ-free conditions do produce serum NAbs reactive with human lymphocytes (Ferrone *et al.*, 1976). Spleen cells and bone-marrow cells from germ-free mice produced as many background IgM plaques, and their antigen specificity repertoires (measured against a variety of haptens) were similar (Hooijkaas *et al.*, 1984). Spleen cells from germ-free mice have been used to develop monoclonal Ab (Underwood *et al.*, 1985). Four additional studies, using monoclonal antibodies, have shown that neonatal mice possess NAbs reactive with self antigens (Underwood *et al.*, 1985; Holmberg *et al.*, 1984; Dighiero *et al.*, 1985; Dighiero *et al.*, 1986). These studies would argue that factors other than evironmental stimulation are responsible for the production of some NAb specificities.

B. Autologous Antigenic Stimulation

As has already been stressed, many of the NAbs are autoreactive, and these specificities are present in mice and humans who have autoimmune diseases, as well as normals (Dighiero *et al.*, 1983; Kissick, 1961; Carson *et al.*, 1981; Slaughter *et al.*, 1978). Therefore, it is possible that some autoantigens are responsible for the stimulation of B cells producing NAbs. This would be the case for natural auto-anti-idiotypic antibodies (Dwyer *et al.*, 1983; Schrater *et al.*, 1979; Geha, 1982; Cleveland *et al.*, 1983; Holmberg *et al.*, 1984). Other self antigens that possibly fulfill this role are those on aged erythrocytes and lymphocytes, which can also be detected after enzymatic treatment of these cell types (Hughes *et al.*, 1973; Cunningham, 1974; Lord and Dutton, 1975; Rogentine and Plocinik, 1974; Rosenberg and Schwarz, 1974; Rogentine, 1975; Rogentine *et al.*, 1977). For example, Cunliffe and Cox (1980) showed that NAb reactive with isologous murine immunoglobulins cross-reacted with bromelain-treated murine erythrocytes. The high frequency of spontaneous murine plaques reactive with sheep erythrocytes could be explained on the basis that sheep-erythrocyte antigens cross-reacted with bromelain-treated murine erythrocytes (Pages and Bussard, 1975), whereas horse erythrocytes, against which few spontaneous plaques were observed, did not display this cross-reactivity. Other laboratories have shown that tumour-reactive NAb could be absorbed by normal plasma cells (Herberman and Aoki, 1972) and brain tissue (Martin and Martin, 1975a). These studies do not, of course, confirm that NAbs are produced as a result of autoantigenic stimulation, since the possibility that these NAbs are reacting with environmental antigens is difficult to rule out.

C. Polyclonal B Cell Activation

B cells can be polyclonally activated by a variety of agents such as bacterial endotoxins and peptidoglycans (Dziarski, 1982a, b). Lipopolysaccharide (LPS) from *E. coli* and other Gram-negative organisms is frequently used for this purpose. Therefore, the role of endogenous bacteria in NAb production could be expanded to include this mechanism in addition to direct antigenic stimulation. Several studies have shown that in vivo and in vitro LPS stimulation increases serum NAb levels as well as the frequency of spontaneous plaque-forming cells in splenic cell populations (Chow *et al.*, 1981a, b; Dziarski 1982a, b; Dresser, 1978; Steele and Cunningham, 1978; Izui *et al.*, 1979; Hang *et al.*, 1983). Glycoprotein bacterial extracts can also be polyclonal activators (Wood and Möller, 1984). Coulie and Van Snick have shown that RF-producing B cells are activated during secondary immune responses to various antigens, such as hen lysozyme, human transferrin in mice (Van Snick and Coulie, 1983; Coulie and Van Snick, 1983) and tetanus toxoid in humans (Coulie and Van Snick, 1985). Therefore, it is conceivable that some of the NAbs detected in the serum of normal individuals are a result of polyclonally activated B cells. This model of NAb production does not explain the presence of NAbs in mice raised under germ-free conditions and neonatal mice (Ferrone *et al.*, 1976; Underwood *et al.*, 1985; Holmberg *et al.*, 1984; Hooijkaas *et al.*, 1984; Dighiero *et al.*, 1985). It also does not answer the question of why, in some instances, NAbs of restricted specifities are produced.

Although agents such as LPS have been termed polyclonal B cell activators, implying a lack of selectivity in this process (Gronowicz and Coutinho, 1975; Möller, 1975; Clagett and Engel, 1978), this is probably not a correct interpretation. For example, Bretscher (1978) has proposed that LPS activates not all B cells, but only those that are undergoing antigen-dependent activation in the host. According to this view polyclonal activators such as LPS increase the levels of NAb specificities already present in the normal serum, but may not be responsible for the 'original' NAb.

Other findings have been that LPS stimulates predominantly autoantibody production, directed against immunoglobulin, ssDNA, and bromelain-treated erythrocytes (Dziarski, 1982a, b; Dresser, 1978; Steele and Cunningham, 1978).

Thus, while polyclonal B cell activation may enhance the levels of NAbs, it does not provide a good explanation for their origin.

D. Natural Antibodies and Germ-line V Region Sequences

Since NAbs can be detected in animals raised under germ-free conditions, and can be produced in monoclonal form from neonatal spleens, it has led some authors to propose that these are representative of germ-line V region sequences coding for autoreactive specificities, that are expressed throughout immune ontogeny (Dighiero *et al.*, 1983; Dighiero *et al.*, 1985; Lymberi *et al.*, 1985). That the NAbs are frequently antibodies of low affinity that react with a variety of self antigens would support this hypothesis, in that it had been established earlier that the antibody repertoire of fetal and neonatal mice is more restricted then that of the adult and that the affinity of these early antibodies is lower (Goidl and Siskind, 1974). The finding that certain NAb specificities seem to be represented at a higher frequency in the neonatal spleen cell population than in the adult has also been interpreted to support this model (Dighiero *et al.*, 1985). According to this model, recombination and somatic mutation taking place in the variable region as these B cells are activated would result in additional specificities being generated, with the consequent dilution of the neonatally expressed germ-line V region sequences (Dighiero *et al.*, 1985). The same authors have also detected frequent cross-reactive idiotypes among NAb populations (Lymberi *et al.*, 1985). The anti-idiotypic antibodies were raised against two monoclonal NAbs, and reacted with natural serum antibodies, as well as with a large number of subsequently raised monoclonal NAbs. Examination of human anti-DNA antibodies has also revealed that some idiotypes are expressed in the serum of different individuals (Solomon *et al.*, 1983). These findings, together with those of Holmberg *et al.*, (1984) that anti-idiotypic antibodies are present among neonatal NAbs would suggest that an internal idiotypic network may be functioning at this level.

Corley (1985) has proposed that co-operation between natural anti-idiotypic antibody and autoreactive T cells is a possible mechanism for continous activation of the B cells expressing the appropriate germ-line-encoded idiotypes. This activation would then allow somatic mutation and antigen-dependent selection for other specificities.

Dominant idiotypes representative of germ-line sequences have been frequently observed in response to bacterial immunisation, and these idiotypes are also present in normal serum. Bottomly (1984) has pointed out that the most frequently analysed idiotypic systems are those in which the first antibody is directed against common environmental pathogens, such as the T15–anti-T15 system in the response to PC containing pneumococcus. She proposed that these V region sequences have been selected throughout the evolutionary history of the host as a protective mechanism against environmental pathogens. In the PC-specific antibody system, three predominant idiotypes have been identified: T15, M603 and M167 (Briles *et al.*, 1982). The $T15^+$ antibodies show less variation due to somatic mutation than the other two idiotypes, in both heavy and light chains (Gearhart *et al.*, 1981; Crews *et al.*, 1981). Exact translation of the T15 V_H gene results in heavy chains characteristic of the $T15^+$ antibody, whereas the M603 and M167 idiotypes, although utilising the same V_H gene, differ on the average of five amino acids from the germ-line gene. Since the $T15^+$ antibodies have been shown to be optimally protective against murine *S. pneumoniae* infections (Briles *et al.*, 1982), these authors have also suggested that evolutionary pressures resulted in the production of these germ-line-encoded NAbs as a protective mechanism against environmental pathogens.

Klinman and Stone (1983) have shown, using the in vivo splenic fragment assay, that the T15 idiotype is already expressed in a dominant manner at the pre-B cell level, although $T15^-$ PC-binding antibodies also exist. Thus they concluded that the dominance of the T15 idiotype is not due to environmental selection. A more recent in vitro culture system has confirmed that antibody specificities are expressed in a well-defined sequence, again in the absence of environmental selection (Teale, 1985). This would appear to contradict earlier studies showing that the T15 idiotype is not represented in the serum of animals raised under germ-free conditions (Lieberman *et al.*, 1974). One explanation would be that the natural production of this antibody in germ-free mice is low, and environmental stimulation is necessary to activate the T15$^+$ B cells sufficiently to bring the serum levels of T15$^+$ antibodies to detectable levels. The finding of Gearhart and Cebra (1979) that detectable levels of T15$^+$ anti-PC antibodies do exist in germ-free animals, but that their levels are enhanced by exposure to a conventional environment, would support this interpretation.

It is likely that all of the models discussed in this section play a role in the origin of NAbs, as defined in Section I. NAbs, or at least a subpopulation of these, may be representative of germ-line sequences and have their production enhanced by either autologous or environmental stimulation. Since anti-self reactive antibodies have been shown to cross-react with bacteria (Springer and Tegtmeyer, 1981; Galili *et al.*, 1985; Carroll *et al.*, 1985; Faaber *et al.*, 1984; Naparstek *et al.*, 1985), the repertoires stimulated by these two mechanisms may be largely overlapping. Furthermore, it cannot be excluded that, as B cells expressing germline sequences are activated and undergo somatic mutation, some of the resulting specificites may also be NAb-like. This is supported by the finding that a somatic mutant of an anti-PC antibody, with a one amino acid substitution, lost its PC-binding specificity and bound to dsDNA, protamine and cardiolipin (Diamond and Scharff, 1984).

Finally, recent work on a subpopulation of B cell (Ly-1$^+$, see below) shows that these cells are largely responsible for the production of self-reactive NAb. These cells undergo clonal expansion in autoimmune and normal strains of mice and show markedly restricted heterogeneity in their V regions, due to lack of somatic hypermutation (Rajewski *et al*, 1988; Tarlinton *et al*, 1988; Forster *et al*, 1988). This is reminiscent of the situation with T-cell receptor (TCR) genes (Davis and Bjorkman, 1988) and the more recently identified TCR-like IgG in Heterodontus (horned shark) (Kobubu, *et al*, 1988). Thus it is possible that mammalian NAb bear a special relationship to ancestral forms of immunoglobulin.

E. Natural-antibody-producing B Cells

Recently, a unique B cell population which is characterised by the Ly 1 marker has been identified in mice. This marker was initially thought to be present only on T cells and was therefore designated Lyt 1, but several laboratories have confirmed its presence on about two per cent of splenic IgM$^+$ cells of normal mice (Hayakawa *et al.*, 1983; Smith *et al.*, 1985). This Ly 1$^+$ B cell is characterised by having high surface IgM and low surface IgD densities (Hayakawa *et al.*, 1983). In spleens of NZB mice, which produce high levels of autoantibodies, the frequency of this population is significantly higher (up to 10 per cent splenic IgM^+ cells) (Hayakawa *et al.*, 1983).

There is a striking difference between Ly 1^+ and Ly 1^- B cells in terms of autoantibody and immune antibody production: Ly 1^+ B cells are responsible for virtually all spontaneous IgM secretion in NZB, as well as LPS-stimulated BALB/c, spleen cell populations, whereas immune antibodies are produced predominantly by the Ly 1^- population (Hayawaka *et al.*, 1983). Specificity studies of these autoantibodies have shown that they include thymocytotoxic and anti-DNA antibodies (Hayakawa *et al.*, 1984).

It is also interesting to note that these cells are more frequent in neonatal spleens. As other B cell subpopulations increase in frequency, the Ly 1^+ B cells are diluted out to a final frequency of about two per cent in adult spleens of non-NZB mice (Hayakawa *et al.*, 1983). This provides an additional explanation for the higher incidence of NAbs directed at autoantigens in neonatal mice (Section IV.C).

Although the Ly 1^+ B cell is rather infrequent in normal spleens, in the peritoneal cavity it represents approximately one-half of all the B cells (Hayakawa *et al.*, 1985). Peritoneal cells have long been known as a particularly good source of autoantibody-producing B cells (Lord and Dutton, 1975; Pages and Bussard, 1975; Steele and Cunningham, 1978). We have also been able to produce auto-antibody secreting hybridomas from peritoneal B cells (see Table 6.1).

Another cell associated with NAb production is the Lyb 5^+ B cell, which is lacking in mice bearing the X-linked immunodeficiency syndrome mutation (*xid*). These mice have lower levels of NAb and do not respond to immunisation with TI-2 antigens (Section IV.A). In terms of total splenic B cells, *xid* mice lack the surface IgM^{low}, IgD^{high} population normally considered to be the mature B cell population (Scher *et al.*, 1983), but their levels of Ly 1^+ B cells are similar to those of other mice. The relationship between these B cell populations is not clear at present. One study has shown that approximately 70 per cent of Ly 1^+ B cells are Lyb 5^+ (as determined by Lyb 5 antisera and complement depletion) and that the level of contribution of Lyb 5^+ B cells to different autoantibody specificities varies, from 96 per cent for anti-DNA antibodies to 67 per cent for anti-bromelain-treated red blood cell antibodies (Smith *et al.*, 1985).

It appears, therefore, that IgM autoantibodies are produced by Ly 1^+ Lyb 5^+ B cells. How these relate to the studies using monoclonal NAbs has not been examined yet. However, it is clear that not all NAbs are produced by this cell population. Included in the exceptions would be the non-IgM NAbs.

IV. REGULATION OF NATURAL ANTIBODY PRODUCTION

From the discussion in Section II it is evident that NAbs are a heterogeneous population in terms of their specificities. This can also be extended to their origin (Section III). It is therefore not surprising that different regulatory mechanisms should be operative in the maintenance of NAb levels. These include genetic, T-cell-dependent and T-cell-independent regulatory mechanisms.

A. T cell Regulation

Several laboratories have shown that the production of NAb is T-cell-independent. NAbs are found in normal quantities in the serum of nude mice, as well as in adult thymectomised, irradiated, and bone-marrow-reconstituted mice (ATXBM) (Gallo and Reitz, 1982; Ando *et al.*, 1978; Martin and Martin, 1974). The antigens tested include induced and spontaneous tumours, as well as haptens. Although the production of NAbs may be T-independent, their levels may be regulated by T suppressor cells (Ménard *et al.*, 1977; Colnaghi *et al.*, 1982; Cunningham, 1976; Colnaghi *et al.*, 1977). This has not, however, been a universal finding (Wolosin and Greenberg, 1981; Colnaghi *et al.*, 1977). Ménard *et al.*, (1977) found that levels of NAb to a syngeneic fibrosarcoma were higher in older BALB/c mice than in young mice, and that T-deprivation of young mice resulted in levels as high as those in 40 week old mice. Levels of anti-thymocyte NAb were, however, not influenced by T cell deprivation. (Colnaghi, *et al.*, 1977). In fact, transfer of young T cells into older mice resulted in lower fibrosarcoma-reactive NAb levels and higher thymocytotoxic NAb levels. T cell suppression of NAb levels has also been documented for NAbs reactive with the EL4 lymphoma (Colnaghi *et al.*, 1982) and anti-erythrocyte antibodies (Cunningham, 1976). The analysis of DBA/2 NAb to syngeneic T cell lymphomas also did not reveal T cell regulation (Wolosin and Greenberg, 1981).

B. Genetic Regulation

1. Studies with mutant mice

The use of mice with immunological deficiencies due to a genetic mutation has proven to be useful in the study of the role of various immunological systems. In relation to NAbs, the models that have been most often used are the nude (*nu*) mutation (see Section IV.A) and the X-linked immunodeficiency (*xid*) mutation in the CBA/N mouse.

CBA/N mice, bearing the *xid* mutation, were found to be incapable of producing antibodies to certain T-independent antigens, termed TI-2 antigens, including pneumococcal polysaccharides, and polyriboino-sinic: polyribocytidilic acid (poly I:C). Other thymus-independent antigens which do elicit a response in CBA/N mice have been designated TI-1 antigens (Berning *et al.*, 1980; Scher, 1982). Mice affected by the *xid* mutation have lower levels of antibodies to tumours (Martin and Martin, 1975c), and are unresponsive to LPS stimulation for a variety of autoantibodies (Marshall-Clarke *et al.*, 1979). The *xid* gene, when congenic in the autoimmune strain NZB, resulted in a much lower level of autoantibody production (Taurog *et al.*, 1981). Although this mutation results in some clear NAb deficiencies, the lack of NAb production and LPS responsiveness is not universal. For example, spontaneous plaque-forming cells to bromelain-treated mouse red blood cells could be stimulated with LPS, although not to the same extent as in normal mice (Rosenberg, 1979). We have also shown that *xid/* − F1 males do respond to LPS by producing antibody to a murine lymphoma (Greenberg and Chow, 1985) but, as with the results of Rosenberg (1979), the increases were not as pronounced as in F1 females or normal CBA/J mice. As discussed in Section III.E, CBA/N mice are deficient in a subpopulation of cells characterised by the Lyb 5 marker. Although initially it was assumed that this deficiency was absolute, more recent findings have shown that a small number of Lyb 5^+ B cells are present in *xid*-bearing mice and that there are qualitative differences between the Lyb 5^- cells of *xid* and normal mice (Smith *et al.*, 1985; Hardy *et al.*, 1983; Ono *et al.*, 1983). This provides an explanation for the fact that their unresponsiveness is not absolute. CBA/N mice also lack the autoantibody-producing Ly 1^+ B cells in the peritoneum (Hayakawa *et al.*, 1986). It has also been possible to examine the effect of the *nu* mutation in a model using double mutant mice which bear both the nude and the *xid* mutation (Wortis *et al.*, 1982; Mond *et al.*, 1982). The fact that these mice had very low serum immunoglobulin levels, as well as low LPS responsiveness, suggests that a sub-population of B cells producing NAb may be controlled by the *nu* locus. Hardy *et al.*, (1984) have developed one model, using monoclonal antibodies against B cell lineage associated antigens (BLA 1 and BLA2), and were able to distinguish deficiencies in CBA/N mice (lacking BLA 1^-2^- and BLA 1^+2^- cells) and CBA/*nu* mice (lacking BLA 1^-2^+ cells, but having more BLA 1^-2^- cells).

2. Other genetic models

The variation in the levels of NAb in different inbred strains of mice suggested that the production of NAb might be under genetic control. Studies of the genetics of NAb production have included viral, hapten, and tumour antibodies. In a genetic analysis of anti-MuLV antibodies, Nowinski *et al.*, (1976) found that in backcrosses (C57L × (AKR × C57L)), the mice could be segregated into those containing infectious MuLV, and those that were virus-negative. The virus-infected mice were all NAb-positive, while the virus-free included both antibody-positive and antibody-negative progeny. Further studies (Nowinski, 1976) revealed that the antibody producers could be divided into high and low producers. The level of antibody production was associated with the $SS^{h/l}$ and $SS^{l/l}$ phenotypes, respectively.

The genetics of the natural thymocytotoxic antibody (NTA) system has been studied extensively, since it was suggested that these antibodies might play a role in the pathogenesis of the autoimmune disease characteristic of strains, such as the NZB, which produce excessive amounts thereof. Genetic analysis revealed, however, that many mice had high levels of NTA, and that the amount of NTA found did not correlate with the presence or absence of autoimmune disease (Eisenberg *et al.*, 1979). In addition, studies of *xid*/NZB congenic mice showed that, although these mice had lower amounts of NTA, the T cell abnormalities seen in normal NZB controls were not abrogated (Taurog *et al.*, 1981). In genetic backcross studies between NZB (high NTA producers) and DBA/2 (low NTA producers), the frequency of NTA producers was intermediate, consistent with a co-dominant pattern of inheritance (Raveche *et al.*, 1978). No evidence for H-2 linkage was found. These studies also showed that the production of anti-DNA and anti-erythrocyte antibodies was regulated independently from that of NTA.

Genetic studies of antitumour NAbs have been carried out in several laboratories, including our own. It was noted initially that the levels of NAb detected were dependent on the strain–tumour combination that was used (Martin and Martin, 1975b; Wolosin and Greenberg, 1981). In an analysis of NAb reactive with a DBA/2 lymphoma, it was found that strains such as CBA/J ($H-2^k$) and C57B1/6 ($H-2^b$) were high producers, and the DBA/2 ($H-2^d$) strain was a low producer (Wolosin and Greenberg, 1981). Analysis of genetic backcrosses revealed a recessive mode of inheritance of high NAb levels, and it was found that low levels of NAb were associated with the $H-2^d$ haplotype. These studies also included an analysis of serum NAb levels of congenic mice, and these confirmed the association of low NAb levels with the $H-2^d$ haplotype.

More recent studies from our laboratory have extended these findings further by combining the effect of the H-2-controlled gene with that of the *xid* mutation, in an analysis of serum NAb reactivity against the $H-2^d$ lymphoma L5178Y (Greenberg and Chow, 1985). It was found that while (CBA/N × CBA/J) F1 males were responsive to LPS induction of NAb,

(CBA/N × DBA/2) F1 males were not. In backcross studies, the frequency of LPS responders was consistent with the frequencies expected on the basis that the H-2^d haplotype was associated with low responsiveness. The interpretation from these studies was that at least two populations of anti-L5178Y-reactive NAbs exist, one controlled by H-2^d, and one by the *xid* locus (Figure 6.1).

Results from other laboratories have led to some different interpretations of the inheritance pattern of tumour-reactive NAbs. For example, Colnaghi *et al.*, (1977) found that high NAb levels were inherited in a dominant pattern, in contrast to the recessive inheritance seen in our studies (Wolosin and Greenberg, 1981). These differences may reflect the heterogeneity of the NAb populations examined, as well as of the tumours, and their subclones.

The last system to be discussed in this section is that of the anti-hapten NAb. These studies, carried out primarily by Mäkelä and colleagues, have provided some interesting results, comparing NAb with induced antibody production. The high antibody level found in normal serum to oxazalone was inherited recessively and was allotype-linked, in contrast to induced antibodies, high levels of which were inherited dominantly (Jormalainen and Mäkelä, 1971; Mäkelä and Imanishi, 1975; Ando *et al.*, 1978). Studies with antibodies to (4-hydroxy-3-nitrophenyl) acetyl NP confirmed the difference in the genetics between induced and naturally occurring antibodies in that high and low affinity anti-NP antibodies were distributed in a co-dominant fashion in F1 hybrids of high and low affinity NAb producing parental strains. Again, in contrast to the NAb pattern, induced antibodies were dominant for the high-affinity strain.

In conclusion, these various genetic models confirm that different genetic mechanisms regulate NAb production, as is expected in view of the heterogeneous nature of NAbs.

V. BIOLOGICAL ROLE OF NATURAL ANTIBODIES

The prevalence of NAbs in all species examined raises the question of their function. The nature of the antigens identified as being NAb-reactive, such as environmental bacteria and aged or damaged erythrocytes, suggests that its antibodies may have various physiological and defensive functions.

A. Physiological Role

Depletion of circulating aged, damaged cells, as well as degradation products, is one of the major physiological functions ascribed to NAbs

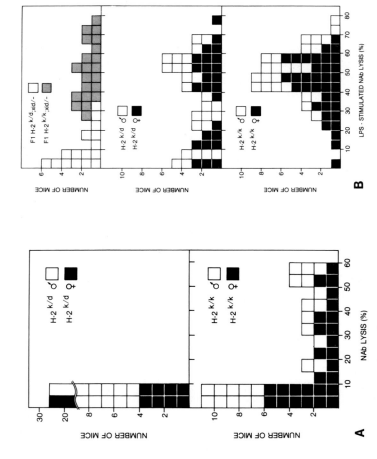

Fig. 6.1A: NAb levels to the L5178Y(H-2^d) tumour in individual mice of the female (CBA/N × DBA/2)F$_1$ × male CBA/N backcross mating. Half of the H-2$^{k/k}$-typed progeny had suppressed NAb levels. All H-2$^{k/d}$ were low but in the normal range of (CBA/J × DBA/2)F$_1$ (H-2$^{k/d}$) mice.

Fig. 6.1B: NAb levels in LPS-stimulated backcrosses. All H-2$^{k/k}$ progeny were LPS-responsive. All H-2$^{k/k}$ progeny were LPS-responsive even though 50% of male and females were *xid/xid*. The H-2$^{k/d}$ progeny were partially responsive, with about 40% exhibiting an NAb lysis of less than 30%. All (CBA/J × DBA/2)F$_1$

(Grabar, 1975; Kay, 1975; Grabar, 1983; Khansari and Fudenberg, 1983a, b). Khansari and Fudenberg (1983a, b) and Kay (1975) have demonstrated that NAb-coated erythrocytes are phagocytosed by macrophages. The antibodies involved in this interaction are predominantly of the IgG class. These studies have included separating young and old erythrocytes from the circulation, as well as artificially aging the erythrocytes, and it was shown that the NAb involved in this opsonisation only bound to naturally aged or enzyme-treated erythrocytes (Kay, 1975). Kay (1975) determined that the IgG from normal human serum responsible for the enhanced phagocytosis was bound in situ to senescent erythrocytes. The anti-α-galactose IgG identified by Galili *et al.*, (1984, 1985) was in relatively high quantities in all normal human sera (one per cent of total IgG, with a titre ranging from 1:800 to 1:1600). This antibody did not bind to normal human red blood cells, not a surprising finding in view of its high titre. It did bind, however, to pronase-treated human red blood cells, as well as to thalassaemic red blood cells, which resemble prematurely aged erythrocytes (Kahane *et al.*, 1980). Although these authors did not carry out studies of phagocytosis by monocytes, it is likely that this antibody is involved in such a function, and representative of the antibody populations described by others.

A role for NAbs in the elimination of aging platelets has also been described (Khansari and Fudenberg, 1983c). In these studies, removal of IgG bound to aging platelets in situ reduced their phagocytosis by autologous monocytes. This antibody could be eluted from senescent red blood cells, indicating that elimination of senescent platelets and red blood cells may be enhanced by the same antibody population.

B. Resistance to Bacterial Infection

A role for NAb in host resistance to bacterial infection is suggested by the fact that many of the specificities that have been identified are those of bacterial antigens (Springer and Tegtmeyer, 1981; Challacombe *et al.*, 1984; Schoolnik *et al.*, 1979; Galili *et al.*, 1985; Carroll *et al.*, 1985; Lieberman *et al.*, 1974; Springer, 1971; Hoskins and Boulding, 1976). It has been argued that the bacterial species commonly associated with NAb reactivity are generally non-pathogenic. However, the relationship between their non-pathogenicity and NAb reactivity needs to be considered.

In an elegant series of experiments, Briles and co-workers have demonstrated the importance of natural serum antibodies in resistance of mice to pneumococcal infections (Briles *et al.*, 1982; Yother *et al.*, 1981; Briles *et al.*, 1981a, b). *S. pneumoniae* is non-pathogenic for most strains of mice, but *xid* mice are 1000 to 10,000 times as susceptible to lethal infections with it, and this susceptibility is associated with reduced NAb levels (Yother *et al.*, 1981; Briles *et al.*, 1981a). Yother *et al.*, (1981) demonstrated that resistance in *xid* mice could be passively acquired with the transfer of normal serum from non-*xid* mice. They extended these findings by passive immunisation with monoclonal antibodies produced against this bacterial strain, and found that the most protective ones were those that were positive for the T15 idiotype, which is representative of the natural anti-pneumococcal antibody population (Briles *et al.*, 1982). Antibodies in human serum that have been implicated in a bacterial resistance function are those against *S. mutans* (Challacombe *et al.*, 1984), an organism which is thought to play an important role in the aetiology of dental caries. Antibodies to this strain are present in all humans, but the titre is significantly greater in individuals with a low frequency of caries than in individuals with a high frequency (Challacombe, 1980).

C. Natural resistance to tumours[1]

That resistance to tumours could be mediated by natural (pre-existing) rather than immune-mediated mechanisms was suggested when it became obvious that mice deficient in thymus-mediated immune responses were not more susceptible to a higher incidence of spontaneous tumours (Stutman, 1974; Rygaard and Povlsen, 1976). Natural killer (NK) cells are thought to be one of the major effector mechanisms for natural resistance, but several groups have proposed that NAbs may also be active (Martin and Martin, 1975b; Aoki *et al.*, 1966; Wolosin and Greenberg, 1981; Ménard *et al.*, 1977; Chow *et al.*, 1981a).

Assays of natural resistance to tumours have included the small tumour cell inoculum assay (Schrater *et al.*, 1979; Chow *et al.*, 1981b; Greenberg and Greene, 1976), in which the incidence, latency and size of tumours, and the time of host death can be examined. However, since this type of experimental design involves relatively long periods of time, a T-cell-mediated influence cannot always be excluded. The use of nude or ATXBM mice has been useful in overcoming this problem (Ménard *et al.*, 1977). The development of the in vivo radio-labelled tumour elimination assay (Chow *et al.*, 1981a; Hofer *et al.*, 1969; Hofer and Hughes, 1971; Carlson and Wegmann, 1977) has provided a convenient system in which to study natural resistance since the time of the assay is relatively short, ranging from hours (if the tumour is injected intraven-

[1] See also Chapters 3, 5, and 25.

ously) (Riccardi *et al.*, 1980) to 3–4 days (if the intraperitoneal, subcutaneous or intra-footpad route is used) (Chow *et al.*, 1981b; Gorelik and Herberman, 1981). These assays, in combination with assays measuring tumour cell susceptibility to various effector mechanisms in vitro have provided the basic approach to the study of the role of NAbs in tumour resistance.

The hypothesis that NAbs are involved in tumour resistance is supported by findings from our laboratory, as well as others. The initial evidence for the role of NAbs came from studies showing correlations between serum NAb levels and tumour resistance. This has been shown to be the case with virally induced tumours (Aoki *et al.*, 1966), transplanted fibrosarcomas (Ménard *et al.*, 1977; Berning *et al.*, 1980), and lymphomas (Chow *et al.*, 1981b). Furthermore, an inverse correlation was found between the sensitivity of cloned tumour lines to in vitro NAb and complement or in vivo NAb binding and host resistance (Chow *et al.*, 1981b; Miller *et al.*, 1983). Recent experiments demonstrated that the reduced tumour binding of serum NAb from *xid* B-cell-deficient CBA/N mutant mice, compared with the normal CBA/J strain, corresponded with a higher frequency of tumours threshold after inocula (Figure 6.2). Analysis of the genetic and ontogenetic properties of natural resistance to NK-cell-resistant tumours indicated that they correlated more closely with NAb activity than with NK activity (Chow *et al.*, 1981a). We have taken advantage of the membrane antigen modulating properties of interferons to examine in more detail the role of NAbs in natural resistance to NK-cell-resistant tumours. Interferon treatment of

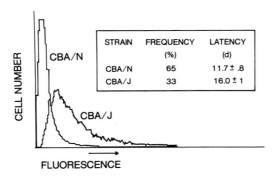

Fig. 6.2: Natural antibody binding and resistance to syngeneic RI(H-2^k) lymphoma in CBA/N (H-2$^{k/k}$; *xid/xid*) and CBA/J (H-2$^{k/k}$; +/+) mice. The RI-28 radiation-induced leukaemia cells were incubated in serum from each strain, then FACS analysed using both fluoresceinated goat anti-IgG and anti-IgM specific antisera. Tumour frequencies of the RI-28 were calculated following subcutaneous inoculation of 10^4 cells and inversely correlated with NAb binding.

the L5178Y-F9 lymphoma, which renders tumours NK-cell-resistant, resulted in increased in vitro NAb binding (Miller *et al.*, 1983). Figure 6.3 shows that interferon-treated L5178Y-F9 tumour cells are rejected more rapidly than control cells in a dose-dependent manner. More recent studies (Chow *et al.*, 1983; Chow, 1984a, b; Brown and Chow, 1985) have extended these findings to in vivo and in vitro selection models. It was found that an NK-cell-resistant tumour which had been passaged in vivo,

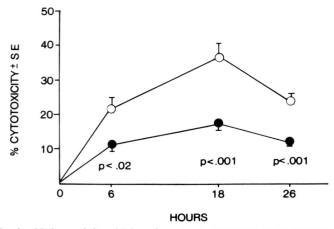

Fig. 6.3A: In vivo NAb reactivity with interferon-treated L5178Y. The L5178Y lymphoma was preincubated with 4000 (u/mL) IFN-containing (O) or control medium (•) for 20 hours then 5×10^6 cells were injected intraperitoneally. Tumour cells were recovered at various times, washed and exposed to rabbit complement. These results were confirmed using ^{125}I-labelled protein-A binding.

in subcutaneous or intraperitoneal sites, exhibited a reduced sensitivity to natural resistance as well as to NAb and complement (Chow *et al.*, 1983; Chow, 1984a). In vitro NAb and complement selection from phorbol ester generated tumour variants produced cells that were more resistant in the rapid elimination assay of natural resistance (Chow, 1984b), while positive selection for high NAb binding subpopulations through fluorescence activated cell sorting yielded less tumorigenic cells (Tough and Chow, 1988). These studies were interpreted to support the hypothesis that NAbs may participate in tumour resistance in vivo, as well as in the selection of variants generated during tumour progression. More direct evidence for the role of NAbs in resistance to a small tumour cell inoculum came from experiments where pretreatment of tumour cells with syngeneic NAb resulted in a lower tumour frequency (Chow *et al.*, 1981a). The conclusion from these studies was that natural resistance is a heterogeneous phenomenon, in which both NK cells (or other naturally cytotoxic cells) and NAbs may play a role. The model of bone-marrow resistance developed by Warner and Dennert (1985) provides another example of how both mechanisms may be acting in combination. We have observed NAb-dependent cell-mediated cytotoxicity against syngeneic tumours using nylon wool passaged spleen cells, and normal serum-coated target cells. Although the levels of cytotoxicity were low, they were in keeping with other studies in which immune

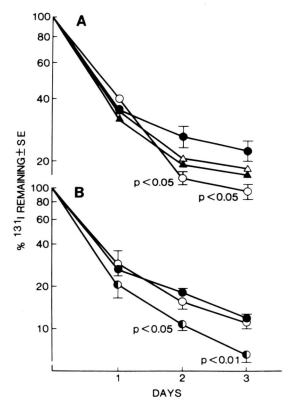

Fig. 6.3B: Resistance of syngeneic DBA/2 mice to interferon-treated L5178Y lymphoma. [131]IdUrd-labelled cells (10^6) were injected into groups of 8- to 10-week-old DBA/2 mice (5 mice/group). (A) The difference between the ^{131}I remaining after injection of cells treated for 20 h with 8000 U IFN/mL (O) and the ^{131}I remaining after injection of untreated (control) tumour cells (•) was statistically significant on days 1 and 2. ▲ = cells treated with 1000 U IFN/mL; △ = cells treated with 100 U IFN/mL. (B) One hour treatment with 8000 U IFN/mL (O) did not result in enhanced ^{131}I elimination on any day. ◑ = cells treated with 8000 U IFN/mL for 20 h; • = untreated (control) tumour cells.

antisera were used (Brunda *et al.*, 1981). That NAbs and NK cells can mediate tumour resistance independently of each other cannot, however, be ruled out. This could possibly be the case in situations where the host is NK-deficient or depleted, and yet able to express natural resistance. Since anti-receptor antibodies seen in autoimmune diseases are known to alter cell function (Blecher and Bar, 1981) it is interesting to speculate that naturally occurring antibodies could affect tumour cells through interference with cell-surface receptors required for essential functions.

Thus, these studies support the hypothesis that NAbs function in natural resistance and suggest mechanisms by which they might do so.

VI. CONCLUSIONS

Natural antibodies are a ubiquitous and, in some ways, enigmatic group of antibodies. They appear to be phylogenetically primitive and have a wide range of distribution in vertebrate species from Agnatha to Mammalia, yet their origins and physiological role remain for the most part undefined. Their importance is suggested by the broad range of specificities recognised, including antigens on environmental pathogens, autologous and neoplastic cells. On the other hand, at the molecular level they recognise common structural features such as specific carbohydrate sequences, alpha helices and phosphate esters, which may or may not have physiological or pathological significance. Much the same can be said of their reactivity with synthetic haptens. This remarkable repertoire has been interpreted as a possible clue to their origin, which includes such hypotheses as autologous or environmental stimulation, and non-specific activation of B cells expressing autoreactive specificities determined by germ-line immunoglobulin V region sequences. At least some B cells expressing the Ly 1$^+$ phenotype produce natural antibodies and can therefore be distinguished from B cells producing immune antibody. This approach of identifying NAb-producing B cells by means of lineage markers, rather than on the basis of their specificity, may help clarify the origins of the NAb repertoire and the genetic control of NAb production. Indeed, a subclassification that distinguishes NAb originating from environmental stimulation from that appearing as a result of autologous activation may be possible with the Ly 1$^+$ B cell lineage. The heterogeneity of the B cell populations producing these antibodies undoubtedly has also led to the description of numerous and varied genetic patterns of regulation.

The biological relevance of natural antibodies remains uncertain. However, the most appealing hypotheses take into account the nature of their specificities for antigens associated with damaged membranes to propose a physiological role in removal of dead and dying cells, as well as abnormal cells with significant alterations in their membrane carbohydrate or protein antigens. A more difficult case to consider, from the view point of its origins and its biological role, is the autoreactive natural antibody. Here one can consider that the autoreactivity is a result of low level cross-reactions to more relevant pathogens in the environment. In this situation, natural autoreactivity would be widespread and maintained at low levels because of active suppression (Cunningham, 1976) or B cell silencing (Goodnow *et al.*, 1988), having little opportunity to damage autologous tissues. Natural antibody of this origin could be considered as an undesirable consequence of the primary response to a pathogen. An alternative view is that the autoreactive natural antibodies have some important role in regulating immune responses. This could take the form of actively maintaining B cell populations by stimulation through natural auto-anti-idiotypic antibodies (Rodkey, 1980). Another possibility is that autoreactivity is necessary for the triggering of B cells, such that this endogenous priming by autoantigen would offer survival advantage by stimulating B cell precursors before confrontation with cross-reacting foreign pathogens. These questions offer interesting challenges to investigators in this field of study.

ACKNOWLEDGMENTS

This work has been supported by the NCI and MRC of Canada.

REFERENCES

Agnello, V., Arbetter, A., Ibanez de Kasep, G., Powell, R., Tan, E. M. and Joslin, F. (1980). Evidence for a subset of rheumatoid factors that cross-react with DNA-histone and have a distinct cross-idiotype. *J. Exp. Med.* 151: 1514.

Ando I., Erdei, J., Mäkelä, O. and Fachet, J. (1978). Correlations between the genetic control of natural and oxazolone-induced antibody production. *Eur. J. Immunol.* 8: 101.

Aoki, T., Boyse, E. A., and Old, L. J. (1966). Occurrence of natural antibody to the G (Gross) Leukemia Antigen in mice. *Cancer Research* 26: 1415.

Arnold, R., Mestecky, J. and McGhee, J. R. (1976). Naturally occurring secretory immunoglobulin A antibodies to *Streptococcus mutans* in human colostrum and saliva. *Infect. Immun.* 14: 355.

Barbacid, M., Bolgnesi, D. and Aaronson, S. A. (1980). Humans have antibodies capable of recognizing oncoviral glycoproteins: Demonstration that these antibodies are formed in response to cellular modification of glycoproteins rather than as a consequence of exposure to virus. *Proc. Natl. Acad. Sci. USA* 77: 1617.

Berning, A., Eicher, E., Paul, W. and Scher, J. (1980). Mapping of the X-linked immune deficiency mutation (*Xid*) of CBA/N mice. *J. Immunol.* 124: 1875.

Blecher, M. and Bar, R. S. (1981). Antireceptor antibodies in autoimmune diseases. In *Receptors and Human Disease*. Baltimore: Williams and Wilkins: 186–265.

Bottomly, K. (1984). All idiotypes are equal, but some are more equal than others. *Immunol. Rev.* 79: 45.

Bray, J., Lemieux, R. U. and McPherson, T. A. (1981). Use of a synthetic hapten in the demonstration of the Thomsen-Friedenreich (T) antigen on neuramini-dase-treated human red blood cells and lymphocytes. *J. Immunol.* 126: 1966.

Bretscher, P. A. (1978). Requirement for antigen in lipopolysaccharide-dependent induction of B cells. *Eur. J. Immunol.* 8: 534.

Briles, D. E., Nahm, M., Schroer, D., Davie, J., Baker, P., Kearney, J. and Barletta, R. (1981a). Antiphosphocholine antibodies found in normal mouse serum are protective against intravenous infection with Type 3 *Streptococcus pneumoniae*. *J. Exp. Med.* 153: 694.

Briles, D. E., Claflin, J. L., Schroer, K. and Forman, C. (1981b). Mouse IgG$_3$ antibodies are highly protective against infection with *Streptococcus pneumoniae*. *Nature* 294: 88.

Briles, D. E., Forman, C., Hudak, S. and Claflin, J. L. (1982). Antiphosphorylcholine antibodies of the T15 idiotype are optimally protective against *Streptococcus pneumoniae*. *J. Exp. Med.* 156: 1177.

Brown, G. W. and Chow, D. A. (1985). Characterization of tumor progression from threshold tumor inocula: Evidence for natural resistance. *Int. J. Cancer* 35: 385.

Brunda, M. J., Herberman, R. B. and Holden, H. T. (1981). Antibody induced augmentation of murine natural killer cell activity. *Int. J. Cancer* 27: 205.

Carlson, G. A. and Wegmann, T. G. (1977). Rapid *in vivo* destruction of semi-syngeneic and allogeneic cells by nonimmunized mice as a consequence of nonidentity at H-2. *J. Immunol.* 118: 2130.

Carroll, P., Stafford, D., Schwartz, R. S. and Stollar, B. D. (1985). Murine monoclonal anti-DNA autoantibodies bind to endogenous bacteria. *J. Immunol.* 135: 1086.

Carson, D. A., Pasquali, J. L., Tsoukas, C. D. *et al.* (1981). Physiology and pathology of rheumatoid factors. *Springer Semin. Immunopath.* 4: 161.

Cerny-Provaznik, R., Radl, J., van Mourk, P., Leupers, T., Brondijk, R., de Greeve, P. and Ivanyi, P. (1985a). Anti-major histocompatibility complex immunity detected prior to intentional alloimmunization: I: Naturally occurring H-2 specific antibodies in C57Bl/KaLwRij (H-2^b) mice. *Nat. Immun. Cell Growth Regul.* 4: 138.

Cerny-Provaznik, R., van Mourik, P., Radl, J., Leupers, T., Limpens, J. C. and Ivanyi, P. (1985b). Anti-major histocompatibility complex immunity detected prior to intentional alloimmunization: II: Monoclonal H-2 specific antibodies obtained from an unimmunized C57Bl/KaLw/Rij (H-2^b) mouse. *Nat . Immun. Cell Growth Regul.* 4: 160.

Cerny-Provaznik, R. C. van Mourik, P., Limpens, J., Leupers, T. and Ivanyi, P. (1985c). Anti-MHC immunity detected prior to intentional alloimmunization: III: Natural autoreactive H-2 specific antibodies. *Immunogenetics.* In press.

Challacombe, S. J. (1980). Serum and saliva antibodies to *Streptococcus mutans* in relation to the development and treatment of human dental caries. *Archs. Oral Biol.* 25: 495.

Challacombe, S. J. and Tomasi, T. B. (1980). Systemic tolerance and secretory immunity after oral immunization. *J. Exp. Med.* 152: 1459.

Challacombe, S. J., Bergmeier, L. A., Czerkinsky, C. and Rees, A. S. (1984). Natural antibodies in man to *Streptococcus mutans*: specificity and quantification. *Immunology* 52: 143.

Chow, D. A. (1984a). Tumor selection *in vivo* for reduced sensitivity to natural resistance and natural antibodies. *J. Natl. Cancer Inst.* 72: 339.

Chow, D. A. (1984b). Variant generation and selection: An *in vitro* model of tumor progression. *Int. J. Cancer* 33: 541.

Chow, D. A., Wolosin, L. B. and Greenberg, A. H. (1981a). Genetics, regulation, and specificity of murine natural antitumor antibodies and natural killer cells. *J. Natl. Cancer Inst.* 67: 445.

Chow, D. A., Wolosin, L. B. and Greenberg, A. H. (1981b). Murine natural antitumor antibodies: II: The contribution of natural antibodies to tumor surveillance. *Int. J. Cancer* 27: 459.

Chow, D. A., Ray, M. and Greenberg, A. H. (1983). *In vivo* generation and selection of variants with altered sensitivity to natural resistance (NR): A model of tumor progression. *Int. J. Cancer* 31: 99.

Clagett, J. A. and Engel, D. (1978). Polyclonal activation: a form of primitive immunity and its possible role in pathogenesis of inflammatory disease. *Dev. Comp. Immunol.* 2: 235.

Cleveland, W. L., Wassermann, N. H., Sarangarajan, R., Penn, A. S. and

Erlanger, B. F. (1983). Monoclonal antibodies to the acetylcholine receptor by a normally functioning auto-anti-idiotypic mechanism. *Nature* 305: 56.

Colnaghi, M. I., Ménard, S. and Della Porta, G. (1977). Natural antitumor serum reactivity in BALB/c mice: II: Control by regulatory T-cells. *Int. J. Cancer* 19: 275.

Colnaghi, M. I., Ménard, S., Tagliabue, E. and Della Torre, G. (1982). Heterogeneity of the natural humoral anti-tumor immune response in mice as shown by monoclonal antibodies. *J. Immunol.* 128: 2757.

Corley, R. B. (1985). Somatic diversification of B cells: a role for autoreactive T lymphocytes. *Immunol. Today* 6: 178.

Coulie, P. and Van Snick, J. (1983). Rheumatoid factors and secondary immune responses in the mouse: II: Incidence, kinetics and induction mechanisms. *Eur. J. Immunol.* 13: 895.

Coulie, P. G. and Van Snick, J. (1985). Rheumatoid Factor (RF) production during anamnestic immune responses in the mouse: III: Activation of RF precursor cells is induced by their interaction with immune complexes and carrier-specific helper T cells. *J. Exp. Med.* 161: 88.

Crews, S., Griffin, J., Juang, H., Calame, K. and Hood, L. (1981). A single V_H gene segment encodes the immune response to phosphorylcholine: somatic mutation is correlated with the class of the antibody. *Cell* 25: 59.

Cunliffe, D. and Cox, K. O. (1980). IgM-autoantibodies against isologous erythrocytes also react with isologous IgG(Fc). *Nature* 286: 720.

Cunningham, A. J. (1974). Large numbers of cells in normal mice produce antibody components of isologous erythrocytes. *Nature* 252: 749.

Cunningham, A. J. (1976). Self-tolerance maintained by active suppressor mechanisms. *Transplant. Rev.* 31: 24.

Davis, M. M. and Bjorkman, P. J. (1988). T-cell antigen receptor genes and T-cell recognition. *Nature* 334: 395.

De Maeyer-Guignard, J., Chachard-Thomas, A. and De Maeyer, E. (1984). Naturally occurring anti-interferon antibodies in Lou/c rats. *J. Immunol.* 133: 775.

Diamond, B. and Scharff, M. D. (1984). Somatic mutation of the T15 heavy chain gives rise to an antibody with autoantibody specificity. *Proc. Natl. Acad. Sci. USA* 81: 5841.

Dighiero, G., Lymberi, P., Mazié, J. C., Rouyre, S., Butler-Browne, G. S., Whalen, R. G. and Avrameas, S. (1983). Murine hybridomas secreting natural monoclonal antibodies reacting with self antigens. *J. Immunol.* 131: 2267.

Dighiero, G., Lymberi, P., Holmberg, D., Lundquist, I., Coutinho, A. and

Avrameas, S. (1985). High frequency of natural autoantibodies in normal newborn mice. *J. Immunol.* 134: 765.

Dighiero, G., Poncet, P., Rouyre, S. and Mazie, J. C. (1986). Newborn Xid mice carry the genetic information for the production of natural autoantibodies against DNA, cytoskeletal proteins, and TNP. *J. Immunol.* 136: 4000.

Dresser, D. W. (1978). Most IgM-producing cells in the mouse secrete auto-antibodies (rheumatoid factor). Nature 274: 480.

Dwyer, D. S., Bradley, R. J., Urquhart, C. K. and Kearney, J. F. (1983). Naturally occurring anti-idiotypic antibodies in myasthenia gravis patients. *Nature* 301: 611.

Dziarski, R. (1982a). Preferential induction of autoantibody secretion in polyclonal activation by peptidoglycan and lipopolysaccharide: I: In vitro studies. *J. Immunol.* 128: 1018.

Dziarski, R. (1982b). Preferential induction of autoantibody secretion in polyclonal activation by peptidoglycan and lipopolysaccharide: II: In vivo studies. *J. Immunol.* 128: 1026.

Eisenberg, R. A., Theofilopoulos, A. N., Andrews, B. S., Peters, C. J., Thor., L. and Dixon, F. J. (1979). Natural thymocytotoxic autoantibodies in autoimmune and normal mice. *J. Immunol.* 122: 2272.

Eldridge, J. H., Kiyono, H., Michalek, S. M. and McGhee, J. R. (1983). Evidence for a mature B cell subpopulation in Peyer's patches of young adult Xid mice. *J. Exp. Med.* 157: 789.

Faaber, P., Capel, P. J. A., Rijke, G. P. M., Vierwinden, G., Van de Putte, L. B. A. and Koene, R. A. P. (1984). Cross-reactivity of anti-DNA antibodies with proteoglycans. *Clin. Exp. Immnol.* 5: 502.

Ferrone, S., Pellegrino, M. A. and Mittal, K. K. (1976). Natural antibodies to human lymphocytes in murine strains. *J. Natl. Cancer Inst.* 56: 75.

Forster, I., Gu, H. and Rajewski, K. (1988). Germline antibody V regions as determinants of clonal persistence and malignant growth in the B cell compartment. *EMBO* 7: 3693.

Galili, U., Rachmilewitz, E. A., Peleg, A. and Flechner, I. (1984). A unique natural human IgG antibody with anti-α-galactosyl specificity. *J. Exp. Med.* 160: 1519.

Galili, E., Macher, B. A., Buehler, J. and Shohet, S. B. (1985). Human natural anti-α-galactosyl IgG: II: The specific recognition of $\alpha(1,3)$-linked galactose residues. *J. Exp. Med.* 162: 573.

Gallo, R. C. and Reitz, M. S. (1982). Human retroviruses and adult T-cell leukemia-lymphoma. *J. Natl. Cancer Inst.* 69: 1209.

Garzelli, C., Taub, F. E., Jenkins, M. C., Drell, D. W., Ginsberg-Fellner, F. and Notkins, A. L. (1986). Human monoclonal autoantibodies that react with both pancreatic islets and thyroid. *J. Clin. Invest.* 77: 1627.

Gearhart, P. J. and Cebra, J. J. (1979). Differentiated B lymphocytes potential to express particular antibody variable and constant regions depends on site of lymphoid tissue and antigen load. *J. Exp. Med.* 149: 216.

Gearhart, P. J., Johnson, N. D., Douglas, R. and Hood, L. (1981). IgG antibodies to phosphorylcholine exhibit more diversity than their IgM counterparts. *Nature* 291: 29.

Geha, R. S. (1982). Presence of auto-anti-idiotypic antibody during the normal human response to tetanus toxoid antigen. *J. Immunol.* 129: 139.

Goidl, E. A. and Siskind, G. W. (1974). Ontogeny of B-Lymphocyte function: I: Restricted heterogeneity of the antibody response of B lymphocytes from neonatal and fetal mice. *J. Exp. Med.* 140: 1285.

Goodnow, C. C., Crosbie, J., Adelstein, S., Lavoie, T. B., Smith-Gill, S. J., Brin, R. A., Pritchard-Briscoe, H., Wotherspoon, J. S., Loblay, R. H., Raphael, K., Trent, R. J. and Basten, A. (1988). Altered immunoglobulin expression and functional silencing of self-reactive B lymphocytes in transgenic mice. *Nature* 334: 676.

Gorelik, E. and Herberman, R. B. (1981). Radioisotope assay for evaluation of *in vivo* natural cell-mediated resistance of mice to local transplantation of tumor cells. *Int. J. Cancer.* 27: 709.

Grabar, P. (1975). Hypothesis: Auto-antibodies and immunological theories: An analytical review. *Clin. Immunol. Immunopath.* 4: 453.

Grabar, P. (1983). Autoantibodies and the physiological role of immunoglobulins. *Immunol. Today* 4: 337.

Greenberg, A. H. and Greene, M. (1976). Non-adaptive rejection of small tumour inocula as a model of immune surveillance. *Nature* 264: 356.

Greenberg, A. H. and Chow, D. A. (1985). Genetic regulation of natural anti-tumor antibodies: The role of H-2 and X-linked genes. In E. Skamene (ed.), *Genetic Control of Host Resistance to Infection and Malignancy.* New York: Alan R. Liss Inc: 713.

Grönberg, A., Hansson, M., Kiessling, R., Andersson, B. and Kärre, K. (1980). Demonstration of natural antibodies in normal rabbit serum with similar specificity pattern as mouse natural killer cells. *J. Natl. Cancer Inst.* 64: 1113.

Grönberg, A., Eriksson, E., Sinangil, F., Rönnholm, M., Feizi, T., Minden, P. and Kiessling, R. (1985). Comparison between murine natural antibodies and natural killer cells: Recognition of separate target structures as revealed by differential *in vitro* expression and dependence on glycosylation. *J. Natl. Cancer Inst.* 74: 67.

Gronowicz, E. and Coutinho, A. (1975). Functional analysis and B cell heterogeneity. *Transplant. Rev.* 24: 3.

Guilbert, B., Dighiero, G. and Avrameas, S. (1982). Naturally occurring antibodies against nine common antigens in human sera: I: Detection, isolation, and characterization. *J. Immunol.* 128: 2779.

Hamilton, R. G. and Adkinson, N. F. (1985). Naturally occurring carbohydrate antibodies: Interference in solid-phase immunoassays. *J. Immunol. Meth.* 77: 95.

Hang, L., Slack, J. H., Amundson, C., Izui, S., Theofilopoulos, A. N. and Dixon, F. J. (1983). Induction of murine autoimmune disease by chronic polyclonal B cell activation. *J. Exp. Med.* 157: 874.

Hannestad, K. and Stollar, B. D. (1978). Certain rheumatoid factors react with nucleosomes. *Nature* 275: 671.

Hardy, R. R., Hayakawa, K., Parks, D. R. and Herzenberg, L. A. (1983). Demonstration of B-cell maturation in X-linked immunodeficient mice by simultaneous three-colour immunofluorescence. *Nature* 306: 270.

Hardy, R. R., Hayakawa, K., Parks, D. R. and Herzenerg, L. A. (1984). Murine B cell differentiation lineages. *J Exp. Med.* 159: 1169.

Haspel, M. V., Onodera, T., Prabhakar, B. S., McClintock, P. R., Essani, K., Ray, U. R., Yagihashi, S. and Notkins, A. L. (1983). Multiple organ-reactive monoclonal autoantibodies. *Nature* 304: 73.

Hayakawa, K., Hardy, R. R., Parks, D. R. and Herzenberg, L. A. (1983). The 'Ly-1 B' cell subpopulation in normal, immunodefective, and autoimmune mice. *J. Exp. Med.* 157: 202.

Hayakawa, K., Hardy, R. R., Honda, M., Herzenberg, L. A., Steinberg, A. D. and Herzenberg, L. A. (1984). Ly-1 B cells: Functionally distinct lymphocytes that secrete IgM autoantibodies. *Proc. Natl. Acad. Sci. USA* 81: 2494.

Hayakawa, K., Hardy, R. R. and Herzenberg, L. A. (1985). Progenitors for Ly-1 B cells are distinct from progenitors for other B cells. *J. Exp. Med.* 161: 1554.

Hayakawa, K., Hardy, R. R. and Herzenberg, L. A. (1986). Peritoneal Ly-1 B cells: Genetic control, autoantibody production, increased lambda light chain expression. *Eur. J. Immunol.* 16: 450.

Herberman, R. B. and Aoki, T. (1972). Immune and natural antibodies to syngeneic murine plasma cell tumors. *J. Exp. Med.* 136: 94.

Hofer, K. G. and Hughes, W. L. (1971). Radiotoxicity of intranuclear Tritium, ^{125}Iodine and ^{131}Iodine. *Radiation Research* 47: 94.

Hofer, K. G., Presnky, W. and Hughes, W. (1969). Death and metastatic distribution of tumor cells in mice monitored with ^{125}I-Iododeoxyuridine. *J. Natl. Cancer Inst.* 43: 763.

Holmberg, D., Forsgren, S., Ivars, F. and Coutinho, A. (1984). Reactions among IgM antibodies derived from normal, neonatal mice. *Eur. J. Immunol.* 14: 435.

Hooijkaas, H., Benner, R., Pleasants, J. R. and Wostmann, B. S. (1984). Isotypes and specificities of immunoglobulins produced by germ-free mice fed chemically defined ultrafiltered 'antigenfree' diet. *Eur. J. Immunol.* 14: 1127.

Hoskins, L. C. and Boulding, E. T. (1976). Degradation of blood group antigens in human colon ecosystems: II: A gene interaction in man that affects the fecal population density of certain enteric bacteria. *J. Clin. Invest.* 57: 74.

Houghton, A. N., Taormina, M. C., Ikeda, H., Watanabe, T., Oettgen, H. F. and Old, L. J. (1980). Serological survey of normal humans for natural antibody to cell surface antigens of melanoma. *Proc. Natl. Acad. Sci. USA* 77: 4260.

Hubbard, S. C. and Ivatt, R. J. (1981). Synthesis and processing of asparagine-linked oligosaccharides. *Ann. Rev. Bioch.* 50: 555.

Hughes, R. C., Palmer, P. D. and Sanford, B. J. (1973). Factors involved in the cytotoxicity of normal guinea pig serum for cells of murine tumor TA3 subline treated with neuraminidase. *J. Immunol.* 111: 1071.

Ihle, J. and Hanna, M. G. Jr (1977). Natural immunity to endogenous oncoviruses in mice. *Contemporary Topics in Immunobiology* 6: 169.

Imai, Y., Nakano, T., Sawada, J. and Osawa, T. (1980). Specificity of natural thymocytotoxic autoantibody developed in New Zealand Black mice. *J. Immunol.* 124: 1556.

Ivanyi, P. van Mourik, P., Breuning, M., Kruisbeek, A. M. and Kröse, C. J. M. (1982). Natural H-2 specific antibodies in sera of aged mice. *Immunogenetics* 15: 95.

Izui, S., Kobayakawa, T., Louis, J. and Lambert, P-H. (1979). Induction of thymocytotoxic autoantibodies after injection of bacterial lipopolysaccharides in mice. *Eur. J. Immunol.* 9: 338.

Jackson S. and Mestecky, J. (1981). Oral-parenteral immunization leads to the appearance of IgG auto-anti-idiotypic cells in mucosal tissues. *Cell Immunol.* 60: 498.

Johnson, P. H. (1979). IgM-rheumatoid factors cross-reactive with IgG and a cell nuclear antigen: apparent 'masking' in original serum. *Scand. J. Immunol.* 9: 461.

Jones, C. (1984). Increased cytotoxicity of normal rabbit serum for lectin-resistant mutants of animal cells. *J. Exp. Med.* 160: 1241.

Jormalainen, S. and Mäkelä, O. (1971). Anti-hapten antibodies in normal sera. *Eur. J. Immunol.* 1: 471.

Kabat, E. A. (1976). *Structural Concepts in Immunochemistry.* New York: Holt, Rinehart and Winston: 174–89.

Kahane, E., Ben Chetrit, E., Shifter, A. and Rachmilewitz, E. A. (1980). The erythrocyte membrane in β-thalassemia. Lower sialic acid levels in glycophorins. *Biochim. Biophys. Acta.* 596: 10.

Kay, M. M. B. (1975). Mechanism of removal of senescent cells by human macrophages *in situ. Proc. Natl. Acad. Sci. USA* 72: 3521.

Khansari, N. and Fudenberg, H. H. (1983a). Phagocytosis of senescent erythrocytes by autologous monocytes: Requirement of membrane-specific autologous IgG for immune elimination of aging red bloodcells. *Cell Immunol.* 78: 114.

Khansari, N. and Fudenberg, H. H. (1983b). Immune elimination of autologous senescent erythrocytes by Kupffer cells *in vivo. Cell Immunol.* 80: 426.

Khansari, N. and Fudenberg, H. H. (1983c). Immune elimination of aging platelets by autologous monocytes: role of membrane-specific autoantibody. *Eur. J. Immunol.* 13: 990.

Kissick, W. L. (1961). Studies of the epidemiology of the rheumatoid factor. *Arthritis Rheum.* 4: 424.

Klassen, L. W., Krakauer, R. S. and Steinberg, A. D. (1977). Selective loss of suppressor cell function in New Zealand mice induced by NTA. *J. Immunol.* 119: 830.

Klinman, N. R. and Stone, M. R. (1983). Role of variable region gene expression and environmental selection in determining the antiphosphorylcholine B cell repertoire. *J. Exp. Med.* 158: 1948.

Knuth, A., Lloyd, K. L., Lipkin, M., Oettgen, H. F. and Old, L. J. (1983). Natural antibodies in human sera directed against blood-group-related determinants expressed on colon cancer cells *Int. J. Cancer* 32: 199.

Kobubu, F., Litman, R., Shamblott, M. J., Hinds, K. and Litman, G. W. (1988) Diverse organization of immunoglobulin V_H gene loci in a primitive vertebrate. *EMBO* 7: 4313.

Kunkel, H. G., Müller-Eberhard, J. K., Fudenberg, H. H. and Tomasi, T. B. (1961). Gamma globulin complexes in Rheumatoid Arithritis and certain other conditions. *J. Clin. Invest.* 40: 117.

Lafer, E. M., Rauch, J., Andrzejewski, C., Mudd, D., Furie, B., Schwartz, R. S. and Stollar, B. D. (1981). Polyspecific monoclonal lupus autoantibodies reactive with both polynucleotides and phospholipids. *J. Exp. Med.* 153: 897.

Lehner, T., Wilton, J. M. A. and Ward, R. G. (1970). Serum antibodies in dental caries in man. *Archs. Oral Biol.* 23: 1061.

Lieberman, R., Potter, M., Mushinski, E. B., Humphrey, W. and Rudikoff, S. (1974). Genetics of a new IgV_H (T15 idiotype) marker in the mouse regulating natural antibody to phosphorylcholine. *J. Exp. Med.* 139: 983.

Longenecker, B. M. and Mosmann, T. R. (1980). 'Natural' antibodies to chicken MHC antigens are present in mice, rats, humans, alligators and allogeneic chickens. *Immunogenetics* 11: 293.

Lord, E. M. and Dutton, R. W. (1975). The properties of plaque-forming cells from autoimmune and normal strains of mice with specificity for autologous erythrocyte antigens. *J. Immunol.* 115: 1199.

Lutz, J. U., Flepp, R. and Stringaro-Wipf, G. (1984). Naturally occurring autoantibodies to exoplasmic and cryptic regions of band 3 protein, the major integral membrane protein of human red blood cells. *J. Immunol.* 133: 2610.

Lymberi, P., Dighiero, G., Ternynck, T. and Avrameas, S. (1985). A high incidence of cross-reactive idiotypes among murine natural autoantibodies. *Eur. J. Immunol.* 15: 702.

McGee, J. R. and Michalek, S. M. (1981). Immunobiology of dental caries: Microbial aspects and local immunity. *Ann. Rev. Microbiol* 35: 595.

Mäkelä, O. and Imanishi, T. (1975). Expression of an immunoglobulin V_H gene in natural anti-hapten antibodies. *Eur. J. Immunol.* 5: 202.

Marchalonis, J. J. and Edelman, G. M. (1968). Phylogenetic origins of antibody structure: III: Antibodies in the primary immune response of the sea lamprey, *Petromyzon marinus. J. Exp. Med.* 127: 891.

Marshall-Clarke, S., Cooke, A. and Hutchings, P. R. (1979). Deficient production of anti-red cell autoantibodies by mice with an X-linked B lymphocyte defect. *Eur. J. Immunol.* 9: 820.

Martin, W. J. and Martin, S. E. (1974). Naturally occurring cytotoxic anti-tumour antibodies in sera of congenitally athymic (nude) mice. *Nature* 249: 564.

Martin, S. E. and Martin, W. J. (1975a). Interspecies brain antigen detected by naturally occurring mouse anti-brain autoantibody. *Proc. Natl. Acad. Sci. USA* 72: 1036.

Martin, S. E. and Martin, W. J. (1975b). Anti-tumor antibodies in normal mouse sera. *Int. J. Cancer* 15: 658.

Martin, S. E. and Martin, W. J. (1975c). X-chromosome linked defect of CBA/HN mice in production of tumor reactive naturally occurring IgM antibodies. *J. Immunol.* 115: 502.

Martin, W. J. and Martin, S. E. (1975d). Thymus reactive IgM autoantibodies in normal mouse sera. *Nature* 254: 716.

Ménard, S., Colnaghi, M. I. and Della Porta, G. (1977). Natural anti-tumor serum reactivity in BALB/c mice: I: Characterization and interference with tumor growth. *Int. J. Cancer* 19: 267.

Miller, V. A., Pohajdak, B. and Greenberg, A. H. (1983). Murine natural antitumour antibodies: III: Interferon treament of a natural killer cell resistant lymphoma: Augmentation of natural antibody reactivity and susceptibility to in vivo natural resistance. *J. Natl. Cancer Inst.* 71: 377.

Mittal, K. K., Ferrone, S., Mickey, M. R., Pellegrino, M. A., Reisfeld, R. A. and Terasaki, P. I. (1973). Serological characterization of natural antihuman lymphocytotoxic antibodies in mammalian sera. *Transplantation* 16: 287.

Möller, G. (1975). One non-specific signal triggers B lymphocytes. *Transplant. Rev.* 23: 126.

Mond, J. J., Scher, I., Cossman, J., Kessler, S., Mongini, P. K. A., Hansen, C., Finkelman, F. D. and Paul, W. E. (1982). Role of the thymus in directing the development of a subset of B lymphocytes. *J. Exp. Med* 155: 924.

Morrison, M. H., Chaney, W. G., and Esselman, W. J. (1984). Molecular weight and charge heterogeneity of Thy-1 glycoprotein in different populations of T-cells. *Mol. Immunol.* 21: 405.

Mosmann, T. R. and Longenecker, B. M. (1982). The high background immune reactivity of mice to polymorphic determinants on xenogeneic erythrocytes: Theoretical and practical implications. *J. Immunol.* 128: 100.

Naparstek, Y., Duggan, D., Schattner, A., Madaio, M. P., Goni, F., Frangione, B., Stollar, B. D., Kabat, E. A. and Schwartz, R. S., (1985). Immunochemical similarities between monoclonal antibacterial Waldenstrom's macroglobulins and monoclonal anti-DNA lupus autoantibodies. *J. Exp. Med.* 161: 1525.

Nowinski, R. (1976). Genetic control of natural immunity to ecotropic mouse leukemia viruses: Immune response genes. *Inf. Immun* 13: 1098.

Nowinski, R. C., Kaehler, S. L. and Baron, J. (1976). Genetic control of natural immunity to exotropic mouse leukemia viruses: Production of endogenous immunogen. *Inf. Immun.* 13: 1091.

Obata, Y., Stockert, E., Boyse, E. A., Tung, J. and Litman, B. W. (1976). Spontaneous autoimmunization to G_{IX} cell surface antigen in hybrid mice *J. Exp. Med.* 144: 533.

Obata. Y., Tanaka, T., Stockert, E. and Good, R. A. (1979). Autoimmune and lymphoproliferative disease in (B6-G_{IX}^+ X 129)F1 mice: Relation to naturally occurring antibodies against murine leukemia virus related cell surface antigens. *Proc. Natl. Acad. Sci. USA* 76: 5289.

Obata, Y., Stockert, E., DeLeo, A. B., O'Donnell, P. V., Snyder, H. W. and Old, L. J. (1981). $G_{(ERALD)}$: A cell surface antigen of the mouse related to xenotropic MuLV defined by naturally occurring antibody and monoclonal antibody. *J. Exp. Med.* 154: 659.

Ono, S., Yaffe, L. J., Ryan, J. L. and Singer, A. (1983). Functional heterogeneity of the Lyb-5⁻ B cell subpopulation: Mutant xid B cells and normal Lyb-5⁻ B

214 Miller, Chow and Greenberg

cells differ in their responsiveness to phenol-extracted lipopolysaccharide. *J. Immunol.* 130: 2014.

Ortega, E., Kostovetzky, M. and Lavalde, C. (1984). Natural DNP binding immunoglobulins and antibody multispecificity. *Molecular Immunol.* 21: 883.

Pages, J. and Bussard, A. E. (1975). Precommitment of normal mouse peritoneal cells by erythrocyte antigens in relation to autoantibody production. *Nature* 257: 316.

Parker, L. M., Chused, T. M. and Steinberg, A. D. (1974). Immunofluorescence studies on thymocytotoxic antibody from New Zealand Black mice. *J. Immunol* 112: 285.

Pearson, R. D. and Steigbigel, R. T. (1980). Mechanism of lethal effect of human serum upon *Leishmania donovani. J. Immunol.* 125: 2195.

Pierce, N. F. and Gowans, J. L. (1975). Cellular kinetics of the intestinal immune response to Cholera Toxoid in rats. *J. Exp. Med.* 142: 1550.

Pierotti, M. A. and Colnaghi, M. I. (1975). Natural antibodies directed against murine lymphosarcoma cells. *J. Natl. Cancer Inst.* 55: 945.

Pierroti, M. and Colnaghi, M. (1976). Natural antibodies directed against murine lymphosarcoma cells: Variability of level in individual mice. *Int. J. Cancer* 18: 223.

Prabhakar, B. S., Saegusa, J., Onodera, T. and Notkins, A. L. (1984). Lymphocytes capable of making monoclonal autoantibodies that react with multiple organs are a common feature of the normal B cell repertoire. *J. Immunol.* 133: 2815.

Rajewsky, K., Forster, I. and Cumano, A. Evolutionary and somatic selection of the antibody repertoire in the mouse. *Science* 238: 1088.

Raveche, E. S., Steinberg, A. D., Klassen, L. W. and Tzio, J. H. (1978). Genetic studies in NZB mice: I: Spontaneous autoantibody production. *J. Exp. Med.* 147: 1487.

Riccardi, C., Santoni, A., Barlozzari, T., Puccetti, P. and Herberman, R. B. (1980) *In vivo* natural reactivity of mice against tumor cells. *Int. J. Cancer* 25: 475.

Risser, R. and Grunwald, D. J. (1981). Production of anti-self H-2 antibodies by hybrid mice immune to a viral tumour. *Nature* 289: 563.

Rodkey, L. S. (1980). Autoregulation of immune responses via idiotype network interactions. *Microbiol. Rev.* 44: 631.

Rogentine, G. N. (1975). Naturally occurring human antibody to neuraminidase-treated human lymphocytes. Antibody levels in normal subjects, cancer patients, and subjects with immunodeficiency. *J. Natl. Cancer Inst.* 54: 1307.

Rogentine, G. N. and Plocinik, B. A. (1974). Carbohydrate inhibition studies of the naturally occurring human antibody to neuraminidase-treated human lymphocytes. *J. Immunol.* 113: 848.

Rogentine, G. N., Doherty, C. M. and Pincus, S. H. (1977). Increase in titer of the naturally occurring human antibody to neuraminidase-treated lymphocytes after influenza. *J. Immunol.* 119: 1652.

Rosenberg, Y. (1979). Influence of the sex-linked defect in CBA/N mice on autoimmune responses to isologous erythrocytes. *J. Exp. Med.* 150: 1561.

Rosenberg, S. A. and Schwarz, S. (1974). Murine autoantibodies to a cryptic membrane antigen: Possible explanation for neuraminidase-induced increase in cell immunogenicity *J. Natl. Cancer Inst.* 52: 1151.

Rygaard, J. and Povlsen, C. O. (1976). *Transplant Rev.* 28: 43–61.

Scher, I. (1982). The CBA/N mouse strain: An experimental model illustrating the influence of the X chromosome on immunity. *Adv. Immunol.* 33: 1.

Scher, I., Titus, J. A. and Finkelman, F. D. (1983). The ontogeny and distribution of B cells in normal and mutant immune-defective CBA/N mice: Two-parameter analysis of surface IgM and IgD. *J. Immunol.* 130: 619.

Schoolnik, G. K., Buchanan, T. M. and Holmes, K. K. (1976). Gonococci causing disseminated gonococcal infection are resistant to the bactericidal action of normal human serum. *J. Clin. Invest.* 58: 1163.

Schoolnik, G. D., Ochs, H. D. Buchanan, T. M. (1979). Immunoglobulin class responsible for gonococcal bactericidal activity of normal human sera. *J. Immunol.* 122: 1771.

Schrater, A. F., Goidl, E. A., Thorbecke, G. J. and Siskind, G. W. (1979). Production of auto-anti-idiotypic antibody during the normal immune response to TNP-Ficoll: I: Occurrence in AKR/J and BALB/c mice of hapten augmentable, anti-TNP plaque-forming cells and their accelerated appearance in recipients of immune spleen cells. *J. Exp. Med.* 150: 138.

Schwartz, R. S. and Stollar, B. D. (1985). Origins of anti-DNA auto-antibodies. *J. Clin. Invest.* 75: 321.

Sela, B. A., Wang, J. L. and Edelman, G. M. (1975). Antibodies reactive with cell surface carbohydrates. *Proc. Natl. Acad. Sci. USA* 72: 1127.

Slaughter, L., Carson, D. A., Jensen, F. C., Holbrook, T. L. and Vaughan, J. H. (1978). *In vitro* effects of Epstein-Barr virus on peripheral blood mononuclear cells from patients with rheumatoid arthritis and normal subjects. *J. Exp. Med.* 148: 1429.

Smith, H. R., Yaffe, L. J., Chused, T. M., Raveche, E. S., Klinman, D. M. and Steinberg, A. D. (1985). Analysis of B-cell subpopulations: I: Relationships among splenic xid, Ly 1[+] and Lyb 5[+] B cells. *Cell Immunol.* 92: 190.

Snyder, H. W. and Fleissner, E. (1980). Specificity of human antibodies to oncovirus glycoproteins: Recognition of antigen by natural antibodies directed against carbohydrate structures. *Proc. Natl. Acad. Sci. USA* 77: 1622.

Solomon, G., Schiffenbauer, J., Keiser, H. D. and Diamond, B. (1983). Use of monoclonal antibodies to identify shared idiotypes on human antibodies to native DNA from patients with systemic lupus erythrematosus. *Proc. Natl. Acad. Sci. USA* 80: 850.

Springer, G. F. (1971). Blood-group and Forssman antigenic determinants shared between microbes and mammalian cells. *Progr. Allergy* 15: 9.

Springer, G. F. (1984). T and Tn, general carcinoma autoantigens. *Science* 224: 1198.

Springer, G. F. and Tegtmeyer, H. (1981). Origin of anti-Thomsen-Friedenreich (T) and Tn agglutinins in man and in White Leghorn chicks. *Br. J. Haematol.* 47: 453.

Springer, G. F., Desai, P. R. and Banatwala, I. (1975). Blood group MN antigens and precursors in normal and malignant human breast glandular tissue. *J. Natl. Cancer Inst.* 54: 335.

Stassin, V., Coulie, P. G., Birshtein, B. K., Secher, D. S. and Van Snick, J. (1983). Determinants recognized by murine rheumatoid factors: Molecular localization using a panel of mouse myeloma variant immunoglobulins. *J. Exp. Med* 158: 1763.

Steele, E. J. and Cunningham, A. J. (1978). High proportion of Ig producing cells making autoantibody in normal mice. *Nature* 274: 483.

Stockert, E., DeLeo, A. B., O'Donnell, P. V., Obata, Y. and Old, L. J. (1979). $G_{(AKSL)}$: A new cell surface antigen of the mouse related to the dual-tropic mink cell focus-inducing class of murine leukemia virus detected by naturally occurring antibody. *J. Exp. Med.* 149: 200.

Stutman, O. (1974). Tumor development after 3-methylcholanthrene in immunologically deficient athymic nude mice. *Science* 183: 534.

Sugamura, K. and Hinuma, Y. (1985). Human retrovirus in adult T-cell leukemia/lymphoma. *Immunol. Today* 6: 83.

Swiedler, S. J., Hart, G. W., Tarentino, A. L., Plummer, T. J. and Freed, J. H. (1983). Stable oligosaccharide microheterogeneity at individual glycosylation sites of a murine major histocompatibility antigen derived from a B cell lymphoma. *J. Biol. Chem* 258: 11515.

Tarlinton, D., Stall, A. M., and Herzenberg, L. A. (1988). Repetitive usage of immunoglobulin V_H and D gene segments in $CD5^+$ Ly-1 clones of (NZB × NZW)F_1 mice. *EMBO* 7: 3705.

Taurog, J., Raveche, S., Smothers, P., Glimcher, L., Huston, D., Hansen, C. and Steinberg, A. (1981). T cell abnormalities in NZB mice occur independently of autoantibody production. *J. Exp. Med.* 153: 221.

Teale, J. M. (1985). B Cell immune repertoire diversifies in a predictable temporal order *in vitro*. *J. Immunol.* 135: 954.

Tough, D. F. and Chow, D. A. (1988). Tumorigenicity of murine lymphomas selected through fluorescence-detected natural antibody binding. *Cancer Res.* 48: 270.

Tung, J., Vitetta, E. S., Fleissner, E. and Boyse, E. A. (1975). Biochemical evidence linking the G_{IX} thymocyte surface antigen to the gp69/71 envelope glycoprotein of murine leukemia virus. *J. Exp. Med.* 141: 198.

Underwood, J. R., Pedersen, J. S., Chalmers, P. J. and Toh, B. H. (1985). Hybrids from normal, germ free, nude and neonatal mice produce monoclonal autoantibodies to eight different intracellular structures. *Clin. Exp. Immunol.* 60: 417.

Van Snick, J. and Coulie, P. (1983). Rheumatoid factors and secondary immune responses in the mouse: I: Frequent occurrence of hybridomas secreting IgM anti-IgG_1 autoantibodies after immunization with protein antigens. *Eur. J. Immunol* 13: 890.

Van Snick, J. L. and Masson, P. L. (1980). Incidence and specificities of IgA and IgM anti-IgG autoantibodies in various mouse strains and colonies. *J. Exp. Med.* 151: 45.

Van Snick, J. L., Stassin, V. and DeLestré, B. (1983). Isotypic and allotypic specificity of mouse rheumatoid factors. *J. Exp. Med.* 157: 1006.

Wade, A. W. and Szewczuk, M. R. (1984). Aging, idiotype repertoire shifts, and compartmentalization of the mucosal-associated lymphoid system. *Adv. Immunol.* 36: 143.

Warner, J. F. and Dennert, G. (1985). Bone marrow graft rejection as a function of antibody-directed natural killer cells. *J. Exp. Med.* 161: 536.

Watkins, W. M. (1966). Blood group substances. *Science* 152: 172.

Wolosin, L. B. and Greenberg, A. H. (1981). Genetics of natural antitumor antibody production: Antibodies to MHC-linked determinants detected in the serum of unstimulated mice. *J. Immunol.* 126: 1456.

Wood, C. D. and Möller, G. (1984). Influence of RU 41.740, a glycoprotein extract from *Klebsiella pneumoniae*, on the murine immune system. *J. Immunol.* 132: 616.

Wortis, H. H., Burkly, L., Hughes, D., Roschelle, S. and Waneck, G. (1982). Lack of mature B cells in nude mice with X-linked immune deficiency. *J. Exp. Med.* 155: 903.

Yother, Y. C., Forman, C., Gray, B. M. and Briles, D. E. (1981). Protection of mice from infection with *Streptococcus pneumoniae* by anti-phosphorylcholine antibody. *Infect. Immun.* 36: 184.

7

Complement

DAVID L. GORDON[1]

Clinical Microbiology,
Flinders Medical Centre,
Bedford Park,
South Australia. 5042.

I. INTRODUCTION

The identification of complement was, along with the discovery of antibody and phagocytosis, one of the three great discoveries in the late 19th century which established the concept of host-defence mechanisms that were the foundation of modern immunology. Observations by Nuttal, Pfeiffer and Bordet late last century defined a heat-labile component of immune serum which had bactericidal activity. Bordet (1898) subsequently described lysis of red blood cells by the serum of animals immunised with red cells of a different species and in 1899 Ehrlich and Morgenroth proposed the term 'complement' for this activity.

[1] Present address: Clinical Microbiology, Royal Newcastle Hospital, Newcastle, NSW 2300, Australia

NATURAL IMMUNITY
ISBN 0 12 5145551

A complement system is present in virtually all vertebrates and comprises a fundamental part of natural defence against infection. Although this property is traditionally associated with the alternative pathway, which can respond immediately to many foreign proteins, direct interaction of antigens with components of the classical pathway in the absence of antibody may also occur. Complement activation is controlled by a complex group of regulatory proteins which prevent uncontrolled deposition on host cells. In addition to providing a natural defence system against micro-organisms, the complement system represents a major effector arm of the humoral immune response, and complement activation generates several non-specific mediators of inflammation.

The major step in complement activation by either the classical or alternative pathways is the cleavage of C3. After this the effector and mediator functions of complement can proceed. Fragments of complement proteins which are recognised by specific receptors on phagocytic and other cells are deposited on micro-organisms, soluble mediators of the inflammatory response are released, and the membrane attack complex which can kill many gram-negative bacteria is generated (Fig. 7.1). A more comprehensive outline of the complement cascade is given in Fig. 7.2. This review will examine the mechanisms of complement activation with emphasis on non-immune activators, regulation of complement activation, the binding of the central protein C3 to diverse surfaces and the biological functions elicited by complement activation.

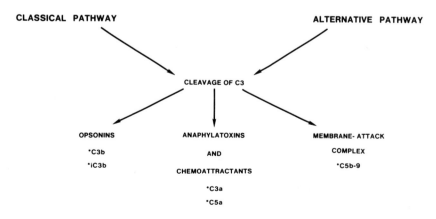

Fig. 7.1 Activation of C3 by the classical or alternative pathway C3 convertases generates the effector and mediator functions of complement.

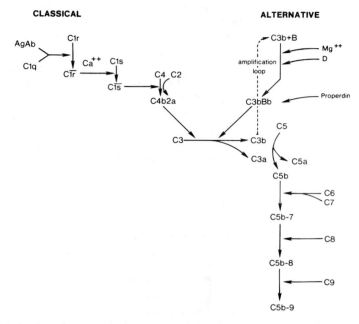

Fig. 7.2 Outline of the reaction sequences of the complement pathway.

II. CLASSICAL PATHWAY ACTIVATION

The classical complement pathway is usually activated following inter-action of antibody (IgG 1,2,3 or IgM) with antigen. Antibody in antibody-antigen complexes binds to C1q, the recognition subunit of the first component of complement, C1, *via* a binding site on its Fc region. The catalytic subunit of C1, $C1r_2s_2$, is a calcium-dependent tetrameric association of the serine proteases C1r and C1s which is activated following C1q binding to the immune complex. How C1q binding initiates activation of the classical complement pathway is not fully understood, but neoantigens present only on bound C1q have been detected (Golan *et al.*, 1982) suggesting a C1q conformational change on binding. This may permit autocatalytic cleavage of C1r to its active form C1r̄ (Ziccardi and Cooper, 1976; Ziccardi, 1982a), which cleaves C1s to C1s̄. C1s̄ maintains classical pathway activation by cleaving C4. C4b covalently attaches to the activating surface, C2 is cleaved and C2a remains associated with the surface-bound C4b. The complex C4b2a, the classical pathway convertase, can cleave C3 into the anaphylatoxic fluid-phase fragment C3a and a larger fragment C3b (Fig. 7.2).

Activation of the classical pathway is controlled by the regulatory protein C1 esterase inhibitor (C1 INH). C1 INH inactivates $C1r_2s_2$ (Harpel and Cooper, 1975) and dissociates it from C1q (Sim *et al.*, 1979; Ziccardi and Cooper, 1979). In addition to controlling activated C1, C1 INH blocks the spontaneous activation of C1 (Ziccardi, 1982b), and inhibits plasmin, kallikrein, clotting factor XI and Hageman factor (Ratnoff, *et al.*, 1969). The importance of this regulatory protein is illustrated by the illnesses, hereditary or acquired angioedema, associated with its deficiency (Donaldson and Evans, 1963; Gelfand *et al.*, 1979). Affected patients have recurrent attacks of non-pitting oedema of the extremities, gastrointestinal tract or airways (Frank *et al.*, 1976) associated with activation of the complement and kinin systems.

The classical pathway can be activated in the non-immune host following interaction of antigen with natural antibodies (Chapter 5). Of additional significance to natural immunity has been the recent recognition that a diverse range of substances can efficiently activate the classical pathway in the absence of antibody. Certain Gram-negative and Gram-positive bacteria (Loos *et al.*, 1978; Betz and Isliker, 1981; Baker *et al.*, 1982), DNA and RNA viruses (Cooper *et al.*, 1976; Martin *et al.*, 1987), cell constituents (Pinckard *et al.*, 1973; Cyong *et al.*, 1982), polyanions and urate crystals (Giclas *et al.*, 1979) directly activate C1 (Table 7.1), initiating in some cases physiological effects such as opsonophagocytosis (Leist-Welsh and Bjornson, 1982; Levy and Kasper, 1985) and virus lysis (Cooper *et al.*, 1976).

Mechanisms by which non-immune activation of the classical pathway occurs might include direct interaction with C1q in the same manner as immune complexes, leading to activation of C1r and C1s, or activation of C1s by a different mechanism, bypassing C1q or C1r. Alternatively, because the spontaneous activation of C1 is inhibited by C1 INH (Ziccardi, 1982b), substances inhibiting C1 INH could indirectly activate the classical pathway. This latter mechanism, however, would be unlikely to specifically deposit complement components on the 'activating' surface, and has been demonstrated not to be the mechanism of non-immune activation of C1 by group B *Streptococcus* (Levy and Kasper, 1986). There is considerable evidence that most non-immune classical pathway activators interact with a collagen-like moiety of C1q (C1as and Loos, 1981; Aubert *et al.*, 1985). There appear, however, to be differences in how immune and non-immune activation of C1 occurs. Immune complex-mediated C1 activation is not affected by C1 INH (Ziccardi, 1982b) whereas at least some non-immune activation of C1 is modulated by C1 INH. Tenner, Ziccardi and Cooper (1984) examined C1 activation by *E. coli* and detected strain differences in C1 binding, C1 activation and modulation by C1 INH. Activation by strain J-5, an efficient

Table 7.1: Examples of non-immune activators of the classical pathway.

Bacteria*
  Group B *Streptococcus*
  E. coli
  Salmonella spp.
  Klebsiella spp.

Viruses
  Retroviruses
  Epstein Barr virus

Cell constituents
  Myelin basic protein
  Mitochondria and cardiolipin vesicles
  DNA and RNA

Polyanions
  Polyanethol sulfonate
  Polyvinyl sulfonate
  Dextran sulfate

Miscellaneous
  Urate crystals

---

* Some strains only. Gram-negative bacteria activate through lipid A portion of lipopoly-saccharide

activator, was not reduced by C1 INH. In addition a C1q- and calcium-dependent C1s binding site on *E. coli* was demonstrated in the absence of C1r. C1q could unmask a $C1s_2$-binding site; alternatively, multivalent interactions of $C1s_2$ with its binding site and C1q could stabilise C1s binding and permit classical pathway activation (Tenner *et al.*, 1984). A similar $C1s_2$-binding site, important in C1 activation, has been identified on retrovirus membranes (Bartholomew and Esser, 1980). Peitsch *et al.*, (1987) and Kovacsovics *et al.*, (1987) have extended these observations on the mechanisms of classical pathway activation, and distinguished 'weak' and 'strong' non-immune activators. Immune complexes and weak activators both require C1r to cleave C1s. Weak activators, unlike immune complexes, are modulated by C1 INH and require C1s for C1r cleavage to occur. Strong activators are not modulated by C1 INH and can cleave C1s, in a calcium- and C1q-dependent manner, in the absence of C1r. It is proposed that different domains on C1q are responsible for the binding of immune complexes and non-immune activators (Kovascovics *et al.*, 1987).

  Binding to C1q does not necessarily result in C1 activation, and the degree of activation does not always correlate with C1q-binding affinity

(Folkerd *et al.*, 1980). Some activators, such as urate crystals, lose the ability to activate C1 at high activator/C1 ratios, despite retaining C1 binding activity (Giclas *et al.*, 1979). There are at least some shared chemical characteristics of C1 activators which determine their ability to bind to C1q and initiate classical pathway activation. Non-immune activators contain repeating subunit structures which probably permit high-affinity-multimeric associations with C1q (Cooper, 1983). In addition non-immune activators have a high density of negatively charged phosphate or sulfate groups which allow ionic interaction with the highly cationic C1q protein. For Gram-negative bacteria the accessibility of the lipid A region of lipopolysaccharide, known to bind and activate C1 (Cooper and Morrison, 1978), is probably a critical requirement for C1q interaction.

Dissociation of C1 by C1 INH leaves uncomplexed C1q bound to the activator. This C1q acts as the ligand for C1q receptors present on B lymphocytes, monocytes, polymorphonuclear leukocytes and other cells (Tenner and Cooper, 1981). Particle-bound C1q enhances the oxidative response of neutrophils (Tenner and Cooper, 1982), the binding of fibronectin to bacteria (Sorvillo and Pearlstein, 1985), and the phagocytosis of particles coated with C3 fragments and fibronectin (Sorvillo *et al.*, 1986). C1q also enhances Fc receptor-mediated phagocytosis by mononuclear phagocytes (Bobak *et al.*, 1987). Thus C1q, which is secreted at sites of inflammation by macrophages, could modulate the interaction between microorganisms and phagocytic cells. In vivo such C1q interactions may be particularly significant in the nonimmune host, or early in the course of an infection when little or no antibody is present.

III. ALTERNATIVE PATHWAY ACTIVATION

Activation of the complement system and cleavage of C3 can also occur by the alternative pathway, without the requirement for the early proteins of the classical pathway, C1, C4 and C2 (Pillemer *et al.*, 1954). The alternative pathway, because it can be activated in the absence of antibody, provides immediate defence against foreign material and is thus an essential component of natural immunity against microbial infection.

Many components of microorganisms and mammalian cells can activate the alternative pathway. They include particulate polysaccharides of bacteria, yeast cell walls and zymosan, bacterial endotoxin, agarose, rabbit erythrocytes, virus-infected cells and some transformed cell lines, aggregated IgA and parasites (Lachmann and Hughes-Jones, 1984). Alternative pathway function may, however, be influenced by antibody. Antigen-antibody precipitates can activate the pathway, initial classical pathway deposition of C3b can be greatly amplified by alternative pathway activity, and occasionally antibody is required for activation (Steele *et al.*, 1984; Gordon, 1988).

The alternative pathway convertase, C3bBb, is formed in the presence of bound or fluid-phase C3b, magnesium, and factors B and D. Through the action of properdin, C3bBb is stabilised, more C3 is cleaved and further C3b is deposited. This in turn interacts with factors B and D to form C3bBb again, thus maintaining and amplifying alternative pathway activity (Fig. 7.2). Initiation of alternative pathway activation occurs when native C3, factors B and D and magnesium interact in solution. It appears that C3 activation occurs naturally in plasma by a continuous 'tick-over' system involving slow, spontaneous hydrolysis of fluid-phase C3 to form $C3.H_2O$. This has 'C3b-like' properties, can bind factor B, and probably serves as a subunit of the initial fluid-phase alternative pathway convertase, $C3.H_2O$ Bb. The first molecules of C3b produced by this enzyme can then form C3bBb and set the amplification loop in motion (Pangburn and Müller-Eberhard, 1980; Pangburn *et al.*, 1981). Because C3b deposition occurs in an indiscriminate manner, uncontrolled deposition on host cells subsequent to the 'tickover' mechanism must be prevented. This is achieved by the regulatory protein factor I (C3b inactivator) which in the presence of factor H ($\beta 1H$) cleaves bound C3b to iC3b. iC3b is unable to bind factor B or C5, so that continued alternative pathway activation and assembly of the membrane attack complex does not occur. The importance of these regulatory proteins in controlling the spontaneous tick-over activation of C3 is illustrated by the recognition of patients with factor I deficiency (Alper *et al.*, 1970). Continued activation of C3 means that virtually all C3 circulates as functionally inactive C3b, resulting in severe predisposition to bacterial infection from what is in essence a C3 deficiency state.

The characteristics of a surface which promote alternative pathway activation are not well understood. There is no common biochemical component amongst the diverse range of activators. However, activators are relatively deficient in sialic acid, and sheep erythrocytes can be converted to activators by its removal. Capsular sialic acid on bacteria retards alternative pathway activation and is a probable virulence factor (Robbins *et al.*, 1974). It is apparent though that many other factors are important determinants of activation. The lipid A region of lipopolysaccharides activates both complement pathways, and antibody enhances alternative pathway deposition of C3b and converts non-activators to activators (Moore *et al.*, 1981, 1982). It is also known that persistence of C3b on activating surfaces is critical. This depends on the

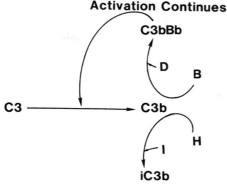

Fig. 7.3 Interaction of C3b with either factor B or H. Alternative pathway activators bind B and generate more C3bBb and cleavage of C3 continues. Non-activators bind H allowing cleavage by factor I of C3b to iC3b, with cessation of alternative pathway activation (from Gordon and Hostetter, 1986).

relative interaction of C3b with factor B, causing continued formation of C3bBb, or with factor H, facilitating cleavage to iC3b (Fig. 7.3). C3b on activators has a high affinity for factor B compared with factor H and must exist in a 'protected site' which is inaccessible to I- and H-mediated cleavage (Fearon and Austen, 1980). Most C3b on *S. aureus* and *E. coli* is very rapidly cleaved to iC3b, yet a small percentage remains as C3b, which is inaccessible to further cleavage and maintains alternative pathway activation (Gordon *et al.*, 1988). Fries *et al.* (1984) have determined a mechanism by which antibody may facilitate alternative pathway activation. C3b bound to IgG as C3b–IgG heterodimers is relatively refractory to factor I- and H-mediated degradation.

Although alternative pathway activation is frequently antibody-independent, auxiliary serum factors may be required for effector functions. Bjornson *et al.* (1987) have reconstructed the pathway from isolated proteins and determined that the effector phase of opsonisation of *Bacteroides sp.* requires additional serum factors. In some cases natural IgM antibodies fulfil this requirement. The effector phase of cytolysis may also require auxiliary factors (Sissons *et al.*, 1980).

The indiscriminate activation of complement on host cells is further prevented by a group of related membrane regulatory glycoproteins including the C3b–C4b receptor (CR1), which acts as a cofactor for factor I-mediated cleavage of C3b, and the widely distributed decay accelerating factor (DAF) and membrane cofactor protein (MCP). DAF accelerates the decay-dissociation of both C3 convertases (Nicholson-Weller *et al.*, 1982) and MCP acts as a cofactor for cleavage of C3b (Seya *et al.*, 1986). Atkinson and Farries (1987) have suggested that these membrane-bound regulatory glycoproteins provide a mechanism for separating self from non-self in the complement system.

IV. BINDING OF C3b

The ability of C3b to attach to a wide variety of biological surfaces provides essential early protection against microorganisms. Regardless of the activator the mechanism of C3b deposition and the subsequent events are identical.

When the C3a fragment is cleaved from the α-chain of C3 during complement activation a labile binding site is exposed in C3b. This endows the protein with a short-lived ability to bind to neighbouring surfaces (Sim *et al.*, 1983). C3b not bound to surfaces remains in the fluid-phase and quickly loses its ability to bind as the labile site is hydrolysed.

It is a necessary requirement that C3b attach firmly to a very diverse range of foreign antigens. Law and Levine (1977) first described the covalent nature of C3b interaction when they determined that C3b bound to erythrocyte membranes or zymosan was resistant to dissociation by detergents, protein denaturants and extremes of temperature, pH and salt — conditions that would normally disrupt hydrophobic interactions. Dissociation did occur after incubation with hydroxylamine, indicating the presence of an ester linkage between C3b and the acceptor surface. Subsequent work showed that C3b could also attach by amide linkages (Sim *et al.*, 1983). The site of covalent binding was localised to the C3d region of the α-chain of C3 (Law *et al.*, 1979).

Further studies have defined the biochemical mechanism involved in C3b binding, which occurs following exposure of an internal thiolester bond. Cleavage of C3 or inactivation by amines results in the appearance of a titratable -SH group (Janatova *et al.*, 1980) localised to a cysteine residue in the C3d region of the α-chain. Studies of the methylamine reactive site in C3 revealed a 1:1:1 stoichiometric relationship between loss of haemolytic activity, incorporation of methylamine in the C3d region of the α-chain and the -SH group titration (Tack *et al.*, 1980). Tryptic peptide analysis indicated that methylamine reacts with a glutamyl carbonyl only three peptides from the cysteine residue containing the titratable -SH. Hostetter *et al.* (1982) subsequently demonstrated that the glutamyl residue of the internal thiolester bond donates its carbonyl group to acceptor carbohydrate or amino groups in a transester-

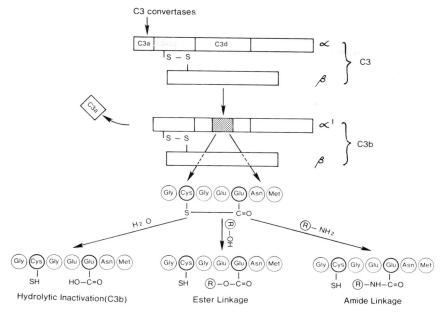

Fig. 7.4 Schematic diagram illustrating activation and binding of C3. In circulating C3 the reactive thiolester resides within a 'hydrophobic pocket'. When C3a is cleaved the molecule undergoes a conformational change and the reactive thiolester site is exposed. C3b then has a transient ability to bind by an ester or amide linkage to suitable acceptor surfaces. C3b which does not bind is rapidly hydrolysed at the thiolester site (from Gordon and Hostetter, 1986).

ification reaction to form ester or amide linkages. The mechanism of activation and binding of C3 is summarised in Fig. 7.4. The ubiquitous presence of hydroxyl and amino groups in nature permits the ester or amide linkage of C3b to a wide range of biological targets.

Attachment of C3b to bacterial surfaces also proceeds through the thiolester site. C3b binds covalently to the capsule, lipopolysaccharide and outer membrane protein of *E. coli* (Joiner, *et al.*, 1984) and thiolester-reactive C3 is required for opsonophagocytosis. Thiolester-disrupted C3, which cannot attach covalently to microorganisms, has no opsonic capacity (Hostetter *et al.*, 1984).

V. BIOLOGICAL EFFECTS OF THE COMPLEMENT SYSTEM

From an evolutionary viewpoint the simplest complement system would consist of a single protein, such as C3, secreted by mononuclear phagocytes and activated in a nonspecific way at the site of inflammation by trypsin or neutrophil proteases. Perhaps the original effects generated in this way were vasodilation and increased vascular permeability. Development of the classical and alternative pathways may have served to regulate these effects more precisely, to increase the spectrum of immune and non-immune activators and, by the classical pathway, to provide a link between the antibody and complement systems (Atkinson and Farries, 1987). The evolution of specific receptors on inflammatory cells led to ligand-receptor interactions, enabling recruitment of cells to the site of infection, facilitation of phagocytosis and release of microbicidal products. The membrane attack complex represents a distinct effector system able to eliminate many microorganisms. An additional recently described role for complement proteins is regulation of the immune response.

A. Soluble Complement Fragments

Complement activation generates the important inflammatory mediators, C3a and C5a anaphylatoxins, small genetically related peptides cleaved from their parent compounds. C4a is also known to have anaphylatoxic activity, but is less potent and probably of less significance in vivo. These peptides are released into the fluid-phase at sites of inflammation and have potent effects on most circulating cells. The biological effects mediated by the anaphylatoxins occur either as a direct result of the interaction with specific cell-surface receptors, which are currently being defined, or as a consequence of release of secondary mediators such as histamine and arachidonic acid metabolites.

C3a induces multiple biological events including smooth muscle contraction, increased vascular permeability, neutrophil adherence to endothelium, degranulation of mast cells, basophils and eosinophils, vasoactive amines and histamine release from basophils and mast cells, lysosomal enzyme release from neutrophils and thromboxane A2 release from macrophages. Studies with synthetic peptides have identified molecular components required for the function of C3a and other anaphylatoxins (Hugli, 1984). The C-terminal region is required for functional activity, and synthetic penta- and hexa-peptides containing a terminal arginyl residue exhibit C3a functional properties.

C5a elicits many of the effects induced by C3a, but in addition has direct effects on neutrophil aggregation and adherence, oxidative metabolism and secretory responses. C5a is best known for its function in directing leukocyte migration, or chemotaxis, of neutrophils, monocytes, eosinophils and basophils. Such effects are mediated by binding to cellular C5a receptors, identified on neutrophils as a Mr 48,000 kD protein (Huey and Hugli, 1985).

The potent physiological properties of these peptides need to be localised at the inflammatory lesion to avoid adverse systemic effects. Serum contains an enzyme, carboxypeptidase N, which rapidly cleaves the carboxyl terminal arginyl from C3a and C5a to form C3a des-arg and C5a des-arg respectively. The biological activities of the des-arg derivatives are generally markedly reduced. For example C5a des-arg has little anaphylatoxic or neutrophil chemotactic activity (Marder *et al.*, 1985). Additional regulation of anaphylatoxic and chemotactic activities may occur locally. Serine esterases, such as chymase, are present in the secretory granules of mast cells. Chymase is released from mast cells in response to C3a, and in the presence of heparin proteoglycan rapidly degrades the bound C3a, thus regulating local mast cell degranulation (Gervasoni *et al.*, 1986). The ability to inactivate chemotaxins may be a bacterial virulence factor. Group A *Streptococcus* produces a chemotactic inhibitor with endoprotease activity which inactivates C5a by cleaving a six-residue peptide from the carboxyl terminus, producing a derivative that has a reduced affinity for C5a receptors (Wexler *et al.*, 1985).

C3e is another soluble C3 fragment, of Mr 12,000 kD, and is formed by treating C3 with trypsin. This peptide has leukocytosis-promoting activity, and is probably involved in inducing leukocytosis during pyogenic infections (Ghebrehiwet and Müller-Eberhard, 1979).

B. Interaction Between Surface-bound C3 Fragments and Cellular Receptors

Once C3b is covalently attached to invading microorganisms interaction with specific cellular receptors for C3b and its cleavage fragments may proceed. This binding is, in contrast to C3b attachment to microorganisms, a non-covalent, reversible, ligand-receptor interaction. Thus C3b provides a bridge by which cells of the immune system can recognise a huge array of antigens.

Two major receptors for C3 fragments exist on neutrophils and mononuclear phagocytes. CR1, the C3b/C4b receptor, is a glycoprotein of 205-260,000 kD present on phagocytic and other cells (Fearon, 1980). CR1 also recognises iC3b, the major cleavage product of C3b, but the affinity of this binding is low and it is of doubtful physiological significance (Gordon *et al.*, 1987). The type 3 complement receptor, CR3, recognises iC3b (Ross and Lambris, 1982) and is a two chain polypeptide antigen of 165,000 and 95,000 kD, defined by monoclonal antibodies anti-Mac 1, Mo1, OKM1 and OKM10 (Wright *et al.*, 1983). CR3 is one of a family of leukocyte glycoproteins, also including LFA-1 and p150,95, important in mediating effector functions related to cell contact.

The role of C3b/iC3b-CR1/CR3 interactions in phagocytosis in the absence of antibody has been controversial. Many studies, using C3b-coated sheep erythrocytes, have defined a role for C3b in the attachment, but not ingestion, phases of phagocytosis, which requires antibody. However, cultured monocytes or macrophages treated with T lymphocyte-derived factors or phorbol esters acquire the ability to ingest C3b- and iC3b-coated erythrocytes (Griffin and Griffin, 1979; Wright and Silverstein, 1982). There is also clear evidence that more physiological particles such as C3-coated *E. coli* can be phagocytised by polymorphs in an antibody-independent manner (Schreiber *et al.*, 1982) and that CR3 is the major phagocytic receptor on polymorphs for *Streptococcus pneumoniae* (Gordon *et al.*, 1986). Monoclonal antibodies to CR3 blocked phagocytosis even in non-immune serum, suggesting that iC3b-CR3 interactions may be important in the early stages of host defense. Thus, both the nature of the opsonised particle and the activation state of the phagocyte determine the biological response mediated by the interaction. Of further significance to natural immunity is the definition of an epitope on CR3 with lectin-like properties. This site does not bind to C3 fragments but can interact with unopsonised yeast and zymosan leading to phagocytosis and stimulation of a respiratory burst (Ross *et al.*, 1985).

Further cleavage of iC3b generates several additional C3 fragments, one of which, C3d, remains attached to the activating surface. A specific receptor, CR2, for C3d is present on B lymphocytes and has been identified as a 145,000 kD membrane protein (Weiss *et al.*, 1984). CR2 is closely associated with the Epstein-Barr virus receptor on B cells and may be a specific membrane site involved in early B cell activation (Frade *et al.*, 1985). Perri *et al.* (1986) have shown that anti-CR2 monoclonal antibodies inhibit human B cell responsiveness to purified B cell growth factor, whilst Hostetter (1986) has demonstrated that highly immunogenic serotypes of *S. pneumoniae* have C3d on their surface, but less immunogenic serotypes do not. Thus the presence of C3d on opsonised bacteria may be important for stimulation of antibody production by B lymphocytes.

C. Membrane Attack Complex

Surface-bound C3b, deposited by either the classical or alternative pathway, serves as the C5 convertase, cleaving C5 to C5a and C5b. Self-assembly of the membrane attack complex (MAC) follows, beginning with binding of C6 and C7. At this point attachment of the complex begins as C5b-7 is anchored in the lipid bilayer of target membranes by a hydrophobic interaction (reviewed by Müller-Eberhard, 1986). C5b-7 binds and inserts C8 into the membrane and subsequently C5b-8 binds and polymerises C9, forming the final MAC, C5b-8.poly-C9. C9 polymerises into tubular structures when the C9 : C5b-8 ratio is high, forming the transmembrane channels leading to osmotic imbalance and ultimately to cell lysis. Observations that phospholipid vesicles and enveloped viruses, which are resistant to hypotonic lysis, can still be lysed by C5b-9 indicates that membrane damage distinct from transmembrane channels also occurs. This appears to result from reorientation and disorganisation of membrane phospholipids following hydrophobic interaction with C5b-9 leading to multiple 'leaky patches' and ejection of MAC-lipid complexes from the outer membrane (Müller-Eberhard, 1986). Such a mechanism may also apply in bacteria. Schreiber *et al.* (1979) assembled a cytolytic pathway from isolated proteins and in the absence of antibody noted membrane lesions and disruption of the outer phospholipid membrane of *E. coli*, leading to cell death without lysis. Dankert and Esser (1987) have also shown that formation of tubular poly-C9 is not required for killing of *E. coli*. They demonstrated that introduction of C9 alone into the periplasmic space induced cell death and suggested that the 'lethal unit' is a C9-derived product which leads to an irreversible dissipation of the membrane potential.

The mechanisms of resistance to complement-mediated killing have been extensively investigated by Joiner, who has demonstrated that resistance generally arises from inability to insert a stable MAC rather than failure of complement activation. For example, although C5b-9 forms on the bacterial cell wall of *S. pneumoniae*, no damage occurs as the MAC cannot penetrate the thick peptidoglycan layer of the Gram-positive cell wall (Joiner *et al.*, 1983). For resistant Gram-negative bacteria complement is efficiently activated, but the C5b-9 complex does not insert into hydrophobic domains of the outer membrane and is subsequently shed from the surface (Joiner *et al.*, 1982).

Nucleated cells are much less susceptible to complement-mediated lysis than erythrocytes, despite assembly of the MAC on the cell surface. Morgan *et al.* (1987) have shown that human neutrophils resist attack from complement by endocytosis of the MAC and proteolysis of C9, and 'shedding' of a large proportion of the MAC formed on the cell surface. Nucleated cells could also resist complement attack by repair of membrane damage, or by utilisation of alternative metabolic processes that compensate for sublethal damage (Schreiber *et al.*, 1980).

MAC formation is, of course, partly controlled at the level of C3 activation, by factors such as DAF. More specifically, a serum glyco-protein, S-protein, regulates the MAC both by binding to C5b-7 in competition with membrane lipids and by preventing C9 polymerisation (Podack *et al.*, 1984). Damage to host cells at the site of complement acti-vation is also minimised by the relative inefficiency of complement to lyse cells from the homologous species. Schonermark *et al.* (1986) have identified a membrane protein of 65,000 kD with homologous C8-binding capacity (C8-binding protein) which inhibits homologous C8- and C9-induced haemolysis. Such a regulatory mechanism would be particularly beneficial because it would allow the unhindered comple-ment attack on invading microorganisms.

D. Complement and Regulation of the Immune Response

A role for the complement system in regulation of the immune response was suggested by Pepys (1976) who demonstrated that C3 depletion by cobra venom factor inhibited the antibody response to T cell-dependent antigens. Such effects, also observed for T-independent antigens, could result from C3 depletion per se, or from generation of C3 fragments with inhibitory activity (Bottger and Bitter-Suermann, 1987). C3a has attracted particular study and has been found to be capable of suppress-ing both antigen-specific and polyclonal antibody responses. C3a inhibits the antibody response of human lymphocytes or murine spleen cells challenged with sheep red blood cells (Morgan *et al.*, 1984), but does not suppress antigen- or mitogen-stimulated lymphocyte proliferation. C3a-mediated immunosuppression may occur through the generation of suppressor T cells (Morgan *et al.*, 1985). In contrast, C5a has immuno-potentiating properties, enhancing antigen-specific and non-specific antibody responses. C5a and C5a des-arg augment the specific response of lymphocyte cultures to sheep red cells and the Fc fragment-mediated polyclonal antibody response, and enhance the T cell proliferative response to tetanus toxoid (Morgan *et al.*, 1984). The contrasting effects of C3a and C5a may serve to generate a potent non-specific suppressor or enhancement circuit affecting humoral and T cell-mediated responses (Morgan, *et al.*, 1984).

Others have proposed that suppression of antibody responses in cobra venom factor-treated animals is merely a result of C3 depletion (Bottger and Bitter-Suermann, 1987). This view is supported by studies in animals genetically deficient in C4, C2 or C3, who show impaired antibody responses, but only to low doses of antigen. C3-related generation of antibody responses may occur secondarily to its role in localising antigen in germinal centres (Klaus and Humphrey, 1977), or the effect of C3d on B cell activation discussed earlier.

VI. SUMMARY

The existence of a complement system throughout vertebrates clearly demonstrates its probable evolutionary importance in protection against micro-organisms. This is further shown by the increased occurrence of infections in patients with inherited deficiencies of some complement proteins or receptors. Complement has a special role in natural immunity because of its ability to recognise a vast array of antigens by either pathway in the absence of antibodies, and to deposit C3b on the activating surface. This alone may sufficiently opsonise micro-organisms, particularly in association with neutrophil activation, or lead to destruction by the membrane attack complex. The soluble mediators of complement are required for the leukocytosis response to infection and for controlling the local inflammatory response. Furthermore, both soluble and surface-bound fragments may be involved in regulation of other components of the immune response. To focus complement attack on microorganisms, a complex set of soluble and membrane-associated regulatory proteins exists, ensuring that indiscriminate deposition of complement and damage to host cells does not occur.

REFERENCES

Alper, C. A., Abramson, N. and Johnston, R. B. (1970). Studies *in vivo* and *in vitro* on an abnormality in the metabolism of C3 in a patient with increased susceptibility to infection. *J. Clin. Invest.* 49: 1975–85.

Atkinson, J. P., and Farries, T. (1987). Separation of self from non-self in the complement system. *Immunol. Today* 8: 212–5.

Aubert, B., Chesne, S., Arland, G. J., and Colomb, M. G. (1985). Antibody-independent interaction between the first component of human complement, C1, and the outer membrane of *Escherichia coli* D31m4. *Biochem. J.* 232: 513–9.

Baker, C. J., Edwards, M. S., Webb, B. J. and Kasper, D. L. (1982). Antibody-independent classical pathway mediated opsonophagocytosis of type Ia group B streptococcus. *J. Clin. Invest.* 69: 394–404.

Bartholomew, R. M. and Esser, A. E. (1980). Mechanism of antibody-independent activation of the first component of complement (C1) on retrovirus membranes. *Biochemistry* 19: 2847–53.

Betz, S. J. and Isliker, H. (1981). Antibody-independent interactions between *Escherichia coli* J5 and human complement components. *J. Immunol.* 127: 1748–54.

Bjornson, A. B., Magnafichi, P. I., Schreiber, R. D. and Bjornson, S. (1987). Opsonization of Bacteroides by the alternative complement pathway reconstructed from isolated plasma proteins. *J. Exp. Med.* 164: 777–98.

Bobak, D. A. Gaither, T. A., Frank, M. M. and Tenner, A. J. (1987). Modulation of FcR function by complement: subcomponent C1q enhances the phagocytosis of IgG-opsonized targets by human monocytes and culture-derived macrophages. *J. Immunol.* 138: 1150–6.

Bordet, J. (1898). Sur l'agglutination et la dissolution des globules rouges par le serum d'animaux injectes de sang defibrine. *Ann. de l'Instit. Pasteur* 12: 688–95.

Bottger, E. C. and Bitter-Suermann, D. (1987). Complement and the regulation of humoral immune responses. *Immunol. Today* 8: 261–4.

Clas, F. and Loos, M. (1981). Antibody-independent binding of the first component of complement (C1) and its subcomponent C1q to the S and R forms of *Salmonella minnesota*. *Infect. Immun.* 31: 1138–44.

Cooper, N. R. (1983). Activation and regulation of the first complement component. *Federation Proc.* 42: 134–8.

Cooper, N. R. and Morrison, D. C. (1978). Binding and activation of the first component of human complement by the lipid A region of lipopolysaccharides. *J. Immunol.* 120: 1862–8.

Cooper, N. R., Jensen, F. C., Welsh, R. M. Jr. and Oldstone, M. B. A. (1976). Lysis of RNA tumour viruses by human serum: direct antibody-independent triggering of the classical complement pathway. *J. Exp. Med.* 144: 970–984.

Cyong, J. C., Witkin, S. S., Reiger, B., Barbarese, E., Good, R. A. and Day, N. K. (1982). Antibody-independent complement activation by myelin via the classical complement pathway. *J. Exp. Med.* 155: 587–98.

Dankert, J. R. and Esser, A. F. (1987). Bacterial killing by complement. C9-mediated killing in the absence of C5b-8. *Biochem. J.* 244: 393–9.

Donaldson, V. H. and Evans, R. R. (1963). A biochemical abnormality in hereditary angioneurotic edema : absence of serum inhibitor of C'1- esterase. *Am. J. Med.* 35: 37–44.

Fearon, D. T. (1980). Identification of the membrane glycoprotein that is the C3b receptor of the human erythrocyte, polymorphonuclear leukocyte, B lymphocyte and monocyte. *J. Exp. Med.* 152: 20–30.

Fearon, D. T. and Austen, K. F. (1980). The alternative pathway of complement - a system for host resistance to microbial infection. *N. Engl. J. Med.* 303: 259–63.

Folkerd, E. J. Gardner, B. and Hughes-Jones, N. C. (1980). The relationship between the binding ability and the rate of activation of the complement component C1. *Immunology* 41: 179–85.

Frade, R., Barel, M., Ehlin-Henriksson, B. and Klein, G. (1985). gp140, the C3d receptor of human B lymphocytes, is also the Epstein-Barr virus receptor. *Proc. Natl. Acad. Sci. USA* 82: 1490–3.

Frank, M. M., Gelfand, J. A. and Atkinson, J. P. (1976). Hereditary angioedema: the clinical syndrome and its management. *Ann. Intern. Med.* 84: 580–93.

Fries, L. F., Gaither, T. A., Hammer, C. H. and Frank, M. M. (1984). C3b covalently bound to IgG demonstrates a reduced rate of inactivation by factors H and I. *J. Exp. Med.* 160: 1640–55.

Gelfand, J. A., Boss, G. R., Conley, C. L., Reinhart, R. and Frank, M. M. (1979). Acquired C1 esterase inhibitor deficiency and angioedema : a review. *Medicine (Baltimore)* 58: 321–8.

Gervasoni, J. E. Jr., Conrad, D. H., Hugli, T. E., Schwartz, L. B. and Ruddy, S. (1986). Degradation of human anaphylatoxin C3a by rat peritoneal mast cells : a role for the secretory granule enzyme chymase and heparin proteoglycan. *J. Immunol.* 136: 285–92.

Ghebrehiwet, B. and Müller-Eberhard, H. J. (1979). C3e : an acidic fragment of human C3 with leukocytosis-inducing activity. *J. Immunol.* 123: 616–21.

Giclas, P. C., Ginsberg, M. H. and Cooper, N. R. (1979). Immunoglobulin G in-dependent activation of the classical complement pathway by monosodium urate crystals. *J. Clin. Invest.* 63: 759–64.

Golan, M., Burger, R. and Loos, M. (1982). Conformational changes in C1q after binding to immune complexes : detection of neoantigens with monoclonal antibodies. *J. Immunol.* 129: 445–7.

Gordon, D. L. (1988). Serum bactericidal activity against *Haemophilus influenzae*. *Pathology* 20: 124–9.

Gordon, D. L. and Hostetter, M. K. (1986). Complement and host defence against microorganisms. *Pathology* 18: 365–75.

Gordon, D. L., Johnson, G. M. and Hostetter, M. K. (1986). Ligand-receptor interactions in the phagocytosis of virulent *Streptococcus pneumoniae* by polymorphonuclear leukocytes. *J. Infect. Dis.* 154: 619–26.

Gordon, D. L., Johnson, G. M. and Hostetter, M. K. (1987). Characteristics of iC3b binding to human polymorphonuclear leukocytes. *Immunology* 60: 553–8.

Gordon, D. L., Rice, J., Finlay-Jones, J. J., McDonald, P. J. and Hostetter, M. K. (1988). Analysis of C3 deposition and degradation on bacterial surfaces after opsonization. *J. Infect. Dis.* 157: 697–704.

Griffin, J. A. and Griffin, F. M. (1979). Augmentation of macrophage comp-lement receptor function in vitro. *J. Exp. Med.* 150: 653–75.

Harpel, P. C. and Cooper, N. R. (1975). Studies on human plasma C1-inactivator-enzyme interactions. I. Mechanisms of interaction with C1s, plasmin and trypsin. *J. Clin. Invest.* 55: 593–604.

Hostetter, M. K. (1986). Serotypic differences in covalently bound C3b and its degradation fragments among virulent pneumococci. I. Implications for phagocytosis and antibody production. *J. Infect. Dis.* 153: 682–691.

Hostetter, M. K., Thomas, M. L., Rosen, F. S. and Tack, B. F. (1982). Binding of C3b occurs by a transesterification reaction at the thiolester site. *Nature* 298: 72–5.

Hostetter, M. K., Krueger, R. A. and Schmelling, D. J. (1984). The biochemistry of opsonization : central role of the reactive thiolester of the third component of complement. *J. Infect. Dis.* 150: 653–61.

Hugli, T. E. (1984). Structure and function of the anaphylatoxins. *Springer Semin. Immunopathol.* 7: 193–219.

Huey, R. and Hugli, T. E. (1985). Characterization of a C5a receptor on human polymorphonuclear leukocytes (PMN). *J. Immunol.* 135: 2063–8.

Janatova, J., Tack, B. F. and Prahl, J. W. (1980). Third component of human complement : structural requirements for its function. *Biochemistry* 19: 4470–85.

Joiner, K. A., Hammer, C. H., Brown, E. J., Cole, R. J. and Frank, M. M. (1982). Studies on the mechanism of bacterial resistance to complement-mediated killing. I. Terminal complement components are deposited and released from *Salmonella minnesota* S218 without causing bacterial death. *J. Exp. Med.* 155: 797–804.

Joiner, K. A., Brown, E., Hammer, C., Warren, K. and Frank, M. (1983). Studies on the mechanism of bacterial resistance to complement-mediated killing. III. C5b-9 deposits stably on rough and type 7 *S. pneumoniae* without causing bacterial killing. *J. Immunol.* 130: 845–9.

Joiner, K. A., Goldman, R., Schmetz, M., Berger, M., Hammer, C. H., Frank, M. M. and Leive, L. (1984). A quantitative analysis of C3 binding to O-antigen capsule, lipopolysaccharide, and outer membrane protein of *E. coli* O111B4. *J. Immunol.* 132: 369–75.

Klaus, G. G. B. and Humphrey, J. H. (1977). The generation of memory cells. I. Role of C3 in the generation of B memory cells. *Immunology* 33: 31–40.

Kovacsovics, T. J., Peitsch, M. C., Kress, A. and Isliker, H. (1987). Antibody-independent activation of C1. I. Differences in the mechanism of C1 activation by nonimmune activators and by immune complexes : C1r-independent activation of C1s by cardiolipin vesicles. *J. Immunol.* 138: 1864–70.

Lachmann, P. J. and Hughes-Jones, N. C. (1984). Initiation of complement activation. *Springer Semin. Immunopathol.* 7: 143–62.

Law, S. K. and Levine, R. P. (1977). Interaction between the third complement protein and cell surface macromolecules. *Proc. Natl. Acad. Sci. USA.* 74: 2701–5.

Law, S. K. Fearon, D. T. and Levine, R. P. (1979). Action of the C3b-inactivator on cell bound C3b. *J. Immunol.* 122: 759–65.

Leist-Welsh, P. and Bjornson, A. B. (1982). Immunoglobulin-independent utilization of the classical complement pathway in opsonophagocytosis of *Eschericia coli* by human peripheral leukocytes. *J. Immunol.* 128: 2643–51.

Levy, N. J. and Kasper, D. L. (1985). Antibody-independent and -dependent opsonization of group B *Streptococcus* requires the first component of complement C1. *Infect. Immun.* 49: 19–24.

Levy, N. J. and Kasper, D. L. (1986). Surface-bound capsular polysaccharide of type 1a group B *Streptococcus* mediates C1 binding and activation of the classical complement pathway. *J. Immunol.* 136: 4157–62.

Loos, M., Wellek, B., Thesen, R. and Opferkuch, W. (1978). Antibody-independent interaction of the first component of complement with gram-negative bacteria. *Infect. Immun.* 22: 5–9.

Marder, S. R., Chenoweth, D. E., Goldstein, I. M. and Perez, H. D. (1985). Chemotactic responses of human peripheral blood monocytes to the complement-derived peptides C5a and C5a des arg. *J. Immunol.* 134: 3325–31.

Martin, H., McConnell, I., Gorick, B. and Hughes-Jones, N. C. (1987). Antibody-independent activation of the classical pathway of complement by Epstein-Barr virus. *Clin. Exp. Immunol.* 67: 531–6.

Moore, F. D., Fearon, D. T. and Austen, K. F. (1981). IgG on mouse erythrocytes augents activation of the human alternative complement pathway by enhancing deposition of C3b. *J. Immunol.* 126: 1805–9.

Moore, F. D., Austen, K. F. and Fearon, D. T. (1982). Antibody restores human alternative complement pathway activation by mouse erythrocytes rendered functionally deficient by pretreatment with pronase. *J. Immunol.* 128: 1302–6.

Morgan, E. L., Weigle, W. O. and Hugli, T. E. (1984). Anaphylatoxin-mediated regulation of human and murine immune responses. *Federation Proc.* 43: 2543–7.

Morgan, E. L., Thoman, M. L., Weigle, W. O. and Hugli, T. E. (1985). Human C3a-mediated suppression of the immune response. I. Suppression of murine *in vitro* antibody responses occurs through the generation of nonspecific Lyt-2$^+$ suppressor T cell. *J. Immunol.* 134: 51–7.

Morgan, B. P., Dankert, J. R. and Esser, A. F. (1987). Recovery of human neutrophils from complement attack : removal of the membrane attack complex by endocytosis and exocytosis. *J. Immunol.* 138: 246–53.

Müller-Eberhard, H. J. (1986). The membrane attack complex of complement. *Ann. Rev. Immunol.* 4: 503–28.

Nicholson-Weller, A., Burge, J., Fearon, D. T., Weller, P. F. and Austen, K. F. (1982). Isolation of a human erythrocyte glycoprotein with decay accelerating activity for C3 convertases of the complement system. *J. Immunol.* 129: 184–9.

Pangburn, M. K. and Müller-Eberhard, H. J. (1980). Relation of a putative thioester bond in C3 to activation of the alternative pathway and the binding of C3b to biological targets of complement. *J. Exp. Med.* 152: 1102–14.

Pangburn, M. K., Schreiber, R. D. and Müller-Eberhard, H. J. (1981). Formation of the initial C3 convertase of the alternative complement pathway : acquisition of C3b-like activities by spontaneous hydrolysis of the putative thiolester in native C3. *J. Exp. Med.* 154: 856–67.

Peitsch, M. C., Kovacsovics, T. J., Tschopp, J. and Isliker, H. (1987). Antibody-independent activation of C1. II. Evidence for two classes of nonimmune activators of the classical pathway of complement. *J. Immunol.* 138: 1871–6.

Pepys, M. B. (1976). Role of complement in the induction of immunological responses. *Transplant. Rev.* 32: 93–120.

Perri, R. T., Wilson, B. S. and Kay, N. E. (1986). Inhibition of B cell growth factor (BCGF) by monoclonal antibodies directed against the C3d receptor (CR2). *Eur. J. Immunol.* 16: 350–5.

Pillemer, L., Blum, L., Lepow, I. H., Ross, O. A., Todd, E. W. and Wardlan, A. C. (1954). The properdin system and immunity. I. Demonstration and isolation of a new serum protein, properdin, and its role in immune phenomena. *Science* 120: 279–85.

Pinckard, R. N., Olson, M. S., Kelley, R. E., De Heer, D. H., Palmer, J. D., O'Rourke, R. A. and Goldfein, S. (1973). Antibody-independent activation of human C1 after interaction with heart subcellular membranes. *J. Immunol.* 110: 1376–13.

Podack, E. R., Preissner, K. T. and Müller-Eberhard, H. J. (1984). Inhibition of C9 polymerization within the SC5b-9 complex of complement by S-protein. *Acta. Pathol. Microbiol. Immunol. Scand.* 92: 89–96.

Ratnoff, O. D., Pensky, J., Ogston, D. and Naff G. B. (1969). The inhibition of plasmin, plasma kallikrein, plasma permeability factor, and the C'1r subcomponent of the first component of complement by serum C'1 esterase inhibitor. *J. Exp. Med.* 129: 315–31.

Robbins, J. B., McCracken, G. H. Jr., Gotschlich, E., Orskov, F., Orskov, I. and Hanson, L. A. (1974). *Escherichia coli* K1 capsular polysaccharide associated with neonatal meningitis. *N. Engl. J. Med.* 290: 1216–20.

Ross, G. D., and Lambris, J. D. (1982). Identification of a C3bi specific membrane complement receptor that is expressed on lymphocytes, monocytes, neutrophils and erythrocytes. *J. Exp. Med.* 155: 96–110.

Ross, G. D., Cain, J. A. and Lachmann, P. J. (1985). Membrane complement receptor type three (CR3) has lectin-like properties analagous to bovine conglutinin and functions as a receptor for zymosan and rabbit erythrocytes as well as a receptor for iC3b. *J. Immunol.* 134: 3307–15.

Schonermark, S., Rauterberg, E. W., Shin, M. L., Loke, S., Roelcke, D. and Hansch, G. M. (1986). Homologous species restriction in lysis of human erythrocytes: a membrane-derived protein with C8-binding capacity functions as an inhibitor. *J. Immunol.* 136: 1772–6.

Schreiber, R. D., Morrison, D. C., Podack, E. R. and Müller-Eberhard, H. J. (1979). Bactericidal activity of the alternative complement pathway generated from eleven isolated plasma proteins. *J. Exp. Med.* 149: 870–82.

Schreiber, R. D., Pangburn, M. K., Medicus, R. G. and Müller-Eberhard, H. J. (1980). Raji cell injury and subsequent lysis by the purified cytolytic alternative pathway of human complement. *Clin. Immunol. Immunopathol.* 15: 384–96.

Schreiber, R. D., Pangburn, M. K., Bjornson, A. B., Brothers, M. A. and Müller-Eberhard, H. J. (1982). The role of C3 fragments in endocytosis and extracellular cytotoxic reactions by polymorphonuclear leukocytes. *Clin. Immunol. Immunopathol.* 23: 335–7.

Seya, T., Turner, J. R. and Atkinson, J. P. (1986). Purification and characterization of a membrane protein (gp45–70) that is a cofactor for cleavage of C3b and C4b. *J. Exp. Med.* 163: 837–55.

Sim, R. B., Arland, G. J. and Colomb, M. G. (1979). C1 inhibitor-dependent dissociation of human complement component C1 bound to immune complexes. *Biochem. J.* 179: 449–57.

Sim, R. B., Twose, T. M., Paterson, D. S. and Sim, E. (1983). The covalent-binding reaction of complement component C3. *Biochem. J.* 193: 115–27.

Sissons, J. G. P., Oldstone, M. B. A. and Schreiber, R. D. (1980). Antibody-independent activation of the alternative complement pathway by measles virus-infected cells. *Proc. Natl. Acad. Sci. USA.* 77: 559–62.

Sorvillo, J. M. and Pearlstein, E. (1985). C1q, a subunit of the first component of complement, enhances binding of plasma fibronectin to bacteria. *Infect. Immun.* 49: 664–9.

Sorvillo, J., Gigli, I. and Pearlstein, E. (1986). The effect of fibronectin on the processing of C1q- and C3b/bi-coated immune complexes by peripheral blood monocytes. *J. Immunol.* 136: 1023–6.

Steele, N. P., Munson, R. S. and Granoff, D. M. (1984). Antibody dependent alternative pathway killing of *Haemophilus influenzae* type b. *Infect. Immun.* 44: 452–8.

Tack, B. F., Harrison, R. A., Janatova, J., Thomas, M. L. and Prahl, J. W. (1980). Evidence for presence of an internal thiolester bond in third component of complement. *Proc. Natl. Acad. Sci. USA.* 77: 5764–8.

Tenner, A. J. and Cooper, N. R. (1981). Identification of types of cells in human peripheral blood that bind C1q. *J. Immunol.* 126: 1174–9.

Tenner, A. J. and Cooper, N. R. (1982). Stimulation of a human polymorphonuclear leukocyte oxidative response by the C1q subunit of the first complement component. *J. Immunol.* 128: 2547–52.

Tenner, A. J., Ziccardi, R. J. and Cooper, N. R. (1984). Antibody-independent C1 activation by *E. coli. J. Immunol.* 133: 886–91.

Thomas, M. L., Janatova, J., Gray, W. R. and Tack, B. F. (1982). Third component of human complement : localization of the internal thiolester bond. *Proc. Natl. Acad. Sci. USA.* 79: 1054–8.

Weiss, J. J., Tedder, T. F. and Fearon, D. T. (1984). Identification of a 145,000 Mr membrane protein as the C3d receptor (CR2) of human B lymphocytes. *Proc. Natl. Acad. Sci. U.S.A.* 81: 881–5.

Wexler, D. E., Chenoweth, D. E. and Cleary, P. P. (1985). Mechanism of action of the group A streptococcal C5a inactivator. *Proc. Natl. Acad. Sci. USA.* 82: 8144–8.

Wright, S. D. and Silverstein, S. C. (1982). Tumour promoting phorbol esters stimulate C3b and C3bi receptor mediated phagocytosis in cultured monocytes. *J. Exp. Med.* 156: 1149–64.

Wright, S. D., Rau, P. E., Van Voorhis, W. C., Craigmyle, L. S., Iida, K., Talle, M. A., Westburg, E. F., Goldlstein, G. and Silverstein, S. C. (1983). Identification of the C3bi receptor of human monocytes and macrophages by using monoclonal antibodies. *Proc. Natl. Acad. Sci. USA.* 80: 5699–703.

Ziccardi, R. J. (1982a). Spontaneous activation of the first component of human complement (C1) by an intramolecular autocatalytic mechanism. *J. Immunol.* 128: 2550–4.

Ziccardi, R. J. (1982b). A new role for C1-inhibitor in homeostasis : control of activation of the first component of human complement. *J. Immunol.* 128: 2505–8.

Ziccardi, R. J. and Cooper, N. R. (1976). Activation of C1r by proteolytic cleavage. *J. Immunol.* 116: 504–9.

Ziccardi, R. J. and Cooper, N. R. (1979). Active disassembly of the first complement component, C1, by C1 inactivator. *J. Immunol.* 123: 788–92.

8

Cytokines

PHILLIP D. SMITH
SHARON M. WAHL

Cellular Immunology Section
Laboratory of Microbiology and Immunology
National Institute of Dental Research
National Institutes of Health
Bethesda, Md 20892, USA

I. INTRODUCTION

During the past two decades a variety of soluble products of various lymphoid cells have become recognised as playing a critical role in natural immunity. These products, referred to collectively as cytokines,

NATURAL IMMUNITY
ISBN 0 12 5145551

are non-immunoglobulin polypeptide molecules produced principally by monocytes and lymphocytes which, among other functions, regulate the activation, maturation and proliferation of certain lymphoid and non-lymphoid cells. Functioning as intercellular mediators, cytokines play an important role in immunological reactions as well as non-immunological inflammatory processes. These functions are facilitated by several unique properties of cytokines. First, some cytokines have the capacity to act upon the same cells from which they are released. Second, many cytokines, in addition to being produced by monocytes and lymphocytes, are produced by a variety of non-lymphoid cells including epithelial cells, endothelial cells, fibroblasts and neural cells. Third, as soluble mediators, cytokines act in a genetically unrestricted manner and, in some cases, across species barriers. Fourth, a single cytokine often stimulates or regulates a multiplicity of biological activities.

In contrast to hormones, which are secreted by glandular tissue and transported in detectable amounts to distant tissues and organs, cytokines are secreted by individual cells and act locally at the site of the immunological, inflammatory or reparative process, as well as at distant sites. Because the amount of cytokine produced by a cell is extremely small, making physicochemical characterisation of the product difficult, cytokines were initially defined according to their biological activity. Subsequently, the development of more sophisticated immunochemical techniques facilitated the biochemical characterisation, purification to homogeneity, and amino acid sequencing of several cytokines. Recently, the complementary DNAs (cDNAs) for several monocyte and lymphocyte cytokines have been cloned, sequenced and transcribed in cell-free systems using recombinant DNA technology. This technology has greatly facilitated our ability to characterise the physicochemical properties and functional activities of these molecules. Therefore, the present chapter will review those cytokines which have been cloned and for which a recombinant molecule is available.

II. CYTOKINES PRODUCED BY MONOCYTES (MONOKINES)

A. Interleukin 1

The host reacts to injury such as that caused by an infectious process or inflammatory disease with a well-orchestrated series of neurological, metabolic and immunological responses, referred to collectively as the acute-phase response (Dinarello, 1984a). Playing a central role in co-ordinating this response, regardless of the nature of the injury, is interleukin 1 (IL-1). This polypeptide is secreted primarily by activated mononuclear phagocytes including circulating monocytes, pulmonary alveolar macrophages, hepatic Kupffer cells, splenic macrophages, peritoneal macrophages and bone-marrow adherent cells (Dinarello, 1984b). Recent evidence suggests that the production of IL-1 is not restricted to monocytes and tissue macrophages since substances with many of the physicochemical and biological characteristics of IL-1 may be produced by other cells, including epithelial cells and keratinocytes (Luger *et al.*, 1982), Langerhans cells (Sander *et al.*, 1984), mesangial cells of the kidney (Lovett *et al.*, 1983), astrocytes and glioma cells (Fountana *et al.*, 1982), fibroblasts (Iribi *et al.*, 1983), B cells (Matsushima *et al.*, 1985) and endothelial cells (Nawroth *et al.*, 1986a).

In 1984 the cloning, sequence analysis and expression of the cDNA for human IL-1 was first reported (Auron *et al.*, 1984). The cDNA encodes a 31,000 dalton 269-amino-acid precursor peptide which is proteolytically processed into the 17,000 dalton (pI 7.0) biologically active form of IL-1. Comparison of the human IL-1 cDNA with the murine IL-1 cDNA, which was cloned and expressed the same year (Lomedico *et al.*, 1984), revealed significant homology at the nucleotide and amino acid levels (Auron *et al.*, 1985). Subsequently, a second human cDNA encoding IL-1 was discovered when two distinct cDNAs encoding two proteins (pI 5.0 and pI 7.0) with IL-1 activity were isolated from a macrophage cDNA library (Marsh *et al.*, 1985). These two cDNAs exhibit 45 per cent nucleotide homology and 26 per cent peptide homology. Thus, two distinct human IL-1 genes appear to encode proteins, termed IL-1α (pI 5.0, 17,000 daltons) and IL-1β (pI 7.0, 17,000 daltons), with IL-1 activity. Recent evidence indicates that the biological activities of Il-1α and IL-1β, as judged by their activity on connective tissue and lymphoid cells, are nearly equivalent (Rupp *et al.*, 1986), suggesting that the two IL-1 molecules act on target cells through a single class of receptor sites.

The production of IL-1 in the acute-phase response is initiated by events which activate macrophages, such as phagocytosis of micro-organisms or exposure to products of micro-organisms including lipopolysaccharide (LPS) and muramyl dipeptide (MDP). One of the more prominent features of the acute-phase reaction is fever. Studies dating back to the 1940s and 1950s (Menkin, 1943; Beeson, 1948; Atkins and Wood, 1955) identified an endogenous pyrogen as capable of causing fever, although it was not until the 1960s and 1970s that purification procedures and cell-culture techniques facilitated identification of bone-marrow-derived phagocytes as the source of endogenous pyrogen (Hahn *et al.*, 1967; Bodel, 1974). That IL-1 is indeed the endogenous pyrogen has been confirmed by the ability of human recombinant IL-1 to induce a monophasic febrile response in rabbits and mice (Dinarello *et al.*, 1986a). This response appears to be due to the ability of IL-1 to stimulate an increase in the synthesis of prostaglandins in the preoptic region of the anterior hypothalamus, the thermoregulatory center of the brain, which in turn act to reset the body's temperature set point (Dinarello and Wolff, 1982).

In addition to its effect on the central nervous system, IL-1 induces important metabolic responses during an acute injury. One such response is muscle wasting. Interleukin 1 likely contributes to this catabolic process by stimulating muscle tissue to release prostaglandin E_2 (PGE$_2$), a mediator that facilitates the oxidation of tissue amino acids (Baracos *et al.*, 1983). Other metabolic responses in the acute-phase reaction which appear to be mediated by IL-1 include a reduction in the serum levels of iron and zinc (Kampschmidt and Upchurch, 1969; Bornstein and Walsh, 1978) and an increase in hepatic production of a group of serum proteins referred to as the acute-phase reactants (Dinarello, 1984b) (see also Chapter 9). The reduced levels of iron and zinc, divalent cations required by micro-organisms for metabolism and growth, may limit the growth of some micro-organisms. The reduced level of serum iron probably also contributes to the anaemia associated with some infections. The acute-phase reactants include fibrinogen, haptoglobin, ceruloplasmin, amyloid A, α2-macroglobulin and C-reactive protein, some of which may participate in host defence and immunoregulatory functions (Benson *et al.*, 1975). For example, the increased hepatic synthesis of ceruloplasmin in response to IL-1 (Kampschmidt, 1981; Kampschmidt and Pulman, 1978) causes an increase in the serum level of copper, a cation that has been shown to have anti-inflammatory properties (Jacka *et al.*, 1983). In addition, the digestion of C-reactive protein by neutrophil-derived proteases has been shown to produce three peptides that are similar in structure to the phagocytic cell activator tuftsin and that augment phagocyte chemotaxis, superoxide production and monocyte IL-1 production (Robey *et al.*, 1987).

Another characteristic feature of the acute-phase reaction is an increase in the number of neutrophils in the circulation and at sites of inflammation. These cells play a critical phagocytic role in acute, particularly bacterial, infections. The systemic and local neutrophilia appears to be due to the ability of IL-1 to induce emigration of mature neutrophils from the bone marrow into the circulation and to act as a chemoattractant for neutrophils at sites of inflammation (Dinarello, 1984b; Luger *et al.*, 1983). Recent evidence also indicates that IL-1 facilitates the adhesion of leukocytes to vascular endothelium (Bevilacqua *et al.*, 1985) and induces the biosynthesis and cell-surface expression of procoagulant activity in vascular endothelial cells (Bevilacqua *et al.*,

1984), two important components of the vascular changes associated with acute, as well as chronic, inflammation. In addition, Il-1 appears capable of stimulating vessel-wall secretion of PGI_2, which plays an important role in platelet aggregation and vascular tone (Rossi et al., 1985). These actions of Il-1 are likely to contribute to the regulation of endothelial-cell-mediated intravascular coagulation.

Many metabolic changes accompanying inflammatory and infectious processes are mediated by an increase in glucocorticoids. This increase may be due, in part, to the ability of IL-1 to stimulate the release of adrenocorticotropic hormone and glucocorticoids (Besedovsky et al., 1986). Moreover, the ability of glucocorticoids to inhibit macrophage function, including cytokine production (Schaffner, 1985; Wahl et al., 1975), suggests the presence of an immunoregulatory feedback circuit which serves to limit the magnitude of the IL-1 response.

One of the most compelling examples of the crucial role which cytokines play in mediating cellular interactions is the IL-1 regulation of lymphocyte proliferation. In the original experiments examining this important function, a product of murine macrophages referred to as lymphocyte-activating factor (LAF) was shown to amplify the mitogen-induced proliferative response of mouse thymocytes (Gery et al., 1981). Since then many studies have confirmed that IL-1 is required for antigen- and mitogen-driven proliferation of human lymphocytes (Oppenheim et al., 1982). The mechanism of this important regulatory function involves the following series of events. Resting macrophages, which do not secrete detectable amounts of IL-1, become activated and produce IL-1. The IL-1, possibly in a membrane-associated form (Kurt-Jones et al., 1985), then interacts with lymphocytes of the helper/inducer phenotype through a high-affinity receptor mediated mechanism (Irle et al., 1978; Dower et al., 1985), stimulating the cells to release the lymphokine IL-2 (Gillis and Mizel, 1981; Maizel et al., 1981). Interleukin 1 also induces increased expression of IL-2 receptors on certain lymphocyte populations (Kaye et al., 1984; McKean et al., 1985). These cells, including helper/inducer and suppressor/cytotoxic lymphocytes (Kelso and McDonald, 1982; Farrar et al., 1980), are in turn induced by the IL-2 signal released from the helper/inducer lymphocytes to undergo clonal expansion.

In addition to the critical role of IL-1 in T lymphocyte proliferation, factors released from activated normal and cell-line macrophages also are involved in the differentiation of B cells, augmenting the terminal differentiation of these cells to immunoglobulin-producing plasma cells (Kawanishi et al., 1983; Hoffman, 1979; Butler et al., 1979). The idea that these factors include IL-1 is supported, in part, by the evidence: (a) that IL-1 acts along with the lymphokine B-cell-derived growth factor (BCGF) to activate B cells (Falkoff *et al.*, 1984; Howard *et al.*, 1983); and (b) that IL-1, even in the absence of other detectable cytokines, can promote B cell activation, division and proliferation (Pike and Nossal, 1985). The immunoregulatory role of IL-1 is not restricted to T cell and B cell responses. In the presence of IL-2 and/or interferon (IFN), IL-1 appears to augment natural killer (NK) cell activity (Dempsey *et al.*, 1982). Interleukin 1 also stimulates monocyte cytotoxic activity as suggested by the ability of the monokine to serve as an autostimulating factor for maintaining monocyte cytotoxic activity against tumour target cells (Onozaki *et al.*, 1985).

The ability of IL-1 to regulate the activities of many types of cells contributes to the host response that leads to chronic tissue inflammation and tissue repair. This has been elucidated by studies in vitro utilising the rheumatoid joint as the prototype of a chronic inflammatory process. These studies have revealed that the tissue-destructive component of an inflammatory process may be mediated, in part, by the ability of IL-1 to stimulate other cells such as chondrocytes, synovial cells and fibroblasts to secrete prostaglandins and collagenase (Mizel *et al.*, 1980; McQuire *et al.*, 1982; Postlewaite *et al.*, 1983), which in turn contribute to connective tissue destruction. Moreover, the secretion of prostaglandins and collagenase by activated macrophages themselves (Wahl *et al.*, 1977) amplifies the IL-1-induced secretion of inflammatory mediators, further augmenting tissue destruction. Interleukin 1 also may be involved in tissue repair, specifically, modulating fibroblast growth and function. This is suggested by the apparent ability of IL-1 to stimulate fibroblast proliferation (Schmidt *et al.*, 1982). In this regard, silica-treated monocytes have been shown to release fibroblast proliferation factors identical to IL-1 (Schmidt *et al.*, 1984). Similarly, monocytes (and lymphocytes) from the synovial tissue of rheumatoid arthritis patients have been shown to produce fibroblast-activating factors (Wahl *et al.*, 1985), consistent with the increased levels of IL-1 which have been identified in synovial fluid from rheumatoid joints (Fontano *et al.*, 1982; Wood *et al.*, 1983). Another area of chronic inflammation in which IL-1 may play a particularly important role is bone resorption (Gowen *et al.*, 1983; Heath *et al.*, 1985).Inflammatory osteolysis involves IL-1 stimulation of osteoblasts which in turn stimulate osteoclastic bone resorption (Thomson *et al.*, 1986).

Thus, serving as an activation and amplification signal, IL-1 plays a key role in acute and chronic inflammatory processes and the regulation of lymphocyte activities. The involvement of IL-1 in these responses illustrates the dependence of many cellular reactions on IL-1 as the host defends itself against infectious and inflammatory injury.

B. Tumour Necrosis Factor α

Another monokine which plays an important role in mediating the host response to injury is tumour necrosis factor α (TNFα, cachectin). As with IL-1, the existence of a soluble mediator with the functional characteristics of TNFα was suspected long before the cytokine was actually characterised. Identified originally as an endotoxin-induced serum factor that caused necrosis of selected tumour cells (O'Malley *et al.*, 1962; Carswell *et al.*, 1975), the factor was found to be a product of macrophages and was named tumour necrosis factor (Mathews, 1981; Mannel *et al.*, 1980). Within a short period of time, TNFα was purified to homogeneity and found to have a molecular weight of approximately 17,000, with an isoelectric point of 5.3, and to contain two cysteines involved in a disulfide bridge (Aggarwal, *et al.*, 1985a). The complementary DNA encoding TNFα was cloned and expressed in *Escherichia coli* (Pennica *et al.*, 1984; Wang *et al.*, 1985; Shirai, *et al.*, 1985). Characterisation of the purified cytokine and the expression product revealed TNFα to be a polypeptide consisting of 157 amino acids with a 30 per cent (Aggarwal *et al.*, 1985a) to 50 per cent (Pennica *et al.*, 1984) homology in amino acid sequence to tumour necrosis factor β (TNFβ, lymphotoxin), a lymphokine with similar biological properties (see below). The genes encoding both TNFα and TNFβ appear to be closely linked on human chromosome 6 to the human major histocompatibility complex, either within the chromosomal segments between HLA-DR and HLA-A or centromeric of HLA-DP (Nedwin *et al.*, 1985; Spies *et al.*, 1986). Moreover, the action of TNFα, as well as TNFβ, appears to be receptor-mediated, both cytokines sharing a common, high-affinity receptor for which (on the human cervical carcinoma cell line ME-180) there are 2000 sites per cell with a K_d of approximately 0.2 nM (Aggarwal *et al.*, 1985b).

In addition to its cytostatic and cytotoxic action on tumour cells and tumour cell lines, TNFα can also induce cachexia. The cachexia which accompanies many infectious, inflammatory and neoplastic diseases was initially investigated simultaneously with, but independently of, studies of the cytotoxic activity of TNFα. In early studies, rabbits infected with *Trypanosoma brucei* were found to develop marked cachexia and hypertriglyceridaemia, the latter apparently due to a reduction in systemic lipoprotein lipase activity (Rouzer and Cerami, 1980). A similar enzyme inhibition was produced in endotoxin-sensitive (C3H/HeN), but not endotoxin-resistant (C3H/HeJ), mice following injection with lipopolysaccharide (LPS) (Kawakami and Cerami, 1981). A serum factor was suspected to be involved since serum from the C3H/HeN mice could induce the inhibition in C3H/HeJ mice. The factor, subsequently named cachectin, was shown to be capable of suppressing lipoprotein lipase activity in isolated preadipocyte cells and adipocytes, and endotoxin-stimulated macrophages were identified as the cell source of cachectin (Kawakami *et al.*, 1982; Mahoney *et al.*, 1985). DNA sequencing studies provided convincing evidence that cachectin and TNFα were homologous, if not identical, molecules (Pennica *et al.*, 1985; Caput *et al.*, 1986). Using the recombinant molecule, the role of TNFα (cachectin) in cytotoxicity and cachexia was confirmed. Specifically, recombinant TNFα has been shown to be an important mediator of monocyte cytotoxicity for tumour target cells such as human rhabdomyosarcoma and colon adenocarcinoma cells (Feinman *et al.*, 1987). Moreover, TNFα appears to be capable of both enhancing monocyte cytotoxicity and mediating it in response to IFN-γ (but not IFN-α), IL-1 or, in an autocrine manner, TNFα itself (Ramila and Epstein, 1986). Recombinant TNFα can also suppress lipoprotein lipase activity (Beutler *et al.*, 1985a), apparently by its ability to suppress adipocyte gene expression (Torti *et al.*, 1985).

The biological action of TNFα is not restricted to its cytotoxic action against tumour cells and role in promoting cachexia. Experiments using recombinant TNFα have provided convincing evidence that TNFα is a pleiotropic cytokine with a broad range of actions. For example, TNFα probably plays an important role in endotoxin-induced shock. This was first suggested by experiments in which mice passively immunised against cachectin resisted the lethal effects of endotoxin (Beutler *et al.*, 1985b). Subsequently, the participation of TNFα in mediating the shock and tissue injury induced by endotoxin was confirmed by experiments in which recombinant TNFα infused into rats elicited hypotension, metabolic acidosis, haemoconcentration, renal tubular acidosis and inflammatory, haemorrhagic and ischaemic changes in certain vital organs (Tracey *et al.*, 1986). In addition, the fever which frequently accompanies endotoxaemia may be due not only to IL-1 but, in part, to TNFα which also can act as an endogenous pyrogen by stimulating PGE_2 release from hypothalamic cells (Dinarello *et al.*, 1986b). Moreover, TNFα is capable of inducing secretion of IL-1, thereby amplifying many of the host responses to endotoxin (Dinarello *et al.*, 1986c; Nawroth *et al.*, 1986b).

Recent evidence indicates that TNFα participates in a spectrum of inflammatory reactions. In reactions involving vascular endothelium TNFα appears to modulate the induction of procoagulant activity (Bevilacqua *et al.*, 1986), the expression of HLA-A,B antigens on vascular endothelial cells (Collins *et al.*, 1986) and the augmentation of neutrophil adherence to vascular endothelial cells (Gamble *et al.*, 1985). Crucial to any inflammatory response is the accumulation of granulocytes, as well as macrophages, at the site of injury. In this connection, the ability of TNFα to augment the production of granulocyte–macrophage colony-stimulating factor (GM-CSF) messenger RNA and protein by various cell types (Munker *et al.*, 1986; Broudy *et al.*, 1986) may have relevance in vivo, since GM-CSF could stimulate the local proliferation and differentiation of granulocytes and macrophages. In addition to augmenting the number of these cells at sites of inflammation or infection, TNFα also appears to enhance the phagocytic and cytotoxic activities of polymorphonuclear neutrophils (Shaloby *et al.*, 1985; Djeu *et al.*, 1986), suggesting a role for TNFα in host defence against micro-organisms.

Accompanying many chronic inflammatory and infectious diseases are changes in mesenchymal tissues. One such change is osteolysis which likely involves the stimulation of osteoclast resorption by activated leukocytes (Horton *et al.*, 1974; Mundy *et al.*, 1974). Recently, TNFα (and TNFβ) was shown to cause osteoclastic bone resorption and inhibit bone collagen synthesis (Bertolini *et al.*, 1986). The mechanism of this cytokine-induced bone resorption appears to involve TNF induction of osteoblasts to produce a factor that stimulates osteoclastic activity (Thomson *et al.*, 1987). In addition, TNFα resembles IL-1 in its ability to stimulate the release of collagenase and PGE_2, important mediators of tissue destruction, from certain cells such as synovial cells and dermal fibroblasts (Dayer *et al.*, 1985). Tumour necrosis factor α also may play a role in the reparative phase of inflammation through its ability to stimulate fibroblast growth (Vilcek *et al.*, 1986). This function of TNFα is inhibited by IFN-β, a cytokine induced by TNFα, providing a potentially important feedback control mechanism for TNFα-induced fibroblast proliferation (Kohase *et al.*, 1986).

Thus, TNFα is similar to IL-1 in its ability to participate in a wide variety of inflammatory processes. Although many of the actions of these cytokines are distinct from each other, it is apparent that the biological functions of TNFα and IL-1 serve to amplify the host's response to neoplastic, inflammatory and infectious injury.

C. Platelet-derived Growth Factor

The ability of serum, but not plasma, to support the growth of various cells in vitro led in 1974 to the discovery of a mitogenic factor that subsequently was named platelet-derived growth factor (PDGF) (Ross *et al.*, 1974). Since that original observation, PDGF has become recognised as an important cytokine involved in the regulation of many cellular reactions in wound healing, atherosclerosis and possibly neoplasia.

Platelet-derived growth factor is a 32,000 dalton dimeric glycoprotein consisting of two smaller peptide chains with molecular weights of 14,000 (A-chain) and 17,000 (B-chain) which are linked by two disulfide bonds (Deuel and Huang, 1983; Deuel and Huang, 1984; Ross *et al.*, 1986). The amino acid sequences for the A-chain (Betsholtz *et al.*, 1986) and the B-chain (Collins *et al.*, 1985; Waterfield *et al.*, 1983; Johnsson *et al.*, 1984; Chiu *et al.*, 1984), determined from the nucleotide sequence of cloned cDNA, appear to have approximately 60 per cent homology. The biological action of the cytokine, mediated through different structural determinants on native PDGF and its constituent poly-peptides (Williams *et al.*, 1983), is initiated at the cellular level by binding to a high-affinity, 170,000 and 180,000 dalton cell-surface receptor which has a K_d of approximately 10^{-11} M and appears to be a tyrosine-specific protein kinase (Bowen-Pope and Ross, 1982; Ek *et al.*, 1982; Huang *et al.*, 1982).

Platelet-derived growth factor circulates stored in the α-granules of platelets (Kaplan *et al.*, 1979). Release of PDGF appears to be induced by platelet adherence and/or aggregation. In contrast, monocytes do not normally contain preformed PDGF but synthesise and secrete the cytokine following activation (Shimiokado *et al.*, 1985; Martinet *et al.*, 1986). In addition to platelets and monocytes, PDGF is expressed by vascular endothelial cells (DiCorleto and Bowen-Pope, 1983) and arterial smooth muscle cells (Walker *et al.*, 1986).

Accumulating experimental evidence implicates PDGF as an impor-tant cytokine in wound healing. Platelets are probably the initial source of PDGF at sites of tissue injury. The chemotactic activity of PDGF for both neutrophils and monocytes (Williams *et al.*, 1983; Deuel *et al.*, 1982) would then facilitate local accumulation of additional inflamma-tory cells. Activation of the monocytes would serve as a continued source of PDGF. At the site of inflammation, the ability of PDGF to act on neu-trophils, stimulating phagocytosis but inhibiting receptor-mediated oxi-dative-burst activity (Wilson *et al.*, 1987), may augment the clearance of micro-organisms but inhibit the toxic effect of oxygen metabolites on tissue and host defence cells. In addition to its chemotactic activity for leukocytes, PDGF is chemotactic for vascular smooth muscle cells (Grotendorst *et al.*, 1982; Grotendorst *et al.*, 1981) and fibroblasts (Seppa *et al.*, 1982; Heldin and Ronnstrand, 1983), cells which partici-pate in the reparative phase of inflammation. Also, the mitogenic action of PDGF, among the first biological activities described for the cytokine (Ross *et al.*, 1974; Williams *et al.*, 1983; Shimiokado *et al.*, 1985), probably augments the accumulation of mesenchymally derived connec-tive tissue-forming cells such as smooth muscle cells and fibroblasts. A disease illustrating the potential clinical relevance of PDGF is idiopathic pulmonary fibrosis, a fibrotic lung disease characterised by increased numbers of mesenchymal cells in alveolar walls and a fourfold increase in the spontaneous release of PDGF by alveolar macrophages (Martinet *et al.*, 1987).

Platelet-derived growth factor has been implicated in the pathogenesis of atherosclerosis. This is supported by studies demonstrating the ability of PDGF to stimulate the proliferation of cellular elements including fibroblasts, smooth muscle cells and, especially, endothelial cells (Walker *et al.*, 1986; Senior, *et al.*, 1985), all important components of the vascular lesion of atherosclerosis. In addition, the major sources of PDGF, macrophages and platelets, are important constituents of the vascular lesion. According to current hypothesis (Ross, 1986), mechanical and/or low-density lipoprotein-induced injury of vascular endothelial cells leads to the attachment of platelets and monocytes to endothelium and the secretion of growth factors, including PDGF, from any or all of these sources. Injury also appears to induce intimal smooth muscle cells to secrete PDGF which is mitogenic for medial smooth muscle cells but not intimal smooth muscle cells (Walker *et al.*, 1986). The potent vasoconstrictor activity of PDGF also may contribute to the vascular reactivity that accompanies certain atherosclerotic vessels (Berk *et al.*, 1986). Thus, the local release of PDGF by platelets, macrophages, endothelium and smooth muscle cells likely plays an important role in the development of atherosclerosis.

The growth-promoting activity of PDGF also may function in mediating cell transformation. This was first suggested by observations that the amino acid sequence of the transforming protein product (p28^{sis}) of the oncogene v-*sis* of simian sarcoma virus exhibited a 96 per cent homology with the B-chain (PDGF2) of PDGF (Waterfield *et al.*, 1983; Doolittle *et al.*, 1983). The v-*sis* oncogene is capable of inducing transformation only in those cells possessing PDGF receptors (Leal *et al.*, 1985). The normal human c-*sis*/PDGF2 gene sequence also has the ability to induce malignant transformation of certain cells (Gazit *et al.*, 1984). The transformation of still other non-neoplastic cells may be caused by the co-ordinated action of three peptide growth factors: PDGF, transforming growth factor β and epidermal growth factor (Assoian *et al.*, 1984). Thus, PDGF may play important roles in wound healing, atherosclerosis and possibly neoplastic transformation.

D. Fibroblast Growth Factor

Originally isolated from brain (Gospodarowicz *et al.*, 1978), fibroblast growth factors (FGFs) are potent mitogens for fibroblasts and for vascular and capillary endothelial cells in vitro and can stimulate angiogenesis in vivo. Two FGFs have been purified to homogeneity from the brain, one (aFGF) with an acidic pI and the other (bFGF) with a basic pI (Thomas *et al.*, 1984; Böhlen *et al.*, 1985). Acidic and basic FGF are similar in size (140 and 146 amino acid residues respectively), and share 53 per cent sequence homology, heparin affinity, and biological activity (Esch *et al.*, 1985a; Gimenez-Gallego *et al.*, 1985; Esch *et al.*, 1985b). Recent evidence suggests that activated macrophages also generate a fibroblast growth factor (FGF) with potent mitogenic activity for fibroblasts (Baird *et al.*, 1985). Macrophage extracts which stimulate vascular endothelial cell proliferation in vitro contain immunoreactive FGF (20 pmol/mL) which binds to a heparin–sepharose affinity column and which elutes by reverse phase high-performance liquid chromatography similar to native pituitary or brain FGF (Baird *et al.*, 1985). Although these studies suggest that macrophages release a growth factor structurally related, if not identical, to pituitary FGF, more recent studies have demonstrated that endotoxin activation of human peripheral blood monocytes induces the expression of the gene for FGF (McCartney-Francis *et al.*, 1987). Hybridisation of endotoxin-activated monocyte RNA with the bFGF cDNA probe (Abrahams *et al.*, 1986) reveals FGF mRNA transcripts not detectable in unstimulated monocytes (McCartney-Francis *et al.*, 1987). Thus, following activation, monocytes express the gene for FGF and synthesise and secrete biologically active FGF.

Receptors for acidic and/or basic FGF have been identified on capillary endothelial cells (Freisel *et al.*, 1986), 3T3 cells and bovine epithelial lens cells (Huang and Huang, 1986). Although it is unclear whether aFGF and bFGF have distinct receptors, the broad specificity of FGFs for a number of target cells including endothelial and connective tissue cells makes these cytokines likely candidates for repair-mediating peptides. Of particular interest is the demonstration that post-translationally processed aFGF and bFGF exhibit similarities to IL-1α and IL-1β by both mass and sequence homology (Gimenez-Gallego *et al.*, 1985). These observations indicate that FGF and IL-1 are members of a family of homologous growth factors. Consequently, the infiltration of monocyte-macrophages at sites of injury and inflammation may provide an important source of angiogenic and fibrogenic factors necessary for wound healing.

E. Colony-stimulating Factors

The growth and differentiation of haemopoietic progenitor cells into mature forms is dependent upon stimulation by specific glycoproteins synthesised by a variety of cell types, including macrophages and T lymphocytes, and referred to as colony-stimulating factor(s) (CSF). To date, four distinct human CSFs have been characterised and their genomic or cDNA clones isolated: granulocyte-CSF (G-CSF), macrophage-CSF (M-CSF or CSF-1), granulocyte–macrophage CSF (GM-CSF) and multilineage-CSF (multi-CSF or interleukin-3) (Metcalf, 1985; Clark and Kamen, 1987). Granulocyte-CSF is produced by monocytes and fibroblasts and M-CSF by monocytes, fibroblasts and endothelial cells. In the murine system G-CSF and M-CSF appear to act on progenitor cells already committed to a specific lineage. In contrast, GM-CSF and IL-3 are produced by T cells and are likely to act on earlier progenitor cells capable of differentiating into multiple lineages. The CSFs produced by monocytes are discussed in this section.

Granulocyte-CSF, a 19,000 dalton glycoprotein, stimulates the proliferation and differentiation of haemopoietic colonies into neutrophilic granulocytes (Metcalf, 1985; Clark and Kamen, 1987; Metcalf and Nicola, 1983). In addition, this CSF also promotes certain granulocyte effector functions including antibody-dependent cell-mediated cytotoxicity (Souza et al., 1986). The action of G-CSF appears to be through a distinct receptor-mediated pathway as suggested by the observation in the murine system that G-CSF does not share its receptor with M-CSF, IL-3 or GM-CSF (Nicola and Metcalf, 1984). The ability of monocytes, which constitutively produce G-CSF, to rapidly increase its production in vitro in response to endotoxin, antigens and phorbol esters may have an important correlation in vivo with acute inflammatory situations such as infection, during which the number of granulocytes may be increased markedly (Souza et al., 1986). The ability of IL-1 and TNF to activate the expression of G-CSF indicates that other cytokines are involved in the regulation of G-CSF (Ramaldi et al., 1987; Munker et al., 1986; Zucali et al., 1987; Sieff et al., 1987; Broxmeyer et al., 1987). Recently, the cDNA for G-CSF was isolated from the cDNA library of CHU-2 cells, a human oral cavity squamous carcinoma cell line which constitutively produces G-CSF (Nagata et al., 1986). Analysis of the CHU-2 cells and normal human leukocytes by Southern hybridisation suggested that human G-CSF is encoded by a single gene. Using the cDNA for G-CSF, the amino acid sequence for G-CSF was deduced and shown to bear little homology with human GM-CSF or murine IL-3.

In addition to G-CSF, monocytes produce M-CSF, a 45,000 dalton heavily glycosylated homodimer which stimulates the formation of macrophages from bone-marrow cells (Metcalf, 1985; Clark and Kamen, 1987; Das et al., 1981). Macrophage-CSF has been distinguished from other CSFs by its biological effect and by specific radioimmunoassays

and radioreceptor assays (Das *et al.*, 1981). More recently, oligonucleotide probes derived from the amino terminal sequence of purified
urinary M-CSF have been used to isolate genomic clones of M-CSF
(Kawaski *et al.*, 1985). The biochemical and functional characteristics of
the expression product of the cDNA for M-CSF are currently under
intense investigation.

In contrast to GM-CSF which stimulates the production of granulocytes and monocytes, M-CSF stimulates the proliferation of cells
exclusively of the mononuclear phagocyte lineage. Like G-CSF, M-CSF is
capable of stimulating certain functional activities in its responder cells.
In this regard, M-CSF has been shown to enhance the capacity of
macrophages to secrete oxygen reduction products (Wing *et al.*, 1985).
These activities are consistent with the observation that the high-affinity
cell-surface receptors mediating the biological effect of M-CSF are
present only on cells of the monocytic series (Guilbert and Stanley, 1980;
Byrne *et al.*, 1981). Interestingly, the M-CSF receptor and the c-*fms*
proto-oncogene product appear to be related or possibly identical
molecules, suggesting the intriguing possibility that the receptor may be
involved in oncogenic transformation (Byrne *et al.*, 1981). However,
unlike PDGF, the CSFs themselves have no homology with oncogenes or
known growth factors. Experiments demonstrating that the transformation of non-leukaemic myeloid cells into leukaemic forms coincides
with the acquisition in the same cells of the ability to synthesise CSF
(Hapel *et al.*, 1981; Schrader and Crapper, 1983) suggest a potential role
for CSF autocrine stimulation in myeloid leukaemias.

F. Transforming Growth Factor β

Monocytes secrete another important regulatory peptide, transforming
growth factor beta (TGF-β) (Assoian *et al.*, 1988). Transforming growth
factor beta is a 25,000 dalton peptide originally defined by its ability to
stimulate the anchorage-independent growth in soft agar of cells which
are otherwise anchorage-dependent (Todaro *et al.*, 1980; Moses *et al.*,
1981; Roberts *et al.*, 1981). Subsequently, TGF-β was shown to both
stimulate and inhibit cell proliferation depending on the cell type and
culture conditions (Tucker *et al.*, 1987; Roberts *et al.*, 1985; Moses *et al.*,
1985). Purification to homogeneity of TGF-β from different sources
including bovine kidney (Roberts *et al.*, 1983a), human placenta (Frolik
et al., 1983), human, platelets (Assoian *et al.*, 1983) and feline sarcoma
virus transformed rat cells (Massagué, 1984) revealed the cytokine to be a
25,000 dalton, disulfide-linked, homodimeric molecule. Amino acid

sequencing of reduced TGF-β confirmed that the two chains of TGF-β are identical and consist of 112 amino acids each (Derynck *et al.*, 1985).

The gene for TGF-β has been cloned from a human genomic library and from cDNA libraries derived from human placenta and the human fibrosarcoma line HT1080 (Derynck *et al.*, 1985). A precursor molecule is encoded by residue 391 in which native TGF-β is encoded by residues 280–391 (Derynck *et al.*, 1985). The gene for TGF-β is transcribed into a 2.5 kilobase mRNA present in many normal and transformed cells. In peripheral blood monocytes, the gene is constitutively expressed (Assoian *et al.*, 1988), but secretion of TGF-β is dependent upon activation of the cells. Furthermore, the U937 histiocytic cell line, a monocyte precursor, also contains mRNA for TGF-β independent of differentiation (Assoian *et al.*, 1988). Since the levels of mRNA for TGF-β are similar in control and activated monocytes, the control mechanism responsible for induction of TGF-β secretion following monocyte activation does not appear to be at the level of RNA. It is likely that different subcellular mechanisms regulate gene expression and secretion of this growth factor in monocyte/macrophages. In association with the TGF-β, the monocytes also generate a binding protein for TGF-β which effectively inhibits the interaction between TGF-β and its cell-surface receptor (Assoian *et al.*, 1988). Activation of this larger molecular weight precursor molecule is likely to be an important regulatory step in TGF-β action.

Although the original studies favored a role for TGF-β as a cancer-specific regulatory peptide, the identification of this mediator in many normal cells including haemopoietic cells such as platelets, lymphocytes and monocytes indicates that TGF-β may have a more fundamental regulatory role in cell biology. One such role, participation in tissue repair, is suggested by evidence that TGF-β induces both angiogenesis and fibrosis in vivo (Roberts *et al.*, 1986). Further evidence supporting a role for TGF-β in tissue repair is provided by experiments in which the subcutaneous injection of TGF-β into newborn mice results in the development of granulation tissue composed of mononuclear cells, fibroblasts, capillaries and collagen (Roberts *et al.*, 1986). The cytokine is also an extremely potent chemoattractant for monocytes with optimal concentrations ranging from 0.04–0.4 pM (Wahl *et al.*, 1987a). At higher concentrations (>40 pM), TGF-β stimulates monocytes to secrete growth-promoting peptides for fibroblasts and endothelial cells, including IL-1 (Wahl *et al.*, 1987). In addition to the effects of TGF-β on monocytes, TGF-β has direct stimulatory effects on the formation of collagen and fibronectin by fibroblasts (Roberts *et al.*, 1986; Ignotz and Massagué, 1986; Raghow *et al.*, 1987). Thus, the ability of monocytes to generate this cytokine at sites of injury may have important implications in the healing process. Although platelets possess and release TGF-β (Assoian *et al.*, 1983), they are unable to synthesise proteins such as TGF-β and their contribution of TGF-β is therefore short-lived. Monocytes which enter the wound prior to fibrosis and angiogenesis, however, can serve as an ongoing source of TGF-β and other mediators of tissue repair.

In contrast to its enhancement of monocyte function in vitro (Wahl *et al.*, 1987) and its induction of granulation tissue in vivo (Roberts *et al.*, 1986; Raghow *et al.*, 1987), TGF-β appears to suppress lymphocyte proliferation (Kehrl *et al.*, 1986a; Kehrl *et al.*, 1986b; Wahl *et al.*, 1988). The ability of TGF-β to inhibit lymphocyte proliferation at femtomolar concentrations makes it significantly more biologically potent than the T-cell-specific immunosuppressant cyclosporin A (Krönke *et al.*, 1984; Bickel *et al.*, 1987). Although one possible level at which TGF-β might act to suppress lymphocyte mitogenesis is inhibition of IL-1 production, TGF-β has been shown to augment IL-1 synthesis by monocytes (Wahl *et al.*, 1987). If the inhibitory action of TGF-β occurred at the level of growth-factor receptors, it would be expected that the signal-transducing activity of the receptors would be markedly impaired after treatment with TGF-β. However, by at least two parameters, the induction of IL-2 synthesis and IL-2 receptor expression, TGF-β does not interfere with IL-1 receptor induced signal transduction. Transforming growth factor β at concentrations up to 20 ng/mL did not inhibit transcription of IL-2 receptor genes nor the phenotypic expression of these receptors on the surface of human peripheral blood lymphocytes (Wahl *et al.*, 1988). Whereas the initiation of T cell cycle progression depends on immuno-stimulatory signals such as antigens, mitogens and/or IL-1, the transition from G_1 into the replicative phases of the cell cycle is mediated by IL-2 alone (Cantrell and Smith, 1984) and IL-2 concentration is a critical determinant of cell cycle progression. Since IL-2 receptor distribution is unimpaired and IL-2 levels are not suppressed in the presence of TGF-β, IL-2 mediated cell cycle progression probably proceeds to some later level in the cell cycle before being arrested by TGF-β (Krönke *et al.*, 1984).

The specificity of the immunosuppressive potential of TGF-β is of significant interest. Transforming growth factor β stimulates monocytes to transcribe and translate IL-1, yet suppresses the ability of IL-1 to promote lymphocyte proliferation and therefore immune responsiveness. These observations suggest that TGF-β might serve as a negative feedback mechanism to reverse the inflammatory response, yet allow monocyte-derived IL-1 and other monokines to continue modulation of tissue repair. In addition, these findings may have significance in defining a mechanism by which tumour cells avoid destruction by the immune system. Thus, the production of TGF-β by neoplastic cells (Roberts *et al.*, 1983b) may provide a potent mechanism for suppression of the host's lymphoid cells and may thereby favour unrestricted tumour cell growth.

III. CYTOKINES PRODUCED BY LYMPHOCYTES (LYMPHOKINES)

A. Interleukin 2

The ability to grow T cells in culture was made possible in 1976 by the discovery of T cell growth factor (TCGF) (Morgan *et al.*, 1976; Ruscetti *et al.*, 1977), subsequently termed interleukin 2 (IL-2) (Smith, 1980). This soluble mediator, originally identified in phytohaemagglutinin (PHA)-stimulated lymphocyte culture media, allowed the long-term proliferation of normal human T lymphocytes from peripheral blood and bone marrow. In contrast to the lectin-induced proliferation of peripheral blood lymphocytes, TCGF acted as a selective mitogen in inducing the proliferation of T lymphocytes following lectin- or antigen-induced blast transformation. This activity was not altered by removal of PHA from the culture media (Kurnick *et al.*, 1979) or purification to homogeneity (Mier and Gallo, 1980), indicating early on that the activity of IL-2 was not due to contaminating lectin, interferon, CSF or other factors. This has been confirmed using recombinant IL-2, which was cloned and sequenced in 1983 (Taniguchi *et al.*, 1983).

Interleukin 2 is a 133-amino-acid glycoprotein with a molecular weight of 15,420 daltons (Lowenthal *et al.*, 1985; Moretta, 1985) produced by helper/inducer and some cytotoxic/suppressor T cells (Moretta, 1985; Maggi *et al.*, 1985). The cytokine, required for the transition of activated T cells from the G_1 to the S phase of the cell cycle (Smith, 1984; Klaus and Hawrylowicz, 1984), plays a crucial role in the generation and maintenance of various cells and factors involved in immune responses. The action of IL-2 on its target cells is dependent upon its binding to a specific, high-affinity membrane receptor (Robb *et al.*, 1981). Characterisation of this receptor has been facilitated by a monoclonal antibody (anti-Tac) to the receptor (Leonard *et al.*, 1982; Leonard *et al.*, 1985). Recently, cDNAs encoding the receptor were cloned, sequenced and expressed, revealing the IL-2 receptor precursor to be a 33,000 dalton, 251-amino-acid peptide separated into two domains by a putative 19-residue transmembrane region that is post-translationally glycosylated into the mature 55,000 dalton, 272-amino-acid Tac peptide (Leonard *et al.*, 1984; Nikaido *et al.*, 1984). In contrast to the presence of a single class of high-affinity receptors for other cytokines, two classes of receptor for IL-2 — a high-affinity (10 pM K_d) and a lower affinity (10 nM K_d) form — are present on cells which respond to IL-2 (Robb *et al.*, 1984). Biological action of IL-2 appears to be mediated by the high-affinity receptors which constitute 5–15 per cent of the IL-2 receptors. Recently, a non-Tac, second IL-2-binding peptide (p75) with a relative molecular weight of 75,000 was identified (Tsudo *et al.*, 1986; Sharon *et al.*, 1986; Teshigawara, 1987). Tac- or p75-binding peptides, but not both, are present on cells expressing low-affinity receptors alone, whereas both peptides are present on cells expressing high-affinity (and low-affinity) peptides (Tsudo *et al.*, 1987). Based on these findings, a multichain model for the high-affinity receptor has been proposed in which expression of Tac or p75 peptides alone represent low-affinity receptors, but the expression of both peptides associated in a receptor complex results in the expression of high-affinity receptors for IL-2 (Tsudo *et al.*, 1987).

The IL-2 receptor is not present on resting T cells, but is rapidly expressed within four hours of stimulation with mitogen or antigen (Depper *et al.*, 1985). The binding of IL-2 to the receptor elicits the expression of additional binding sites on the cell surface and simultaneously a 20 to 30 per cent reduction in detectable high-affinity IL-2 receptors. Following internalisation of the IL-2, the proliferative phase of cell growth is initiated. Resembling a hormone receptor, the IL-2 receptor exhibits high affinity, saturability, ligand specificity and target-cell specificity (Cantrell and Smith, 1983). Thus, the specificity of T cell clonal expansion is derived not from IL-2 but from the receptor for IL-2 present on certain cells.

Interleukin 2 is a soluble factor required for the growth and differentiation of certain cells, including helper T cells which produce it. Other cells responding to IL-2, all of which express the IL-2 receptors, include precursors of cytotoxic T lymphocytes (Erard *et al.*, 1985; Orosz *et al.*, 1985), precursors of natural killer cells (Williams *et al.*, 1985; Rook *et al.*, 1985) and B cells (Waldmann *et al.*, 1984; Lowenthal *et al.*, 1985; Jung *et al.*, 1984; Tsudo *et al.*, 1984). Interleukin 2 also regulates the function of natural killer cells and resting cytotoxic non-T cells (referred to as lymphokine-activated killer [LAK] cells), inducing increased cytotoxic activity for tumour target cells, a fact which has important therapeutic implications (Rosenberg *et al.*, 1985). In addition, IL-2 regulates the production of immune interferon by T cells and T cell subsets (Kasahara *et al.*, 1983). Recently, IL-2 receptors were detected on stimulated normal monocytes and promonocyte cell lines (Hermann *et al.*, 1985; Holter *et al.*, 1986; Holter *et al.*, 1987; Wahl *et al.*, 1987b). The IL-2 receptor–ligand complex on monocytes may mediate lymphocyte–

monocyte interactions and appears to promote monocyte effector function by augmenting the generation of reactive oxygen intermediates and cytotoxic activity (Wahl *et al.*, 1987b).

Abnormal expression of the IL-2 receptor is associated with several types of T-cell leukaemias, in particular adult T-cell leukaemia (ATL). The IL-2 receptors on ATL cells are increased quantitatively, do not exhibit normal down-regulation following long-term culture or the addition of anti-Tac and are spontaneously phosphorylated (Waldmann, 1986; Tsudo *et al.*, 1986), features which may contribute to the aberrant proliferation of T cells in ATL. In this regard, human T-cell leukaemia virus type 1 (HTLV-1), which is associated with ATL, induces expression of IL-2 receptors on T cells, possibly by encoding a transactivator of transcription (tat) protein which may activate the host genes for IL-2 and its receptor (Hazeltine, 1984). Although the role of IL-2 and the IL-2 receptor in ATL remains to be elucidated, therapy with anti-Tac has induced remission in several patients (Waldmann *et al.*, 1985), providing cause for cautious optimism in the treatment of this aggressive leukaemia.

B. Interleukin 3

Murine interleukin 3 (IL-3) or multilineage-CSF (multi-CSF) was first identified as a factor that induced the expression of 20α-hydroxysteroid dehydrogenase, an enzyme associated with early T-cell differentiation (Ihle *et al.*, 1982). Subsequently, the factor was shown to have multi-potent colony-stimulating properties by its ability to promote the proliferation of early haemopoietic progenitor cells of multiple lineages (Ihle *et al.*, 1983; Ihle *et al.*, 1985; Goldwasser *et al.*, 1983). The molecular cloning of the murine cDNA encoding IL-3 followed shortly thereafter (Fung, 1984; Yokota *et al.*, 1984). In contrast, the identification of human IL-3 and the isolation of its cDNA have proved elusive. Moreover, the observations that IL-3 can be replaced by other cytokines such as GM-CSF (Hapel *et al.*, 1984) and IL-2 (Le Gros, 1985) for initially IL-3-dependent (FDC-P and FDC-P1) cell lines raised the possibility that human IL-3 was replaced evolutionarily by other growth factors. However, a cDNA clone encoding a novel gibbon CSF capable of supporting the proliferation, differentiation and function of human myeloid and erythroid progenitor cells recently was identified by a mammalian cell expression cloning system (Yang *et al.*, 1986; Lopez *et al.*, 1987). The cDNA and the deduced amino acid sequence of this primate CSF were shown to have low but significant homology with the murine IL-3 nucleotide (49 per cent) and amino acid (29 per cent) sequences. The gibbon cDNA clone has been used as a hybridisation probe to isolate and clone the corresponding human gene (Yang *et al.*, 1986). The amino acid sequence of the recombinant human IL-3 product differed from the gibbon IL-3 molecule by only 11 amino acids. The difficulty in identifying human IL-3 may have been due to the low level of expression of the cytokine by stimulated T cells (Yang *et al.*, 1986). The availability of recombinant human IL-3 should now aid in the study of this potentially important cytokine.

C. Interleukin 4

As was the case with other cytokines, the existence of a factor with biological properties that were eventually ascribed to interleukin 4 (IL-4) was proposed several years before the cytokine was actually identified. In the original description of IL-4, culture fluid from phorbol myristate acetate (PMA)-stimulated EL-4 thymoma cells was shown to promote the entry of resting murine B cells into cell cycle S phase in the presence of anti-IgM antibodies (Howard *et al.*, 1982). The factor in the culture fluid responsible for this activity was named B cell stimulatory factor 1 (BSF-1). Later designated IL-4 because of its pleiotropic effects, the factor was purified to homogeneity by affinity and high-pressure chromatography and identified as a 20,000 dalton glycoprotein (Farrar *et al.*, 1983; Ohara *et al.*, 1985; Ohara *et al.*, 1987). In the murine system, IL-4 also has been shown to stimulate B cell expression of class II major histocompatibility complex antigens (Roehm *et al.*, 1984; Noelle *et al.*, 1984) and the secretion of IgGl and IgE by lipopolysaccharide-stimulated B cells (Vitetta *et al.*, 1985; Sideras *et al.*, 1985; Coffman *et al.*, 1985). Besides stimulating certain B cell activities, IL-4 exhibits a range of biological activities distinct from those of IL-1, IL-2 and IL-3 on cells of other lineages. In this regard, the cytokine promotes the viability and/or growth of normal T cells (Hu-Li *et al.*, 1987) and certain T cell, mast cell and macrophage cell lines (Fernandez-Botran *et al.*, 1986; Grabstein *et al.*, 1986; Mossman *et al.*, 1986; Smith and Rennick, 1986; Ohara and Paul, 1985). In addition, evidence that IL-4 promotes murine macrophage expression of Ia and tumoricidal activity (Crawford *et al.*, 1984) indicates that IL-4 is a potent macrophage-activating factor. Consistent with the ability of these diverse cell types to respond to IL-4 is the demonstration that B cells, T cells, mast cells, macrophages and undifferentiated haemopoietic cells each express a high-affinity IL-4-binding molecule on their surface (Ohara and Paul, 1987). Thus, the biological activities of IL-4 clearly extend beyond B cells.

Recently, cDNA clones for IL-4 were isolated from a cDNA library constructed from the mRNA of concanavalin-A-activated mouse helper T cell lines (Noma *et al.*, 1986; Lee *et al.*, 1986). The DNA sequence encodes a polypeptide of 140 amino acid residues including a hydrophobic region of 20 amino acids presumed to be the leader sequence. Partial homology at the amino acid level has been reported between IL-4 and GM-CSF and IFN-γ (Noma *et al.*, 1986) and between IL-4 and IL-2 and the IL-3 precursor molecule (Lee *et al.*, 1986). However, the significance of these homologies is unclear in view of the distinctive biological activity of IL-4 (Mossman *et al.*, 1986; Smith and Rennick, 1986; Ohara and Paul, 1985) and the absence of nucleotide homology between IL-4 and other cytokines (Lee *et al.*, 1986).

Although in the human system at least two B cell growth factors and one B cell differentiation factor have been reported to promote B cell proliferation and differentiation (Kashimoto, 1985), the identification of human IL-4 was made possible only very recently by the isolation of a human cDNA clone which expresses IL-4 activities (Yokota *et al.*, 1986). This clone was isolated from a concanavalin-A-activated human T cell (helper cell line 2F1) cDNA library based on homology with the murine IL-4 cDNA. The human cDNA encodes a 153-amino-acid residue with a probable 24-amino-acid hydrophobic leader sequence. The deduced amino acid sequence shares extensive homology and at least two biological activities (B cell and T cell growth factor activity) with murine IL-4. Very recent studies showing that this expression product induces the proliferation of preactivated B cells (DeFrance *et al.*, 1987) and promotes the growth of T cells (Spits *et al.*, 1987) indicate that for the biological activities tested thus far recombinant human IL-4 is functionally homologous to murine IL-4.

D. Granulocyte–macrophage Colony-stimulating Factor

In addition to producing the multilineage-CSF(IL-3), activated T cells (as well as endothelial cells and fibroblasts) produced GM-CSF. This 22,000 dalton glycoprotein shares with IL-3 the ability to stimulate myeloid and erythroid progenitor cells (Metcalf, 1985; Clark and Kamen, 1987). However, GM-CSF appears to act on later haemopoietic target cells than IL-3. In the presence of GM-CSF, bone-marrow-derived colonies are stimulated to form granulocyte, macrophage, granulocyte–macrophage and eosinophil colonies and erythrocyte and megakaryocyte precursors (Metcalf *et al.*, 1980; Gasson *et al.*, 1984; Sieff *et al.*, 1985; Metcalf *et al.*, 1986; Tomonaga *et al.*, 1986). Similar to G-CSF, GM-CSF also promotes effector functions including chemotaxis, phagocytosis, superoxide anion production and cytotoxicity by stimulated granulocytes or eosinophils (Gasson *et al.*, 1984; Weisbart *et al.*, 1986); Fleishman *et al.*, 1986; Silberstein *et al.*, 1986). These biological activities are initiated by the binding of GM-CSF to specific and saturable high-affinity receptors on the surface of responding cells (Walker and Burgess, 1985; Park *et al.*, 1986a). Characterisation of the receptor for GM-CSF (100–500 receptors per cell with a K_a of 10^9–10^{10} M^{-1}) (Park *et al.*, 1986b) has been facilitated by the use of recombinant GM-CSF for which the human gene has been cloned, sequenced and expressed (Cantrell *et al.*, 1985; Wong *et al.*, 1985; Lee *et al.*, 1985). In certain myeloid leukaemias receptors for GM-CSF may play a role similar to the suspected role of the IL-2 receptor in adult T cell leukaemia. In this regard, low levels of receptors for the cytokine on GM-CSF-responsive promyelocytic (HL-60) and myelogenous (KG-1) leukaemia cell lines suggest that at least some myeloid leukaemias may express GM-CSF receptors (Gasson *et al.*, 1986). However, the similarity in GM-CSF receptor binding properties of mature neutrophils and undifferentiated cells of the HL-60 line suggest that factors other than an alteration in the binding of GM-CSF to its receptor contribute to maturational changes (Park *et al.*, 1986b).

The gene encoding GM-CSF is a 2.5 kb sequence with at least three intervening spaces and has been mapped to human chromosome 5 at bands of 23–32 (Huebner *et al.*, 1985; Le Blou *et al.*, 1986), a region where the genes for M-CSF and the c-*fms* proto-oncogene are located. The importance of this localisation lies in the fact that loss of chromosome 5 or a portion of the long arm of the chromosome (del [5q]) frequently occurs in the malignant cells of patients with myeloid dysplastic syndrome and acute nonlymphocytic leukaemia secondary to cytotoxic therapy, suggesting that these genes may be involved in the altered haemopoiesis associated with these diseases.

E. Tumour Necrosis Factor β

The host response to certain stimuli includes, along with many of the cytokines described above, the secretion of tumour necrosis factor β (TNFβ, or lymphotoxin). Tumour necrosis factor β is a glycoprotein produced by activated lymphocytes which exhibits structural and functional similarities to cachectin or TNFα. Analysis of TNFβ produced by a lymphoblastoid cell line and purified by reverse-phase high-performance liquid chromatography has revealed a protein of 171 amino acids in length with a molecular weight of 18,600 (Aggarwal *et al.*, 1985c). Also cloned, the cDNA for TNFβ expressed in *Escherichia coli* encodes a protein with the same characteristics as the purified product (Aggarwal *et al.*, 1985c). Recent Southern blot analysis and in vitro hybridisation studies have revealed the genes for TNFβ and TNFα to be closely linked to the human major histocompatibility complex on chromosome 6 (Gray *et al.*, 1984). Moreover, the proteins encoded by these genes share approximately 30 per cent homology at the amino acid level (Pennica *et al.*, 1984; Aggarwal *et al.*, 1985c; Spies *et al.*, 1986) and appear to bind to a common receptor (Nedwin *et al.*, 1985). However, TNFβ is produced by activated T cells and lymphoblastoid B cell lines (Le Blou *et al.*, 1986; Aggarwal *et al.*, 1985b) whereas TNFα, as noted above, is produced by activated macrophages. Tumour necrosis factor β exhibits potent cytostatic and cytolytic activity towards certain tumour cell lines and certain virally and chemically transformed cell lines but not for primary cell cultures and normal cell lines (Aggarwal *et al.*, 1985c; Rundell and Evans, 1981; Granger *et al.*, 1982; Ruddle *et al.*, 1983). This antitumour activity can be augmented by IFN-α (Williams and Bellanti, 1983) and IFN-γ (Williams and Bellanti, 1983; Stone-Wolff *et al.*, 1984; Shalaby *et al.*, 1985). The mechanism of action of TNFβ and its potential use as a therapeutic agent are currently being investigated.

F. Transforming Growth Factor β

Transforming growth factor β, recently identified as a monocyte product (see above), is also produced by T lymphocytes (Kehrl *et al.*, 1986a). Human peripheral blood lymphocytes stimulated with phytohaemagglutinin (PHA) release 10–50-fold higher levels of TGF-β into their culture medium than unstimulated cells. Using Northern analysis with a TGF-β cDNA hybridisation probe, unstimulated T lymphocytes were shown to have low to undetectable levels of TGF-β mRNA, whereas within two hours after PHA stimulation the T cells expressed TGF-β mRNA. Significant levels of TGF-β were not secreted until 2–4 days later. Both T4 and T8 subpopulations of T lymphocytes produce TGF-β with the T4 subset expressing higher levels of TGF-β mRNA than the T8 cells. Thus, activated T cells of both subsets express mRNA for TGF-β and secrete TGF-β (Kehrl *et al.*, 1986a).

T lymphocytes also possess receptors for TGF-β (Kehrl *et al.* 1986a), and TGF-β may be important in lymphocyte immunoregulation. The evidence supporting a role for TGF-β in regulation of T cell growth includes the demonstration that the addition of exogenous TGF-β to T cells inhibits IL-2 dependent T cell proliferation (Kehrl *et al.*, 1986a). Furthermore, TGF-β is a potent inhibitor of IL-1-dependent induction of

T cell proliferation Wahl *et al.*, 1988) and appears to be significantly more active as a T cell immunosuppressant than cyclosporin A. Interestingly, a number of cultured cells, including lymphocytes, produce TGF-β and have specific TGF-β membrane receptors, yet are not continuously inhibited by the TGF-β. This may reflect, in part, the secretion of an inactive precursor form of the factor with requires activation before it can exert its biological effects. The precursor or latent form of TGF-β appears to be associated with a binding protein (Assoian *et al.*, 1988). Considering the ubiquity of TGF-β and cells possessing TGF-β receptors, activation of this latent form of TGF-β may represent an important regulatory step in TGF-β action.

G. Interferon

Originally identified for its antiviral action (Isaacs and Lindemann, 1957; Wheelock 1965), interferon (IFN) is now recognised as a family of proteins with immunoregulatory as well as antiviral activities. Interferon is present in three species-specific, antigenically and biochemically distinct forms: IFN-α (leukocyte IFN) produced by T and B lymphocytes, monocytes, NK cells and large granular lymphocytes; IFN-β produced by fibroblasts and epithelial cells; and IFN-γ (immune IFN) produced by T lymphocytes (Kirchner and Marucci, 1984; Epstein, 1984).

The genes encoding human IFNs were isolated in the early 1980s by several groups and have been expressed in bacterial, yeast and mammalian systems (summarised by Lengyel, 1982). The large amounts of recombinant IFN made available by these expression systems have facilitated the biochemical and functional characterisation of the three species. Although exhibiting significant homologies at the nucleotide and amino acid levels and similar molecular weights (20,000 daltons) (Yip *et al.*, 1982), IFNs differ in their physicochemical properties, cell-surface receptors and biological activity. In contrast to IFN-γ, IFN-α and IFN-β are acid-stable (pH 2) and relatively heat-resistant. Interferon-α and IFN-β appear to bind to a common receptor, whereas IFN-γ binds to a distinct receptor with 4000 sites per monocyte with a K_a of $4 \times 10^9 \text{ M}^{-1}$ (Branca and Baglioni, 1981; Anderson *et al.*, 1982; Finebloom *et al.*, 1985). Comparison of the immunostimulatory properties of the three IFNs reveals that IFN-γ is considerably more potent in certain functions such as inducing macrophage activation (Nathan *et al.*, 1984; Varesio *et al.*, 1984).

Interferons are produced by cells in response to a variety of stimuli including viruses, certain bacteria and parasites, endotoxin, tumour cells, allogeneic cells, polyribonucleotide complexes, mitogens and antigens. Following its release, IFN rapidly binds to a specific receptor on responder cells, triggering a series of biochemical events which have antiviral effects (Torrence, 1985). Among these events is the IFN-mediated induction of a 2′,5′-oligoadenylate synthetase. This enzyme becomes activated by double-stranded RNA (dsRNA) to synthesise from ATP the molecule 2′,5′-oligoadenylate (2–5A). The 2–5A molecule then activates a latent endonuclease which degrades mRNA, causing inhibition of virus-directed coat proteins and enzymes. A second enzyme system probably involved in antiviral activity is the protein P_1 kinase system. In this scheme, IFN induces a protein kinase which, following activation by dsRNA, phosphorylates a protein synthesis initiation factor, thereby inhibiting initiation complex formation and viral protein synthesis. In a third system which is not dependent on dsRNA activation, IFN appears to inhibit the methylation of viral mRNA, thereby reducing translation of the mRNA. In addition to its effect on these biochemical pathways, IFN stimulates the activity of host defence cells (see below), many of which are active against virally infected cells. One or more of these antiviral mechanisms are likely to contribute to host defence against certain viruses (see chapter 18).

Interferons exhibit a broad range of immunoregulatory activities through their ability to modify certain macrophage, B and T lymphocyte and NK cell functions. Although both IFN-α and IFN-γ are capable of stimulating macrophages, the stimulatory action of IFN-γ has been the most widely studied. Convincing evidence now implicates IFN-γ as the macrophage-activating factor responsible for stimulating macrophage oxidative metabolism and microbicidal activity (Nathan et al., 1983; Murray et al., 1983; Nathan et al., 1984). Macrophage phagocytosis, an important component of microbicidal activity, is enhanced by IFN, possibly through increased Fc receptor expression (Vogel et al., 1983) and augmented association between actin filaments and the plasma membrane (Wang et al., 1984). Acting through a specific receptor (Celada et al., 1984), IFN-γ also augments macrophage tumoricidal activity (Pace et al., 1983a; Pace et al., 1983b; Schultz and Kleinschmit, 1985). In addition to stimulating cytotoxicity, IFN-γ stimulates the expression of macrophage surface class II histocompatibility antigens (Steeg et al., 1982; Basham and Merigan, 1983) which are critical for T lymphocyte recognition of antigen on the macrophage surface.

All three species of IFN are capable of modulating B and T lymphocyte activities. Depending on the experimental conditions, IFN exhibits the ability to increase or decrease antibody production in response to both T-dependent and T-independent antigens (Brodeur and Merigan, 1975; Parker *et al.*, 1981; Levinson *et al.*, 1982). The ability of IFN-α to directly inhibit B cell differentiation and Ig production has been demonstrated in vitro (Peters *et al.*, 1986a) and in vivo in patients receiving IFN-α for chronic type B hepatitis (Peters *et al.*, 1986b). Interferon gamma, which may be more potent than IFN-α or IFN-β in modulating antibody responses, also acts directly on B cells by promoting B cell differentiation and antibody secretion (Leibson *et al.*, 1984; Sidman *et al.*, 1984). Interferon also modulates T cell function as reflected by its ability to modify allograft and graft-versus-host reactions (DeMaeyer-Guignard, 1984). The activation of suppressor T cells by IFN-α appears to be one mechanism by which IFN can suppress both antibody production and T cell proliferation (Schnapper *et al.*, 1983). Also, NK cell cytotoxic activity, which may contribute to host defence mechanisms against tumour cells and viral infections, can be augmented by IFN (Trinchieri and Santoli, 1978: Ortaldo *et al.*, 1983). In addition to direct stimulation or inhibition of immune cells, IFN frequently interacts with other cytokines such as IL-2, TNF (Ramila and Epstein, 1986; Stone-Wolff *et al.* 1984; Shalaby *et al.*, 1985) and IL-4 (Ohara *et al.*, 1987) to augment or modulate target cell function. This potentiation of the biological actions of other cytokines is an important mechanism by which IFN amplifies certain immunological and host defence mechanisms.

The first cytokine to be cloned, IFN was also the first cytokine to be used clinically in the treatment of certain viral infections. The infections for which IFN has been shown to have at least some effect include herpes zoster, herpes simplex, hepatitis B, papilloma viruses, and some viruses which cause upper respiratory tract infections (Ho, 1987). Factors including dosage, dosage schedule, duration of infection at the time therapy is initiated, and underlying immune status appear to affect the efficacy of IFN antiviral therapy. More recently, the administration of recombinant IFN-γ to patients with advanced malignancies was shown to induce monocyte activation in vivo (Nathan *et al.*, 1985), suggesting that IFN therapy may be beneficial for immunosuppressed patients who are highly susceptible to certain pathogens.

Clearly, the rapidly expanding field of cytokines is one of the most exciting areas in immunology. With the use of recombinant DNA technology, the role of cytokines in regulating immune responses and host defence mechanisms is being elucidated. A knowledge of the precise mechanisms of action of the various cytokines may soon provide the rationale for their use in various clinical settings.

REFERENCES

Abrahams, J. A., Mergia, A., Whang, J. L., Tumolo, A. Friedman, J., Hjerrild, K. A., Gospodarowicz, D., and Fiddes, J. C. (1986), *Science* 233: 545.

Aggarwal, B. B., Moffat, B. and Harkins, R. N. (1984). *J. Biol. Chem.* 259: 686.

Aggarwal, B. B., Kohr, W. J., Hass, P. E., Moffat, B., Spencer, S. A., Henzel, W. J., Bringman, T. S. Nedwin, G. E., Goeddel, D. V. and Harkins, R. N. (1985a). *J. Biol. Chem.* 260: 2345.

Aggarwal, B. B., Eessolu, T. E. and Hass, P. E. (1985b). *Nature* 318: 665.

Aggarwal, B. B., Henzel, W. J., Moffat, B., Kohr, W. J. and Harkins, R. N. (1985c) *J. Biol. Chem.* 260: 2334.

Anderson, P., Yip, Y. K. and Vilcek, J. (1982). *J. Biol. Chem.* 259: 11301.

Assoian, R. K., Komoriya, A., Meyers, C. A., Smith, D. M. and Sporn, M. B. (1983). *J. Biol. Chem.* 255: 7155.

Assoian, R. K., Grotendorst, G. R., Miller, D. M., and Sporn, M. B. (1984). *Nature* 309: 804.

Assoian, R. K., Fleurdelys, B. E., Stevenson, H. C., Miller, P. J., Madtes, D. K., Ranies, E. W., Ross, R. and Sporn, M. B. (1988). *Proc. Natl. Acad. Sci. USA* 84: 6020.

Atkins, E. and Wood, W. B. Jr. (1955). *J. Exp. Med.* 102: 499.

Auron, P. E., Webb, A. C., Rosenwasser, L. J., Mucci, S. F., Rick, A., Wolff, S. M. and Dinarello, C. A. (1984). *Proc. Natl. Acad. Sci. USA* 81: 7907.

Auron, P. E., Rosenwasser, L. J., Matsushima, K., Copeland, T., Dinarello, C. A., Oppenheim, J. J. and Webb, A. C. (1985). *J. Mol. Cell. Immunol.* 2: 169.

Baird, A., Mormede, P. and Böhlen, P. (1985). *Biochem. Biophys. Res. Chem.* 126: 358.

Baracos, V., Rodermann, H. A., Dinarello, C. A. and Goldberg, A. L. (1983). *N. Engl. J. Med.* 308: 553.

Basham, T. Y. and Merigan, T. C. (1983). *J Immunol.* 130: 1492.

Beeson, P. B. (1948). *J. Clin. Invest.* 27: 524.

Benson, M. D., Aldo-Benson, M. A., Shirahama, T., Borel, Y. and Cohen, Y. S. (1975). *J. Exp. Med.* 142: 236.

Berk, B. C., Alexander, R. W., Brock, T. A., Gimbrone, M. A. Jr and Webb, R. C. (1986). *Science* 232: 87.

Bertolini, D. R., Nedwin, G. E., Bringman, T. S., Smith, D. D. and Mundy, G. R. (1986). *Nature* 319: 516.

Besedovsky, H., Del Rey, A., Sorkin, E. and Dinarello, C. A. (1986). *Science* 233: 652.

Betsholtz, C., Johnsson, A., Heldin, C.-H., Westermark, B., Lind, P., Urdea, M. S., Eddy, R., Shows, T. B., Philpott, K., Mellor, A. L., Knott, T. J. and Scott, J. (1986). *Nature* 320: 695.

Beutler, B. D., Greenwald, D., Hulmes, J. D., Chang, M., Pan, Y.-C.E., Mathison, J., Ulevitch, R. and Cerami, A. (1985a) *Nature* 316: 552.

Beutler, B., Milsark, I. W. and Cerami, A. (1985b) *Science* 229: 869.

Bevilacqua, M. P., Pober, J. S., Majeau, G. R., Cotran, R. S. and Gimbrone, M. A. (1984). *J. Exp. Med.* 160: 618.

Bevilacqua, M. P., Pober, J. S., Wheeler, M. E., Cotran, R. S. and Gimbrone, M. A. (1985). *J. Clin. Invest.* 76: 2003.

Bevilacqua, M.P., Pober, J. S., Majeau, G. R., Fiers, W, Cotran, R. S. and Gimbrone, Jr., M. A. (1986). *Proc. Natl. Acad. Sci. USA* 83: 4533.

Bickel, M., Tsuda, H., Amstad, P., Evequoz, V., Mergehangen, S. E., Wahl, S. M. and Pluznik, D. H. (1987). *Proc. Natl. Acad. Sci. USA* 84: 3274.

Bodel, P. T. (1974) *J. Exp. Med.* 140: 954.

Böhlen, P., Esch, F., Baird, A., Jones, K. L. and Gospodarowicz, D. (1985). *FEBS Lett* 185: 177.

Bornstein, D. L. and Walsh, E. C. (1978). *J. Lab. Clin. Med.* 91: 236.

Bowen-Pope, D. F. and Ross, R. (1982). *J. Biol. Chem.* 257: 5161.

Branca, A. A. and Baglioni, C. (1981). *Nature* 294: 768.

Brodeur, B. R. and Merigan, T. C. (1975). *J. Immunol.* 114: 1323.

Broudy, V–C., Kaushansky, K., Segal, G. M., Harlan, J. M. and Adamson, J. W. (1986). *Proc. Natl. Acad. Sci. USA* 83: 7467.

Broxmeyer, H. E., Dinarello, C. A., Oblon, D. J., Gross, M. A., Anderson, L. and Weiner, R. S. (1987). *Blood* 69: 33.

Butler, R. C., Notwotny, A. and Friedman, H. (1979). *Ann. N. Y. Acad. Sci.* 332: 564.

Byrne, P. V., Guilbert, L. J. and Stanley, E. R. (1981). *J. Cell. Biol.* 91: 848.

Cantrell, D. A. and Smith, K. A. (1983). *J. Exp. Med.* 158: 1895.

Cantrell, D. A. and Smith, K. A. (1984). *Science* 224: 1312.

Cantrell, M. A., Anderson, D., Ceretti, D. P., Price, V., McKereghan, K., Tushinski, R. J., Mochizaki, D. Y., Larsen, A., Grabstein, K., Gillis, S., and Cosman, D. (1985). *Proc. Natl. Acad. Sci. USA* 82: 6250.

Caput, D., Beutler, B., Hartog, K., Brown-Shimer, S. and Cerami, A. (1986). *Proc. Natl. Acad. Sci. USA* 83: 1670.

Carswell, E. A., Old, L. J., Kassel, R. L., Green, S., Fiore, N. and Williamson, B. (1975). *Proc. Natl. Acad. Sci. USA* 72: 3666.

Celada, A., Gray, P. W., Ruiderknecht, E. and Schreiber, R. D. (1984). *J. Exp. Med.* 160: 55.

Chiu, I-M., Reddy, E. D., Gival, D., Robbins, K. C., Tronick, S. R. and Aaronson, S. A. (1984). *Cell* 37: 123.

Clark, S. C. and Kamen, R. (1987). *Science* 236: 1229.

Coffman, R. L., Ohara, J., Bond, M. W., Carty, J., Zlotnik, A. and Paul, W. E. (1985). *J. Immunol.* 136: 4538.

Collins, T., Ginsburg, D., Boss, J. M., Orkin, S. H. and Pober, J. S. (1985). *Nature* 316: 748.

Collins, T., La Pierre, L. A., Fiers, W., Strominger, J. and Pober, J. S. (1986). *Proc. Natl. Acad. Sci. USA* 83: 446.

Crawford, R. M., Finebloom, D.S., Ohara, J., Paul, W.E. and Meltzer, M. S. (1984). *J. Immunol.* 139: 135.

Das, S. K., Stanley, E. R., Guilbert, L. J. and Forman, L. W. (1981). *Blood* 58: 630.

Dayer, J. M., Beutler, B. and Cerami, A. (1985). *J. Exp. Med.* 162: 2163.

DeFrance, T., Vanbervliet, B., Aubry J. P., Takabe, Y., Arai, N., Miyajima, A., Yokota, T., Lee, F., Arai, K. I., deVries, J. E. and Banchereau, J. (1987). *J. Immunol.* 139: 1135.

DeMaeyer-Guignard, J. (1984). In J. Vilcek and E. DeMaeyer (eds), *Interferon and the Immune System*, vol. 2. Amsterdam: Elsevier Sci. Publ. 133.

Dempsey, R. A., Dinarello, C. A., Mier, J. W., Rosenwasser, L. J., Allegretta, M., Brown, T. E. and Parkinson, D. R. (1982). *J. Immunol.* 129: 2504.

Depper, J. M., Leonard, W. J., Drogula, C., Krönke, M., Waldmann, T. A. and Greene, W. C. (1985). *Proc. Natl. Acad. Sci. USA* 82: 4230.

Derynck, R., Jarrett, J. A., Chen, E. Y., Eaton, D. H., Bell, J. R., Assoian, R. K., Roberts, A. B., Sporn, M. B. and Goeddel, D. V. (1985). *Nature* 316: 701.

Deuel, T. F. and Huang, J. S. (1983). *Prog. Hematol.* 13: 201.

Deuel, T. F. and Huang, J. S. (1984). *J. Clin. Invest.* 74: 669.

Deuel, T. F., Senior, R. M., Huang, J. S. and Griffin, G. L. (1982). *J. Clin. Invest.* 69: 1046.

DiCorleto, P. E. and Bowen-Pope, D. F. (1983). *Proc. Natl. Acad. Sci. USA* 80: 1919.

Dinarello, C. A. (1984a). *N. Engl. J. Med.* 811: 1413.

Dinarello, C. A. (1984b). *Rev. Infect. Dis.* 6: 51.

Dinarello, C. A. and Wolff, S. M. (1982). *Am. J. Med.* 72: 799.

Dinarello, C. A., Cannon, J. G., Mier, J. W., Bernheim, H. A., LoPreste, G., Lynn, D. L., Love, R. N., Webb, A. C., Auron, P. E., Reuben, R. C., Rich, A., Wolff, S. M. and Putney, S. D. (1986a). *J. Clin. Invest.* 77: 1734.

Dinarello, C. A., Cannon, J. G., Wolfe, S. M., Bernheim, H. A., Beutler, B., Cerami, A., Figari, I., Palladino, Jr., M. A. and O'Connor, J. V. (1986b). *J. Exp. Med.* 163: 1363.

Djeu, J. Y., Blanchard, D. K., Holkias, D. and Friedman, H. (1986). *J. Immunol.* 137: 2980.

Doolittle, R. F., Hunkapillar, M. W., Hood, L. E., Devare, S. G., Robbins, K. C., Aaronson, S. A., and Antoniades, H. N. (1983). *Science* 221: 275.

Dower, S. K., Kronheim, S. R., Marsh, C. J., Conlon, P. J. Hopp, T. P., Gillis, S., and Urdal, D. L. (1985). *J. Exp. Med.* 162: 501.

Ek, B., Westermark, B., Wasteson, A. and Heldin, C. H. (1982). *Nature* 295: 419.

Epstein, L. B. (1984). In J. Vilcek and E. De Maeyer (eds), *Interferons and the Immune System*, vol. 2. Amsterdam: Elsevier Sci. Publ. 185.

Erard, F., Corthesy, P., Nabholz, M., Lowenthal, J. W., Zalch, P., Plaetinck, G., and MacDonald, H. R. (1985). *J. Immunol.* 134: 1644.

Esch, F., Euno, N., Baird, A., Hill, F., Denoroy, L., Gospodarowicz, D. and Guillemin, R. (1985a) *Biochem. Biophys. Res. Comm.* 133: 554.

Esch, F., Baird, A., Ling, N., Ueno, N., Hill, D., Denoroy, L., Klepper, R., Gospodarowicz, D., Böhlen, P. and Guillemin, R. (1985b) *Proc. Natl. Acad. Sci. USA* 82: 6507.

Falkoff, R. J. M., Butler, J. L., Dinarello, C. A. and Fauci, A. S. (1984). *J. Immunol.* 133: 692.

Farrar, W. L., Mizel, S. B. and Farrar, J. L. (1980). *J. Immunol.* 124: 1371.

Farrar, J. J., Howard, M., Fuller-Farrar, J. and Paul, W. E. (1983). *J. Immunol.* 131: 1838.

Feinman, R., Henriksen-DeStefano, D., Tsujimoto, M. and Vilcek, J. (1987). *J. Immunol.* 138: 635.

Fernandez-Botran, R., Krammer, P. H., Diamenstein, T., Uhr, J. W. and Vitetta, E. S. (1986). *J. Exp. Med.* 164: 850.

Finebloom, D. S., Hoover, D. L. and Wahl, L. M. (1985). *J. Immunol.* 135: 300.

Fleishman, J., Golde, D. W., Weisbart, R. H. and Gasson, J. C. (1986). *Blood* 68: 708.

Fontano, A., Hengartner, H., Weber, E., Fehr, K., Grob, P. J. and Cohen, G. (1982). *Rheumatol. Int.* 2: 49.

Fountana, A, Kristensen, F., Dubo, R., Geinsa, D. and Weber, E. (1982). *J. Immunol.* 129: 2413.

Freisel, R., Burgess, W. H., Mehlman, T., and Maciag, T. (1986). *J. Biol. Chem.* 261: 7581.

Frolik, C. A., Dart, L. L., Meyers, C. A., Miller, D. M. and Sporn, M. B. (1983). *Proc. Natl. Acad. Sci. USA* 80: 3676.

Fung, M. C., Hapel, A. J., Ymer, S., Cohen, D. R., Johnson, R. N., Campbell, H. D. and Young, I. G. (1984). *Nature* 307: 233.

Gamble, J. R., Harlan, J.M., Klebanoff, S. J. and Vadas, M. A. (1985). *Proc. Natl. Acad. Sci USA* 82: 8667.

Gasson, J. C., Weisbart, R. H., Kaufman, S. E., Clark, S. C., Hewick, R. M., Wong, G. G. and Golde, D. W. (1984). *Science* 226: 1339.

Gasson, C. G., Kaufman, S. E., Weisbart, R. H., Tomonaga, M. and Golde, D. W. (1986). *Proc. Natl. Acad. Sci USA* 83: 669.

Gazit, A., Igarashi, H., Chiu, I. M., Srinivasan, A., Yaniv, A., Tronick, S. R., Robbins, K. C., and Aaronson, S. A. (1984). *Cell* 39: 89.

Gery, I., Gershon, R. K. and Waksman, B. H. (1981). *J. Exp. Med.* 153: 470.

Gillis, S. and Mizel, S. B. (1981). *Proc. Natl. Acad. Sci. USA* 78: 1133.

Gimenez-Gallego, G. L., Rodkey, J., Bennett, C., Rios-Caldelore, M., DiSalvo, J. and Thomas, K. (1985). *Science* 230: 1385.

Goldwasser, E., Ihle, J. N., Prystowsky, M. B., Rich, I. and Van Zani, G. (1983). In D. W. Golde and P. A. Marks (eds), *Normal and Neoplastic Hemopoiesis*, UCLA Symposia on Molecular and Cellular Biology. New York: Alan R. Liss: 301.

Gospodarowicz, D., Bialecki, H. and Greenburg, G. (1978) *J. Biol. Chem.* 253: 3736.

Gowen, M., Wood, D. D., Ihrie, E.J., McGuire, M. and Russell, R. G. G. (1983). *Nature* 306: 378.

Grabstein, K., Eiseman, J., Mochizuki, D., Shanebeck, K., Conlon, P., Hopp, T., March, C. and Gillis, S. (1986). *J. Exp. Med.* 163: 1405.

Granger, G. A., Yamamoto, R. S., Devlin, J. J. and Klostergaard, J. (1982). *Lymphokine Res.* 1: 45.

Gray, P. W., Aggarwal, B. B., Benton, C. V., Bringman, T. S., Henzel, W. J., Jarrett, J. A., Leung, D. W., Moffat, B., Ng, P., Svendersky, L. P., Polladino, M. A. and Nedwin, G. E. (1984). *Nature* 312: 712.

Grotendorst, G. R. Seppa, H. E. J., Kleinman, H. K. and Martin, G. R. (1981). *Proc. Natl. Acad. Sci. USA* 78: 3669.

Grotendorst, G. R., Chang, T., Seppa, H. E. J., Kleinman, H. K. and Martin, G. R. (1982). *J. Cell. Physiol.* 113: 261.

Guilbert, L. J. and Stanley, E. R. (1980). *J. Cell Biol.* 85: 153.

Hahn, H. H., Char, D. C., Posted, W. B. and Wood, W. B. Jr. (1967). *J. Exp. Med.* 126: 385.

Hapel, A. J., Lee, J. C., Farrar, W. L. and Ihle, J. N. (1981). *Cell* 25: 179.

Hapel, A. J., Warren, H. S. and Hume, D. A. (1984). *Blood* 64: 786.

Hazeltine, W. A. (1984). *Science* 225: 419.

Heath, J. K., Saklatvola, J., Meikle, M. C., Atkinson, S. J. and Reynolds, J. J. (1985). *Calcif. Tissue Int.* 37: 95.

Heldin, C. H. and Ronnstrand, L. (1983). *J. Biol. Chem.* 258: 10054.

Hermann, F., Cannistra, S. A., Levine, H. and Griffin, J. D. (1985). *J. Exp. Med.* 162: 1111.

Ho, M. (1987). *Ann. Rev. Med.* 38: 51.

Hoffman, M. K. (1979). *Ann. N. Y. Acad. Sci.* 332: 557.

Holter, W., Grunow, R., Stockinger, H. and Knapp, W. (1986). *J. Immunol.* 135: 2171.

Holter, W., Goldman, C. K., Casabo, L., Nelson, D. L., Greene, W. C. and Waldmann, T. A. (1987). *J. Immunol.*138: 2917.

Horton, J. E., Oppenheim, J. J., Mergenhagen, S. E. and Raisz, L. G. (1974). *J. Immunol.* 113: 1278.

Howard, M., Farrar, J., Hilfiker, M., Johnson, B., Takatsu, K., Hamaoka, T. and Paul, W. E. (1982). *J. Exp. Med.* 155: 914.

Howard, M., Mizel, S. B., Lachman, L., Ansel, J., Johnson, B. and Paul, W. E. (1983). *J. Exp. Med.* 175: 1529.

Huang, S. S. and Huang, J. S. (1986). *J. Biol. Chem.* 261: 9568.

Huang, J. S., Huang, S. S., Kennedy, B. and Duel, T. F. (1982). *J. Biol. Chem.* 257: 8130.

Huebner, K., Isobe, M., Croce, C. M., Golde, D. W., Kaufman, S. E. and Gasson, J. C. (1985). *Science* 230: 1282.

Hu-Li, J., Shevach, E. M., Mizuguchi, J., Ohra, J., Mossman, T. and Paul, T. E. (1987). *J. Exp. Med.* 165: 157.

Ignotz R. A. and Massagué, J. (1986). *J. Biol. Chem.* 261: 4337.

Ihle, J. H., Rebar, L., Keller, J., Lee, J. C. and Hapel, A. (1982). *Immunol. Res.* 63: 5.

Ihle, J. N., Keller, J., Oroszlan, S., Henderson, L. E., Copeland, T. D., Fitch, F., Prystowsky, M. B., Goldwasser, E., Schrader, J. W., Palaszynski, E., Dy, M. and Lebel, B. (1983). *J. Immunol.* 131: 282.

Ihle, J. N., Keller, J., Rein, A., Cleveland, I. and Rapp, U. (1985). In *Cancer Cells: Growth Factors and Transformation*, vol. 3. New York: Cold Spring Harbor Laboratory Press: 211.

Iribi, H., Koga, T., Kotani, S., Kusumoto, S. and Shiba, T. (1983). *J. Exp. Med.* 157: 2190.

Irle, C., Piguet, P. F. and Vassalli, P. (1978). *J. Exp. Med.* 148: 32.

Isaacs, A. and Lindemann, J. (1957). *Proc. Roy. Soc.* Ser. B 147: 258.

Jacka, T., Bernard, C. C. A. and Singer, G. (1983). *Life Sci.* 32: 1023.

Johnsson, A., Heldin, C.-H, Wasteson, A., Westermark, B., Deuel, T. F., Huang, J. S., Seeburg, P. H., Gray, A., Ullrich, A., Scrace, G., Stoobant, P., and Waterfield, M. D. (1984). *Eur. Mol. Biol. Organ. J.* 3: 921.

Jung, L. K. L., Hara, T. and Fu, S. M. (1984). *J. Exp. Med.* 160: 1597.

Kampschmidt, R. F. (1981). In M. C. Powanda and P. G. Canoncio (eds), *The physiologic and metabolic responses of the host.* Amsterdam: Elsevier/North-Holland: 55.

Kampschmidt, R. F. and Pulman, L. A. (1978). *Proc. Soc. Exp. Biol. Med.* 158: 32.

Kampschmidt, R. F. and Upchurch, H. (1969). *Am. J. Physiol.* 216: 1287.

Kaplan, D. R., Chao, F. C., Stiles, C. D., Antoniades, H. N. and Sher, C. D. (1979). *Blood* 53: 1043.

Kasahara, T., Hooks, J. J., Dougherty, S. F. and Oppenheim, J. J. (1983). *J Immunol.* 130: 1784.

Kashimoto, T. (1985). *Ann. Rev. Immunol.* 3: 133.

Kawakami, M. and Cerami, A. (1981). *J. Exp. Med.* 154: 631.

Kawakami, M., Pekola, P. H., Lane, M. D. and Cerami, A. (1982). *Proc. Natl. Acad. Sci. USA* 79: 912.

Kawaski, E. S., Ladner, M. B., Wang, A. M., Van Arsdell, J., Warren, M. K., Coyne, M. Y., Schweikart, V. L., Lu, M.-T., Wilson, K. J., Boosman, A., Stanley, E. R., Ralph, P. and Mark, D. F. (1985). *Science* 230: 291.

Kaye, J., Gillis, S. and Mizel, S. B. (1984). *J. Immunol.* 133: 1339.

Kehrl, J. H., Wakefield, L. M., Roberts, A. B., Jakowlew, S., Alvarez-Mon, M., Derynck, R., Sporn, M. B. and Fauci, A. S. (1986a) *J. Exp. Med.* 163: 1037.

Kehrl, J. H., Roberts, A. B., Wakefield, L. M., Jakowlew, S., Sporn, M. B. and Fauci, A. S. (1986b), *J. Immunol.* 137: 3855.

Kelso, A. and McDonald, H. R. (1982). *J. Exp. Med.* 156: 1366.

274   *Smith and Wahl*

Kirchner, H. and Marucci, F. (1984). In J. Vilcek and E. De Maeyer *Interferons and the Immune System*, vol. 2. Amsterdam: Elsevier Sci. Publ.: 7.

Klaus, G. G. B. and Hawrylowicz, C. M. (1984) *Immunology Today* 5: 15.

Kohase, M., Henriksen-DeStefano, D., May, L. T., Vilcek, J. and Sehgal, P. B. (1986). *Cell* 45: 659.

Krönke, M., Leonard, W. J., Depper, J. M., Arya, S. K., Wong-Staal, F., Gallo, R. C., Waldmann, T. A. and Greene, W. C. (1984). *Proc. Natl. Acad. Sci. USA* 81: 5214.

Kurnick, J. T., Gronvik, K., Kimura, A., Lindbom, J., Skoog, V. T., Sjoberg, O., and Wigzell, H. (1979). *J. Immunol.* 122: 1255.

Kurt-Jones, E. A., Beller, D. I., Mizel, S. B. and Unanue, E. R. (1985) *Proc. Natl. Acad. Sci. USA* 82: 1204.

Le Gros, G., Gillis, S. and Watson, J. D. (1985). *J. Immunol.* 135: 4009.

Leal, F., Williams, L. T., Robbins, K. C., and Aaronson, S. A. (1985). *Science* 230: 327.

Le Blou, M. M., Westbrook, C. A., Diaz, M. O., Larson, R. A., Rowley, J. D., Gasson, J. C., Golde, D. W. and Sherr, C-J. (1986). *Science* 231: 984.

Lee, F., Yokota, T., Otsuka, T., Gremmell, L., Larsen, N., Luh, J., Arai, K.-I. and Rennick, D. (1985). *Proc. Natl. Acad. Sci. USA* 82: 4360.

Lee, F., Yokota, T., Otsuka, T., Meyerson, P., Villaret, D., Roehm, N., Smith, C., Zlotnick, A. and Arai, K. (1986). *Proc. Natl. Acad. Sci. USA* 83: 2061.

Leibson, H. J., Gefter, M., Zlotnik, A., Marrack, P. and Kappler, J. W. (1984). *Nature* 309: 799.

Lengyel, P. (1982). *Ann. Rev. Biochem.* 51: 251.

Leonard, W. J., Depper, J. M., Uchiyama, T., Smith, K. A., Waldmann, T. A. and Greene, W. C. (1982). *Nature* 300: 267.

Leonard, W. J., Depper, J. M., Crabtree, G. R., Rudikoff, S., Pumphrey, J., Robb, R. J., Krönke, M., Svetlik, P. B., Peffer, N. J., Waldmann, T. A. and Greene, W. C. (1984). *Nature* 311: 626.

Leonard, W. J., Depper, J. M., Robb, R. J., Waldmann, T. A. and Greene, W. C. (1985). *Proc. Natl. Acad. Sci. USA* 82: 4230.

Levinson, A. I., Dziarski, M. S. and Hooks, J. Y. (1982). *Clin. Exp. Immunol.* 49: 677.

Lomedico, P. T., Gubler, U., Hellman, C. P., Dukovich, M., Giri, J. G., Pan, Y-C. E., Collier, K., Semionow, R., Chua, A. O. and Mizel, S. B. (1984) *Nature* 312: 458.

Lopez, A. F., To, L. B., Yang, Y.-C., Gamble, J. R., Shannon, M. F., Burns, G. F.,

Dyson, P. G., Juttner, C. A., Clark, S. and Vadas, M. A. (1987) *Proc. Natl. Acad. Sci. USA* 84: 2761.

Lovett, D. M., Ryan, J. L. and Sterzel, R. B. (1983). *J. Immunol.* 130: 1796.

Lowenthal, J. W., Zubler, R. H., Nabholz, M. and MacDonald, H. R. (1985). *Nature* 315: 669.

Luger, T. A., Stadler, B. M., Luger, B. M., Mathieson., B. J., Mage, M., Schmidt, J. A. and Oppenheim, J. J. (1982). *J. Immunol.* 128: 2147.

Luger, T. A., Charon, J. A., Colot, M., Michsche, M. and Oppenheim, J. J. (1983). *J. Immunol.* 131: 816.

McCartney-Francis, N., Wong, H. and S. M. Wahl. (1989). Manuscript submitted.

McKean, D. J., Nilson, A., Beck, B. N., Giri, J., Mizel, S. B. and Handwerger, B. S. (1985). *J. Immunol.* 135: 3205.

McQuire, M. K. B., Wood, D. D., Meats, J. E., Ebsworth, N. M., Gowen, M. and Russell, R. G. G. (1982). *Calcif. Tissue Int.* 34: 510.

Maggi, E., Mingari, M. C., Almerigogna, F., Gerosa, F., Moretta, L., Romaguani, S. (1985). *Clin. Immunol. Immunopathol.* 36: 168.

Mahoney, J. R. Jr., Beutler, B. A., LeTrang N., Vine, W., Ikeda, Y., Kawanami, M. and Cerami, A. (1985). *J. Immunol.* 134: 1673.

Maizel, A. L., Mehta, S. R., Ford, R. J. and Lachman, L. B. (1981) *J. Exp. Med.* 153: 470.

Mannel, D. N., Moore, R. W. and Mergenhagen, S. E. (1980). *Infect. Immun.* 30: 523.

Martinet, Y., Bitterman, P. B., Mornex, J. F. Grotendorst, G. R., Martin, G. R., and Crystal, R. G. (1986). *Nature* 319: 158.

Martinet, Y., Rom, W. N., Grotendorst, G. R., Martin, G. R. and Crystal, R. G. (1987). *N. Engl. J. Med.* 317: 202.

Marsh, C. J., Mosley, B., Alf, L., Ceretti, D. P., Braedt, G., Price, V., Gillis, S., Henney, C. S., Kronheim, S. R., Grabstein, K., Conlon, P. J., Hopp, T. D. and Cosman, D. (1985). *Nature* 315: 641.

Matsushima, K., Procopio, A., Abe, H., Scala, G., Ortaldo, J. R. and Oppenheim, J. J. (1985). *J. Immunol.* 135: 1132.

Massagué, J. (1984). *J. Biol. Chem.* 259: 9756.

Mathews, N. (1981). *Br. J. Cancer* 38: 310.

Menkin, V. (1943). *Arch. Path.* 36: 269.

Metcalf, D. (1985). *Science* 229: 16.

Metcalf, D. and Nicola, N. A. (1983). *J. Cell. Physiol.* 116: 198.

Metcalf, D., Johnson, G. R. and Burgess, A. W. (1980). *Blood* 55: 138.

Metcalf, D., Begley, C. G., Johnson, G. R., Nicola, N. A., Lopes, V. A. F., Williamson, D. J., Wong, G. G., Clark, S. C. and Wang, E. A. (1986). *Blood* 67: 37.

Mier, J. W. and Gallo, R. C. (1980). *Proc. Natl. Acad. Sci. USA* 10: 6134.

Mizel, S. B., Dayer, J. M., Krane, S. M. and Mergenhagen, S. E. (1980). *Proc. Natl. Acad. Sci. USA* 78:2474.

Moretta, A. (1985). *Eur. J. Immunol.* 15: 148.

Morgan, D. A., Ruscetti, F. W. and Gallo, R. C. (1976). *Science* 193: 1007.

Moses, H. L., Branum, E. L., Proper, J. A. and Robinson, R. A. (1981). *Cancer Res.* 41: 4842.

Moses, H. L., Tucker, R. F., Leof, E. B., Coffey, R. J. Jr., Halper, J. and Shipley, G. D. (1985). In J. Feramisco, B. Ozanne and C. Stiles (eds), *Growth Factors and Transformation: Cancer Cells.* Cold Spring Harbor, N. Y.: Cold Spring Harbor Press: 65.

Mossman, T. R., Bond, M. W., Coffman, R. L., Ohara, J. and Paul, W. E. (1986). *Proc. Natl. Acad. Sci. USA* 83: 5654.

Mundy, G. R., Raisz, L. G., Cooper, R. A., Schlecter, G. P. and Salmon, S. E. (1974). *N. Engl. J. Med.* 291: 1041.

Munker, R., Gasson, J., Ogawa, M. and Koeffler, H. P. (1986). *Nature* 323: 79.

Murray, H. W., Rubin, B. Y. and Rothermel, C. D. (1983). *J. Clin. Invest.* 72: 1506.

Nagata, S., Tsuchiya, M., Asano, S., Kaziro, Y., Yamazaki, T., Yamamoto, O., Hirata, Y., Kuboto, N., Oheda, M., Nomura, H. and Ouo, M. (1986). *Nature* 319: 415.

Nathan, C. F., Murray, H. W., Wiebe, M. W. and Rubin, B. Y. (1983). *J. Exp. Med.* 158: 670.

Nathan, C. F., Prendergast, T. J., Wiebe, M. E., Stanley, E. R., Platzer, E., Remold, H. G., Welte, K., Rubin, B. Y. and Murray, H. W. (1984). *J. Exp. Med.* 160: 600.

Nathan, C. F. Horowitz, C. R., de la Harpe, J., Vadhan-Raj, S., Sherwin, S. A., Oettgen, H. F. and Krown, S. E. (1985). *Proc. Natl. Acad. Sci. USA* 82: 8686.

Nawroth, P. P., Bank, I., Handley, D., Cassimeris, J., Chess, L. and Stern, L. (1986a) *J. Exp. Med.* 163: 1363.

Nawroth, P. P., Bank, I., Handley, D., Cassimeris, J., Chess, L. and Stern, D. (1986b) *J. Exp. Med.* 163: 1433.

Nedwin, G. E., Naylor, S. L., Sakaguchi, A. Y., Smith, D., Jarrett-Nedwin, J., Pennica, D., Goedell, D. V. and Gray, P. W. (1985). *Nucleic Acids Res.* 13: 6361.

Nicola, N. A. and Metcalf, D. (1984). *Proc. Natl. Acad. Sci. USA* 81: 3765.

Nikaido, T., Shimizu, A., Ishida, N., Sabe, H., Teshigawara, K., Maeda, M., Uchiyama, T., Yodoi, J. and Honjo, T. (1984). *Nature* 311: 631.

Noelle, R., Krammer, P. H., Ohara, J., Uhr, J. W. and Vitetta, E. S. (1984). *Proc. Natl. Acad. Sci. USA* 61: 6149.

Noma, Y., Sideras, T., Naito, T., Bergstedt-Lindquist, S., Azuma, C., Severinson, E., Tanabe, T., Kinashi, T., Matsuda, F., Yaoita, Y. and Honja T. (1986). *Nature* 319: 640.

Ohara, J. and Paul, W. E. (1985). *Nature* 315: 333.

Ohara, J. and Paul, W. E. (1987). *Nature* 325: 537.

Ohara, J., Lahet, S., Inman, J. and Paul, W. E. (1985). *J Immunol.* 135: 2518.

Ohara, J., Coligan, J. E., Zoon, K., Maloy, W. L. and Paul, W. E. (1987). *J. Immunol.* 139: 1127.

O'Malley, W. E., Achinstein, B and Shear M. J. (1962). *J. Natl. Cancer Inst.* 29: 1169.

Onozaki, K., Matsushima, K., Kleinerman, E. S., Saito, T. and Oppenheim, J. J. (1985). *J. Immunol.* 135: 314.

Oppenheim, J. J., Stadler, B. M., Siraganian, R. P., Mage, M. and Mathieson, B. (1982). *Fed. Proc.* 41: 257.

Orosz, C. G., Scott, J. W., Gillis, S., and Finke, J. H. *J. Immunol.* (1985). 134: 324.

Ortaldo, J. R., Mantovani, A., Hobbs, D., Rubinstein, M., Petska, S. and Herberman, R. B. (1983). *Int. J. Cancer* 31: 285.

Pace, J. L., Russell, S. W., Torres, B. A., Johnson, H. M. and Gray, P. W. (1983a). *J. Immunol.* 130: 2011.

Pace, J. L., Russell, S. W. Schreiber, R. D., Oltman, A. and Katz, D. H. (1983b). *Proc. Natl. Acad. Sci. USA* 80: 3782.

Park, L. S., Friend, D., Gillis, S. and Urdal, D. L. *J. Biol. Chem.* (1986a). 261: 4177.

Park, L. S., Friend, D., Gillis, S. and Urdal, D. L. (1986b). *J. Exp. Med.* 164: 251.

Parker, M. A., Mandel, A. D., Wallace, J. H. and Sonnenfeld, G. (1981) *Cell Immunol.* 58: 464.

Pike, B. L. and Nossal, G. J. V. (1985). *Proc. Natl. Acad. Sci. USA* 82: 8153.

Pennica, D., Nedwin, G. E., Hayflick, J. S., Seeburg, P. H., Derynck, R., Palladino, M. A., Kohr, W. J., Aggarwal, B. B. and Goeddel, D. V. (1984). *Nature* 312: 724.

Pennica, D., Hayflick, J. S., Bringham, T. S., Palladino, M. A. and Goeddel, D. V. (1985). *Proc. Natl. Acad. Sci. USA* 82: 6060.

Peters, M., Ambrus, J. Zheleznyak, A., Walling, D. and Hoofnagle, J. H. (1986a). *J. Immunol.* 137: 3153.

Peters, M., Walling, D. M., Kelly, K., Davis, G. L. Waggoner, J. G. and Hoofnagle, J. H. (1986b) *J. Immunol.* 137: 3147.

Postlewaite, A. E., Lachman, L. B., Mainardi, C. L. and Kang, A. H. (1983). *J. Exp. Med* 157: 801.

Raghow, R., Postlewaite, A. E., Keski-Oja, J., Moses, H. L. and Kang, A. H. (1987). *J. Clin. Invest.* 79: 1285.

Ramaldi, A., Young, D. C. and Griffin, J. D. (1987). *Blood* 69: 1409.

Ramila, P. and Epstein, L. B. (1986). *Nature* 323: 86.

Robb, R. J., Munck, A. and Smith, K. A. (1981). *J. Exp. Med.* 154: 1455.

Robb, R. J., Greene, W. C. and Rusk, C. M. (1984). *J. Exp. Med.* 160: 1126.

Roberts, A. B., Anzano, M. A., Lamb, L. C., Smith, J. M. and Sporn, M. B. (1981). *Proc. Natl. Acad. Sci. USA* 78: 5339.

Roberts, A. B., Anzano, M. A., Meyers, C. A., Wildeman, J., Blacher, R., Pan, V.-C. E., Stein, S., Lehrman, S. R., Smith, L. C., Lamb, L. C. and Sporn, M. B. (1983a). *Biochemistry* 22: 5692.

Roberts, A. B., Frolik, C. A., Anzano, M. and Sporn, M. B. (1983b). *Fed. Proc.* 42: 2621.

Roberts, A. B., Anzano, M. A., Wakefield, L. M., Roche, N. S., Stern, D. F. and Sporn, M. B. (1985). *Proc. Natl. Acad. Sci. USA* 82: 119.

Roberts, A. B., Sporn, M. B., Assoian, R. K., Smith, J. M., Roche, N. S., Wakefield, L. M., Heine, U. I., Liotta, L. A., Falanga, V., Kehrl, J. H. and Fauci, A. S. (1986). *Proc. Natl. Acad. Sci. USA* 83: 4167.

Robey, F. A., Ohura, K., Futaki, S., Fujii, N., Yajima, H., Goldman, N., Jones, K. D. and Wahl, S. M. (1987). *J. Biol. Chem.* 262: 7053.

Roehm, N. W., Liebson, J., Zlotnick, A., Kappler, J., Marrack, P. and Cambier, J. C. (1984). *J. Exp. Med.* 160: 679.

Rook, A. H., Hooks, J. J., Quinnan, C. V., Lane, H. C., Manischewitz, J. F., Macher, A. M., Masur, H., Fauci, A. S. and Djeu, J. Y. (1985). *J. Immunol.* 135: 1503.

Rosenberg, S. A., Lotze, M. T., Muul, L. M., Leitman, S., Chang, A. E., Ettinghausen, S. E., Matory, Y. L., Skibber, J. M., Shiloni, E., Vetto, J. T., Skeipp, C. A., Simpson, C. and Reichert, C. M. (1985). *N. Engl. J. Med.* 313: 1485.

Ross, R. (1986). *N. Engl. J. Med.* 314: 488.

Ross, R., Glomset, J. A., Kariya, B. and Harker, L. (1974). *Proc. Natl. Acad. Sci. USA* 71: 1207.

Ross, R., Raines, E. W. and Bowen-Pope, D. F. (1986). *Cell* 46: 155.

Rossi, V., Breviario, F., Ghezzi, P. Dejana, E. and Mantovani, A. (1985). *Science* 229: 174.

Rouzer, C. A. and Cerami, A. (1980). *Mol. Biochem. Parasitol.* 2: 31.

Ruddle, N. H., Powel, M. B. and Conta, B. S. (1983). *Lymphokine Res.* 2: 23.

Rundell, J. O. and Evans, C. H. (1981). *Immunopharmacology* 3: 9.

Rupp, E. A., Cameron, P. M., Ranawat, C. S., Schmidt, J. A. and Bayne, E. K. (1986). *J. Clin. Invest.* 78: 836.

Ruscetti, F. W., Morgan, D. A. and Gallo, R. C. (1977). *J. Immunol.* 119: 131.

Sander, D. N., Dinarello, C. A. and Morheim, V. B. (1984) *J. Invest. Dermatol.* 82: 605.

Schaffner., A. (1985). *J. Clin. Invest.* 76: 1755.

Schmidt, J. A., Mizel, S. B., Cohen, D. and Green, I. (1982). *J. Immunol.* 128: 2177.

Schmidt, J. A., Oliver, C. N., Lepe-Zuniga, I. L., Green, I. and Gery. I. (1984). *J. Clin. Invest.* 73: 1462.

Schnapper, H. W., Aune, T. M. and Pierce, C. W. (1983). *J. Immunol.* 131: 2301.

Schrader, J. W. and Crapper, R. M. (1983). *Proc. Natl. Acad. Sci. USA* 80: 6892.

Schultz., R. M. and Kleinschmidt, W. J. (1985). *Nature* 305: 239.

Senior, R. M., Huang, J. S., Griffin, G. L. and Deuel, T. F. (1985). *J. Cell. Biol.* 100: 351.

Seppa, H., Grotendorst, G., Seppa, S., Schiffman, E. and Martin, G. R. (1982). *J. Cell. Biol.* 92: 584.

Shaloby, M. R., Aggarwal, B. B., Rinderknecht, E., Snedersky, L. P., Finkle, B. S. and Palladino, M. A. (1985). *J. Immunol.* 135: 2069.

Sharon, M., Klausner, R. D., Cullen, B. R., Chizzonite, R. and Leonard, W. J. (1986). *Science* 234: 859.

Sherr, C. J., Rettenmier, C. W., Sacca, R., Roussel, M. F., Look, A. T. and Stanley, E. R. (1985). *Cell* 41: 665.

Shimiokado, K., Raines, E. W., Madtes, D. K., Barrett, T. B., Benditt, E. P. and Ross, R. (1985). *Cell* 43: 277.

Shirai, T. H., Yamaguchi, H., Ito, H., Todd, C. W. and Wallace, R. B. (1985). *Nature* 313: 803.

Sideras, P., Bergstedt-Lindqvist, S. and Severeinson, E. (1985). *Eur. J. Immunol.* 15: 593.

Sidman, C. L., Marshall, J. D., Shultz, L. D., Gray, P. W. and Johnson, H. M. (1984). *Nature* 309: 801.

Sieff, C. A., Emerson, S. G., Nathan, D. G., Wang, E. A., Wong, G. G. and Clark, S. C. (1985). *Science* 230: 1171.

Sieff, C. A., Tsai, S. and Faller, D. V. (1987). *J. Clin. Invest.* 79: 48.

Silberstein, D. S., Owen, W. F., Gasson, J. C., DiPersio, J. F., Golde, D. W., Bina, J. C., Soberman, R., Austen, K. F. and David, J. R. (1986). *J. Immunol.* 137: 3290.

Smith, K. A. (1980). *Immunol. Rev.* 51: 337.

Smith, K. A. (1984). *Ann. Rev. Immunol.* 2: 319.

Smith, K. A. and Rennick, D. M. (1986). *Proc. Natl. Acad. Sci. USA* 83: 1857.

Sonnenfeld, G., Mandel, A. D. and Merigan, T. C. (1978). *Cell. Immunol.* 40: 285.

Souza, L. M., Boone, T. C., Gabrilove, J., Lai, P. H., Zsebo, K. M., Murdock, D. C., Chazin, V. R., Bruszewski, J., Lu, H., Chen, K. K., Barendt, J., Platzer, E., Moore, A. S., Mertelsmann, R. and Welte, K. (1986). *Science* 232: 61.

Spies, T., Morton, C. C., Nedosposov, S. A., Fiers, W., Pious, D. and Strominger, J. L. (1986). *Proc. Natl. Acad. Sci. USA* 83: 8699.

Spits, H., Yssel, H., Takebe, Y., Arai, N., Yokota, T., Lee, F., Arai, K.-I., Banchereau, J. and deVries, J. E. (1987). *J. Immunol.* 139: 1142.

Steeg, P. S., Moore, R. N., Johnson, H. M. and Oppenheim, J. J. (1982). *J. Exp. Med.* 156: 780.

Stone-Wolff, D. S., Yip, Y. K., Kelker, H. C., Le, J., Henriksen-Destefano, D., Rubin, B. Y., Rinderknecht, E., Aggarwal, B. B. and Vilcek, J. (1984). *J. Exp. Med.* 159: 828.

Svedersky, L. P., Benton, C. V., Berger, W. H., Rinderknecht, E., Harkins, R. N. and Palladino, M. A. (1984). *J. Exp. Med.* 159: 812.

Taniguchi, T., Matsui, H., Fujita, T., Takaoka, C. and Kashima, N. (1983). *Nature* 302: 305.

Tracey, K. J., Beutler, B., Lowry, S. F., Merryweather, J., Wolpe, S., Milsark, I. W., Hariri, R. J., Fahey, T. J., Zentella, A. (1986). *Science* 234: 470.

Teshigawara, K., Wang, H., Kato, K. and Smith, K. A. (1987). *J. Exp. Med.* 16: 223.

Thomas, K. A., Rios-Caldelore, M. and Fitzpatrick, S. (1984). *Proc. Natl. Acad. Sci. USA* 81: 357.

Thomson, B. M., Saklatvola, J. and Chambers, T. J. (1986). *J. Exp. Med.* 164: 104.

Thomson, B. M., Mundy, G. R. and Chambers, T. J. (1987). *J. Immunol.* 138: 775.

Todaro, G. J., Fryling, C. and DeLarco, J. E. (1980). *Proc. Natl. Acad. Sci. USA* 77: 5258.

Tomonaga, M., Golde, D. W. and Gasson, J. C. (1986). *Blood* 67: 31.

Torrence, P. F. (1985). In Torrence, P. F. (ed.) *Biological response modifiers: new approaches to disease intervention.* New York: Academic Press: 77.

Torti, F. M., Dieckmann, B., Beutler, B., Cerami, A. and Ringold, G. M. (1985). *Science* 229: 867.

Trinchieri, G. and Santoli, D. (1978). *J. Exp. Med.* 147: 1314.

Tsudo, M., Uchiyama, T., and Uchino, H. (1984). *J. Exp. Med.* 160: 612.

Tsudo, M., Kozak, R. W., Goldman, C. K. and Waldmann, T. A. (1986). *Proc. Natl. Acad. Sci. USA* 83: 9694.

Tsudo, M., Kozak, R. W., Goldman, C. K. and Waldmann, T. A. (1987). *Proc. Natl. Acad. Sci. USA* 84: 4215.

Tucker, R. F., Shipley, G. D., Moses, H. L. and Holley, R. W. (1987). *Science* 226: 705.

Varesio, L., Blasi, E., Thurman, G. B., Talmadge, J. E., Wiltrout, R. H. and Herberman, R. B. (1984). *Cancer Res.* 44: 4465.

Vilcek, J., Palombella, V. J., Henrikson-DeStefano, D., Swenson, C., Feinman, R., Hiri, M. and Tsujimoto, M. (1986). *J. Exp. Med.* 163: 632.

Vitetta, E. S., Ohara, J., Myers, C., Layton, J., Krammer, P. H. and Paul, W. E. (1985). *J. Exp. Med.* 162: 1726.

Vogel, S. N., Finebloom, D. S., English, K. E., Rozenstreich, D. L. and Langreth, S. G. (1983). *J. Immunol.* 130: 1210.

Wahl, S. M., Altman, L. C. and Rosenstreich, D. L. (1975). *J. Immunol.* 115: 476.

Wahl, L. M., Olsen, C. E., Sandberg, A. L. and Mergenhagen, S. E. (1977). *Proc. Natl. Acad. Sci. USA* 74: 4955.

Wahl, S. M., Malone, D. G. and Wilder, R. L. (1985). *J. Exp. Med.* 161: 210.

Wahl, S. M., Hunt, D. A., Wakefield, L. M., McCartney-Francis, N., Wahl, L.M., Roberts, A. B. and Sporn, M. B. (1987a) *Proc. Natl. Acad. Sci. USA* 84: 5788.

Wahl, S. M., McCartney-Francis, N., Hunt, D. A., Smith, P. D., Wahl, L. M. and Katona, I. M. (1987b). *J. Immunol.* 139: 1342.

Wahl, S. M., Hunt, D., Wong, H., Dougherty, S., McCartney-Francis, N., Wahl, L. M., Ellingsworth, L., Schmidt, J. A., Hall, G., Roberts, A. B. and Sporn, M. B. (1988). *J. Immunol* 140: 3026.

Waldmann, T. A. (1986). *Science* 232: 727.

Waldmann, T. A., Goldman, C. K., Robb, R. J., Depper, J. M., Leonard, W. J., Sharrow, S. O., Bongiovanni, K. F., Korsmeyer, S. J. and Green, W. C. (1984). *J. Exp. Med.* 160: 1450.

Waldmann, T. A., Longo, D. L., Leonard, W. J., Depper, J. M., Thompson, C. B. Krönkee, M., Goldman, C. K., Sharrow, S., Bongiovanni, K. and Greene, W. C. (1985). *Cancer Res.* 45 (Suppl.): 4559.

Walker, F. and Burgess, A. W. (1985). *Eur. Mol. Biol. Organ. J.* 4: 933.

Walker, L. N., Bowen-Pope, D. F., Ross, R. and Reidy, M. A. (1986). *Proc. Natl. Acad. Sci. USA* 83: 7311.

Wang, E., Michl, J., Pfeffer, L. M., Silverstein, S. C. and Tamm, I. (1984). *J. Cell Biol.* 98: 1328.

Wang, A. M., Creasy, A. A., Ladner, M. B., Lin, L. S., Strickler, J., Van Arsdell, J. N., Yamamoto, R. and Mark, D. F. (1985). *Science* 228: 149.

Waterfield, M. D., Scrace, G. T., Whittle, N., Stroobant, P., Johnsson, A., Wasteson, A., Westermark, B., Heldin, C.-H., Huang, J. S. and Deuel, T. F. (1983). *Nature* 304: 35.

Weisbart, R. H., Golde, D. W., Clark, S. C., Wong, G. G. and Gasson, J. C. (1985). *Nature* 314: 361.

Wheelock, E. F. (1965). *Science* 149: 310.

Williams, T. W. and Bellanti, J. A. (1983). *J. Immunol.* 130: 518.

Williams, L. T., Antoniades, H. N. and Goetzl, E. J. (1983). *J. Clin. Invest.* 72: 1759.

Williams, J. B., Akbud-Filho, M., Kelly, V. E., and Strom, T. B. (1985). *Cell. Immunol.* 94: 383.

Wilson, E., Laster, S. M., Gooding, L. R. and Lambeth, J. D. (1987). *Proc. Natl. Acad. Sci. USA* 84: 2213.

Wing, E. J., Ampel, N. M., Waheed, A. and Shadduck, R. K. (1985). *J Immunol.* 135: 2052.

Wong, G. G., Witek, J. S., Temple, P. A., Williams, K. M., Leary, A. C., Luxenberg, D. P., Jones, S. S., Brown, E. L., Kay, R. M., Orr, E. C., Shoemaker, C., Golde, D. W., Kaufman, R. J., Hewick, R. M., Wang, E. A. and Clark, S. C. (1985). *Science* 228: 810.

Wood, D. D., Ihrie, E. J., Dinarello, C. A. and Cohen, P. L. (1983). *Arthritis Rheum.* 26: 975.

Yang, Y.-C., Ciarletta, A. B., Temple, P. A., Chung, M. D., Kövacic, S., Witek-Giannotti, J. S., Leary, A. C., Kriz, R., Donahue, R. E., Wong, G. G. and Clark, S. C. (1986). *Cell* 47: 3.

Yip, Y. K., Barrowclough, B. S., Urban, C. and Vilcek, J. (1982). *Science* 215: 411.

Yokota, T., Lee, F., Renwick, D., Hall, C., Arai, N., Mosmann, T., Nabel, G., Cantor, H. and Arai, K. (1984). *Proc. Natl. Acad. Sci. USA* 81: 1070.

Yokota, T., Otsuka, T., Mosmann, T., Banchereau, J., DeFrance, T., Blanchard, D., DeVries, J., Lee, F. and Arai, K. (1986). *Proc. Natl. Acad. Sci. USA* 83: 5894.

Zucali, J. R., Dinarello, C. A., Gross, M. A. and Weiner, R. S. (1987). *Blood* 69: 33.

9

Plasma Proteins

SAMUEL N. BREIT

Centre for Immunology
St Vincent's Hospital and University of New South Wales
Sydney, NSW 2010, Australia

I. INTRODUCTION

Plasma contains, in addition to antibodies and complement, a large number of other proteins that are important in natural immunity. Many of these substances, notably the plasma protease inhibitors, function largely to dampen down the overexuberant response, which, if unchecked, would lead to excess tissue damage. Some, like the opsonins, facilitate the rapid elimination of the eliciting material. Others, like C-reactive protein (CRP), have multiple roles and it is very difficult to be

284

NATURAL IMMUNITY
ISBN 0 12 5145551

certain what their major biological function really is. Rather than having a direct effect, the majority of these substances act by modulating the functions of neutrophils, macrophages or natural killer (NK) cells, the major direct mediators of natural immunity. Many of these proteins are acute-phase reactants, which means that they are present in the greatest amounts at times of particular need. It is clear that the factors regulating natural immunity and inflammation are subtle and complex and represent an interplay between most biological systems in the body. This complexity is still beyond our current comprehension.

For the purposes of this discussion, plasma proteins may be conveniently considered in three broad groups — opsonins, protease inhibitors, and a collection of miscellaneous proteins affecting natural immunity.

II. OPSONINS

Opsonins are substances which greatly facilitate the phagocytosis of invading organisms by macrophages or neutrophils and are essential to their efficient function. Undoubtedly the most important of these are immunoglobulins and complement (see Chapters 1, 2, 6 and 7). There are, however, also a number of other plasma proteins, including fibronectin and CRP, that have considerable opsonic activity. These substances generally exert their actions in the presence of the primary opsonin, and seem to act by enhancing its effects.

A. Fibronectin

Fibronectin is the most important of what might be regarded as the secondary opsonic proteins. Following its isolation in 1948 by cold precipitation, it was called cold-insoluble globulin (Morrison *et al.*, 1948), but has been known under a variety of different names since then, alluding to the multiplicity of functions it is now known to subserve. These names included, α-2 surface-binding (SB) glycoprotein, large external transformation-sensitive protein (LETS), soluble fibroblast antigen, and cell-spreading factor. Its role as an opsonin became clearer in the 1970s when it was shown to facilitate macrophage phagocytosis (Saba *et al.*, 1978a; Blumenstock *et al.*, 1978) and was noted to be reduced in plasma in patients who developed sepsis following serious injury or major surgery. This deficiency could be demonstrated by either a liver-slice bioassay of particle uptake or immunochemical determination and could be improved by infusion into the patient of cryoprecipitate known to be rich in this material. It has been suggested by a number of workers that infusion of fibronectin preparations in such patients results in clinical improvement (Saba *et al.*, 1978b; Scovill *et al.*, 1978,1979). The final evaluation of this issue however, depends on carefully controlled clinical studies that still have not been undertaken (Snyder and Luban, 1986).

Fibronectin is a polymorphic molecule that circulates as two nearly identical disulphide-linked polypeptide chains, each with a molecular weight of about 220,000 daltons. It is widely distributed throughout the body, both in the fluid phase and bound in an insoluble form to many connective tissue components and basement membranes (Stenman and Vaheri,1978; Linder *et al.*, 1978; Mosher,1980). The fibronectin polypeptide chain can be divided into at least three distinct functional regions of sizes 32,000, 40,000 and 140–150,000 daltons by sequential digestion with trypsin and thermolysin. Only the largest fragment promotes cell spreading whilst both smaller fragments are capable of inducing cell attachment, but not cell spreading. The 40,000 dalton fragment contains almost all the carbohydrate and is the region containing the gelatin-binding site (Sekiguchi and Hakomori, 1980). The part of the molecule responsible for cell attachment has been futher localised to a tetrapeptide fragment Arg-Gly-Asp-Ser, only the first three residues of which are crucial. This sequence is also found on a number of other proteins which interact with cells suggesting the possible use of a single receptor or binding site (Pierschbacher and Ruoslahti, 1984). Somewhat surprisingly for a protein of this type, fibronectin is not an acute-phase reactant and in fact its plasma levels tend to drop transiently following injury. It may well be, however, that this transient decrease represents utilisation of the material on a massive scale, well in excess of any possible increase in production.

Many of the functions of fibronectin are due to its capacity to bind avidly to a variety of different structures, including collagen, sulfated proteoglycans, hyaluronic acid, gangliosides, fibrin and bacterial cell walls (Stenman and Vaheri, 1978; Linder *et al.*, 1978; Mosher, 1980). Its extraordinary adhesive nature may therefore be one of the primary reasons for its activity as an opsonin. Fibronectin probably exercises its opsonic function by a number of different mechanisms. This is suggested by the differences in the literature as to its mode of action. The predominant view is that it, along with other matrix proteins like laminin and serum amyloid P component, interacts with monocytes and macrophages and enhances their ingestion of targets, provided the cells have previously been stimulated by agents such as complement components (Wright *et al.*, 1984; Pommier *et al.*, 1984; Bohnsack *et al.*, 1985; Brown, 1986). The same probably applies to neutrophils as shown by increased phagoctosis in in vitro and in vivo experiments using opsonised group B streptococci (Hill *et al.*, 1984). However, there is some disagreement on this issue, as, in some studies, ingestion of the target is enhanced by fibronectin through an effect on the target rather than the phagocyte (Cosio, 1984; Pommier *et al.*, 1984). It is possible that this is due to direct binding of the fibronectin to an epitope on the C3d molecule (Johnson *et al.*, 1985). Prior opsonisation by immunoglobulin or complement does not always have to occur for fibronectin to exhibit its opsonic effect. This is particularly so for removal of debris by the mononuclear phagocyte system. In a liver-slice assay, phagocytosis of collagenous and non-collagenous membranes was increased by fibronectin (Rovin *et al.*, 1984). A 180,000 dalton fragment of fibronectin isolated from plasma, increased the monocyte uptake of particulate activators of the human alternative complement pathway (Czop *et al.*, 1982). This effect has been duplicated with a cathepsin D digest of intact fibronectin, occurring in the absence of serum and mediated by direct binding to the target material (Czop *et al.*, 1985). The effect of fibronectin on monocytes and macrophages may be more complex than that purely related to op-sonisation. There is some evidence that it can alter other aspects of macrophage function. It enhanced the cytostatic effect of activated macrophages on tumours in vitro (Martin *et al.*, 1984). Whilst it cannot enhance macrophage bactericidal activity, its presence in the cell cultures was required for the maintenance of this function over a 7–10 day period (Proctor *et al.*, 1985).

It therefore appears that, in addition to the numerous other roles it fills, fibronectin is an important opsonic protein, aiding considerably in the phagocytosis of infective organisms and particulate material. For this action it usually requires the presence of other opsonic proteins (e.g. immunoglobulin and complement) but in some instances it may act alone. Its widespread distribution, its production by many different cell types and its pronounced adhesive properties suggest that it plays an important role in natural immunity.

B. C-reactive Protein

CRP is an acute-phase reactant with strong functional similarities, but only weak homology, to the C1q binding (CH2) domain of IgG (Dayhoff, 1976). Its discovery in 1930 was based on its capacity to bind to a pneumococcal polysaccharide antigen (Tillet and Francis, 1930), later identified to be a phosphocholine determinant (Volanakis and Kaplan. 1971). This phosphocholine reactivity endows it with the capacity to bind to a variety of phospholipids containing this determinant (Kaplan and Volanakis, 1974). Like IgG it binds C1q and is able to activate the classical complement pathway (Kaplan and Volanakis,1974), but presumably does so more efficiently because of its pentameric structure. Once activated in this way, the complement cascade is able to proceed to completion, permitting complement-dependent phenomena such as adherence, phagocytosis (Mortensen *et al.*, 1976) and solubilisation of immune complexes (Volanakis, 1982). CRP will induce activation of the classical complement pathway on the surface of human or rabbit erythrocytes treated with phospholipase A2, or human red cell ghosts (Narkates and Volanakis, 1982). CRP can induce complement-mediated red cell lysis of sheep erythrocytes passively coated with phosphocholine just as efficiently as antibody (Osmand *et al.*,1975). Additionally, fragments of C4 and C3 are deposited on the cell surface, resulting in its efficient phagocytosis by monocytes (Mortensen *et al.*, 1976). On reaction with polyanions such as DNA, ENA, heparin and hyaluronic acid, or with polyanion–polycation complexes, CRP is able to initiate complement activation with all the expected consequences including membrane lysis (Siegel *et al.*, 1974, 1975; Claus *et al.*, 1977; Richards *et al.*, 1977, 1979).

The opsonic effect of CRP seems to be due largely, but perhaps not exclusively, to its capacity to activate complement (Mortensen *et al.*, 1976; Kilpatrick and Volanakis, 1985). It is possible that CRP is also associated with the Fc receptor or a structure closely related to it. CRP can facilitate opsonisation by monocytes in vitro (Mortensen *et al.*, 1976) and markedly enhanced splenic clearance of phosphocholine-coated sheep red cells in vivo (Nakayama *et al.*, 1982). CRP given 30 minutes prior to administration of *S. pneumoniae* was protective in mice made tolerant to phosphocholine (Mold *et al.*, 1981).

The functional similarity of CRP to IgG is further enhanced by its capacity to influence a number of presumed Fc-receptor-mediated phenomena. Aggregated CRP, like aggregated IgG, is able to induce platelet aggregation and mediator release (Fiedel *et al.*, 1982). Of greater relevance, however, is its capacity to bind to lymphocytes and perhaps modulate their function. There appears to be little doubt that it can bind to lymphocytes and it has also been found in sparse amounts on a small percentage of normal resting cells. It appears to bind to both T, B and NK cells, which have in common the presence of Fc receptors (Williams *et al.*, 1978; James *et al.*, 1981a, b, 1982). More controversial is the effect of this binding on the function of the cells. Some authors indicate it can stimulate lymphocyte blastogenesis and that these stimulated cells can destroy tumour cell lines in vitro (Hornung and Fritschi, 1971; Hornung, 1972). It also appears to be capable of inducing heightened macrophage tumoricidal activity (Barna *et al.*, 1984). Highly purified CRP markedly enhanced cell-mediated cytotoxicity and slightly enhanced allogeneic responses but did not affect antibody-dependent cell-mediated cyto-toxicity (ADCC), mitogen-induced proliferation or rosette formation (James *et al.*, 1982; Vetter *et al.*, 1986). Still others found that it could in-hibit phytohaemagglutinin (PHA) blastogenesis (Hokama *et al.*, 1973) rosette formation and blastogenic responses to antigens and allogeneic cells, but not ADCC or mitogen responses (Mortensen *et al.*, 1975). Whilst CRP has no apparent effect on NK cell function, treatment of NK cells with anti-CRP antiserum and complement resulted in marked impairment of cytotoxicity, suggesting that CRP is already present on the surface of the cells (Baum *et al.*, 1983).

The phosphocholine determinant is present in many eukaryotic and non-eukaryotic cell membranes and is distributed very widely in bac-terial species, some fungal species and even some nematodes (Volanakis, 1982). These determinants, whether present on infective organisms or red cells, are often not exposed unless the cell membrane is damaged (Volanakis, 1982; Kilpatrick and Volanakis, 1985). However, once it is exposed, CRP is able to bind avidly to it, and activate the complement cascade efficiently, thus greatly facilitating opsonisation, and allowing rapid clearance of the material from circulation. It also appears likely that CRP binds to and possibly influences the function of Fc-receptor-bearing lymphocytes, predominantly NK cells, although its exact role in this area is still much less clear. The rapid and marked rise in plasma levels of CRP in response to injury suggests that it has a significant biological role in non-specific defence against infection and in inflam-mation.

III. PROTEASE INHIBITORS

Human plasma contains a large number of protease inhibitors, but in the main their substrate specificity is restricted, often to an enzyme of an inflammatory pathway such the complement, coagulation or kinin systems. Two protease inhibitors, α-1-antitrypsin and α-2-macro-globulin, have a much broader range of enzyme reactivity, suggesting a wider role in natural immunity, with the potential capacity to modulate many types of inflammatory and immunological processes.

A. Alpha-1-antitrypsin

Alpha-1-antitrypsin is an inhibitor of serine proteases, which comprise the largest group of mammalian enzymes. It is an acute-phase reactant, with a molecular weight of about 51, 000 daltons and a molar concentration in plasma greater than that of all the other circulating protease inhibitors combined (Aubry and Bieth, 1977). It has a very broad spectrum of inhibitory activity (Breit *et al.*, 1985) and this, coupled with its small size and acute-phase reactant properties, suggests a very important role for it, in both the intra- and the extra-vascular compartments. Although α-1-antitrypsin has been shown to inhibit a wide variety of serine proteases, in vivo the bulk of the α-1-antitrypsin is needed to inactivate leukocytic neutral proteases, especially elastase (Ohlsson, 1971, 1975). This situation is considerably complicated by the fact that α-1-antitrypsin itself may be inactivated by two different mechanisms at sites of inflammation. A critical methionine residue at its active site is susceptible to oxidation, resulting in the destruction of its enzyme-inhibitory capacity (Travis *et al.*, 1977; Nakajima *et al.*, 1979). A recombinant α-1-antitrypsin has recently been constructed in which this critical residue has been replaced by valine, with a resultant 10-fold increase in protection against neutrophil-mediated damage (George *et al.*, 1984). Additionally, an exposed loop of the molecule is itself susceptible to enzymic degradation, with a resultant loss of most of its inhibitory activity (Banda *et al.*, 1985; Carrell and Owen, 1985).

The codominant allelic genes coding for α-1-antitrypsin are markedly polymorphic, some alleles being associated with a reduction in plasma levels of this protein. The phenotypes ZZ, MZ and MS are associated with mean plasma levels reduced to 12 per cent, 57 per cent and 79 per cent of normal respectively (Kueppers, 1972). It is produced predominantly within hepatocytes (Gitlin and Biasucci, 1969; Bhan *et al.*,1976) but also by macrophages (Isaacson *et al.*, 1979; Wilson *et al.*, 1980; Takemura *et al.*, 1986). Synthesis by the latter is at least in part regulated by cytokines (Takemura *et al.*, 1986), suggesting the possibility that local synthesis of this protein may also be important. By contrast with the other circulating protease inhibitors, deficient variants of α-1-antitrypsin are common, with an incidence of about 10 per cent in Caucasian populations, and are associated with an large number of inflammatory and immunologically mediated disorders, including emphysema, chronic liver disease, rheumatoid arthritis, systemic lupus erythematosus (SLE), uveitis, asthma, Weber Christian Disease, contact dermatitis and cold urticaria (reviewed by Breit *et al.*, 1985). Its physicochemical properties and the disorders associated with its deficiency suggest that it plays a fundamental role in regulating aspects of immunity and inflammation.

Because of the ubiquitous nature of serine proteases in mammalian function, the number of means by which α-1-antitrypsin and other protease inhibitors could potentially influence natural immunity is enormous. However, the two major areas of importance probably relate to the capacity of α-1-antitrypsin to influence directly the function of lymphocytes and phagocytic cells, and its inhibition of critical enzymes such as elastase, which not only have direct effects on inflammation, but are also potent amplifiers and secondary activators of many humoral and cellular inflammatory mechanisms. Whilst it is beyond the scope of this publication to review this area in depth, neutral proteases which α-1-antitrypsin inhibits in a highly efficient manner are capable of destroying elastin (Kueppers and Bearn, 1966; Baumstark, 1967; Janoff and Scherer, 1968), cartilage and structural collagen (Malemiud and Janoff, 1975; Laskowski and Kato, 1980), basement membranes (Sanders *et al.*, 1976; Davies *et al.*, 1978), fibrin (Plow, 1980) and fibronectin (Mc-Donald *et al.*, 1979). They can generate chemotactic factors from fibrin (Plow, 1980) and complement (Hugli *et al.*, 1976; Taubman *et al.*, 1980), produce an enhancing factor for IgG synthesis (Morgan and Weigle, 1980), activate mediators such as complement (Hugli *et al.*, 1976; Taubman *et al.*, 1980), kininogen (Wasi *et al.*, 1978) and angiotensinogen (Wintroub *et al.*, 1974), and activate cells such as lymphocytes and monocytes. Alpha-1-antitrypsin is also an important inhibitor of some coagulation proteins, most especially Xa, XIa (Heck and Kaplan, 1974; Gitel *et al.*, 1984) and, to a minor extent, thrombin (Downing *et al.*, 1977).

As has been indicated in both this and other chapters, complement plays a crucial role in natural immunity. Whilst α-1-antitrypsin probably has no direct effect on complement regulation, it is important in inhibition of neutral-protease-induced activation of the complement cascade. Two groups have demonstrated selective elevation of alternative pathway and attack sequence proteins C3, factor B, and C5 (Arnaud *et al.*, 1975; Breit *et al.*, 1982) and functional alternative pathway activity (Breit *et al.*, 1982) in α-1-antitrypsin-deficient subjects. Alpha-1-antitrypsin has also been shown to bind to C3 by a non-active-site-mediated mechanism and inhibit C3-mediated phagocytosis (Landen *et al.*, 1979; Mod *et al.*, 1981). Alpha-1-antitrypsin deficient serum could also induce enhanced activation of monocytes and neutrophils in a complement-dependent chemiluminescence assay (Breit *et al.*, 1983a). Purified α-1-antitrypsin, however, could not inhibit activation of these cells, suggesting that the effect was secondary. As the chemiluminescence assay is dependent on alternative pathway induced zymosan activation, this secondary effect may perhaps reflect changes in complement proteins in this deficient sera.

There is also evidence that α-1-antitrypsin can influence various aspects of the function of mononuclear cells. Alpha-1-antitrypsin deficient subjects show markedly accelerated delayed-type hypersensitivity reactions (Breit *et al.*, 1982). That this is not just a non-specific exaggeration of inflammatory responses is suggested by the fact that there appeared to be no changes in cutaneous Arthus reactions in the same subjects. Alpha-1-antitrypsin has been detected on the surface of resting and mitogen-stimulated lymphocytes (Lipsky *et al.*, 1979; Boldt *et al.*, 1982) and monocytes (Boldt *et al.*, 1982) and its level appears to increase with cell activation. Alpha-1-antitrypsin is able to inhibit the proliferative response of mononuclear cells to phytohaemagglutinin and concanavalin A, but not pokeweed mitogen (PWM) (Bata *et al.*, 1977, Vischer, 1979; Breit *et al.*, 1983b). This is reflected by increased proliferation in response to mitogens in otherwise well subjects with α-1-antitrypsin deficiency and phenotype zz. That this effect is mediated by α-1-antitrypsin itself is indicated by the fact that addition of the purified material in physiological amounts to the cultures returns the proliferative responses to normal. It is interesting that α-1-antitrypsin cannot completely suppress proliferation, indicating that its effect may be on some modifier, such as interleukin 1 production. This is further supported by studies suggesting that this effect is mediated by monocytes and not by a direct effect on proliferating T cells (Breit *et al.*, 1983b). Others have suggested that α-1-antitrypsin inhibits an enzyme on the surface of T-cell-depleted tonsillar cells (Bata *et al.*, 1981a, b). The presumption was that the latter was a B cell, but it may well have been a macrophage. There is direct evidence for the presence of an elastase on the surface of macrophages (Lavie *et al.*, 1980) and perhaps α-1-antitrypsin binds to this enzyme.

Subjects with α-1-antitrypsin deficiency exhibit no alteration in the levels of any immunoglobulin classes compared with control subjects (Breit *et al.*, 1982). In mice, α-1-antitrypsin inhibits the plaque-forming cell responses to sheep erythrocytes (Arora *et al.*, 1978), but in humans it enhances PWM-driven IgG synthesis in an exponential manner — a mirror image of the suppressive effect noted on mitogen-induced T cell proliferation (Breit *et al.*, 1984). The results at first glance appear paradoxical, and are probably due to inhibition of macrophage function by α-1-antitrypsin. They may therefore represent an in vitro artifact of the PWM system, which is known to be very sensitive to the ratio of adherent to non-adherent cells.

Alpha-1-antitrypsin can inhibit the cytotoxic reactions of lymphocytes including both antibody and cell mediated cytotoxicity (Redelman and Hudig, 1980; Ades *et al.*, 1982) and NK cell activity (Hudig *et al.*, 1981; Ades *et al.*, 1982). There is weak evidence for inhibition of T cell cytotoxicity (Redelman and Hudig, 1980). Alpha-1-antitrypsin probably does not inhibit monocyte tumour-cell killing (Colotta *et al.*, 1985). The mechanism of action of α-1-antitrypsin in cytotoxic responses is as yet unknown, but in the case of NK cells there is evidence that serine esterases and an elastase-like enzyme on the cell surface are involved in cytotoxicity and it is possible that they represent the site of action of α-1-antitrypsin (Hudig *et al.*, 1981; Ades *et al.*, 1982; Dawson *et al.*, 1985; Lavie *et al.*, 1985).

The role of alpha-1-antitrypsin in regulating cell motility has not been extensively studied but as it is believed that an active and an activatable serine esterase are involved in phagocyte motility (Ward and Becker, 1967a, b; Goetzl, 1975; Damerau *et al.*, 1980), it would not be surprising if α-1-antitrypsin were involved. This issue has really only been directly addressed in one study that suggested that α-1-antitrypsin inhibited the chemokinetic response of monocytes and neutrophils by about 35 per cent (Breit *et al.*, 1983b). There has also been one report of defective neutrophil chemotaxis in five infants with severe alpha-1-antitrypsin deficiency and recurrent infections (Khan *et al.*, 1986), but it is difficult to interpret the data in the light of the infant's clinical state.

B. Alpha-2-macroglobulin

Alpha-2-macroglobulin is unique among protease inhibitors because of both its large size and its surprising mode of action. It has a molecular weight of about 720,000 daltons (Hall and Roberts, 1978), which means that its access to the extravascular compartment is severely impeded. It is not an acute-phase reactant in humans, and there are no well-documented cases of its deficiency, as in the case of many of the other protease inhibitors. It is by far the least substrate-specific of any of the circulating protease inhibitors and will in fact bind to almost any endoproteinase, irrespective of class (Hartley, 1960). It is probably able to do this because the enzyme hydrolyses susceptible peptides in the α-2-macroglobulin, triggering a comformational change which results in its being trapped within the α-2-macroglobulin (Barrett and Starkey, 1973). The active site of the enzyme is however, not activated, which means that while it can no longer hydrolyse large substrates because of steric hindrance, it can continue to do so to small ones (Haverback *et al.*, 1962). Additionally, the trapped enzyme may still be inhibited by smaller protease inhibitors (Eddeland and Ohlsson, 1978). Because of this, and the irreversible nature of the binding of protease to α-2-macroglobulin, active enzymes from other enzyme-inhibitor complexes tend to be 'transferred' to α-2-macroglobulin which then rapidly clears them from the circulation (Ohlsson and Laurell, 1976; Balldin *et al.*, 1978) probably by way of macrophages, which express receptors for this material (James *et al.*, 1985).

Like α-1-antitrypsin, α-2-macroglobulin can also inhibit lymphocyte proliferation (Stein-Streilein and Hart, 1978; Hubbard, 1978; Vischer,

1979; Hubbard *et al.*, 1981; Rastogi and Clausen, 1985) and it is conceivable that it does so by reacting with the same cell-surface enzyme (Bata *et al.*, 1981a, b). This view, however, is at least in part contradicted by 2 groups, whose experiments indicate that inhibition is greatest if α-2-macroglobulin is complexed to enzyme rather than in its native configuration (Hubbard *et al.*, 1981; Mannhalter *et al.*, 1986), suggesting that it may be the enzyme, not α-2-macroglobulin, that is responsible for this effect (Mannhalter *et al.*, 1986). It is not clear whether α-2-macroglobulin is acting on lymphocytes, macrophages or both cells in exhibiting this effect.

Whilst there is no direct evidence for the role of α-2-macroglobulin in other aspects of natural immunity, a recent paper has suggested another rather novel mechanism. Human α-2-macroglobulin, and soya bean trypsin inhibitor, greatly decreased the infectivity of bloodstream trypomastigotes of *Trypanosoma cruzi* (de Araujo-Jorge *et al.*, 1986), suggesting that this protease inhibitor is acting on an enzyme important in the infectivity of the parasite. This suggests yet another mechanism whereby protease inhibitors such as α-2-macroglobulin and α-1-antitrypsin can influence natural immunity to infective organisms and perhaps also tumours.

C. Other Protease Inhibitors

There are many other circulating plasma protease inhibitors, including α-2-antiplasmin, inter-α-trypsin inhibitor, antithrombin III and C1 inhibitor, but it is beyond the scope of this chapter to discuss them in detail. Generally, they have a much greater restriction in substrate specificity, interacting with one active enzyme in the appropriate inflammatory pathway. Deficiences of these inhibitors are generally very rare, in marked contrast to α-1-antitrypsin. It is interesting to speculate that α-1-antitrypsin deficiency, especially in its minor form, may provide enhanced reactivity to a variety of stimuli, thus resulting in heightened natural immunity and resulting in genetic pressure to maintain a high frequency of deficiency in the population.

IV. OTHER PROTEINS

A. Ceruloplasmin

Ceruloplasmin is an acute-phase reactant which, because of its extremely high copper content, has been considered a copper transport protein. More recently evidence has appeared which suggests it may also function as an anti-inflammatory agent. In physiological concentrations, both free in solution and within liposomes, this material can scavenge superoxide anion radicals (Goldstein and Weissman, 1977). It could therefore be the extracellular counterpart of the copper-containing superoxide dismutase found within cells, which is so vital in limiting tissue damage generated by the highly reactive superoxide species.

B. Lipoproteins

Human serum has long been known to be toxic to some parasites. This effect is peculiar to the serum of some species and has been shown to be due to high-density lipoprotein, which is capable of slowly lysing trypanosomes (Rifkin, 1978). That this is of some physiological significance is suggested by the fact that human serum, or purified high-density lipoprotein, can clear *T. brucei* from the circulation of infected mice (Rifkin, 1978).

Both high and low density lipoproteins are also known to have an effect on humoral and cell-mediated immune processes (Curtiss and Edgington, 1976; Hsu *et al.*, 1982). They tend to be immunosuppressive, probably by interfering with early events in activation. It is suggested that changes in serum lipids are reflected by similar changes within the lipid membrane of cells, causing increased viscosity and decreased responsiveness to activation signals (Rivnay *et al.*, 1980).

CONCLUSION

Natural immunity can be influenced by many plasma factors which are capable of interacting with each other in a complex manner. This chapter has concentrated on the assessment of the current state of knowledge of two broad groups: the potentiating factors such as CRP and fibronectin, and the inhibitory factors that limit excessive responses such as α-1-antitrypsin and α-2-macroglobulin. The challenge of the future is to define the links and interactions between these and other biological systems that are important in natural immunity.

REFERENCES

Ades, E. W., Hinson, A., Chapuis-Cellier, C. and Arnaud P. (1982). Modulation of the immune response by plasma protease inhibitors: I: Alpha 2-macroglobulins and alpha 1-antitrypsin inhibit natural killing and antibody-dependent cell-mediated cytotoxicity. *Scand. J. Immunol.* 15: 109–13.

Arnaud, P, Creyssel, R. Bertoux, F.C., Chapuis-Cellier, C. and Freyria, A. M. (1975). High serum complement levels in patients with alpha 1-antitrypsin deficiency. *Protides Biol. Fluids.* 23: 387–93.

Arora, P. K., Miller, H. C. and Aronson, H. C. (1978). Alpha-1-antitrypsin is an effector of immunological stasis. *Nature* 274: 589–90.

Aubry, M. and Bieth J. (1977). Kinetics of the inactivation of human and bovine trypsins and chymotrypsins by alpha 1 proteinase inhibitor and of their reactivation by alpha 2 macroglobulin. *Clin. Chim. Acta.* 78: 371–80.

Balldin, G. Laurell, C.-B. and Ohlsson, K. (1978). Increased catabolism of alpha-macroglobulins after intravenous infusion of trypsin–alpha 1-antitrypsin complexes in dogs. *Hoppe-Seylers Z. Physiol. Chem.* 359: 699–708.

Banda, M. J., Clark, E. J. and Werb Z. (1985). Regulation of alpha 1 protease inhibitor function by rabbit alveolar macrophages: Evidence for proteolytic rather than oxidative inactivation. *J. Clin. Invest.* 75: 1758–62.

Barna, B. P., Deadhar, S. D., Gautam, S., Yen-Lieberman, B. and Roberts, D. (1984). Macrophage activation and generation of tumoricidal activity by liposome-associated human C-reactive protein. *Cancer Res.* 44: 305–10.

Barrett, A. J. and Starkey, P. M. (1973). The interaction of alpha 2-macroglobulin with proteinases: Characteristics and specificity of the reaction and a hypothesis concerning its molecular mechanism. *Biochem. J.* 133: 709–24.

Bata, J. Deviller, P. Colbert, L. and Lepine, M. P. (1977). Inhibition de la biosynthese du DNA chez les lymphocytes humains par l'effet de l'alpha-1-antitrypsine. *CR Acad. Sci. Paris* 285: 1499–1501.

Bata, J. Deviller, P. and Revillard, J. P. (1981a). Binding of alpha 1 antitrypsin (alpha 1 protease inhibitor) to human lymphocytes. *Biochem. Biophys. Res. Commun.* 98: 709–16.

Bata, J. Martin, J. P. and Revillard, J. P. (1981b). Cell surface protease activity of human lymphocytes: Its inhibition by alpha-1-antitrypsin. *Experientia.* 37: 518–19.

Baum, L. L. James, K. Glaviano, R. and Gewurz, H. (1983). Possible role for C-reactive protein in the human natural killer cell response. *J. Exp. Med.* 157: 301–11.

Baumstark, J. S. (1967). Studies on the elastase – serum protein interaction: 1: Molecular identity of the inhibitors in human serum and direct demonstration of inhibitor–elastase complexes by zone and immunoelectrophoresis. *Arch. Biochem. Biophys.* 118: 619–30.

Bhan, A. K., Grand, R. J., Colten, H. R. and Alper, C. A. (1976). Liver in alpha-1-antitrypsin deficiency: Morphologic observations and in vitro synthesis of alpha-1-antitrypsin. *Pediatr. Res.* 10: 35–40.

Blumenstock, F. A., Saba, T. M., Weber, P. and Laffin, R. (1978). Biochemical and alpha 2 immunological characterization of human opsonic alpha 2 SB glycoprotein: Its identity with cold insoluble globulin. *J. Biol. Chem.* 253: 4287–91.

Bohnsack, J. F., O'Shea, J. J., Takahashi, T. and Brown, E. J. (1985). Fibronectin enhanced phagocytosis of an alternative pathway activator by human culture-derived macrophages is mediated by the C4b/C3b complement receptor (CR1). *J. Immunol.* 135: 2580–6.

Boldt, D. H., Chan, S. K. and Keaton, J. (1982). Cell surface alpha 1-protease inhibitor on human peripheral mononuclear cells in culture. *J. Immunol.* 129: 1830–6.

Breit, S. N., Robinson, J. P., Luckhurst, E, Clark, P. and Penny R. (1982). Immunoregulation by alpha 1 antitrypsin. *J. Clin. Lab. Immunol.* 7: 127–32.

Breit, S. N., Robinson, J. P. and Penny, R. (1983a). The effect of alpha 1 antitrypsin on phagocyte function. *J. Lab. Clin. Immunol.* 10: 147–9.

Breit, S. N., Luckhurst, E. and Penny, R. (1983b). The effect of alpha 1 antitrypsin on the proliferative response of human peripheral blood lymphocytes. *J. Immunol.* 130: 681–6.

Breit, S. N., Maclean, P., Zaunders, J., Robinson, J. P., Wakefield, D., Cooper, D. A. and Penny, R. (1984). The effect of alpha 1 antitrypsin on PWM driven Ig synthesis. *J. Lab. Clin. Immunol.* 14: 191–3.

Breit, S. N., Wakefield, D., Robinson, J. P., Luckhurst, E., Clark, P. and Penny R. (1985). The role of alpha 1 antitrypsin in the pathogenesis of immune disorders. *Clin. Immunol. Immunopathol.* 35: 363–80.

Brown, E. J. (1986). The role of extracellular matrix proteins in the control of phagocytosis. *J. Leukocyte Biol.* 39: 579–91.

Carrell, R. W. and Owen, M. C. (1985). Plakaalbumin, alpha-1-antitrypsin, antithrombin, and the mechanism of inflammatory thrombosis. *Nature* 317: 730–2.

Claus, D. R., Siegel, J., Petras, K., Skor, D., Osmand, A. P. and Gewurz, H. (1977). Complement activation by interaction of polanions and polycations in the presence of C-reactive protein. *J. Immunol.* 118: 83–7.

Colotta, F., Bersani, L., Lazzarin, A., Poli, G. and Mantovani, A. (1985). Rapid killing of actinomycin D-treated tumor cells by human monocytes: II: Cytoxicity is dependent on secretion of reactive oxygen intermediates and is suppressed by protease inhibitors. *J. Immunol.* 134: 3524–31.

Cosio, F. G. (1984). Human fibronectin is an opsonin for IgG antibody-coated sheep erythrocytes. *J. Lab. Clin. Med.* 103: 613–19.

Curtiss, L. K. and Edgington, T. S. (1976). Regulatory serum lipoproteins: regulation of lymphocyte stimulation by species of low density lipoprotein. *J. Immunol.* 116: 1452–8.

Czop, J. K., Kadish, J. L. and Austen, K. F. (1982). Purification and characterisation of a protein with fibronectin determinants and phagocytosis-enhancing activity. *J. Immunol.* 129: 163–7.

Czop, J. K., Kadish, J. L., Zepf, D. M. and Austen, K. F. (1985). Characterization of the opsonic and monocyte adherence functions of the specific fibronectin fragment that enhances phagocytosis of particulate activators. *J. Immunol.* 134: 1844.

Damerau, B., Grunefeld, E. and Vogt, W. (1980). Aggregation of leukocytes induced by the complement derived peptides C3a and C5a and by three synthetic formyl-methionylpeptides. *Int. Archs. Allergy Appl. Immunol.* 63: 159–69.

Davies, M., Barret, A. J., Travis, J., Sanders E. and Coles, G. A. (1978). The degradation of human glomerular basement membrane with purified lyso-somal proteinases. *Clin. Sci. Molec. Biol.* 54: 233–40.

Dawson, M. M., Shipto, U. and Moore, M. (1985). Involvement of cell surface macromolecules sensitive to alkylating ketones in lysis of human peripheral blood NK cells. *Clin. Exp. Immunol.* 59: 91–100.

Dayhoff, M. O. (ed.) (1976). *Atlas of Protein Sequence and Structure*, vol.5, suppl. 2: 3–8. Maryland, USA: National Biomedical Research Foundation.

de Araujo-Jorge, T. C., Sampaio, E. P. and de Souza, W. (1986). *Trypanosoma cruzi*: inhibition of host cell uptake of infective bloodstream forms by alpha-2-macroglobulin. *Z. Parasitenkd.* 72: 3232–9.

Downing, M. R., Bloom, J. W. and Mann, K. G. (1977). Alpha 1 antitrypsin inhibition of thrombin. In RL Lundblad *et al* (eds), *Chemistry and Biology of Thrombin*. Ann Arbor Science: 441–50.

Eddeland, A. and Ohlsson, K. (1978). A radioimmunoassay for the measure-ment of human pancreatic secretory trypsin inhibitor in different body fluids. *Hoppe-Seylers Z. Physiol. Chem.* 359: 379–84.

Fiedel, B. A., Simpson, R. M. and Gewurz, H. (1982). Activation of platelets by modified C-reactive protein. *Immunol.* 45: 439–47.

George, P. M., Vissers, M. C., Travis, J., Winterbourn, C. C. and Carrell, R. W. (1984). A genetically engineered mutant of alpha 1-antitrypsin protects connective tissue from neutrophil damage and may be useful in lung disease. *Lancet* 2: 1426–8.

Gitel, S. N., Medina, V. M. and Wessler, S. (1984). Inhibition of human activated Factor X by antithrombin III and alpha 1-proteinase inhibitor in human plasma. *J. Biol. Chem.* 259: 6890–5.

Gitlin, D. and Biasucci, A. (1969). Development of gamma G, gamma A, gamma M, beta 1C/beta 1A, C1 esterase inhibitor, ceruloplasmin, transferrin, hemopexin, haptoglobin, fibrinogen, plasminogen, alpha-1-antitrypsin, orosomucoid, beta lipoprotein, alpha 2 macroglobulin and prealbumin in the human conceptus. *J. Clin. Invest.* 48: 1433–46.

Goetzl, E. J. (1975). Modulation of human neutrophil polymorphonuclear leukocyte migration by plasma alpha globulin inhibitors and synthetic esterase inhibitors. *Immunology* 29: 163–74.

Goldstein, I. M. and Weissman, G. (1977). Effects of the generation of superoxide anion on permeability of liposomes. *Biochem. Biophys. Res. Commun.* 75: 604–9.

Hall, P. K. and Roberts, R. C. (1978). Physical and chemical properties of human plasma alpha 2 macroglobulin. *Biochem. J.* 171: 27–38.

Hartley, B. S. (1960). Proteolytic enzymes. *Ann. Rev. Biochem.* 29: 45–72.

Haverback, B. J., Dyce, B., Bundy, H. F. *et al.* (1962). Protein binding of pancreatic proteolytic enzymes. *J. Clin. Invest.* 41: 972–80.

Heck, L. W. and Kaplan, A. P. (1974). A role for alpha 1 antitrypsin in the regulation of coagulation. *Fed. Proc.* 33: 642.

Hill, H. R., Shigeoka, A. O., Augustine, N. H., Pritchard, D., Lundblad, J. L. and Schwartz, R. S. (1984). Fibronectin enhances the opsonic protective activity of monoclonal and polyclonal antibody against group B streptococci. *J. Exp. Med.* 159: 1618–28.

Hokama, Y., Paik, Y. P., Yanagihara, E., Kimura, L. *et al* (1973). Effect of C-reactive protein and blood group substances on 3H-thymidine incorporation into DNA of leukocytes. *J. Reticuloendothel. Soc.* 13: 111–21.

Hornung, M. O. (1972). Growth inhibition of human melanoma cells by C-reactive protein (CRP) activated lymphocytes. *Proc. Soc. Exp. Biol. Med.* 139: 1166–9.

Hornung, M. O. and Fritchi, S. (1971). Isolation of C reactive protein and its effect on human lymphocytes in vitro. *Nature New Biol.* 230: 84–5.

Hsu, K. H., Hiramoto, R. N. and Ghanta, V. K. (1982). Immunosuppressive effects of mouse serum lipoproteins: II: In vivo studies. *J. Immunol.* 128: 2107–10.

Hubbard, W. J. (1978). Alpha-2-macroglobulin–enzyme complexes as suppressors of cellular activity. *Cell. Immunol.* 39: 388–94.

Hubbard, W. J., Hess, A. D., Hsia, S. and Amos, D. B. (1981). The effects of electophoretically 'slow' and 'fast' alpha 2 macroglobulin on mixed lymphocyte cultures. *J. Immunol.* 126: 292–9.

Hudig, D., Haverty, T., Fulcher, C., Redelman, D. and Mendelsohn, J. (1981). Inhibition of human natural cytotxicity by macromolecular antiproteases. *J. Immunol.* 126: 1569–74.

Hugli, T. E., Taylor, J. C. and Crawford, I. P. (1976). Selective cleavage of C3 by human leukocyte elastase (HLE). *J. Immunol.* 116: 1737–42.

Isaacson, P., Jones, D. B. and Judd, M. A. (1979). Alpha 1-antitrypsin in human macrophages. *Lancet* 2: 964–5.

James, K., Hansen, B. and Gewurz, H. (1981a). Binding of C-reactive protein to lymphocytes: 1: Requirement for binding specificity. *J. Immunol.* 127: 2539–44.

James, K., Hansen, B. and Gewurz, H. (1981b). Binding of C-reactive protein to lymphocytes: II: Interaction with a subset of cells bearing the Fc receptor. *J. Immunol.* 127: 2545–50.

James, K., Baum, L. L., Vetter, M. L. and Gewurz, H. (1982). Interactions of C-reactive protein with lymphoid cells. *Ann. NY Acad. Sci.* 389: 274–85.

James, K., Milne, I. and Donaldson, K. (1985). Fluoresceinated alpha 2-macroglobulin as a probe for studying macrophages. *J. Immunol. Methods.* 82: 281–93.

Janoff, A. and Scherer, J. (1968). Mediators of inflammation in leukocyte lysosomes: IX: Elastinolytic activity in granules of human polymorphonuclear leukocytes. *J. Exp. Med.* 128: 1137–55.

Johnson, E., Gaupera, T. and Eskeland, T. (1985). Fibronectin binds to complement-coated agarose beads and increases their association to mouse macrophages. *Scand. J. Immunol.* 22: 315–20.

Kaplan, M. D. and Volanakis, J. E. (1974). Interaction of C-reactive protein complexes with the complement system: I: Consumption of human complement associated with the reaction of C-reactive protein with pneumococcal C-polysaccharide and with choline phosphatides, lecithin and sphingomyelin. *J. Immunol.* 112: 2135–47.

Khan, A. J., Evans, H. E. and Agbayani, M. M. (1986). Defective neutrophil chemotaxis in patients with alpha-1-antitrypsin deficiency. *Eur. J. Pediatr.* 144: 464–6.

Kilpatrick, J. M. and Volanakis, J. E. (1985). Opsonic properties of C-reactive protein: Stimulation by phorbol myristate acetate enables human neutrophils to phagocytize C-reactive protein-coated cells. *J. Immunol.* 134: 3364–70.

Kueppers, F. (1972). Alpha 1-antitrypsin levels and electrophoretic patterns of several deficient phenotypes. *Humangenetik* 15: 1–6.

Kueppers, F. and Bearn, A. G. (1966). A possible experimental approach to the association of hereditary alpha 1 antitrypsin deficiency and pulmonary emphysema. *Proc. Soc. Exp. Biol. (NY)* 121: 1207–15.

Landen, B., Schmitt, M. and Dierich, M. P. (1979). Alpha 1-antitrypsin serves as a C3 receptor molecule. *Fed. Proc.* 38: 1467.

Laskowski, M. and Kato, I. (1980). Protein inhibitors of proteinases. *Ann. Rev. Biochem.* 49: 593–626.

Lavie, G., Zucker-Franklin, D. and Franklin, E. C. (1980). Elastase type proteases on the surface of human blood monocytes: Possible role in amyloid formation. *J. Immunol.* 125: 175–80.

Lavie, G., Leib, Z. and Servadio, C. (1985). The mechanism of human NK cell mediated cytotoxicity: Mode of action of surface associated proteases in early stages of the lytic reaction. *J. Immunol.* 135: 1470–6.

Linder, E., Stenman, S., Lehto, V. P. and Vaheri, A. (1978). Distribution of fibronectin in human tissues and relationship to other connective tissue components. *Ann. NY Acad. Sci.* 312: 151–9.

Lipsky, J. J., Berninger, R. W., Hyman, L. R. and Talamo, R. C. (1979). Presence of alpha-1-antitrypsin on mitogen stimulated human lymphocytes. *J. Immunol.* 122: 24–6.

McDonald, J. A., Baum, B. J., Rosenberg, D. M., Kelman, J. A. *et al.* (1979). Destruction of a major extracellular adhesive glycoprotein (fibronectin) of human fibroblasts by neutral proteases from polymorphonuclear leukocyte granules. *Lab. Invest.* 40: 350–7.

Malemiud, C. F. and Janoff, A. (1975). Human polymorphonuclear leukocyte elastase and cathepsin G mediate the degradation of lapine articular cartilage proteoglycan. *Ann. NY Acad. Sci.* 256: 254–62.

Mannhalter, J. W., Borth, W. and Eibl, M. M. (1986). Modulation of antigen induced T cell proliferation by alpha 2M-trypsin complexes. *J. Immunol.* 136: 2792–9.

Martin, D. E., Reece, M. and Reese, A. C. (1984). Effects of plasma fibronectin, macrophages, and glycosaminoglycans on tumor cell growth. *Cancer Res.* 2: 339–45.

Mod, A., Fust, G., Gergely, J., Hollan, S. and Dierich, M. P. (1981). Alpha-1-antitrypsin induced inhibition of complement dependent phagocytosis. *Immunobiol.* 158: 338–46.

Mold, C., Nakayama, S., Holzer, T. J., Gewurz, H. and Du Clos, T. W. (1981). C-reactive protein is protective against *Streptococcus pneumoniae* infection in mice. *J. Exp. Med.* 154: 1703–8.

Morgan, E. L. and Weigle, W. O. (1980). Regulation of Fc fragment induced murine spleen cell proliferation. *J. Exp. Med.* 151: 1–11.

Morrison, P. R., Edsall, J. T. and Miller, S. G. (1948). Preparation and properties of serum and plasma proteins XVIII: The separation of purified fibrinogen from fraction I of human plasma. *J. Am. Chem. Soc.* 70: 3103.

Mortensen, R. F., Osmand, A. P. and Gewurz, H. (1975). Effects of C-reactive protein on the lymphoid system: I: Binding to thymus-dependent lymphocytes and alteration of their function. *J. Exp. Med.* 141: 821–39.

Mortensen, R. F., Osmand, A. P., Lint, T. F. and Gewurz, H. (1976). Interaction of C-reactive protein with lymphocytes and monocytes: Complement dependent adherence and phagocytosis. *J. Immunol.* 117: 774–81.

Mosher, D. F. (1980). Fibronectin. *Progress in Hemostasis and Thrombosis* 5: 111–51.

Nakajima, K., Powers, J. C., Ashe, B. M. and Zimmerman, M. (1979). Mapping the extended subtrate binding site of cathepsin G and human leukocyte elastase: Studies with peptide substrates related to the alpha 1-protease inhibitor reactive site. *J. Biol. Chem.* 254: 4027–32.

Nakayama, S., Mold, C., Gewurz, H. and Du Clos, T. (1982). Opsonic properties of C-reactive protein in vivo. *J. Immunol.* 128: 2435–8.

Narkates, A. J. and Volanakis, J. E. (1982). C-reactive protein binding specificities: Artificial and natural phospholipid bilayers. *Ann. NY Acad. Sci.* 389: 172–82.

Ohlsson, K. (1971). Neutral leukocyte proteases and elastase inhibited by alpha 1-antitrypsin. *Scand. J. Clin. Lab. Invest.* 28: 251–3.

Ohlsson, K. (1975). Alpha 1 antitrypsin and alpha 2 macroglobulin: Interactions with human neutrophil collagenase and elastase. *Ann. NY Acad Sci.* 256: 4409–19.

Ohlsson, K. and Laurell, C. B. (1976). The disappearance of enzyme–inhibitor complexes from the circulation of man. *Clin. Sci. Molec. Med.* 51: 87–92.

Osmand, A. P., Mortensen, R. F., Seigel, J. and Gewurz, H. (1975). Interactions of C-reactive protein with the complement system: III: Complement dependent passive hemolysis intitiated by CRP. *J. Exp. Med.* 142: 1065–77.

Pierschbacher, M. D. and Ruoslahti, E. (1984). Cell attachment activity of fibronectin can be duplicated by small synthetic fragments of the molecule. *Nature* 309: 30–3.

Plow, E. F. (1980). The major fibrinolytic proteases of human leukocytes. *Biochim. Biophys. Acta.* 630: 47–56.

Pommier, C. G., O'Shea, J., Chused, T., Yancey, K., Frank, M. M., Takahashi, T. and Brown, E. J. (1984). Studies on the fibronectin receptors of human peripheral blood leukocytes: Morphological and functional characterization. *J. Exp. Med.* 159: 137–51.

Proctor, R. A., Textor, J. A., Vann, J. M. and Mosher, D. F. (1985). Role of fibronectin in human monocyte and macrophage bactericidal activity. *Infect. Immun.* 47: 629–37.

Rastogi, S. C. and Clausen, J. (1985). Kinetics of inhibition of mitogen induced proliferation of human lymphocytes by alpha 2-macroglobulin serum free medium. *Immunobiology* 169: 37–44.

Redelman, D. and Hudig, D. (1980). The mechanism of cell mediated cytotoxicity: I: Killing by murine cytotoxic T lymphocytes requires cell surface thiols and activated proteases. *J. Immunol.* 124: 870–8.

Richards, R. L., Gewurz, H., Osmand, A. P. and Alving, C.R. (1977). Interactions of C-reactive protein and complement with liposomes. *Proc. Natl. Acad. Sci. USA* 74: 5672–6.

Richards, R. L., Gewurz, H., Siegel, J. and Alving, C.R. (1979). Interactions of C-reactive protein and complement with liposomes: II: Influence of membrane composition. *J. Immunol.* 122: 1185–9.

Rifkin, M. R. (1978). Identification of the trypanosomal factor within normal human serum: high density lipoprotein. *Proc. Natl. Acad. Sci. USA* 75: 3450–4.

Rivnay, B., Bergman, S., Shinitsky, M. and Globerson, A. (1980). Correlations between viscosity, serum cholesterol, lymphocyte activation and aging in man. *Mech. Aging Dev.* 12: 119–26.

Rovin, B., Molnar, J., Chevalier, D. and Ng, P. (1984). Interaction of plasma fibronectin (pFN) with membranous constituents of peritoneal exudate cells and pulmonary macrophages. *J. Leukocyte Biol.* 36: 601–20.

Saba, T. M., Blumenstock, F. A., Weber, P. and Kaplan, J. E. (1978a). Physiological role of cold insoluble globulin in systemic host defence: implications of its characterisation as the opsonic alpha 2 surface binding glycoprotein. *Ann. NY Acad. Sci.* 312: 43–55.

Saba, T. M., Blumenstock, F. A., Scovill, W. A. and Bernard, H. (1978b). Cryoprecipitate reversal of opsonic surface binding glycoprotein deficiency in septic surgical and trauma patients. *Science* 203: 622–4.

Sanders, E., Coles, G. A. and Davies, M. (1976). Polymorphonuclear leukocyte enzyme activity in human glomerulonephritis. *Proc. Europ. Dialysis. Transpl. Ass.* 13: 541–5.

Scovill, W. A., Saba, T. M., Blumenstock, F. A., Bernard, H. and Powers, S. R. Jr. (1978). Opsonic alpha 2 surface binding glycoprotein therapy during sepsis. *Ann. Surg.* 188: 521–9.

Scovill, W. A., Annest, S., Saba, T. M., Blumenstock, F. A., Newell, J. C. *et al.* (1979). Cardiovascular haemodynamics after opsonic alpha 2 SB glycoprotein therapy in injured patients. *Surgery* 86: 284–93.

Sekiguchi, K. and Hakomori, S.-I. (1980). Functional domain structure of fibronectin. *Proc. Natl. Acad. Sci. USA* 77: 2661–5.

Siegel, J., Rent, R. and Gewurz, H. (1974). Interactions of C-reactive protein with the complement system: I: Protamine induced consumption of complement in acute phase sera. *J. Exp. Med.* 140: 631–47.

Siegel, J., Osmand, A. P., Wilson, M. F. and Gewurz, H. (1975). Interactions of C-reactive protein with the complement system: II: C-reactive protein mediated consumption of complement by poly-L-lysine polymers and other polycations. *J. Exp. Med.* 142: 709–21.

Snyder, E. L. and Luban. N. L. (1986). Fibronectin: applications to clinical medicine. *CRC Crit. Rev. Clin. Lab. Sci.* 23: 15–34.

Stein-Streilen, J. and Hart, D. A. (1978). Role of alpha globulins in nonspecific regulation of the immune response: Possible mechanisms for external and internal signals. *Fed. Proc.* 37: 2042–4.

Stenman, S. and Vaheri, A. (1978). Distribution of a major connective tissue protein, fibronectin, in normal human tissues. *J. Exp. Med.* 147: 1054–64.

Takemura, S., Rossing, T. H. and Perlmutter, D. H. (1986). A lymphokine regulates expression of alpha 1 proteinase inhibitor in human monocytes and macrophages. *J. Clin. Invest.* 77: 1207–13.

Taubman, S. B., Goldschmidt, P. R. and Lepow, I. H. (1980). Effects of lysosomal enzymes from human leukocytes on human complement components. *Proc. 4th Intern. Congress. Immunol.* : 434.

Tillet, W. S. and Francis, T. (1930). Serological reactions in pneumonia with a non-protein somatic fraction of pneumococcus. *J. Exp. Med.* 52: 561–71.

Travis, J., Matheson, N., Johnson, D. and Beatty, K. (1977) Human alpha-1-proteinase inhibitor and human alpha-1-antichymotrypsin: Properties and mechanism. In D. H. Bing (ed.), *The Chemistry and Physiology of the Human Plasma Proteins.* Ann Arbor Science: 441–50.

Vetter, M. L., Gewurz, H. and Baum, L. L. (1986). The effects of C-reactive protein on human cell mediated cytotoxicity. *J. Leukocyte Biol.* 39: 13–25.

Vischer, T. L. (1979). Protease inhibitors reduce mitogen induced lymphocyte stimulation. *Immunology.* 36: 811–13.

Volanakis, J. E. (1982). Complement activation by C-reactive protein complexes. *Ann. NY Acad. Sci.* 389: 235–50.

Volanakis, J. E. and Kaplan, M. D. (1971). Specificity of C-reactive protein for choline phosphate residues of pneumococcal C-polysaccharide. *Proc. Soc. Exp. Biol. Med.* 136: 612–14.

Ward, P. A. and Becker, E. L. (1967a). Mechanisms of the inhibition of chemotaxis by phosphonate esters. *J. Exp. Med.* 125: 1001–20.

Ward, P. A. and Becker, E. L. (1967b). The deactivation of rabbit neutrophils by chemotactic factor and the nature of the activatable esterase. *J. Exp. Med.* 127: 693–709.

Wasi, S., Movat, H. Z., Pass, E. and Chan, J. Y. C. (1978). Production of conversion and destruction of kinins by human neutrophil leukocyte proteases. In K. Havemann and A. Janoff (eds), *Neutral Proteases of Human Polymorphonuclear Leukocytes.* Urban and Schwarzenberg: Baltimore: 245–60.

Williams, R. C., Kilpatrick, K. A., Kassaby, M. and Abdin, Z. H. (1978). Lymphocytes binding C-reactive protein during acute rheumatic fever. *J. Clin. Invest.* 61: 1384–93.

Wilson, G. B., Walker, J. H., Watkins, J. H. and Wolgroch, D. (1980). Determination of subpopulations of leukocytes involved in the synthesis of alpha 1 antitrypsin in vitro. *Proc. Soc. Exp. Biol. Med.* 164: 105–14.

Wintroub, B. Y., Goetzl, E. and Austen, K. F. (1974). A neutrophil dependent pathway for the generation of a neutral peptide mediator. *J. Exp. Med.* 140: 812–24.

Wright, S. D., Licht, M. R., Craigmyle, L. S. and Silverstein, S. C. (1984). Communication between receptors for different ligands on a single cell : ligation of fibronectin receptors induces a reversible alteration in the function of complement receptors on cultured human monocytes. *J. Cell Biol.* 99: 336–9.

10

Hormones

NICOLA FABRIS
MAURO PROVINCIALI

Immunology Centre
Gerontology Research Department
Italian National Research Centres on Aging (INRCA)
Via Birarelli 8
Ancona
Italy

NATURAL IMMUNITY
ISBN 0 12 5145551

I. INTRODUCTION

It is generally accepted that the immune system, although regulated to a large extent by intrinsic cellular and humoral events, is sensitive to signals generated in the nervous and endocrine systems. This assumption is supported by two lines of experimental evidence: first, that spontaneous or induced alterations in the neuroendocrine system may cause functional modifications of immune reactivity (Fabris, 1981a); and, second, that the membranes of various lymphoid cells contain receptor sites for many hormones (Gavin, 1977), neuropeptides (Shavit *et al.*, 1985; Blalock *et al.*, 1985a) and substances, such as the autacoids (Schafer, 1916; Hadden, 1983), released under stressful and inflammatory reactions.

The neuroendocrine system, however, seems to act not only as a modulator of the immune network, but also as a target itself for signals generated within the immune system. Alterations can be induced in the neuroendocrine balance, in fact, either by removal of relevant lymphoid organs, such as the thymus (Pierpaoli *et al.*, 1971) or the bursa (Pedernera *et al.*, 1983), or by the functioning of the immune system itself, such as reactions to immunogenic or tolerogenic doses of antigen (Besedovsky *et al.*, 1975; Besedovsky and Sorkin, 1977). Moreover, it has been recently shown that activated T cells are able, in some circumstances, to produce hormone-like substances that may directly interfere with the neuroendocrine network (Blalock *et al.*, 1985a).

With regard to the lymphoid branch of such interactions, most studies have, however, dealt with specific immune reactions, and therefore, with the cells that are responsible for them, i.e. mature T or B cells, and their humoral products.

These studies, together with those dealing with the interactions between the thymus as an endocrine gland and the neuroendocrine network (Fabris and Piantanelli, 1982; Fabris *et al.*, 1986), have sought to identify definite pathways of neuroendocrine–immune interactions.

The evidence for the role played in such interactions by the cells deputed to carry on natural resistance against infections and neoplastic diseases is relatively sparse and somewhat fragmentary.

The aim of this work is to summarise the evidence in favour of the existence of neuroendocrine–immune pathways, and to analyse the available data on the modulation of natural resistance by means of neuroendocrine signals.

II. THE NEUROENDOCRINE NETWORK

The neuroendocrine network represents a quite complex system sensitive both to external stimuli, via its connections with the central nervous system, and to internal signals as generated by other organs directly or indirectly involving critical metabolic processes.

Because the network is so complex, it is worthwhile to summarise the most important neuroendocrine pathways and the interactions and regulation of various components of the neuroendocrine tissue.

A. Functional Organisation of the Neuroendocrine System

According to the historical view, the co-ordinated function of the body is regulated by two interdependent systems (Fig. 10.1): the central nervous system, whose messages are mediated by low molecular weight sub-

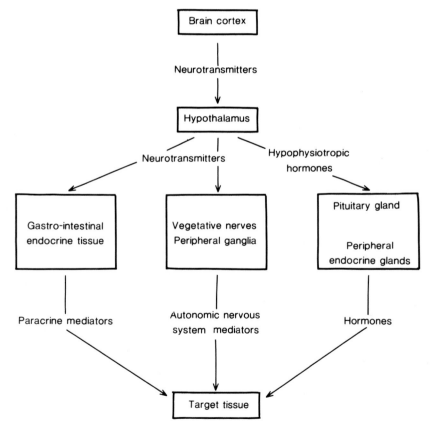

Fig. 10.1 Schematic representation of the functional organisation of the neuroendocrine system (see text for explanation).

stances (neurotransmitters); and the endocrine system, working by means of the 'classical' hormones (Timiras, 1972). The former, through one of its subdivisions, the autonomic nervous system (ANS), is concerned with rapid responses to stress, danger or demands (Best and Taylor, 1943). Generally speaking, the autonomic nervous system consists of two opposing subsystems: the sympathetic nervous system, whose action is mediated through two hormone-like substances epinephrine and norepinephrine, secreted by the adrenal medulla and nerve endings respectively; and the parasympathetic nervous system, whose action is mediated by acetylcholine liberated from nerve endings. These two opposing subsystems, working simultaneously in alternation, control a number of vascular and metabolic processes in response to stress.

The endocrine system, again according to the classical view, is directed by the 'master' pituitary gland, which is in turn regulated by neurohormonal substances released by the hypothalamus (hypophysiotropic hormones), and through its hormonal products (pituitary hormones) modulates the activity of peripheral endocrine glands, such as the thyroid, sexual glands, adrenals, etc.

A third homeostatic system has been added in the last decades: the diffuse endocrine epithelial organ associated with the gastrointestinal tract which, through the secretion of different peptides (gastrin, cholecystokinin, substance P, vasointestinal peptides, etc.) modulates various functions at the digestive level. The term 'paracrine' has been used to distinguish these humoral secretions (Jackson and Mueller, 1982).

Feedback mechanisms ensure the autoregulation of the endocrine system. The hormones of the peripheral endocrine glands can act back on the hypothalamus, pituitary or both, to regulate the secretion of hypophysiotropic and pituitary hormones (long-loop feedback) (Jackson and Mueller, 1982). The pituitary hormones can also act on the hypothalamus to inhibit their own secretion (short-loop feedback) (Fig. 10.2). Some of these classical neuroendocrinological views have been modified during the last decades and new, sometimes revolutionary, concepts have arisen.

First of all, it has been recognised that the cascade of hypothalamus – pituitary – target glands, in addition to the long-loop feedback mechanism, is regulated by a number of neurotransmitters produced in different brain areas, ensuring a relationship with brain-mediated perception of external stimuli and with ANS-mediated rapid responses (Jackson and Mueller, 1982).

Furthermore, in addition to some neuronal mediators already known, such as serotonin, histamine, dopamine and norepinephrine, a new class of neuronal mediators has been identified in the endogenous opioid

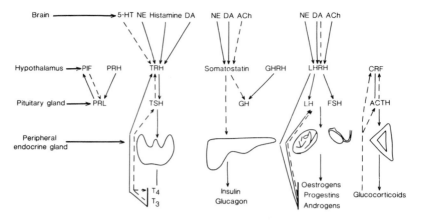

Fig. 10.2 Schematic representation of the long- and short-loop feedback mechanisms ensuring the autoregulation of the endocrine system. The continuous line indicates enhancement; the dashed line indicates inhibition. Abbreviations: 5-HT, 5-hydroxytryptamine; NE, norepinephrine; DA, dopamine; ACh, acetylcholine; PIF, prolactin-inhibiting factor; PRH, prolactin-releasing hormone; TRH, thyrotropin-releasing hormone; GHRH, growth hormone releasing hormone; LHRH, luteinising hormone releasing hormone; CRF, corticotropin-releasing factor; PRL, prolactin; TSH, thyrotropic hormone; GH, growth hormone; LH, luteinising hormone; FSH, follicle-stimulating hormone; ACTH, adrenocorticotropic hormone.

system (Khachaturian *et al.*, 1985). This new class, of neuropeptides, was discovered following the demonstration on brain cells of membrane receptors for derivatives of opium. The findings suggested that such receptors probably had a physiological role in recognising endogenous products more or less related to opioid alkaloids. Three major groups of endogenous opioid peptides are now known: the enkephalins, the peptides related to β-endorphins, and the peptides related to dynorphin. These peptides are not individually synthesised but are secreted as cleavage products of polyprotein precursors, which have recently been biochemically characterised (Fig. 10.3). Peptides derived from proopiomelanocortin (POMC) include the opioid β-endorphin and the nonopioid hormones adrenal corticotropic hormone (ACTH) and α-melanocyte stimulating hormone (α-MSH). The POMC precursor is synthesised in both the pituitary gland and the hypothalamus. The proenkephalin precursors of met-enkephalin and leu-enkephalin are more widely distributed than POMC. Pro-enkephalin precursors are found in different brain areas, particularly at the hypothalamic level, in adrenal medulla, and in many peripheral nerves (Khachaturian *et al.*, 1985). The prodynorphin precursor of A and B dynorphin and α-neo-endorphin is present in the pars nervosa of the pituitary.

PROOPIOMELANOCORTIN

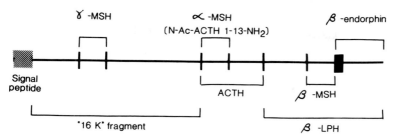

PROENKEPHALIN

PRONEOENDORPHIN-DYNORPHIN

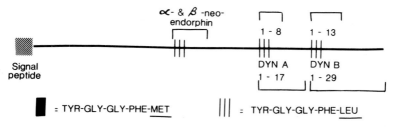

Fig. 10.3 Schematic representation of the structure of the three opioid peptide precursors. Note that the opiate-active core sequence Tyr-Gly-Gly-Phe-Met (met-enkephalin) appears in both proopiomelanocortin and proenkephalin, while the opiate-active sequence Try-Gly-Gly-Phe-Leu (leu-enkephalin) is common to both proenkephalin and pro-neoendorphin-dynorphin. (From Khachaturian *et al.*, 1985 Trends in Neurosciences 8: 111).

The major role of endorphins and enkephalins seems to be the control of sensitivity to analgesia. Other actions have been attributed to endogenous opioids, such as the control of blood pressure, blood temperature and the secretion of some hormones, particularly those which mediate reactions to stressors.

It is worth noting that not all kinds of stress are mediated by the actions exerted on the opioid receptors. There exist forms of naturally occurring or experimentally inducible stressors which do not evoke opioid-mediated reactions. That there is a distinction between opioid stress and non-opioid stress is supported by the fact that the former, but not the latter, can be counteracted by the opioid antagonist naloxone, which blocks the activity of opioid receptors (Shavit *et al.*, 1984).

A second main conceptual change is that the sharp distinction among the humoral mediators of the three major systems of co-ordination and communication of cellular activity, i.e. 'hormone', 'neurotransmitters' and 'paracrine peptides', is no longer tenable in respect either of the biological function of single humoral substances or of the topography of the cells producing them (Jackson and Mueller, 1982).

With regard to the specific functions of various neuroendocrine signals, many mediators, generally characterised by short amino-acid sequences (endorphins, enkephalins, neurotensin, vasointestinal peptide, substance P, etc.), may in some circumstances provide signals within the nervous tissues while in others they may enter the circulation and act as hormones (Jackson and Mueller, 1982).

Also, the hypothalamic releasing factors (thyrotropin releasing hormone [TRH], luteinizing hormone releasing hormone [LHRH] and somatostatin), which were initially discovered in the hypothalamus and have a hypophysiotropic function (modulation of the secretion of pituitary hormones), were subsequently found to be capable of influencing transmission of nervous signals (electrophysiological function) and of conditioning some behavioural reactions (Table 10.1).

Multi-functional humoral mediators of the neuroendocrine system can be secreted by different anatomical sites. Thus at least two hypophysiotropic hormones, somatostatin and TRH, are produced not only in the hypothalamus but also in sensory neurones (Hökfelt *et al.*, 1978) and in the motorneurones of the anterior horn of the spinal cord respectively. In addition, somatostatin is produced by the D cells of the pancreas and the gut (Polak *et al.*, 1975) and TRH by cells of the intestinal tract (Hökfelt *et al.*, 1978) (Table 10.1). Furthermore, hormones and neuropeptides such as cholecystokinin (CCK), vasoactive intestinal peptide (VIP) and insulin, which are produced by secretory cells or nerve endings associated with the gut, have been found to be produced also by the brain (Dockray, 1978; Haurankova *et al.*, 1978). Such distribution of hormones and neuropeptide secreting cells may be linked to the diversification of functions of these peptides which may behave as neurotransmitters in one setting and as hormones in another.

Moreover, the same secretory cell can synthesise and release more than one hormone or neuropeptide. The best examples of this are

Table 10.1: The main hypophysiotropic, behavioural and electrophysiological effects of several hypothalamic hormones

Hormone	Thyrotropin releasing hormone (TRH)	Luteinising hormone releasing hormone (LHRH)	Somatostatin
Effects:			
Hypophysiotropic:	releases TSH and PRL	releases LH and FSH	inhibits GH and TSH release
Behavioural:	on motor activity on food and water intake	on mating sexual performance on water intake	on food and water intake on insomnia on tonic-clonic seizures
Electrophysiological:	on firing of brain neurones on excitability of neurones in midbrain and medulla	on firing of brain neurones	on firing of brain neurones on firing of cerebro-cortical neurones
Sites of production	Extrahypothalamic brain Hypothalamus Spinal cord (anter.) Gastrointestinal tract	Extrahypothalamic brain Hypothalamus Pineal gland	Extrahypothalamic brain Hypothalamus Spinal cord (dorsal) Gastrointestinal tract

pituitary cells which secrete both the opioid β-endorphin and the non-opioid hormones ACTH and α-MSH (Khachaturian *et al.*, 1985). It is noteworthy that there exist intracellular cleavage enzymatic systems which may modulate the proportions of active molecules derived from the same precursor: thus N-acetylation during cleavage reduces the opioid activity of β-endorphin and enhances the biological potency of α-MSH (O'Donohue *et al.*, 1982).

In addition to these neurohormonal mediators, a number of other substances released during inflammatory and stressful conditions, such as histamine, prostaglandins and leukotrienes, can exert an action quite similar to that of neurotransmitters or paracrine mediators (Hadden, 1983).

Many authors now prefer to classify humoral mediators as: hormones (protein and non-protein hormones [Tata, 1984]), neuropeptides (neuro-transmitters and paracrine secretions [Jackson and Mueller, 1982]) and autacoids (mediators of inflammation), though this last group requires further definition.

B. Mode of Action

An exhaustive examination of the different pathways by which hormones and neuropeptides act on target cells is beyond the scope of this review, but it is necessary to focus on two major aspects of hormone action.

The first is related to the fact that hormones may exert two relatively distinct actions: some hormones rapidly modulate metabolic activities without altering the nature of the target cells (Table 10.2a); others, such as those listed in Table 10.2b, change the mass or composition of the tar-

Table 10.2a: Hormones with rapid and transient metabolic actions

Hormone	Major physiological and biochemical actions
Adrenalin (epinephrine)	Cardiac activity; thermogenesis; glycogenolysis; regulation of cyclic AMP level
Insulin	Carbohydrate metabolism; sugar transport
Growth hormone (somatotropin)	Lipolysis; amino acid uptake
Vasopressin	Water and ion transport in bladder; regulation of cyclic AMP levels; modulation of Na^+ pump
Prostaglandins	Inflammatory responses; uterine tonicity and contraction; regulation of phosphodiesterase and breakdown of cyclic AMP

Table 10.2b: Hormones with relatively slow growth and development actions

Hormone	Major physiological and biochemical actions
L-thyroxine	Amphibian metamorphosis; brain development in mammalian embryos; regulation of basal metabolic rate and growth in neonatal mammals; control of RNA and protein synthesis
Oestradiol	Growth and maturation of accessory sexual tissues in mammals; regulation of prolactin synthesis; control of gene expression
Growth hormone	Regulation of growth and hypertrophy in vertebrates; control of overall protein synthesis
Prolactin	Control of lactation and milk protein synthesis; regulation of transcription and translation in mammary gland

get cells themselves (Tata, 1984). In some cases, a single hormone, such as growth hormone, may have promoting effects on cellular mass, particularly during development, while having rapid lipolytic activity in the adult (Scharf, 1974). In other cases, the metabolic and growth-promoting properties may represent different manifestations of the same hormone: thyroid hormones regulate basal metabolic rate which, in turn, modulates the slow process of synthesis (Tata, 1966).

The second point is that all hormones and neuropeptides exert their action by binding to specific receptors present on the membrane, cytosol or nuclei of the target cells and that the expression of such receptors is 'autoregulated' by the specific hormone. Thus, down-regulation of receptors, i.e. reduction in number or binding affinities of receptor sites, may provide a tool to protect cells from excessive hormonal stimulation (Kaplan, 1981). Other hormones may display an 'up-regulation' of receptors: administration of some hormones such as thyroid hormones or oestrogens may increase the expression of the specific receptors (Hayward *et al.*, 1980). It should also be noted that the activities of some receptors are modulated not only by the homologous hormones but also by others. This phenomenon is quite evident in some multihormone regulatory systems, such as the oestrous cycle and lactation (Waters *et al.*, 1978), but it may also be present in apparently more simple systems (Table 10.3).

III. NEUROENDOCRINE–IMMUNE INTERACTIONS

Despite the common concept of the 'constancy of the internal milieu', no biological system is ever constant, or in a state of equilibrium (Spector, 1983). Cyclical changes with varying periodicity (e.g. in hormone levels, neuronal activity, hormone-metabolic functions) continually change the internal milieu (Takahashi and Menaker, 1984). It is therefore extremely difficult to define clearly interactions between such an inconstant neuroendocrine system and the immune system, which is itself changing in response to different external stimuli. Nevertheless, investigations using circumscribed experimental settings, and critical clinical observations, have provided evidence for the physiological relevance of neuroendocrine – immune interactions.

A. Neurohormonal Modulation of Immune Functions

A large and growing number of hormones and neurostransmitters have been identified as exerting a critical action on discrete immune functions (Table 10.4). This identification is supported by functional studies based

Table 10.3: Examples of heterologous hormonal regulation of receptors

Regulator hormone	Hormone whose receptor is regulated	Target tissue	Change in receptor number	Physiological consequence
Progesterone	Oestrogen	Rat and hamster uterus	↓	Inhibition of oestrogen action
		Cat uterus and oviduct	↓	Decreases morphogenetic maturation
		Rat uterus	↓	Diminution of sensitivity to oestrogen
		Rat pituitary	↓	Inhibition of oestrogenic induction of prolactin synthesis
		Rabbit uterus	↓	Inhibition of uteroglobin synthesis
Oestrogen	Progesterone	Hamster uterus rat uterus	↓	Increased sensitivity to progesterone
		Mouse mammary gland (virgin)	↑	Prevents maturation
	Prolactin	Rat liver	↑	Increased sensitivity to prolactin
Glucocorticoids	Prolactin	Mouse mammary cells	↑	Enhanced milk protein synthesis
Androgen	Prolactin	Rat prostate	↑	Enhanced cyclic AMP production
Thyroid hormone	Prolactin	Rat kidney and adrenal	↑	Increased sensitivity to prolactin
	TRH	Rat pituitary mammotrophs	↓	Decreased response to TRH

Epinephrine	Rat heart	↑	Enhanced cathecolamine sensitivity
Glucagon Triiodothyronine	Rat liver	↓	Decreased inducibility of malic enzyme

From: Tata, J. R., in R. F. Goldberger and K. R. Yamamoto (eds), *Biological Regulation and Development*, New York: Plenum Press: 1984: 35.

Table 10.4: Functional, binding, and competitive analysis for the evidence of cellular receptors for neuro-hormonal substances on lymphocytes (L) or natural killer cells (NK)

	F[a]		B		C	
	L	NK	L	NK	L	NK
AUTACOIDS						
Histamine	X	X	X		X	
5-HT	X		X			
PG	X	X	X			
Leukotrienes	X	X				
NEUROPEPTIDES						
Endorphins	X	X	X			X
Enkephalins	X	X	X			
Somatostatin	X		X			
VIP	X	X	X			
Substance P	X		X			
GH	X	X	X			
PRL	X	X				
ACTH	X		X			
TSH	X					
LH		X				
PROTEIN HORMONES						
Insulin	X		X			
Calcitonin			X			
PTH	X					
NON-PROTEIN HORMONES						
Thyroxine	X	X	X			
Glucocorticoids	X	X		X		
Androgens	X					
Oestrogens	X	X				
Progesteroids	X					
ACh			X			
Catecholamine	X	X	X		X	X

[a] F, functional study; B, binding study; C, competitive antagonism

either on deprivation designs (such as endocrine gland ablation, or brain or peripheral neural lesions), on exogenous administration of specific substances to otherwise normal animals, or on studies *in vitro*. Because of the multiple functions of various hormones and neuropeptides and the wide distribution of the secretory cells within the organism, all these experimental designs are in some way flawed. More decisive, though functionally limited, is the identification of receptors for different hormones, neuropeptides and autacoids on lymphoid cells (Table 10.4). Specific binding has also been documented for somatotropic hormone, insulin, calcitonin, T3 and T4, and steroid hormones (Archer *et al.*, 1973; Gavin, 1977; Lemarchand-Beraud *et al.*, 1977; Lesniak, 1974), as well as for hormonal mediators of the parasympathetic system (acetylcholine-muscarinic), sympathetic system (norepinephrine-alpha-adrenergic), and the neuro-adrenalinic system (epinephrine-beta-adrenergics) (Melmon *et al.*, 1977). Lymphoid cells also possess receptors for autacoids such as prostaglandins of the E and F series, serotonin and histamine (H1 and H2). More recently, receptors for brain neuropeptides such as enkephalins have been found on some lymphoid cells (Ausiello and Roda, 1984).

Without examining the information about each hormonal substance and its properties as an immunoregulating agent, a general picture of immune–endocrine relationships should include the following features.

The modulating effect of a single hormone may be positive (i.e., it may increase the efficiency of a given immune function) or negative (reducing it). Because of the concomitant presence of both stimulator and antagonist hormones, and the periodicity of most hormonal secretion (Takahashi and Menaker, 1984), the efficiency of an immune function at any one time will be affected by the current balance of neurohormonal influence.

The impact, however, of such balance in the economy of the immune system may vary according to the relevance of the target function of the neuroendocrine signals. Thus hormones acting on developmental stages of the immune system induce more relevant modifications, sometimes irreversible, than hormonal substances acting on the functional performance of mature cells. The positive action exerted on the proliferation of stem cells towards more mature stages by developmental hormones, such as somatotropin, thyroxine and insulin, as well as the suppressive effect due to corticosteroids, gonadotropins, progesteroids and testosterone, may have a long-lasting effect on the development of the major branches of the immune system (Fabris, 1977, 1982).

Neurohormonal substances influencing effector systems may have a more restricted and transient action. Clearly, many hormonal substances may act much more dramatically on development than on the actual performance of mature cells. Furthermore, during development a higher hormonal supply or a more critical hormone concentration seems to be required compared with that needed in adult age (Fabris, 1981a). This is probably linked to the relevance of some hormones to the proliferation of lymphoid cells.

The effect of hormones is not exerted equally on all kinds of lymphoid cells. Insulin and gonadotropins seem to act differently on humoral and cell-mediated immune responses. Many hormones are quite active on thymocyte differentiation, though their requirement by mature lymphocytes is extremely limited (Arrembrecht, 1974). Such a differential action may be due, in some instances, to different concentrations of hormone receptor on the surfaces of different populations of lymphocytes. Thus, insulin receptors are found in greater concentration on B than on T cells (Gavin, 1977). Higher binding of somatotropic hormone occurs on thymocytes than on mature lymphocytes.

Moreover, even at different stages of an immune response, the sensitivity to hormones may vary: thus, corticosteroids may play a positive role during the inductive phase of an immune response, whereas in later phases they are not required or are even harmful (Stavy, 1974). Insulin receptors, which are not usually found on the membrane of lymphocytes responsive to concanavalin A, appear during the early phase after mitogen stimulation (Krug *et al.*, 1972).

Of the non-protein hormones and autacoids, beta-adrenergic amines, histamine, and prostaglandin E, in addition to their known effect on the inflammatory processes, act on both B and T cells. In particular they inhibit both cytolytic functions and the production of lymphokines by effector T cells and suppressor T cell activity. Antibody-dependent lymphocyte-mediated cytotoxicity seems also to be inhibited. They can also (except for histamine) inhibit the production and the release of antibody by B cells. On the other hand, cholinergic drugs, particularly of the muscarinic type, increase T cell proliferation after mitogen stimulation and T cell mediated cytolysis (Hadden, 1977; Hadden, 1983). These findings have been interpreted in the light of the role played by cyclic nucleotides, cAMP and cGMP, in the physiological control of proliferation and differentiation of lymphocytes (Hadden, 1983).

A final effect of different neurohormonal stimulators depends on a complex system of intracellular regulation varying widely in the final effects, depending on the cell lineage involved, the stage of differentiation, and the degree of activation of the cells.

In addition to the effects on peripheral lymphoid cells, hormones and neuropeptides may also influence the thymus as a producer of hormonal factors. The circulating level of the 'facteur thymique sérique' (FTS)

(Bach *et al.*, 1972), more recently called thymulin in its zinc-bound form (Bach, 1984), has been used as a marker of the endocrine function of the thymus. Many experimental and human endocrinopathies were found to be associated with modifications of the rate of synthesis and/or release of this thymic hormone (Fabris *et al.*, 1983; Fabris and Mocchegiani, 1985).

In mice, congenital hypopituitarism, experimental diabetes and thyroidectomy all cause a reduction in the plasma level of thymulin, whereas removal of the gonads or of the adrenals does not induce any significant modification (Fabris and Mocchegiani, 1985). In humans, congenital hypopituitarism, juvenile diabetes and hypothyroidism are associated with consistent reduction of thymulin levels; by contrast, hyperthyroidism, due to diffuse nodular goitre, is associated with high levels of thymulin, particularly evident in old individuals, since at this age the physiological level of thymulin is usually quite low (Fabris *et al.*, 1986).

These findings, together with the demonstration of a hormone-dependent circadian rhythmicity of thymic secretion (Hall and Goldstein, 1983), strongly support the idea of a physiological neurohormonal modulation of thymic activity, though the relevance of such neuroendocrine – thymus interaction for the peripheral efficiency of the immune system remains to be established.

B. Effects of the Immune System on the Neuroendocrine System

A growing body of experimental evidence supports the idea that modifications of the immune system may influence a number of extra-immunological functions, particularly the physiological balance of the neuroendocrine network. Several experimental models support this idea:

1. The removal or the congenital absence of primary lymphoid organs, such as the thymus or the bursa, can induce alterations either of the endocrine balance (as suggested by variations in blood hormonal levels, by delayed sexual development and by the absence of sexual dimorphism in submandibular glands) or of the activity of the autonomic nervous system (as revealed by the altered response to beta-adrenergic agonists). All these abnormalities can be corrected by transplanting a neonatal thymus, whereas isolated thymocytes or lymphocytes are ineffective (Piantanelli *et al.*, 1978, Fabris, 1981c).
2. Consistent variations in the physiological antigenic challenge, such as those achieved by keeping animals under germ-free conditions or by overloading the organism with tolerogenic doses of antigen, are associated with modifications in the development of the neuroendocrine system (Besedovsky and Sorkin, 1977).
3. During the immune response to an antigen injected at an optimal dose, variations in the blood levels of corticosteroids and thyroxine

and in the spleen content of neurotransmitters have been observed. These modifications do not occur shortly after the antigenic challenge, thus ruling out possible interference by injection stress (Besedovsky and Sorkin, 1977).

4. Finally, the lymphoid cells may interfere in the immune–neuroendo-crine interactions by means of the direct production by activated T cells of ACTH, TSH, FSH, GH, LH and gamma-endorphins (Blalock *et al.*, 1985b).

From all these observations two conclusions emerge: first, that there exist bidirectional interactions between the immune and neuroendocrine systems and second, that such interactions occur during the whole life of the organism, though their impact may be more relevant at the extremes of life, during ontogenetic development and during age-associated deterioration (Fabris, 1982).

Information about the mechanisms by which these interactions are exerted is still fragmentary. As a working hypothesis it might be proposed that two major levels of interactions are present. The first would be represented by the thymus – hypophysis axis (Fig. 10.4). Neuroendocrine alterations can modify the production of some thymic factors

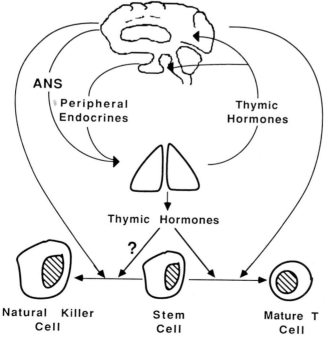

Fig. 10.4 Schematic representation of the interrelationship between thymic hormones and the neuroendocrine network.

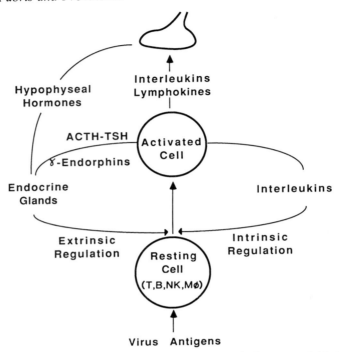

Fig. 10.5 Schematic representation of the interrelationship between soluble factors produced by lymphocytes and the neuroendocrine network.

(Fabris and Piantanelli, 1982). On the other hand, thymic factors might act at the hypophyseal level by augmenting the secretion of some pituitary hormones and probably also at the hypothalamic level, since receptors for thymosines have been demonstrated on neurones (Grossman, 1985; Spangelo *et al.*, 1987). The main role of such interactions is in immune cell differentiation, as well as with neuroendocrine influences on both development and aging. The second level of interaction may be at the periphery (Fig. 10.5): hormones and neurotransmitters may influence the efficiency of mature immune cells; in turn, cytokines produced during immune reactions can probably modify, via the hypophyseal gland, the turnover of many hormones and neurotransmitters (Dumonde *et al.*, 1983). The role played in this context by the direct production of hormone-like substances from activated accessory or lymphoid cells (Lolait *et al.*, 1984; Blalock, 1985b), remains to be established.[1]

---

[1] The effects of interleukin 1 on thermoregulation and sleep provide an excellent example of the effects of products of the immune system on the central nervous system; see Chapter 8.

The main roles of these interactions should be to modulate the actual performance of mature cells and to restore body homeostasis that has been suddenly altered by stress or antigenic challenge. Other reasons for discriminating between these two levels are that long-term hormonal actions are operating in the first level, whereas short-term effects are required in the second level (Fabris *et al.*, 1988).

IV. NEUROHORMONAL MODULATION OF NATURAL KILLER (NK) ACTIVITY

The experimental designs used in order to evaluate the effect of hormones and neuropeptides on NK-mediated cytotoxicity and/or resistance to tumour growth have been quite similar to those chosen for studies on specific immunity: in vivo models based primarily on deprivation of relevant endocrine glands or of nervous centres or on administration of hormones or neuropeptides; and in vitro designs aimed to demonstrate direct effects of these substances on the capacity of NK cells to bind to target cells and/or to lyse them.

Both types of design have limitations. First, any manipulation in vivo may reveal a role for some hormones or neuropeptides in NK activity, without indicating whether the effect is direct or mediated by other hormonal substances or hormone-dependent metabolic events. Second, NK cells have a life-span of at least two weeks (Hochman *et al.*, 1978) and the generation of functional elements from undifferentiated precursors may require several weeks (Hochman *et al.*, 1978; Haller *et al.*, 1977). Studies in vitro are therefore unlikely to reveal effects at the level of generation or survival of NK cells, which, in contrast, may be suggested by studies in vivo.

Third, NK activity is physiologically regulated by macrophages with suppressor activity (Brunda *et al.*, 1982) as well as by different lymphokines, such as interferon (IFN) (Herberman *et al.*, 1979) and interleukin 2 (IL-2) (Henney *et al.*, 1981). Since all these functions may be sensitive to the action of various hormones and neuropeptides, and the experiments often involve mixed cell populations, the interpretation of data on neurohormonal modulation of NK activity should aim to discriminate direct effects on NK cells or their precursors from actions mediated through the activation of macrophages or lymphokine-secreting cells.

Fourth, the sensitivity of NK cells to the boosting effect of IL-2 and IFN appears at different stages during ontogenetic development, and it has been suggested that basal activity, IL-2 sensitivity and IFN sensitivity may represent three consecutive stages in the maturation of the NK lineage (Yoshiki *et al.*, 1985; Provinciali *et al.*, 1989). Most of the studies on neurohormonal modulation of NK activity have taken this into account and have tried to define the stage at which a neurohormonal influence is exerted.

With regard to the demonstration of receptors for hormones and neuropeptides on NK cells, the available data mainly concern glucocorticoids and β-endorphins (Table 10.4).

Binding techniques have demonstrated receptors for glucocorticoids (Katz *et al.*, 1985), but receptors for β-endorphin and enkephalin have been demonstrated only by competitive antagonism with naloxone (Mathews *et al.*, 1983). This last assumption is, however, quite controversial, since a variety of different receptors for endogenous opioids have been identified and in lymphoid cells non-opiate receptors have also been found (Hazum *et al.*, 1979).

A. The Hypothalamus–Hypophysis Axis

Ablation of the left neocortex or of the anterior hypothalamus causes a reduction or even a disappearance of NK activity (Forni *et al.*, 1983; Cross *et al.*, 1984; Belluardo *et al.*, 1987) from spleen cells, attributable to a decrease in large granular lymphocytes (LGLs), which are responsible for the majority of NK cytotoxicity. Neither the release of substances from the electrolytically lesioned nervous tissue, nor recruitment of suppressor cells (Roszman *et al.*, 1982), likely to belong to a macrophage population, is responsible for the reduction of NK activity. The observations that the diminished NK activity is present only in the adherent cell fraction of the spleen, leaving unaltered the non-adherent activity, and that killing by the adherent population is not the result of macrophage-mediated cytotoxicity (Cross *et al.*, 1984), suggest that the target of the neural lesion is a specific population of NK cells, sensitive to the boosting effect either of IFN and IFN-inducers or of IL-2 (Forni *et al.*, 1983).

The mediators of such an effect are not known. Although the involvement of neurotransmitters produced by the lesioned neural tissue cannot be excluded, the majority of authors agree that a primary role should be assigned to the connection of the hypothalamus with the pituitary and perhaps with the pineal gland.

In fact, hypophysectomy (Saxena *et al.*, 1982) strongly reduces NK activity and abrogates the decreased NK activity observed in hypothalamus-lesioned animals (Cross *et al.*, 1984), suggesting that the effect observed in this model is due to modification induced by the neural lesion of the production and/or release of pituitary hormones or peptides.

From the available data, it does not seem that a single pituitary hormone is involved in the modulation of NK activity. Several different pituitary hormones and peptides affect NK activity.

Thus, *in vivo* administration of growth hormone is able to restore NK activity depressed after hypophysectomy (Saxena *et al.*, 1982). Support for a role played by growth hormone comes from the clinical observation that NK activity is reduced in growth hormone deficient children (Kiess *et al.*, 1986); acute administration of growth hormone releasing factor failed, however, to restore NK activity in these patients.

Another pituitary hormone involved may be prolactin. NK activity is decreased in hyperprolactinaemic patients and recovers following treatment with bromocriptine, a powerful agonist of dopaminergic neurones in the tubero-infundibular region of the hypothalamus, which exerts an inhibitory action on prolactin secretion (Gerli *et al.*, 1986). It is beyond doubt that tubero-infundibular dopaminergic neurons are physiologically involved, in both rodents and primates, in the inhibitory control of pituitary hormone production (Neill, 1980) and that prolonged oestradiol administration or tubero-infundibular destruction, both of which have been demonstrated to inhibit NK activity, are also associated with the development of hyperprolactinaemia in rodents (Brawer *et al.*, 1976: Sarkar *et al.*, 1982). It is, however, difficult at present to relate these findings to those obained in hypophysectomised animals. Prolactin *per se* does not seem to have any modulatory effect on NK cell function in vitro. This suggests that if an effect is exerted in vivo, either such an action is mediated by other neurohormonal or metabolic alterations, or prolactin affects NK cell progenitors (Gerli *et al.*, 1986).

Other pituitary hormones such as thyrotropic hormone, ACTH, gonadotropins and peptides like endorphins, which may be involved as well in hypothalamus–hypophysis-dependent modulation of NK activity, will be considered together with the hormones produced by the target glands (see below).

With regard to the role played by the pineal gland, it has been recently shown that melatonin, a hormone produced by the pineal gland, can enhance or inhibit NK activity depending on the time of the day when it is administered (Lissoni *et al.*, 1986). While these data may be in agreement with the role of melatonin in determining the circadian cycling of the pineal–pituitary–adrenal intermodulation (Sanchez de la Pena *et al.*, 1983) and also explain the circadian rhythmicity of NK cells (Fernandes *et al.*, 1979), the proof of a direct cortisone-independent action of melatonin on NK cells still waits for further evidence.

B. The Hypophysis–Thyroid Network

Thyroid hormones when administered in vivo enhance or inhibit the cytotoxic activity of NK spleen cells in mice depending on the length of treatment. Short treatment with thyroxine (up to five days) increases NK cytotoxicity without modifying either the number of target-binding cells, or the production of IFN (Sharma *et al.*, 1982; Provinciali *et al.*, submitted for publication). When thyroxine is administered for longer than six weeks, no NK activity is detectable in the spleen and lung of treated mice (Stein-Streilein *et al.*, 1987). The lack of NK cell activity is not ascribed to a decrease in the number of target-binding cells but rather, to a defect either in the ability of NK cells to respond to IL-2 or in the release of factors than can lyse NK targets (Strein-Streilein *et al.*, 1987).

In vitro, thyroxine does not modify NK activity per se but increases the sensitivity of NK cells to IFN and induces IFN responsiveness in an otherwise unresponsive cell population, such as those from very young or very old mice (Provinciali *et al.*, 1987, Provinciali *et al.*, submitted for publication). IL-2 responsiveness further supports the idea of hormonal effects discriminating among different cell subsets. Furthermore, the relatively short time (1–5 days) required to observe the in vivo thyroid hormone induced increment of NK activity (Sharma *et al.*, 1982) and the extremely reduced preincubation time needed in vitro (30 minutes) (Provinciali and Fabris, submitted for publication) argue against an action of thyroid hormone on the generation of precursor cells, but rather support an effect at the level of functional performance of NK cells. Hyperthyroidism in humans has been associated with cytotoxic activity or peripheral blood NK/K cell numbers higher than normal (Calder *et al.*, 1976); normal (Bogner *et al.*, 1986); or decreased (Papic *et al.*, 1987).

C. The Hypophysis–Gonad Network

The effect of sex hormones on NK activity is still controversial. In some studies NK cell activity was similar in males and females (Kiessling *et al.*, 1975), but in others females showed lower cytotoxic activity (Trinchieri *et al.*, 1977; Barret *et al.*, 1982). Reduced NK activity has also been reported to occur during pregnancy. NK reactivity is significantly depressed during the third trimester of gestation and in the immediate postpartum period (Baines *et al.*, 1978; Okamura *et al.*, 1984; Baley and Schacter, 1985). According to other authors maternal NK activity is also decreased in the first and second trimesters (Gregory *et al.*, 1985; Lee *et al.*, 1987).

In some studies the depression of lytic activity was associated with a normal number of LGLs and of target binding cells, while in others a reduced number of Leu-11[+] lymphocytes and of target binding cells was reported (Baley and Schacter, 1985; Gregory *et al.*, 1987).

However, although reduced in the number, active NK cells present during pregnancy seem to have a similar capacity to recycle and kill target cells as NK cells from non-pregnant females (Gregory *et al.*, 1987). It would therefore appear that the observed defect in NK cell function during pregnancy is due to a reduction in both binding capacity of NK cells and the ability of a proportion of the bound NK cells to lyse their target while unimpaired NK cells are essentially normal (Gregory *et al.*, 1987). Serum from pregnant females has been reported to suppress NK cytotoxicity, but specific factors have not yet been identified (Barrett *et al.*, 1982).

Castration has no effect on NK activity in either female or male mice (Seaman *et al.*, 1978).

Chronic administration of oestrogen to mice causes, in addition to thymic involution, a decrease in antibody production and mitogen responsiveness (Sljivic and Warr, 1973) and reduction of the cytotoxic potential of T lymphocytes (Luster *et al.*, 1980) and NK cells (Seaman *et al.*, 1978). The suppression of NK activity is achieved over a period of several weeks (Seaman *et al.*, 1978); the effects, however, are reversible and full immunocompetence returns after the cessation of treatment (Kalland *et al.*, 1979). The reduced NK activity is not due, in this experimental model, to inhibition by accessory cells or humoral factors (Seaman *et al.*, 1978). Perinatal treatment with oestrogen leads to persistent reduction in NK cell activity, apparently not due to either humoral or cellular suppressor factors (Kalland and Forsberg, 1981). Treatment of mice with other sex hormones such as androgens (Seaman *et al.*, 1978) had no substantial effects on NK activity nor caused a reduction of splenic NK cell function (Hov and Zheng, 1988).

In vitro, HCG and LH reduced NK activity, but testosterone and progesterone had no effect (Sulke *et al.*, 1985). In some experiments oestrogens had no effect in vitro (Seaman *et al.*, 1978), but in others suppression of NK activity was observed (Ferguson and McDonald, 1985). It was suggested that the suppression might be due to the interaction of oestrogens with the peroxidase – oxygenase enzyme system (Ferguson and McDonald, 1985).

The findings with in vivo models support the hypothesis of an effect of oestrogens on the generation and/or differentiation of NK precursors, because of the long time required to induce the depression and the slow recovery. In contrast with the effect of hypothalamic lesions, the depressed NK activity observed after oestrogen treatment cannot be boosted, or can be only slightly boosted, by IFN (Kalland, 1980). These findings would not exclude the possibility of direct effects of oestrogens on NK effector mechanisms (Ferguson and McDonald, 1985).

D. The Hypophysis–Adrenal Network

This regulatory system is not only one of the more complex systems, but also one in which the distinction between hormone and neurotransmitter is hardest to make. Furthermore, in the response to acute stress there is concomitant activation of this network, the autonomic nervous system and the endorphin–enkephalin system (Shavit *et al.*, 1985). We will examine here only the effects of single hormones/neuropeptides on NK cell activity in vitro.

A further difficulty in interpretation arises from the fact that one of the most effective NK inducers, IFN, is antigenically related to ACTH and endorphins and therefore might compete with these neuropeptides for binding sites on NK cells (Smith and Blalock, 1981).

Treatment with glucocorticoids such as hydrocortisone reduces NK activity both in experimental animals (Hochman and Cudkowicz, 1979) and in humans (Parrillo and Fauci, 1978; Onsurd and Thorsby, 1981). In vitro, glucocorticoids depress NK activity. The decrease is already maximal after two hours, cannot be reversed by washing of lymphocytes, and is not due to decreased cell viability (Nair and Schwartz, 1984). Since glucocorticoids reduce the number of target-binding lymphocytes, the inhibition of NK cytotoxicity may be due to interference by glucocorticoids with the target recognition structure (Nair and Schwartz, 1984). Glucocorticoid-induced depression of NK activity can be antagonised by concomitant exposure to IFN, but not IL-2. THe IFN-induced reversal has been interpreted as being due to reactivation of mature NK cells temporarily inhibited by glucocorticoid treatment (Oehler and Herberman, 1978).

The NK activity of human peripheral blood lymphocytes (PBLs) can be inhibited in vitro by glucocorticoids at physiological, as well as therapeutic, levels (Holbrook *et al.*, 1983). An interesting observation made by these authors is that pretreatment of cells with IFN did not modify glucocorticoid sensitivity as would be expected if the effect of IFN were to stimulate steroid-resistant precursor NK cells (Oehler and Herberman, 1978).

Epinephrine or beta-agonists can modulate the cytotoxic activity of PBLs in vitro either negatively or positively. Preincubation of PBLs with epinephrine enhances NK activity, but addition of the hormone directly to the cytotoxic assay reduces it (Hellstrand *et al.*, 1985). Other factors, such as prostaglandins and vasoactive intestinal peptide (see below), have a similar dual action.

In vivo administration of epinephrine enhanced NK activity in PBLs (Tonnensen *et al.*, 1984; Hellstrand *et al.*, 1985) and increased the percentage of Leu-7 positive cells (Crary *et al.*, 1983), though it is not known whether the effect was due to recruitment of pre-NK cells, to activation of NK cells already present or to a mobilisation of active NK cells into peripheral blood (Hellstrand *et al.*, 1985). Interestingly, the simultaneous infusion of cortisol and epinephrine for five hrs causes an increase in the NK cell activity and in the number of Leu 11 + cells in peripheral blood, equivalent to the increase seen during epinephrine infusion alone (Tonnesen *et al.*, 1987). This fact might explain the transient increase of NK activity demonstrated during the early steps of anaesthesia and surgical procedures (Griffith *et al.*, 1984).

Beta-endorphin and met-enkephalin enhanced the NK activity of human PBLs in vitro (Mathews *et al.*, 1983; Mandler *et al.*, 1986). Leu-enkephalin increased NK activity in some studies (Faith *et al.*, 1984) but not in others (Mathews *et al.*, 1983). Alpha-endorphin and morphine do not augment NK activity (Mandler *et al.*, 1986). The enhancement of NK activity induced by β-endorphin and met-enkephalin is inhibited by naloxone, suggesting that opiate receptors are involved (Mathews *et al.*, 1983). However, the intervention of opioid receptors in the modulation of NK activity remains to be elucidated, since non-opioid fragments of β-endorphin are much more potent that β- and γ-endorphin in enhancing human lymphocyte NK activity (Kay *et al.*, 1987).

Experiments in vivo though still few and fragmentary, support the modulating role of endogenous opioid peptides. Thus a stress paradigm (footshock) diminished NK activity in rats (Shavit *et al.*, 1984): since naltrexone reversed the stress-induced NK depression, a role of endogenous opioid peptides was postulated.

E. Other Neurohormonal Factors

A growing body of evidence supports the view that most of the other neuropeptides listed in Table 10.4 may affect immune responsiveness. While, however, neuropeptides such as neurotensin (Bar-Shavit *et al.*, 1982), substance P (Payan *et al.*, 1984) and vasoactive intestinal peptide (VIP) (Danek *et al.*, 1983) have been shown to affect lymphocyte or macrophage function, their effect on NK activity has not been studied extensively. Among those peptides, the functional role of VIP on modulating NK activity has been studied in detail.

VIP is a 28-amino-acid peptide that has been localised in nerve elements in the brain (Said and Rosemberg, 1976), in respiratory and genital tracts (Polak and Bloom, 1982) and in circulating platelets, mast cells (Giachetti *et al.*, 1978) and neutrophils (O'Dorisio *et al.*, 1980). Incubation of human NK cells with VIP in vitro led to a bimodal modulation of NK cytotoxicity. When VIP was present during the entire cytotoxic assay NK activity was inhibited whereas it was enhanced by a short preincubation of NK cells with VIP before the cytotoxic assay (Rola-Pleszczynski *et al.*, 1985). The increase was due to augmented effector – target cell binding, rather than to an increase in cytotoxic activity per cell.

Reports of the effects of autacoids on NK activity are still contradictory. Prostaglandins have been reported to inhibit NK activity when added to the cytotoxic assay (Brunda *et al.*, 1980: Droller *et al.*, 1978; Kendall and Targan, 1980; Lanefelt *et al.*, 1983). This is probably linked to the augmented level of cAMP, the major mediator of prostanoid effects. In one study, however, NK activity was enhanced by preincubation with prostaglandins (Kendall and Targan, 1980), thus suggesting a dual effect, similar to that reported for adrenalin and VIP. Serotonin is stored together with histamine in thrombocytes and, in some species, also in mast cells. Because both substances have been reported to suppress tumour growth in certain animal models in vivo (Burtin *et al.*, 1981), they were studied for their role in the regulation of NK cell cytotoxicity.

Experimentally induced reduction in brain serotonin levels causes a marked reduction of NK activity in rats (Steplewski and Vogel, 1985). In vitro, serotonin strongly augments the cytotoxic activity of NK enriched human mononuclear cells (Hellstrand and Hermodsson, 1987). Although the effect of serotonin is dependent on the presence of monocytes, these cells are not required as effector cells during target cell lysis (Hellstrand and Hermodsson, 1987). It seems that serotonin may directly affect the cytotoxic activity of NK cells perhaps through specific receptors (Bonnet *et al.*, 1987).

Contradictory data have been reported on the effect of histamine on NK function: according to some authors (Nair and Schwartz, 1983) preincubation of PBLs with histamine induces a decrease in NK activity. More recently the same authors have demonstrated that lymphocytes may, under histamine stimulation, secrete soluble factors with a suppressive effect on NK activity (Nair *et al.*, 1986). In contrast, other authors have demonstrated that histamine in vitro increased NK activity in PBLs, but only in the presence of monocytes. Thus suggests that the effect should be ascribed to a histamine-mediated interference with monocyte-mediated suppression of NK lysis (Hellstrand and Hermodsson, 1986). While it seems clear that an increased level of cAMP is associated with reduced NK activity (Goto *et al.*, 1983; Hellstrand *et al.*, 1985), further work is needed to define the effects due to the involvement of cells other than putative NK cells.

The recent discovery of an endocrine activity of the thymus has added a further series of immunomodulating agents, which have been proved to regulate a number of differentiative steps in the maturation of the immune system (Low and Goldstein, 1984; Dardenne *et al.*, 1984). The hypothesis linking NK cells to a pre-thymic compartment has suggested a possible role of thymic hormones on NK activity. The experiments which have followed this suggestion have so far been contradictory. A positive as well as negative action of some thymic preparations on the expression on NK activity has been reported (Bardos and Bach, 1982; Serrate *et al.*, 1987).

F. Mode of Action

As with the majority of target functions of hormones and neuropeptides, the modulation of NK activity also shows a great variety of possible mechanisms of action. While at present it is difficult to define clearly any simple hormone-target action, a general picture for NK cells should include at least two levels of action: (a) a direct action on different steps of maturation or on the actual performance of NK cells; and (b) the involvement of other humoral and/or cellular events, which may be under hormonal influence and which may in turn affect NK activity.

With regard to the first point, and assuming that IL-2- and IFN-inducible NK activity represent distinct steps of NK maturation (Yoshiki *et al.*, 1985; Provinciali *et al.*, 1989), the available data suggest that some hormones, such as oestrogens, affect the generation of NK cells, while others, such as glucocorticoids and β-endorphins, may affect IL-2 sensitivity and consequently IFN sensitivity, and still others, such as thyroxine and epinephrine, influence only IFN sensitivity leaving IL-2 responsiveness unaffected. Although the picture is at present incomplete, these examples clearly suggest that different hormones and neuropeptides may act at different functional stages of NK cells, and in some cases on more than one stage.

With regard to the effect on the actual performance of NK cells, many different mechanisms may be involved. Thus endorphins may accelerate the kinetics of cytotoxicity through either a reduced lytic time per target cell or a more rapid movement of effector cells from one target to another (Mathews *et al.*, 1983). Such mechanisms are also activated by IFN (Targan and Dorey, 1980; Kuribayashi *et al.*, 1981). Unlike IFN, however, β-endorphin can also increase the number of effector–target cell conjugates.

A further mechanism of action has been recently demonstrated by experiments showing that supernatants of NK cell cultures, stimulated with opioid peptides, contain factors that increase the NK activity of naive blood mononuclear cells from a different donor (Wybran, 1985).

In addition, opioids have been shown to control calmodulin distribution (Baram and Simantov, 1983) and to increase calmodulin levels in the brain (Clovet and Williams, 1982). Beta-endorphin has also been shown to bind calmodulin (Geidroc *et al.*, 1983). It has been found that calmodulin is required for NK activation (Moon *et al.*, 1983).

One crucial point of action of many hormones is represented by the activation of the cyclic nucleotide messengers (cAMP and cGMP). By using a number of drugs known to increase intracellular cAMP, it has been demonstrated that a good inverse correlation exists between intracellular cAMP concentration and NK cytotoxic activity, and that such a correlation is observable regardless of the stimulus used to increase the cAMP level (Lanefelt *et al.*, 1983). Such a correlation has been demonstrated experimentally for only a limited number of hormonal factors, particularly prostanoids. It seems likely, however, that other hormones modulating NK activity will also be found to act by way of cyclic nucleotides.

The second level of action of hormones and neuropeptides on NK activity may be mediated by the activation or inhibition of the synthesis and/or release of the lymphokines which modulate NK activity, in

Table 10.5: Cyclic nucleotides in NK cell regulation

DA			
[a]PGE			
[b]Histamine			
[b]Beta-adrenergics			ACh
TSH			5-HT
TRH			PGF
ACTH			Alpha-adrenergics
[b]LH	→ cAMP →	NK CELL	Endorphins[b]
FSH		FUNCTION	Insulin
MSH		← cGMP ←	Enkephalins[b]
Vasopressin			Thymosin[b]
Glucagon			Thymopoietin[b]
Parathormone			
[b]VIP			
Thyrocalcitonin			

(cAMP — NK CELL FUNCTION + cGMP)

[a] Experimental evidence available on the effect on NK function via cyclic nucleotides.
[b] Experimental evidence available on the effect of NK function: the role of cyclic nucleotides remains to be established.

For the other cyclic nucleotide modulating substances the role in NK function remains to be established.

particular IL-2 and IFN. ACTH and glucocorticoids depress the production of both IFN and IL-2, whereas β-endorphins increase their synthesis (Johnson *et al.*, 1984; Gillis *et al.*, 1979; Mandler *et al.*, 1986). In contrast, other hormonal factors that may influence NK activity, such as epinephrine, thyroxine and histamine, do not seem to have any action on IFN production (Hellstrand *et al.*, 1985; Hellstrand and Hermodsson, 1986; Sharma *et al.*, 1982; Provinciali *et al.*, submitted).

Finally, since macrophages may exert a suppressive action on NK activity, it is possible that some of the observed effects of hormones and neuropeptides might be mediated by functional alterations in macrophages.

V. NEUROENDOCRINE INFLUENCES ON THE RETICULO-ENDOTHELIAL SYSTEM

The role played by macrophages, neutrophils and more generally by the reticulo-endothelial system[2] (RES) in body resistance to infections and neoplastic diseases is quite diverse, depending on the cells involved and on the specific function exerted by those cells in the given conditions. The primary function of the RES is the continuous cleansing of bodily fluids to remove particulate matter, but such an action is often associated with the induction of specific immune responses. The modulating influence of the neuroendocrine network may be exerted on both the RES and specifically reactive cells of the immune system. Furthermore, the mutual interactions between the neuroendocrine and reticulo-endothelial systems still represent a scientifically undercultivated field. Our knowledge of neurohormonal modulation of the RES is in fact mostly restricted to the effect of sex hormones, stress-related humoral mediators and agents acting through the cAMP/cGMP system, on the phagocytic function of macrophages and neutrophils.

A. Sex Hormones

The relevance of sex hormones to the RES is clearly shown by the existence of cyclical variations in RES activity during the oestrous cycle and pregnancy in rats and mice (Nicol *et al.*, 1964; Nicol and Vernon-Roberts, 1965; Mattsson *et al.*, 1984). Various studies in women have demonstrated a close correspondence between phagocytic activity and the variations in the production of oestrogenic hormones during the

---

[2] The term reticulo-endothelial system is used here in a very broad sense. (Ed.)

menstrual cycle and pregnancy (Enfinger, 1932; Brown, 1956). Moreover there is a sex difference in phagocytic activity, females showing a higher activity than males (Northdurft and Flemming, 1971). Such an increased activity is not due to a rise in the number of phagocytic cells, but to a high efficiency per cell. Administration of natural or synthetic oestrogens to mice and rats stimulates the RES, as shown by hypertrophy of the liver and spleen, proliferation of macrophages and a marked increase in phagocytic activity (Nicol, 1935; Biozzi *et al.*, 1957; Trejo *et al.*, 1972). The increased phagocytic activity is due to both an augmented number of cells and a marked increase in the activity of existing RES macrophages (Heller *et al.*, 1957).

Similar results have been reported in humans. The phagocytic activity of polymorphonuclear leukocytes is also increased by oestrogens (Burger and Leonardt, 1952).

With regard to androgens, it has been reported that testosterone depresses the phagocytic activity of both liver (Snell and Nicol, 1956) and alveolar macrophages (Schorn and Walter, 1975).

B. Corticosteroids

The effects of glucocorticoids on RES activity have been extensively investigated in both animals and humans. The majority of glucocorticoids depress phagocytic activity (Nicol and Snell, 1955; Gotjamanos, 1970; Flemming, 1974) either by reducing the number of active cells (Gotjamanos, 1970) or by decreasing their phagocytic efficiency (Lurie, 1960). These effects are exerted on liver and spleen macrophages, as well as on alveolar macrophages (Schorn and Walter, 1975; Gudewicz, 1979). Corticosteroids also depress phagocytosis in vitro: for example, the phagocytosis of yeast cells by peritoneal macrophages is greatly inhibited by hydrocortisone (Gemsa *et al.*, 1974; Raz and Goldman, 1976).

Although high doses of corticosteroids depress phagocytic activity, small doses have no effect or may even stimulate RES activity (Benveniste *et al.*, 1970; Flemming, 1974). The opposite effects of large and small doses of corticosteroids on phagocytic activity may explain the finding that a large cortisone dose led to depression shortly after administration, followed by increased phagocytosis (Heller *et al.*, 1957). In this context, it has been recently reported that corticosteroid treatment of monocytes in vitro may enhance the number of recepor sites for IFN and the IFN-induced macrophage Fc receptor capacity (Fertsch and Vogel, 1984; Girard *et al.*, 1984; Strickland *et al.*, 1986).

In vitro, glucocorticoids inhibited the activation of macrophages to a fully tumoricidal state (Hogan and Vogel, 1988). Non-glucocorticoid sex hormones failed to inhibit tumoricidal activity in this system under identical culture conditions (Hogan and Vogel, 1988). In agreement with this report, previous observation demonstrated that macrophages derived from mice stressed by immobilisation, or treated with glucocorticoids, failed to become activated (Pavlidis and Chirigos, 1980).

C. Catecholamines and Autacoids

The balance between the two intracellular second messengers, cAMP and cGMP, plays a fundamental role in determining the actual performance of both macrophages and polymorphs (Table 10.6). Both these cell lineages are sensitive to agents increasing cAMP, such as epinephrine, histamine and prostaglandins (PGE) and agents which increase cGMP, such as acetylcholine, serotonin, prostaglandins (PGF) and insulin (Hadden, 1983).

Cyclic AMP and agents which increase cAMP have been associated with inhibition of proliferation of both macrophage precursors (Taetle and Koessler, 1980) and mature cells (Hadden *et al.*, 1978). Macrophage activities that are affected by elevated cAMP levels include phagocytosis, chemiluminescence, lysosomal enzyme release (Weissmann *et al.*, 1971; Smith and Weidemann, 1980), locomotion (Pick, 1972; Oropeza-Rendon *et al.*, 1979), aggregation (Rouveix *et al.*, 1980), fusion (Papadimitrious and Sforcina, 1975) and tumoricidal activity (Schultz *et al.*, 1978; Koff and Dunegan, 1985, 1986). Some of these functions also show a negative correlation with cAMP levels in neutrophils (Ignarro, 1977;

Table 10.6: Cyclic nucleotides in macrophage and neutrophil regulation

cyclic AMP [a]M	N		cyclic GMP M	N
−	−	Phagocytosis	+	+
−		Chemiluminescence	+	
−	−	Lysosomal enzyme release	+	+
−		Aggregation	+	
−		Fusion	+	
−	−	Chemotaxis	+	+
−		Proliferation	+	
	−	Antibody-dependent cytotoxicity	−	+
		Killing	+	
		Fc receptor display	+	
−		Tumoricidal activity		
+		Collagenase production		

[a] M, macrophage; N, neutrophil

Weissman *et al.*, 1980). Conversely, agents which increase cGMP stimulate a variety of functions in both macrophages and neutrophils (Rhodes, 1975; Hadden and England, 1979; Ignarro, 1977; Weissman *et al.*, 1980).

D. Other Neurohormonal Factors

Treatment with either native or recombinant somatotropin increased the production of superoxide anion by both peripheral blood derived and alveolar macrophages stimulated with opsonised zymosan in vitro. In hypophysectomised rats somatotropin caused an activation of peritoneal macrophages equivalent to that of macrophages from rats primed with interferon-gamma (Edwards *et al.*, 1988).

Insulin has been of special interest, because diabetes is associated with depressed movement, phagocytosis and bactericidal activity of phagocytes, (Miller, 1984; Wilson and Reeves, 1986). This depression has been considered a major contributing factor to infection in diabetic hosts (Bagdade, 1976). Some of these defects, however, require fairly extreme conditions in order to be of clinical significance, and other abnormalities in diabetes, such as vascular disease or neuropathy, may also contribute to the poor resistance to infection.

The spectrum of hormones and neuropeptides acting on macrophage and neutrophil function is probably very wide. For example, substance P, a neuropeptide with a widespread distribution in the nervous system, has recently been shown to increase chemotaxis and lysosomal enzyme release in polymorphonuclear leukocytes and to enhance phagocytosis by neutrophils and macrophages, (Hartung *et al.*, 1986). Moreover, inhibition of prolactin release by bromocryptine has been shown to prevent the induction of tumoricidal macrophages after the intraperitoneal injection of bacteria in mice (Benton *et al.*, 1988). Much more work is required to define the hormonal substances involved in RES modulation and their integration at functional level.

VI. CONCLUDING REMARKS

A good body of experimental evidence now supports the concept that the neuroendocrine network modulates both the development and the actual performance of the immune system. The influence of various hormones and neuropeptides on T and B lymphocytes, as well as the presence of hormonal receptors at membrane, cytosol or nuclear level, has been deeply investigated, but our knowledge on the neurohormonal modulation of natural resistance is much more limited. Nevertheless, the available data clearly reveal that the two major systems of natural host defence, i.e. natural cytotoxicity and phagocytic activity, are both sensitive to signals generated in the neuroendocrine network. The exact roles played by the different hormones, neuropeptides or autacoids need further investigation for a comprehensive picture.

In spite of these limits, the fact that the neuroendocrine system modulates natural resistance is of great importance, since it suggests a physiological way to regulate and potentiate host defence against infections and neoplastic diseases.

Furthermore, the available data on the interactions between the neuroendocrine and the immune system are opening new and interesting fields of research, some of which may have a great impact on our general understanding of homeostasis of the organism. The discoveries that 'immunological' products of the thymus or of lymphocytes, such as thymic hormones and lymphokines, may modulate the neuroendocrine balance, and that lymphocytes may, in some cases, produce hormone-like substances such as ACTH, TSH and gamma-endorphins, clearly suggest that the lymphoid system may offer, in addition to the natural immune defence mechanism, a 'non-immune' help to the homeostatic systems which cooperate in maintaining the integrity of the body.

ACKNOWLEDGMENTS

This has been in part supported by grant number 86.01765.56 from the Consiglio Nazionale delle Ricerche, Italy.

REFERENCES

Archer, J. A., Gorden, P., Gavin, J. R. III, Lesniak, M. A. and Roth, J. (1973). *Journal Clinical Endocrinology Metabolism* 36: 627.

Arrembrecht, S. (1974) *Nature* 252: 225.

Ausiello, G. M. and Roda, L. G. (1984). *Cell Biology International Reports* 8: 97.

Bach, J. F. (1984). In Yamamura and T. Tada (eds), *Progress in Immunology.* London: Academic Press: 5: 1563.

Bach, J. F., Dardenne, M., Papiernik, M., Barvis, A., Levasseur, P. and Lebrand, H. (1972). *Lancet* 2: 1056.

Bagdade, J. D. (1976). *Acta Endocrinologica* 83 (suppl. 205): 27.

Baines, M. G., Pross, H. F. and Millar, K. G. (1978). *American Journal of Obstetrical Gynecology* 130: 741.

Baley, J. E., and Schacter, B. Z. (1985). *Journal of Immunology* 134: 3042.

Baram, D. and Simantov, R. (1983). *Journal of Neurochemistry* 40: 55.

Bardos, P. and Bach, J. F. (1982). *Scandinavian Journal of Immunology* 12: 321.

Barrett, D. S., Rayfield, L. S. and Brent, L. (1982). *Clinical and Experimental Immunology* 47: 742.

Bar-Shavit, Z., Terry, S., Blumberg, S. and Goldeman, R. (1982). *Neuropeptides* 2: 325.

Belluardo, N., Mudò, G., Cella, S., Santoni, A., Forni, G. and Bindoni, M. (1987). *Immunology* 62: 321.

Benton, E. W., Meitzer, R. S., Holaday, J. W. (1988) *Science* 239: 401.

Benveniste, J., Higouwet, F. and Salomon, J. C. (1970). *Journal of the Reticuloendothelial Society* 8: 499.

Besedovsky, H. O. and Sorkin, E. (1977). *Clinical and Experimental Immunology* 27: 1.

Besedovsky, H. O., Sorkin, E., Keller, M. and Muller J. (1975). *Proceedings of the Society for Experimental Biology and Medicine* 150: 466.

Best, C. H. and Taylor, W. B. (1943). *The Physiological Basis of Medical Practice*. Baltimore, Maryland: Williams and Wilkins: 353.

Biozzi, G., Halpern, B. N., Bilbey, D., Stiffel, C., Benacerraf, B. and Mouton, D. (1957). *C. R. Soc. Biol.* 151: 1326.

Blalock, J. E., Bost, K. L. and Smith, E. M. (1985a). *Journal of Neuroimmunology* 10: 31.

Blalock, J. E., Harbour-McMenamin, D. and Smith, E. M. (1985b). *Journal of Immunology* 135: 858s.

Bogner, U., Wall, J. R. and Schleusener, H. (1986). In G. Medeirds-Neto and E. Gaitan (Eds.), *Frontiers in Thyroidology*, vol. 2, New York: Plenum: 1395–1399.

Bonnet, M., Lespinats, G. and Burtin, G. (1987) *International Journal of Immunopharmacology* 9: 551.

Brawer, J. R., Naftolin, F., Martin, J. and Sonnenschein, C. (1976). *Endocrinology* 103: 501.

Brown, J. B. (1956). Lancet 1: 704.

Brunda, M. J., Herberman, R. B. and Holden, H. T. (1980). *Journal of Immunology* 124: 2682.

Brunda, M. J., Taramelli, D., Holden, H. T. and Varesio, L. (1982). In R. B. Herberman (ed.), *NK Cells and Other Natural Effector Cells*. New York: Academic Press: 535.

Burger, H. and Leonhardt, K. (1952). *Arch. Gynaekol.* 181: 300.

Burtin, C., Scheinmann, P., Salomon, J. C., Lespinats, G., Loisillier, F. and Canu, P. (1981) *Cancer Letters* 12: 195.

Calder, E. Q., Irvine, W. J., Davidson, N. M. and Wu, F. (1976) *Clinical and Experimental Immunology* 75: 17.

Clovet, D. H. and Williams, N. (1982). *Life Sciences* 31: 2283.

Crary, B., Hansen, S. L., Borynzenko, M., Kutz, I., Hoban, C., Ault, K. A., Weiner, H. L. and Benson, H. (1983). *Journal of Immunology* 131: 1178.

Cross, R. J., Markesbery, W. R., Brooks, W. H. and Roszman, T. L. (1984). *Immunology* 51: 399.

Danek, A., O'Dorisio, M. S. and George, J. M. (1983). *Journal of Immunology* 131: 1173.

Dardenne, M., Savino, W., Gastinel, L. and Bach, J. F. (1984). In A.L. Goldstein (ed.), *Thymic Hormones and Lymphokines.* New York: Plenum Press: 37–42.

Dockray, G. L. (1978). In M. Grossman, V. Speranza, N. Basso and E. Lezoche (eds), *Gastrointestinal Hormones and Pathology of the Digestive System.* New York: Plenum Press: 263–9.

Droller, M. J., Scheider, N. U. and Perlmann, P. (1978). *Cellular Immunology* 39: 165.

Dumonde, D. C., Hamblin, A. S., Kasp-Grochowska, E., Pulley, M. S. and Wolstencroft, R. (1983). In N. Fabris, N. Garaci, J. Hadden and N. A. Mitchison (eds), *Immunoregulation.* New York: Plenum Press: 177–99.

Edwards, C. K. III., Ghiasuddin, S. M., Schepper, J. M., Yunger, L. M. and Kelley, K. W. (1988) *Science,* 239: 769.

Enfinger, K. (1932). *Monatsschr. Geburtshilfe Gynaekol.* 91: 312.

Fabris, N. (1977). *Comprehensive Immunology* 1: 72.

Fabris, N. (1981a). In T. Makinodan and M. M. B. Kay (eds) *Immunology of Aging.* Palm Beach: CRC Press: 61–78.

Fabris, N. (1981b). In R. D. Hesch (ed.), *The Low T3 Syndrome.* New York: Academic Press: 199–216.

Fabris, N. (1981c). *Developmental Comparative Immunology* 5: 49.

Fabris, N. (1982). In E. Cooper (ed.), *Developmental Immunology: Clinical Problems and Aging:* New York: Academic Press: 291–298.

Fabris, N. and Mocchegiani, E. (1985). *Cellular Immunology* 91: 325.

Fabris, N. and Piantanelli, L. (1982). In R. C. Adelman and G. S. Roth (eds), *Hormones and Aging.* Palm Beach: CRC Press: 167.

Fabris, N., Mocchegiani, E., Muzzioli, M. and Imberti, R. (1983). In N. Fabris, J. W. Hadden and N. A. Mitchison (eds), *Immunoregulation.* New York: Plenum Press: 341–62.

Fabris, N., Mocchegiani, E., Mariotti, S., Pacini, F. and Pinchera, A. (1986). *Journal of Clinical Endocrinology and Metabolism* 62: 474.

Fabris, N., Mocchegiani, E., Muzzioli, M., Provinciali, M. (1988) *Progress in Neuroendocrine Immunology*, in press.

Faith, R. E., Liang, H. J., Murgo, A. J. and Plotnikoff, N. P. (1984). *Clinical Immunology and Immunopathology* 31: 412.

Ferguson, M. M. and McDonald, F. G. (1985). *FEBS Letters* 191: 145.

Fernandes, G., Carandente, F., Halberg, F. and Good, R. A. (1979). *Journal of Immunology* 123: 622.

Fertsch, D. and Vogel, S. N. (1984). *Journal of Immunology* 132: 2436.

Flemming, K. (1974). *Excerpta Med. Ind. Congr. Ser.* 325: 280.

Forni, G., Bindoni, M., Santoni, A., Belluardo, N., Marchese, A. E. and Giovanelli, M. (1983). *Nature* 306: 181.

Gavin, J. R. III (1977). In J. W. Hadden, R. G. Coffey and F. Spreafico (eds), *Immunopharmacology*. New York: Plenum Medical Book Company: 357–87.

Geidroc, D. P., Pvett, D., Ling, N. and Staros, J. V. (1983). *Journal of Biological Chemistry* 258: 16.

Gemsa, D., Fudenberg, H. and Schmid, R. (1974). In W. H. Wagner and H. Hahn (eds), *Activation of Macrophages*. Amsterdam: Excerpta Medica: 58–70.

Gerli, R., Rambotti, P., Nicoletti, I., Orlandi, S., Migliorati, G. and Riccardi, C. (1986). *Clinical and Experimental Immunology* 64: 399.

Giachetti, A., Goth, A. and Said, S. I. (1978). *Federation Proceedings* 37: 657.

Gillis, S., Crabtree, G. R. and Smith, K. A. (1979). *Journal of Immunology* 123: 1624.

Girard, M. T., Guyre, P. N., Tejes-Toth, A. N. and Munck, A. (1984). *Federation Proceedings* 43: 1434 (abstr.)

Gotjamanos, T. (1970). *Journal of the Reticuloendothelial Society* 8: 421.

Goto, T., Herberman, R. B., Maluish, A. and Strong, D. M. (1983). *Journal of Immunology* 130: 1350.

Gregory, C. D., Lee, H., Rees, G. B., Scott, I. V., Shah, L. P. and Golding, P. R., (1985) *Clinical and Experimental Immunology* 62: 121.

Gregory, C. D., Lee, H., Scott, I. V. and Golding, P. R. (1987) *Journal of Reproductive Immunology* 11: 135.

Griffith, C. D., Rees, R. C., Platts, A., Jermy, A., Peel, J. and Rogers, K. (1984). *Annals of Surgery* 200: 753.

Grossman, C. J. (1985). *Science* 227: 257.

Gudewicz, P. W. (1979). *16th Ann. Natl. Meet. R. E. Soc.*: 28a (abstr.).

Hadden, J. W. (1977). *Comprehensive Immunology* 3: 1.

Hadden, J. W. (1983). In N. Fabris, E. Garaci, J. W. Hadden and N. A. Mitchison (eds), *Immunoregulation.* New York: Plenum Press: 201–30.

Hadden, J. W. and Englard, A. (1979). In *10th Int. Congress on Transplantation and Clinical Immunology.* Amsterdam: Excepta Medica: 279.

Hadden, J. W., Sadlik, J. R. and Hadden, E. M. (1978). *Journal of Immunology* 121: 231.

Hall, N. R. and Goldstein, A. L. (1983). In N. Fabris, E. Garaci, J. Hadden and N. A. Mitchison (eds), *Immunoregulation.* New York: Plenum Press: 141–63.

Haller, O., Kiessling, R., Orn, A. and Wigzell, H. (1977). *Journal of Experimental Medicine* 145: 1411.

Hartung, H. P., Wolters, K. and Toyka, K. V. (1986). *Journal of Immunology* 136: 3856.

Haurankova, J., Schmechel, D., Roth, J. and Brownstein, M. (1978). *Proceedings of the National Academy of Sciences, USA* 75: 5737.

Hayward, M. A., Mitchell, T. A. and Shapiro, D. J. (1980). *Journal of Biological Chemistry* 255: 11308.

Hazum, E., Chang, K. J. and Cuatrecasas, P. (1979). *Science* 205: 1033.

Heller, J. H., Meier, R. M., Zucker, R. and Mast, G. W. (1957). *Endocrinology* 61: 235.

Hellstrand, K. and Hermodsson, S. (1986). *Journal of Immunology* 137: 656.

Hellstrand, K. and Hermodsson. S. (1987). *International Journal of Immunopharmacology* 9: 551.

Hellstrand, K., Hermodsson, S. and Strannegard, 0. (1985). *Journal of Immunology* 134: 4095.

Henney, C. S., Kuribayashi, K., Kern, D. E. and Gillis, S. (1981). *Nature* 291: 335.

Herberman, R. B., Ortaldo, J. R. and Bonnard, G. D. (1979). *Nature* 277: 221.

Hochman, P. S. and Cudkowicz, G. (1979). *Journal of Immunology* 123: 968.

Hochman, P. S., Cudkowicz, G. and Dausset, J. (1978). *Journal of National Cancer Institute* 61: 265.

Hogan, M. M. and Vogel, S. W. (1988) *Journal of Immunology* 140: 513.

Hökfelt, T., Elde, R., Fuxe, K, Johansson, L., Ljungdahl, A., Goldestein, M., Luft, R., Efendic, S., Nilsson, G., Terenius, L., Ganten, D., Jeffcoate, S. L., Rehfeld, J.,

Said, S., Perez de la Mora, M., Possani, L., Tadia, R., Teran, L. and Palacios, R. (1978). In S. Reichlin, R. J. Baldessarini and J. B. Martin (eds), *The Hypothalamus.* New York: Raven Press: 69–135.

Holbrook, N. J., Cox, W. I. and Horner, H. C. (1983). *Cancer Research* 43: 4019.

Hov, J. and Zheng, W. F. (1988). *International Journal of Immunopharmacology* 10: 15.

Ignarro, G. (1977). In J. W. Hadden, R. G. Coffey and F. Spreafico (eds), *Immunopharmacology,* vol. 3. New York: Plenum Publishing Corp.: 61.

Jackson, I. M. D. and Mueller, G. P. (1982). In A. Goldberger and K. R. Yamamoto (eds), *Biological Regulation Development,* vol. 3a, *Hormone Action.* New York: Plenum Press: 127–202.

Johnson, H. M., Torres, B. A., Smith, E. M., David Dion, L. and Blalock, J. E. (1984). *Journal of Immunology* 132: 246.

Kalland, T. (1980). *Journal of Immunology* 124: 1297.

Kalland, T. and Forsberg, J. G. (1981). *Cancer Research* 41: 5134.

Kalland, T., Strand, O. and Forsberg, J. G. (1979). *Journal of National Cancer Institute* 63: 413.

Kaplan, J. (1981). *Science* 212: 14.

Katz, P., Zaytoun, A. M. and Lee, J. H. Jr (1985). *Cellular Immunology* 94: 347.

Kay, N., Morley, J. E. and Van Ree, J. M. (1987) *Life Sciences* 40: 1083.

Kendall, R. A. and Targan, S. (1980). *Journal of Immunology* 125: 2770.

Khachaturian, H., Lewis, M. E., Schafer, M. K. H. and Watson, S. J. (1985). *Trends in Neurosciences* 8: 111.

Kiess, W., Doerr, H., Butenandt, O. and Belohradsky, B. H. (1986). *New England Journal of Medicine* 314: 321.

Kiessling, R., Klein, E. and Wigzell, H (1975). *European Journal of Immunology* 5: 112.

Koff, W. C. and Dunegan, M. A. (1985). *Journal of Immunology* 135: 350.

Koff, W. C. and Dunegan, M. A. (1986). *Journal of Immunology* 136: 705.

Krug, U., Krug, F. and Cuatrecasas P. (1972). *Proceedings of the National Academy of Sciences, USA* 9: 2604.

Kuribayashi, K., Gillis, S., Kern, D. E. and Henny, C. S. (1981). *Journal of Immunology* 126: 2321.

Lanefelt, F., Ullberg, M., Jondal, M. and Fredholm, B. B. (1983). *Medical Biology* 61: 324.

Lee, H., Gregory, C. D., Rees, G. B., Scott, I. V. and Golding, P. R. (1987) *Journal of Reproductive Immunology* 11: 135.

Lemarchand-Beraud, T., Holm, A. C. and Scazziga, B. R. (1977). *Acta Endocrinologica* 85: 44.

Lesniak, M. A. (1974). *Journal of Biological Chemistry* 249: 1661.

Lissoni, P., Marelli, O., Mauri, R., Resentini, M., Franco, P., Esposti, D., Esposti, G., Fraschini, F., Halberg, F., Sotern, R. B. and Cornelissen, G. (1986). *Chronobiologia.* (In press).

Lolait, S. J., Lim, A. T. W., Toh, B. H. and Funder, J. W. (1984) *Journal of Clinical Investigation* 73: 277.

Low, T. L. K. and Goldstein, A. L. (1984). In A. L. Goldstein (ed.), *Thymic Hormones and Lymphokines.* New York: Plenum Press: 21–36.

Lurie, M. B. (1960). *Ann. NY Acad. Sci.* 88: 83

Luster, M. I., Boorman, G. A., Dean, J. H., Luebke, R. W. and Lawson, L. D. (1980). *Journal of the Reticuloendothelial Society* 28: 561.

Mandler, R. N., Biddison, W. E., Mandler, R. and Serrate, S. A. (1986). *Journal of Immunology* 136: 934.

Mathews, P. M., Froelich, C. J., Sibbitt, W. L. Jr and Bankhurst, A. D. (1983). *Journal of Immunology* 130: 1658.

Mattsson, R., Ocklind, G. and Andersson, M. (1984). *Developmental and Comparative Immunology* 8: 443.

Melmon, K. L., Wenstein, J., Poon, T. C., Bourne, M. R., Shearer, G. M., Coffino, P. and Insel, P. A. (1977). *Comprehensive Immunology* 3: 331.

Miller, M. E. (1984). In S. Gupta (ed.), *Immunology of Clinical and Experimental Diabetes.* New York: Plenum Publishing Corp.: 369–83.

Moon, T. D., Morley, J. E., Lange, P. H. and Vessella, R. L. (1983). *Scandinavian Journal of Immunology* 18: 255.

Nair, M. P. N. and Schwartz, S. A. (1983). *Cellular Immunology* 81: 45.

Nair, M. P. N. and Schwrtz, S. A. (1984). *Journal of Immunology* 132: 2876.

Nair, M. P. N, Cilik, J. M. and Schwartz, S. A. (1986). *Journal of Immunology* 136: 2456.

Neill, J. D. (1980). In L. Martini and W. F. Ganong (eds), *Frontiers in Neuroendocrinology*, vol. 6: New York: Raven Press: 129.

Nicol, T. (1935). *Trans. R. Soc. Edinburgh* 58: 449.

Nicol, T. and Snell, R. S. (1955). *Nature* 175: 995.

Nicol, T. and Vernon-Roberts, B. (1965). *Journal of the Reticuloendothelial Society* 2: 15.

Nicol, T., Bilbey, D. L. J., Charles, L. M., Cordingley, J. L. and Vernon-Roberts, B. (1964). *Journal of Endocrinology* 30: 277.

Northdurft, W. and Flemming, K. (1971). In N. R. Diluzio and K. Flemming (eds), *The Reticuloendothelial System and Immune Phenomena*. New York: Plenum Press: 95–110.

O'Donohue, T. L., Handelmann, G. E., Miller, R. L. and Jacobowitz, D. M. (1982). *Science* 215: 1125.

O'Dorisio, M. S., O'Dorisio, T. M., Cataland, S. and Balcerzak, S. P. (1980). *Journal of Laboratory and Clinical Medicine* 86: 666.

Oehler, J. R. and Herberman, R. B. (1978). *International Journal of Cancer* 30: 229.

Okamura, K., Furukawa, K., Nakakuki, M., Kanunori, Y. and Suzuki, M. (1984). *American Journal of Obstetrics and Gynecology* 28: 149.

Onsurd, M. and Thorsby, E. (1981). *Scandinavian Journal of Immunology* 13: 573.

Oropeza-Rendon, R. L., Speth, V., Hiller, G., Weber, K. and Fischer, H. (1979). *Experimental Cell Research* 119: 365.

Papadimitrious, J. M. and Sforcina, D. (1975). *Experimental Cell Research* 91: 233.

Papic, M., Stein-Streilein, J., Zakarija, M., McKenzie, J. M., Guffee, J., and Fletcher, M. A. (1987). *Journal of Clinical Investigation* 79: 404.

Parrillo, J. E. and Fauci, A. S. (1978). *Scandinavian Journal of Immunology* 8: 99.

Pavlidis, N. and Chirigos, M. (1980). *Psychosomatic Medicine* 42: 47.

Payan, D. G., Brewster, D. R., Missirian-Bastian, A. and Goetzl, E. J. (1984). *Journal of Clinical Investigation* 74: 1532.

Pedernera, E., Romano, M., Besedovsky, H. and Del Carmine Anguilar, M. (1983). *Journal of Endocrinology* 5: 325.

Piantanelli, L., Basso, A., Muzzioli, M. and Fabris, N. N. (1978). *Mechanisms of Ageing and Development* 7: 171.

Pick, E. (1972). *Nature New Biology* 238: 176.

Pierpaoli, W., Bianchi, E. and Sorkin, E. (1971). *Clinical and Experimental Immunology* 9: 889.

Polak, J. M. and Bloom, S. R. (1982). In Said, S. I. (ed), *Vasoactive Intestinal Peptide*. New York: Raven Press: 107.

Polak, J. M., Pearse, A. G. E., Grimelius, L., Bloom, S. R. and Arimura, A. (1975). *Lancet* 1: 1220.

Provinciali, M., Muzzioli, M. and Fabris, N. (1987). *Journal of Experimental Pathology* 3: 617.

Provinciali, M., Muzzioli, M. and Fabris, N. (1989). *Experimental Gerontology*, in press.

Raz, A. and Goldman, R. (1976). *Journal of the Reticuloendothelial Society* 20: 177.

Rhodes, J. (1975). *Nature* 257: 597.

Rola-Pleszczynski, M., Boldue, D. and St-Pierre, S. (1985). *Journal of Immunology* 135: 2569.

Roszman, T. L., Cross, R. J., Brooks, W. H. and Markesbery, W. R. (1982). *Immunology* (1982). 45: 737.

Rouveix, B., Badenoch-Jones, P., Larno, S. and Turk, J. L. (1980). *Immunopharmacology* 2: 319.

Said, S. I. and Rosemberg, R. N. (1976). *Science* 192: 907.

Sanchez de la Pena, S., Harberg, F., Ungar, F., Haus, E., Lakatua, D., Scheving, L. E., Sanchez, E. and Vecsei, P. (1983). *Brain Research Bulletin* 10: 559.

Sarkar, D. K., Gottschall, P. L. and Meites, J. (1982). *Science* 218: 684.

Saxena, Q. B., Saxena, R. K. and Adler, W. H. (1982). *International Archives of Allergy and Applied Immunology* 67: 169.

Schafer, E. A. (1916). In Longnans (ed.), *The Endocrine Organs: An Introduction to the Study of Internal Secretion.* New York: Green and Co. 33–49.

Scharf, J. H. (1974). In Scharf, J. H. (ed.), *Das Somatotrope Hormon.* Halle/Saale: Deutsche Akademie der Natur Forscher 20–31.

Schorn, H. and Walter, C. (1975). *Journal of the Reticuloendothelial Society* 18 (suppl.): 35a.

Schultz, R. M., Pavlidis, N. A., Stylos, W. A. and Chirigos, M. A. (1978). *Science* 202: 320.

Seaman, W. E., Blackman, M. A., Gindhart, T. D., Roubinian, J. R., Loeb, J. M. and Talal, N. (1978). *Journal of Immunology* 121: 2193.

Serrate, S. A., Schulof, R. S., Leondaridis, L., Goldstein, A. L. and Sztein, M. B. (1987). *Journal of Immunology* 139: 2338.

Sharma, S. D., Tsai, V. and Proffitt, M. R. (1982). *Cellular Immunology* 73: 83.

Shavit, Y., Lewis, J. W., Terman, G. W., Gale, R. P. Liebeskind, J. C. (1984). *Science* 223: 188.

Shavit, Y., Terman, G. W., Martin, F. C., Lewis, J. W., Liebeskind, J. C. and Gale, R. P. (1985). *Journal of Immunology* 135: 834s.

Sljivic, V. S. and Warr, G. W. (1973). *Periodicum Biologorum* 75: 231.

Smith, E. M. and Blalok, J. E. (1981) *Proceedings of the National Academy of Sciences, USA* 78: 7530.

Smith, R. L. and Weidemann, M. L. (1980). *Biochemical and Biophysical Research Communications* 96: 973.

Snell, R. S. and Nicol, T. (1956). *Nature* 178: 1405.

Spangelo, B. L., Judd. A. M., Ross, P. C., Login, I. S., Jarvis. W. D., Badamchian, M., Goldstein, A. L. and MacLeod, R. M., (1987). *Endocrinology* 121: 2035.

Spector, N. H. (1983). In N. Fabris, E. Garaci, J. Hadden and N. A. Mitchinson (eds), *Immunoregulation.* New York: Plenum Press: 231–58.

Stavy, L. (1974). *Transplantation* 17: 173.

Stein-Streilein, J., Zakarija, M., Papic, M. and Maxwell McKenzie, J. (1987) *Journal of Immunology* 139: 2502.

Steplewski, Z. and Vogel, W. H. (1985) *Neuroscience Letters* 62: 277.

Strickland, R. W., Wahl, L. M. and Finebloom, D. S. (1986). *Journal of Immunology* 137: 1577.

Sulke, A. N., Jones, D. B. and Wood, P. J. (1985). *Journal of Reproductive Immunology* 7: 105.

Taetle, R. and Koessler, A. (1980). *Cancer Research* 40: 1223.

Takahashi, J. S. and Menaker, M. (1984). In R. E. Goldberger and K. R. Yamamoto (eds), *Biological Regulation and Development,* vol. 3B, *Hormone Action,* New York: Plenum Press: 285–303.

Targan, S. and Dorey, F. (1980). *Journal of Immunology* 124: 2157.

Tata, J. R. (1966). In J. M. Tager, S. Papa, E. Quagliariello and E. C. Slater (eds), *Regulation of Metabolic Processes in Mitochondria,* Amsterdam: Elsevier: 489–505.

Tata, J. R. (1984). In R. F. Goldberger and K. R. Yamamoto (eds), *Biological Regulation and Development,* vol. 3B, *Hormone Action.* New York: Plenum Press: 1–58.

Timiras, P. S. (1972). In P. S. Timiras (ed.), *Developmental Physiology and Aging.* New York: Macmillan: 542–63.

Tonnesen, E., Tonnesen, J. and Christensen, N. J. (1984). *Acta Pathologica, Microbiologica et Immunologica Scandinavica* 92C: 81.

Tonnesen, E., Christensen, N. J. and Brinlov, M. M. (1987) *European Journal of Clinical Investigation* 17: 497.

Trejo, R. A., Loose, L. D. and Diluzio, N. R. (1972). *Journal of the Reticuloendothelial Society* 11: 88.

Trinchieri, G., Santoli, D. and Zmijewski, J. (1977). *Transplantation Proceedings* 9: 112.

Yoshiki, U., Miyawaki, T., Seki, H., Matsuda, A., Taga, K., Sato, H. and Taniguchi, N. (1985). *Journal of Immunology* 135: 180.

Waters, M. J., Frisen, H. G. and Bohnet, H. G. (1978). In L. Birnbaumer and B. W. O'Malley (eds), *Receptors and Hormone Action*, vol. 3. New York: Academic Press: 457–77.

Weissemann, G., Dukor, P. and Zurier, R. B. (1971). *Nature New Biology* 231: 131.

Weissemann, G., Smolen, J. and Korchak, H. (1980). *New England Journal of Medicine* 303: 27.

Wilson, R. M. and Reeves, W. G. (1986). *Clinical and Experimental Immunology* 63: 478.

Wybran, J. (1985). *Neuropeptides* 5: 371.

11

Genetic Factors

SUZANNE LEMIEUX

Immunology Research Centre, Institut Armand-Frappier
Université du Québec,Laval, Québec

MARY M. STEVENSON

EMIL SKAMENE

Division of Clinical Immunology and Allergy
Montreal General Hospital Research Institute, Montreal, Quebec

348

NATURAL IMMUNITY
ISBN 0 12 5145551

I. INTRODUCTION

History provides numerous examples of variable susceptibility of human populations to viral, bacterial and parasitic infections, both during epidemics and in the endemic areas of the world. Similar observations have been made with respect to the incidence of various malignant conditions. Although the influence of environmental factors must be considered in any explanation of such variability, it has recently become clear, mainly on the basis of studying experimental infections and tumorigenesis in inbred animals, that genetic factors play a decisive role in individual susceptibility.

In principle, the entire basis of susceptibility or resistance to infection and malignancy is genetically determined but, because of the immense variety of offenders and the complexities of host defences, few common patterns of resistance are discernible. Thus, we are compelled to study stepwise processes affecting individual micro-organisms or individual tumour target cells with the hope of extending the studies to other infections, other malignancies, and other hosts. It furthermore follows that no natural infection or host response to malignant transformation could be expected to be solely regulated by a single gene. It is true that possession of a particular allele at one genetic locus may dramatically influence the course of disease in certain individuals, but at the level of whole populations many genes would be expected to be responsible for the variable disease profile which is frequently observed.

Koch, about a century ago, demonstrated the importance of 'isolating' and studying pure genotypes of a *pathogen* if studies of pathogenesis were to have critical value. Similar considerations must surely apply to *host populations* if disease is to be understood. Through genetic means, different host genotypes may be isolated and stratified into relatively pure categories. The sum of variations observed in these categories should equal that for the original heterogenous population.

The genetic basis of innate susceptibility and resistance is, therefore, best viewed as a composite interplay of inherited mechanisms which manifest themselves as a programmed sequence of events. Only by separating the particular pattern of host response to a given invader into discrete steps may we reconstruct its genetic regulation. This chapter will deal first with the strategy of such analysis, using as an example the two best-analysed genetic models of natural immunity, namely, that of resistance to infections with intracellular pathogens (*Ity-Lsh-Bcg* gene) and that of resistance to influenza virus (*Mx* gene). In the subsequent parts, the genetic mechanisms controlling the function of the two key effector cellular compartments of natural resistance, namely the natural killer (NK) cells and macrophages, will be discussed. The attempt will be made to discuss genetically-determined phenomena which can be expected to have a broad relevance across species. Most of the experimental foundation in studies of natural immunity employs the inbred mouse as a convenient model. Therefore, unless stated otherwise, the mechanisms described in this chapter pertain to the mouse.

II. STRATEGY OF THE GENETIC ANALYSIS OF NATURAL IMMUNITY

The prerequisite of genetic analysis is a variation, quantitative or qualitative, in the host response to a pathogen or to a tumour target. When found among inbred mouse strains which are kept in a defined environment, such variation is usually the result of either mutation or a polymorphism at one or more chromosomal loci. While death of the animal exposed to infection or to malignancy is often used as a typing criterion for susceptibility, it is preferable to use more defined end points, such as the number of micro-organisms in the tissue at various times after infection, the number of labelled tumour cells remaining in tissues at a particular time after implantation, or the size and appearance of tissue lesions (tumour nodule, necrosis, granuloma etc.). It is often seen that variables such as the dose of infectious agent, the virulence of the pathogen, the tumour cell variant or the route of inoculation can dramatically alter the observed genetic variation in the response of the host. This fact was alluded to by Gowen (1960) but it is often ignored when seemingly discrepant results from different laboratories are being compared. In order to probe one variable (i.e. host genes), one has to fix the other side of the equation (i.e. standardise the conditions of infection or of tumour induction/implantation) and thus transform the three-dimensional problem into a two-dimensional one.

In the first model selected as an illustrative example, mice of various inbred strains were infected intravenously with *Mycobacterium bovis* BCG and the number of bacillary colonies in their spleens was studied at various times after infection. Two patterns of response were seen.

Approximately half of the strains were resistant, not allowing any bacterial proliferation to occur. There was logarithmic growth of the mycobacteria in the spleens of the other half of the inbred strains. Such a clear, discontinuous, inter-strain pattern of response immediately suggested that the character may be under the control of a single gene, named *Bcg* (Forget *et al.*, 1981).

Genetic variation in natural resistance to influenza virus, the other model used here as an example, originated sometime between 1942 and 1950 at Glaxo Laboratories in England as a true experiment of nature. An unwanted visitor somehow managed to mate illegitimately with a mouse of the strain A inbred colony. Unknowingly, the progeny of this mating were taken for inbreeding. Only years later was the new strain identified as distinct from A and named A2G. Among many deviations from the strain A phenotypic characteristics, the A2G mice were found to be resistant to influenza virus (myxovirus): the virus grew in the brains of A2G mice to a titre 100 times lower than in susceptible A mice (Lindenmann *et al.*, 1963). Interestingly, the A2G mice were fully susceptible to a wide variety of other viruses including yellow fever, poliovirus, herpes simplex and encephalomyocarditis. Later it was found that mice of several other strains (e.g. SL/NiA and strains derived from outbred wild *Mus musculus*) were as resistant to influenza as A2G mice, while most of the other inbred laboratory strains were susceptible, thus suggesting a simple mode of genetic control. The putative gene which was seen as regulating natural resistance to influenza virus (and to other myxoviruses) was named *Mx*.

A. Segregation Mendelian Analysis of Natural Immunity

Having defined a discontinuous variation in the phenotype of natural resistance or susceptibility among inbred strains, one may embark on further analysis to estimate the number of genetic loci involved in the control of such a trait. This means setting up numerous crosses of the typical resistant and susceptible progenitors and typing the individual animals of the segregating populations (F_2 and backcrosses) for the trait of resistance/susceptibility. Where the distribution of a given trait in mice of progenitor strains can clearly be differentiated from that of F_1 hybrids, single-locus control of resistance leads to a bimodal distribution of resistant and susceptible animals among the backcross progeny. Such is the case for genetic resistance to both BCG and the influenza virus, where individuals of numerous segregating populations always express one of the parental types with the proportion of susceptible and resistant phenotypes approaching the predicted Mendelian ratio for monogenic control, i.e., the gene 'breeds true' (Gros *et al.*, 1981; Lindenmann *et al.*, 1963).

More often than not, however, such a clear distinction of variant phenotypes is not seen and a considerable degree of overlap in the expression of the traits of resistance and susceptibility exists in the genetically homogeneous populations of parental and F_1 strains. Understandably, the distributions of phenotypic classes in the segregating generations also overlap extensively in these situations. This type of data is being obtained in genetic studies of resistance and susceptibility to infection and cancer much more frequently than that of clear segregation into distinct phenotypic categories. The strategies for analysis of such data have recently been provided by Curtis *et al.* (1985) and by McCall (1985).

B. Mapping of the Genes of Natural Immunity

The identification of a single gene controlling the phenotype of resistance or susceptibility leads to an immediate temptation to map its locus in the genome. There are several reasons why it is useful to embark on a long and often difficult path of determining the chromosomal location of the host resistance gene. These reasons can be summarised as follows:

1. To uncover a pleiotropic effect of the gene (this may contribute to our understanding of the mechanism of natural resistance).
2. To map the host resistance gene to a previously identified locus carrying an already known gene which codes for a product that may be involved in the phenotype of resistance/susceptibility.
3. To identify closely linked chromosomal markers which are useful in (a) typing for resistance/susceptibility; (b) creation of congenic lines; or (c) searching for the gene using the tools of molecular biology.
4. To search for conservation of homologous domains containing similar host resistance genes in different species.

There are several feasible ways of mapping genes of natural resistance. The classical one employs the strategy of linkage analysis using known linkage groups and it is based on the search for co-segregation of the phenotype of host resistance with one of the previously identified allotypic markers in the backcross and F_2 generation. This approach has successfully been used by Plant and Glynn (1979) in the location of the *Ity* gene which controls innate resistance of mice to *Salmonella typhimurium* to chromosome 1. The practical problem with this methodology is the necessity of making precise measurements of the variable phenotype (resistant *vs.* susceptible) on individual animals of the segregating progeny. It is, therefore, applicable only in those circumstances where there is a well-defined, 'tight' typing method available. Once typed by exposure to destructive infection or to a tumour, the same animal is never available for repeated measurements. The other limitation is the availability of only a small number of testing stocks with appropriately identified linkage groups. For this reason, a newer genetic tool, namely recombinant inbred (RI) strains, has been widely used in the analysis of genetic control of resistance to a variety of infectious agents.

RI mouse strains are derived by inbreeding the F_2 progeny of a cross between two inbred parental strains. Once inbred, such a set of RI strains can be thought of as a stable, segregant population. Unlinked genes are randomised in the RI strains while linked genes will tend to become fixed in the same (parental) combination as when they entered the cross. If the parental strains carry different alleles at a locus one wants to map, its chromosomal location may be determined by typing each RI strain for the presence of one or other parental allele.

A basic feature of analysing data sets derived from typing RI strains for a given character is the assignment of one of the progenitor phenotypes to each of the RI strains, in order to determine a strain distribution pattern (SDP) for the RI set. For a trait controlled by a single gene, one may expect a bimodal distribution of parental phenotypes among the RI mice. By comparing the SDP of the new locus to a table of SDPs for other, already known loci, one determines whether alleles at any other loci are inherited in a similar fashion. The more closely two loci are linked, the more likely it is that their SDPs will be identical or nearly identical.

When mice of various RI strains were typed for their response to BCG, the SDP of this trait was concordant (but not identical) with the SDP of two chromosome 1 genes, namely *Idh-1* and *Pep-3*. The recombination frequency of the gene of resistance to *M. bovis* BCG with the *Idh-1* and *Pep-3* loci signalled a putative location of the *Bcg* gene on chromosome 1, in the vicinity of those 2 marker genes.

The RI strain analysis of the resistant (Bcg^r) and susceptible (Bcg^s) phenotypes, furthermore, resulted in a most valuable appreciation of an absolute concordance between the Bcg^r/Bcg^s pattern and the SDP of resistant and susceptible alleles of two other genes of natural resistance which were identified previously, namely the *Ity* (*Salmonella typhimurium* resistance) gene (Plant and Glynn, 1979) and the *Lsh* gene (controlling innate resistance to *Leishmania donovani*) (Bradley *et al.*, 1979). Thus, a single gene was found which controlled innate resistance to a group of immunologically distinct and taxonomically unrelated pathogens. Already at this early stage of the genetic studies it was suggested that perhaps the inherited mechanism operates via macrophages, since all three pathogens identified as being genetically restricted by this gene are intracellular parasites of the macrophage (Skamene *et al.*, 1982).

When the phenotype of natural resistance is identified at a cellular level, the location of the responsible gene may be detected using the methods of somatic cell hybridisation. Co-segregation of the loss of the known chromosomal markers with the loss of natural resistance in the hybrid cell signals the gene location. This methodology was employed in the search for chromosomal assignment for the *Mx* gene and led to its mapping to chromosome 16 (Dreiding *et al.*, 1985).

C. Phenotypic Expression of the Genes of Natural Immunity

The availability of mutant and congenic lines, which were developed or discovered in the course of genetic analysis of host resistance, allows us to embark on functional studies dealing with the control mechanisms. These studies can be performed without the interfering effect of the rest of the genome which is always a problem when functional correlates of resistance and susceptibility are sought in regular inbred strains exhibiting the alternative resistant or susceptible phenotypes.

The search for the phenotypic expression of *Bcg(Ity,Lsh)* gene in congenic mice revealed that the genetic mechanism was operating very early after infection, with its clear effects being seen already at 24 hours (Swanson and O'Brien, 1983; Gros *et al.*, 1983). The functional depletion of T cell, B cell and NK cell subsets did not influence the phenotype of genetic resistance. *Bcg*^{r} mice remained resistant even after total body irradiation with 550 R and 900 R. Experiments with reciprocal *Bcg*^{s} → *Bcg*^{r} chimeras showed clearly that the cell population expressing the resistant phenotype originated from bone marrow. The only manoeuvre which transformed the genetically resistant mouse strain into the phenotypically susceptible one was chronic treatment with silica (Gros *et al.*, 1983). All these lines of evidence pointed to the mature macrophage as the cell expressing the resistant or susceptible form of the *Bcg* gene.

In the case of the *Mx* gene (alleles: resistant, *Mx*$^+$ and susceptible, *Mx*$^-$) a spectrum of possibilities to explain the genetic basis of resistance to influenza was also explored. The participation of T cells, B cells, NK cells and macrophages was ruled out and the investigators turned to interferon (IFN). Although studies with other viruses had shown that antibodies to IFN block IFN-mediated resistance, it seemed unlikely that IFN itself was the product of the *Mx* gene. Not only is the *Mx*-controlled resistance specific for myxoviruses but the levels of IFN (α and β) in susceptible mice were significantly higher than those in resistant mice. Nevertheless, antibody to IFN did abolish the resistance of Mx^+ mice. This apparent paradox was explained when cell cultures (macrophages or embryonic cells) from Mx^+ and Mx^- animals were exposed first to IFN and then to a variety of viruses, namely VSV (vesicular stomatitis virus), EMC (encephalomyocarditis virus) or influenza virus. Increasing doses of IFN led to the acquisition of antiviral state against VSV and EMC in both phenotypic variants. However, in the case of influenza virus infection, IFN decreased the virus titre only in Mx^+ cells. The Mx^- cells showed only a minimal response. These results led to the hypothesis of co-operation between a non-specific extrinsic factor (IFN) with an intrinsic element (the product of the natural resistance Mx gene) resulting in a significant degree of antiviral specificity. Thus, the resistance gene was envisaged either as modulating the antiviral state induced by IFN or as coding for an antiviral mechanism activated by IFN (Haller *et al.*, 1980).

The availability of Mx congenic mice later in the course of investigation proved to be invaluable in unravelling the molecular basis of the Mx^+ phenotype. The combination of two-dimensional gel analysis of protein fingerprints of the congenic Mx^- and Mx^+ macrophages and immunoprecipitation with congenic Mx^- anti-Mx^+ alloantibodies led to the identification of the gene product, a 75 kilodalton protein induced by IFN and localising in the nucleus. Segregation linkage analysis confirmed the identity of this molecule with the Mx^+ gene product and functional studies revealed that it specifically inhibits the influenza viral mRNA synthesis (Krug *et al.*, 1985).

D. Human Equivalents of the Murine Genes of Natural Resistance

The $Bcg(Ity,Lsh)$ locus seems to have considerable biological significance, as it regulates natural resistance to infections with very diverse intracellular pathogens. The resistant allele confers a survival advantage on the mouse as attested by the fact that wild mice from a variety of locations all over the world have been typed as resistant to infection (Blackwell, 1983). One would intuitively expect that a mouse gene with such a survival advantage for *Mus musculus* might have a homologue in other species, including humans. Genetic polymorphism in resistance and susceptibility to tuberculosis in rabbits had been well characterised by the pioneering studies of Lurie (1964); its basis was found to be differential handling by macrophages of virulent mycobacteria. Resistance of human populations to tuberculosis has often been postulated to have a genetic basis and twin studies as well as familial segregation of the disease support this hypothesis (Skamene, 1986). Similarly, there are multiple lines of evidence suggesting that the spectral character of other diseases with intracellular pathogens, such as leprosy and leishmaniasis, may have a genetic basis.

The case of the *Mx* gene suggests another rationale for the search for its homologues in other species. Obviously, host genetic factors are extremely important in IFN-mediated responses. The variety of proteins induced by interferons have, as yet, unknown functions. Spriggs (1986) speculated that a host's IFN response to viruses is regulated by its specific ability to respond to an IFN signal. For example, certain persons may not efficiently clear a viral infection, not because they fail to make IFN but because they cannot synthesise a specific protein in response to IFN and, therefore, cannot limit the spread of infection. Perhaps a specific host protein inhibits only a specific class of infectious agents in a manner analogous to the *Mx* protein and the myxoviruses.

There are three possible approaches to the search for the homologues of genes of natural resistance, such as *Bcg* or *Mx*, in other species. The first one takes advantage of our current knowledge of the phenotypic expression of these genes and involves the application to other species of the techniques of host cell – pathogen interaction, which were developed to recognise the resistant and susceptible phenotypes at the cellular level in the mouse. Another possibility would be the isolation of the murine gene as a biochemical entity and probing the genome of other species for homologous sequences. This task has already been achieved in the case of the *Mx* gene. Its sequence has been cloned and, furthermore, the Mx^+ gene has successfully been used to transfect Mx^- cells, resulting in a change of the genetically susceptible phenotype into the resistant one (Staeheli *et al.*, 1986). As predicted, gene homologues of *Mx* have recently been discovered in the rat and humans (Staehali and Haller, 1985).

A similar approach applied to the *Bcg* gene has not succeeded as yet, mainly because the gene product is still, in 1987, an elusive molecule. The strategy proposed for the isolation and characterisation of the *Bcg* gene is based on the use of genetic linkage techniques to identify the DNA sequences which encode these genes (Housman and Gros, 1985). This approach involves the saturation of the region of the chromosome surrounding the *Bcg* locus with genetic markers which are defined by specific cloned DNA segments. The location of the *Bcg* gene within a cloned segment of DNA can then be determined by examining its segregation pattern in genetic linkage studies with respect to other markers defined by DNA probes within that chromosomal segment.

This line of investigation has led to the recent discoveries of new polymorphisms in the vicinity of the *Bcg* gene. The *Len-1* gene (coding for the polymorphic variants of the γ-crystallin protein of the lens) was found to be located a few centimorgans proximal to the *Bcg* gene (Skow, 1982) and the *Fn* gene coding for the fibronectin variants seems to map almost precisely (by the RI strain analysis) to the *Bcg* locus. The examination of this sequence of linked genes on chromosome 1 in the approximate order *Idh-1 – Len-1 – Fn – Bcg* reveals a striking homology with a similar linkage group which is conserved on the arm of human chromosome 2. The hypothesis raised by this finding is that the presence of the gene of host resistance in this region is *the* reason for the conservation of this chromosomal segment. This hypothesis, further supported by the fact that a similar sequence homology is also found in the cow, is now being tested by examination of co-segregation of these chromosomal markers with the pattern of resistance and susceptibility to tuberculosis in families living in endemic areas of the world.

Although, as covered in Part II of this book, there exist numerous levels of natural resistance to infections and tumours, the role of genetic factors in the regulation of natural resistance has been analysed best in the response of two effector cell populations, NK cells and macrophages. The detailed discussion of those two areas of investigation is the topic of the following sections.

III. GENETIC CONTROL OF NATURAL KILLER CELL ACTIVITY

By consensus, natural killer (NK) cell activity is defined as the capacity of non-adherent, non-phagocytic effector cells to lyse a variety of target cells without a requirement for prior priming, MHC-restricted target cell recognition or the further acquisition of immunological memory (Koren and Herberman, 1983). Although all lymphoid in nature, effector cells involved in natural killing have been found to be extremely heterogeneous, differing in cell-surface antigen phenotypes, in organ and strain distribution, in target cell specificity, in the cellular and molecular requirements for their full development, and in their response to immunomodulators (see Lotzova and Herberman, 1986, for review). Endogenous lymphocyte-mediated natural cytotoxicity is mostly associated with two distinct cell subtypes, designated natural killer (NK) and natural cytotoxic (NC) cells (reviewed by Lattime and Stutman, 1983).[1]

The discussion of the genetic factors involved in the control of NK cell activity will deal almost exclusively with the data accumulated in studies with mice. Given the large number of inbred, congenic and recombinant inbred strains available, as well as the numerous well-characterised

[1] See Chapters 3 and 5.

mutations associated with, or responsible for, other immune-related defects, the mouse has been by far the best animal model to investigate the genetic control of differentiation, function and regulation of NK cells and other related natural effector cells and their relative contributions to various biological functions.

A. Phenotypic Expression of the Genetic Control of Lymphocyte-Mediated Natural Killing

NK cell activity is predominantly exerted by Ly-5$^+$ Qa-5$^+$ Ly-1$^-$ Ly-2$^-$ asialo GM1$^+$ cells which can also express Thy-1 and other alloantigens of the Qa and Ly series (see Pollack, 1986, for review). In addition, NK cells of most mouse strains express NK-1, NK-2 or both NK-specific markers (Glimcher *et al.*, 1977; Burton and Winn, 1981; Pollack and Emmons, 1982). Operationally, murine NK cell activity is usually estimated by measuring the lysis of radiolabelled prototypic YAC-1 tumour target cells by fresh splenic lymphoid cells in a four-hour ^{51}Cr-release assay (Kiessling *et al.*, 1975a). As environmental conditions influence the NK cell activity level, endogenous NK cell activity is considered to be the level of NK cytotoxicity reached with cells from mice housed under conventional conditions. It is obvious that a significant part of this activity is due to IFN-activated killers (IAK) which have been stimulated by naturally occurring pathogens (Clark *et al.*, 1979). Few studies dealing with the genetic control of the natural killing of normal cells or antibody-coated tumour targets have indicated that the cells involved in these functions are not under the same genetic control as NK cells (Kiessling and Welsh, 1980; Altman *et al.*, 1983).

Different inbred mouse strains express either a low, intermediate or high NK phenotype (Kiessling *et al.*, 1975a). The high NK phenotype is usually inherited as a dominant trait (Kiessling *et al.*, 1975a; Petranyi *et al.*, 1975; Petranyi *et al.*, 1976). The absence of bimodal distribution of low and high NK phenotypes among [A × C57BL]F$_1$ × A backcross progeny suggests that NK cell function is under polygenic control (Petranyi *et al.*,1975). The same conclusion emerged when [A × SM/J]F$_1$ hybrids expressing very high NK cell activity were backcrossed to the A (low NK) progenitor (Clark, 1986). On the other hand, a single gene was suspected to be involved in the difference between the endogenous NK cell activity of SJL (low) and B10.S (high) strains when a similar analysis of their backcross progeny was performed (Kaminsky *et al.*, 1985). The occurrence of an NK cell activity higher than that observed in either parental strain in hybrids derived from specific strain combinations has been interpreted as an example of either gene complementation or heterosis of different alleles at the same locus (Klein *et al.*, 1978; Blair, 1980; Kaminsky *et al.*, 1985).

H-2-linked genes influence NK cell activity level but only on certain defined genetic backgrounds (Petranyi *et al.*, 1975; Petranyi *et al.*, 1976; Clark *et al.*, 1979; Klein *et al.*, 1980; Klein, 1982). One such H-2-linked gene appears to map telomeric of H-2D, probably in the Qa region (Klein, 1982). The influence of H-2-linked genes on the control of NK cell activity is very similar to their control of hybrid or allogeneic resistance to bone-marrow grafts. This is not surprising, as NK cells participate in this resistance (Lotzova, 1983). According to Afifi *et al.* (1985), NK cells contribute to the genetic resistance to bone-marrow grafts as a separate step following the recognition of haemopoietic histocompatibility (Hh) antigens by other host cells. The parallel genetic control of the two functions has been extensively discussed in previously published reviews (Clark and Harmon, 1980; Clark, 1986).

Several genes mapping outside the H-2 histocompatibility complex are also involved in NK cell activity control (Petranyi *et al.*, 1976; Clark *et al.*, 1979; Kaminsky *et al.*, 1983; Kaminsky *et al.*, 1985). Recently, such background genes of various origin have been successfully introduced into the A/Sn mouse, creating diverse congenic lines with variable resistance to the NK-susceptible YAC lymphoma (Ährlund-Richter *et al.*, 1983; Ährlund-Richter *et al.*, 1985). Some of the non-H-2-linked genes involved in the control of NK cell activity appear to modulate the expression of the H-2-linked genes but others act independently (Klein and Taylor, 1985).

Clark *et al.* (1979) have analysed the genetic control of natural killing against YAC-1 target cells following the transfer of mice from a specific pathogen-free environment to conventional facilities. They estimate that the splenic NK cell activity measured in these conditions is most likely attributable to activated NK cells stimulated by naturally acquired infections due to the endogenous pathogens present in the colony. Like endogenous NK cell activity, the cytotoxicity mediated by the naturally activated NK cells (presumably IAK) is under polygenic control involving complementation between H-2-linked and non-H-2-linked genes. A positive influence of the H-2D^d haplotype was detected in congenic mice of the B10 background. This observation was confirmed by Klein *et al.* (1980) for the control of endogenous NK cell activity.

On the basis of their spontaneous NK cell activity and their capacity to respond to the IFN-inducer poly I : C, Kaminsky *et al.* (1983) classified different mouse strains as low, inducible or high NK strains. Following the genetic analysis of these two NK cell functions in several kinds of F_1 hybrids and selected backcross progeny, they reported that both high endogenous NK cell activity and the capacity to respond to poly I : C are dominant (Kaminsky *et al.*, 1985). No H-2^s-linked influence on spontaneous NK cell activity or on its inducibility by poly I : C was detected in the progeny of SJL (low) and B10.S (high) congenic strains. Depending on the strain combination tested, at least two genes could be shown to influence endogenous NK cell activity whereas three genes seem to be involved in controlling the response to poly I : C.

We are currently studying the inheritance of NK cell activity using the RI strains derived from A/J (A) and C57BL/6J (B6) progenitors (Lemieux *et al.*, 1985). This set of RI strains is of particular interest in that, compared with the B6 progenitor, the A strain has a low number of target-binding cells (TBC) (Roder and Kiessling, 1978), and low endogenous and non-inducible NK cell activity (Kaminsky *et al.*, 1985), but expresses the H-2D^d haplotype previously associated with high NK cell activity in mice of B6 and B10 backgrounds (Clark *et al.*, 1979; Klein *et al.*, 1980; Klein, 1982).

The distribution of NK cell activity among 29 RI strains examined thus far is extremely heterogeneous, confirming that new combinations of the progenitor genes have been created. Statistical analysis revealed the existence of five NK cell phenotypic groups; a minimum of three loci are involved in the control of the NK cell activity in this system. Two B6-derived dominant genes are involved. The third gene, derived from the A progenitor, needs to be in a homozygous state and requires the presence of a B-derived gene(s) for its full expression (Lemieux *et al.*, manuscript in preparation). It remains to be established if the A-derived gene involved in our system is related to the H-2D^d-linked gene previously associated with the high NK phenotype. The effect of this gene was detected in both the homozygous and the heterozygous state (Harmon *et al.*, 1977; Clark *et al.*, 1979), whereas in our system, the effect of the A-derived gene is seen only in the homozygous state. Prototype H-2^a-matched RI strains, corresponding to each of the five phenotypes, have been selected to create a unique model for NK cell analysis. In a first series of experiments, we have demonstrated that the in vivo lung clearance of [^{111}In]-Ox-labelled YAC-1 cells correlates with the in vitro splenic NK cell activity levels of the selected RI strains. This observation illustrates the usefulness of our model for further in vivo studies concerning the involvement of NK cells in innate resistance to pathogens and tumours.

Compared with NK cell activity, murine natural cytotoxic (NC) cell activity also shows a variable strain distribution pattern (SDP) of high and low phenotypes in regard to the lysis of the Meth 113 sarcoma cell line (Stutman *et al.*, 1978). The testing of a large variety of inbred, congenic and recombinant strains, as well as F_1 hybrids of diverse combinations, led to the hypothesis that an A/AKR background gene and two other genes, respectively associated with the T1a and the Qa regions, were contributing to the control of NC cell activity levels. High NC cell activity required any combination of at least two of these three genes. As previously reported for the control of NK cell activity, gene complementation was noted in F_1 hybrids derived from some but not all strain combinations tested (Stutman and Cuttito, 1982). In our opinion, the hypothesis presented in this paper is not totally convincing for three reasons. First, in a later paper from the same laboratory, the Meth 113 cell line was shown to be both NK- and NC-susceptible, whereas both the Meth A and WEHI-164 cell lines were identified as the real NC prototype targets (Lattime *et al.*, 1983). Second, only small strain-dependent variations of natural cytotoxicity to Meth A target cells have been reported (Stutman *et al.*, 1978). Finally, the cells responsible for the natural cytotoxicity of WEHI-164 sarcoma cells have recently been shown to belong to a multilineage system (Bykowsky and Stutman, 1986). Thus, we consider that the genetic factors putatively involved in the control of NC cell activity need to be re-evaluated.

B. Modulation of NK Cell Activity by Mouse Mutations

At various steps along their differentiation pathway, NK cells or their precursors interact with other cell subsets or their secretory products. Few mutations are known which selectively act on NK cells themselves; however, several influence the non-NK cells involved in NK cell development and could, therefore, indirectly modulate NK cell activity. Given the pleiotropic effect of many mutations, the exact mechanism by which a particular mutation interferes with NK cell function often remains unknown, but a better understanding of the NK cell lineage has emerged from studies of mutant mouse strains. Only the modulation of lymphocyte-mediated natural killing by mutations impairing immunological functions will be discussed here. The effects of other mutations have been recently reviewed by Clark (1986).

1. Mutations affecting the development of the immune system

Most of the mutations responsible for immunodeficiencies affecting T cells, B cells, or their precursors have been tested for their effects on NK cell activity. Athymic nude mice (*nu/nu*) usually express higher NK cell activity than do heterozygous litter-mates, which behave like normal controls (Kiessling *et al.*, 1975b; Herberman *et al.*, 1975; Clark *et al.*, 1981a). Environmental conditions as well as genetic background determine the NK cell activity level reached in nude mice (Hanna *et al.*, 1982).

Roder and Kiessling (1978) have shown that the percentage of nylon wool non-adherent spleen cells binding to YAC-1 NK-susceptible target cells is identical in homozygous and heterozygous nude mice. Thus it is unlikely that the *nu* gene in mice influences the proliferation of NK cell precursors or the expression of the target recognition structures. On the other hand, in the rat, both NK cell activity and the number of large granular lymphocytes (LGLs) are enhanced in the presence of the nude mutation (*rnu*) (Reynolds *et al.*, 1982).

Various hypotheses can be invoked to explain the high NK cell activity in homozygous nude mice. As NK cell activity is increased following transfer of nude mice from barrier to conventional conditions (Minato *et al.*, 1980; Hanna *et al.*, 1982) and as they are more susceptible to viral infections, a virus-induced increase in serum IFN titre could be responsible for the NK cell activation. Absence of the suppressor T cells known to participate in NK cell regulation (Nair *et al.*, 1981; Zoller and Wigzell, 1982; Tarkkanen *et al.*, 1983) could also contribute to the high NK cell activity. Kaminsky *et al.* (1985) recently shed new light on this question by studying the NK cell activity of nude mice on the SJL background. SJL mice had previously been classified as being of low NK phenotype, because of their low endogenous NK cell activity and their unresponsiveness to IFN-inducers (Kaminsky *et al.*, 1983). SJL-*nu/nu* mice still have a low endogenous NK cell activity but they respond very well to poly I : C, whereas, SJL-*nu/+* litter-mates or normal controls do not. Similar differences were observed when spleen cells from SJL-*nu/nu* and SJL-*nu/+* mice were incubated in vitro with IFN-*β*. This suggests that the introduction of the *nu* gene into the SJL background is responsible for the conversion from IFN-unresponsiveness to responsiveness. Hyporesponsiveness to IFN-*γ* has recently been shown to be involved in the defective tumoricidal activity of A/J mouse macrophages (Hamilton *et al.*, 1986). Like SJL mice, A/J mice have a low, non-inducible NK phenotype (Kaminsky *et al.*, 1983); it would be interesting to know if the introduction of the *nu* gene into A/J mice would also correct their macrophage defect.

MRL/Mp–*lpr/lpr* mice develop a T cell lymphoproliferative disease associated with a lupus-like syndrome (Murphy and Roths, 1977). The NK cell activity of these mice was originally reported to be elevated compared to syngeneic controls (Clark *et al.*, 1981a). More recently, the effect of the homozygous *lpr* mutation on mice of three different backgrounds was explored (Pan *et al.*, 1986). Depressed NK cell activity accompanied the development of autoimmunity and coincided with the reduced production of IL-2 known to occur in autoimmune mice (Dauphinée *et al.*, 1981). Treatment of homozygous *lpr/lpr* mice with poly I : C restored NK cell activity and reduced the production of autologous plaque-forming cells to bromelin-treated mouse red blood cells. This inverse correlation supports the putative contribution of NK cells to the down-regulation of B cell function.[2] Also in agreement with this is the observation of high NK cell activity in CBA/N mice suffering from a sex-linked B cell defect (*Xid*) (Herberman *et al.*, 1975).

A reduced number of cortical thymocytes and perturbation of the histological structure of the thymus are observed in murine congenital muscular dystrophy (DeKretser and Livett, 1976; Karmali and Harrobin, 1976). Spleen cells from C57BL/6 dy^{2J}/dy^{2J} mice express a higher NK cell activity, associated with an increased number of target-binding cells (TBC) (Semple and Szewczuk, 1983). In young dystrophic mice, an increased sensitivity of thymocytes to NK-cell-mediated killing was also observed. Enhanced NK cell activity was later shown in lymph nodes and thymus, sites which are usually almost devoid of NK cell activity (Semple *et al.*, 1984). Of all the mouse mutations known to affect NK cell function, the dy^{2J} mutation is the only one which has an enhancing effect on NK cell number.

Depending on the exact location of the defect in the lymphocyte differentiation pathway, severe combined immunodeficiency diseases (SCID) in human patients are classified into 4 subgroups depending on the T and B cell function impairments (Chandra *et al.*, 1979). On account of the variable deficiency in NK cell activity of 8 SCID patients, Peter *et al.* (1983) have proposed an ontogenetic model in which NK cells are derived from a lineage different from T cells, B cells and monocytes. An animal model of human SCID became available following the emergence of a mutation affecting both T cell and B cell functions in C.B-17 mice (Bosma *et al.*, 1983). Since myeloid cells and myeloid progenitors are normal in C.B-17 SCID mice, the defect must interfere with early lymphoid differentiation (Dorshkind *et al.*, 1984). Homozygous C.B-17 SCID mice express endogenous and inducible NK cell activity (Dorshkind *et al.*, 1985) and have a normal frequency of transplantable NK progenitors (Hackett *et al.*, 1986). These observations give strong support to the concept that NK cells arise from an independent lineage. The exact site at which the SCID mutation acts in the mouse remains undefined, with the existence of a putative common early progenitor for T cells and NK cells not yet ruled out. This is, however, unlikely, as it was

[2]See also Chapter 26.

recently shown that enriched NK-2$^+$ cells from C.B-17 SCID mice do not rearrange or express T cell antigen receptor α, β and γ genes (Lauzon *et al.*, 1986). Similar observations concerning human and rat LGLs (Reynolds *et al.*, 1985; Young *et al.*, 1986), enriched CD3$^-$CD16$^+$ human NK cells (Lanier *et al.*, 1986a; Lanier *et al.*, 1986b) and enriched NK-1$^+$ mouse NK cells (Tutt *et al.*, 1986) have also been reported.

A normal frequency of transplantable bone marrow NK progenitors was also observed in W/W^v mutant mice, which have a defect in the generation of multipotent myeloid stem cells (CFU-S), and in Steel Dickie (Sl/Sl^d) mice, which possess a defective microenvironment for the development of CFU-S (Hackett *et al.*, 1985). This suggests that NK cell precursors are not CFU-S nor their immediate progeny. In an earlier study, the severe anaemias present in these two mutant strains were associated with deficient splenic NK cell activity (Clark *et al.*, 1981a).

The *me* (moth-eaten) gene is another mutation responsible for a severe immunodeficiency involving both T cell and B cell functions (Shultz *et al.*, 1978). The defect affects bone marrow cell progenitors as it can be adoptively transferred to normal recipients with these cells (Shultz *et al.*, 1978) or cured by transfer of normal bone-marrow cells to irradiated mutant mice (Shultz *et al.*, 1983a). The *me* mutation produces a marked depression of NK cell activity and of antibody-dependent cell-mediated cytotoxicity (ADCC) against tumour target cells (Clark *et al.*, 1981a). Moreover, *me/me* mice are more susceptible to tumour growth than are *me/+* littermate controls (Shultz *et al.*, 1983b).

Impaired development of NK cell activity in 4–5 week old unweaned CBA and Gruneberg congenitally osteopetrotic mice was also reported (Seaman *et al.*, 1979). These mice carry the *mi/mi* (microphthalmia) mutation responsible for at least 50 per cent replacement of the marrow by bone. This NK cell defect is, however, non-selective, as osteopetrotic mice and rats are also deficient in their responses to T and B cell mitogens (Milhaud *et al.*, 1977; Olsen *et al.*, 1978).

2. The beige mouse as a model for NK deficiency[3]

The identification of severe NK cell deficiency in the beige (*bg/bg*) mutant mouse was an important turning point in the history of NK cells (Roder, 1979; Roder and Duwe, 1979; Roder *et al.*, 1979). The deficiency of beige mouse cytotoxic cells in the lysis of antibody-coated or untreated tumour cells was first reported to be restricted to NK cells, as macrophage, granulocyte and T cell-mediated cytotoxicities are all normal

---

[3]See also Chapters 3 and 25.

(Roder and Duwe, 1979). Beige mice are also not deficient in NC activity (Stutman and Cuttito, 1981) but they are unable to generate lymphokine-activated killer (LAK) cells (Merluzzi *et al.*, 1986a). The frequency of target-binding cells (TBCs) in homozygous and heterozygous litter-mates is identical to that observed in normal controls of the same background, so the defect is suspected to involve the activation and/or regulation of the lytic phase (Roder and Duwe, 1979). As the NK cell defect of the beige mouse is transferable to bone-marrow chimeras, it is considered to be a predetermined stem-cell defect (Roder, 1979). In agreement with this observation, Kärre *et al.* (1983) reported a significantly higher tumour incidence in beige mice inoculated with NK-susceptible leu-kaemic cells and demonstrated that, in lethally irradiated mice reconsti-tuted with bone-marrow cells from either *bg/bg* or *bg/+* donors, susceptibility to tumour take was of the donor type. In confirmation of the selectivity of the NK cell defect, the in vivo cytotoxic T cell response to allogeneic tumour cells, skin graft rejection, as well as in vitro T cell proliferation in mixed lymphocyte cultures or mitogen-stimulated cul-tures were all shown to be normal in beige mice (Roder *et al.*, 1979). However, subsequent reports from other laboratories have demonstrated that, under certain circumstances, homozygous beige mice show a defect in the generation of cytotoxic T cells in response to primary or secondary challenge with allogeneic cells (Saxena *et al.*, 1982) and the capacity of their macrophages to acquire cytostatic or cytotoxic competence is delayed (Mahoney *et al.*, 1980). A reduced B cell response of NK-deficient beige mice to LPS mitogen has also been reported (Clark *et al.*, 1982; Fodstad *et al.*, 1984a). This is in contrast with the increased number of cells with surface immunoglobulin (sIg) and the higher response to B cell mitogens observed in mice deprived of NK cell activity by inoculation of anti-asialo GM1 alloantibodies (Suzuki *et al.*, 1986). Considering the contradictory results obtained in various laboratories, and despite the usefulness of the beige mutation in characterisation of the in vivo role of NK cells, great care must be taken in interpreting the data collected from this animal model.

C57BL/6 beige mice have a reduced capacity to resist low doses of both a virally and a chemically induced syngeneic leukaemia (Kärre *et al.*, 1980a). A faster growth rate and an increased metastatic spread of NK-susceptible melanoma cell lines has also been reported in beige mice compared with normal controls (Talmage *et al.*, 1980; Hanna and Fidler, 1981; Gorelik *et al.*, 1982). The lung clearance of radiolabelled YAC-1 cells inoculated i.v. was markedly reduced in beige mice, but to a lesser extent than in nude mice treated with anti-asialo GM1 antibodies (Gorelik *et al.*, 1982). Over a period of 2 to 2.5 years, the incidence of death due to spontaneous lymphomas was slightly higher in C57BL/6 *bg/bg* mice than in the *bg/*+ controls (Haliotis *et al.*, 1985). Both higher frequencies of primary tumours and shorter latency periods for appearance of the tumours were reported following the injection of homozygous beige mice with benzo(alpha)pyrene (Haliotis *et al.*, 1985), but no differences between *bg/bg* and *bg/*+ mice were observed with regard to resistance to many other oncogenic treatments (Salomon *et al.*, 1980; Kärre *et al.*, 1982; Haliotis *et al.*, 1985). In addition, beige mice are as susceptible as heterozygous litter-mates to the oncogenic action of the Moloney sarcoma virus (MSV) (Kärre *et al.*, 1982) and they are more susceptible than normal (+/+) syngeneic controls to MuLV-induced tumorigenesis (Truesdale *et al.*, 1982).

Mice of different genetic backgrounds homozygous for the *bg* gene have lower resistance to allogeneic and xenogeneic bone-marrow grafts (Kaminsky and Cudkowicz, 1980). On the C57BL/6 background, homozygosity at the beige locus reduced but did not abrogate the short-term growth of allogeneic bone-marrow cells; on the other hand, long-term resistance to systemic erythropoietic repopulation was totally eliminated when the bone-marrow cells were inoculated into lethally irradiated beige mutant mice (Harrison and Carlson, 1983).

The presence of the beige gene in SB/Le mice reduces the mortality of male mice due to the spontaneous autoimmune disease of this strain (Clark *et al.*, 1982). Fewer immune-complex deposits and autoantibodies are detected in young SB/Le male mice carrying the beige gene, suggesting that NK cells are involved in the regulation of B cell functions. This concept is now supported by many other observations (Robles and Pollack, 1986).[4]

NK cells participate in the innate resistance against some infectious diseases (reviewed by Fitzgerald and Lopez, 1986; Welsh, 1986). The beige mouse model has been extremely useful in demonstrating that, although viral glycoproteins or virus-induced IFN stimulate NK cell activity, this stimulation does not necessarily contribute to the resistance to the virus. As an example, lymphocytic choriomeningitis virus (LCMV) stimulates NK cell activity to a lesser extent in beige mice than in the heterologous controls, but in spite of the differences in both endogenous and activated NK cell activities, identical virus titres can be detected in LCMV-infected *bg/bg* and *bg/*+ mice (Welsh and Kiessling, 1980).

Studies of the experimental infection of beige mice with murine cytomegalovirus (MCMV) provide probably the strongest support of the contribution of NK cells in resistance to viruses. Compared to *bg/*+

[4]See also Chapter 26.

controls, *bg/bg* mice are more susceptible to MCMV infection and this susceptibility is transferable by *bg/bg* bone-marrow cells (Shellam *et al.*, 1981). The low resistance of the beige mouse to MCMV infection also depends on the genetic background of the mouse (Shellam *et al.*, 1985) and on the route of inoculation of the virus (Bukowski *et al.*, 1984). NK cells in the lung do not seem to contribute to resistance to intranasally inoculated MCMV (Bukowski *et al.*, 1984). Beige mice are not totally devoid of NK cell activity, as significant NK lysis is usually detected after virus infection (Brunda *et al.*, 1980; Welsh and Kiessling, 1980; McKinnon *et al.*, 1981). Moreover, activated NK cells are more efficient than endogenous NK cells in lysing virus-infected target cells. This is supported by experiments in nude mice in which the reduced tumorigenicity of HeLa and BHK cells persistently infected with measles, mumps, influenza, vesicular stomatitis or rabies viruses has been attributed to the high level of naturally activated NK cells in these immunodeficient mice (Minato *et al.*, 1980).

The beige mouse model has also been helpful in identifying the role of NK cells in resistance to parasites and fungi. For example, beige mice are more susceptible than their heterozygous litter-mates to infection with *Leishmania donovani* (Kirkpatrick and Farrell, 1982) and *Cryptococcus neoformans* (Marquis *et al.*, 1985; Hidore and Murphy, 1986). Conversely, contradictory results concerning the level of parasitaemia reached in *bg/bg* and *bg/+* mice infected with *Babesia microti* have been reported (Ruebush and Burgess, 1982; Wood and Clark, 1982). In our hands, C57BL/6 beige mice were not more susceptible than heterozygous litter-mates or normal controls to infection with *Plasmodium chabaudi* at a dose lethal for susceptible A/J mice (Skamene *et al.*, 1983). This indicates that, if NK cells are in any way involved in malaria infection by controlling the level of early parasitaemia, as suggested by Eugui and Allison (1980), their action is not a determinant of the final outcome of the disease.

3. Multi-mutant Strains

Various laboratories have been interested in studying the effect of the beige gene in combination with other genes controlling immunodeficiencies. Several double mutant strains and a triple one have been created by diverse breeding methods. The first double mutant mouse was produced by crossing C57BL/6 *bg/bg* mice with *nu/nu* mice of different genotypes (Kärre *et al.*, 1980b; Clark *et al.*, 1981a; Fodstad *et al.*, 1984a; Fodstad *et al.*, 1984b; Hoki *et al.*, 1987). In all cases, the in vitro NK cell activity of the *bg/bg–nu/nu* double mutant mice was only slightly higher than in the beige homozygous control. Equal numbers of TBCs were observed in beige, nude, beige–nude and normal mice of the appropriate genetic backgrounds (Clark *et al.*, 1981a). The percentage of asialo GM1-positive cells was also the same in these four strains (Hoki *et al.*, 1987). Surprisingly, no differences in tumour cell rejection and metastatic spread were detected when adult nude (high NK), young nude (immature NK) and beige–nude (deficient NK) mice were compared in a single study (Fodstad *et al.*, 1984b). Compared with the nude progenitor, beige–nude mice also have a reduced capacity to generate lymphokine-activated killer (LAK) cells (Andriole *et al.*, 1985).

As observed with the introduction of the beige gene into mice carrying the NK-enhancing nude mutation, the construction of a *bg/bg–dy^{dJ}/dy^{dJ}* double mutant strain resulted in low splenic NK cell activity (Semple and Szewczuk, 1986). Unfortunately, the relative number of TBCs in these mice compared with normal, beige, and dystrophic control mice has not yet been tested. A synergistic effect in the depression of NK cell activity was reported in mice simultaneously carrying the beige and the satin genes in the homozygous state (McGarry *et al.*, 1984).

Another double mutant was constructed by the association of the beige gene with the *Xid* mutation. These *bg/bg–Xid/Xid* double mutant mice have a low NK phenotype but are capable of generating LAK cells (Andriole *et al.*, 1985). This observation is in agreement with the fact that, on the basis of their cell-surface phenotype and target-cell specificity (Rosenstein *et al.*, 1984; Merluzzi, 1985; Merluzzi *et al.*, 1986a) as well as on the properties of the bone-marrow precursors required for their generation (Ballas, 1986; Merluzzi *et al.*, 1986a; Merluzzi *et al.*, 1986b), at least some of the LAK cells are distinct from both NK and NC cells. Through a complex breeding plan, three mutations were then associated together in a triple homozygous (*bg/bg–nu/nu–Xid/Xid*) mutant strain which was theoretically expected to be deficient in NK, T and B cell functions. Surprisingly, although a total abrogation in the generation of LAK cells was observed, the level of endogenous NK cell activity was normal. This genetic study is a beautiful illustration of the complex cellular interactions governing the regulation of cells mediating natural cytotoxic functions. Given the results obtained with the triple mutant mice, it would be interesting to associate the beige and the SCID mutations.

IV. GENETIC CONTROL OF MACROPHAGE RESPONSES TO INFECTION AND MALIGNANCY

Macrophage-mediated defence against tumour growth and infectious disease represents a cascade of events involving both differentiation within the mononuclear cell lineage and modulation by numerous host-derived cytokines. Genes may influence or control any number of steps in this cascade. Severe defects in macrophage responses are likely to be incompatible with the survival of the host, mainly because of the role of this cell in antimicrobial defenses. However, more subtle qualitative or quantitative differences in macrophage responses to infection and to tumour cells have often been observed among individuals of a given species and have been found to be the result of genetic variation.

The overall function of the macrophage defence system may be considered as a sequence of processes which must proceed in a stepwise fashion so that the demands of infections and tumours on the host can be met:

1. Production of adequate numbers of macrophage precursors in the bone marrow;
2. Recruitment and delivery of macrophage precursors to the blood;
3. Margination and emigration of macrophages into tissues and immobilisation of macrophages within infectious foci and growing tumours;
4. Establishment of contact between macrophages and target cells; and
5. Microbicidal and tumoricidal activity.

Each of these steps represents unique cellular mechanisms which are regulated by distinct gene products. The genetic control of macrophage responses is therefore best considered as an interplay of genetically determined events at each of these steps.

A. Genetic Control of Monocytopoiesis

The relationship between genetic variation in the proliferative potential of mononuclear phagocyte precursors and host responses to infection or neoplasia is poorly defined. Genetic variation among inbred strains of mice has been demonstrated at each of several distinct stages of mononuclear phagocyte development beginning with the proliferation of the multipotential stem cell (Russell and Bernstein, 1968; Suzuki and Axelrad, 1980; van Zant et al., 1983). In vitro assay of granulocyte-macrophage colony-forming cells (CFC-GM), the earliest step of myelo-monocytopoiesis, has been found to vary quantitatively among inbred mouse strains, with the C57BL-derived strains exhibiting high bone-marrow responsiveness to colony-stimulating factors(CSF) (McNeill and Fleming, 1973; Metcalf and Russell, 1976). Similarly, the longevity of myelopoiesis in vitro (that is, the duration of generation of CFC-GM formation) varies markedly with the mouse strain used, suggesting that the genetic regulation of CFC-GM formation is expressed as an intrinsic property of the precursor cells itself (Sakakeeny and Greenberger, 1982).

Genetically determined differences in monocytopoiesis have been related to variations in host response to infection in two models, namely, resistance to *Salmonella typhimurium* and *Listeria monocytogenes*. In examining the responses of colony-forming cells in vitro in the bone marrow of *Salmonella*-resistant CBA and susceptible C57BL mice, Wilson *et al.* (1982) demonstrated that the resistant strain responded within hours after infection with increased numbers of CFC-GMs. Increased macrophage production was evident for the first 2–3 days after infection. In contrast, susceptible mice exhibited a slowly increasing response which never exceeded 1.2 times normal and eventually fell to less than normal by 2–3 days after infection.

Infection with *Listeria*, another facultative, intracellular bacterium, also results in differences in monocytopoiesis at both the cellular and humoral levels. During the course of listeriosis, changes in the number of colony-forming cells and increases in the level of serum CSF have been described (Wing *et al.*, 1984; Young and Cheers, 1986). A transient increase in CSF was apparent in both resistant C57BL-derived and susceptible BALB/c mice following *Listeria* infection, so the ability to produce CSF is apparently not related to resistance to *Listeria* (Young and Cheers, 1986). In this study, resistant C57BL mice were found to have a larger and more responsive population of colony-forming cells or CFC-GMs than either susceptible BALB/c or CBA mice.

Superior monocytopoiesis in response to infection thus appears to be related to the infecting organism and the level of the genetically determined host response to that organism. The in vitro colony-forming potential of macrophage precursors in the bone marrow of tumour-bearing mice is altered during the course of tumorigenesis (Baum and Fisher, 1972; Otu *et al.*, 1970; Balducci and Hardy, 1983). This is also likely to be dependent on the genetic background of the host as well as the origin and type of tumour (e.g., spontaneous or chemically or virally induced).

B. Genetic Control of Peripheral Blood Monocytosis

If an infectious focus or the site of tumour development is considered as an inflammatory focus, monocytosis would be a likely consequence due to the same sequence of events as occurs following the induction of inflammation by a non-specific phlogistic agent. For example, inflammation induced in the peritoneal cavity by injection of a non-specific, sterile stimulus (e.g., thioglycollate, proteose peptone or foetal calf serum) or of sterile particulate material (e.g., latex beads) is characterised by the accumulation of young, recently blood-derived macrophages. This response is accompanied by monocytosis in the peripheral blood as a result of increased bone-marrow production of mononuclear phagocytes in response to a soluble factor — FIM or factor increasing monocytopoiesis — produced by macrophages at the site of inflammation (Sluiter *et al.*, 1982; van Furth and Sluiter, 1985). It is quite likely that monocytosis during tumour development (Braun and Harris, 1981; Wood *et al.*, 1979; Normann *et al.*, 1981) and infectious episodes is due to a bone marrow stimulatory factor which is either FIM or a similar molecule produced by the growing tumour or pathogenic organism.

Genetic variation among inbred strains of mice in monocytosis in response to non-specific inflammatory stimuli and during infection has been described. For example, Sluiter and his colleagues (1984) described genetic variation in the response of monocyte precursors to a standard source of FIM in mice given various inflammatory stimuli. In contrast, no genetic restriction in the production of FIM was evident.

A correlation between genetic variation of monocytosis in inbred mice and the outcome of *Listeria* infection has been observed (Punjabi *et al.*, 1984). *Listeria*-resistant C57BL-derived B10.A strain mice responded to infection or to the injection of a *Listeria* cell-wall extract with a rapid decrease of promonocyte generation time, whereas there was no such shortening in susceptible mice (strain A/J). It is not known if the genes regulating the monocyte response to FIM and to components of *Listeria* are genetically linked. Likewise, it is not known if the gene(s) described as controlling monocytosis during acute inflammation and infection also regulate the response to tumours.

C. Genetic Control of Macrophage Inflammatory Responses

The level of macrophage accumulation in inflammatory foci has been found to be genetically controlled in inbred mice (Stevenson *et al.*, 1981). Variations in the level of this response were initially described because of linkage of the level of the macrophage response with the trait of resistance to infection with Listeria. *Listeria*-resistant mouse strains (C57BL-derived strains, SJL) were found to have effective accumulation of macrophages in the peritoneal cavity and in subcutaneous sites in response to non-specific inflammatory agents and *Listeria* (Stevenson *et al.*, 1981; Kongshavn, 1986). In contrast, *Listeria*-susceptible mouse strains (BALB/c, CBA, DBA/2, DBA/1 and A/J) have a defective response which results in a 2–3 fold lower number of macrophages at the inflammatory or infective foci. In the case of the A/J mice, susceptibility to *Listeria* and the defective macrophage response have been found to be due to C5 deficiency, controlled by the Hc locus on mouse chromosome 2 (Gervais *et al.*, 1984).

The existence of an alternative and, as yet, undefined genetic mechanism, which would also control the inflammatory responsiveness of macrophages, has been postulated on the basis of defective responses in some C5 sufficient strains, such as BALB/c and CBA. Genetic analysis of the BALB/c defect using the CXB series of recombinant inbred strains (C = BALB/c; B = C57BL/6) suggests that an allelic difference at a single locus is responsible for the deficiency of macrophage accumulation in BALB/c mice (Kongshavn and Anthony, 1985).

The observation of the presence of macrophages at the site of progressing tumours has led to the development of the concept that macrophages play a major role in surveillance against neoplastic cells (Eccles and Alexander, 1974). Further studies have revealed that macrophage accumulation at the site of a growing tumour is not dependent on the presence of an intact immune system, that is, it occurs in T cell or B cell deficient mice (Szymaneic and James, 1976; Evans and Eidlen, 1981); nor does it require the C5 component of complement, that is, macrophage accumulation in tumours occurs equally well in C5-sufficient and C5-deficient mice (Evans, 1980). For a host to accumulate macrophages effectively at the site of a growing tumour an intact bone marrow is required (Kaizer and Lala, 1977; Evans and Eidlen, 1981; Acero *et al.*, 1984). By analogy with inflammation and infection, genetic control of macrophage accumulation in growing tumours seems likely. Observations of genetic differences in responsiveness of bone-marrow precursors to stimulatory signals, such as CSF or FIM, suggest the likelihood of genetic control of a response which is so dependent on a functional bone marrow compartment of mononuclear phagocytes.

The macrophage response to chemoattractants in vitro is also genetically controlled (Stevenson *et al.*, 1981; Stevenson *et al.*, 1985; Stevenson *et al.*, 1986). Recombinant inbred strain analysis using the AXB series (A = A/J, low responder; B = C57BL/6, high responder) revealed, furthermore, that the level of host macrophage response to chemoattractants in vitro was correlated with the level of their accumulation in vivo and their response in the leukocyte adherence inhibition assay (LAI) in vitro (Thomson *et al.*, 1985).

D. Genetic Modulation of Macrophage Ia Expression and of Antigen Presentation

Expression of Ia antigen on the membranes of macrophages controls the initiation and level of host immune responses to both infection and tumours (Unanue, 1984; Unanue *et al.*, 1984). For example, exposure to infectious agents leads to an increase in the percentages of macrophages expressing Ia antigens. The kinetics of the influx of Ia$^+$ macrophages, moreover, have been found to correlate with the development of acquired resistance to infection. Macrophage Ia antigen expression is finely regulated, as demonstrated by Unanue, Beller and their colleagues (Beller and Ho, 1982; Unanue, 1984; Unanue *et al.*, 1984). They found that in in vitro cultures, young, recently blood-derived macrophages expressed Ia antigens in the presence of IFN-γ. Ia antigen expression was found to be transient in nature; synthesis of this protein was terminated within two days of in vitro culture (Beller and Unanue, 1981). It has, however, been demonstrated that infection of mice of different inbred strains with *Mycobacterium bovis* strain BCG induced continuous Ia expression in those strains which are genetically resistant to this pathogen (Zwilling *et al.*, 1985). Whether this phenomenon has a cause and effect relationship with the trait of natural resistance/susceptibility to BCG is now under investigation.

E. Genetic Control of Macrophage Adhesion to Targets

A family of human leukocyte antigens (Mac-1, LFA-1) that share certain structural and functional characteristics has been recently described (Anderson and Springer, 1985). These glycoprotein antigens exist on the cell surface as non-covalently linked heterodimers composed of different α subunits associated with a common β subunit. The α subunits have been characterised with specific monoclonal antibodies and have been designated as αL, αM, and αX. These antigens are expressed on different populations of leukocytes and are important in mediating effector functions related to cell contact. The αL molecule (with common β subunit) is present on T lymphocytes, monocytes and polymorpho-nuclear leukocytes (PMNs) and has been shown to mediate the adhesive interaction responsible for cytolytic T lymphocyte killing. The αM subunit (with the common β subunit) is present on monocytes, PMNs and natural killer cells; it has been shown to mediate adherence to C3bi-coated particles and appears to be closely associated with, if not identical to, the human C3bi receptor (CR3). The function of the αX subunit remains unknown. These glycoproteins share considerable amino acid sequence homology and may have arisen from gene duplication.

The importance of this antigenic family in regulating normal cell physiology is underscored by the devastating consequences of their genetically determined absence. Children with this deficiency experience recurrent bacterial infections from birth, a defect related to abnormalities in PMN adherence and in PMN ingestion of particles coated with

C3bi. Investigations of PMNs, monocytes and lymphocytes from affected children have been important in delineating the role of these antigens in cellular physiology (Springer *et al.*, 1984).

F. Genetic Control of Monokine Release

Genetically determined variations among inbred mouse strains in the ability to produce, and/or the level of production, of a wide variety of monokines have been demonstrated. In several instances, the level of host response to infection or tumour induction correlated with the level of monokine release.

Differences among inbred strains of mice in the ability to produce interleukin 1 (IL-1), a soluble immunoregulatory peptide produced by macrophages in response to immune or inflammatory stimuli (Dinarello, 1984), were initially described by Mortensen and his colleagues (Mortensen *et al.*, 1983). The observation was confirmed and extended by Brandwein *et al.* (1987) using the AXB/BXA recombinant inbred strains derived from high responder C57BL/6 and low responder A/J progenitor mice. They showed that production of IL-1 in response to lipopolysaccharide (LPS) is genetically controlled by multiple genes. The major gene appears to control the production of IL-1 and to be located on chromosome 1. The additional gene or genes appear to control the magnitude of the response.

In other studies peritoneal macrophages from C3HeB/Fe mice released IL-1 in response to LPS but not muramyl dipeptide (MDP) while macrophages from C57BL/6J mice produced IL-1 in response to both LPS and MDP (Abehsira *et al.*, 1985). Thus, the issue of the dependence of genetic control of IL-1 production on the identity of the stimulus needs to be addressed. That production of IL-1, regardless of the stimulus, is a complex process requiring at least two genes, is evident from a recent study showing multigenic control of IL-1 production in the mouse at the molecular level (Gray *et al.*, 1986).

Production of another monokine, procoagulant activity or PCA, is also under genetic control (Dindzans *et al.*, 1986). PCA production is regulated by T cell products and the molecule is detected by its prothrombin-cleaving activity (Levy *et al.*, 1981; Dindzans *et al.*, 1985). Susceptibility of inbred mice to mouse hepatitis virus, strain 3, (MHV-3) was found to correlate with the level of spontaneous expression of PCA activity (Levy *et al.*, 1981; Dindzans *et al.*, 1985). By recombinant inbred strain analysis, inheritance of the two traits, resistance or susceptibility to MHV-3 and the level of PCA activity, was found to be identical and to be genetically determined by two recessive, non-H-2-linked genes (Dindzans *et al.*, 1986).

The release of several other macrophage-derived soluble mediators which are related to host antitumour and antimicrobial mechanisms also varies among inbred mice. These mediators include tumour necrosis factor (TNFα) or cachectin, reactive oxygen intermediates, arachidonic acid metabolites and, as will be discussed in the next section, a neutral protease cytolytic factor (CF).

TNFα (Carswell *et al.*, 1975), which has recently been shown to be identical to cachectin (Beutler and Cerami, 1986), is produced by macrophages in vivo or in vitro following priming with a stimulus, such as infection with BCG or *Corynebacterium parvum*, followed by exposure to bacterial endotoxin (LPS). When BCG is used as the priming signal, differences in the production of TNF are apparent among inbred strains: C57BL/6, SJL and AKR produce TNF while A/J mice do not (Carswell *et al.*, 1975). This strain difference was apparent only when BCG was used; all of the strains produced TNF when *C. parvum* was used. In a later study by Mannel and her colleagues (Mannel *et al.*, 1980), it was demonstrated that C3H/HeJ mice were also unable to produce TNF in response to BCG followed by LPS. A similar finding was demonstrated by Beutler and his colleagues (Beutler *et al.*, 1986a; Beutler *et al.*, 1986b). These investigators found that although there was no production of cachectin (TNF) in vivo, macrophages from C3H/HeJ mice produced the molecule in vitro following incubation with IFN-γ and LPS. As is evident here with production of TNF (cachectin) and in the studies examining differences among inbred strains in IL-1 production, the identity of the stimulating agent is critical in determining genetic regulation.

TNFα (cachectin) also exerts an inhibitory effect on parasite multiplication in vivo and a cytotoxic effect in vitro on a variety of intra- and extra-cellular parasites, including human and murine *Plasmodium* species (Clark *et al.*, 1981b; Taverne *et al.*, 1981; Haidaris *et al.*, 1983), *Trypanosoma cruzi* (De Titto *et al.*, 1986), *T. musculi* (Kongshavn and Ghadirian, 1988) and *Entamoeba histolytica* (Ghadirian *et al.*, 1987). The relationship between a host's ability to produce TNFα and resistance to either infection or tumour development is not yet defined.

The release from macrophages of reactive oxygen intermediates (H_2O_2 and O_2^-) whose antitumour and antimicrobial effects are well documented in the literature, and of metabolites of arachidonic acid has also been studied in different inbred strains of mice. The discrepancy in the results of some of these studies may be attributed to the use of peritoneal macrophages elicited by various agents and induction of mediator release by various inducers.

Lewis and Adams (1986) studied the release of H_2O_2 and O_2^- and metabolites of arachidonic acid by casein-elicited peritoneal macrophages from SENCAR and C57BL/6 mice following exposure to phorbol esters. SENCAR mice have been bred for their sensitivity to the promotion of skin tumours by a tumour-promoting agent (TPA) following initiation with a chemical carcinogen while C57BL/6 mice are almost totally resistant to promotion of skin tumours by TPA (Reiners *et al.*, 1984). Macrophages from SENCAR mice were found to be more sensitive to phorbol ester exposure and to produce significantly more H_2O_2 and metabolites of arachidonic acid than macrophages from C57BL/6 mice. Release of the two groups of mediators was similar when macrophages from the two mouse strains were stimulated with zymosan. These investigators concluded that the enhanced response to phorbol ester of inflammatory cells or macrophages from SENCAR mice correlated with the enhanced sensitivity of the strain to tumour promotion by phorbol ester. This conclusion can only be confirmed by backcross studies showing linkage of the two traits.

In contrast to the results obtained by Lewis and Adams in their studies, Boraschi *et al.* (1983) found that saline-induced macrophages from mice with known defects in macrophage-mediated non-specific tumour cytotoxicity produced normal levels of reactive oxygen intermediates and metabolites of arachidonic acid after exposure in vitro to macrophage-activating factors. In this study, opsonised zymosan was used to induce mediator production by macrophages. Comparison of the results of the studies by Lewis and Adams (1985) and Boraschi *et al.* (1983) again stresses the importance of the identity of the stimulus used to induce mediator production.

G. Genetic Control of Macrophage Activation for Destruction of Extracellular Targets

One of the most intensely studied areas of genetic control of macrophage antitumour and antimicrobial responses is destruction of these invaders by activated macrophages. Macrophages are able to destroy extracellular targets via two distinct mechanisms (Adams and Hamilton, 1984; Adams *et al.*, 1982; Adams and Nathan, 1983). In the presence of target-specific antibody, macrophages are able to lyse target cells by antibody-dependent cell-mediated cytotoxicity (ADCC), which occurs within a relatively short period of time (within hours). Normal macrophages and activated macrophages are both effective, the latter being more active. The second mechanism, non-specific macrophage-mediated cytotoxicity, involves activated macrophages, which are able to recognise and destroy tumour cells selectively. This process may be fast (hours) or slow (1–2 days), depending on the target cell.

Using mouse strains with genetically determined defects in the development of activated macrophages, Meltzer *et al.* (1982) studied the series of reactions required for the full expression of tumoricidal activity. The non-responder strains could be grouped into three categories (Boraschi and Meltzer, 1979a): (1) strains (C3H/HeJ, C57BL/10ScSn) having defective responses to the lipid A region of bacterial endotoxins, a defect which is controlled by the *Lps* gene on chromosome 4 (Ruco and Meltzer, 1978; Ruco *et al.*, 1978); (2) strains (A/J, A/HeJ, AL/N) derived from the A strain (Boraschi and Meltzer, 1979b, c); and (3) P/J strain mice (Boraschi and Meltzer, 1980b, c). Although the phenotypic expression of the defect in macrophage activation was found to be almost identical in all three groups of defective strains, the gene(s) controlling the expression of the defect in each strain appears to be unique (Boraschi and Meltzer, 1980a). In the case of A/J mice, the defect was found to be the inability of activated macrophages to bind to the tumour target cells. Activated macrophages from C3H/HeJ mice were found to be unable to produce a neutral serine protease, termed cytolytic factor or CF (Adams *et al.*, 1980, 1981). Both of these events, binding to tumour targets and release of CF, have been demonstrated to be necessary for completion of macrophage-mediated tumour cytotoxicity (Adams and Nathan, 1983). Further analysis of these two events suggested that binding to target cells is induced principally by lymphokines while secretion of CF is induced by LPS (Adams *et al.*, 1981; Adams *et al.*, 1982). Thus, the defect of C3H/HeJ mice is the inability of their macrophages to respond to LPS — not surprising, as they lack the receptor for LPS (Forni and Coutinho, 1978). In contrast, the defect of A/J mice appears to be the inability of their macrophages to respond to lymphokines. Recent studies have confirmed this possibility: macrophages from A/J mice have membrane receptors for IFN-γ but these macrophages do not undergo biochemical changes associated with activation by IFN-γ (Hamilton *et al.*, 1985; Hamilton *et al.*, 1986). The genetic defect of P/J mice is expressed as a defect not only in the response of macrophages to activating stimuli but also in the production of macrophage-activating lymphokines (Boraschi and Meltzer, 1980b, c).

It is now clear that the defects in the activation of macrophages from C3H/HeJ, A/J and P/J mice described in vivo and in vitro are manifest as alterations in host defence against both neoplasia and infectious diseases (numerous examples were described by Skamene *et al.*, 1980 and Skamene, 1985). For example, both A/J and P/J mice have a very high incidence of tumours after administration of carcinogens (Diwan and Meier, 1976; Malkinson *et al.*, 1985). Tumour-bearing C3H/HeJ mice have been found to be unresponsive to intralesional BCG treatment (Meltzer *et al.*, 1979). The capacity of C3H/HeJ, A/J and P/J mice to develop activated macrophages for the in vitro killing of extracellular targets (tumour cells and larvae of *Schistosoma mansoni*) was found to correlate with the development in vivo of concomitant immunity in schistosomiasis (James *et al.*, 1983). Linkage analysis showed that both macrophage tumoricidal and schistosomulicidal activities are genetically controlled by the same dominant, autosomal, non-H-2-linked gene (James *et al.*, 1983; Skamene *et al.*, 1984).

BCG-activated macrophages from C3H/HeJ and A/J mice do, however, have an augmented capacity to mediate ADCC against both erythroid and neoplastic targets, in spite of the defect in non-specific cytotoxicity (Koren *et al.*, 1981). It has been demonstrated that H_2O_2 released from activated macrophages is the mediator of ADCC (Adams *et al.*, 1982). Additional evidence that activated macrophages from C3H/HeJ, A/J and P/J are not defective in mediating ADCC and that the defect is restricted to non-specific macrophage-mediated cytotoxicity, is the finding that in vitro activation of these macrophages with lymphokines resulted in enhanced production of oxygen metabolites and metabolites of arachidonic acid, similar to that produced by macrophages from strains which exhibit normal development of tumour cytotoxicity (Boraschi *et al.*, 1983).

These findings demonstrate that ADCC and macrophage-mediated tumour cytotoxicity do not share the same genetic regulation and suggest that at least one mechanism will function in the absence of another.

In addition to macrophages of A/J mice being able to destroy tumour cells via ADCC, these animals are resistant to infection with a variety of micro-organisms, including BCG, *Salmonella typhimurium* and *Leishmania donovani* (Skamene *et al.*, 1982). This strain is also resistant to the development of certain inflammatory diseases, for example, secondary amyloidosis (Wolgethan and Carthcart, 1979). These findings of variations within a given inbred strain of mice stress the importance of the concept that there are multiple mechanisms of host antitumour and antimicrobial defence whose operations are dependent on the identity of the invading organism or the neoplastic target.

H. Genetic Control of Macrophage Activation for Destruction of Intracellular Pathogens

Functional analysis of the models of natural resistance to infections with intracellular pathogens controlled by the chromosome 1 locus *Ity-Lsh-Bcg* (Skamene *et al.*, 1982) led to the conclusion that the macrophage expresses the phenotype of genetic resistance or susceptibility. Macrophages explanted from the peritoneal cavity of normal, noninfected, genetically resistant (*Bcg^r*) donors were shown to be superior to macrophages from susceptible (*Bcg^s*) strains in their ability to interfere with the intracellular growth of BCG as detected by the assay of uracil incorporation into BCG (Stach *et al.*, 1984) or by the plating efficiency of the BCG micro-organisms released (Stokes *et al.*, 1985). Similar experiments using a temperature-sensitive mutant of *Salmonella* (Lissner *et al.*, 1983) or its wild type (van Dissel *et al.*, 1985) showed the identical pattern of genetic restriction as an intrinsic function of the resident (peritoneal) macrophage. Interaction of *Leishmania donovani* with macrophages in vitro (*Lsh* gene) also follows the same pattern except for the superior activity of liver macrophages compared with peritoneal macrophages (Crocker *et al.*, 1984). A most interesting observation on natural resistance to *L. donovani*, not made in the *Bcg* or *Ity* models, was reported. There was a definite 2–3 day time lag between the infection and the expression of the resistance in the macrophages either in vivo or in Kupffer cells in vitro. Furthermore, the resistance of *Lsh*^{r} congenic mice was selectively enhanced following pre-treatment with *S. typhimurium* LPS or with purified *L. donovani* membranes in vivo. These effects could not be demonstrated in *Lsh*^{s} congenic mice. A hypothesis has been advanced that the chromosome 1 *Lsh* (*Bcg, Ity*) gene regulated some form of T-cell-independent macrophage activation process (Crocker *et al.*, 1984).

Recent experiments clearly established that the accessory role of *Bcg*^{r} macrophages (compared with those of *Bcg*^{s} congenic counterparts) was superior in responses to alloantigens, to mitogens, and to bacterial antigens such as BCG, *Salmonella typhimurium*, *Brucella abortus* and *Listeria monocytogenes* (Denis *et al.*, 1986). These accessory functions are Ia-dependent and vary quantitatively with the density of Ia antigens on the macrophage surface. The up-regulation of Ia antigens being one of the markers of macrophage activation, the presence of other markers associated with that event was investigated. Among those examined was the downregulation of membrane ectoenzyme 5′nucleotidase and an enhanced respiratory burst in the macrophages. A functional corollary of macrophage activation, listericidal activity, was also examined. In all instances tested so far, the *Bcg*^{r} macrophages, when compared with their *Bcg*^{s} controls, showed a quantitatively enhanced ability to become activated by a variety of specific and non-specific stimuli.

Macrophage activation is a stepwise chain of events in which cells in different stages of maturation and/or differentiation become receptive to priming and activating signals to acquire cytotoxic effector responses. In its simplified form, the cascade involves the stimulation of responsive macrophages into the primed state by molecules such as IFN-γ. Primed macrophages are then able to respond to a variety of membrane stimuli, among them LPS and other components of bacterial cell walls, to become activated for microbicidal function. According to this concept and based on our results and those of others, the difference between the genetically resistant and susceptible macrophages may be thought of as follows.

The resistant macrophage is at a more advanced level in the activation sequence; it seems to have many characteristics of a *primed* cell. The phagocytosis of a pathogen or an interaction with other activating stimuli leads to membrane perturbation and to a cascade of events which are characteristic of activated macrophages: upregulation of Ia, downregulation of 5'nucleotidase, increased oxidative burst and enhanced nonspecific bactericidal activity. These processes should only be considered *markers* of the activated state of the macrophage — it is not implied that any one of these particular markers is actually the expression of the resistant phenotype at a molecular level.

The susceptible macrophage, on the other hand, is quantitatively lower in the cascade of macrophage activation; it appears to be in the responsive, but not yet primed, state. The phagocytosis of an intracellular pathogen does not lead to the full activation of the susceptible macrophage — the stage of priming in that cell has not yet been achieved under natural conditions. The susceptible macrophage does, however, have the capacity to develop into a fully activated cell when exposed to such priming stimuli as, for example, T-cell-derived lymphokines in the course of acquired immunity. The genetically susceptible mice are able to control the bacterial load later on in the course of natural infection, in its immune phase, through the process of T-cell-dependent macrophage activation. It seems that the resistant macrophage can respond very early on in the course of infection, by activation to the phagocytic BCG stimulus without the need for priming by the specifically sensitised T cell.

V. CONCLUSION

There are two major aspects of studies dealing with the genetic control of natural resistance which were discussed in this chapter.

The first one takes advantage of the observed variation in the given trait of natural resistance in vivo or its equivalent in vitro to define the mode of inheritance, to map the responsible genes where possible and to uncover the often pleiotropic effect of such genes. Such studies are descriptive in nature and, at the moment, are largely self-limiting. They hold, however, great promise for the future when the genes can be isolated and the gene products identified. Besides that, DNA polymorphisms may be employed for typing the linked genes of resistance.

The other, currently more important, approach to genetic studies in natural resistance is to use the genetic analysis not as the ultimate aim, but as a tool. Such a strategy can be used to prove formally, by linkage analysis, the cause-and-effect relationships of various traits of innate resistance in vivo with the postulated cellular or molecular mechanisms studied in vitro. Both aspects of the genetic analysis of natural resistance will certainly continue their rapid growth.

The identification of the genes or closely linked polymorphisms should enable us to determine the genetically susceptible individuals, first in the defined strains of animals or in human families and later in the general population. Knowledge of the genetically controlled mechanisms at the cellular and molecular level should allow us to selectively target our knowledge of early detection, prevention and institution of remedial measures of defects in natural resistance.

REFERENCES

Abehsira, A. O., Demais, C., Parent, M. and Chedid, L. (1985). *J. Immunol.* 134: 365.

Acero, R., Polentarutti, N., Bottazzi, B., Alberti, S., Ricci, M. R., Bizzi, A. and Mantovani, A. (1984). *Int. J. Cancer* 33: 95.

Adams, D. O. and Hamilton, T. A. (1984). *Ann. Rev. Immunol.* 2: 283.

Adams, D. O. and Nathan, C. F. (1983). *Immunology Today* 4: 166.

Adams, D. O., Johnson, W. J. and Marino, P. A. (1982). *Fed. Proc.* 41: 2212.

Adams, D. O., Kao, K. J., Farb, R. and Pizzo, S. V. (1980). *J. Immunol.* 124: 293.

Adams, D. O., Marino, P. A. and Meltzer, M. S. (1981). *J. Immunol.* 126: 1843.

Afifi, M. S., Kumar, V. and Bennett, M. (1985). *J. Immunol.* 134: 3739.

Ährlund-Richter, L., Klein, G. and Klein, E. (1983). *Immunogenetics* 18: 221.

Ährlund-Richter, L., Nordstedt, C., Klein, G. and Klein, E. (1985). *Immunogenetics* 22: 517.

Altman, J., Bardos, P., Van der Gaag, R. and Carnaud, C. (1983). *Scand. J. Immunol.* 17: 455.

Anderson, D. C. and Springer, T. A. (1985). *Prog. Leukocyte Biol.* 3: 611.

Andriole, G. L., Mulé, J. J., Hansen, C. T., Linehan, W. M. and Rosenberg, S. A. (1985). *J. Immunol.* 135: 2911.

Balducci, L. and Hardy, C. (1983). *Cancer Res.* 43: 4643.

Ballas, Z. K. (1986). *J. Immunol.* 137: 2380.

Baum, M. and Fisher, B. (1972). *Cancer Res.* 32: 2813.

Beller, D. I. and Ho, K. (1982). *J. Immunol.* 129: 971.

Beller, D. I. and Unanue, E. R. (1981). *J. Immunol.* 128: 163.

Beutler, B. and Cerami, A. (1986). *Nature* 320: 584.

Beutler, B., Krochin, N., Milsark, I. W., Luedke, C. and Cerami, A. (1986a). *Science* 232: 977.

Beutler, B., Tkacenko, V., Milsark, I., Krochin, N. and Cerami, A. (1986b). *J. Exp. Med.* 164: 1791.

Blackwell, J. M. (1983). *J. Trop. Med. Hyg.* 86: 17.

Blair, P. (1980). In R. B. Herberman (ed.), *Natural Cell-Mediated Immunity Against Tumors.* New York: Academic Press: 401–8.

Boraschi, D. and Meltzer, M. S. (1979a). *Cell. Immunol.* 45: 188.

Boraschi, D. and Meltzer, M. S. (1979b). *J. Immunol.* 122: 1587.

Boraschi, D. and Meltzer, M. S. (1979c). *J. Immunol.* 122: 1979.

Boraschi, D. and Meltzer, M. S. (1980a). *J. Immunol.* 124: 1050.

Boraschi, D. and Meltzer, M. S. (1980b). *J. Immunol.* 125: 771.

Boraschi, D. and Meltzer, M. S. (1980c). *J. Immunol.* 125: 777.

Boraschi, D., Pasqualetto, E., Ghezzi, P., Salmon, M., Bartalini, M., Barbarulli, G., Censini, S., Soldateschi, D. and Tagliabue, A. (1983). *J. Immunol.* 131: 1707.

Bosma, G. C., Custer, R. P. and Bosma, M. J. (1983). *Nature* 301: 527.

Bradley, D. J., Taylor, B. A., Blackwell, J. M., Evans, E. P. and Freeman, J. (1979). *Clin. Exp. Immunol.* 37: 7.

Brandwein, S. R., Skamene, E., Aubut, J. A., Gervais, F. and Nesbitt, M. N. (1987). *J. Immunol.* 138: 4263.

Braun, D. P. and Harris, J. E. (1981). *J. Natl. Cancer Inst.* 67: 809.

Brunda, M. J., Holden, H. T. and Herberman, R. B. (1980). In R. B. Herberman (ed.), *Natural Cell-Mediated Immunity Against Tumors.* New York: Academic Press: 411–15.

Bukowski, J. F., Woda, B. A. and Welsh, R. M. (1984). *J. Virol.* 52: 119.

Burton, R. C. and Winn, H. J. (1981). *J. Immunol.* 126: 1985.

Bykowsky, M. J. and Stutman, O. (1986). *J. Immunol.* 137: 1120.

Carswell, E. A., Old, O. J., Kassel, R. L., Green, S., Fiore, N. and Williamson, B. (1975). *Proc. Natl. Acad. Sci. USA* 72: 3666.

Chandra, R. K., Cooper, M. D., Hitzig, W. H., Rosen, F. S., Seligmann, M., Soothill, J. F. and Terry, R. J. (1979). *Clin. Immunol. Immunopathol.* 13: 296.

Clark, E. A. (1986). In E. Lotzova and R. B. Herberman (eds), *Immunobiology of Natural Killer Cells,* vol. 1. Boca Raton: CRC Press: 73–86.

Clark, E. A. and Harmon, R. C. (1980). *Adv. Cancer Res.* 31: 227.

Clark, E. A., Russell, P. H., Egghart, M. and Horton, M. A. (1979). *Int. J. Cancer* 24: 688.

Clark, E. A., Shultz, L. D. and Pollack, S. B. (1981a). *Immunogenetics* 12: 601.

Clark, E. A., Roths, J. B., Murphy, E. D., Ledbetter, J. A. and Clagett, J. A. (1982). In R. B. Herberman (ed.), *NK Cells and Other Natural Effector Cells.* New York: Academic Press: 301–6.

Clark, I. A., Virelizier, J. L., Carswell, E. A. and Wood, P. R. (1981b). *Infect. Immun.* 32: 1058.

Crocker, P. R., Blackwell, J. M. and Bradley, D. J. (1984). *Infect. Immun.* 43: 1033.

Curtis, J., Curtis, C. F. and Barton, N. H. (1985). *Prog. Leukocyte Biol.* 3: 65.

Dauphinée, M. J., Kipper, S. B., Wopfsy, D. and Talal, N. (1981). *J. Immunol.* 127: 2483.

DeKretser, T. A. and Livett, B. G. (1976). *Nature* 263: 682.

Denis, M., Buschman, E., Forget, A., Pelletier, M., and Skamene, E. (1986a). *6th International Congress of Immunology,* Toronto. (Abstract).

De Titto, E. H., Catterall, J. R. and Remington, J. S. (1986). *J. Immunol.* 137: 1342.

Dinarello, C. A. (1984). *Rev. Infect. Dis.* 61: 51.

Dindzans, V. P., MacPhee, P., Fung, L. S., Leibowitz, J. L. and Levy, G. A. (1985). *J. Immunol.* 135: 4189.

Dindzans, V. P., Skamene, E. and Levy, G. A. (1986). *J. Immunol.* 137: 2355.

Diwan, B. A. and Meier, H. (1976). *Proc. Am. Assoc. Cancer Res.* 17: 106.

Dorshkind, K., Keller, G. M., Phillips, R. A., Miller, R. G., Bosman, G. C., O'Toole, M. and Bosma, M. J. (1984). *J. Immunol.* 132: 1804.

Dorshkind, K., Pollack, S. B., Bosma, M. J. and Phillips, R. A. (1985). *J. Immunol.* 134: 3798.

Dreiding, P., Staeheli, P. and Haller, O. (1985). *Virology* 140: 192.

Eccles, S. A. and Alexander, P. (1974). *Nature* 250: 667.

Eugui, E. M. and Allison, A. C. (1980). *Parasite Immunol.* 2: 277.

Evans, R. (1980). *Int. J. Cancer* 26: 227.

Evans, R. and Eidlen, D. M. (1981). *J. Reticul. Society* 30: 425.

Fitzgerald, P. A. and Lopez, C. (1986). In E. Lotzova and R. B. Herberman (eds), *Immunobiology of Natural Killer Cells,* vol. 2. Boca Raton: CRC Press: 107–31.

Fodstad, O., Hansen, C. T., Cannon, G. B. and Boyd, M. R. (1984a). *Scand. J. Immunol.* 20: 267.

Fodstad, O., Hansen, C. T., Cannon, G. B., Statham, C. N., Lichtenstein, G. R. and Boyd, M. R. (1984b). *Cancer Res.* 44: 4403.

Forget, A., Skamene, E., Gros, P., Miailhe, A. C. and Turcotte, R. (1981). *Infect. Immun.* 32: 42.

Forni, L. and Coutinho, L. (1978). *Eur. J. Immunol.* 8: 56.

Gervais, F., Stevenson, M. and Skamene, E. (1984). *J. Immunol.* 132: 2078.

Ghadirian, E., Kongshavn, P. A. L. and Hasegawa, H. J. *J. Leuk. Biol.* (1987), 42: 422.

Glimcher, L., Shen, F. W. and Cantor, H. (1977). *J. Exp. Med.* 145: 1.

Gorelik, E., Wiltrout, R. H., Okumura, K., Habu, S. and Herberman, R. B. (1982). *Int. J. Cancer* 30: 107.

Gowen, J. W. (1960). *Bact. Rev.* 24: 192.

Gray, P. W., Glaister, D., Chen, E., Goeddel, D. V. and Pennica, D. (1986). *J. Immunol.* 137: 3644.

Gros, P., Skamene, E. and Forget, A. (1981). *J. Immunol.* 127: 2417.

Gros, P., Skamene, E. and Forget, A. (1983). *J. Immunol.* 131: 1966.

Hackett, J. Jr., Bennett, M. and Kumar, V. (1985). *J. Immunol.* 134: 3731.

Hackett, J. Jr., Bosma, G., Bosma, M. J., Bennett, M. and Kumar, V. (1986). *Proc. Natl. Acad. Sci. USA* 83: 3427.

Haidaris, C. G., Haynes, J. D., Meltzer, M. S. and Allison, A. C. (1983). *Infect. Immun.* 42: 385.

Haliotis, T., Ball, J. K., Dexter, D. and Roder, J. C. (1985). *Int. J. Cancer* 35: 505.

Haller, O., Arnheiter, H., Lindenmann, J. and Gresser, I. (1980). *Nature* 283: 660.

Hamilton, T. A., Becton, D. L., Somers, S. D., Gray, P. W. and Adams, D. O. (1985). *J. Biol. Chem.* 260: 1378.

Hamilton, T. A., Somers, S. D., Becton, D. L., Celada, A., Schreiber, R. D. and Adams, D. O. (1986). *J. Immunol.* 137: 3367.

Hanna, N. and Fidler, I. J. (1981). *J. Natl. Cancer Inst.* 66: 1183.

Hanna, N., Davis, T. W. and Fidler, I. J. (1982). *Int. J. Cancer* 30: 371.

Harmon, R. C., Clark, E. A., O'Toole, C. and Wicker, L. S. (1977). *Immunogenetics* 4: 601.

Harrison, D. E. and Carlson, G. A. (1983). *J. Immunol.* 130: 484.

Herberman, R. B., Nunn, M. E. and Lavrin, D. H. (1975). *Int. J. Cancer* 16: 216.

Hidore, M. R. and Murphy, J. W. (1986). *J. Immunol.* 137: 3624.

Hoki, K., Marwo, K., Suzuki, S., Kato, H., Shimamura, K., Saito, M. and Nimura, T. (1987). *Lab. Animals* 21: 72.

Housman, D. E. and Gros, P. (1985). *Prog. Leukocyte Biol.* 3: 101.

James, S. L., Skamene, E. and Meltzer, M. S. (1983). *J. Immunol.* 131: 948.

Kaizer, L. and Lala, P. K. (1977). *Cell Tissue Kinetics* 10: 279.

Kaminsky, S. and Cudkowicz, G. (1980). *Fed. Proc.* 39: 466.

Kaminsky, S. G., Nakamura, I. and Cudkowicz, G. (1983). *J. Immunol.* 130: 1980.

Kaminsky, S. G., Nakamura, I. and Cudkowicz, G. (1985). *J. Immunol.* 135: 665.

Karmali, R. A. and Harrobin, D. F. (1976). *Nature* 263: 684.

Kärre, K., Klein, G. O., Kiessling, R., Klein, G. and Roder, J. C. (1980a). *Nature* 284: 624.

Kärre, K., Klein, G. O., Kiessling, R., Klein, G. and Roder, J. C. (1980b). *Int. J. Cancer* 26: 789.

Kärre, K., Klein, G. O., Kiessling, R., Argov, S. and Klein, G. (1982). In R. B. Herberman (ed.), *NK Cells and Other Natural Effector Cells*. New York: Academic Press: 301–6.

Kärre, K., Klein, G. O., Kiessling, R. and Klein, G. (1983). *Tokai J. Exp. Med.* 8: 429.

Kiessling, R. and Welsh, R. M. (1980). *Int. J. Cancer* 25: 611.

Kiessling, R., Klein, E. and Wigzell, H. (1975a). *Eur. J. Immunol.* 5: 112.

Kiessling, R., Klein, E., Pross, H. and Wigzell, H. (1975b). *Eur. J. Immunol.* 5: 117.

Kirkpatrick, C. E. and Farrell, J. P. (1982). *Infect. Immun.* 38: 1208.

Klein, G. O. (1982). In R. B. Herberman (ed.), *NK Cells and Other Natural Effector Cells*. New York: Academic Press: 275–80.

Klein, G. O. and Taylor, B. A. (1985). *Prog. Leukocyte Biol.* 3: 757.

Klein, G. O., Klein, G., Kiessling, R. and Kärre, K. (1978). *Immunogenetics* 6: 561.

Klein, G. O., Kärre, K., Klein, G. and Kiessling, R. (1980). *J. Immunogenetics* 7: 401.

Kongshavn, P. A. L. (1986). *Curr. Top. Microbiol. Immunol.* 124: 67.

Kongshavn, P. A. L., and Anthony, L. S. D. (1985). *Curr. Top. Microbiol. Immunol.* 122: 134.

Kongshavn, P. A. L. and Ghadirian, E. (1988). *Parasite Immunol.* 10: 581.

Koren, H. S. and Herberman, R. B. (1983). *J. Natl. Cancer Inst.* 70: 785.

Koren, H. S., Meltzer, M. S. and Adams, D. O. (1981). *J. Immunol.* 126: 1013.

Krug, R. M., Shaw, M., Broni, B., Shapiro, C. and Haller, O. (1985). *J. Virology* 56: 201.

Lanier, L. L., Cwirla, S., Federspiel, N. and Phillips, J. H. (1986a). *J. Exp. Med.* 163: 209.

Lanier, L. L., Cwirla, S. and Phillips, J. H. (1986b). *J. Immunol.* 137: 3375.

Lattime, E. C. and Stutman, O. (1983). *Surv. Synth. Path. Res.* 2: 57.

Lattime, E. C., Pecoraro, G. A., Cuttito, M. J. and Stutman, O. (1983). *Int. J. Cancer* 32: 523.

Lauzon, R. J., Siminovitch, K. A., Fulop, G. M., Phillips, R. A. and Roder, J. C. (1986). *J. Exp. Med.* 164: 1797.

Lemieux, S., Lusignan, Y. and Skamene, E. (1985). *Prog. Leukocyte Biol.* 3: 763.

Levy, G. A., Leibowitz, J. L. and Edgington, T. S. (1981). *J. Exp. Med.* 154: 1150.

Lewis, J. G. and Adams, D. O. (1985). *Cancer Res.* 45: 1270.

Lewis, J. G. and Adams, D. O. (1986). *Cancer Res.* 46: 5696.

Lindenmann, J., Lance, C. A. and Hobson, D. (1963). *J. Immunol.* 90: 942.

Lissner, C. R., Swanson, R. N. and O'Brien, A. D. (1983). *J. Immunol.* 131: 3006.

Lotzova, E. (1983). *Surv. Synth. Pathol. Res.* 2: 41.

Lotzova, E. and Herberman, R. B. (eds) (1986). *Immunobiology of Natural Killer Cells.* Boca Raton: CRC Press.

Lurie, M. B. (1964). *Resistance to Tuberculosis: Experimental Studies in Native and Acquired Defensive Mechanisms.* Cambridge: Harvard University Press.

Mahoney, K. H., Morse, S. S. and Morahan, P. S. (1980). *Cancer Res.* 40: 3934.

Malkinson, A. M., Nesbitt, M. N. and Skamene, E. (1985). *J. Natl. Cancer Inst.* 75: 971.

Mannel, D. N., Meltzer, M. S. and Mergenhagen, S. E. (1980). *Infect. Immun.* 28: 204.

Marquis, G., Montplaisir, S., Pelletier, M., Mousseau, S. and Auger, P. (1985). *Infect. Immun.* 47: 288.

McCall, R. D. (1985). *Prog. Leukocyte Biol.* 3: 71.

McGarry, R. C., Walker, R. and Roder, J. C. (1984). *Immunogenetics* 20: 527.

McKinnon, K. P., Hale, A. H. and Ruebush, M. J. (1981). *Infect. Immun.* 32: 204.

McNeill, T. A. and Fleming, W. A. (1973). *J. Cell. Physiol.* 82: 49.

Meltzer, M. S., Ruco, L. P., Boraschi, D. and Nacy, C. A. (1979). *J. Reticul. Soc.* 26: 403.

Meltzer, M. S., Occhionero, M. and Ruco, L. P. (1982). *Fed. Proc.* 41: 2198.

Merluzzi, V. J. (1985). *Cell. Immunol.* 95: 95.

Merluzzi, V. J., Smith, M. D. and Last-Barney, K. (1986a). *Cell. Immunol.* 100: 563.

Merluzzi, V. J., Trail, P. A. and Last-Barney, K. (1986b). *J. Immunol.* 137: 2425.

Metcalf, D. and Russell, S. (1976). *Exp. Hematol.* 4: 339.

Milhaud, G., Labat, M. -L., Parant, M., Damais, C. and Chedid, L. (1977). *Proc. Natl. Acad. Sci. USA* 74: 339.

Minato, N., Reid, L., Cantor, H., Lengyel, P. and Bloom, B. R. (1980). *J. Exp. Med.* 152: 124.

Mortensen, R. F., Beisel, K., Zeleznik, N. J. and Le, P. T. (1983). *J. Immunol.* 120: 885.

Murphy, E. D. and Roths, J. B. (1977). *Fed. Proc.* 36: 1246.

Nair, M. P. N., Schwartz, S. A., Fernandes, G., Pahwa, R., Ikehara, S. and Good, R. A. (1981). *Cell. Immunol.* 58: 9.

Normann, S. J., Schardt, M. and Sorkin, E. (1981). *J. Natl. Cancer Inst.* 66: 157.

Olsen, C. E., Wahl, S. M., Sanberg, A. L. and Mergenhagen, S. E. (1978). In J. E. Horton, T. M. Tarpley and W. F. Davis (eds), *Mechanisms of Localized Bone Loss.* Washington: Information Retrieval: 389–98.

Otu, A. A., Russell, R. J., Wilkinson, P. C. and White, R. G. (1970). *Br. J. Cancer* 36: 330.

Pan, L. -Z., Dauphinée, M. J., Ansar Ahmed, S. and Talal, N. (1986). *Scand. J. Immunol.* 23: 415.

Peter, H. H., Friedrich, W., Dopper, R., Muller, W., Kortmann, C., Pichler, W. J., Heinz, F. and Rieger, C. H. (1983). *J. Immunol.* 131: 2332.

Petranyi, G., Kiessling, R. and Klein, G. (1975). *Immunogenetics* 2: 53.

Petranyi, G., Kiessling, R., Povey, R., Klein, G., Herzenberg, L. and Wigzell, H. (1976). *Immunogenetics* 3: 15.

Plant, J. and Glynn, A. A. (1979). *Clin. Exp. Immunol.* 37: 1.

Pollack, S. B. (1986). In E. Lotzova and R. B. Herberman (eds), *Immunobiology of Natural Killer Cells*, vol. 1. Boca Raton: CRC Press: 87–105.

Pollack, S. B. and Emmons, S. L. (1982). *J. Immunol.* 129: 2277.

Punjabi, C., Galsworthy, S. B. and Kongshavn, P. A. L. (1984). *Clin. Invest. Med.* 7: 165.

Reiners, J. J., Newnow, S. and Slaga, T. J. (1984). *Carcinogenesis* 5: 301.

Reynolds, C. W., Timonen, T. T., Holden, H. T., Hansen, C. T. and Herberman, R. B. (1982). *Eur. J. Immunol.* 12: 577.

Reynolds, C. W., Bonyhadi, M., Herberman, R. B., Young, H. A. and Hedrick, S. M. (1985). *J. Exp. Med.* 161: 1249.

Robles, C. P. and Pollack, S. B. (1986). *Nat. Immun. Cell Growth Regul.* 5: 64.

Roder, J. C. (1979). *J. Immunol.* 123: 2168.

Roder, J. C. and Duwe, A. K. (1979). *Nature* 278: 451.

Roder, J. C. and Kiessling, R. (1978). *Scand. J. Immunol.* 8: 135.

Roder, J. C., Lohmann-Matthes, M.-L., Domzig, W. and Wigzell, H. (1979). *J. Immunol.* 123: 2174.

Rosenstein, M., Yron, I., Kaufmann, Y. and Rosenberg, S. A. (1984). *Cancer Res.* 44: 1946.

Ruco, L. P. and Meltzer, M. S. (1978). *J. Immunol.* 120: 329.

Ruco, L. P., Meltzer, M. S. and Rosenstreich, D. L. (1978). *J. Immunol.* 121: 543.

Ruebush, M. J. and Burgess, D. E. (1982). In R. B. Herberman (ed.), *NK Cells and Other Natural Effector Cells*. New York: Academic Press: 1483–9.

Russell, E. S. and Bernstein, S. E. (1968). In E. L. Green (ed.), *Biology of the Laboratory Mouse*. New York: Dover Publications: 351–65.

Sakakeeny, M. A. and Greenberger, J. S. (1982). *J. Natl. Cancer Inst.* 68: 305.

Salomon, J. C., Creau-Goldberg, N. and Lynch, N. R. (1980). *Cancer Immunol. Immunother.* 8: 67.

Saxena, R. K., Saxena, Q. B. and Adler, W. H. (1982). *Nature* 295: 240.

Seaman, W. E., Gindhart, T. D., Greenspan, J. S., Blackman, M. A. and Talal, N. (1979). *J. Immunol.* 122: 2541.

Semple, J. W. and Szewczuk, M. R. (1983). *Cell. Immunol.* 82: 316.

Semple, J. W. and Szewczuk, M. R. (1986). *Cell. Immunol.* 100: 20.

Semple, J. W., Wade, A. W. and Szewczuk, M. R. (1984). *Clin. Immunol. Immunopathol.* 33: 144.

Shultz, L. D., Sidman, C. L., and Unanue, E. R. (1978). In M. R. Gershwin and E. L. Cooper (eds), *Animal Models of Comparative and Developmental Aspects of Immunity and Disease.* New York: Pergamon Press: 260–9.

Shultz, L. D., Bailey, C. L. and Coman, D. R. (1983a). *Exp. Hematol.* 11: 667.

Shultz, L. D., Bailey, C. L., Carlson, G. A., Coman, D. R., Evans, R. and Outzen, H. C. (1983b). In B. Sordat (ed.), *Immuno-Deficient Animals.* Basel: Karger: 224–9.

Shellam, G. R., Allan, J. E., Papadimitriou, J. M. and Bancroft, G. J. (1981). *Proc. Natl. Acad. Sci. USA* 78: 5104.

Shellam, G. R., Flexman, J. P., Farrell, H. E. and Papadimitriou, J. M. (1985). *Scand. J. Immunol.* 22: 147.

Skamene, E. (ed.) (1985). *Progress in Leukocyte Biology.* Vol. 3. New York: Alan R. Liss.

Skamene, E. (1986). *Curr. Topics Microbiol. Immunol.* 124: 49.

Skamene, E., Kongshavn, P. A. L. and Landy, M. (eds) (1980). *Genetic Control of Natural Resistance to Infection and Malignancy.* New York: Academic Press.

Skamene, E., Gros, P., Forget, A., Kongshavn, P. A. L., St. Charles, C. and Taylor, B. A. (1982). *Nature* 297: 506.

Skamene, E., Stevenson, M. M. and Lemieux, S. (1983). *Parasite Immunol.* 5: 557.

Skamene, E., James, S. L., Meltzer, M. S. and Nesbitt, M. N. (1984). *J. Leuk. Biol.* 35: 65.

Skow, L. C. (1982). *Exp. Eye Res.* 34: 509.

Sluiter, W., Hulsing-Hesselink, E. and van Furth, R. (1982). In F. Rossi and P. Patriaca (eds), *Biochemistry and Function of Phagocytes.* New York: Plenum Press: 225–45.

Sluiter, W., Elzenga-Claasen, I., van der Voort van der Kleÿ-van Andel, A. and van Furth, R. (1984). *J. Exp. Med.* 159: 524.

Spriggs, D. R. (1986). *J. Infect. Dis.* 154: 381.

Springer, T. A., Thompson, W. S., Miller, L. F., Schmalstieg, F. C. and Anderson, D. C. (1984). *J. Exp. Med.* 160: 1901.

Stach, J.-L., Gros, P., Forget, A. and Skamene, E. (1984). *J. Immunol.* 132: 888.

Staeheli, P. and Haller, O. (1985). *Molec. Cell Biol.* 5: 2150.

Staeheli, P., Haller, O., Boll, O., Lindenmann, J. and Weissmann, C. (1986). *Cell* 44: 147.

Stevenson, M. M., Kongshavn, P. A. L. and Skamene, E. (1981). *J. Immunol.* 127: 402.

Stevenson, M. M., Shenouda, G., Thomson, D. M. P. and Skamene, E. (1985). *Prog. Leukocyte Biology* 3: 577.

Stevenson, M. M., Skamene, E. and McCall, R. D. (1986). *Immunogenetics* 23: 11.

Stokes, R. W., Orme, I. M. and Collins, F. (1985). *Infect. Immun.* 54: 811.

Stutman, O. and Cuttito, M. J. (1981). *Nature* 290: 254.

Stutman, O. and Cuttito, M. J. (1982). In R. B. Herberman (ed.), *NK Cells and Other Natural Effector Cells.* New York: Academic Press: 281–9.

Stutman, O., Paige, C. J. and Figarella, E. F. (1978). *J. Immunol.* 121: 1819.

Suzuki, S. and Axelrad, A. A. (1980). *Cell* 19: 225.

Suzuki, S., Suzuki, R., Onta, T. and Kumagai, K. (1986). *Nat. Immun. Cell Growth Regul.* 5: 75.

Swanson, R. N. and O'Brien, A. D. (1983). *J. Immunol.* 131: 3014.

Szymaneic, S. and James, K. (1976). *Brit. J. Cancer* 33: 36.

Talmage, J. E., Meyers, K. M., Prieur, D. J. and Starkey, J. R. (1980). *Nature* 284: 622.

Tarkkanen, J., Saksela, E. and Paavolainen, M. (1983). *Clin. Immunol. Immunopathol.* 28: 29.

Taverne, J., Dockrell, H. M. and Playfair, J. H. L. (1981). *Infect. Immun.* 33: 83.

Thomson, D. M. P., Stevenson, M. M. and Skamene, E. (1985). *Cell. Immunol.* 94: 547.

Truesdale, A. T., Johnson, D. A., Bedigian, H. G., Outzen, H. C. and Carlson, G. A. (1982). *Cell. Immunol.* 74: 120.

Tutt, M. M., Kuziel, W. A., Hackett, J. Jr., Bennett, M., Tucker, P. W. and Kumar, V. (1986). *J. Immunol.* 137: 2998.

Unanue, E. R. (1984). *Ann. Rev. Immunol.* 2: 395.

Unanue, E. R., Beller, D. I., Lu, C. Y. and Allen, P. M. (1984). *J. Immunol.* 132: 1.

van Dissel, J. T., Stikkelbroeck, J. J. M., Sluiter, W., Leijh, P. C. J. and van Furth, R. (1985). *Prog. Leukocyte Biol.* 3: 245.

van Furth, R. and Sluiter, W. (1985). *Prog. Leukocyte Biol.* 4: 111.

van Zant, G., Eldridge, P. W., Behringer, R. R. and Dewey, M. J. (1983). *Cell* 35: 639.

Welsh, R. M. (1986). *Nat. Immun. Cell Growth Regul.* 5: 169.

Welsh, R. M. and Kiessling, R. (1980). *Scand. J. Immunol.* 11: 363.

Wilson, B. M., Rosendaal, M. and Plant, J. E. (1982). *Immunology* 45: 395.

Wing, E. J., Waheed, A. and Shadduck, R. K. (1984). *Infect. Immun.* 45: 180.

Wolgethan, J. R. and Cathcart, E. S. (1979). *Nature* 278: 452.

Wood, G. W., Neff, J. E. and Stephens, R. (1979). *J. Natl. Cancer Inst.* 63: 587.

Wood, P. R. and Clark, I. A. (1982). *Parasite Immunol.* 4: 319.

Young, A. M. and Cheers, C. (1986). *Cell. Immunol.* 97: 227.

Young, H. A., Ortaldo, J. R., Herberman, R. B. and Reynolds, C. W. (1986). *J. Immunol.* 136: 2701.

Zoller, M. and Wigzell, H. (1982). *Cell. Immunol.* 74: 27.

Zwilling, B. S., Johnson, S., Vespa, L. and Kwasniewski, M. (1985). *Prog. Leukocyte Biol.* 3: 299.

12

Developmental Biology and Senescence

JACQUES J. PROUST
BRADLEY S. BENDER
JAMES E. NAGEL
WILLIAM H. ADLER

Clinical Immunology Section
Gerontology Research Center
National Institute on Aging
4940 Eastern Avenue
Baltimore, Md 21224, USA

NATURAL IMMUNITY
ISBN 0 12 5145551

I. INTRODUCTION

This chapter will attempt to describe changes in development and senescence of some of the major components of the natural immunity system. Not all of the reported changes are consistent, and sometimes there is not general agreement that there are changes, or whether levels of components or activity increase or decrease in the young and old. The topic is further confused by the comparison of results obtained in humans and different species of experimental animals. This is not surprising, since it is easy to appreciate that human peripheral blood lymphocytes and mouse or rat spleen cells are entirely different kinds of sources of cells for assay systems. However, there are other factors which also may cause variations in many of these studies of natural immunity, and some are not quite so obvious. Genetics, including sex, is an obvious factor: not only does it influence the results obtained in studies of inbred species of animals but, in a more subtle manner, it can influence results obtained in different human populations and in family studies. Nutrition is another important factor; when this is added to the variable of age in an experimental model, it is easy to appreciate how discordant results may be obtained by different laboratories. There are also geographic factors that are tied to the genetic and nutritional considerations. Even the variable of age itself needs to be considered. Studies on 70-year-old humans from populations with a life expectancy of 50 years probably yield different results than do studies based on populations with a much longer life expectancy. The same is true at the other end of the scale for studies in populations of neonates with high and low infant mortality. Also, how does one equate relative life spans in different animal species to compare results? Lastly, many assay systems are not very precise, so that a 50 per cent decrease or increase in the level of a function may not be significant in one study and may be highly significant in another. With these considerations, we have attempted to present a broad picture of the effects of development and age on natural immunity, and to point out where differences in results do exist and where they might exist. As it will become evident, in many instances sufficient information is simply not available to allow firm conclusions to be made regarding age-related alterations in natural immunity.

II. NATURAL KILLER AND NATURAL CYTOTOXIC CELLS

Natural killer (NK) cells are so named because they have the unique ability to recognise and kill, without the necessity of prior sensitisation, certain tumour and virus-infected cells. They are believed to play a first-line role in host defence against many malignancies and infections, in resistance to allografts, and in bone-marrow development (Herberman and Ortaldo, 1981; Mangan *et al.*, 1984; Ortaldo and Herberman, 1984). NK cells are more fully described in Chapter 3.

It is currently believed that NK cells arise from the bone marrow (Haller *et al.*, 1977), undergo further processing in lymph nodes and spleen, and finally are released into the peripheral blood (Abo *et al.*, 1984). The thymus is not required for their processing, as is best shown by the fact that NK cells develop normally in nude (athymic) mice (Kiessling *et al.*, 1975) and in children with congenital thymic aplasia (DiGeorge syndrome) (Sirianni *et al.*, 1983). Further, they traffic through thymus-independent areas of lymphoid tissue (Banerjee and Thibert, 1983) and lack surface-membrane markers typically associated with mature T lymphocytes (Lanier *et al.*, 1983).

In both animal models and humans, NK cell activity is either low or absent at birth (Table 12.1). Human NK cell activity is virtually absent in fetal blood (Uksila *et al.*, 1983; Seki *et al.*, 1985) and very low in cord blood (Antonelli *et al.*, 1981; Kaplan *et al.*, 1982; Uksila *et al.*, 1983; Noble and Warren, 1985). This correlates with extremely low numbers of Leu-7[+] cells even though the number of Leu-11[+] cells in cord blood approximates adult levels (Abo *et al.*, 1982, 1984; Noble and Warren, 1985; Seki *et al.*, 1985). Under laboratory conditions, interferon and

Table 12.1: Development of NK cell activity

Species	Newborn NK activity	Age peak NK activity is reached	References
Mouse	Absent	3–8 weeks	Herberman *et al.* (1975) Kiessling *et al.* (1975)
Rat	Absent	5–20 weeks	Nunn *et al.* (1976) Shellam and Hogg (1977)
Hamster	Low	4–12 months	Tsang *et al.* (1983)
Guinea Pig	NT[a]	13 weeks	Altman and Rapp (1978)
Miniature swine	Absent	NT[a]	Koren *et al.* (1978) Kim *et al.* (1980)
Human	Low	4–5 years	Antonelli *et al.* (1981) Kaplan *et al.* (1982) Uksila *et al.* (1983) Noble and Warren (1985)

[a] NT = not tested

interleukin 2 (IL-2) can boost NK activity of cord blood cells to adult levels (Antonelli *et al.*, 1981; Uksila *et al.*, 1983; Seki *et al.*, 1985; Ueno *et al.*, 1985).

In animals, it is easier to investigate possible mechanisms underlying alterations in NK activity. Roder (1980) found that as infant mice mature, their NK cells become more avid by binding greater numbers of target cells. Further, Savary and Lotzova (1978) have shown that splenic lymphocytes from infant mice are capable of suppressing NK cell activity, while adult spleen lymphocytes lack this ability. In the one human study we are aware of, Baley and Schacter (1985) found that cord blood lymphocytes have decreased target-cell binding and lysis as determined by a single-cell cytotoxicity assay.

The level of NK cell activity in senescence is not clear, as there are conflicting reports not only between different species but also within the same species. In rodents, spleen cell preparations are typically used to evaluate NK cell activity. There is general agreement that splenic NK function is virtually absent in old mice and rats (Herberman *et al.*, 1975; Kiessling *et al.*, 1975; Albright and Albright, 1983) and one study shows a decline in guinea pig splenic NK cell activity at 40 weeks (Altman and Rapp, 1978), though older animals were not studied. Investigations into the mechanism of the decline of murine NK activity by Saxena *et al.* (1984) have shown that the lower NK activity in senescence is correlated with a four-fold decrease in splenic NK precursor cells. Additionally, when Haller *et al.*, (1977) transferred bone-marrow cells from variably aged mice into irradiated recipients, they found that cells from old donors were less effective than cells from young donors in restoring splenic NK cell activity. Roder (1980) reported that the age-associated impairment in murine NK cell activity is due to a decrease in the number of effector cells. The NK cells that are present bind target cells as avidly as cells from young mice.

The level of NK cell activity in aging humans is even more confusing. Of 14 studies of NK activity, three report that the elderly have decreased NK cell function (Penschow and Mackay, 1980; Mysliwska *et al.*, 1985; Tsang *et al.*, 1985), four report increased NK cell function (Bátory *et al.*, 1981; Fernandes and Gupta, 1981; Onsrud, 1981; Bátory *et al.*, 1985) and six report no change in NK activity (Nagel *et al.*, 1981; Marcano *et al.*, 1982; Pross and Baines, 1982; Sugiyama *et al.*, 1983; Yamashita *et al.*, 1984; Ventura *et al.*, 1985; Bender *et al.*, 1986). Two studies have examined NK cell phenotypes in aging. Abo *et al.* (1982) used the Leu-7 (HNK-1) monoclonal antibody and reported that there is an increase in the numbers of reactive cells with aging. However, scrutiny of their data shows that most of the increase in Leu-7$^+$ cells occurs during the first two decades of life, and they had only four subjects over age 70 years.

We have recently completed a study of NK phenotypes and function of 67 adults aged 17–84 years (Bender *et al.*, 1986). Using dual-colour immunofluorescence and the monoclonal antibodies Leu-7 and Leu-11, we found that there was no difference between young and aged adults in the expression of Leu-7$^+$, Leu-11$^+$, Leu-7$^-$ Leu-11$^+$, or Leu-7$^+$ Leu-11$^+$ cells. In older subjects, a significant decrease was seen in both percentage representation and absolute number of Leu-7$^+$ Leu-11$^-$ cells, a subset that has very little cytotoxic ability (Lanier *et al.*, 1983). We also found a significant correlation between NK cell function and either the percentage representation or the absolute number of the various peripheral blood Leu-11$^+$ subsets that was valid for both young and old subjects.

The discrepancy between the decline in NK function in aged animals and a maintenance of NK function in elderly humans may be due to several factors. First, murine NK assays are typically done with spleen cell preparations, while human NK assays use peripheral blood lymphocytes. Lanza and Djeu (1982) have shown that NK activity of murine peripheral blood was comparable in young and aged animals. Secondly, an old human has been exposed to a larger number of and more prolonged environmental stimuli than an aged mouse. These stimuli could conceivably diminish a decline in NK cell activity. Finally, there may be true interspecies differences in NK cell function.

The possibility of enhancing immune function in the elderly has attracted increasing attention in recent years. Since NK cell function responds to many immunomodulators, it has been frequently studied. Isoprinosine has been shown to augment NK cell activity of lymphocytes from elderly subjects (Tsang *et al.*, 1985). Interferon (IFN) can enhance the natural cytotoxic action of lymphocytes from the elderly (Sato *et al.*, 1979). Polyinosinic acid – polycytidylic acid (poly I : C), an IFN-inducer, also can increase the NK cell activity of elderly donors (Sugiyama *et al.*, 1983). IL-2 has emerged as one of the most important immunoregulatory molecules. Yamashita *et al.* (1984) found that peripheral blood lymphocytes obtained from aged subjects and treated with IL-2 were able to proliferate to the same extent as cells from young donors, and that the IL-2-propagated cells had the same NK activity as did cells from young adults. Further, short-term (4 h) incubation of lymphocytes from aged donors with IL-2 has been shown to increase NK activity (Bender *et al.*, 1986).

Natural cytotoxic (NC) cells are another class of lymphoid cells that mediate spontaneous killing. They differ from NK cells in target-cell specificity, surface-membrane markers, responsiveness to various biological response modifiers, and strain and tissue distribution (Stutman *et al.*, 1978; Rola-Pleszczynski *et al.*, 1985). Natural cytotoxic cells are covered in Chapter 5. Of importance to this chapter is that in hamsters and in mice, unlike NK cells, NC activity is present at birth and is maintained in senescence (Stutman *et al.*, 1978; Datta *et al.*, 1979). IFN can enhance the NC activity of cord blood (Sato *et al.*, 1979; Kohl *et al.*, 1981) and peripheral blood of the aged (Sato *et al.*, 1979).

III. POLYMORPHONUCLEAR LEUKOCYTES[1]

Bacterial killing by polymorphonuclear leukocytes (PMNs) is a complex process. The attachment to the cell surface of a bacterium fully opsonised by antibody and the third component of complement induces a sudden rise in the concentration of intracellular free Ca^{2+}. This increase in intracellular free Ca^{2+} triggers a series of metabolic events (endocytosis, locomotion, secretion of lysosomal enzymes) and initiates the respiratory burst. The oxidative respiratory burst is characterised by a dramatic increase in oxygen consumption and hexose monophosphate shunt activity resulting in the generation of bactericidal products: superoxide anion, singlet oxygen, hydrogen peroxide, and hydroxyl radical.

Assays for PMN function vary widely in concept and design. Several aspects of the experimental designs influence the results of the studies on PMN function and may explain the discrepancies among published observations. The variability may be mainly attributed to the choice of the test organism, the concentration and source of opsonin, and the bacteria to PMN ratio. Subtle differences in PMN function can be demonstrated only when the cells are placed in stress conditions, i.e. low concentrations of opsonin and/or high bacteria to PMN ratio. The marked susceptibility of the newborn, as well as the aged, to infections has prompted numerous studies of the PMN function in these two populations. A number of developmental deficiencies have been observed in the function of neonatal PMNs which may account for the high prevalence of neonatal sepsis. Impairment of PMN function has also been reported in association with advanced age. However, the degree to which PMN dysfunction contributes to the recognised impairment of host defences in aged humans has yet to be determined (Pesanti, 1977).

A. Phagocytosis

In the presence of a normal concentration of opsonin no differences were observed between cord blood PMNs and adult PMNs (Matoth, 1952; Miller, 1969; Miyazaki *et al.*, 1982). However, neonatal PMN phagocytosis was found deficient when the opsonic concentration was

---

[1] See also Chapter 2.

decreased. Forman and Stiehm (1969) also observed an impairment in the phagocytic function of stressed neonates. Whether the deficient phagocytosis, under stress conditions in vitro as well as in vivo, is clinically relevant is still unknown. Studies concerning the effect of age on phagocytosis yield conflicting results. Corberand *et al.* (1981) did not witness any age-related defect in endocytosis, whereas Charpentier and co-workers (1981) reported a dramatic decrease in the phagocytic activity of PMNs from aged individuals. Bongrand *et al.* (1984) found that aged people displayed a selective decrease of Fc-receptor-mediated phagocytosis by granulocytes. An age-related decrease in phagocytosis was also reported by Antonaci *et al.* (1984). In a recent study, Nagel *et al.* (1986), using flow cytometry to examine the phagocytic capacity of individual cells, showed an age-related increase in the proportion of a population of PMNs which have a defect in phagocytic ability.

B. Bactericidal Activity

The numerous studies of bactericidal activity of PMNs from newborns over the past several years have led to the accumulation of conflicting data. Both normal and decreased bactericidal activity have been documented in neonates by Forman and Stiehm (1969), Coen *et al.* (1969), Park *et al.* (1970), Wright *et al.* (1975), Orlowski *et al.* (1976), Stoerner *et al.* (1978), Miyazaki *et al.* (1982) and Stroobant *et al.* (1984). However, in most cases, the results obtained in studies of bactericidal activity are similar to those found for phagocytosis in that results obtained under normal conditions differ from those obtained under stress conditions. Mills and co-workers (1979a) were able to demonstrate a decreased bactericidal activity when PMNs from neonates were compared to PMNs derived from their mothers or healthy adults using a high bacteria to PMN ratio. Decreased bactericidal activity has also been described under clinical conditions in which stress varied from mild to severe (Forman and Stiehm, 1969; Wright *et al.*, 1975). Investigations of oxidative metabolism yield more consistent results. Hexose monophosphate shunt activity was found lower in newborn infants (Coen *et al.*, 1969; Park *et al.*, 1970; Anderson *et al.*, 1974; Stoerner *et al.*, 1978; Strauss and Seifert, 1978). The generation of superoxide anion (weakly bactericidal) was found normal in the newborn PMN (Ambruso *et al.*, 1979; Miyazaki *et al.*, 1982). In contrast, a significant defect in the generation of hydroxyl radical (highly bactericidal) was observed upon stimulation by phorbol esters or opsonised zymosan (Ambruso *et al.*, 1979). Chemiluminescence, which is initiated by the respiratory burst, has also been reported to be decreased in some neonates (Strauss and Seifert, 1978; van Epps *et al.*, 1978). With aging, no change in PMN bactericidal activity has been observed (Phair *et al.*, 1978; Palmblad and Haak, 1978; Johnson *et al.*, 1984). Corberand *et al.* (1981), however, reported a diminished *Candida*-killing activity in the PMNs of humans over 60 years of age. Nagel and co-workers (1982) also reported a diminished production of superoxide with age, although the bactericidal activity of PMNs from elderly subjects was not found significantly different from that of the PMNs from young individuals.

C. Mobility

Studies of movement of neonatal PMNs, unlike studies of phagocytic and bactericidal activities, have shown a consistent deficiency. Miller (1971) observed a marked deficiency of neonatal PMNs in movement toward chemotactic stimuli and also showed that neonatal sera were deficient in chemotactic activities. Similar findings were reported by Klein *et al.* (1977); Pahwa *et al.* (1977); Tono-Oka *et al.* (1979) and Miyazaki *et al.* (1982). According to Repo and co-workers (1980), the impaired chemotaxis of cord PMNs was due to a defect in both responsiveness to chemotactic stimulus, and deformability of the cell membrane. However, later studies by Anderson *et al.* (1981) do not support the concept that sensory function is deficient in the neonatal PMNs. PMN mobility is also impaired in the elderly. Phair *et al.* (1981) found a chemotactic defect in seven per cent of the elderly subjects examined. Corberand *et al.* (1981) also observed a decrease in the chemotactic response of individuals aged 80 and over. McLaughlin *et al.* (1986) showed that human peripheral blood granulocytes from elderly subjects exhibit reduced chemotaxis in response to stimulation with a synthetic tripeptide. Silverman and Silverman (1975) found that granulocyte adherence increased with age. This finding was confirmed by Corberand *et al.* (1981) in humans age 80 and older. However, other investigators (Antonaci *et al.*, 1984; Kelly *et al.*, 1985) found that PMN adherence in elderly individuals was similar to that of healthy young adults.

IV. MONOCYTES AND MACROPHAGES

Over the past 100 years various experiments have demonstrated that peripheral blood monocytes, tissue-fixed macrophages and their precursors are closely related and belong in the same system, referred to as either the reticulo-endothelial system (RES) or the mononuclear phagocyte system. The most immature cell that is still recognisable as being part of the RES is the bone-marrow promonocyte. The promonocyte, by cell division, gives rise to two monocytes, which are then released into the circulation. The tissue macrophages in such diverse areas as the lung, liver, spleen, and peritoneal cavity are derived from both circulating monocytes and local proliferation of macrophages (van Furth *et al.*, 1972). Monocytes and macrophages are covered in detail in Chapter 1.

One of the most important functions of the RES cells is phagocytosis. In the newborn, studies are essentially restricted to ingestion and killing of micro-organisms. Studies on monocytes from cord blood generally show normal phagocytosis and killing of *Staphylococcus aureus* (Orlowski *et al.*, 1976; Weston *et al.*, 1977) and *Escherichia coli* (Kretschmer *et al.*, 1976; Orlowski *et al.*, 1976). This correlates with normal quantitative nitroblue-tetrazolium dye reduction by monocytes from newborns (Kretschmer *et al.*, 1977). There are, however, differences in chemotaxis. Cord blood monocytes have decreased movement towards endotoxin-activated human serum (Weston *et al.*, 1977); Maródi *et al.*, 1980) and zymosan-activated human serum (Klein *et al.*, 1977). Depending on the chemoattractant, chemotaxis reaches adult levels by either ages 3–8 (Maródi *et al.*, 1980) or ages 11–16 (Klein *et al.*, 1977). Arenson *et al.* (1979), by enumerating monocyte subsets, showed that the impaired chemotactic ability of cord blood monocytes was due to an intrinsic functional deficiency rather than a reduced number of chemotactically active cells. In studies on the biochemical requirements for killing of pathogens, Das *et al.* (1979) found that monocytes from cord blood had reduced pyruvate kinase activity and adenosine triphosphate content. This suggests that newborn monocytes, by virtue of their relative depletion of energy stores, may be particularly susceptible to stress.

Human newborns are particularly susceptible to disseminated viral infections. It is well established in laboratory animals that macrophage antiviral activity is strongly age-related, with macrophages from suckling mice having decreased ability to inhibit replication of herpes simplex virus (Johnson, 1964; Hirsch *et al.* 1970). It appears that alveolar macrophages obtained by bronchoalveolar lavage from human neonates also have impaired ability to inhibit growth of herpes simplex virus (Mintz *et al.*, 1980). This study is flawed, however, since the cells were obtained by post-mortem lavage from newborns who died in the intensive care nursery. In a related study, Sullivan *et al.* (1975) found that 2–9 % of cord blood monocytes could be infected with measles virus as compared to 0.4 % of monocytes obtained from non-immune adults.

The prototype organism for testing resistance to intracellular organisms is *Toxoplasma gondii*. Wilson and Haas (1984) found that survival of *T. gondii* was equal in newborn and adult monocytes, but that lymphocytes from newborns produced decreased amounts of a macrophage-activating factor, probably IFN-γ.

Many T-lymphocyte activities require that an accessory cell (usually a monocyte or a macrophage) process and present the antigen to the responding cell, usually in association with Class II antigens of the major histocompatibility complex Ia in the mouse, and DR and others in humans. Class II antigen representation may determine the speed and efficiency of a specific immune response.

Lu *et al.* (1979) showed that peritoneal macrophages from newborn mice were unable to support proliferation of T lymphocytes from adult donors. This defect was present until 3–4 weeks of age and correlated with a deficiency of Ia^+ macrophages. A recent study by this group indicates that a neonatal splenic cell blocked Ia expression (Snyder *et al.*, 1982). The suppression was probably mediated by arachidonic acid metabolites and the suppressor cell appeared to be a precursor of the monocyte–macrophage cell line. This suggests that mononuclear phagocytes are self-regulatory. Stiehm *et al.* (1984) also found deficient DR antigen expression on human cord blood monocytes: only 19–33 % of newborn monocytes were DR^+ as compared to 71–82 % of adult peripheral blood monocytes. They also found that DR^- cord blood monocytes can be induced to express the DR antigen by the addition of IFN-α.

Recent experiments performed by van Tol and colleagues (1984) indicate that cord blood monocytes also differ in their ability to process antigen. They found that the optimal dose of the T-cell-dependent antigen ovalbumin to produce an IgM plaque-forming cell (PFC) response was consistently 100-fold lower in neonatal cultures than in adult cell cultures. Their data suggest that this may be due to increased secretion of prostaglandin E_2 by neonatal monocytes.

The sequence of pulmonary alveolar macrophage development has received intense investigation in animal models. In both rabbits and monkeys, there is an influx of alveolar macrophages at birth, followed by a rapid increase in the first postnatal week of life (Bellanti *et al.*, 1979; Jacobs *et al.*, 1985). The signal for this migration of macrophages seems to be surfactant-related phospholipids. The postnatal influx may also be related to the inhalation of particles that are phagocytosed, resulting in the release of chemoattractants (Bellanti *et al.*, 1979).

Alveolar macrophages from newborn and adult monkeys are similar in their ability to phagocytose and kill *S. aureus* and group B streptococcus (Jacobs *et al.*, 1983). They are also able to clear *T. gondii* with an equal ability. Alveolar macrophages from neonatal rabbits, however, have

phagocytic ability equal to adult, but decreased intracellular killing of
Candida albicans (Zeligs *et al.*, 1984), *S. aureus* and *E. coli* (Bellanti *et al.*,
1979). This may be due to defects in biochemical mechanisms respon-
sible for the respiratory burst (Bellanti *et al.*, 1979).

Two clinical observations suggesting defective in vitro clearance by
the neonatal RES have been reported. Holroyde *et al.* (1969) used
interference contrast microscopy to study peripheral red blood cell
surface morphology. They found that in adults, 2.6 per cent of red cells
had small surface pits. Premature and term infants had 47 per cent and
24 per cent pitted cells respectively, with a progressive age-related
decrease to adult values by two months of age. Acevedo and Maurer
(1963) found decreased clearance of erythrocytes containing Heinz
bodies in premature infants. Since pitted erythrocytes and Heinz bodies
are characteristic post-splenectomy findings, this suggests that newborns
have a physiological splenic RES dysfunction.

It is logical, when investigating the possible mechanisms involved in
age-related changes in immune function, to quantify the number of cells
in the peripheral blood. Ligthart *et al.* (1985) studied 48 volunteers and
Nielsen *et al.* (1984) studied 60 volunteers and found no change in the
number of peripheral blood monocytes with age. Munan and Kelly
(1979), however, collected data on 2347 non-institutionalised persons.
They found that in men, there is an increase in the absolute number of
peripheral blood monocytes to age 45, then a decrease in the number of
cells, while in women there was a continual post adolescent decrease in
the absolute number of peripheral blood monocytes.

Phagocytosis has received the most attention in young subjects.
Surprisingly, monocyte phagocytosis appears to be increased with aging.
This has been shown in mice by Wustrow *et al.* (1982), who found that
the percentage of peritoneal macrophages that can phagocytose latex
beads increases markedly in senescence. Increased monocyte phagocytosis with aging was also suggested by studies of Løvik and North (1985),
who infected aging mice with *Listeria monocytogenes*, an organism that
requires monocytes for effective control. They found that aged mice had
increased resistance to *L. monocytogenes* and that this property was
independent of T lymphocytes, thus suggesting that there was increased
function of mononuclear phagocytes from senescent mice. It is presumed
that this increased monocyte phagocytic ability is a result of a non-
specific activation that occurs as a result of lifelong exposure to micro-
organisms (Løvik and North, 1985; Matsumoto *et al.*, 1979).

Antibody-dependent cell-mediated cytotoxicity (ADCC) is a form of
cell killing in which an effector cell kills an antibody-coated target cell via
recognition of the Fc portion of the attached antibody by Fc-receptors on

the surface membrane of the effector cell. Three studies on monocyte ADCC in aging humans have been published, and all three report an increase in killing by cells from aged humans. All three studies, however, appear to be flawed. First, Bátory *et al.* (1985) and Fernandes and Gupta (1981) used as effector cells, peripheral blood that had been depleted of many phagocytes by carbonyl iron and magnet treatment. Fülöp *et al.* (1984) used 'inmates of an old peoples home' as their source of blood cells, and it is thus difficult to ascertain whether their results are secondary to age or illness.

In two relevant studies, Whisler *et al.* (1985) showed that the percentage of peripheral blood monocytes that are Fc receptor positive is the same in young and old persons, and Bongrand *et al.* (1984) found no difference between young and old adults in the ability of monocytes to ingest IgG-coated sheep erythrocytes, but did find age-related impairment of non-specific phagocytosis of glutaraldehyde-treated sheep red cells.

Other studies of monocyte phagocytosis in aging have been performed. Gardner *et al.* (1981) found no changes with age in human peripheral blood monocyte phagocytosis of *Candida albicans*, chemotaxis to zymosan-activated serum, or adherence to glass. Likewise, Kelly *et al.* (1985) found no age-related differences in monocyte adherence. Tsang *et al.* (1983) found that monocyte chemotaxis was impaired in aging hamsters, but could be restored with isoprinosine. In more detailed studies, Antonaci *et al.* (1984) found a normal chemotactic response to zymosan-activated serum in the elderly, but did find that monocyte chemotactic activity induced by leukocyte-derived chemotactic factor was decreased. They also found monocyte phagocytosis of *C. albicans* to be decreased in the elderly, as did Nielsen *et al.* (1984).

The literature on in vitro function of the RES in aging as assessed by the clearance of intravenously injected substances has been recently reviewed by Brouwer and Knook (1983). They concluded that in humans, the RES shows an age-related decrease of approximately 15 per cent between 30 and 80 years of age. In senescent mice no changes were seen in the clearance of injected non-murine erythrocytes, but an age-related decline was found for the clearance of murine erythrocytes. The experiments do not distinguish whether these observed changes were due to circulatory disturbances, declining opsonic ability, or intrinsic splenic or hepatic macrophage dysfunction (Brouwer and Knook, 1983).

Recently, the accessory cell function of monocytes has received increased attention. There is a decreased ability of B cells from aged humans to make antibody to protein A derived from *Staphylococcus aureus* that appears to be due to both a decline in intrinsic B cell function and an increase in the monocyte's suppressive function (Whisler *et al.*, 1985). This increased monocyte suppressive effect can be blocked by inhibitors of prostaglandin synthesis (Antonaci *et al.*, 1983).

Schwab *et al.* (1985) studied the proliferative response of human T cells to the monoclonal antibody OKT3. This assay requires monocytes as accessory cells. They found a decreased proliferative response of T cells from aged donors that could not be improved by co-culture with monocytes from young donors. Thus, in this assay, there was an age-related decline in T-cell function, but there was no age-associated change in monocyte function. However, in studies on the regulatory function of monocytes in a cell-mediated cytotoxicity assay (Becker *et al.*, 1981) and an autologous mixed lymphocyte reaction (Klajman *et al.*, 1983) it was found that there was a loss of monocyte-mediated suppressor activity with aging.[2]

Interleukin 1 (IL-1) production is discussed in Section V.

V. CYTOKINES

The alterations of the immune response with aging have been correlated with a decreased production and/or a diminished response of the immunocompetent cells to various soluble mediators. Although there has been considerable progress in the purification and biochemical characterisation of these products, only a few of them have been studied in relation to aging. It has become evident that some of these mediators have the ability to modulate the production and/or release of other mediators. There are now data suggesting that certain thymic hormones can regulate the production of lymphokines like IL-2, IFN and CSF (Zatz *et al.*, 1975; Shoham *et al.*, 1980; Huang *et al.*, 1981; Svedersky *et al.*, 1982; Neta and Salvin, 1983; Zatz *et al.*, 1984) and that IL-2 induces IFN production (Handa *et al.*, 1983). IL-1 has also been shown to trigger IL-2 synthesis by activated T cells (Smith *et al.*, 1980). Given the level of interaction between these soluble mediators, it may not be easy to recognise the primary defect responsible for the age-associated decreased production of a particular lymphokine. Moreover, lymphoid cells from aged donors display an impaired response (in terms of proliferation as well as release of immunoregulatory molecules) to normal concentrations of exogenous lymphokines (Gillis *et al.*, 1981). Although other mechanisms may be involved, the age-related decreased response to lymphokines is more likely due to the loss of high-affinity receptors for these immunoregulatory products.

---

[2] Thus in different systems there have been reports of increased suppressor activity, decreased suppressor activity and normal function of monocytes. Generalisations would be more than usually hazardous. (Ed.)

A. Thymic Hormones

The thymus produces a number of immunoregulatory hormones which, among other properties, induce the maturation and differentiation of prethymic T cell precursors and also the maturation of B lymphocytes (Szewczuk *et al.*, 1980). During the past 15 years, numerous thymic hormones (thymosin fraction 5, thymic humoral factor, thymic factor X, thymostimulin) have been isolated and partially purified. Thymosin fraction 5 (TF-5) is probably the best characterised of these preparations. It includes a family of polypeptides, collectively termed thymosins (α and β thymosins, facteur thymique sérique [FTS], thymopoietin [TP-5]) that have been purified to homogeneity, sequenced and even synthesised. The serum concentration of most of these thymosins has been shown to decrease with age. Lewis *et al.* (1978) found that thymopoietin levels in human serum decline linearly after the age of 30. Thymopoietin activity is no longer present in the serum of healthy humans over the age of 60. Similarly, the concentration of FTS begins to decrease after the age of 20 and becomes undetectable after the age of 50 (Bach *et al.*, 1972). The concentration of thymosin α_1 is extremely elevated prior to birth. It decreases shortly after birth to remain fairly constant during the first 15 years of life. Maternal blood levels of thymosin α_1 are elevated during pregnancy (McClure *et al.*, 1982). Thymosin β_4 levels are high in the newborn and decline with age (Naylor *et al.*, 1984). The age-associated immune dysfunction has been shown to be partly related to the decreased production of thymic hormones. Synthetic thymosin α_1 is able to partially restore the impaired helper T cell response observed during aging (Frasca *et al.*, 1982; Ershler *et al.*, 1984, Frasca *et al.*, 1985). The decreased IL-2 production in aged humans, however, could not be corrected in vitro by thymosin α_1 (Ershler *et al.*, 1985). The treatment of aged or thymectomised mice with FTS prevented the decline of lymphocyte-mediated cytotoxicity (Bach, 1977). Weksler *et al.* (1978) showed that the age-related loss of IgG and high-affinity PFCs could also be reversed in old mice after in vivo or in vitro treatment with thymopoietin. Aside from their T cell differentiating activities, the mechanism of action of most of the thymosins is still unclear. The enhancing effect observed on the senescent immune response may be due to a direct action of the thymic hormones but could also be mediated by a modulation of lymphokine (IL-2, IFN, CSF) production or release.

B. Interleukins

Although the immune response of the newborn is qualitatively and quantitatively different from that of adults, this is not attributable to a defect in IL-2 synthesis since newborn T cells have been shown to be

efficient producers of IL-2 (Hayward and Kurnick, 1981). The lymphocytes from elderly humans, as well as from aged mice, proliferate less in
culture upon mitogenic stimulation than do lymphocytes from younger
counterparts. The reasons for the impaired proliferative response are not
fully understood. However, mitogen-induced proliferation of human and
murine T cells strictly depends on their capacity to release and to respond
to IL-2. Gillis *et al.* (1981) showed that the impaired proliferative
response of human lymphocytes from elderly donors could be attributed
to a decreased production of and response to IL-2. Similar data were
presented by Rabinowich *et al.* (1985). Thoman and Weigle (1981)
demonstrated that spleen cells from elderly mice produce 5 to 10 times
less IL-2 than do spleen cells from young mice. Miller and Stutman
(1981), Chang *et al.* (1982), and Effros and Walford (1983) also reported
lower IL-2 levels in old mice. The data reported by Gilman *et al.* (1982)
also suggest a defect in the synthesis and/or recognition of IL-2 in aged
rats. The decline does not appear to be due to a decreased number of cells
engaged in IL-2 production (Thoman and Weigle, 1981; Chang *et al.*,
1982), nor is it associated with the presence of suppressor activity (Gillis
et al., 1981; Chang *et al.*, 1982). Cheung *et al.* (1985) were able to
demonstrate a considerable age-associated decrease in the level of IL-2
mRNA in rat lymphocytes incubated with the mitogen concanavalin A.
Thus, the impaired proliferative response of T lymphocytes from aged
donors can be in part explained by low levels of IL-2. However, the fact
that the deficient T cell proliferative response could not be totally
reconstituted by exogeneous IL-2 (Gillis *et al.*, 1981) suggests that other
mechanisms are involved. Although the expression of IL-2 receptors
during aging has not been thoroughly examined, the data provided by
Gillis *et al.* (1981) and Chang *et al.* (1982) indicate an age-related
decrease in the expression of IL-2 receptors by activated T lymphocytes.
Aside from its role in antigen- or mitogen-induced T cell proliferation,
the contribution of IL-2 to age-related immune dysfunction has been
examined by Thoman and Weigle (1981, 1982) and Miller and Stutman
(1981). They observed that the failure to produce sufficient amounts of
IL-2 resulted in a decreased mixed lymphocyte reaction, a decline in
cytotoxic T cell response and diminished antibody production to T-
dependent antigens. The defects could be partially corrected by supplementation with exogenous IL-2.

The participation of IL-1 in the age-related immune deficiency has
been investigated. In mice, Chang *et al.* (1982) provided evidence that
the decreased level of IL-2 activity with age is attributable to both T
helper cells and adherent cells, reflecting a possible decrease in IL-1
production. The age-associated decline in IL-1 production was con-

firmed in later studies (Bruley-Rosset and Vergnon, 1984; Inamizu *et al.*, 1985). However, in humans no age-related decrease in IL-1 production has been observed (Jones *et al.*, 1984; Whisler *et al.*, 1985).

C. Interferons

Studies of IFN production in newborn infants have been prompted by their marked susceptibility to severe disseminated virus infections. Cantell *et al.* (1968) and Carter *et al.* (1971) showed that fetal and newborn fibroblasts and mononuclear cells can produce adult levels of virus-induced IFN. However, conflicting data have been reported concerning the production of lectin-induced IFN-γ. Bryson *et al.* (1980) and Taylor and Bryson (1981) observed a deficient to absent IFN-γ production in newborns, whereas Handzel *et al.* (1980) and Hahn *et al.* (1980) found that cord-blood lymphocytes were as capable of producing both viral and immune IFN as lymphocytes from older individuals. Contradictory results have also been reported concerning the production of IFN later in life. Cantell *et al.* (1968) found that human lymphocytes produce a constant amount of IFN per cell irrespective of the age of the donor. Abb *et al.* (1984) observed an age-related decline of IFN-α and IFN-γ production by human peripheral blood mononuclear cells. In mice IFN-γ production has been shown to increase with age (Heine and Adler, 1977).

As part of their pleiotropic biological activity, IFNs can modulate the immune responses. They enhance some immunological functions (NK activity, T-cell-mediated cytotoxicity, macrophage phagocytosis, expression of surface antigens) and inhibit others (cell activation, cell proliferation). Their effect on antibody synthesis is time and dose dependent: the enhancing effect is mediated by helper T cells while the suppressive activity is due to a direct effect on B cells. Because it is still unclear whether a physiological production exists and because of the complexity of its immunoregulatory activity, the exact contribution of an eventual defect in IFN production in the age-related decline of the immune function may prove difficult to evaluate.

D. Prostaglandins

Prostaglandins of the E series (PGE) are potent immunoregulatory molecules mostly synthesised by mononuclear phagocytes. The modulation of certain immunological functions by macrophages, in particular suppression of lymphocyte activity, is often mediated by PGEs. Conveniently, PGE production is completely suppressed by indomethacin.

Investigating the mechanism of T suppressive activity in the newborn, Durandy and co-workers (1982) showed that newborn monocytes produce a significantly smaller amount of PGE_2 than adult monocytes. In contrast, PGEs appears to play a significant role in the age-associated decrease in immune responsiveness. Rosenstein and Strausser (1980) demonstrated that T cell responsiveness to mitogen in old mice could be restored by the addition of indomethacin to the cell culture. Culture of adherent spleen cells from old mice produced six times more PGE than that of young mice. Goodwin and Messner (1979) reported that lymphocytes from humans over age 70 were significantly more sensitive to inhibition by PGE_2 in mitogen-stimulated cultures and postulated that endogenous PGE_2 may partially account for the depressed cellular immune response in the elderly. This finding was confirmed and extended in a later publication (Goodwin, 1982). The more sensitive lymphocytes were to inhibition by PGE_2, the lower was the mitogenic response, and the greater was the increase of the response in the presence of indomethacin.

VI. IMMUNOGLOBULINS AND ANTIBODIES

Age-dependent variation in immunoglobulin (Ig) levels in humans has been extensively studied during the past 20 years. Despite the relatively large number of publications on the subject, a definitive interpretation of the results is still difficult. The discrepancies among the published figures can be attributed to (1) the use of different methods for Ig quantitation, (2) the significant circadian and circannual rhythm effects on Ig levels (Reinberg *et al.*, 1977; Casale *et al.*, 1983), (3) the number of subjects within each age group, (4) the selection of the appropriate age intervals, (5) the sex-related changes in Ig concentration (which appear to vary among different age groups), (6) the health and nutritional status of the population under study (probably a major cause of variation among elderly people), (7) the cross-sectional or longitudinal characteristics of the studies, and (8) ethnic or other population differences.

In mice, Haaijman *et al.* (1977) observed an increase of serum Ig between birth and six months of age. Between six and 24 months of age individual classes and subclasses of Ig did not show much change except for significant increases in the IgG_1 and IgG_{2b} subclasses. From 24 months on the mean Ig level did not show any distinct trend except for a greater variation among the individual animals. Since antibody-forming potential declines with age, Quinn *et al.* (1973) attempted to explain the age-related increase of IgG by studying the catabolism of Ig as a function of age in mice. It was found that the half-life of radioiodinated IgG decreases sharply until about six months of age followed by a more gradual decrease throughout the remainder of life. In contrast the half-life of albumin remained relatively constant until very late in life when a marked increase was observed.

Numerous studies have been published concerning Ig concentrations in newborn humans and children (Orlandini *et al.*, 1955; West *et al.*, 1962; Huntley and Lyerly, 1963; Fulginiti *et al.*, 1966; Stiehm and Fudenberg, 1966; Johansson and Berg, 1967; Butterworth *et al.*, 1967; Collins-Williams *et al.*, 1967; Buckley *et al.*, 1968; Hardy *et al.*, 1969; Stoop *et al.*, 1969; Evans *et al.*, 1971; Cederquist *et al.*, 1978; Belldegrin *et al.*, 1980). Cord blood IgM and IgG both increase with gestational age until term while IgA remains unaffected by gestational age. Although there are conflicting reports concerning the age at which adult Ig levels are attained, the data from the largest series indicate that serum IgG reaches high concentrations at birth, drops dramatically after two weeks to attain a minimum level at three months and rises again to the adult level by the age of nine. However, the high IgG level at birth is due to maternal IgG crossing the placenta. The decrease observed between two weeks and three months is consistent with the half-life of serum IgG. In contrast, IgA and IgM, which do not cross the placenta, are low at birth and rise gradually to reach adult levels by the age 17–18. A significantly higher concentration of IgM has been observed in females over six years old (West *et al.*, 1962; Buckley *et al.*, 1968; Stoop *et al.*, 1969). Belldegrin *et al.* (1980) also found slightly higher levels of IgM in females in all age groups up to 18 years old, but none of the differences reached statistical significance.

Studies of Ig concentrations in humans after maturity seem to be more controversial. Nevertheless, when careful attention is paid to the selection of age ranges, analysis of the literature shows mainly two distinct trends. In some studies, Ig appears to rise with age, while in others Ig levels decline between the third and the sixth decade of life and then increase again up to the ninth decade. Although consensus has not been established on IgM levels or on sex-related changes in Ig concentrations, there is a general agreement that IgA and IgG levels are significantly increased in humans beyond the seventh decade. Buckley and Dorsey (1970) found that IgG decreases from the third to the sixth decade and that the IgM concentration decreases significantly by the sixth decade, whereas changes in serum IgA after maturity were small and non-significant. No sex-related differences were noted for any of the Ig classes. In a longitudinal study on older people, the same authors (Buckley *et al.*, 1974) observed a gradual upward trend in serum IgG and IgA in two-thirds of the eldest subjects. They also noticed that IgG was significantly lower in subjects studied proximate to death. Similarly, Bátory *et al.* (1984) observed low IgG values between 60 and 69 years of age, but also showed that IgA and IgG levels increase through the seventh, eighth and ninth decades of life whereas the IgM level remained identical or slightly higher in old individuals. Leslie *et al.* (1975) reported a moderate decrease in serum IgD with advancing age. Grundbacher and Shreffler, (1970) found a significant increase in IgG and IgA levels up to old age while IgM levels decreased significantly. Cassidy *et al.* (1974) also found a continuous rise of both IgA and IgG levels with age. Lamy *et al.* (1974) found that IgA levels increase with age and appear significantly higher in males than in females between the age 45 and 65. Cox *et al.* (1983) confirmed that older males have a higher IgA median value than age-matched females. Finkelstein *et al.* (1984) reported high concentrations of IgA, IgG and IgM in the saliva of older persons. Hallgren *et al.* (1973) and Riesen *et al.* (1976) found that IgG and IgA were significantly increased in the serum of aged persons living beyond the seventh decade. Radl *et al.* (1975) showed an important increase in serum IgA and IgG in humans over 95 years of age. Increase in the IgG_1 and IgG_3 subclasses was responsible for the elevated level of IgG.

Since most of these studies were only descriptive, the biological significance of an age-related increase in immunoglobulin levels in the serum as well as in other biological fluids (saliva, spinal fluid) is unknown. The studies of Hallgren *et al.* (1973), Buckley *et al.* (1974), Radl *et al.* (1975), Riesen *et al.* (1976) and Bátory *et al.* (1984) would seem to indicate that an increase in serum IgG and IgA is associated with a survival advantage. However, in the absence of conclusive longitudinal studies the prognostic significance of high Ig levels has still to be established: the relationship between survival and high Ig concentrations may be coincidental. The mechanism of such an increase in Ig levels with age remains unexplained. The influence of pathology, however, may not be ignored. High concentrations of IgA and IgG have been found in association with chronic pulmonary diseases (Stiehm and Fudenberg, 1966; Michel *et al.*, 1974) which have an extremely high prevalence among elderly people. B cells from elderly humans are functionally impaired in their ability to differentiate into Ig-secreting cells. Whether this impairment is due to a restriction in T–B cell collaboration and/or to an intrinsic B cell defect, it is unlikely that the age-related increase in Ig level may be attributed to an increased Ig synthesis at a single-cell level. Accordingly, it has been found that the concentration of isohaemagglutinin as well as natural antibodies (e.g., anti-sheep erythrocyte, anti-flagellin) decreased with age (Rowley *et al.*, 1968; Sommers and Kihns, 1972; Baumgarten *et al.*, 1976). However, the exposure to antigenic triggers (extrinsic antigens as well as altered intrinsic antigens) increases with age and may account, as a result of a continous stimulation of the immune system, for elevated Ig levels. In this respect, Glimcher and Cantor (1982) found that B cells from senescent mice spontaneously produce 'non-specific' IgG as if permanently activated.

A. Auto-anti-idiotypic Antibodies

The idiotypic network has proved to be an important regulatory feature of the immune system. Auto-anti-idiotypic antibodies have been shown to be partly responsible for the down-regulation of immunoglobulin synthesis. These auto-anti-idiotypic antibodies can be reliabily detected by the anti-idiotypic blocked, hapten-augmentable PFC assay. Alternatively, the presence of such antibodies can be detected using the ability of the immune sera to inhibit plaque formation by idiotype-producing cells. Szewczuk and Campbell (1980) demonstrated that the age-related decline in the number and heterogeneity of avidity of PFCs was due to the high concentrations of auto-anti-idiotypic antibodies in the immune sera of aged mice. The data reported by Goidl *et al.* (1980) also suggested that part of the age-associated decline in the humoral immune response is due to an increased production of auto-anti-idiotypic antibodies by old mice. An increased auto-anti-idiotypic response by aged mice was also suggested by the studies of Klinman (1981). In a later study, Goidl and co-workers (1983) showed that the serum of old mice contained twofold higher levels of auto-anti-idiotypes than did the serum of young mice. Transfer experiments indicated that the marked auto-anti-idiotypic response of aged mice was an inherent property of their B cell population

B. Autoantibodies

In experimental animals, aging increases the spontaneous expression of autoantibody-secreting B cells (Meredith *et al.*, 1979; Goidl *et al.*, 1981). Autoreactive lymphocytes exist in young animals, but the expression of their autoimmune potential is inhibited. Interestingly, IL-2 seems to be involved in the expression of autoimmunity. IL-2 deficiency correlates with the appearance of autoimmune manifestations in murine models of systemic lupus erythematosus (Dauphinée *et al.*, 1981). However, it is unclear whether IL-2 deficiency occurs as the primary defect or secondary to the autoimmune process. In humans, autoantibodies directed against a wide variety of antigens (nuclear antigens, thyroglobulin, gastric parietal cells, smooth and striated muscles, mitochondria, lipoproteins, submaxillary and adrenal glands, liver and kidney microsomes, lymphocytes, immunoglobulins) have been detected with an increased frequency in the serum of aged individuals (Hackett *et al.*, 1960; Heimer *et al.*,

1963; Cannat and Seligmann, 1965; Litwin and Singer, 1965; Cammarata *et al.*, 1967; Willikins *et al.*, 1967; Rowley *et al.*, 1968; Whittingham *et al.*, 1971; Hooper *et al.*, 1972; Mackay, 1972; Stobo and Tomasi, 1972; Hallgren *et al.*, 1973; Valtuena *et al.*, 1973; Fixa *et al.*, 1975; Riesen *et al.*, 1976; Pandey *et al.*, 1979; Delespesse *et al.*, 1980; Strelkauskas *et al.*, 1981; Goodwin *et al.*, 1982; Bátory *et al.*, 1985). Although the presence of such antibodies has been reported to be associated with shortened survival in humans (Hooper *et al.*, 1972), their pathologic significance is unknown and elderly people with these autoantibodies do not have the clinical manifestations of autoimmune diseases nor do they develop further immunological impairment as compared to age-matched controls without autoantibodies (Goodwin *et al.*, 1982). However, the coexistence of autoantibodies and autoantigens may result in the formation and circulation of immune complexes. Indeed, an increase frequency of circulating immune complexes was observed in aged individuals (Delespesse *et al.*, 1980; Goodwin *et al.*, 1982; Bátory *et al.*, 1985). Delespesse and co-workers reported a highly significant association between the presence of circulating immune complexes and that of autoantibodies. Although circulating immune complexes may play a role in the pathogenesis of vascular degenerative diseases, further epidemiological studies are needed to ascertain the link between circulating immune complexes and atherosclerosis in the elderly.

C. Monoclonal Immunoglobulins

In humans, the incidence of benign monoclonal gammopathy increases with age (Hallen, 1963; Axelsson *et al.*, 1966; Englisova *et al.*, 1968; Radl *et al.*, 1975; Riesen *et al.*, 1976). The frequency of idiopathic paraproteinaemia is reported to be about 0 % in the third decade, 0.1 to 1 % below the age of 50, 2 % over 70 years of age and increasing gradually up to 19 % in the tenth decade (Radl *et al.*, 1975). These homogeneous proteins reflect an impaired regulation of B cell function and not a neoplastic transformation of plasma cells. The occurrence of monoclonal Ig does not seem to influence the life expectancy of the affected individual (Axelsson, 1977). In mice, Radl and Hollander (1974) also reported the appearance of homogeneous immunoglobulins during aging. Abnormalities of T cell function seem to be involved in the pathogenesis of idiopathic paraproteinaemia. Thymectomised mice showed a markedly increased frequency and an earlier onset of idiopathic paraproteinaemia, often preceded by a restriction in Ig heterogeneity, and the appearance of transient homogeneous Ig. No increased incidence of lymphoreticular neoplasms or of malignant paraproteinaemia was observed in the thymectomised animals as compared with the control groups (Radl *et al.*, 1980).

The age-related alterations in humoral immunity are mainly qualitative. The total number of antibody-producing cells and the total amount of antibody synthesised following antigenic stimulation remain essentially unchanged. The age-associated impairment of B cell function results in a decreased response (in terms of affinity) to foreign antigen in reciprocal relation with an increased response to self antigens (Rowley *et al.*, 1968). Whether this impairment is attributed to B cells and/or to a restricted B–T cooperation, the primary underlying defect seems to be an age-dependent loss of high-affinity receptors for the antigen and for the lymphokines that mediate the control mechanisms between cells. The loss of high-affinity lymphocyte receptors accounts for the characteristics of the humoral response during aging, i.e. the requirement for a high dose of antigen to elicit a maximal response and the preferential loss of high-affinity antibodies. The same proposed mechanism explains the observation that an increased dose of tolerogen is necessary to induce tolerance in old animals. Under these conditions, a low concentration of self antigen may no longer be sufficient to maintain self-tolerance. The loss of self-tolerance may result in the emergence of autoreactive clones of lymphocytes and explain the increased incidence of autoantibodies. The increased anti-idiotypic response observed during aging may be due to a similar mechanism. Although little is known about the specificity of monoclonal immunoglobulins, idiopathic paraproteinaemias may arise from the expansion of one of these derepressed autoreactive clones. It is of particular interest that a normal thymic function is required for the production of high-affinity antibodies and that thymectomy increased the incidence of monoclonal immunoglobulins. The relative hypergammaglobulinaemia observed in aged humans may be partly attributed to an increased concentration of antibody to autologous antigens.

VII. COMPLEMENT

The 20 or more interacting serum proteins that constitute the complement system are critical components both in host defence against infection and in the inflammatory process (Johnston and Stroud, 1977; Kohler, 1978; Hadding, 1980). Complement proteins are activated by one of two general mechanisms; the classical pathway operates via Cl, C4 and C2, and the alternative pathway via C3 and factors B, D and P. The terminal complement proteins (C3–C9), which are responsible for most of the biological activities of complement, are a final common pathway for both systems. The classical pathway is activated by the recognition of antigen by IgM or IgG. This, in turn, leads to the binding of Clq by the Fc portion of antibody and initiates the conversion of inactive complement proteins into their enzymatically active forms (Porter and Reid, 1979). The alternative pathway proteins, which exist in a constant state of low-level activation, provide a humoral surveillance system that removes the need for specific antibody. Alternative pathway proteins are activated by many bacteria, certain viruses and virus-infected cells, fungi, and some tumour cell lines.

The effects of complement activation are at the heart of many inflammatory and autoimmune processes. Many cell types, including, neutrophils, monocytes/macrophages, T and B lymphocytes, basophils, mast cells and eosinophils, have specific receptors for complement components; these allow complement to regulate or modulate a variety of cellular responses (Fearon and Wong, 1983; Weigle *et al.*, 1983; Schreiber, 1985). Numerous and diverse clinical diseases are associated with decreased levels of serum complement proteins. Although rare, there are many different inherited complement deficiencies. They are frequently associated with an increased susceptibility to infection and/ or autoimmune diseases (Johnston and Stroud, 1977; McLean and Winkelstein, 1984; Ross and Densen, 1984).

As previously detailed in Section VI, many published studies of age-related changes in serum complement also suffer from a variety of methodological problems. Although there are studies examining age-related changes in CH_{50}, C3 or C4, the levels of most of other individual complement proteins have not been systematically examined. Measurement of CH_{50} tests the functional (haemolytic) activity of C1–C9 and does not assay components unique to the alternative pathway (factors B, D, or P). While this test is capable of detecting major deficiencies of classical pathway components, it is relatively insensitive to subtle alterations that might accompany age-related changes. Individual components such as C3 or C4 are commonly measured by immunochemical or haemolytic techniques that do not quantitate function. Further discussions of the components, molecular structure, and operation of the complement system may be found in reviews (Frank, 1979; Müller-Eberhard and Schreiber, 1980; Reid and Porter, 1981; Fearon, 1983; Joiner *et al.*, 1984; Müller-Eberhard and Miescher, 1985; Campbell *et al.*, 1986).

In the human fetus, synthesis of complement proteins begins as early as the first month of gestation and precedes immunoglobulin production. Gitlin and Biasucci (1969) were able to demonstrate synthesis of C3 and C1 inhibitor (C1 INH) from fetal yolk-sac cultures as early as 29 days of gestation. Production of C1 has been found in cultures of intestinal epithelium from 14-week-old fetuses (Colten *et al.*, 1968). Biologically active C2 and C4 are detectable in the supernatant of liver-cell cultures from 8-week-old fetuses, but it now appears that both C2 and C4 are actually synthesised in large part by cells of the macrophage–monocyte lineage (Adinolfi and Gardner, 1967; Adinolfi *et al.*, 1968; Colten, 1972; Einstein *et al.*, 1976; Colten *et al.*, 1979). Studies of pregnant women with complement deficiencies have further demonstrated the synthesis of C1 INH and C2 by the fetus (Alper and Rosen, 1976). C3 production has been detected in cultured liver cells from a 5.5-week-old fetus, but fetal serum levels of C3 remain very low until 26–28 weeks of gestation when the liver undergoes rapid growth (Adinolfi and Gardner, 1967; Propp and Alper, 1968; Gitlin and Biasucci, 1969; Adinolfi, 1970; Colten, 1972). In vitro synthesis of C5 by 8–14-week-old fetuses has been observed in a number of different tissues including liver, spleen, lung, thymus, bone marrow and colon, as well as the placenta (Kohler, 1973; Colten, 1973; Colten, 1976). The rate of synthesis of C5 by fetal liver is similar to that of the adult liver (Colten, 1973). C7 and C9 are detectable in the sera of fetuses over 16 weeks of age (Adinolfi and Beck, 1975). Synthesis of C3b inactivator (C3bINA) and factor H also occur at less than 12 weeks of gestation (Adinolfi *et al.*, 1981). The observation that all complement components are synthesised to some extent during human fetal life has been reproduced in animal species including the guinea pig, mouse, lamb, goat, rabbit, pig, monkey, and chicken (Adinolfi, 1977; Colten, 1977; Colten and Goldberger, 1979). In addition, haemolytic complement analogues are present in all vertebrate species (Rosen, 1974).

There is apparently no transplacental transport of complement components. This has been documented, to date, for C4, factor B, C3 and C6 (Propp and Alper, 1968; Alper and Rosen, 1976). Maternal C3 nephritic factor (C3NeF), an oligoclonal antibody to C3bBb, does pass the placenta and can decrease the serum C3 levels of the newborn (Kim *et al.*, 1978; Fearon and Austen, 1980).

CH_{50} levels are lower in cord blood than in adult sera (Dancis and Kunz, 1954; Eward *et al.*, 1961; Fishel and Pearlman, 1961; Fireman *et al.*, 1969; Drew and Arroyave, 1980). Although there are contradictory studies (Sawyer *et al.*, 1971; Norman *et al.*, 1975), it is now clear that the healthy term infant has levels of classical pathway complement components approximately 50–100 % of those of the adult (Adinolfi *et al.*, 1968; Ballow *et al.*, 1974; Davis *et al.*, 1979; Johnston *et al.*, 1979; Strunk *et al.*, 1979; Notarangelo *et al.*, 1984). The activation of C3, a critical component of both the classical and alternative pathways, is especially defective in the newborn (Winkelstein *et al.*, 1979). Alternative pathway components are even more deficient than classical pathway components (Stossel *et al.*, 1973; Ballow *et al.*, 1974; Feinstein and Kaplan, 1975; Davis *et al.*, 1979; Mills *et al.*, 1979b). Factors B and P in cord sera are at least three standard deviations below the adult mean. Despite these low levels, consumption of C3–C9 following alternative pathway activation by either zymosan or cobra venom factor is relatively normal. The functional activity (i.e. lytic activity) of the neonatal alternative pathway is, however, markedly deficient, probably because the low serum levels of factors B and P result in fewer active lytic enzyme sites per cell (Adamkin *et al.*, 1978). This reduction in alternative pathway complement activity and its effect on opsonisation underlie, in part, the increased susceptibility of the neonate to both viral and bacterial infections (Forman and Stiehm, 1969; McCracken and Eichenwald, 1971; Everaerts *et al.*, 1985). Several studies of premature infants indicate a significant correlation between birth weight and alternative pathway complement activity (Arditi and Nigro, 1957; Geisert *et al.*, 1971; McCracken and Eichenwald, 1971; Sawyer *et al.*, 1971; Strunk *et al.*, 1979; Shapiro *et al.*, 1981; Notarangelo *et al.*, 1984). Small premature infants, especially those with a birth weight below 1500 grams, seem to be especially deficient in complement components.

The precise age at which various complement components reach adult levels is largely unknown. CH_{50}, C3 and C4 levels rise through the first 1–2 years of life (Kaufman *et al.*, 1968; Fireman *et al.*, 1969; Geisert *et al.*, 1971; Büsse and Ströder, 1973). C1q and properdin reach adult levels at 18–21 months of age (Davis *et al.*, 1979). Two studies found no charge in CH_{50} (Norman *et al.*, 1975) or C3 (Coker *et al.*, 1972) levels from birth to the mid-teenage years. Norman *et al.* (1975) did, however, find in this same group increases with age in C3 and C4, and decreases in C5.

Although all studies do not agree (André and Lennes, 1965; Weeke and Krasilnikoff, 1972; Phair *et al.*, 1978; Sakamoto *et al.*, 1985), there appears to be a trend with age toward higher serum complement activity (Hartmann, 1958; Marucci and Chapman, 1964; Del Campo *et al.*, 1966; Papanayiotou *et al.*, 1969; Kalliomäki *et al.*, 1974). It is difficult to determine whether this is a gradual increase throughout adult life or is limited to the elderly groups, since some studies found increases limited to individuals older than 70 years of age, while others found increasing values only up to the fourth or fifth decade of life. Levels of C3 were found to increase in the aged (Thompson and Buckley, 1973; Riesen *et al.*, 1976; Phair *et al.*, 1978; Yonemasu *et al.*, 1978; Nagaki *et al.*, 1980); however, this was not the case for C4 (Riesen *et al.*, 1976; Jernigan *et al.*, 1980). Other studies have found age-related increases in C4

(Palmblad and Haak, 1978, Jernigan *et al.*, 1980; Nagaki *et al.*, 1980) and C1q (Yonemasu *et al.*, 1978). Nagaki *et al.* (1980) reported age-related increases in C5 and C9 and a decrease in factor B. Phair *et al.* (1978) found no age differences in factor B, but a slight increase in the elderly in serum properdin levels.

Polymorphism within the complement system has been known to exist since the late 1960s (Alper and Propp, 1968; Azen and Smithies, 1968). Currently seven of nine classical pathway proteins, and factors B and D of the alternative pathway, have been shown to be polymorphic (Hauptmann, 1979; McLean and Winkelstein, 1984). Of interest is the demonstration that C3 phenotype distribution differs significantly between young and old persons (Sørenson and Dissing, 1975a). The presence of the *C3*F* allele was found to be correlated with the occurrence of atherosclerosis in the elderly (Dissing *et al.*, 1972; Sørensen and Dissing, 1975b). It is not known whether certain complement phenotypes confer a biological advantage or whether phenotype expression is stable throughout life (Colten and Alper, 1972; Avrilommi, 1974).

At present there are many unanswered questions regarding age-related changes in complement levels and activity. Since elderly individuals have an increased incidence of conditions such as the presence of autoantibodies whose activities are mediated by complement, it is important to obtain further information about complement levels and function in the elderly. Recent advances, such as the development of cDNA clones for individual complement components, will obviously facilitate more precise investigations of age-related alterations of complement biology (DeBruijn and Fey, 1985; DiScipio *et al.*, 1984; Campbell *et al.*, 1986).

VIII. CONCLUSIONS

Many infectious diseases have increased morbidity in both the young and the old. This can be seen in terms of length of illness, degree of susceptibility, and length of hospitalisation. However, in many infectious diseases there is a markedly higher mortality in the elderly, and in most cases this is not understood. Also, it is well documented that the efficacy of antibiotic therapy is less in the elderly. These considerations support a proposal that natural immune mechanisms are deficient in both the young and the old, but the deficiency and lack of reserve capacity is more severe in the elderly. This also introduces the concept of activity levels. In the young, the absolute level of any natural immune function may be low, but the trend is generally upward toward adult levels, while in the elderly the level may again be low, but the trend is away from adult levels. Thus, the reserve capacity of the system is less and the ability of the host to deal with a pathogen is compromised. The infective dose of a pathogen is lower in both the young and the old, but the infective dose becomes a lethal dose in the elderly. Therefore, the critical function of a natural immune defence becomes one of eliminating pathogens to lower the challenge dose and prevent illness and/or death. Humoral immune mechanisms are also important, but generally require that the pathogen has been previously seen. Therefore, time becomes critical. Natural immunity, functioning optimally, provides time for the initiation of an immune response and for antibiotic action. Any decrement of natural immune ability increases the alloted time and shifts the advantage in the host–pathogen interaction to the pathogen. Mechanisms for dealing with less than optimal levels of natural immunity become important considerations in the care of the young and old and therefore studies to detail the development and senescence of natural immunity are crucial.

REFERENCES

Abb, J., Abb, H. and Deinhardt, F. (1984). Age related decline of human interferon alpha and interferon gamma production. *Blut* 48: 285.

Abo, T., Cooper, M. D. and Balch, C. M. (1982). Postnatal expansion of the natural killer and killer cell population in humans identified by the monoclonal HNK-1 antibody. *J. Exp. Med.* 321: 321.

Abo, T., Miller C. A. and Balch, C. M. (1984). Characterization of human granular lymphocyte subpopulations expressing HNK-1 (Leu-7) and Leu-11 antigens in the blood and lymphoid tissues from fetuses, neonates and adults. *Eur. J. Immunol.* 14: 616.

Acevedo, G. and Mauer, A. M. (1963). The capacity for removal of erythrocytes containing Heinz bodies in premature infants and patients following splenectomy. *J. Pediatr.* 63: 61.

Adamkin, D., Stitzel, A., Urmson, J., Farnett, M. L., Post, E. and Spitzer, R. (1978). Activity of the alternative pathway of complement in the newborn infant. *J. Pediatr.* 93: 604.

Adinolfi, M. (1970). Levels of two components of complement (C'4 and C'3) in human fetal and newborn sera. *Dev. Med. Child. Neurol.* 12: 306.

Adinolfi, M. (1977). Human complement: onset and site of synthesis during fetal life. *Am. J. Dis. Child.* 131: 1015.

Adinolfi, M. and Beck, S. (1975). Human complement — C7 and C9 — in fetal and newborn sera. *Arch. Dis. Child.* 50: 562.

Adinolfi, M. and Gardner, B. (1967). Synthesis of β_{1E} and β_{1C} components of complement in human foetuses. *Acta Paediatr. Scan.* 56: 450.

Adinolfi, M., Gardner, B. and Wood, C. B. S. (1968). Ontogenesis of two components of human complement: β_{1E} and β_{1C1A} globulins. *Nature* 219: 189.

Adinolfi, M., Dobson, N. C. and Bradwell, A. R. (1981). Synthesis of two components of human complement, β_{1H} and C3bINA, during fetal life. *Acta Paediatr. Scand.* 70: 705.

Albright, J. W. and Albright, J. F. (1983). Age-associated impairment of murine natural killer activity. *Proc. Natl. Acad. Sci USA* 80: 6371.

Alper, C. A. and Propp, R. P. (1968). Genetic polymorphism of the third component of human complement (C'3). *J. Clin. Invest.* 47: 2181.

Alper, C. A. and Rosen, F. S. (1976). Genetics of the complement system. *Adv. Human Genet.* 7: 141.

Altman A. and Rapp, H. J. (1978). Natural cell-mediated cytotoxicity in guinea pigs: Properties and specificity of natural killer cells. *J. Immunol.* 121: 2244.

Ambruso, D. R., Altenburger, K. M. and Johnston, R. B. (1979). Defective oxidative metabolism in newborn neutrophils: discrepancy between superoxide anion and hydroxyl radical generation. *Pediatrics* 64S: 722.

Anderson, D. C., Pickering, L. K. and Feigin, R. D. (1974). Leukocyte function in normal and infected neonates. *J. Pediatr.* 85: 420.

Anderson, D. C., Hugues, B. J. and Smith, C. W. (1981). Abnormal mobility of neonatal polymorphonuclear leukocytes: relationship to impaired redistribution of surface adhesion sites by chemotactic factor or colchicine. *J. Clin. Invest.* 68: 863.

André, A., and Lennes, G. (1965). La valeur moyenne du taux de complément total dans la population adulte normale est-elle en relation avec les groupes sanguins, ABO, MN, le sexe, l'âge et le poids? *Bibl. Haematol.* 23: 845.

Antonaci, S., Jirillo, E., Lucivero, G., Gallitelli, M., Garofalo, A. R. and Bonomo, L. (1983). Humoral immune response in aged humans: suppressor effect of monocytes on spontaneous plaque forming cell generation. *Clin. Exp. Immunol* 52: 387.

Antonaci, S., Jirillo, E., Ventura, M. T., Garofalo, A. R. and Bonomo, L. (1984). Non-specific immunity in aging: Deficiency of monocyte and polymorpho-nuclear cell-mediated functions. *Mech. Ageing Dev.* 24: 367.

Antonelli, P., Stewart, W. and DuPont, B. (1981). Distribution of natural killer cell activity in peripheral blood, cord blood, thymus, lymph nodes and spleen, and the effect of in vitro treatment with interferon preparation. *Clin. Immunol. Immunopathol* 19: 161.

Arditi, E. and Nigro, N. (1957). Ricerche sul complemento serico nell'immaturo. *Minerva Pediatr.* 9: 921.

Arenson, E. B., Epstein, M. B. and Seeger, R. C. (1979). Monocyte subsets in neonates and children. *Pediatrics* 64 (suppl): 740.

Avrilommi, H. (1974). Capacity of complement C3 phenotypes to bind on mononuclear cells in man. *Nature* 251: 740.

Axelsson, U. (1977). An eleven year follow up on 64 subjects with M components. *Acta Med. Scand.* 201: 173.

Axelsson, U., Bachmann, R. and Hallen, J. (1966). Frequency of pathological proteins (M-components) in 6995 sera from an adult population. *Acta Med. Scand.* 179: 235.

Azen, E. A and Smithies, O. (1968). Genetic polymorphism of C'3 (β1c-globulin) in human serum. *Science* 162: 905.

Bach, J. F., Papiernik, M., Levasseur, P., Dardenne, M., Barois, A. and Le Brigand, H. (1972). Evidence for a serum factor secreted by the human thymus. *Lancet* 2: 1056.

Bach, M-A. (1977). Lymphocyte mediated cytotoxicity: effect of aging, adult thymectomy and thymic factor. *J. Immunol.*, 119: 641.

Baley, J. E. and Schacter, B. Z. (1985). Mechanisms of diminished natural killer cell activity in pregnant women and neonates. *J. Immunol.* 134: 3042.

Ballow, M., Fang, F., Good, R. A. and Day, N. K. (1974). Developmental aspects of complement components in the newborn: The presence of complement components and C3 proactivator (properdin factor B) in human colostrum. *Clin. Exp. Immunol.* 18: 257.

Banerjee, D. and Thibert, R. F. (1983). Natural killer-like cells found in B-cell compartment of human lymphoid tissues. *Nature* 304: 270.

Bash, J. A., and Vogel, D. (1984). Cellular immunosenescence in F344 rats: decreased natural killer (NK) cell activity involves changes in regulatory interactions between NK cells, interferon prostaglandins and macrophages. *Mech. Ageing Dev.* 24: 49.

Bátory, G., Benczur, M., Varga, M., Garam, T., Onody, C. and Petranyi, G. G. (1981). Increase killer cell activity in aged humans. *Immunobiol.* 158: 383.

Bátory, G., Jancso, A., Puskás, E., Rédi, A., and Lengyel, E. (1984). Antibody and immunoglobulin levels in aged humans. *Arch. Gerontol. Geriatr.* 3: 175.

Bátory, G., Szondy, E., Falus, A., Füst, G., Beregi E., Onody, C. and Benzur, M. (1985). Autoimmunity and normal immune functions in aged humans. *Arch. Gerontol. Geriat.* 4: 261.

Baumgarten, A., Kruchok, A. H. and Weinrich, F. (1976). High frequency of IgG anti-A and -B antibody in old age. *Vox Sang.* 30: 253

Becker, M. J., Drucker, I., Farkas, R., Steiner, Z. and Klajman, A. (1981). Monocyte-mediated regulation of cellular immunity in humans: loss of suppressor activity with ageing. *Clin. Exp. Immunol.* 45: 439.

Bellanti, J. A., Nerurkar, L. S. and Zeligs, B. J. (1979). Host defenses in the fetus and neonate: Studies of the alveolar macrophage during maturation. *Pediatrics* 64 (suppl.): 726.

Belldegrin, A., Shoenfield, Y., Pick, A. I. and Vana, D. (1980). Age related distribution of serum immunoglobulin concentration in 1003 healthy children and adults. *Biomedicine* 33: 8.

Bender, B. S., Chrest, F. J. and Adler, W. H. (1986). Phenotypic expression of natural killer cell associated membrane antigens and cytolytic function of peripheral blood cells from different aged humans. *J. Clin. Lab. Immunol.* 21: 31.

Bongrand, P., Bartolin, R., Bouvenot, G., Arnaud, C., Delboy, C. and Depieds, R. (1984). Effect of age on different receptors and functions of phagocytic cells. *J. Clin. Lab. Immunol.* 15: 45.

Brouwer, A. and Knook, D. L. (1983). The reticuloendothelial system and aging: A review. *Mech. Ageing Dev.* 21: 205.

Bruley-Rosset, M. and Vergnon, I. (1984). Interleukin-l synthesis and activity in aged mice. *Mech. Ageing Dev.* 24: 247.

Bryson, Y. S., Winter, H. S., Gard, S. E., Fischer, T. J. and Stiehm, E. R. (1980). Deficiency of immune interferon production by leukocytes of normal newborns. *Cell. Immunol.,* 55: 191.

Buckley, C. E. III and Dorsey, F. C. (1970). The effect of aging on human serum immunoglobulin concentrations. *J. Immunol.* 105: 964.

Buckley, C. E. III, Buckley, E. G. and Dorsey, F. C. (1974). Longitudinal changes in serum immunoglobulin levels in older humans. *Fed. Proc.* 33: 2036.

Buckley, R. G., Dees, S. C. and O'Fallon, W. H. (1986). Serum immunoglobulin: I: Levels in normal children and in uncomplicated childhood allergy. *Pediatrics* 41: 600.

Büsse, M. and Ströder, J. (1973). Haemolytic complement activity in infants. *Z. Kinderheilkd.* 115: 267.

Butterworth, M. M., McClellan, B. and Allansmith, M. (1967). Influence of sex on immunoglobulin levels. *Nature* 214: 1224.

Cammarata, R. J., Rodnan, G. P. and Fennel, R. H. (1967). Serum anti γ globulin and antinuclear factors in the aged. *J. Am. Med. Ass.,* 199: 455.

Campbell, R. D., Carroll, M. C. and Porter, R. R. (1986). The molecular genetics of components of complement. *Adv. Immunol.* 38: 203.

Cannat, A. and Seligmann, M. (1965). Les anticorps anti-nucleaires décelés par immunofluorescence et par d'autres methodes immunologiques. *La Semaine des Hopitaux* 41: 1090.

Cantell, K., Stranger, H., Saxén, L. and Meyer, B. (1968). Interferon response of human leukocytes during intrauterine and postnatal life. *J. Immunol.* 100: 1304.

Carter, W. A., Hande, K. R., Essien, B., Prochownik, E. and Kaback, M. M. (1971). Comparative production of interferon by human fetal and neonatal and maternal cells. *Infect. Immun.* 3: 671.

Casale, G., Marinoni, G. L., d'Angelo, R. and de Nicola, P. (1983) Circadian rhythm of immunoglobulin in aged persons. *Age Ageing* 12: 81.

Cassidy, J. T., Nordy G. L. and Dodge, H. J. (1974). Biologic variations of human serum immunoglobulin concentrations: Sex-age specific effects. *J. Chronic Dis.* 27: 507.

Cederquist, L. L., Ewool, L. C. and Litwin, S. O. (1978). The effect of fetal age, birth weight, and sex on cord blood immunoglobulin values. *Am. J. Obstet. Gynecol.* 131: 520.

Chang, M. P., Makinodan, T., Peterson, W. J. and Strehler, B. L. (1982). Role of T cells and adherent cells in age-related decline in murine interleukin 2 production. *J. Immunol.* 129: 2426.

Charpentier, B., Fournier, C., Fries, D., Mathieu, D., Noury, J. and Bach, J. F. (1981). Immunological studies in human aging: I: In vitro function of T cells and polymorphs. *J. Clin. Lab. Immunol.* 5: 87.

Cheung, H. T., Wu, W. T., Pahlavani, M. and Richardson, A. (1985). Effect of age on the interleukin 2 messenger RNA level. *Fed. Proc.* 44: 573.

Coen, R., Grush, O. and Kauder, G. (1969). Studies of bactericidal activity and metabolism of the leukocyte in full-term neonates. *J. Pediatr.* 75: 400.

Coker, S. B., Nunnery, A. W. and Wenzel J. E. (1972). Determination of β_{1C}/β_{1A} globulin in children. *Southern Med. J.* 65: 61.

Collins-Williams, C., Tkachyk, S. J., Toft, B. and Moscarello, M. (1967). Quantitative immunoglobulin levels (IgG, IgA and IgM) in children. *Int. Arch. Allergy Appl. Immunol.* 31: 94).

Colten, H. R. (1972). Ontogeny of the human complement system: in vitro biosynthesis of individual complement components by fetal tissues. *J. Clin. Invest.* 51: 725.

Colten, H. R. (1973). Biosynthesis of the fifth component of complement (C5) by human fetal tissues. *Clin. Immunol. Immunopathol.* 1: 346.

Colten, H. R. (1976). Biosynthesis of complement. *Adv. Immunol.* 22: 67.

Colten, H. R. (1977). Development of host defenses: the complement and properdin systems. In M. D. Cooper and D. H. Dayton (eds), *Development of Host Defenses.* New York: Raven Press 165–173.

Colten, H. R. and Alper, C. A. (1972). Hemolytic efficiencies of genetic variants of human C3. *J. Immunol.* 108: 1184.

Colten, H. R. and Goldberger, G. (1979). Ontogeny of serum complement proteins. *Pediatrics* 64 (suppl.): 775

Colten, H. R., Gordon, J. M., Borosos, T. and Rapp, H. J. (1968). Synthesis of the first component of human complement in vitro. *J. Exp. Med.* 128: 55.

Colten, H. R., Ooi, Y. M. and Edelson, P. J. (1979). Synthesis and secretion of complement proteins by macrophages. *Ann. NY Acad. Sci.* 332: 482.

Corberand, J., Ngyen, F., Laharrague, P., Fontanilles, A-M., Gleyzes, B., Gyard, E. and Senegas, C. (1981). Polymorphonuclear functions and aging in humans. *J. Am. Geriatr. Soc.* 29: 391.

Cox, M. L., Freeman, H. G. M., Hodkinson, H. M., Pepys, M. B. and Ogle, S. J. (1983). Serum proteins in the elderly: Reference Ranges II. *J. Clin. Exp. Gerontol.* 5: 295).

Dancis, J. and Kunz, H. W. (1954). Studies of the immunology of the newborn infant: VI: Bacteriostatic and complement activity of the serum. *Pediatrics* 13: 339.

Das, M., Henderson, T. and Feig, S. A. (1979). Neonatal mononuclear cell metabolism: Further evidence for diminished moncyte function in the neonate. *Pediatr. Res.* 13: 632.

Datta, S. K., Gallagher, M. T. and Trentin, J. J. (1979). Natural cell-mediated cytotoxicity in hamsters. *Int. J. Cancer* 23: 728.

Dauphinée, M. J., Kipper, S. B., Wofsy, D. and Talal, N. (1981). Interleukin 2 deficiency is a common feature of autoimmune mice. *J. Immunol.* 127: 2483.

Davis, C. A., Vallota, E. H. and Forristal, J. (1979). Serum complement levels in infancy: age related changes. *Pediatr. Res.* 13: 1043.

DeBruijn, M. H. L. and Fey, G. H. (1985). Human complement component C3: cDNA coding sequence and derived primary structure. *Proc. Natl. Acad. Sci. USA* 82: 708.

Dekruyff, R. J., Kim, Y. T., Siskind, G. W. and Weksler, M. E. (1980). Age related changes in the in vitro immune response: increased suppressor activity in immature and aged mice. *J. Immunol.* 125: 142.

Del Campo, A. Castellani, G. and Franzoni, A. (1966). I fattori naturali de resistenza immunitaria nell'età senile. *G.Gerontol.* 14: 1123.

Delespesse, G., Gausset, P. H., Sarfati, M., Dubi-Rucquoy, M., Debisschop, M. J. and Van Haelst, L. (1980). Circulating immune complexes in old people and diabetics: correlation with autoantibodies. *Clin. Exp. Immunol.* 40: 96.

DeMaeyer, E., and DeMaeyer-Guignard, J. (1968). Influence of animal genotype and age on the amount of circulating interferon induced by Newcastle disease virus. *J. Gen. Vir.* 2: 445.

DiScipio, R. G., Gehring, M. R., Podack, E. R., Kan, C. C., Hugli, T. E. and Fey, G. H. (1984). Nucleotide sequence of cDNA and derived amino acid sequence of human complement component C9. *Proc. Natl. Acad. Sci. USA* 81: 7298.

Dissing, J., Lund, J. and Sorensen, H. (1972). C3 polymorphism in a group of old arteriosclerotic patients. *Hum. Hered.* 22: 466.

Drew, J. H. and Arroyave, C. M. (1980). The complement system of the newborn infant. *Biol. Neonate* 37: 209.

Durandy, A, Fischer, A., Mamas, S., Dray, F. and Griscelli, C. (1982). Respective roles and interactions of T lymphocytes and PGE_2-mediated monocyte suppressive activities in human newborns and mothers at the time of delivery. *Am. J. Reprod. Immunol.* 2: 127.

Effros, R. B. and Walford, R. L. (1983). The immune response of aged mice to influenza: diminished T cell proliferation, interleukin 2 production and cytotoxicity. *Cell. Immunol.* 81: 298.

Einstein, L. P., Schneeberger, E. E. and Colten, H. R. (1976). Synthesis of the second component of complement by long-term primary cultures of human monocytes. *J. Exp. Med.* 143: 114.

Englisova, M., Englis, M., Kyral, V., Kourilek, K. and Dvorak. K. (1968). Changes of immunoglobulin synthesis in old people. *Exp. Gerontol.* 3: 125.

Ershler, W. B., Moore, A. L. and Socinski, M. A. (1984). Influenza and aging: Age related changes and the effects of thymosin on the antibody response to influenza vaccine. *J. Clin. Immunol.* 4: 445.

Ershler, W. B., Moore, A. L., Roessner, K. and Ranges, G. E. (1985). Interleukin 2 and aging: Decreased interleukin 2 production in healthy elder people does not corrrelate with reduced helper cell numbers or antibody response to influenza vaccine and is not corrected in vitro by thymosin α_1. *Immunopharmacology* 10: 11.

Evans, H. E., Akpata, S. O. and Glass, L. (1971). Serum immunoglobulin levels in premature and full-term infants. *Am. J. Clin. Path.* 56: 416.

Everaerts, M. C., Van den Berghe, G., Saint-Remy J. M. and Corbeel, L. (1985). Effect of age-dependent enzymatic degradation of zymosan into oligosaccharides during incubation with serum and its opsonization by complement. *Pediatr. Res.* 19: 1293.

Eward, R. A., Williams, J. H. and Bowden, D. H. (1961). Serum complement in the newborn: an investigation of complement activity in normal infants and in Rh and AB haemolytic disease. *Vox Sang.* 6: 312.

Fearon, D. T. (1983). Complement. *J. Allergy Clin. Immunol.* 71: 520.

Fearon, D. T. and Austen, K. F. (1980). The alternative pathway of complement — a system for host resistance to microbial infection. *N. Engl. J. Med.* 303: 259.

Fearon, D. T. and Wong, W. W. (1983). Complement ligand–receptor interactions that mediate biological responses. *Ann. Rev. Immunol.* 1: 243.

Feinstein, P. A. and Kaplan, S. R. (1975). The alternative pathway of complement activation in the neonate. *Pediatr. Res.* 9: 803.

Fernandes, G. and Gupta, S. (1981). Natural killing and antibody-dependent cytotoxicity by lymphocyte subpopulations in young and aging humans. *J. Clin. Immunol.* 3: 141.

Finkelstein, M. S., Tanner, M. and Freedman, M. L. (1984). Salivary and serum IgA levels in a geriatric outpatient population. *J. Clin. Immunol.* 4: 85.

Fireman, P., Zuchowski, D. A. and Taylor, P. M. (1969). Development of human complement system. *J. Immunol.* 103: 25.

Fishel, C. W. and Pearlman, D. S. (1961). Complement components of paired mother–cord sera. *Proc. Soc. Exp. Biol. Med.* 107: 695.

Fixa, B., Komarkova, O. and Nozicka, Z. (1975). Ageing and autoimmunity. *Gerontologia* 21: 117.

Forman, M. L. and Stiehm, E. R. (1969). Impaired opsonic activity but normal phagocytosis in low-birth-weight infants. *N. Engl. J. Med.* 281: 926.

Frank, M. M. (1979). The complement system in host defense and inflammation. *Rev. Infect. Dis.* 1: 483.

Frasca, D., Garavini, M. and Doria, G. (1982). Recovery of T cell functions in aged mice injected with synthetic thymosin α_1. *Cell. Immunol.* 72: 384.

Frasca, D., Adorini, L. and Doria, G. (1985). Enhancement of helper and suppressor T cells activities by thymosin α_1 injection in old mice. *Immunopharmacology* 10: 41.

Fulginiti, V. A., Sieber, O. F. Jr., Claman, H. N. and Merrill, D. (1966). Serum immunoglobulin measurement during the first year of life and in immunoglobulin-deficiency states. *J. Pediatr.* 68: 723.

Fülöp, T., Fóris, G., Wórum, I. and Leövey, A. (1984). Age-dependent changes of the Fcγ-receptor-mediated functions of human monocytes. *Int. Archs. Allergy Appl. Immunol.* 74: 76.

Gardner, I. D. (1980). The effect of aging on susceptibility to infection. *J. Infect. Dis.* 131: 295.

Gardner, I. D., Lim, S. T. K. and Lawton, J. W. M. (1981). Monocyte function in ageing humans. *Mech. Ageing Dev.* 16: 233.

Geisert, J., Sacrez, R., Malgras, J., Hauptmann, G., Peter, M. O. and Duvivier, B. (1917). Variations physiologiques du complement serique chez l'enfant. *Pediatrie* 26: 619.

Gillis, S., Kozak, R., Durante, M. and Weksler, M. E. (1981). Immunological studies of aging: decreased production of and response to T cell growth factor by lymphocytes from aged humans. *J. Clin. Invest* 64: 937.

Gilman, S. C., Rosenberg, J. S. and Feldman J. D. (1982). T lymphocytes of young and aged rats: II. Functional defects and the role of interleukin-2. *J. Immunol.* 128: 644.

Gitlin, D. and Biasucci, A. (1969). Development of γG, γA, γM, β_{1C}/β_{1A}, C1'-esterase inhibitor, ceruloplasmin, transferrin, hemopexin, haptoglobin, fibrinogen, plasminogen, α_1-antitrypsin, orosomucoid, β-lipoprotein, α_2-macroglobulin and prealbumin in the human conceptus. *J. Clin. Invest.* 48: 1433.

Glimcher, L. H. and Cantor, H. (1982). T cell sets that control B-cell secretion of antigen specific immunoglobulin also control secretion of nonspecific immunoglobulin. *Cell. Immunol.* 70: 271.

Goidl, E. A., Thorbecke, G. J., Weksler, M. E. and Siskind, G. W. (1980). Production of auto-anti-idiotypic antibody during the normal immune response: changes in the auto-anti-idiotypic antibody response and the idiotype repertoire associated with aging. *Proc. Natl. Acad. Sci. USA* 77: 6788.

Goidl, E. A., Michelis, M. A., Siskind, G. W. and Weksler, M. E. (1981). Effect of age on the induction of autoantibodies. *Clin. Exp. Immunol.* 44: 24.

Goidl, E. A., Choy J. W., Gibbons, J. J., Weksler, M. E., Thorbecke, G. J. and Siskind, G. W. (1983). Production of auto-anti-idiotypic antibodies during the normal immune response: VIII: Analysis of the cellular basis for the increased auto-anti-idiotype antibody production by aged mice. *J. Exp. Med.* 157: 1635.

Goodwin, J. S. (1982). Changes in lymphocyte sensitivity to prostaglandin E, histamine, hydrocortisone, and x-irradiation with age: studies in a healthy elderly population. *Clin. Immunol. Immunopathol.* 25: 243.

Goodwin, J. S. and Messner, R. P. (1979). Sensitivity of lymphocytes to prostaglandin E_2 increases in subjects over 70. *J. Clin. Invest.* 64: 434.

Goodwin, J. S., Searles, R. P. and Tung, K. S. K. (1982). Immunological responses of a healthy elderly population. *Clin. Exp. Immunol.* 48: 403.

Grundbacher, F. J. and Shreffler, D. C. (1970). Changes in human serum immunoglobulin levels with age and sex. *Z. Immun. Forsch. Bd.* 141: S20.

Guimbretiere, J. and Audran, R. (1961). Etude of complement serique humain en fonction du sexe, du groupe sanguin ABO at Rh, de l'age et de la gravidie. *Nouv. Rev. Fr. Hematol.* 1: 694.

Haaijman, J. J., Van den Berg P. and Brinkhof, J. (1977). Immunoglobulin class and subclass levels in the serum of CBA mice throughout life. *Immunology* 32: 923.

Hackett, E., Beech, M. and Forbes, I. J. (1960). Thyroglobulin antibodies in patients without clinical diseases of the thyroid gland. *Lancet* 2: 402.

Hadding, U. (1980). Possible contribution of the complement system to the inflammatory state. *Agents Actions* 7: 24.

Haferkamp, O., Schlettwein-Gsell, D., Schwick. H. G. and Storiko, K. (1966). Serum protein in an aging population with particular reference to evaluation of immune globulin and antibodies. *Gerontologia* 12: 30.

Hahn, T., Levin, S. and Handzel, Z. T. (1980). Production of immune and viral interferon by lymphocytes of newborn infants. *Isr. J. Med. Sci.* 16: 33.

Hallen, J. (1963). Frequency of abnormal serum globulines (M-component) in the aged. *Acta Med. Scand.* 173: 737.

Haller, O., Kiessling R., Orn, A. and Wigzell, H. (1977). Generation of natural killer cells: an autonomous function of the bone marrow. *J. Exp. Med.* 145: 1411.

Hallgren, H. M., Buckley, C. E. III, Gilbertsen, V. A. and Yunis, E. J. (1973). Lymphocyte phytohemagglutinin responsiveness, immunoglobulins and auto-antibodies in aging humans. *J. Immunol.* 111: 1101.

Handa, K., Suzuki, R., Matsui, H., Shimizu, Y. and Kumagai, K. (1983). Natural killer (NK) cells as a response to interleukin 2 (IL-2): II: IL2 induces interferon γ production. *J. Immunol.* 130: 988.

Handzel, Z. J., Levin, S. and Dolphin, Z. (1980). Immune competence of newborn lymphocytes. *Pediatrics* 65: 491.

Hardy, J. B., McCracken, G. H., Mellits, E. D., Gilkeson, M. R. and Sever, J. L. (1969). Serum immunoglobulin levels in newborn infants: III: Some preliminary observations from a survey of cord blood levels in 2500 infants. *J. Pediatr.* 75: 1211.

Hartmann, J. (1958). Complement determination: 2: Determination of haemo-lytic complement activity in human sera as a function of age. *Acta Pathol. Microbiol. Scand.* 42: 164.

Hauptman, G. (1979). Genetic polymorphism of human complement proteins. *Rev. Fr. Transfus. Immunohematol.* 22: 587.

Hayward, A. R. and Kurnick, J. (1981). Newborn T cell suppression: early appearance, maintenance in culture, and lack of growth factor suppression. *J. Immunol.* 126: 50.

Heimer, R., Levin, F. M. and Rudd, E. (1963). Globulins resembling rheumatoid factor in serum of the aged. *Am. J. Med.* 35: 175.

Heine, J. W. and Adler, W. H. (1977). The quantitative production of interferon by mitogen stimulated mouse lymphocyte as a function of age and its effect on the lymphocyte proliferative response. *J. Immunol.* 118: 1366.

Herberman, R. B. and Ortaldo, J. R. (1981). Natural killer cells: Their role in defenses against disease. *Science* 214: 24.

Herberman, R. B., Nunn, M. E. and Lavrin, D. H. (1975). Natural cytotoxic reactivity of mouse lymphoid cells against syngeneic and allogeneic tumours: I: Distribution of reactivity and specificity. *Int. J. Cancer* 16: 216.

Hirsch, M. S., Ziman, B. and Allison, A. C. (1970). Macrophages and age-dependent resistance to Herpes simplex virus in mice. *J. Immunol.* 104: 1160.

Holroyde, C. P., Oski, F. A. and Gardner, F. H. (1969). The 'pocked' erythrocyte. Red-cell surface alterations in reticuloendothelial immaturity of the neonate. *N. Engl. J. Med.* 281: 516.

Hooper, B., Whittingham, S. Mathews, J. D., Mackay, I. R. and Curnow, D. H. (1972). Autoimmunity in a rural community. *Clin. Exp. Immunol.* 12: 79.

Huang, K. Y., Kind, P. D., Jagoda, E. M. and Goldstein, A. L. (1981). Thymosin treatment modulates production of interferon. *J. Interferon Res.* 1: 411.

Huntley, C. C. and Lyerly, A. (1963). Immunoglobulin determination in allergic children. *Am. J. Dis. Child.* 106: 545.

Inamizu, T., Chang, M. P. and Makinodan, T. (1985). Influence of age on the production and regulation of interleukin-1 in mice. *Immunology* 55: 447.

Jacobs, R. F., Wilson, C. B., Smith, A. L. and Haas, J. E. (1983). Age-dependent effects of aminobutyryl muramyl dipeptide on alveolar macrophage function in infant and adult *Macaca* monkeys. *Am. Rev. Respir. Dis.* 128: 862.

Jacobs, R. F., Wilson, C. B., Palmer, S., Springmeyer, S. C., Henderson, W. R., Glover, D. M., Kessler, D. L. Jr, Murphy, J. H., Hughes, J. P., Van Belle, G., Chi, E. Y. and Hodson, W. A. (1985). Factors related to the appearance of alveolar macrophages in the developing lung. *Am. Rev. Respir. Dis.* 131: 548.

Jernigan, J. A., Gudat, J. C., Blake, J. L., Bowen, L. and Lezotte, D. C. (1980). Reference values for blood findings in relatively fit elderly persons. *J. Am. Geriatr. Soc.* 28: 308.

Johansson, S. G. O. and Berg, T. (1967). Immunoglobulin levels in healthy children. *Acta Pediatr. Scand.* 56: 572.

Johnson, D. D., Renshaw, H. W., Warner, D. H., Browder, G. J. and Williams, J. D. (1984). Characteristics of the phagocytically induced respiratory burst in leukocytes from young adult and aged beagle dogs. *Gerontology* 30: 167.

Johnson, R. T., (1964). The pathogenesis of herpes virus encephalitis: II: A cellular basis for the development of resistance with age. *J. Exp. Med.* 20: 359.

Johnston, R. B. Jr, and Stroud, R. M. (1977). Complement and host defense against infection. *J. Pediatr.* 90: 169.

Johnston, R. B. Jr, Altenberger, K. M., Atkinson, A. W. Jr, and Curry, R. H. (1979). Complement in the newborn infant. *Pediatrics* 64 (suppl.): 781.

Joiner, K. A., Brown, E. J. and Frank, M. M. (1984). Complement and bacteria: chemistry and biology in host defense. *Ann. Rev. Immunol.* 2: 46.

Jones, P. G., Kauffman, C. A., Bergman, A. G., Hayes, C. M., Kluger, M. J. and Cannon, J. G. (1984). Fever in the elderly: Production of leukocytic pyrogen by monocytes from elderly persons. *Gerontology* 30: 182.

Kalff, M. W. (1970). A population study of serum immunoglobulin levels. *Clin. Chim. Acta* 28: 277.

Kalliomäki J. L., Mustakallio, E. and Mustakallio-Cook, S. (1974). Hemolytic and conglutinating complement in normal and pathologic human sera. *J. Am. Geriatr. Soc.* 22: 67.

Kaplan, J., Shope, T. C., Bollinger, R. O. and Smith, J. (1982). Human newborns are deficient in natural killer acitivty. *J. Clin. Immunol.* 2: 350.

Kaufman, H. S., Frick, O. L. and Fink, D. (1968). Serum complement (β_{1c}) in young children with atopic dermatitis. *J. Allergy* 42: 1.

Kelly, M. K., Brown, J. M. and Thong, Y. H. (1985). Neutrophil and monocyte adherence in diabetes mellitus, alcoholic cirrhosis, uraemia and elderly patients. *Int. Archs. Allergy Appl. Immunol.* 78: 132.

Kiessling, R., Klein, E., Pross, H. and Wigzell, H. (1975). 'Natural' killer cells in the mouse: II: Cytotoxic cells with specificity for mouse Moloney leukemia cells: Characteristics of the killer cell. *Eur. J. Immunol.* 5: 117.

Kim, Y., Shvil, Y. and Michael, A. F. (1978). Hypocomplementemia in a newborn infant caused by placental passage of C3 nephritic factor. *J. Pediatr.* 92: 88.

Kim, Y. B., Huh, N. D., Koren, H. S. and Amos, D. B. (1980). Natural killing (NK) and antibody-dependent cellular cytotoxicity (ADCC) in specific pathogen-free (SPF) miniature swine and germfree piglets: I: Comparison of NK and ADCC. *J. Immunol* 125: 755.

Klajman, A., Drucker, I. and Manor, Y. (1983). Autologous mixed lymphocyte reaction in man: further characterization of responding cells. *Immunol. Lett.* 6: 13.

Klein, R. B., Fisher, T. J. Gard, S. E., Biberstein, M., Rich, K. C. and Stiehm, E. R. (1977). Decreased mononuclear and polymorphonuclear chemataxis in newborns, infants, and young children. *Pediatrics* 60: 467.

Klinman, N. R. (1981). Antibody-specific immunoregulation and the immuno-deficiency of aging. *J. Exp. Med.* 154: 547.

Kohl, S., Frazier, J. J., Greenberg, S. B., Pickering, L. K. and Loo, L.-S. (1981). Interferon induction of natural killer cytotoxicity in human neonates. *J. Pediatr.* 98: 379.

Kohler, P. F. (1973). Maturation of the human complement system, onset time and sites of fetal C1q, C4, C3 and C5 synthesis. *J. Clin. Invest.* 52: 671.

Kohler, P. F. (1978). Human complement system. In M. Samter, D. W. Talmage, B. Rose, K. F. Austen and J. H. Vaughan (eds) *Immunological Diseases.* Waltham, Mass.: Little, Brown and Co.: 244–80.

Koren, H. S., Amos, D. B. and Kin, Y. B. (1978). Natural killing and antibody-dependent cellular cytotoxicity are independent immune functions in the Minnesota miniature swine. *Proc. Natl. Acad. Sci. USA* 75: 5127.

Kretschmer, R. R., Stewardson, P. B., Papierniak, C. K. and Gotoff, S. P. (1976). Chemotactic and bactericidal capacities of human newborn monocytes. *J. Immunol.* 117: 1303.

Kretschmer, R. R., Papierniak, C. K., Stewardson-Krieger, P., Bamzai, A. K. and Gotoff, S. P. (1977). Quantitative nitrobluetetrazolium reduction by normal newborn monocytes. *J. Pediatr.* 90: 306.

Lamy, J., Titeca, C. and Weill, J. (1974). Valeurs de reference des IgA seriques humaines: variation avec l'age et le sexe. *Ann. Biol. Clin.* 32: 529.

Lanier, L. L., Le, A. M., Phillips, J. H., Warner, N. L. and Babcock, G. F. (1983). Subpopulations of human natural killer cells defined by expression of the Leu-7 (HNK-1) and Leu-11 (NK-15) antigens. *J. Immunol.* 131: 1789.

Lanza, E. and Djeu, J. Y. (1982). Age-independent natural killer cell activity in murine peripheral blood. In R. B. Herberman (ed.), *NK Cells and Other Natural Effector Cells*: New York, Academic Press: 335–40.

Leslie, G. A., Correa, L. R. H. and Holmes, J. N. (1975). Structure and biological function of human IgD: IV: Ontogeny of human serum immunoglobulin D (IgD) as related to IgG, IgA and IgM. *Int. Arch. Allergy Apppl. Immunol.* 49: 350.

Lewis, V. M., Twomey, J. J., Bealmear, P., Goldstein, G. and Good, R. A. (1978). Age, thymic involution and circulating thymic hormone activity. *J. Clin. Endocrinol. Metab.* 47: 145.

Ligthart, G. J., Schuit, H. R. E. and Hijmans, W. (1985). Subpopulations of mononuclear cells in ageing: expansion of the null cell compartment and decrease in the number of T and B cells in human blood. *Immunology* 55: 15.

Litwin, S. D. and Singer, J. M. (1965). Studies of the incidence and significance of anti-gammaglobulin factors in the aged. *Arthritis Rheum.* 8: 538.

Løvik, M. and North, R. J. (1985). Effect of aging on antimicrobial immunity: old mice display a normal capacity for generating protective T cells and immunologic memory in response to infection with *Listeria monocytogenes. J. Immunol.* 135: 3479.

Lu, C. Y., Calamai, E. G. and Unanue, E. R. (1979). A defect in the antigen-presenting function of macrophages from neonatal mice. *Nature* 282: 327.

McClure, J. E., Lameris, N., Wara, D. W. and Goldstein, A. L. (1982). Immunochemical studies on thymosin: radioimmunoassay of thymosin α_1, *J. Immunol.* 128: 368.

McCracken G. H. Jr and Eichenwald, H. F. (1971). Leukocyte function and the development of opsonic activity and complement activity in the neonate. *Am. J. Dis. Child.* 121: 120.

Mackay I. (1972). Aging and immunological function in man. *Gerontologia* 18: 285.

McLaughlin, B., O'Malley, K. and Cotter, T. G. (1986). Age-related differences in granulocyte chemotaxis and degradation. *Clin. Sci.* 70: 59.

McLean, R. H. and Winkelstein, J. A. (1984). Genetically determined variation in the complement system: relationship to disease. *J. Pediatr.* 105: 179.

Mangan, K. F., Hartnett, M. E., Matis, S. A., Winkelstein, A. and Abo, T. (1984). Natural killer cells suppress human erythroid stem cell proliferation in vitro. *Blood* 62: 260.

Marcano, N. B., Rivas, A., Figarella, E. F., Blanca, I., Penchaszakeh, G. K., Perez-Rojas, G. and Bianco, N. E. (1982). Cell-mediated effector mechanisms in aging humans. *Int. Arch. Allergy Appl. Immunol.* 69: 7.

Maródi, L, Scorba, S. and Nagy, B. (1980) Chemotactic and random movement of human newborn monocytes. *Pediatrics* 135: 73.

Marucci, A. A. and Chapman, O. D. (1964). Complement activity in sera of normal adult blood donors: its relation to blood group, Rho(D) type, sex, age, and weight. *Transfusion* 4: 39.

Matoth, Y. (1952). Phagocytic and ameboid activity of the leukocytes in the newborn infant. *Pediatrics* 9: 748.

Matsumoto, T., Miake, S., Mitsuyama, M., Takeya, K. and Nomoto, K. (1979). Augmented resistance to *Listeria monocytogenes* in mice at an early stage of aging. *J. Clin. Lab. Immunol* 2: 55.

Meredith, P. J., Kristie, J. A. and Walford, R. L. (1979). Aging increases expression of LPS-induced autoantibody-secreting B cells. *J. Immunol.* 123: 87.

Michel, F. B., Mellet, J. M., Prefaut, C., Robinet-Levy, M. and David, P. (1974). Immunoglobulin A, G. M et bronchopneumopathies chroniques. *Nouv. Presse. Med.* 3: 258.

Miller, M. E. (1969). Phagocytosis in the newborn infant: humoral and cellular factors. *J. Pediatr.* 74: 255.

Miller, M. E. (1971). Chemotactic function in the human neonate: humoral and cellular aspects. *Pediatr. Res.* 5: 487.

Miller, R. A. and Stutman, O. (1981). Decline, in aging mice of the anti-2,4,6 trinitrophenyl (TNP) cytotoxic T cell response attributable to loss of Lyt-2$^-$, interleukin-2 producing helper cell function. *Eur. J. Immunol.* 11: 751.

Mills, E. L., Thompson, T. and Björkstén, B. (1979a). The chemiluminescence response and bactericidal activity of neutrophils from newborns and their mothers. *Pediatrics* 63: 429.

Mills, E. L., Björkstén, B. and Quie, P. G. (1979b). Deficient alternative complement pathway activity in newborn sera. *Pediatr. Res.* 13: 1341.

Mintz, L., Drew, W. L., Hoo, R. and Finley, T. N. (1980). Age-dependent resistance of human alveolar macrophages to herpes simplex virus. *Infect. Immun.* 28: 417.

Miyazaki, S., Shin, H., Kabuba, S., Tomooka, Y. and Goya, N. (1982). Neutrophil function in newborns. *Tohoku J. Exp. Med.* 137: 207.

Müller-Eberhard, H. J. and Miescher, P. A. (1985). *Complement.* Berlin: Springer-Verlag.

Müller-Eberhard, H. J. and Schreiber, R. D. (1980). Molecular biology and chemistry of the alernative pathway of complement. *Adv. Immunol.* 29: 1.

Munan, L. and Kelly, A. (1979). Age-dependent changes in blood monocyte populations in man. *Clin. Exp. Immunol.* 16: 161.

Mysliwska, J., Mysliwski, A. and Witkowski, J. (1985). Age-dependent decline of natural killer and antibody-dependent cell mediated cytotoxicity activity of human lymphocytes is connected with decrease of their acid phosphatase activity. *Mech. Ageing Dev.* 31: 1.

Nagaki, K., Hiramatsu, S., Inai, S. and Sasaki, A. (1980). The effect of aging on complement activity (CH_{50}) and complement protein levels. *J. Clin. Lab. Immunol.* 3: 45.

Nagel, J. E., Collins, G. C. and Adler, W. H. (1981). Spontaneous or natural killer cytotoxicity of K562 erythroleukemic cells in normal patients. *Cancer Res.* 41: 2284.

Nagel, J. E., Pyle, R. S., Chrest, F. J. and Adler, W. H. (1982). Oxidative metabolism and bactericidal capacity of polymorphonuclear leukocytes from normal young and aged adults. *J. Gerontol.* 37: 829.

Nagel, J. E., Han, K., Coon, P. J., Adler, W. H. and Bender, B. S. (1986). Age differences in phagocytosis by polymorphonuclear leukocytes measured by flow cytometry. *J. Leukocyte Biol.* 39: 399.

Naor, D., Bonavida, B. and Walford, R. L. (1976). Autoimmunity and ageing, the age related response of mice of a long lived strain to trinitrophenylated syngeneic mouse red blood cells. *J. Immunol.* 117: 2204.

Naylor, P. H., McClure, J. E., Spangelo, B. L., Low, T. L. K. and Goldstein, A. L. (1984). Immunochemical studies on thymosin: radioimmunoassay of thymosin β_4. *Immunopharmacology* 7: 9.

Neta, R. and Salvin, S. B. (1983). Resistance and susceptibility to infection in in-bred murine strains: II: Variation in the effect of treatment with thymosin fraction 5 on the release of lymphokines in vivo. *Cell. Immunol.* 75: 173.

Nielsen, H., Blom, J. and Larsen, S. O. (1984). Human blood monocyte function in relation to age. *Acta Path. Microbiol. Immunol. Scand.* 92: 5.

Noble, R. L. and Warren, R. P. (1985). Age-related development of human natural killer cell activity. *N. Engl. J. Med.* 313: 641.

Norman, M. E., Gall, E. P., Taylor, A., Laster, L. and Nilsson, U. R. (1975). Serum complement profiles in infants and children. *J. Pediatr.* 87: 912.

Notarangelo, L. D., Chirico, G., Chiara, A., Colombo, A., Rondini, G., Plebani, A., Martini, A. and Ugazio, A. G. (1984). Activity of classical and alternative pathways of complement in preterm and small for gestational age infants. *Pediatr. Res.* 18: 281.

Nunn, M. E., Djeu, J. Y., Glaser, M., Lavrin, D. H. and Herberman, R. B. (1976). Natural cytotoxic reactivity of rat lymphocytes against syngeneic Gross virus-induced lymphoma. *J. Natl. Cancer Inst.* 56: 393.

Onsrud, M. (1981). Age dependent changes in some human lymphocyte subpopulations. Changes in natural killer cell activity. *Acta Path. Microbiol. Scand.* 89: 55.

Orlandini, T. O., Sass-Kortsak, A. and Ebbs, J. H. (1955). Serum gammaglobulin levels in normal infants. *Pediatrics* 16: 575.

Orlowski, J. P., Sieger, L. and Anthony, B. F. (1976). Bactericidal capacity of monocytes of newborn infants. *J. Pediatr.* 89: 797.

Ortaldo, J. R. and Herberman, R. B. (1984). Heterogeneity of natural killer cells. *Ann. Rev. Immunol.* 2: 359.

Pahwa, S. G., Pahwa, R. and Grimes, E. (1977). Cellular and humoral components of monocyte and neutrophil chemotaxis in cord blood. *Pediatr. Res* 11: 677.

Palmblad, J., and Haak, A. (1978). Ageing does not change blood granulocyte bactericidal capacity and levels of complement factors 3 and 4. *Gerontology* 24: 381.

Pandey, J. P., Fudenberg, H. H., Ainsworth, S. K. and Loadholt, C. B. (1979). Autoantibodies in healthy subjects of different age groups. *Mech. Ageing Dev.* 10: 399.

Papanayiotou, P., Papanayiotou, K., Papavassiliou, J. and Mastoraki, D. (1969). Variations physiologiques de complément sérique. Influence de l'age et du sexe sur le taux C'H$_{50}$. *Ann. Inst. Pasteur.* 117: 796.

Park, B. H., Holmes, B. and Good, R. A. (1970). Metabolic activities in leukocytes of newborn infants. *J. Pediatr.* 76: 237.

Penschow, J. and Mackay, I. R. (1980). NK and K cell activity of human blood: differences according to sex, age, and disease. *Ann. Rheum. Dis.* 39: 82.

Pesanti, E. L. (1977). When phagocytic dysfunction increases susceptibility to infectious diseases. *Geriatrics* 32: 110.

Phair, J. P., Kauffman, C. A., Bjornson, A., Gallagher, J., Adams, L. and Hess, E. V. (1978) Host defenses in the aged: evaluation of components of the inflammatory and immune response. *J. Infect. Dis.* 138: 67.

Porter, R. R. and Reid, K. B. M. (1979). Activation of the complement system by antibody-antigen complexes: the classical pathway. *Adv. Prot. Chem.* 33: 1.

Propp, R. A. and Alper, C. A. (1968). C3 synthesis in the human fetus and lack of placental passage. *Science* 162: 672.

Pross, H. F. and Baines, M. G. (1982). Studies of human natural killer cells: I: *In vivo* parameters affecting normal cytotoxic function. *Int. J. Cancer* 29: 383.

Quinn, R. P., Price, G. B., Ellis, J. M. and Makinodan, T. (1973). Catabolic half-lives of immunoglobulin and albumin as a function of age in mice. *J. Gerontol.* 28: 257.

Rabinowich, H., Goses, Y., Reshef, T. and Klajman, A. (1985). Interleukin-2 production and activity in aged humans. *Mech. Ageing Dev.* 32: 213.

Radl, J. and Hollander, C. F. (1974). Homogenous immunoglobulins in sera of mice during aging. *J. Immunol.* 112: 2271.

Radl, J., Sepers, J. M., Skvaril, F., Morell, A. and Hijmans, W. (1975). Immunoglobulin patterns in humans over 95 years of age. *Clin. Exp. Immunol.* 22: 84.

Radl, J., De Glopper, E., Van Den Berg, P. and Van Zwieten, M. J. (1980). Idiopathic paraproteinemia: III: Increased frequency of paraproteinemia in thymectomized aging C57BL/KaLwRij and CBA/BrArRij mice. *J. Immunol.* 125: 31.

Reid, K. B. M. and Porter, R. R. (1981). The proteolytic activation systems of complement. *Ann. Rev. Biochem.* 50: 433.

Reinberg, A., Schuller, E., Delasnerie, N., Clench, J. and Helary, M. (1977). Rythmes circadiens et circannuel des leucocytes, proteines totales, immuno-globulines A, G et M. *Nouv. Presse Med.* 6: 3819.

Repo, H., Jokipii, A. M. M., Leirisalo, M. and Kosunen, T. U. (1980) Leukocyte motility in the newborn: determination of spontaneous movement is essential in the in vitro assessment of neutrophil chemotaxis. *Clin. Exp. Immunol.* 40: 620.

Riesen, W., Keller, H., Skvaril, F., Morell, A. and Barandun, S. (1976). Restriction of immunoglobulin heterogeneity, autoimmunity and serum protein levels in aged people. *Clin. Exp. Immunol.* 26: 280.

Roder, J. C. (1980). Target–effector interaction in the natural killer (NK) cell system: VI: The influence of age and genotype on NK binding characteristics. *Immunology* 41: 483.

Rola-Pleszczynski, M., Lieu, H., Sullivan, A. K. and Girard, J. (1985). Membrane markers, target cell specificity, and sensitivity to biological response modifiers distinguish human natural cytotoxic from human natural killer cells. *J. Clin. Invest.* 76: 1927.

Rosen, F. S. (1974). Complement: ontogeny and phylogeny. *Transplant. Proc.* 6: 47.

Rosenstein, M. M. and Strausser, H. R. (1980). Macrophage-induced T cell mitogen suppression with age. *J. Reticuloendothel. Soc.* 27: 159.

Ross., S. C. and Densen, P. (1984). Complement deficiency states and infection: epidemiology, pathogenesis and consequences of neisserial and other infections in an immune deficiency. *Medicine (Baltimore)* 63: 243.

Rowley, M. J., Buchanan, H. and Mackay, I. R. (1968). Reciprocal change with age in antibody to extrinsic and intrinsic antigens. *Lancet* 2: 24.

Sakamoto, M., Ooyamma, T., Tango, T. and Nishioka, K. (1985). Association of nutritional indices and immunological parameters in elderly patients, including those with cancer. In R. K. Chandra (ed.), *Nutrition, Immunity and Illness in the Elderly*. New York: Pergamon: 234–41.

Sato, T., Fuse, A. and Kuwata, T. (1979). Enhancement by interferon of natural cytotoxic activities of lymphocytes from human cord blood and peripheral blood of aged persons. *Cell. Immunol.* 45: 458.

Savary, C. A. and Lotzova, E. (1978). Suppression of natural killer cell cytotoxicity by splenocytes from *Corynebacterium parvum*-injected, bone marrow-tolerant, and infant mice. *J. Immunol.* 120: 239.

Sawyer, M. K., Forman, M. L., Kuplic, L. S. and Stiehm, E. R. (1971). Developmental aspects of the human complement system. *Biol. Neonate* 19: 148.

Saxena, R. K., Saxena, Q. B. and Adler, W. H. (1984). Interleukin-2 induced activation of natural killer activity in spleen cells from old and young mice. *Immunology* 51: 719.

Schreiber, R. D. (1985). The chemistry and biology of complement receptors. In H. J. Müller-Eberhard and P. A. Miescher (eds), *Complement*. Berlin: Springer-Verlag: 115–43.

Schwab, R., Hausman, P. B., Rinnooy-Kan, E. and Weksler, M. E. (1985). Immunological studies of ageing: X: Impaired T lymphocytes and normal monocyte response from elderly humans to the mitogenic antibodies OKT3 and Leu4. *Immunology* 55: 677.

Seki, H., Ueno, Y., Taga, K., Matsuda, A., Miyawaki, T. and Taniguchi, N. (1985). Mode of in vitro augmentation of natural killer cell activity by recombinant human interleukin 2: A comparative study of Leu-11$^+$ and Leu-11$^-$ cell populations in cord blood and adult peripheral blood. *J. Immunol.* 135: 2351.

Shapiro, R., Beatty, D. W., Woods, D. L. and Malan, A. F. (1981). Serum complement and immunoglobulin values in small-for-gestational-age infants. *J. Pediatr.* 99: 139.

Shellam, G. R. and Hogg, N. (1977). Gross-virus-induced lymphoma in the rat: IV: Cytotoxic cells in normal rats. *Int. J. Cancer* 19: 212.

Shoham, J., Eshel, I., Aboud, M. and Salzberg, S. J. (1980). Thymic hormonal activity in vitro: II: Enhancement of the production of immune interferon by activated cells. *J. Immunol.* 125: 54.

Silverman, E. M. and Silverman, A. G. (1977). Granulocyte adherence in the elderly. *Am. J. Clin. Path.* 67: 49.

Sirianni, M. C., Businco L., Seminara, R. and Aiuti, F. (1983). Severe combined immunodeficiencies, primary T-cell defects and DiGeorge syndrome in humans: Characterization by monoclonal antibodies and natural killer cell activity. *Clin. Immunol. Immunopath.* 28: 361.

Smith, K. A., Lachman, L. B., Oppenheim, J. J. and Favata, M. F. (1980). The functional relationship of the interleukins. *J. Exp. Med.* 151: 1551.

Snyder, D. S., Lu, C. Y. and Unanue, E. R. (1982). Control of macrophage Ia expression in neonatal mice — role of a splenic suppressor cell. *J. Immunol.* 128: 1458.

Sommers, H. and Kihns, W. J. (1972). Blood group antibodies in old age. *Proc. Soc. Exp. Biol. Med.* 141: 1104.

Sørensen, H. and Dissing, J. (1975a). C3 polymorphism in relation to age. *Hum. Hered.* 25: 284.

Sørensen, H. and Dissing, J. (1975b). Association between the C3F gene and atherosclerotic vascular diseases. *Hum. Hered.* 25: 279.

Stiehm, E. R. and Fudenberg, H. H. (1966). Serum levels of immunoglobulins in health and diseases: a survey. *Pediatrics* 37: 715.

Stiehm, E. R., Sztein, M. B., Steeg, P. S., Mann, D., Newland, C., Blaese, M. and Oppenheim J. J. (1984). Deficient DR antigen expression on human cord blood monocytes: reversal with lymphokines. *Clin. Immunol. Immunopath.* 30: 430.

Stobo, J. D. and Tomasi, J. B. (1972). Aging and the regulation of immune reactivity. *J. Chronic Dis.* 28: 437.

Stoerner, J. W., Pickering, L. K., Adcock, E. W. and Morriss, F. H. Jr (1978). Polymorphonuclear leukocyte function in newborn infants. *J. Pediatr.* 93: 862.

Stoop, J. W., Zegers, B. J. M., Sander, P. C. and Ballieux, R. E. (1969). Serum immunoglobulin levels in healthy children and adults. *Clin. exp. Immunol.* 4: 101.

Stossel, T. P., Alper, C. A. and Rosen, F. S. (1973). Opsonic activity in the newborn: role of properdin. *Pediatrics* 52: 134.

Strauss, R. G. and Seifert, M. J. (1978). Oxidative metabolism in cord blood polymorphonuclear leukocytes. *Arch. Dis. Child.* 53: 78.

Strelkauskas, A. J., Andrew, J. A. and Yunis, E. J. (1981). Autoantibodies to a regulatory T cell subset in human ageing. *Clin. Exp. Immunol.* 45: 308.

Stroobant, J., Harris, M. C., Cody, C. S., Polin, R. A. and Douglas, S. D. (1984). Diminished bactericidal capacity for group B streptococcus in neutrophils from 'stressed' and healthy neonates. *Pediatr. Res.* 18: 634.

Strunk, R. C., Fenton, L. J. and Gaines, J. A. (1979). Alternative pathway of complement activation in full term and premature infants. *Pediatr. Res* 13: 641.

Stutman, O., Christopher, J. P. and Figarella, E. F. (1978). Natural cytotoxic cells against solid tumours in mice. I. Strain and age distribution and target cell susceptibility. *J. Immunol.* 121: 1819.

Sugiyama, E., Ito, M., Suzuki, H., Yamashita, N., Maruyama, M. and Yano, S. (1983). Natural killer cell activity associated with aging and sex in humans. *Jap. J. Med.* 22: 195.

Sullivan, J. L., Barry, D. W., Lucas, S. J. and Albrecht, P. (1975). Measles infection of human mononuclear cells: I: Acute infection of peripheral blood lymphocytes and monocytes. *J. Exp. Med.* 142; 773.

Svedersky, L. P., Hui, A., May, L., McKay, P. and Stebbing, N. (1982). Induction and augmentation of mitogen-induced immune interferon production in human peripheral blood lymphocytes by N^{α} — desacetylthymosin α_1. *Eur. J. Immunol.* 12: 244.

Szewczuk, M. R. and Campbell, R. J. (1980). Loss of immune competence with age may be due to anti-idiotypic antibody regulation. *Nature* 286: 164.

Szewczuk, M. R., DeKruyff, R. H., Weksler, M. E. and Siskind, G. W. (1980). Ontogeny of B lymphocyte function: VIII: Failure of thymus cells from aged donors to induce the functional maturation of B lymphocytes from immature donors. *Eur. J. Immunol.* 10: 918.

Taylor, S. and Bryson, Y. J. (1981). Impaired production of immune (PHA induced) interferon in newborns is due to a functionally immature macrophage *Pediatr. Res.* 15: 604.

Thoman, M. L. and Weigle, W. O. (1981). Lymphokines and ageing: interleukin-2 production and activity in aged animals. *J. Immunol.* 127: 2102.

Thoman, M. L. and Weigle, W. O. (1982). Cell-mediated immunity in aged mice: an underlying lesion in IL-2 synthesis. *J. Immunol.* 128: 2358.

Thompson, J. and Buckley, C. E. (1973). Serum β_{1A} levels in older humans. *J. Gerontol.* 28: 434.

Tono-Oka, T., Nakayama, M., Uehara, H. and Matsumoto, S. (1979). Characteristics of impaired chemotactic function in cord blood leukocytes. *Pediatr. Res.* 13: 148.

Tsang, K. Y., Fudenberg, H. H. and Gnagy, M. J. (1983). Restoration of immune responses of aging hamsters by treatment with isoprinosine. *J. Clin. Invest.* 71: 1750.

Tsang, K. Y., Pan, J. F., Swanger, D. L. and Fudenberg. H. H. (1985). In vitro restoration of immune responses in aging humans by isoprinosine. *Int. J. Immunopharmacol.* 7: 199.

Ueno, Y., Miyawaki, T., Seki, H., Matsuda, A., Taga, K., Sato, H. and Taniguchi, N. (1985) Differential effects of recombinant human interferon-γ and interleukin 2 on natural killer cell activity of peripheral blood in early human development. *J. Immunol.* 135: 180.

Uksila, J., Lassila, O., Hirvonen, T. and Toivanen, P. (1983). Development of natural killer cell function in the human fetus. *J. Immunol.* 130: 153. *J. Immunol.* 130: 153.

Umiel, T., Pecht, M. and Trainin, N. (1984). THF, a thymic hormone, promotes IL-2 production in intact and thymus deprived mice. *J. Biol. Response Mod.* 3: 423.

Valtuena, J. P., Gonzalez Guilabert, M. I., Del Pozo Perez, M. A., Del Pozo Crespo, F. and Velasco Alonzo, R. (1973). Autoimmunity, immunoglobulin and T lymphocyte population in old age. *Biomedicine* 19: 301.

van Epps, D. E., Goodwin, J. S. and Murphy, S. (1978). Age dependent variations in polymorphonuclear leukocyte chemiluminescence. *Infect. Immun.* 22: 57.

van Furth, R., Cohn, Z. A., Hirsch, J. G., Humphrey, J. H., Spector, W. G. and Langevoort, H. L. (1972). The mononuclear phagocytes system: A new classification of macrophages, monocytes, and their precursor cells. *Bull. WHO* 46: 845.

van Tol, M. J. D., Zijlstra, J., Thomas, C. M. G., Zegers, B. J. M. and Ballieux, R. R. (1984). Distinct role of neonatal and adult monocytes in the regulation of the *in vitro* antigen-induced plaque-forming cell response in man. *J. Immunol.* 134: 1902.

Ventura, M. T., Troccoli, G., Crollo, R., Lasaracina E. and Bonomo L. (1985). Modifying effects of monocytes and autologous serum on natural killer capacity in the elderly. *IRCS Med. Sci.* 13: 1172.

Weeke, B. and Krasilnikoff, P. A. (1972). The concentration of 21 serum proteins in normal children and adults. *Acta Med. Scand.* 192: 149.

Weigle, W. O., Goodman, M. G., Morgan, E. L. and Hugli, T. E. (1983). Regulation of immune response by components of the complement cascade and their activated fragments. *Springer Semin. Immunopathol.* 6: 173.

Weksler, M. E., Innes, J. B. and Goldstein, G. (1978). Immunological studies of aging: IV: The contribution of thymic involution to the immune deficiencies of aging mice and reversal with thymopoietin. *J. Exp. Med.* 148: 996.

West, C. D., Hong, R. and Holland, N. H. (1962). Immunoglobulin levels from the newborn period to adulthood and in immunoglobulin deficiency states. *J. Clin. Invest.* 41: 2054.

Weston, W. L., Carson, B. S., Barkin, R. M., Slater, G. D., Dustin, R. D. and Hecht, S. K. (1977). Monocyte–macrophage function in the newborn. *Am. J. Dis. Child.* 131: 1241.

Whisler, R. L., Newhouse, Y. G., Ennist, D. and Lachman, L. B. (1985). Human B-lymphocyte colony responses: Suboptimal colony responsiveness in aged humans associated with defective function of B cells and monocytes. *Cell. Immunol.* 94: 133.

Whittingham, S., Matthews, S. D., Mackay, I. R., Stocks, A. E., Ungar, B. and Martin, F. I. R. (1971). Diabetes mellitus, autoimmunity and aging. *Lancet* 1: 763.

Willikins, R. F., Whitaker, R. R., Anderson, R. V. and Bevven, D. (1967). Significance of anti-nuclear factors in older persons. *Ann. Rheum. Dis.* 26: 306.

Wilson, C. B. and Haas, J. E. (1984). Cellular defenses against *Toxoplasma gondii* in newborns. *J. Clin. Invest.* 73: 1606.

Winkelstein, J. A., Kurlandsky, L. E. and Swift, A. J. (1979). Defective activation of the third component of complement in the sera of newborn infants. *Pediatr. Res.* 13: 1093.

Wright, W. C. Jr, Ank, B. J. and Herbert, S. (1975). Decreased bactericidal activity of leukocytes of stressed newborn infants. *Pediatrics* 56: 578.

Wustrow, T. P. U., Denny, T. N., Fernandes, G. and Good, R. A. (1982). Changes in macrophages and their functions with aging in C57BL/6J, AKR/J, and SJL/J mice. *Cell. Immunol.* 69: 227.

Yamashita, N., Suzuki, H., Maruyama, M., Sugiyama E. and Yano, S. (1984). Effects of aging in the *in vitro* response of human lymphocytes to interleukin-2. *Jap. J. Med.* 23: 211.

Yonemasu, K., Kitajima, H., Tanabe, S., Ochi, T. and Shinkai, H. (1978). Effect of age on C1q and C3 levels in human serum and their presence in colostrum. *Immunology* 35: 523.

Zatz, M. M., White, Z., Schulof, R. S. and Goldstein, A. L. (1975). The effect of anti-thymosin globulin in the recovery of T cells in ATS-treated mice. *Ann. NY Acad. Sci.* 249: 499.

Zatz, M. M., Oliver, J., Samuels, C., Skotnicki, A., Sztein, M. and Goldstein, A. L. (1984). Thymosin increases production of T cell growth factor by normal human peripheral blood lymphocytes. *Proc. Natl. Acad. Sci. USA* 81: 2882.

Zeligs, B. J., Nerurkar, L. S. and Bellanti, J. A. (1984). Chemotactic and candidacidal responses of rabbit alveolar macrophages during postnatal development and the modulating roles of surfactant in these responses. *Infect. Immun.* 44: 379.

13

Nutritional Factors

M. ERIC GERSHWIN
CARL L. KEEN
MARK P. FLETCHER
LUCILLE S. HURLEY

*Division of Clinical Immunology and the Departments of Internal Medicine and Nutrition
University of California at Davis
TB 192, Davis, CA 95616, USA*

I. INTRODUCTION

The importance of nutritional factors for immune responses has received much attention in the past several years. While the influence of severe malnutrition upon disease has been well categorised in Third World nations, the influence of selective deprivation on immunity has received only modest attention. Clearly nutritional factors are best studied and

440

NATURAL IMMUNITY
ISBN 0 12 5145551

defined during periods of rapid growth and development, i.e., when imposed during gestation and the postnatal period. In this chapter we will therefore emphasise the role of selective nutritional deprivation on immune ontogeny.

In considering the influences of nutritional factors upon immunocompetence, it is extremely important to distinguish between the effects of nutrition on immunological function in adults from those upon neonatal or developing organisms. Young animals undergo rapid growth and development and are therefore subjected to a heightened degree of physiological stress; thus insufficient availability of essential nutrients is a more critical factor for them than for adults. Nutritional deficiencies which might not result in an impaired immune response in adult animals or humans might cause notable dysfunction in the developing fetus or neonate, rendering it more susceptible to a variety of infectious agents. Moreover, should the essential nutrient deficiency occur during a particularly critical period of development or embryogenesis, the capacity for normal immune ontogenesis may be permanently compromised. Consequently, even prolonged periods of subsequent nutritional rehabilitation in such animals may not result in an acceptable level of immunological function.

II. EXPERIMENTAL ANIMAL STUDIES

A number of studies have attempted to reproduce dietary manipulations in experimental animals similar to dietary conditions of malnourished human populations. While it is difficult to duplicate such dietary deficiencies, empirical studies in animals allow one to observe precisely and serially the effects of early nutritional deficiencies and allow for specific antigenic challenge. The results have helped to elucidate the role of specific nutrients in the immunodeficiency observed in undernourished populations.

Based upon field studies suggesting possible long-term impairment of immune function in humans and studies in experimental animals indicating that the thymus was one of the organs most affected by nutritional deprivation during development, Jose et al., (1973) investigated the influence of a defined period of nutritional deficiency during postnatal development upon immunological function in mice. In addition to a carefully defined period of nutritional deprivation, some animals were also subjected to intensive antigenic stimulation simultaneously, so as to simulate conditions observed in developing nations. Mice were fed a diet low in total kilojoules and protein for a two-week period during the latter stages of postnatal development and specific humoral and cellular immune responsiveness to transplantation antigens was assessed. A decreased capacity to develop cellular cytotoxicity in response to allogeneic stimuli was seen in animals fed low-protein, low-kilojoule diets, even 12 weeks after nutritional restitution had commenced. Protein deficiency alone had a similar effect, but by 12 weeks of age, the cell-mediated immune responsiveness had returned to normal. Lower levels of haemagglutinating antibodies were observed in deprived mice after five weeks of nutritional rehabilitation; beyond this time period, responses were within normal ranges (Jose *et al.*, 1973). A reduced number of Thy-1-positive lymphocytes was also observed in thymus, spleen and lymph nodes of deprived animals after five weeks of nutritional rehabilitation; however, 12 weeks of such supplementation resulted in a more normal profile of splenic Thy-1^+ cells. Of particular interest, the animals subjected to simultaneous intense antigenic stimulation did not experience a deficient level of immune function, despite being fed the low-protein diet (Jose *et al.*, 1973). Therefore, both depressed cell-mediated immunity and the relative lack of thymus-derived lymphoid cells present in thymus, spleen and lymph nodes were directly related to the magnitude of early nutritional deprivation of protein and energy, in terms of both the extent and the duration of immunosuppression.

When pregnant mice were fed a diet deficient in total kilojoules and containing low levels of protein (6 per cent protein during the first 14 days of lactation and then either 6 per cent or 2 per cent protein to 40 days of age) the immune responsiveness of first generation offspring at 40 days of age was significantly compromised (Hook and Hutcheson, 1976). Direct plaque-forming cell responses to heterologous erythrocytes from control animals were 93-fold and 3-fold greater than those of mice fed the diets containing 2% and 6% protein respectively. These differences between dietary groups remained significant even after adjustment for decreased spleen size and total spleen cell number, which were significantly lower in the mice fed the protein–energy-deficient diets during development. In addition, the mean titres of serum haemagglutinating antibody to sheep erythrocytes reflected a similar trend, being markedly lower in the protein–energy-malnourished mice (Hook and Hutcheson, 1976). It would therefore appear that, in experimental animals, cell-mediated immunity and possibly humoral immunity may both be significantly affected by protein–energy malnutrition. Similar observations have been made in inbred rats fed a diet restricted, in protein and calories, to 25 per cent of the levels fed to control counterparts prior to and during gestation but then returned to a control diet at parturition.

This limited the period of nutritional deprivation to fetal development (except for possible effects on lactation) (Chandra, 1975b). Such rats displayed a marked reduction in the plaque-forming cell responsiveness of spleen cells; both direct IgM plaques and, especially, indirect IgG plaques were substantially reduced. Serum haemolysin titres to heterologous erythrocytes were also significantly reduced by nutritional deprivation. In addition, despite nutritional repletion of F_1 offspring beginning at birth, immunodeficiency persisted in the F_2 generation offspring of F_1 females mated with healthy control male rats (Chandra, 1975b).

Wade *et al.* (1983) have reported that when the duration of the protein–energy undernutrition is limited to the period of lactation, there is little impact on the immune system in mice. These investigations utilised a design in which female mice were bred in litters of four, nine or 20 pups. Litters of nine pups were considered controls. Overfeeding (litters of four pups) during lactation had no effect on immune system function when tested at four and seven weeks of age, as judged by their plaque-forming cell responses to sheep red blood cells (SRBC) and lymphocyte stimulation in vitro to concanavalin A or lipopolysaccharide (LPS). Similarly, if the undernourished pups (litters of 20) were allowed unlimited access to food following weaning, they also showed normal immune responses at four and seven weeks of age. However, if the undernourished pups were allowed access to food only every other day after weaning, by seven weeks of age they showed marked atrophy of the lymphoid tissue and depressed immune responsiveness to SRBCs and they showed a diminished delayed-type hypersensitivity to dinitrofluorobenzene (DNFB) (Wade *et al.*, 1983). The above results show that the length of the dietary deficiency, rather than its severity, may explain some of the conflicts in reports on functional immune tests in protein–energy undernutrition.

Mechanisms which may account for the immunodeficiency observed in animals fed restricted levels of protein and calories during development have been suggested (Srivastava *et al.*, 1981). In particular, abnormal metabolism of nucleotides and nucleosides in both thymus and spleen of neonatal offspring of rats who experienced such dietary deprivation has been seen. For example, thymocytes and splenocytes from the malnourished rats had altered intracellular levels of ATP, ADP, cAMP, 5'AMP and adenosine, suggesting that such metabolic alterations may be fundamental to the immunodeficiency observed in animals deprived of essential nutrients during critical periods of development. Srivastava *et al.* (1987) have recently reported a lower content of poly A^+ RNA in the lymphoid organs of rat pups exposed to protein–energy undernutrition during their second week of life. However, despite the lower content of poly A^+ RNA, the translational efficiency of poly A^+ RNA was higher in the thymus and spleens collected from the undernourished pups. These results support the idea that protein–energy undernutrition early in life can modulate the metabolism of mRNA and hence protein synthesis in lymphoidal tissues. To what extent these changes are influencing the immune responsiveness of the animal is not known.

An additional biochemical lesion which may in part underlie the immunodeficiency of protein–energy undernutrition is impaired histidine metabolism (Enwonwu, 1986). It has been established in several experimental animals, including non-human primates, that protein-energy undernutrition can result in a marked increase in the free histidine pool in several tissues, due to increased synthesis of the amine (Enwonwu, 1986). It has been shown that some functional subsets of T lymphocytes have a greater density of histamine receptors than other lymphocytes (Plaut *et al.*, 1980), and the cytolytic activity of the former is inhibited by histamine through a histamine-induced increase in cAMP (Plaut *et al.*, 1985; Strom *et al.*, 1977). Histamine can also have a suppressive effect on lymphocyte proliferation, which is thought to be due to a histamine-induced increase in prostaglandins (Bach *et al.*, 1985; Rocklin, 1985), or a histamine-induced reduction in interleukin 2 production and activity (Rocklin, 1985; Huchet, 1985).

A. Studies of Protein Deficiency During Immune Ontogeny

Because protein has been considered to be one of the key essential nutrients frequently deficient in diets of socio-economically deprived populations, there have been several animal studies focusing only on protein deficiency. One of the most interesting studies was an attempt to simulate the synergistic interaction between nutritional deficiencies and increased risk of pathogenic challenge during the neonatal period (Cruz and Waner, 1978). These investigators studied the interactive influences upon growth and immune development of concurrent sublethal cytomegalovirus infection in mice fed a low-protein diet introduced at the 21st day post partum. Infection with cytomegalovirus resulted in stunted growth of offspring as well as immunosuppression, as reflected by impaired mitogen responsiveness and decreased direct plaque-forming cell responsiveness to sheep erythrocytes (Cruz and Waner, 1978). However, when all nutritional requirements were met during the postnatal period, mice were able to respond effectively to the cytomegalovirus infection; growth rates rebounded to normal levels within 28–42 days after infection. In neonatal mice, the effects of protein deficiency upon growth and immunosuppression in uninfected protein-malnour-ished mice were similar to those in infected well-nourished mice (e.g., decreased body weight, impaired T cell function), leading the authors to suggest that protein malnutrition during the prenatal period mimics the detrimental influences of cytomegalovirus infection. When neonatal cytomegalovirus infection and undernutrition (protein deficiency) were introduced simultaneously, there was a synergistically accentuated negative impact upon growth and immune function, resulting in a significantly more profound immunosuppression and a much greater delay in response to cytomegalovirus challenge. This experimental model closely resembles the situation in less developed countries. In children, however, there is often more than a single agent involved and the infectious dose is sublethal. In addition, the diet of human populations would most likely be deficient in more than a single nutrient. Similarly, such nutritional deprivation, to a variable degree, would have existed prenatally, during the immediate postnatal period, as well as during the latter stages of postnatal development. An increased susceptibility to infectious agents after protein deficiency during gestation has been confirmed by other investigators (Watson *et al.*, 1976).

There are many studies of immune function following gestational protein deficiency. Examination of lymphoid organ weights after protein deprivation *in utero* revealed that thymic weights were low at birth and tended to remain significantly low at five months of age, even after nu-tritional rehabilitation at birth (Olusi *et al.*, 1976). Histological examin-ation of such thymus glands indicated that this form of intra-uterine growth retardation is associated with a delay in thymic development (Lansdown, 1977). Thymus tissue obtained from protein-deprived rats and mice contained fewer small lymphocytes and showed an aberrant organisation of cortex and medulla. The clear distinction between cortex and medulla was lost in protein-deficient animals; there was also a relative increase in epithelial cells in both the cortex and medulla. In contrast, Hassall's corpuscles were largely absent (Lansdown, 1977).

The immune responsiveness of rodents deprived of protein during gestation was markedly altered. When rats were fed a protein-deficient diet for four days prior to mating and then throughout gestation there was a delay in the appearance of IgG2b in malnourished offspring (Olusi *et al.*, 1976). Additionally, while serum levels of IgG2a in well-nourished control offspring began to increase on day 16 post partum, no such increase occurred in protein-malnourished progeny. Moreover, even when offspring of malnourished dams were rehabilitated nutritionally for four months with a high-protein diet, IgG levels in serum were still significantly lower in formerly malnourished offspring. Offspring born to dams who had been fed a diet deficient in protein for three months before and throughout gestation had a prolonged period of reduced immune function (Gebhardt and Newberne, 1974). Even when progeny of such deprived dams were fed a high-protein diet for four months, there was decreased antibody response to antigenic challenge. For example, offspring of deprived dams formed only 58 ± 4 plaques/10^6 spleen cells in response to SRBC immunisation, as compared to 275 ± 13 plaques/10^6 spleen cells in control offspring (Gebhardt and Newberne, 1974). In addition, in vitro mitogen responsiveness of splenic lymphocytes to phytohaemagglutinin (PHA) continued to show a 60 per cent reduction even after months of nutritional rehabilitation. Thus protein deficiency alone can impair immune responsiveness for prolonged periods, perhaps permanently, if imposed during critical periods of immune ontogeny.

Studies of the influence of protein deficiency during gestation upon non-specific immune functions have also been performed. Rats were fed an 8 per cent casein diet between days 5 and 19 of gestation (compared with a 25 per cent protein diet fed to control dams), thereby limiting the period of deprivation to only the end of pregnancy. Serum complement levels were not similar in both groups of dams. Offspring of control dams developed normal CH50 levels by 35 days of age. At 35 days of age, levels of serum complement in the protein-deficient offspring were only one-third those of controls. Even at 90 days of age, the progeny of protein-deficient dams had not attained the normal levels of complement. Protein-deficient dams also had significantly lower levels of complement in milk. Control dams had levels of milk complement approximately twofold greater than serum complement levels, whereas no differences between milk and serum complement were seen in protein-deficient dams. This may explain the decreased complement levels in their respective offspring.

B. Experimental Vitamin Deficiencies During Immune Ontogeny

Vitamin deficiency during development and its influence upon the ontogenesis of intact immune function has been investigated rather sporadically. It is difficult to generalise about vitamin deficiencies and their impact upon any physiological parameter, as vitamins represent a heterogeneous group of compounds. Nonetheless the potential importance of such deficiencies is becoming apparent as methodology to detect marginal degrees of deficiency is developed.

One of the water-soluble vitamins that has been investigated more extensively than most is pyridoxine. Davis *et al.* (1970) first noted that when pyridoxine was withheld during gestation, both dams and offspring

experienced thymic involution. Others utilised a diet devoid of pyridoxine fed from day 4 of pregnancy until birth and also fed a pyridoxine antagonist. There was an elevated mortality rate among progeny of
pyridoxine-deficient dams. Even after three months of a complete
control diet, rats deprived of pyridoxine during gestation exhibited
significantly low levels of mixed lymphocyte reactivity and a defective
graft-versus-host reaction (Robson and Schwarz, 1975). This immunodeficiency was due to an impaired reactivity of individual lymphocytes,
because the total number of lymphocytes was not decreased at three
months of age. When the dams were deprived of pyridoxine during both
gestation and lactation, low levels of pyridoxine were found in spleen and
thymus of the deficient offspring. At nine days of age, IgG levels in the
sera of dams and pups were within normal ranges, indicating that passive
transfer of antibodies was not altered by dietary deficiency of pyridoxine.
However, on day 35, the spleen-cell number of the pups was decreased
and there was a marked reduction in plaque-forming cell responses to
SRBC immunisation; there was a 40-fold reduction in plaques/spleen
and a 20-fold reduction in plaques/10^6 spleen cells. Because pyridoxine
deficiency has been shown to alter food intake levels, pair-fed controls
were also included in this study. While plaque-forming cell responsiveness of these food-restricted controls was also affected, the influence was
not nearly of the magnitude observed in the pyridoxine deficiency
progeny. Therefore, if pyridoxine deficiency is induced during critical
periods of development, whether by dietary or non-dietary means, an
apparently permanent alteration of immunocompetence can result in
mice. Marginal pyridoxine deficiency has also been reported to affect
humoral immunity in chicks. Blalock *et al.* (1984) found that, in chicks
fed a marginal B6 diet from hatching until seven weeks of age, there was a
reduction in antibody production to SRBCs and in relative levels of IgM
and IgG during the peak and degradation phases of the primary response.
They suggested that the effect of B6 deficiency on the immune system
was secondary to an overall reduction in protein synthesis in the B6-
deficient chicks compared to controls. The reversibility of the immune
defects observed in the B6-deficient chicks was not reported.

Other water-soluble B vitamins have been investigated to a far lesser
extent; however, limited studies have underscored the possible importance of folate in immune ontogeny. Neonatal guinea pigs, which
ordinarily are not susceptible to infection with *Shigella flexneri*, were
fatally susceptible after consuming a folate-deficient diet for 13–15 days
after birth: 89 per cent of deficient animals died after challenge, 50
per cent within the first 24 hours, indicating an almost total inability to
resist infection (Haltalin *et al.*, 1970). The presence of a virulent

bacteraemia in the folate-deficient animals correlated closely with a fatal outcome. In contrast to the frequently fatal outcome in folate-deficient guinea pigs, control counterparts showed no evidence of infection. No information on parameters of immune function is available for animals subjected to folate deficiency during prenatal development.

Information regarding biotin and vitamin B12 deficiencies during development is available only through preliminary observations of individuals with congenital disorders involving the metabolism of these essential B vitamins. In children with biotin-responsive carboxylase deficiency, immunodeficiency of both B and T cell mediated systems may be present (Cowan *et al.*, 1979). However, in other instances, this biotin-responsive carboxylase deficiency may not be associated with deficient immunological function. Lymphocytes from such patients are deficient in the activity of three biotin-associated enzymes (propionyl-CoA carboxylase, 3-methylcrotonyl-CoA carboxylase and pyruvate carboxylase); these enzyme activities returned to normal levels, along with parameters of immune function, upon biotin supplementation (Cowan *et al.*, 1979). Similarly, in infants with congenital transcobalamin II (a vitamin-B12-binding protein) deficiency, one sees agammaglobulinaemia along with granulocyte dysfunction. Phagocytic cells from such patients exhibit a lack of intracellular bactericidal killing activity; other parameters of granulocyte function, e.g. nitroblue tetrazolium reduction and phagocytosis, appear to be normal. Therefore, studies of humans with disordered metabolism of biotin and vitamin B12 during the postnatal period indicate that both may play key roles in the development of an effective immune defence. Appropriate experimental models need be developed to investigate the role of these two B vitamins in immune ontogeny.

There have only been a limited number of studies of the effects on the immune system of deficiencies of fat-soluble vitamins during development. When hens were fed diets supplemented with either 150 or 450 ppm vitamin E and then immunised with *Brucella abortus*, offspring had significantly higher than normal levels of passively transferred antibodies at two and seven days of age (Jackson *et al.*, 1978). Such passive antibody transfer in chicks takes place via the yolk sac. This was particularly impressive since dietary supplementation with vitamin E did not increase maternal serum antibody levels significantly (Jackson *et al.*, 1978). In contrast, supplementation with 90, 300 or 900 ppm vitamin E had no such positive influence upon antibody transfer to offspring. Thus, one sees a biphasic dose-dependent response with two peaks of maximal effect; such a biphasic pattern was also observed at other stages of the life cycle and in other species. Additionally, these results underscore the potential importance of nutritional–immunological interactions in successful veterinary practice.

The feeding of diets deficient in vitamin E from the time of hatching can result in retardation of the development of T-dependent humoral immune function in chicks (Marsh *et al.*, 1981). It has also been reported that, in the chick, vitamin E deficiency results in a significant depression of lymphoid organ growth, particularly in the bursa (Marsh *et al.*, 1986). A reduction in spleen growth was also noted in the vitamin-E-deficient chicks, but thymus growth was not influenced by simple vitamin E deficiency (thymus growth was reduced in chicks fed diets deficient in both vitamin E and selenium). The reversibility of the above immune system defects has not been reported.

In rats and mice, vitamin E deficiency imposed at weaning results in a marked reduction in T and B lymphocyte responses to mitogenic stimulation. Significantly, the effect of vitamin E deficiency on the immune system occurs before other gross signs of the deficiency develop (Saxena *et al.*, 1984; Bendlich *et al.*, 1986; Eskew *et al.*, 1985; Corwin and Schloss, 1980). The biochemical lesion(s) underlying the effects of vitamin E deficiency on the immune system in mammals have not been defined, but it is possible that given its interaction with membrane arachidonic acid, a deficiency of vitamin E results in an increase in immunodepressive prostaglandins (Meydani *et al.*, 1984). In addition, specific changes in receptor concentration in the plasma membranes of macrophages from vitamin-E-deficient mice have been reported (Gebremichael *et al.*, 1984). Aberrations in the mitochondrial membranes of lymphocytes from vitamin-E-deficient rats have also been reported (Lehman and McGill, 1982).

It is well established that laboratory animals fed vitamin-A-deficient diets are more vulnerable to natural or experimentally induced infections (Bang *et al.*, 1973; Darip *et al.*, 1979; Nauss and Newberne, 1985). Vitamin-A-deficient rats are characterised by low macrophage activity, impaired antigen-stimulated lymphocyte trapping in lymph nodes and a reduced response to polyclonal mitogens (Nauss *et al.*, 1985; Ongsakul *et al.*, 1985; Takagi and Nakano, 1983). The effects on the immune system of vitamin A deficiency imposed during pregnancy alone have not been reported. Smith and co-workers (1987) have reported that vitamin A deficiency imposed in mice during the last third of pregnancy and continued until 11 weeks after birth, results in marked immunological dysfunction. At six weeks of age the vitamin-A-deficient mice were characterised by impaired delayed-type hypersensitivity responses to skin antigens such as dinitrofluorobenzene. The biochemical lesion underlying the decreased cell-mediated immunity observed in these mice has not been identified. At eight weeks of age, these mice were also characterised by reduced serum IgM responses to a protein antigen. The vitamin A deficiency did not affect lymphoid organ weight or total lymphoid organ cellularity, but splenomegaly occurred in some of the animals. Information on the reversibility of the above lesions was not reported.

C. Experimental Lipotrope Deficiency During Immune Ontogeny

Newberne and his colleagues have used diets deficient in lipotropes (e.g. choline, methionine, folacin) to investigate the influences of prenatal and postnatal nutritional deficiencies upon development of the immune response. Initial studies were conducted in dams deprived of lipotropes for three months, then mated with healthy males, and maintained on the deficient diet throughout gestation. After parturition, the groups were differentially manipulated to investigate possible differences between lipotrope deficiency during prenatal and postnatal periods. The most dramatic effects were obtained in animals deprived of lipotropes, even with only a marginal deficiency, during both gestation and lactation (Newberne and Gebhardt, 1973). Even after three months of nutritional rehabilitation post-weaning, animals deprived of lipotropes during development exhibited markedly increased mortality rates due to *Salmonella typhimurium*. The size of spleen and thymus in the deprived offspring was also low, even after three months of nutritional supplementation; the cellular densities of these organs were also reduced. Such rats also exhibited decreased serum antibody titres to SRBC immunisation. In addition, the direct plaque-forming cell response was only 37 ± 8 plaques/10^6 spleen cells in deprived rats versus 275 ± 13 plaques/10^6 spleen cells in controls. Spleen-cell mitogen responsiveness to PHA was decreased markedly, but thymus-cell response to PHA was intact. This may have indicated a lack of normal thymocyte mobilisation in lipotrope-deficient offspring. In addition, when animals were deprived during both gestation and lactation, a decreased skin-test response to PHA and a substantially reduced response of non-immune splenocytes in the one-way mixed leukocyte culture were also observed (Williams *et al.*, 1979). If rats were deprived of lipotropes during gestation only, a decreased primary response to SRBCs was observed. If the deficient diet was imposed during lactation only, the offspring did not exhibit a reduced response to heterologous erythrocytes but did show decreased mitogen responsiveness and a reduced skin-test response to PHA (Williams *et al.*, 1979). When lipotrope-deficient diets are fed post-weaning, the impact on the immune system is blunted relative to the effects of these diets during lactation (Nauss *et al.*, 1982). In all of the lipotrope-deprived groups, with repeated sensitisation with alloantigen in vivo, no further differences between deprived and control groups were noted in either cell-mediated or humoral immunity. This may emphasise that one of the principal defects in such nutritionally depleted animals is an impaired ability to recognise an antigen as foreign.

D. Experimental Mineral Deficiencies During Immune Ontogeny

The most comprehensively studied dietary mineral and possibly one of the best studied of all nutrients with regard to its effect upon the development of the immune response has been zinc (Table 13.1). When a deficiency of zinc was imposed on mice beginning at parturition and continuing throughout the postnatal period, profound depression of a number of immune functions was observed. Such postnatally zinc-deprived mice experienced a selective retardation of lymphoid organ growth, most notably the thymus (Beach *et al.*, 1979, 1980a, 1980b, 1980c). Moreover, a variety of immune functions were depressed by postnatal zinc deprivation, including in vitro blast transformation response to mitogens, especially T cell mitogens (Beach *et al.*, 1979), and

Table 13.1: Effects of Zn deficiency on immune function

1. Found in immunodeficiency associated with protein–energy malnutrition
2. Increased susceptibility to infection:
   hypogammaglobulinaemia
   abnormal proportions of immunoglobulin classes
3. Abnormal cell-mediated immunity:
   decreased mitogenic responses to lectins
   decreased delayed-type hypersensitivity to skin-test antigens
   decreased circulating T lymphocytes and T-related function
   profound thymic atrophy/involution
   depressed plaque-forming cell responses
4. Depressed cytotoxicity
5. Depressed levels of natural killer cell activity
6. Depressed circulating thymic hormones
7. Decreased Thy 1.2^+ cells with (proportional) increase of Fc^+ cells
8. Impaired B cell-dependent responses (PWM, PPD, diphtheria toxoid)
9. Thymic involution
10. Lowered serum zinc associated with increased hepatic zinc is seen in response to pathogenic organism invasion (mediated by adrenal steroids and leukocytic endogenous mediators)
11. Depressed/retarded growth of lymphoid organs during fetal or early postnatal deprivation (especially T-dependent tissues) and mobility of B-cell surface markers with exposure to the high/normal levels of Zn.

direct plaque-forming cell response (both per spleen, and per 10^6 spleen cells) to SRBC immunisation (Beach *et al.*, 1980b). There was a highly abnormal serum immunoglobulin profile with elevated levels of IgG1, and no detectable IgM, IgG2a or IgA (Beach *et al.*, 1980b). Even marginal dietary deprivation of zinc during postnatal development was associated with a significant degree of impairment of immunological function, notably an altered response to T cell mitogens and an abnormal serum immunoglobulin profile (Beach *et al.*, 1979).

Zwickl and Fraker (1980) have shown that when mice consumed a zinc-deficient diet for 7–11 days beginning at two weeks of age, there was a profound depression of plaque-forming cell responses to SRBC (7–35% of controls). The response of postnatally zinc-deprived mice to dextran was also reduced to 40 per cent of control levels. Nutritional repletion for as little as four days returned the plaque-forming cell responsiveness to normal. The effect was similar when the period of zinc deficiency was from day 5 through day 17 post partum (Fraker *et al.*, 1984). The effect of a marginal zinc deficiency on ontogeny of the immune system has also been investigated in rhesus monkeys. Haynes *et al.* (1985) reported that rhesus monkey infants fed a marginally zinc-deficient diet (4 ppm Zn) from conception through 12 months postnatal life had low responses to PHA, concanavalin A (Con A) and pokeweed mitogen (PWM), compared with infants born to mothers fed diets containing 100 ppm Zn. They also had low serum IgM levels. Thus, with regard to the immune system, the response of a non-human primate model to zinc deficiency during early development is very similar to that observed for rodent models. Similar abnormalities, e.g., thymic atrophy, abnormal serum immunoglobulin profile and impaired T cell function, along with an increased incidence of infectious disease, have been observed in children with acrodermatitis enteropathica, a congenital disorder of zinc metabolism which tends to mimic postnatal zinc deficiency. Phagocyte chemotaxis is also defective in such children. The defects can be corrected by zinc administration (Weston *et al.*, 1977; Wilson *et al.*, 1982; Businco *et al.*, 1980). Recently, it has been recognised that a significant number of protein–energy malnourished children have low levels of serum zinc, and the immuno-deficiency syndromes observed in such patients are partially corrected by zinc administration (Golden *et al.*, 1977, 1978; Castillo-Duran *et al.*, 1987). To what extent the immune deficiency syndrome associated with protein–energy malnutrition (PEM) in humans is due to zinc deficiency is not clear. If, however, zinc deficiency is common in PEM in adults as well as children, this could result in exposure of the infant to prenatal, as well as postnatal, zinc deficiency. Based on the work conducted with experimental animals, such a prolonged exposure to zinc deficiency during the ontogeny of the immune system would be predicted to have devastating effects on development of immune function. Finally, patients fed intravenously during the postnatal period are at risk of developing zinc deficiency unless they are specifically supplemented (Srouji *et al.*, 1978).

Experimental zinc deficiency during the fetal period only has also been examined. Offspring of dams moderately deprived of zinc between days 7 and 20 of gestation experienced a profound suppression of serum IgM levels along with an impaired direct plaque-forming cell responsiveness to heterologous erythrocytes early in life. This immunodeficiency persisted even at six months of age in F_1 progeny. Perhaps the most remarkable evidence from these experiments is that such immunodeficiency was passed on to F_2 and F_3 generations, although of a lesser magnitude than that seen in first generation offspring (Beach *et al.*, 1982a, 1983). It is important to point out that this persistence of impaired immuno-competence occurred even though there was rehabilitation of the overall structure (i.e. normal spleen and thymus weight) of the offspring deprived of adequate zinc nutriture during gestation (Beach *et al.*, 1982b). Recently, Keller and Fraker (1986) have reported that, in mice, gestational zinc deficiency results in a retardation of B-cell development *in utero* which persists into the neonatal and young adult period in spite of nutritional repletion. Similar observations were made by Chandra (1975b) when both first and second generation offspring experienced immunosuppression as a result of energy restriction in F_0 dams. The mechanism whereby defective immunocompetence is passed to subsequent generations after deprivation of essential nutrients *in utero* remains a mystery. However, intensive investigation should be directed at elucidating this mechanism; such processes may help to explain the persistent immune dysfunction in children of Third World countries.

Far less is known about the influence of other trace elements upon the development of immune function (Tables 13.2 and 13.3). It has been reported that, in experimental animals, dietary copper deficiency can result in an increased susceptibility to bacterial infections (Newberne *et al.*, 1968; Jones and Suttle, 1983) and decreased resistance to tumour challenge (Lukasewycz and Prohaska, 1982). Similarly, it has been reported that, for sheep and cattle, dietary copper deficiency can result in increased infection rates, impaired neutrophil function and decreased bactericidal activity (Boyne and Arthur, 1981; Jones and Suttle, 1981). In mice a copper-deficient diet imposed from the time of parturition throughout the early postnatal period results in a decreased antibody response to SRBCs, a reduction in lymphocyte stimulation by Con A, and a reduced mixed lymphocyte reaction (Prohaska and Lukasewycz, 1981;

454   *Gershwin, Keen, Fletcher and Hurley*

Table 13.2: Effects of copper and manganese on immune function

Copper deficiency
    Increased T-cell-controlled infections
    Inhibition of T cell mitogen responses
        (especially T helper activity)

B-cell function
    Decreased phagocytic cell number
    Pro-inflammatory effects

Copper excess
    Inhibits complement-mediated haemolyis
        of sensitised SRBCs
    Inhibits binding of C9

Miscellaneous
    Copper is important in the three-dimensional structure of immunoglobulin molecules;
    thermal aggregation of human gammaglobulin (of possible importance in pathogenesis
    of rheumatoid arthritis).

Lukasewycz *et al.*, 1985; Prohaska *et al.*,1983; Lukasewycz *et al.*, 1987). Consistent with these observations, Prohaska *et al.* (1983) have demonstrated that copper deficiency in mice has a profound effect on thymus and spleen morphology. They examined mice which had been subjected to a copper-deficient diet from birth through to six weeks of age. The copper-deficient mice had small thymus glands, enlarged spleens, and livers similar in size to copper-adequate mice. Liver, spleen, and thymus tissues from the deficient mice had low cytochrome oxidase and Cu,Zn-superoxide dismutase activities compared with control mice. That the

Table 13.3: Effects of iron on immune function

Iron deficiency
    Reduced blastogenic responses
    Reduced circulating T cells
    Reduced antigen-specific antibody titres in iron-deficient mice
    Long-term impairment of humoral immunity in pre- and postnatal iron-
        deficient rats not corrected by iron repletion

Iron excess/overload
    Enhanced mitogen responses of PWM-stimulated human mononuclear
        cells, but suppression of PHA and Con A driven
        mixed lymphocyte reactions
    Suppression of generation of cytotoxic T cells
    Suppressed chemotactic, phagocytic and/or bactericidal activity.

reduction in the activities of these copper enzymes was functionally significant is suggested by electron microscopy studies which showed that thymic cells from the deficient mice had misshapen nuclei, areas of necrosis and hypertrophied and pleomorphic mitochondria. There were similar morphological lesions in the spleens of deficient animals. These spleens were characterised by a high number of B cells and a low number of T cells, the reduction in T cell number mainly occurring in the T helper cells (Lukasewycz *et al.*, 1985).

The biochemical lesion(s) underlying the effects of copper deficiency on the immune system during early development have not been characterised. Lukasewycz *et al.* (1987) have suggested that one of the primary lesions may be alterations in splenocyte membranes due in part to lipid peroxidative damage secondary to low Cu,Zn superoxide dismutase activity. Flynn and Yen (1981), Flynn *et al.*, (1984) have reported that copper deficiency results in a reduction in splenocyte production of interleukin 1 and T cell replacing factor in vitro. Thus, some of the immune defects observed in copper-deficient animals may be the result of reductions in hormonal (cytokine) signals. At present, the long-term consequences of perinatal copper deficiency for immune function in adulthood have not been identified.

When iron deficiency was imposed in rats for 30 days before gestation, throughout gestation, and then during lactation, an enhanced suscepti-bility to infection with *Salmonella typhimurium* was noted (Baggs and Miller, 1973). Even rat pups exposed to iron deficiency during the suckling period alone, through cross-fostering experiments, were more than normally susceptible to such infections. The authors suggested that one possible mechanism for decreased resistance to infection might be a reduced number of myeloperoxidase-containing cells, the total number of such cells being too low to respond effectively to the infectious challenge. Other parameters of immune function, however, many of which are known to be altered by iron deficiency, were not measured in this study.

Kochanowski and Sherman (1985) have reported that prenatal and early postnatal iron deficiency can result in a long-term impairment of humoral immunity in rats. Rats were fed diets containing 6, 12, or 250 ppm iron throughout gestation and lactation. On day 17, the pups were immunised with SRBCs and antibody synthesis was evaluated by the Jerne plaque assay. It was found that in both iron-deficient groups, antibody formation was decreased by over 50 per cent compared with controls. In the second phase of this study, for three weeks beginning on day 21, iron-deficient pups were fed either a control iron diet or the same iron-deficient diet as was fed to the dam. Despite a three week repletion period, antibody production remained depressed in pups from dams fed iron-deficient diets during pregnancy and lactation. One interpretation of these results is that the perinatal iron deficiency resulted in a persistent effect in thymus and/or spleen function. It is known that suckling iron-deficient rat pups have involuted thymuses and decreased number of cells in thymus as well as in spleen (Kochanowski and Sherman, 1982). Thus it is possible that both T-cell and B-cell production may be limited in these animals, which would explain their decreased antibody production to T-cell-dependent antigens. It is not known if these cell populations can return to normal levels following nutritional rehabilitation. An additional observation of Kochanowski and Sherman (1985) was that circulating IgG and IgM levels were lower in the iron-deficient pups than in controls at day 17 and day 42. Repletion of iron in the diet from day 21 through to day 42 resulted in a 50 per cent increase in IgG and IgM levels in the deficient pups, but the concentrations were still less than half those of control pups. Control pups which were switched to an iron-deficient diet at day 21 had low IgG and IgM levels at day 42. Thus, an effect of iron deficiency on immunoglobulin concentrations can be shown in both the perinatal and the weanling periods of life. Sherman and Lockwood (1987) have recently reported that natural killer cell activity is also significantly impaired in rat pups subjected to iron deficiency during gestation and lactation. It has not been established if this effect of perinatal iron deficiency on natural killer cell activity is reversible with postnatal iron supplementation, or if the impairment is permanent.

Mulhern *et al.* (1985) have reported that mice exposed to selenium-deficient diets during gestation, lactation and post-weaning development have low IgM and IgG antibody responses to SRBCs, while mice exposed to the deficient diet only during post-weaning development have a normal IgM response but a reduced IgG response. Previous work from these investigators demonstrated that the deficient mice in both groups (F_0 and F_1) had normal cell-mediated lympholysis, mixed lymphocyte and mitogenic responses (Mulhern *et al.*, 1981). The lymphoid organs in the selenium-deficient mice were not found to be atrophied; thus the reduced immune response observed in these animals is not the result of a preferential involution of lymphatic tissue (Mulhern *et al.*, 1985).

Similarly, Marsh and co-workers (1986) have reported normal spleen and thymus growth in chicks fed selenium-deficient diets from the day of hatching until 35 days of age. However, bursa development was retarded by selenium deficiency, with bursa weights being 50 per cent lower in the selenium-deficient chicks than in controls after four weeks of dietary treatment. The finding of depressed bursal development in selenium-deficient chicks is consistent with an earlier report of an impaired humoral immune response to SRBCs in two-week-old selenium-deficient chicks (Marsh *et al.*, 1981). The reversibility of the immune defects associated with developmental selenium deficiency has not been reported.

From the above, it is quite clear that trace metal deficiencies during critical periods of development can profoundly influence the ultimate ability of the host to respond to pathogenic challenge. However, the biochemical lesions underlying these defects are not well understood.

E. Alteration of the Progression of Autoimmunity and Oncogenesis by Zinc Deprivation

To ascertain whether manipulation of zinc nutriture in older animals could modify immune status, Beach *et al.* first determined whether feeding a diet low in zinc altered the progression of autoimmune disease in (New Zealand black (NZB), NZB/W) and MRL/1 mice (Beach *et al.*, 1981b, 1982c, d). Beginning at either 6 weeks or 6 months of age, NZB mice consumed diets containing 100 ppm zinc (control), or 9, 5, or 2.5 ppm zinc. In addition, a group of mice was pair-fed the control diet in amounts equal to the intake of the mice fed 5 ppm zinc. NZB mice fed 9 ppm zinc from the age of six weeks had less severe autoimmune haemolytic anemia and lower anti-erythrocyte autoantibody titres, and lived longer. Mice fed 5 ppm zinc also had higher packed cell volumes and lower anti-erythrocyte titres than their pair-fed controls. These findings indicate that deprivation of zinc may account for a significant influence on the development of autoimmunity that is produced by nutritional manipulation. NZB mice started on the zinc-restricted diets at 6 months of age also showed a reduction in autoimmune haemolytic anemia. Similar results were obtained when NZB/W and MRL/1 mice were used (Beach *et al.*, 1981b, 1982c, d). In addition to zinc, restriction of protein, energy and lipids have all been found to modulate the expression of autoimmune disease in mice (Fernandes *et al.*, 1978; Hurd *et al.*, 1981; Kubo *et al.*, 1984). With respect to the dietary treatment of autoimmune disorders in humans, it must be pointed out that, clinically, nutrient intervention in humans would begin only after the disease is manifest. Recently, Vruwink *et al.* (1987) have reported that when dietary zinc deficiency is initiated in NZB mice with established autoimmunity, there is no improvement in the animals' outcome. Thus, if dietary treatment of autoimmune disorders is to be efficacious, it may be imperative that the treatment be initiated prior to, or during, the initial development of the disease.

Second, Beach *et al.* (1981a) explored the relationship between dietary zinc and Moloney sarcoma virus (MSV) oncogenesis. BALB/c mice were fed diets that contained four levels of zinc, as described above, including pair-fed controls. After three weeks of limited zinc availability before MSV injection, mice fed a diet containing 9 or 5 ppm zinc showed an increase in sarcoma growth when compared with control animals. Mice fed 2.5 ppm zinc had a decreased incidence of sarcomas and reduced tumour size. Feeding low-zinc diets for six weeks before MSV injection resulted in reductions in initiation and progression of sarcoma in the groups restricted to 9, 5, and 2.5 ppm zinc groups (Beach *et al.*, 1981a, 1982e). This experiment underscores the critical influence of both the magnitude and duration of zinc deficiency in the development of one form of cancer in mice.

III. HUMAN STUDIES

While the influence of nutritional deficiencies imposed during later periods of life has been well characterised, much less is known about the impact of very early nutrient shortages. Several types of protocol have been developed to study the immediate and long-term effects of nutritional stress imposed during either gestation or the postnatal period, i.e., while the immune system is developing.

Most clinical studies of the fetal period have focused on fetuses characterised as displaying intrauterine growth retardation (IUGR) (also known as small-for-gestational-age or small-for-date). This means that gestation was of normal duration (38–40 weeks), but the birth weight was low when compared with some arbitrary standard (e.g. third percentile of the Harvard growth standards, 2500 grams). A number of factors may contribute to such IUGR, including maternal malnutrition, environmental insults such as viral infections, or various pathological conditions such as placental insufficiency. Studies of IUGR related to nutritional factors ideally should be confined to cases where maternal malnutrition can be adequately demonstrated; in addition, premature infants should be considered separately, as in these infants it is very difficult to distinguish between the disparate influences of gestational age and low birth weight. Thus, the most important studies of this sort have confined observations to infants of normal gestational length, but low birth weight, born to mothers who experienced nutritional deprivation during pregnancy. Studies of postnatal influences are plagued by similarly variable causative factors and circumstances.

The initial indication of prolonged impairment of immunological function were studies indicating that children who had experienced IUGR were more than normally susceptible to infection during later periods of childhood (Chandra, 1976). In actuality, offspring born to inadequately nourished mothers in Third World countries are the product of both a prenatal and a postnatal environment characterised by a synergistic interaction between infection and an inadequate supply of nutrients. Fetuses carried by such mothers are often confronted with early and excessive antigenic stimulation as exemplified by high levels of cord-blood IgM which cannot cross the placenta (Urrutia *et al.*, 1975). Approximately 40 per cent of newborns studied in rural Guatemala and more than 60 per cent of those examined in Peru had elevated levels of cord-blood IgM (higher than 0.20 mg/mL) (Urrutia *et al.*, 1975). Levels of cord-blood complement component C3 were also elevated in over 50 per cent of the Peruvian samples, confirming this premature antigenic stimulation. In addition, newborn infants had a high frequency of elevated antibody titres to bacterial and viral antigens immediately after birth, indicating prior antigenic confrontation.

The point has also been raised that if antigenic components of bacteria and viruses cross the placenta at an early age, it may be possible for such infants to be rendered partly or wholly tolerant to these antigens, impairing their ability later in life to respond to them (Koster *et al.*, 1981). More attention is now being directed to the possibility that such interactions, though of lesser magnitude, may also affect children in developed nations (Sever, 1975). There, however, it is far more difficult to establish such a relationship because of the more moderate nature of the maternal malnutrition and the lesser degree of antigenic stimulation.

The consequences of nutritional deprivation during gestation can be quite pervasive and may persist for many years, possibly permanently compromising immune function. Studies of small-for-date infants at autopsy indicated a notable atrophy of lymphoid tissue, particularly spleen and thymus (Naeye *et al.*, 1971). With regard to humoral immunity, others have observed a significant correlation between low birth weight and serum immunoglobulin levels (Chandra, 1976).

Other studies have found a significant relationship between cord-blood IgA levels and birth weight in small-for-gestational-age infants when birth weight was less than 2550 g. IgA titres following immunisation were also depressed (Chandra, 1975a). For such a profound decrease in serum immunoglobulin levels to occur, the nutritional insult must be initiated prior to the seventh month *in utero*. Ghavami *et al.*, (1979) have confirmed some of these findings and furthermore found a correlation between severe infections, low levels of IgG, and birth weights below 3500 g; this includes many infants who at most were marginally malnourished. Serum levels of IgA were in the low-normal region which, considering the excessive antigenic stimulation these children underwent, may indicate a relatively deficient serum IgA production. In many of these infants, elevated levels of IgM were found and the authors suggested that this might represent compensatory serum immunoglobulin production in the face of decreased levels of IgG. It may also represent excessive antigenic stimulation *in utero* leading to elevated IgM synthesis. Virtually nothing is known regarding the effects of gestational nutrient deficits upon titres of serum IgD or IgE. Certainly both merit considerable attention: studies of serum IgD levels may help elucidate the role of nutritional factors in the evolution of a normal immunoglobulin profile and studies of IgE may unlock some of the mystery surrounding the burgeoning pediatric problem of food allergies.

Low birth weight infants (birth weights ranging from 1800 to 2800 g) had a markedly decreased percentage of surface-immunoglobulin-positive cells (only 380 ± 195 Ig$^+$/mm^3 compared with 1485 ± 810 in age-matched control subjects) (Moscatelli *et al.*, 1976). In most cases, differences between IUGR infants and controls were narrowed after 3–4 weeks of nutritional supplementation, but in some children no significant improvement was observed even at 2–3 months of age.

The influence of IUGR upon antibody response to specific antigenic challenge seems to depend upon the nature of the particular antigen in question. When typhoid and tetanus toxoid vaccines were administered, antibody responses were within normal ranges in infants who had suffered significant degrees of IUGR (Chandra, 1975a). In contrast, when live attenuated poliovirus vaccine was administered, while most IUGR infants did experience seroconversion, the mean titre of antibodies was significantly low both four and eight weeks after immunisation. Such findings have significance for any public health vaccination programs including infants with IUGR.

An early study of humoral immunity in infants malnourished early in postnatal life revealed marked immunosuppression, which persisted for prolonged periods. Children with kwashiorkor who experienced clinical disease prior to the age of seven months showed deficient production of all immunoglobulin classes studied (IgM, IgA and IgG). Serum levels of IgA and IgM were especially low even at four months of age, with most of the children studied not having any detectable IgM; many children still had undetectable levels of IgM even at 7–8 months of age (Aref *et al.*, 1970). In children aged 1–4 years who had experienced early-onset kwashiorkor, the serum immunoglobulin levels remained abnormal. While total serum immunoglobulin levels were normal or high, IgG levels tended to be high and serum IgM was consistently quite low, some infants as old as 4 1/2 years having no detectable IgM. IgA levels in serum were quite variable. For example, many infants subjected to early nutritional deprivation showed only a trace of detectable IgA, while others had only slightly reduced or even elevated levels of serum IgA. Thus, despite years of nutritional rehabilitation, the serum immunoglobulin profile remained highly aberrant if nutritional insults occurred early in life. Although it was not specifically stated, it is quite possible that nutritional deficiencies of these children also occurred *in utero*, as most of these children were born to mothers from a deprived socio-economic environment. Different degrees of coincident nutritional deficiencies during gestation, along with complicating specific nutrient deficiencies, may have contributed to the variability in some immune parameters. It is also important to recognise that in the human population, malnutrition such as protein–energy undernutrition can involve numerous nutrient imbalances. Thus children with protein–energy undernutrition (either kwashiorkor or marasmus) may be deficient in ascorbic acid (Enwonwu, 1973), folate (Tomkins, 1985), zinc (Golden *et al.*, 1977, 1978), selenium (Golden and Golden, 1981) and manganese (Lehmann *et al.*, 1971). In addition, these children may have excessive plasma histamine concentrations (Enwonwu, 1986). All of the above nutritional imbalances may contribute to the immunodeficiency syndrome observed with protein-energy undernutrition, and the variety of imbalances which occur may explain in part why the expression of the syndrome can vary from child to child (Tomkins, 1985).

More recently, the persistence of defects in serum immunoglobulin levels in children who had experienced early postnatal nutritional deprivation (e.g. during the first six months of life) have been confirmed. Children between one and nine years of age continued to exhibit significantly decreased levels of serum IgM, while most other immune parameters were within normal ranges. The influence of protein in the diet during this early postnatal period has been studied, both retrospectively and prospectively. In particular, studies have been performed utilising isocaloric diets containing either 2.5 g/kg body weight/day or 4.0 g/kg body weight/day throughout the first year of life (Zoppi *et al.*, 1978). Both serum IgG and total gammaglobulin levels were significantly lower in children on the lower protein diet when monitored at five, seven or ten months of age. Serum IgM and IgA levels were also slightly lower, but these differences were not significant. As expected, reduced serum immunoglobulin levels correlated with morbidity in children fed the lower-protein diet, both in terms of the number of children experiencing infections and in the number of infectious episodes per child; this was especially true of upper respiratory tract infections, bronchitis, and gastroenteritis (Zoppi *et al.*, 1978). Serum levels of IgD and IgE have been studied to a far lesser extent; titres of both have been shown to be elevated in children deprived of essential nutrients during the early postnatal period. In many malnourished children, detectable and often markedly elevated levels of both IgD and, especially, IgE were observed, whereas in age-matched control children, these two serum constituents were not detectable. Levels of IgG were particularly high in children with early-onset marasmus and marasmic kwashiorkor and in most cases remained elevated even after extensive nutritional rehabilitation. Levels of IgE, in contrast, generally did respond to nutritional treatment and may have been related to the high incidence of parasitism seen in association with all forms of PEM. Even though high levels of IgE are frequently seen in PEM, allergy is seldom associated with such nutritional deficiencies. Nonetheless, antibodies to a variety of food proteins (e.g. eggs, milk, gluten) are frequently observed in children with PEM (Chandra, 1975a).

Not all studies of the development of humoral immunity following nutritional deprivation during the early postnatal period have found such depressed levels of serum immunoglobulins. Berg (1968) found a significant correlation between serum levels of IgG and gestational age, but no correlation between full-term low birth weight infants and serum IgG levels. Infants of lower gestational age had a tendency toward pronounced hypogammaglobulinaemia during the first months of life. In addition, the early ability to synthesise IgM was notably impaired in premature infants and this persisted for some time. Such defects could not be found in full-term infants of low birth weight. In all infants studied, the levels of serum IgA and IgD were within normal ranges. Other investigators were also unable to document an influence of prenatal nutritional deprivation upon levels of serum immunoglobulins (Bhaskaram *et al.*, 1977). It should be pointed out, however, that none of the infants in these studies showed evidence of severe nutritional deprivation (nearly all birth weights were approximately 2000 g). In addition, excessive antigenic stimulation in these children may have resulted in serum immunoglobulin levels within normal ranges, but perhaps the specific immune response would have been compromised.

Studies of cell-mediated immune function have also given varying results, although there is general agreement that if nutritional insults occur during critical periods of gestation or postnatally within six months after parturition, such children will have impaired cell-mediated immune responses and the defect in immunological function may be long-term. In infants of low birth weight, there is thymic atrophy (Naeye *et al.*, 1971), and a reduced number of rosette-forming T lymphocytes, especially in those with birth weights less than 2550 g (Bhaskaram *et al.*, 1977). Moscatelli *et al.* (1976) showed that when T lymphocytes obtained from IUGR infants were incubated with thymosin prior to performance of the rosette assay, there was a significant increase in the relative proportion of lymphocytes able to form rosettes with SRBCs. As has been demonstrated with older children who experienced PEM, it is possible that the serum of these IUGR infants contained some factor which inhibits rosette formation by T lymphocytes (Olusi *et al.*, 1980). Even after years of nutritional rehabilitation, the relative percentage of lymphocytes forming rosettes, i.e. T lymphocytes, remained significantly low in older children who had experienced IUGR, although the absolute number of T cells, although lower in IUGR children, was not statistically significantly different. No definitive data have been generated using monoclonal reagents.

As further indication that cell-mediated immune function is impaired in IUGR, delayed cutaneous hypersensitivity responses to a battery of skin-test antigens including PHA, streptokinase-streptodornase, dinitrochlorobenzene, *Candida* and *Trichophyton* have all been found to be consistently low (Ghavami *et al.*, 1979). Not only did IUGR children respond poorly to these skin-test antigens, most small-for-gestational-age children responded to at most only one of the battery of the antigens employed and many IUGR children failed to respond to any antigens. Additionally, as with the reduced ability of T lymphocytes to form rosettes, this decreased ability to demonstrate a delayed-type hypersensitivity response to skin-test antigens persisted for many years (Ghavami *et al.*, 1979). The defective cell-mediated immunocompetence often coincided with the low levels of serum immunoglobulins. Many small-for-gestational-age infants also demonstrated a decreased level of in vitro blast transformation in response to mitogens such as PHA (Bhaskaram *et al.*, 1977).

Decreased responsiveness to T cell mitogens in IUGR infants has not always been a consistent finding. In one study, investigators found that when such infants were followed later in life (up to nine years of age) many exhibited a hyperresponsiveness to PHA. This suggests that defects in immune regulation have occurred at the level of suppressor T cell function. It may also represent an inherent hyperactivity residing in a specific T cell subpopulation, e.g. helper T cells. These same children also expressed persistently low levels of serum IgM, although all had clinically experienced intensive antigenic confrontation; however, other parameters of immunological function were within normal ranges. While the pathogenesis of such immune dysfunction remains unclear, the potential importance of malnutrition during either the prenatal or early postnatal period is altogether too clear.

Non-specific parameters of immunity, e.g. phagocytic cell function, complement component levels, and total haemolytic complement activity in children subjected to IUGR, have also been investigated.

While phagocytosis is normal in such children, intracellular bactericidal killing is significantly low. Nitroblue tetrazolium reduction by polymorphonuclear leukocytes is markedly depressed. In low birth weight infants, phagocytic cell mobility, whether directed or random, was also substantially decreased. Keusch (1981) and Keusch *et al.* (1976) found many of these findings in infants who had been severely malnourished during the gestational period. However, they were able to localise the defect in these IUGR children more precisely. Cord-blood phagocytic cell intracellular bactericidal killing activity with preopsonised *Staphylococcus aureus* or *Escherichia coli* was within normal ranges. However, without preopsonisation, the intracellular bactericidal killing activity was defective, indicating an opsonic defect (Keusch *et al.*, 1976). The limiting humoral factor was heat-labile, suggesting it was a complement component. Chandra (1974) found that such IUGR infants had significantly low serum levels of complement component C3 and these low levels of C3 correlated closely with the observed opsonic defect and the decreased level of intracellular bactericidal activity. While this opsonic defect was most serious in infants with very low birth weights, it was also present in many infants of only moderately low birth weights. Very little is known regarding the possible persistence of these non-specific immune defence defects in later life.

In infants, postnatal nutritional copper deficiency is characterised by recurrent infections that can lead to pulmonary sepsis (Al-Rashid and Spangler, 1971; Karpel and Peden, 1972). Recently, it has been suggested that, similarly to zinc, copper supplementation may be of value in reducing the infection frequency in infants recovering from severe undernutrition (Castillo-Duran *et al.*, 1982). That prenatal copper deficiency may affect the ontogeny of the immune system is suggested by the observation that infants with Menkes' disease, a genetic disorder mimicking copper deficiency, have a T-lymphocyte defect, as reflected by their increased susceptibility to T-cell mediated infections (Danks *et al.*, 1972; Pedroni *et al.*, 1975; Haas *et al.*, 1981). Currently there is no effective therapy for Menkes' disease and individuals with this disease normally die before five years of age. Thus, at present, it is not known if the immune defects which occur with this disorder can be corrected with postnatal copper supplementation.

During infancy, postnatal iron deficiency has been linked to an impairment of cell-mediated immune functions, including decreased circulating T-lymphocytes (Chandra and Saraya, 1975; MacDougall *et al.*, 1975; Prema *et al.*, 1982). Iron deficiency in humans does not result in marked changes in circulating immunoglobin concentrations (Krantman *et al.*, 1982). To date, persistent effects of perinatal iron deficiency on immune function have not been reported.

REFERENCES

Al-Rashid, R. A. and Spangler, J. (1971) Neonatal copper deficiency. *New Engl. J. Med.* 285: 841–3.

Aref, G. H., Badr El-Din, M. K., Hassan, A. I. and Draby, I. I. (1970) II: Immunoglobulins in kwashiorkor. *J. Trop. Med. Hyg.* 73: 186.

Bach, J. F., Chatenoud, L. and Dy, M. (1985). Lymphocytes; histamine, a new entry to immunoregulation. In C. R. Ganellin and J. C. Schwartz (eds), *Frontiers in Histamine Research.* Oxford: Pergamon: 353.

Baggs, R. B. and Miller, S. A. (1973). Nutritional iron deficiency as a determinant of host resistance in the rat. *J. Nutr.* 103: 1554.

Bang, B. G., Foard, M. A. and Bang, F. B. (1973). The effect of vitamin A deficiency and Newcastle disease on lymphoid cell systems in chickens. *Proc. Soc. Exp. Biol. Med.* 143: 1140–6.

Beach, R. S., Gershwin, M. E. and Hurley, L. S. (1979). Altered thymic structure and mitogen responsiveness in postnatally zinc-deprived mice. *Develop. Comp. Immunol.* 3: 725.

Beach, R. S., Gershwin, M. E. and Hurley, L. S. (1980a). Growth and development of postnatally zinc-deprived mice. *J. Nutr.* 110: 201.

Beach, R. S., Gershwin, M. E. and Hurley, L. S. (1980b). Zinc deprivation and the immune response. *Fed. Proc.* 39: 888.

Beach, R. S., Gershwin, M. E., Makishima, R. K. and Hurley, L. S. (1980c). Impaired immunologic ontogeny in postnatal zinc deprivation. *J. Nutr.* 110: 805.

Beach, R. S., Gershwin, M. E. and Hurley, L. S. (1981a). Dietary zinc modulation of Moloney sarcoma virus oncogenesis. *Cancer Res.* 41: 552.

Beach, R. S., Gershwin, M. E. and Hurley, L. S. (1981b). Nutritional factors and autoimmunity: I: Immunopathology of zinc deprivation in New Zealand mice. *J. Immunol.* 126: 1999.

Beach, R. S., Gershwin, M. E. and Hurley, L. S. (1981c). T cell function in the lethal milk (lm/lm) mutant mouse. *Proc. Fourth Int. Congress of Immunol., 1981.* (Abstract).

Beach, R. S., Gershwin, M. E. and Hurley, L. S. (1982a). Gestational zinc deprivation in mice: persistence of immunodeficiency for three generations. *Science* 218: 469.

Beach, R. S., Gershwin, M. E. and Hurley, L. S. (1982b). Reversibility of developmental retardation following murine fetal zinc deprivation. *J. Nutr.* 112: 1169.

Beach, R. S., Gershwin, M. E. and Hurley, L. S. (1982c). Nutritional factors and autoimmunity: II: Prolongation of survival in zinc deprived NZB/W mice. *J. Immunol.* 128: 308.

Beach, R. S., Gershwin, M. E. and Hurley, L. S. (1982d). Nutritional factors and autoimmunity: III: Zinc deprivation versus restricted food intake in MRL/1 mice; the distinction between interacting dietary influences. *J. Immunol.* 129: 2686.

Beach, R. S., Gershwin, M. E. and Hurley, L. S. (1982e). Zinc, copper and manganese in immune function and experimental oncogenesis. *Nutr. Canc.* 3: 172.

Beach, R. S., Gershwin, M. E. and Hurley, L. S. (1983). Persistent immunological consequences of gestation in zinc deprivation. *Am. J. Clin. Nutr.* 38: 579.

Bendich, A., Gabriel, E. and Machlin, L. J. (1986). Dietary vitamin E requirement for optimum immune responses in the rat. *J. Nutr.* 116: 675.

Berg, T. (1968). Immunoglobulin levels in infants with low birth weights. *Acta Pediat. Scand.* 57: 369.

Bhaskaram, P., Prasad, J. S. and Krishnamachari, K. A. V. R. (1977). Anemia and the immune response. *Lancet* 1: 1000.

Blalock, T. L., Thaxton, P. and Garlich, J. D. (1984). Humoral immunity in chicks experiencing marginal vitamin B-6 deficiency. *J. Nutr.* 114: 312–322.

Boyne, R. and Arthur, J. R. (1981). Effects of selenium and copper deficiency on neutrophil function in cattle. *J. Comp. Path.* 91: 271–6.

Businco, L., Menghi, A. M., Rossi, P., D'Amelio, R. and Galli, E. (1980). Zinc dependent chemotactic defect in an infant with acrodermatitis. *Arch. Dis. Child.* Vol. 55: 966.

Castillo-Duran, C., Fisber, M., Valenzuela, A., Egana, J. I. and Uauy, R. (1982). Controlled trial of copper supplementation during recovery from marasmus. *Am. J. Clin. Nutr.* 37: 898–903.

Castillo-Duran, C., Heresi, G., Fisberg, M. and Uauy, R. (1987). Controlled trial of zinc supplementation during recovery from malnutrition: effects on growth and immune function. *Am. J. Clin. Nutr.* 45: 602.

Chandra, R. K. (1974). Rosette-forming T lymphocytes and cell-mediated immunity in malnutrition. *Brit. Med. J.* 3: 608.

Chandra, R. K. (1975a). Reduced secretory antibody response to live attenuated measles and poliovirus vaccines in malnourished children. *Brit. Med. J.* 2: 583.

Chandra, R. K. (1975b). Antibody formation in first and second generation offspring of nutritionally deprived rats. *Science* 190: 289.

Chandra, R. K. (1976). Nutrition as a critical determinant in susceptibility to infection. *Wld. Rev. Nutr. Diet* 25: 166.

Chandra, R. K. and Saraya, A. K. (1975). Impaired immunocompetence associated with iron deficiency. *J Pediat.* 86: 899.

Corwin, L. M. and Schloss, J. (1980). Influence of vitamin E on the mitogenic response of murine lymphoid cells. *J. Nutr.* 110: 916–23.

Cowan, M. J., Wara, D. W., Packman, S. and Ammann, A. J. (1979). Multiple biotin-dependent carboxylase deficiencies associated with defects in T-cell and B-cell immunity. *Lancet* 2: 115.

Cruz, J. R. and Waner, J. L. (1978). Effect of concurrent cytomegaloviral infection and undernutrition on the growth and immune response of mice. *Inf. Immun.* 21: 436.

Darip, M. D., Sirisinha, S. and Lamb, A. (1979). Effect of vitamin A deficiency on susceptibility of rats to Angiostrongylus cantonensis. *Proc. Soc. Exp. Biol. Med.* 161: 600–4.

Dauks, D. M., Campbell, P. E., Stevens, B. J., Mayne, V. and Cartwright, E. (1972). Menk's kinky-hair syndrome. An inherited defect is copper absorption with widespread effects. *Pediatrics* 50: 188.

Davis, S., Nelson, T. and Shepard, T. (1970). Teratogenicity of Vitamin B$_6$ deficiency: Omphalocele, skeletal and neural defects, and splenic hypoplasia. *Science* 169: 1329.

Enwonwu, C. D. (1973) Experimental protein-calorie malnutrition in the guinea pig and evaluation of the role of ascorbic acid status. *Lab. Invest.* 29: 17–26.

Enwonwu, C. (1986). Potential relevance of impaired histidine metabolism to the immunodeficiency in human protein–energy malnutrition. *Nutr. Res.* 6: 337.

Eskew, M. L., Scholz, R. W., Reddy, C. C., Todhunter, D. A. and Zarkower, A. (1985). Effects of vitamin E and selenium deficiencies on rat immune function. *Immunology* 54: 173–80.

Fernandes, G., Friend, P., Yunis, E. J. and Good, R. A. (1978). Influence of dietary restriction on immunologic function and renal disease in (NZB × NZW)F$_1$ mice. *Proc. Natl. Acad. Sci.* 75: 1500–4.

Flynn, A. and Yen, B. R. (1981). Mineral deficiency effects on the generation of cytotoxic T-cells and T-helper cell factors *in vitro. J. Nutr.* 111: 907–13.

Flynn, A., Loftus, M. A. and Finke, J. H. (1984). Production of interleukin-1, and interleukin-2 in allogeneic mixed lymphocyte cultures under copper, magnesium and zinc deficient conditions. *Nutr. Res.* 4: 673–9.

Fraker, P., Hildebrandt, K. and Luecke, R. (1984). Alteration of antibody mediated responses of suckling mice to T-cell dependent and independent antigens by maternal marginal zinc deficiency: Restoration of responsivity by nutritional repletion. *J. Nutr.* 114: 170.

Gebhardt, B. M. and Newberne, P. M. (1974). Nutrition and immunological responsiveness: T cell function in the offspring of lipotrope- and protein-deficient rats. *J. Immunol.* 26: 489.

Gebremichael, A., Levy, E. M. and Corwin, L. M. (1984). Adherent cell requirement for the effect of vitamin E on *in vitro* antibody synthesis. *J. Nutr.* 114: 1297–1305.

Ghavami, H., Dutz, W., Mohallattee, M., Rossipal, E. and Vessal, K. (1979).

Immune disturbances after severe enteritis during the first six months of life. *Israeli J. Med. Sci.* 15: 364.

Golden, M. H. N. and Golden, B. E. (1981). Trace elements: potential importance in human nutrition with particular reference to zinc and vanadium. Br. Med. Bull. 37: 31–36.

Golden, M. H. N., Jackson, A. A. and Golden, B. E. (1977). Effect of zinc on thymus of recently malnourished children. *Lancet* 2: 1057.

Golden, M. H. N., Golden, B. E., Harland, P. S. E. G. and Jackson, A. A. (1978). Zinc and immunocompetence in protein–energy malnutrition. *Lancet* 1: 226–30.

Haas, R. H., Chir, B., Robinson, A., Evans, K., Lascelles, P. T. and Dubowitz, V. (1981). An X-linked disease of the nervous system with disordered copper metabolism and features differing from Menkes' disease. *Neurology* 31: 852–9.

Haltalin, K. C., Nelson, J. D. Woodman, E. B. and Allen, A. A. (1970). Fatal Shigella infection induced by folic acid deficiency in young guinea pigs. *J. Inf. Dis.* 121: 275.

Haynes, D. C., Gershwin, M. E., Golub, M. S., Cheung, A. T. W., Hurley, L. S. and Hendrickx, A. G. (1985). Studies of marginal zinc deprivation in rhesus monkeys: VI: Influence on the immunohematology of infants in the first year. *Am. J. Clin. Nutr.* 42: 252.

Hook, R. R. and Hutcheson, D. P. (1976). Impairment of the primary immune response in early-onset protein–calorie malnutrition. *Nutr. Reports Intl.* 13: 541.

Huchet, R. (1985). Histamine induced inhibition of interleukin-2 synthesis: activity in man. In C. R. Ganellin and J. C. Schwartz (eds), *Frontiers in Histamine Research*. Oxford: Pergamon: 365.

Hurd, E. R., Johnston, J. M., Okita, J. R., MacDonald, P. C., Ziff, M. and Gilliams, J. N. (1981). Prevention of glomerulonephritis and prolonged survival in New Zealand Black/New Zealand White F$_1$ hybrid mice fed an essential fatty acid deficient diet. *J. Clin. Invest.* 67: 476–85.

Jackson, D. W., Law, G. R. J. and Nockels, C. F. (1978). Maternal vitamin E alters passively acquired immunity of chicks. *Poult. Sci.* 57: 70.

Jones, D. G. and Suttle, N. F. (1981). Some effects of copper deficiency on leucocyte function in sheep and cattle. *Res. Vet. Sci.* 31: 151–6.

Jones, D. G. and Suttle, N. F. (1983). The effect of copper deficiency on the resistance of mice to infection with *Pasteurella haemolytica*. *J. Comp. Pathol.* 93: 143–9.

Jose, D. G., Stutman, O. and Good, R. (1973). Long term effects on immune function of early nutritional deprivation. *Nature* 241: 57.

Karpel, J. T. and Peden, V. H. (1972). Copper deficiency in long-term parenteral nutrition. *J. Pediatr.* 80: 32–6.

Keller, P. and Fraker, P. (1986). Gestational zinc requirement of the A/J mouse:

Effects of a marginal zinc deficiency on *in utero* B cell development. *Nutr. Res.* 6: 41.

Keusch, G. T. (1981). Host defense mechanisms in protein energy malnutrition. *Adv. Exp. Med. Biol.* 135: 183.

Keusch, G. T., Urrutia, J. J., Fernandez, R. and Kovacs, I. B. (1976). Protein–calorie malnutrition (PCM) in a Mayan community: effects on neutrophil function at birth. *Am. J. Clin. Nutr.* 29: 472.

Kochanowski, B. A. and Sherman, A. R. (1982). Cellular growth in iron-deficient rat pups. *Growth* 46: 126.

Kochanowski, B. A. and Sherman, A. R. (1985). Decreased antibody formation in iron-deficient rat pups — effect of iron repletion. *Am. J. Clin. Nutr.* 41: 278.

Koster, F. T., Curlin, G. C., Aziz, K. M. A. and Haque, A. (1981). Synergistic impact of measles and diarrhoea on nutrition and mortality in Bangladesh. *Bull. World Health Org.* 59: 901.

Krautman, H. J., Young, S. R. and Awk, B. J. (1982). Immune function in pure iron deficiency. Am. J. Dis Child. 136: 840–844.

Kubo, C., Johnson, B. C., Day, N. K. and Good, R. A. (1984). Calorie source, calorie restriction, immunity and aging of (NZB/NZW) F_1 mice. *J. Nutr.* 114: 1884–99.

Lansdown, A. B. G. (1977). Histological observations on thymic development in fetal and newborn mammals subject to intrauterine growth retardation. Biol. Neonate. 31: 252.

Lehman, J. and McGill, M. (1982). Biochemical and ultrastructural alterations in platelets, reticulocytes, and lymphocytes from rats fed vitamin E-deficient diets. *J. Lipid Res.* 23: 299–306.

Lehman, B. H., Hansen, J. A. L., and Warren, P. J. (1971). The distribution of copper, zinc and manganese in various regions of the brain and other tissues of children with protein-calorie malnutrition. *Br. Journal Nutr.* 26: 197–202.

Lukasewycz, O. A. and Prohaska, J. R. (1982). Immunization against transplantable leukemia impaired in copper-deficient mice. *J. Natl. Canc. Inst.* 69: 489–93.

Lukasewycz, O. A. and Prohaska, J. R. (1983). Lymphocytes from copper-deficient mice exhibit decreased mitogen reactivity. *Nutr. Res.* 3: 335–41.

Lukasewycz, O. A., Prohaska, J. R., Meyer, S. G., Schmidtke, J. R., Hatfield, S. M. and Marder, P. (1985). Alterations in lymphocyte subpopulation in copper-deficient mice. *Infect. Immun.* 48: 644–7.

Lukasewycz, O. A., Kolquist, K. L. and Prohaska, J. R. (1987). Splenocytes from copper-deficient mice are low responders and weak stimulators in mixed lymphocyte reactions. *Nutr. Res.* 7: 43.

MacDougall, L. G., Anderson, R., McNab, G. N., Khatz, J. (1975). The immune response in iron-deficient children: impaired cellular defense mechanisms with altered humoral components. *J. Pediatr.* 86: 833–843.

Mark, D. A., Nauss, K. M., Baliga, B. S. and Suskind, R. M. (1981). Depressed transformation response by splenic lymphocytes from vitamin A-deficient rats. *Nutr. Res.* 1: 489–97.

Marsh, J. A., Dietert, R. R. and Combs, G. F. Jr. (1981). Influence of dietary selenium and vitamin E on the humoral response of the chick. *Proc. Soc. Exp. Biol. Med.* 166: 228–36.

Marsh, J. A., Combs, G. F., Whitacre, M. E. and Dietert, R. R. (1986). Effects of selenium and vitamin E dietary deficiencies on chick lymphoid organ development. *Proc. Soc. Exp. Biol. Med.* 182: 425.

Meydani, S. N., Meydani, M., Verdon, C. P. and Blumberg, J. B. (1984). PGE_2 control of vitamin E-enhanced immunity in old mice. *Fed. Proc.* 43: 478.

Moscatelli, P., Bricarelli, F. D., Piccinini, A., Tomatis, C. and Dufour, M. A. (1976). Defective immunocompetence in fetal undernutrition. *Helv. Paediat. Acta* 31: 241.

Mulhern, S. A., Morris, V. C., Vessey, A. R. and Levander, O. A. (1981). Influence of selenium and chow diets on immune function in first and second generation mice. *Fed. Proc.* 40: 935.

Mulhern, S. A., Taylor, G. L., Magruder, L. E. and Vessey, A. R. (1985). Deficient levels of dietary selenium suppress the antibody response in first and second generation mice. *Nutr. Res.* 5: 201–10.

Naeye, R. L., Diener, M. M., Harcke, H. T. and Blanc, W. A. (1971). Relation of poverty and race to birth weight and organ and cell structure in the newborn. *Pediat. Res.* 5: 17.

Nauss, K. M., Connor, A. M., Kavanaugh, A. and Newberne, P. M. (1982). Alterations in immune function in rats caused by dietary lipotrope deficiency: effect of age. J. Nutr. 12: 2333–2341.

Nauss, K. M. and Newberne, P. M. (1985). Local and regional immune function of vitamin A-deficient rats with ocular herpes simplex virus (HSV) infections. *J. Nutr.* 115: 1316.

Nauss, K. M., Mark, D. A. and Suskind, R. M. (1979). The effect of vitamin A deficiency on the *in vitro* cellular immune response of rats. *J. Nutr.* 109: 1815–23.

Nauss, K. M., Phua, C.–C., Ambros, L. and Newberne, P. M. (1985). Immunological changes during progressive stages of vitamin A deficiency in the rat. *J. Nutr.* 115: 909.

Newberne, P. M. and Gebhardt, B. M. (1973). Pre and postnatal malnutrition and responses to infection. *Nutr. Int.* 7: 407.

Newberne, P. M., Hunt, C. E. and Young, V. R. (1968). The role of diet and the reticuloendothelial system in the response of rats to *Salmonella typhimurium* infection. *Br. J. Exp. Path.* 49: 448–57.

Olusi, S. O., Thurman, G. B. and Goldstein, A. L. (1980). Effect of thymosin on T-lymphocyte rosette formation in children with kwashiorkor. *Clin. Immunol. Immunopath.* 15: 687.

Olusi, S. O., Wallwork, J. C. and McFarlane, H. (1976). Intrauterine malnutrition and Igb allotypes in the rat. *Biol. Neonate* 30: 187.

Ongsakul, M., Sirisinha, S. and Lamb, A. J. (1985). Impaired blood clearance of bacteria and phagocytic activity in vitamin A-deficient rats. *Proc. Soc. Exp. Biol. Med.* 178: 204–8.

Pedroni, F., Bianchi, F., Vgazio, A. G., Burgib, G. R. (1975). Immunodeficiency and steely hair. *Lancet* 1: 1303.

Plaut, M., Marone, G., Thomas, L. L. and Lichtenstein, L. M. (1980). Cyclic nucleotides in immune responses and allergy. *Adv. Cyclic Nucleotide Res.* 12: 116.

Plaut, M., Kagey-Sobotka, A. and Jacques, A. R. (1985). Modulation of cytotoxic T-lymphocyte responses by histamine. In C. R. Ganellin and J. C. Schwartz (eds), *Frontiers in Histamine Research.* Oxford: Pergamon: 379.

Premer, K., Ramalaskshmi, B. A., Madhava peddi, R. and Babu, S. (1982). Immune status of anemic pregnant women Br. J. Obstet. Gynaecol. 89: 222–225.

Prohaska, J. and Lukasewycz, O. A. (1981). Copper deficiency suppresses the immune response of mice. *Science* 213: 559–61.

Prohaska, J. R., Downing, S. W. and Lukasewycz, O. A. (1983). Chronic dietary copper deficiency alters biochemical and morphological properties of mouse lymphoid tissues. *J. Nutr.* 113: 1583–90.

Puffer, R. R. and Serrano, C. V. (1973). The role of nutritional deficiency in mortality findings of the inter-American investigation of mortality in childhood. Pan. Am. Health Organ. 7: 1.

Robson, L. C. and Schwarz, M. R. (1975). Vitamin B_6 deficiency and the lymphoid system: I: Effects on cellular immunity and in vitro incorporation of ^{3}H-Uridine by small lymphocytes. *Cell. Immunol.* 16: 135.

Rocklin, R. E. (1985). Histamine-induced suppressor cell responses in normal and atopic subjects. In C. R. Ganellin and J. C. Schwartz (eds), *Frontiers in Histamine Research.* Oxford: Pergamon: 357.

Saxena, Q. B., Saxena, R. K. and Adler, W. H. (1984). Effect of feeding a diet with half of the recommended levels of all vitamins on the natural and inducible levels of cytotoxic activity in mouse spleen cells. *Immunology* 52: 41–8.

Sever, J. L., Fuccillo, D. A., Ellenberg, J. and Gilkeson, M. R. (1975). Infection and low birth weight in an industrialized society. *Am. J. Dis. Child.* 129: 557.

Sherman, A. R. and Lockwood, J. F. (1987). Impaired natural killer cell activity in iron-deficient rat pups. *J. Nutr.* 117: 567.

Sirisinha, S., Darip, M. D., Moongkarndi, P., Ongsakul, M. and Lamb, A. J. (1980). Impaired local immune response in vitamin A-deficient rats. *Clin. Exp. Immunol.* 40: 127–35.

Smith, S. M., Levy, N. S. and Hayes, C. E. (1987). Impaired immunity in vitamin A-deficient mice. *J. Nutr.* 117: in press.

Srivastava, U. S., Rakshit, A. K., Seebag, M., Omoloko, C. and Thakur, M. L.

(1981). Metabolism of adenine nucleosides and nucleotides, nucleic acids and proteins in the thymus and spleen of neonatal progeny of dietary restricted rats. *Nutr. Reports Intl.* 23: 1035.

Srivastava, U. S., Thakur, M., Majumdar, P., Bhatnagar, G. and Supakar, P. (1987). Lymphoid organ mRNA transplantability in rats: effect of protein energy undernutrition in early life. *J. Nutr.* 117: 242.

Srouji, M. N., Balistreri, W. F., Caleb, M. H., South, M. A. and Starr, S. (1978). Zinc deficiency during parental nutrition: Skin manifestations and immune incompetence in a premature infant. *J. Ped. Surg.* 13: 570.

Strom, T. B., Lundin, A. P. and Carpenter, C. B. (1977). The role of cyclic nucleotides in lymphocyte activation: function. *Prog. Clin. Immunol.* 3: 115.

Takagi, H. and Nakano, K. (1983). The effect of vitamin A depletion on antigen-stimulated trapping of peripheral lymphocytes in local lymph nodes of rats. *Immunology* 48: 123–8.

Tomkins, A. (1986). Symposium on nutrition: Resistance to infection: Protein-energy malnutrition and risk of infection. *Proc. Nut. Soc.* 45: 289.

Urrutia, J. J., Mata, L. J., Trent, F., Cruz, J. R., Villatoro, E. and Alexander, R. E. (1975). Infection and low birth weight in a developing country. *Am. J. Dis. Child.* 129: 558.

Vruwink, K. G., Keen, C. L., Gershwin, M. E. and Hurley, L. S. (1987). Studies of nutrition and autoimmunity: Failure of zinc deprivation to alter autoantibody production when initiated in disease-established mice. *J. Nutr.* 117: 177.

Wade, S., Lemonnier, D., Bleiberg, F. and Delorme, J. (1983). Early nutritional experiments: Effects on the humoral and cellular immune responses in mice. *J. Nutr.* 113: 1131.

Watson, R. R., Rister, M. and Baehner, R. L. (1976). Superoxide dismutase activity in polymorphonuclear leukocytes and alveolar macrophages of protein malnourished rats and guinea pigs. *J. Nutr.* 103: 1801.

Weston, W. L., Huff, J. C., Humbert, J. R., Hambidge, M., Neldner, K. H. and Walravens, P. A. (1977). Zinc correction of defective chemotaxis in acrodermatitis enteropathica. *Arch. Dermatol.* 113: 422.

Williams, E. A. J., Gebhardt, B. M., Morton, B. and Newberne, P. M. (1979). Effects of early marginal methionine-choline deprivation on the development of the immune system in the rat. *Amer. J. Clin. Nutr.* 32: 1214.

Wilson, M. C., Fischer, T. J. and Riordan, M. M. (1982). Isolated IgG hypogammaglobulinemia in acrodermatitis enteropathica: correction with zinc therapy. *Ann. Allergy* 48: 288.

Zoppi, G., Zamboni, G., Siviero, M., Bellini, P. and Cancellieri, M. L. (1978). γ-globulin level and dietary protein intake during the first year of life. *Ped.* 62: 1010.

Zwickl, C. M. and Fraker, P. J. (1980). Restoration of the antibody mediated response of zinc/caloric deficient neonatal mice. *Immunol. Com.* 9: 611.

Environmental Stress

VERNON RILEY

Pacific Northwest Research Foundation
Seattle, Washington 98194, USA

The considerable body of information on the effects of environmental stress on natural resistance to microbes, viruses, and tumours is in large part the cumulative product of years of research by Vernon Riley, terminated by his untimely death. As his work is so compellingly relevant to establishing a role for stress in a broad consideration of mechanisms of natural immunity, such as is sought in this volume, we have taken the unusual step of constructing this brief chapter utilising selections from a number of Riley's publications. In giving prominence to these correlates our intent is to foster a better appreciation of the ubiquitous factors that impinge on the expression of natural resistance. This chapter was composed by Maurice Landy.

It has been observed by Riley and his colleagues that a number of uncontrolled environmental circumstances and technical procedures produce physiological alterations in experimental and control animals, and that these uncontrolled stress-associated changes interfere with and distort various experimental parameters impinging on natural resistance to tumours and viruses. These findings provide disquieting evidence that the most carefully done studies using animal models can be subject to misinterpretation unless such stress-inducing environmental and animal-handling factors can be identified and controlled.

Anxiety or other varieties of psychosocial stresses in experimental animals produce a series of biochemical events that are mediated through

NATURAL IMMUNITY
ISBN 0 12 5145551

the neuroendocrine system.[1] These biochemical responses have demonstrable destructive effects upon specific cells and tissues that are involved in immune defence. As a consequence, the stress-compromised animal is less capable of defending itself against cancer cells, infectious agents, and other disease processes. Accordingly, uncontrolled stress factors are important components to be reckoned with in assessing the non-induced kinds of immunity.

There are many varieties of stress which may activate separate physiological systems, either singly or as complexes. For purposes of this chapter data and discussion are restricted to the effects of uncomplicated anxiety-involving, emotionally aroused stress, which is associated with the activation of the adrenal cortex.

A characteristic expression of such stress is an abrupt and dramatic increase in circulating plasma glucocorticoids (in rodents, this is corticosterone). Such stress-induced hormone elevations also evoke secondary stress effects involving T cells and thymic components, and other elements of the immune system. Relevant metabolic and related biochemical alterations also occur through the influence of increased glucocorticoid action.

Within the framework of this limited definition of stress, it is assumed that the adrenal medulla either is not significantly activated by mild stress, or does not greatly alter the effects of the adrenal cortex. However, activation of the adrenal medulla system does occur in rodents under more drastic stressful conditions where fear or rage is the inciter.

The rationale of stress-induced or stress-mediated disease follows logically from a series of known physiological events. Although the overall biochemical phenomena associated with stress are complex and have many subtle consequences, the primary events relevant to disease processes appear to be straightforward, at least those involving the adrenal cortex.

The rapid physiological response to handling-induced anxiety stress is attested to by the measurable elevation in plasma corticosterone levels observed only minutes after animals have been agitated by simple capturing procedures. This is illustrated by a rapidly ascending corticosterone curve which attests to the response to handling being so rapid that its biochemical manifestation in the form of plasma corticosterone elevation is initiated within 3½ minutes. This imposes a rigorous time limitation upon the investigator who seeks to establish the baseline levels of plasma corticosterone in control animals as well as for measuring the physiological effects of experimentally induced stress. Rapid rises in

---

[1] See Chapter 10.

plasma corticosterone can be generated by the routine process of capturing animals for injections, cage transfer, bleeding, or other experimental procedures, or even by simply transporting the animals from their protective holding facilities to the laboratory bench. Unless these operations are carried out in less than a four-minute period, anxiety stress is manifested by initiation of the typical physiological stress syndrome, resulting in elevated plasma corticosterone levels. If sufficient time elapses, leukopoenia and eventually thymus involution may occur.

As a consequence of several interrelated developments, it has been demonstrated that experiments using mouse models for the study of immunological and neoplastic relationships are frequently compromised by the inadvertent and unappreciated stress that intrudes when mice are maintained in conventional housing facilities and handled in the usual manner.

The protective animal facilities we have devised constitute one of the important conditions that permit work upon environmental and anxiety stress to be placed on a quantitative basis. It is such quiescent conditions that permit the low baseline values of 0–35 ng/mL for plasma corticosterone to be obtained. In contrast, plasma corticosterone values observed in mice maintained in conventional communal animal rooms where the animals are routinely exposed to rack motion, cage cleaning, noise, drafts, dust, odours, pheromones, and experimental manipulation have usually been in the range of 150–500 ng/mL. This constitutes an elevation of 10 to 20 times the quiescent plasma corticosterone level. Such physiological corticosterone elevations cause thymus involution, lymphocytopoenia and alterations in amino acid metabolism, and lead to various effects upon tumour growth, latent periods, and incidence. These effects imply that animals housed under conventional, non-protective conditions may well have relatively impaired immunocompetence.

A subenvironmental factor to be considered in maintaining mice under optimal conditions is the type of holding cage to be employed within the animal facilities. For example, we have compared plasma corticosterone levels of mice housed in hanging wire-bottom cages and analogous mice housed in plastic cages with corn-cob bedding. Both types of holding cages were maintained with the same loss-stress protective facilities. A statistically significant plasma corticosterone elevation ($p < .005$) was observed in the mice housed in wire-bottom cages. In addition to the hormone increase, a differential adrenomegaly ($p < .01$) and a shortening of life span ($p < .0001$) were observed. These data strongly suggest that wire-bottom cages are stressful for mice, even when employed within protective facilities.

From the standpoint of the low stress that is essential for reliable biological research, individually ventilated shelf units offer several beneficial features. For example, the enclosed shelves provide substantial soundproofing, which is of special significance, since we established that animals are stressed by a wide variety of noises that stimulate immunologically adverse neuroendocrine reactions. Stressful noises and cage motion are prevalent in most conventional animal rooms, particularly where there are rolling metal racks, metal cages, radios, shouting, frequent cage cleaning with rough handling, and other noise and stressful operations.

To minimise these experimental problems, certain modified animal handling procedures and animal housing have been established which should be considered essential prerequisites for animal experimentation. These improved techniques allow the investigator to distinguish between truly quiescent and chronically stressed mice, as well as to determine the authentic consequences of experimentally imposed stress: (a) avoidance of previous contact with the animals; (b) partial soundproofing of storage shelves to protect the animals from stressful noises; (c) elimination of vibrations and high-pitched sounds of centrifuges, vacuum cleaners and heavy equipment; (d) elimination of drafts and air turbulence; (e) control of lighting to stabilise circadian rhythms; (f) segregation of males and females with respect to transmissible odours, pheromones, and other signals; (g) segregation of experimental animals that are experiencing stress from normal or experimental control animals; and (h) introduction of special minimal-stress animal-handling techniques and cage-cleaning procedures.

Plasma corticosterone levels were also found to be elevated tenfold in mice during and after air shipment, and thymus involution was initiated as expected in response to the increased corticoid concentrations. The physiological effects induced by shipping stress take approximately two weeks to return to quiescent levels after the mice are placed in protective facilities. It has been our practice to allow animals to equilibrate for at least two weeks prior to their being placed in experiments. A persuasive example is provided by differences in host mortality rates ($p < .005$) if tumours are implanted into newly received mice as compared to analogous equilibrated mice.

There was a need for a simple, non-traumatic and reproducible means for inducing controlled stress in experimental animals. It was sought to produce such stress without activating other hormonal systems, significantly altering the metabolism of the host, or changing caloric intake. A simple stress-inducing device was developed that provides a controlled quantitative form of stress which is readily reproducible, and lends itself to automation with a wide variety of intermittent stress-rest programming. This machine is a modified phonograph turntable that has the four standard speeds of 16, 33, 45, and 78 rpm. The instrument has been designed so that an entire cage of animals can be placed on the machine for rotation without changing the established arrangement of their living facilities. With this device it is not necessary to alter the availability of food and water, inasmuch as the slow rotational speeds and intermittent on–off cycles permit the animals to move about their cage and to continue eating and drinking. It may also be noted that the lateral gravitational force involved in less than 1 g. This stress-inducing instrument is thus not a centrifuge device, but merely a mechanical means for inducing mild spatial disorientation, and possibly vertigo or dizziness, with its associated anxiety.

This instrument can induce variable intensities of stress. When plasma corticosterone values are plotted against the various rotational speeds, it is seen that, following the rotation of separate mice for 20 minutes at each of the four speeds, a systematic increase in plasma corticosterone occurs. For most stress-inducing purposes, the intermediate speed of 45 rpm has been employed, and the animals are usually rotated for 10 minutes followed by a 50-minute rest. This, or other cycles, can be repeated for any desired period of time by employing programmed automation.

Such programmed rotation has a striking effect on the white blood cell count. The leukopoenia immediately follows as a consequence of the elevated plasma corticosterone levels induced by the anxiety stress.

Intermittent rotational stress influences the subsequent growth rate of the Gardner lymphosarcoma (6C3HED) in C3H/He mice. In this experiment the tumour-bearing mice were exposed to intermittent rotational stress (45 rpm) for 10 minutes out of each hour during the first six days following subcutaneous implantation of the transplantable lymphosarcoma. A logical interpretation of these observations suggests that those animals receiving rotational stress had some elements of their cell-mediated immunological competence compromised, permitting this sensitive tumour to grow at a more rapid rate than in the control animals, who possessed the immune capability to restrain the optimal growth of this tumour. Such a stress-induced decrease in immunological competence is a natural consequence of the corticosterone elevation induced by anxiety stress.

An extremely mild 'handling' stress is capable of inducing anxiety in mice which, in turn, produces an immediate and substantial increase in plasma corticosterone. 'Abnormal' quiescent plasma corticosterone values of individual mice were obtained when groups of 10 animals were removed from protective storage and all 10 bled by the rapid orbital bleeding technique within 3.5 minutes. This short time period is sufficient for the overt expression of any stress or anxiety to be manifested biochemically by an elevation of plasma corticosterone. However, when analogous cages of mice were similarly removed from protective storage, and one animal was captured and bled every two or three minutes, so that the total elapsed handling time was about 30 minutes between the first and last animal captured, corticosterone became markedly elevated in the blood plasma of such mildly stressed animals. Such results have been obtained with four different mouse strains, (BDF1, BAF1, C3H, and CBA), and attest to the need for quiescent, protective housing facilities, and the need to employ special animal-handling techniques for studies on biochemical and biological effects of stress.

The lactate dehydrogenase (LDH) virus is a benign passenger in most biological materials transplanted serially in mice. The infectious vehicles include the classical transplanted tumours and leukaemias as well as preparations of oncogenic viruses and other entities perpetuated by mouse passage. Awareness of the presence or absence of this virus in experimental mice and in their harvested biological materials is of critical importance, since this silent infectious entity is capable of inducing or mediating a wide range of subtle modifications in the host or in tumour responses under various experimental conditions. These modifications include alterations in the immune competence of the host. More specifically, the LDH virus induces a temporary thymolytic effect and a significant lymphopoenia. In contrast, however, it may cause a hyperplasia of the peripheral lymph nodes and spleen and it has substantial but unidentified effects on macrophages. It also is a good interferon inducer.

In addition, this ubiquitous virus induces permanent biochemical lesions, most conspicuously expressed by substantial elevations in a variety of plasma enzymes, notably LDH. The virus ordinarily is non-pathogenic, and as a consequence, its presence is generally unsuspected. However, it can combine synergistically with other biological entities such as *Eperythrozoon coccoides*, a frequent murine contaminant, and with most malignancies to produce enhanced biological and biochemical effects both in the host and in tumour behaviour.

The unappreciated presence of such inapparent viral contaminants in commonly used biological preparations has led to the introduction of an increasing burden of erroneously interpreted information into the cancer literature.

The LDH virus has been found as contaminant in over 100 different varieties of mouse tumours and leukaemias and is now distributed worldwide. Investigators must, therefore, assume that it is present in *all* transplantable mouse tumours unless each preparation has *recently* been tested by adequate techniques. The same precautions apply to all mouse-passaged virus preparations, both oncogenic and nononcogenic.

Probably the most persuasive reason to warrant the effort required for establishing the absence or controlled presence of this virus in experimental animals and biological materials is that it is scientifically risky to interpret the most carefully obtained experimental data that are complicated or compromised by the presence of any uncontrolled entity known to exert potent physiological and immunological effects upon the host and to act synergistically with the introduced tumours or oncogenic viruses.

A change in host resistance to infection, brought about by psychosocial factors, has been noted by several groups. Rasmussen, Friedman, Grundbert, Hirsch, Jensen and others have shown that the stress induced by avoidance learning procedures (electric shock, etc.) increased susceptibility to herpes simplex virus, coxsackie B virus, and polyoma virus infection. Physical restraint was also found to enhance herpes simplex infection.

Our own studies, as well as those of others, on the tangible effects of psychosocial or anxiety stress upon tumour processes appear to be most closely related to the immune impairment resulting from elevated levels of plasma adrenal corticoids. There is abundant evidence that the basic cellular elements constituting the immune system, including macrophages, T cells and B cells, are all subject to modulation, impairment and/or destruction by specific adrenal cortical hormones. A particularly conspicuous cellular effect of these stress-elevated hormones is thymus involution. The lymphopenia resulting from stress-induced plasma corticosterone undoubtedly includes sequestration, destruction, or disappearance of T cells and probably B cells as well.

Adrenal corticoid-induced immunological impairment thus logically accounts for the enhancement of tumour growth seen in mice stressed by rotation, as well as the shorter survival of tumour-bearing mice stressed as a result of cross-country air shipment, or psychosocial confrontation and competition. Since the administration of synthetic corticoids also has effects upon tumour growth, regression and host survival similar to those produced by stress, this mechanism would seem to provide a plausible explanation for the physiological effects of certain forms of stress resulting in the enhancement of growth of some tumours.

All living organisms exhibit circadian rhythms in certain of their biological and biochemical control systems. Circadian fluctuations in plasma corticosterone concentrations in mice, which are nocturnal creatures, amount to a three- to fivefold increase between the early morning low plasma concentration and the evening high concentrations.

Humans, by comparison, exhibit high plasma cortisol levels between 6 a.m. and noon, and the lowest concentrations late in the evening. Thus, the time of day at which stress-affected plasma hormone levels are determined is relevant in experimental design and interpretation.

The phase of the circadian cycle during which experimental stresses are initiated can greatly affect the subsequent influences of such stress on the physiological, biochemical, cellular, and immunological events under consideration. The LDH virus, when inoculated at 5 p.m., just prior to the nocturnal increase in corticosterone, produces peak corticosterone levels much higher than those resulting from a similar virus inoculation made at 9 a.m. Thus, the timing of experimental stress may be of critical importance. Such subtle procedural differences may also account for many of the apparent contradictions in the literature. Therefore, the time of day at which experimental stresses are initiated should be both regulated and recorded. It is now known that the time of day that therapeutic drugs are administered also relates to their efficacy. Additional studies of such rhythmic physiological phenomena could result in further insights into demonstrating relationships between stress and neoplastic disease.

Our studies have thus shown that mice held in conventional animal storage facilities undergo chronic or intermittent stress, which may be inapparent to the unsuspecting researcher. When examined more carefully, such control animals show an increase in circulating corticosterone, a lymphopoenia, early thymus involution, and other physiological manifestations of stress, as compared with mice maintained in protective housing.

If such conventionally maintained chronically stressed animals are then used for stress experiments, and are thus subjected to additional stress factors, the potential experimental difficulties are obvious. It is therefore essential that studies on stress employ originally non-stressed experimental animals, as well as permanently non-stressed controls, with both groups maintained in environmental circumstances that assure quiescent baseline levels of the various stress-related biological components to be compared in the experimental and control animals.

Viewed in the context of Vernon Riley's extensive documentation of rapid and profound diminution by environmental stress of natural host resistance to viruses, microbes, and tumours, it is evident that the parameters of natural immunity affected are varied, significant, and rather uniformly sensitive to this particular form of physiological alteration by glucocorticoids. The rapidity and magnitude of this suppression of host resistance implies that under normal conditions this system either is in delicate balance or equipoise, or is *inordinately* sensitive to glucocorticoids.

In view of more recent (1982) work[2] attesting to significant changes in macrophage performance upon exposure in vitro to hydrocortisone, it may well be that in many of the Riley experiments on stress, the host effectors involved included macrophages. What is needed to resolve the issue of whether macrophage involvement is critical, is to explore whether in stressed mice there occurs a down-regulation in the performance of host macrophages in various sites, with respect to their array of relevant functions such as target cytotoxicity, elaboration of monokines, and phagocytic efficiency. It seems a reasonable expectation that such studies would broadly affirm the proposition that this 'first line' of host defence against threats from the environment is promptly and profoundly compromised by glucocorticoid-mediated stress, however induced.

BIBLIOGRAPHY

Fitzmaurice, M. A., Riley, V. and Santisteban, G. A. (1972). Biological synergism between the LDH-virus and *Eperythrozoon coccoides*: Studies on the mechanism. *Path. Biol.* 20: 743–50.

Riley, V. (1961). Virus–tumour synergism. *Science* 134: 666–8.

Riley, V. (1964). Synergism between a lactate dehydrogenase-elevating virus and *Eperythrozoon coccoides*. *Science* 146: 921–3.

Riley, V. (1966). Spontaneous mammary tumours: Decrease of incidence in mice infected with an enzyme-elevating virus. *Science* 153: 1657–8.

Riley, V. (1968). Lactate dehydrogenase in the normal and malignant state in mice and the influence of a benign enzyme-elevating virus. Busch (ed.), *Methods in Cancer Research,* vol. 4. New York: Academic Press: 493–619.

Riley, V. (1969). Role of the LDH-elevating virus in leukemia therapy. *Nature* 220: 1245–6.

Riley, V. (1970). Influence of a benign virus upon mouse leukemia. *Path. Biol.* 18: 757–64.

Riley, V. (1972). Protective ventilated shelves for experimental animal storage. Proc. 23rd Annual Session, Amer. Assoc. Lab. Animal Sci., St. Louis, #22A.

Riley, V. (1973). Persistence and other characteristics of the lactate dehydrogenase-elevating virus (LDH-virus). In, J. L. Melnick and J. Hotchin (eds), *Progr. Med. Virol.: Slow Virus Diseases,* vol. 18. Basel: S. Karger: 198–213.

[2] Ozaki, T., Yasuoka, S., Nakayama, T. and Tsubura, E. (1982). Glucorticoid receptors on human alveolar macrophages and peripheral blood cells. *Clin. Exp. Immunol.* 47: 505. Masur, H., Murray, H. W. and Jones, T. C. (1982) Effect of hydrocortisone on macrophage response to lymphokine. *Infect. Immun.* 35: 709.

Riley, V. (1974). Biological contaminants and scientific misinterpretations. *Cancer Research.* 34: 1752–4.

Riley, V. (1974). Erroneous interpretation of valid experimental observations through interference by the LDH-virus. *J. Natl. Cancer Inst.* 52: 1673–7.

Riley, V. (1974). Persistence and other characteristics of the lactate dehydrogenase elevating virus (LDH-virus). In Melnick (ed.), *Progress in medical virology: Slow Virus Diseases,* vol. 13. Basel: Karger: 198–213.

Riley, V. (1975). Mouse mammary tumours: alteration of incidence as an apparent function of stress. *Science.* 189: 465–7.

Riley, V. (1978). Stress and cancer: Fresh perspectives. *Proc. 3rd Int. Symp. Detect. Prev. Cancer.* 1976. New York: Marcel Dekker Inc.; 1769–76.

Riley, V. (1979). Introduction: Stress–cancer contradictions: A continuing puzzlement. *Cancer Detect. Prev.* 2: 159–62.

Riley, V. (1979). Cancer and stress: Overview and critique. *Cancer Detect. Prev.* 2: 163–95.

Riley, V. and Spackman, D. H. (1976). Modifying effects of a benign virus on the malignant process and the role of physiological stress on tumour incidence. *Fogarty Int. Cent. Proc.* 28: 319–36.

Riley, V. and Spackman, D. H. (1976). Melanoma enhancement by viral-induced stress. In V. Riley (ed), *The Pigment Cell; Melanomas: Basic Properties and Clinical Behaviour,* vol. 2. Basel: Karger: 163–73.

Riley, V. and Spackman, D. H. (1977). Housing stress. *Lab Animal* 6: 16–21.

Riley, V. and Spackman, D. H. (1977). Cage crowding stress: Absence of effect on melanoma within protective facilities. *Proc. Am. Assoc. Cancer Res.* 18: 173.

Riley, V., Lilly, F., Huerto, E. and Bardell, D. (1960). Transmissible agent associated with 26 types of experimental mouse neoplasms. *Science* 132: 545–7.

Riley, V., Huerto, E., Lilly. F., Bardell, D., Loveless, J. D. and Fitzmaurice, M. A. (1961). Some characteristics of virus-like entities associated with thirty varieties of experimental tumours. *Proc. Amer. Ass. Cancer Res.* 3: 261.

Riley, V., Huerto, E., Bardell, D., Loveless, J. D. and Fitzmaurice, M. A. (1962). Influence of LDH-elevating viruses on normal and tumour-bearing hosts. *Proc. Amer. Ass. Cancer Res.* 3: 354.

Riley, V., Huerto, E., Loveless, J. D., Bardell, D., Fitzmaurice, M. A. and Forman, C. (1963). Inapparent transmissible agents in oncology and their influence on tumour and host. *Acta Union Internationale Contre le Cancer* 19: 263–70.

Riley, V., Loveless, J. D., Fitzmaurice, M. A. and Siler, W. M. (1965). Mechanism of lactate dehydrogenase (LDH) elevation in virus-infected hosts. *Life Sci.* 4: 487–507.

Riley, V., Fitzmaurice, M. A. and Loveless, J. D. (1966). Decrease in 'spontaneous' mammary tumour incidence. *Proc. Amer. Ass. Cancer Res.* 7: 59.

Riley, V., Loveless, J. D., Fitzmaurice, M. A., Smullyan, I. and Fischer, S. W. (1967). Characteristics of the Friend leukemia disease in the presence and absence of a benign enzyme-elevating (LDH) virus. *Proc. Amer. Ass. Cancer Res.* 8: 56.

Riley, V., Spackman, D. and Santisteban, G. (1975). The role of physiological stress on breast tumour incidence in mice. *Proc. Amer. Assoc. Cancer Res.* 16: 152.

Riley, V., Braun, W., Ishizuka, M. and Spackman, D. H. (1976). Antibody-producing cells: Virus-induced alteration of response to antigen. *Proc. Natl. Acad. Sci. U.S.A.* 73: 1707–11.

Riley, V., Spackman, D. H., Hellstrom, K. E. and Hellstrom, I. (1978). Growth enhancement of murine sarcoma by LDH-virus, adrenocorticoids, and anxiety stress. *Proceedings of the American Association for Cancer Research* 19: 57.

Riley, V., Spackman, D., McClanahan, H. and Santisteban, G. A. (1979). The role of stress in malignancy. *Cancer Detection and Prevention* 2: 235–55.

Riley, V., Fitzmaurice, M. A. and Spackman, D. H. (1981). Biobehavioral factors in animal work on tumorigenesis. In S. Weiss (ed.), *Proc. Acad. Behav. Med. Res.* New York: Academic Press: 183–214.

Riley, V., Fitzmaurice, M. A. and Spackman, D. H. (1981). Animal models in biobehavioral research: Effects of anxiety stress on immunocompetence and neoplasia. In S. Weiss *et al.* (eds), Perspectives in Behavioral Medicine. New York: Academic Press.

Riley, V., Fitzmaurice, M. A. and Spackman, D. H. (1981). Psychoneuroimmunological factors in neoplasia: Studies in animals. In R. Ader (ed.), *Psychoneuroimmunology.* New York: Academic Press: 31–102.

Santisteban, G. and Riley, V. (1973). Thymo-lymphatic organ response to the LDH-virus. *Proc. Am. Ass. Cancer Res.* 14: 112.

Santisteban, G. A., Riley, V. and Fitzmaurice, M. A. (1972). Thymolytic and adrenal cortical responses to the LDH-elevating virus. *Proc. Soc. Exp. Biol. Med.* 139: 202–6.

Spackman, D. and Riley, V. (1974). Increased corticosterone, a factor in LDH-virus induced alterations of immunological responses in mice. *Proc. Amer. Assoc. Cancer Res.* 15: 143.

Spackman, D. and Riley, V. (1975). Stress effects of the LDH-virus in altering the Gardner tumour in mice. *Proc. Amer. Assoc. Cancer Res.* 16: 170.

15

Radiation

MICHAEL BENNETT

Department of Pathology
University of Texas Southwestern Medical Center
5323 Harry Hines Blvd
Dallas, Texas 75235, USA

I. ANALYSIS OF EFFECTS OF RADIATION

In this chapter, I will discuss only the effects of ionising irradiation, even though much has been written about the immunosuppressive effects of ultraviolet light irradiation, and something is known about the effects of high frequency radio waves on immune cells. If you are an immunologist and 'discover' a new cell type or immune phenomenon, you will eventually characterise the cell or the phenomenon by testing the effects

NATURAL IMMUNITY
ISBN 0 12 5145551

of irradiation. Ironically, radiation of animals can 'uncover' a new immune cell type or phenomenon. For example, in the early days of experimental bone-marrow transplantation, prospective recipient mice or rats were exposed to supralethal doses of X-rays or gamma rays. Gustavo Cudkowicz discovered the phenomenon of 'hybrid resistance' to parental strain bone-marrow cell grafts and to graft-versus-host cells by infusing cells into irradiated mice (Cudkowicz and Stimpfling, 1964). Fifteen years after the discovery of hybrid resistance, natural killer (NK) cells were co-discovered, as such, by Rolf Kiessling, Ronald Herberman and colleagues. NK cells mediate the rejection of incompatible bone-marrow cell grafts, and therefore NK cells are thought to be radioresistant. But are they really resistant to radiation?

How should one analyse the effects of radiation on natural immune functions? Let us take NK cells as an example. Suppose that you have just discovered them and want to characterise their sensitivity to irradiation. NK cells lyse their prototypic target cells, YAC-1 lymphoma cells, within a four-hour period of incubation (Herberman *et al.*, 1975). Therefore, you expose NK cells (contained in murine spleen-cell suspensions) to doses of radiation from 0 to 4000 or so centigray (cGy). Immediately after irradiation, you add the cells to ^{51}Cr-labelled YAC-1 cells and perform the assay. At low doses of radiation, you will observe no diminution of function; this is the 'shoulder' of the curve relating dose of irradiation to suppression of function. (The curve is formed by plotting function or percentage of function on the ordinate on a log scale and dose of X-rays or gamma rays on the abscissa on a linear scale.) At increasing doses thereafter, a steady linear decrease in function will occur. The D_0 value is that dose of irradiation which inhibits function to 37 percent ($1/e$) of the control value on the linear portion of the curve. The straight portion of the curve is extrapolated to the y-axis. The intercept is the value n (extrapolation number), when the control 100% value equals 1. The value of n is determined largely by the number of 'hits' required to inactivate the cell's function. The quasithreshold dose, D_q, is the dose where the extrapolated line reaches 1, and is the measure of the 'shoulder'. The ability of the cell type to repair the injury determines the D_q value. If the ionising radiation is very dense, there may be no shoulder or D_q value and n is very close to 1.0 (Hamilton, 1964). The equation $\log_e n - D_q/D_0$ describes the relationships between these above-mentioned values.

Were you to irradiate mice and rapidly remove the spleen to perform the NK cell assay, the D_0 value in vitro and in vivo would be similar. If you were to irradiate the mice and remove the spleens one, two or three days afterwards, you would obtain different results. The NK cell function as expressed by the numbers of cells plated might be increased or normal, but the spleen would be drastically less cellular, the cells decreasing in number from 100 million to 3–5 million. You would then have to interpret your results in two different ways. The NK cells could be said to be relatively (compared to other spleen cells) radioresistant. However, in absolute terms 80 to 95 percent of the NK cell function has been lost. One can express the results in terms of 'lytic units', where 1 unit = 30% (for example) specific cytotoxicity. If 5×10^5 cells/well results in 30% cytotoxicity, and there 4 $\times$ 10^6 cells/spleen two days after 800 cGy, then there are 8 lytic units/spleen. If 10^6 control cells cause 30% cytotoxicity and there are 100×10^6 cells/spleen, then there are 100 lytic units per spleen. Thus, NK cell function, i.e., lysis of tumour cells, is radioresistant but maintenance of NK cell numbers is quite radiosensitive.

The next set of experiments you can perform, which is far more complex, is to determine the radiosensitivity of precursor and 'stem cells' for NK cells. Koo and Manyak have recently developed an in vitro assay to detect NK precursors (Koo and Manyak, 1986). Mouse bone-marrow cells are cultured in the presence of sources of interleukin 2 (IL-2) for a number of days and NK cell function is assessed. Assuming that linear relationships exist between numbers of marrow cells cultured and NK cell function that appears, you can determine the radiosensitivity of the precursor. An in vivo assay for NK stem cells or progenitor cells has been developed by Hackett et al (1985). Mice are lethally irradiated and infused with graded numbers of syngeneic marrow cells. At different intervals later, such as 12 days, the spleen cells can be harvested to assess NK cell function. To preclude any host NK cell contamination, the host mice are injected with anti-asialo-GM1 serum to eliminate host NK cell two days before irradiation and cell transfer. An alternative in vivo NK cell assay (Riccardi *et al.*, 1979) has proven superior; in this assay, radiolabelled YAC-1 cells are infused intravenously into the mice. The lungs are removed four hours later and radioactivity is measured. Riccardi observed that 80% or more of its cells are trapped in the lungs within 15–20 minutes. In mice with normal NK cell function there is a rapid clearing of cells from the lungs between 2 and 4 hours, such that the percentage retention of radiolabelled YAC-1 cell in the lungs is inversely related to in vivo NK cell function. In unirradiated mice with good NK cell function 0.5–1.5% retention is detected four hours after infusion. To determine radiosensitivity of marrow precursors or stem cells, the marrow should be exposed to 25 to 600 cGy just prior to plating or infusion. These experiments have not yet been done. From experience with other haemopoietic cells, I would predict that the D_0 values for the precursors and stem cells would be 75–140 cGy, whereas the D_0 value for NK cell function itself would be more than 1200 cGy (Till and McCulloch, 1961, Mayhew and Bennett, 1971).

II. SENSITIVITY OF STEM CELLS, PRECURSOR CELLS AND MATURE FUNCTIONAL EFFECTOR CELLS TO RADIATION

A. Granulocytes

In recent years considerable knowledge has been gained about the stem cells and precursor cells for granulocytes and related myelopoietic cells, particularly from the work of Metcalf and his colleagues (Walker *et al.*, 1986). In vitro studies have demonstrated a multi-colony-forming cell (CFC) which can give rise to erythrocytes (RBC), platelets, eosinophils, granulocytes, macrophages and even mast cells. Colony stimulating factors (CSFs) determine the pattern of differentiation of the CSFs which are derived from the multi-CFC; multi CSF (IL-3) dominates other CSFs and is followed by GM-CSF which induces the formation of colonies containing granulocytes and macrophages. GM-CSF dominates 'lower-order' CSF's, M-CSF and G-CSF, which induce the formation of macrophage and granulocyte colonies respectively. The in vivo colony-forming unit-spleen (CFU-S) is the immediate precursor of the in vitro multi-CFC. Therefore, radiation affects of all the abovementioned cell types equally at the CFU-S level. CFU-Ss are quite sensitive to gamma radiation, with a D_0 value of 95 cGy (McCulloch and Till, 1962).

Large domestic animals and humans are much more sensitive to total-body irradiation than rodents or rabbits with respect to the haemopoietic system (Leong *et al.*, 1964). The LD50/30s (LD50/30 = lethal dose which kills 50% of animals within 30 days) for mice, rabbits, goat and sheep were 940, 800, 412 and 360 cGy, respectively. Do these species show similar difference in susceptibility of the stem cells or precursor cells? Dog GM-CFCs were indeed quite sensitive to radiation, with D_0 values of 26.1 and 60.0 cGy for blood and marrow GM-CFCs (Nothdurft *et al.*, 1983). In contrast, human and murine GM-CFCs were much more resistant, with D_0 values of 127–160 cGy and 160–190 cGy, respectively (Senn and McCulloch, 1970). But since the LD50/30 for humans is about 400 cGy (low), one cannot conclude that CFCs reflect inherent differences in susceptibility to radiation. Patients exposed to therapeutic doses of radiation exhibited an 86 per cent decrease in frequency of marrow CFCs but there was very little effect on cells capable of secreting CSFs (Hornstein *et al.*, 1985). Similar results were observed in dogs exposed to low doses of total-body irradiation (Nothdurft *et al.*, 1984.) In mice, 600 cGy of X-rays was superior to anti-granulocyte serum and nitrogen mustard in depleting granulocytes 3–10 days later (Bogman *et al.*, 1984), indicating that stem cells and precursor cells for granulocytes are quite radiosensitive.

In great contrast to the production of granulocytes, the function of mature granulocytes is quite radioresistant. The metabolic response (stimulation of hexose monophosphate shunt) to phagocytosis of bacteria, and the bactericidal ability and the mobility of granulocytes in response to bacterial culture factors were resistant to doses as high as 40 000 cGy (Holley *et al.*, 1974; Valerius *et al.*, 1981). Of those three functions, mobility was somewhat more susceptible than the other functions to radiation. Therefore, the loss of granulocytic function in natural immunity after radiation is due to a decrease in the number of cells.

B. Macrophages

The picture with macrophages is rather more complicated. Whereas granulocytes are found in the marrow, the red pulp of the spleen and the blood, macrophages are found in every organ of the body. If mice receive injection of the long-lived bone-seeking isotope ^{89}Sr, there is a severe monocytopenia that lasts at least 30 days (Sawyer *et al.*, 1982). Granulocytes are not so severely suppressed, presumably because the increased splenic haemopoiesis results in granulocyte production and release of granulocytes into the blood. Monocytopoiesis in the spleen is not reflected in the blood, where monocytopoenia may be extreme. Nevertheless, pulmonary and peritoneal macrophage numbers are maintained. These findings are potentially puzzling, since marrow and blood monocytes are thought to be the immediate precursors of tissue macrophages (van Furth and Cohn, 1968; Thompson and van Furth, 1970). Whereas maintenance of tissue macrophage numbers under 'resting' conditions can occur in irradiated animals, such animals fail to mobilise macrophages to sites to inflammation (Volkman and Gowans, 1965). Instillation of carbon particles into the lung normally causes an outpouring of alveolar macrophages which take up the carbon and aid in the expulsion of the material. In irradiated mice there is a poor increase in numbers of alveolar macrophages in response to the carbon, and an increase in the deposition of carbon in the lung interstitium and hilar nodes (Adamson and Bowden, 1982). This presumably would decrease the 'natural immunity' to any fibrogenic response of the lung to inhaled particulate matter. A similar decrease or delay in response of alveolar macrophages to carbon was noted in mice treated with [89]Sr (Evans *et al.*, 1986).

If genetically resistant mice are infected with *Listeria moncytogenes* intraperitoneally, the macrophages harvested two days later have greatly increased bactericidal activity (Sadarangani *et al.*, 1980; Wood *et al.*, 1986). If the mice are irradiated just prior to harvesting the macrophages, bactericidal activity is less. Therefore, the production of activated macrophages and/or the activation of macrophages by some other cell type were the radiosensitive elements of the process. These findings illustrate a general point: that as the complexity of a natural immune function becomes more apparent, it becomes more difficult to pinpoint the cell type or component that is affected by radiation.

The effect of radiation on the ability of adjuvants such as Bacillus Calmette Guérin (BCG), pyran copolymer or glucan to induce tumoricidal macrophages in the peritoneal cavities of mice has been studied (Schultz *et al.*, 1978). Surprisingly, exposure of mice to 400 to 800 cGy alone stimulated function for several days. Mice exposed to 600 cGy and injected with the various adjuvants had no diminution of antitumour activity per cell. The yield of cells per peritoneal cavity was not given, but one would expect that radiation would have greatly reduced cell numbers at the high doses. Macrophages taken from irradiated mice were normally responsive to the stimulatory effects of lymphokines (supernatants of concanavalin-A-stimulated lymphocyte cultures) or interferon.

Human monocytes from peripheral blood can survive for some time in vitro and can function, e.g. kill bacteria. If the cells are exposed to large doses of gamma rays (2500 or 5000 cGy), the survival, two-dimensional growth, and ability to kill *Listeria monocytogenes* are impaired (Bueschner and Gallin, 1984). Similar findings were obtained with mouse peritoneal macrophages irradiated in vitro and tested three to ten days later. The cell numbers and the ability to bind to and to phagocytose IgG antibody-coated RBCs were decreased and the release of lactic dehydrogenase (measure of cell injury) was increased (Gallin *et al.*, 1984). These two studies indicate that macrophages exhibit a 'delayed' type of functional deficiency after direct irradiation. This delay may be able to explain the surprising findings of Gallily and her colleagues. Mice exposed to 550 cGy of X-rays were unable to make anti-*Shigella* antibodies well, and this defect could be restored by injection of 15 million peritoneal cells enriched in macrophages previously exposed to *Shigella* antigens (Gallily and Feldman, 1967). It is of interest that the mice were challenged two days after irradiation and not immediately after irradiation. If the host mice were exposed to 750 or 900 cGy the transferred macrophages were less able to restore antibody formation, indicating that host B cells and T helper cells were inactivated. Macrophages from irradiated donors were inactive. Thus bacterial antigen processing and presentation by macrophages appear to be significantly affected two days after irradiation. Under similar conditions, phagocytosis, enzyme function and degradation of ^{125}I-labelled *Shigella* were normal or somewhat increased (Geiger and Gallily, 1974).

Mice were exposed to 10 or 100 cGy of ^{60}Co irradiation per day to achieve total doses of 50 to 650 and 400 to 2000 cGy respectively. The phagocytic index, using colloidal carbon injections in vivo, and serum lysozyme (a macrophage product) levels were measured. At 10 cGy/day, the phagocytic index was actually stimulated at 50 cGy, but gradually decreased and was suppressed at 400 cGy (Hlavaty, 1978). At 100 cGy/day, the phagocytic index was stimulated at 400 and 800 cGy, but decreased and was quite low at 2000 cGy. Serum lysozyme activity was progressively suppressed with doses at 100 cGy/day and was suppressed at 450 and 600 cGy following exposure to 10 cGy/day. Thus, over time, whole body irradiation does compromise the functions of macrophages.

In a very careful study of the effects of direct irradiation on the ability of mouse macrophages to engulf and later to degrade sheep RBCs, the effect of time was again noted. The ability to engulf the RBCs was unaffected even after 50 000 cGy if tested directly after irradiation (Perkins *et al.*, 1966), but the phagocytic ability steadily declined between 6 and 24 hours. The ability to degrade intracellular RBCs was unaffected by irradiation. Death of the macrophages appeared to explain the results of decreased function with time after irradiation. Although the data were not presented, examination of the dose–response curves indicates that the D_0 values were 1500 cGy at 6 hours, 800 cGy at 12 hours and 150 cGy at 24 hours.

A major function of macrophages is to present antigens to T helper cells and B cells in antibody response. Macrophages exposed to 1000 cGy were perfectly able to present sheep RBC antigens in an in vitro system to detect antibody formation (Roseman, 1969). In a more detailed analysis, this function was shown to decrease between doses of 500 and 6000 cGy. The cells were irradiated and antibody-forming cells were determined five days afterward (Cosenza *et al.*, 1971). In contrast, irradiated macrophages (to doses of 10 000 cGy) were better able than normal macrophages to present protein (keyhole limpet haemocyanin or human gamma globulin) antigens to normal mice (Schmidtke and Dixon, 1972). The uptake and degradation were not significantly affected by irradiation and more antigen/cell was bound to the irradiated macrophages. The continued immune function, including perhaps antigen presentation, would be expected to be normal in the unirradiated mice. A major antigen-presenting cell, the dendritic cell, appears to function in immune responses continually. Rowley and colleagues have demonstrated that immune functions, including antibody responses, can be inhibited by exposing the antigen-presenting cells to potent NK cells, even after the first day or so of culture (Abruzzo and Rowley, 1983; Shah *et al.*, 1985). Thus, if antigen presentation is required for prolonged times during the immune response, irradiation will eventually inhibit that function. The failure to appreciate that antigen presentation was required throughout the immune response might be ascribed to data in vitro, which indicated that adherent cells were only required for the first 24 hours of a response. However, dendritic cells become non-adherent after 24 hours in culture (Abruzzo and Rowley, 1983; Shah *et al.*, 1985).

The ability of macrophages to phagocytose colloidal carbon in vivo is resistant to large doses of irradiation (Benacerraf *et al.*, 1959). Klimpel and colleagues observed that mouse bone-marrow cells produce large amounts of interferon in response to alloantigens (Klimpel *et al.*, 1982). In that system, T cells secrete IL-2, which induces marrow monocytes/ macrophages to secrete interferon beta (IFN-β). The ability of the cells to secrete IFN is not diminished after exposure to 2000 cGy of gamma rays.

C. Mast Cells

Although we usually associate mast cells with anaphylactic type I hypersensitivity responses mediated by IgE (and other) antibodies, the secretory products of mast cells indicate that they must participate in a number of inflammatory responses. Mast cell granules secrete primary mediators, including histamine, heparin, eosinophil chemotactic factor of anaphylaxis, and neutrophil chemotactic factor (Austen, 1982). Secondary mediators are formed within the cell membrane and include slow reactive substance of anaphylaxis, made up of leukotrienes (LT) C_4, D_4 and E_4. LTC_4 and LTD_4 are powerful smooth muscle contractants. LTB_4 is the most powerful chemotactic agent known and is made by mast cells. PGD_2 is a potent vasodilator and PGI_2 causes platelet disaggregation; both are products of mast cells (O'Flaherty, 1982). Exposure of monkeys to 4000 cGy of a mixture of neutrons and gamma rays (total body irradiation) resulted in the rapid secretion of histamine from mast cells (Doyle and Strike, 1977). The femoral artery was cannulated to obtain the blood sample rapidly. If mast cells were degranulated with compound 48/80, the irradiation failed to cause a release of histamine.

Mast cell numbers in the skin of mice remained stable for over 11 days after exposure to 600 cGy. Exposure of mice to doses between 0 and 1200 cGy 24 hours before enumerating mast cells in the skin revealed a very modest loss of cells, even at 1200 cGy (Carter, 1977). A D_0 value could not be determined. The radiosensitivity of bone-marrow versus skin precursors of mast cells was evaluated (Kitamura *et al.*, 1983). Bone-marrow donors were (WB $\times$ B6)F_1 $+/+$ or C57BL/6-bg^j/bg^j (beige) and recipients were (WB $\times$ B6)F_1 W/W^V (dominant spotted anaemia). The anaemic mice have no mast cells, and the transferred cells form small colonies of mast cells 35 days after inoculation of the marrow into sites in the skin. The characteristic granules of the beige mutants allow easy identification of donor-type mast cells. Kitamura *et al.* observed 'hybrid resistance' by the (WB $\times$ B6)F_1 hosts to B6 beige marrow cells, but colonies were detected. The D_0 values for (WB $\times$ B6)F_1 $+/+$ and B6 beige marrow cells were 123 and 103 cGy, respectively. These values are not very different from those for CFU-S. B6 beige mice were exposed to 0 to 2400 cGy one hour before their skin was removed and transplanted onto C57BL/6 $+/+$ hosts. Mast cells in the skin grafts were enumerated 45 days later and the large granules were used to distinguish between beige and $+/+$ mast cells. The D_0 value for skin precursors of beige origin was 795 cGy. Finally, they exposed mice to doses up to 4000 cGy before removing the skin 24 hours later to determine mast cell numbers. No decreases was seen even after 4000 cGy. Thus, in this slowly turning over cell population, great differences are seen in radiosensitivities when stem cells, fairly immediate precursor cells and mature cells are compared.

Rats were exposed to local abdominal irradiation (800 cGy) and mast cell numbers and histamine content were studied for the next 14 days. The numbers of mast cells were decreased by 50 per cent four days after irradiation (Norby *et al.*, 1984). Thus, mesenteric mast cells or their immediate precursors are apparently more radiosensitive than skin mast cells. The secretory capacities of the remaining mesenteric mast cells, in response to compound 48/80, were also diminished.

D. Natural Killer (NK) Cells

The radiosensitivity of NK cells has been competently reviewed by Lotzová (1981). She observed that in vivo irradiation to 1200 cGy or in vitro exposure to 1500 cGy did not affect NK cell function, if it was tested within 24 hours (Lotzová and McCredie, 1978; Lotzová and Savary, 1977). Mice exposed to 1100, but not to 2200, cGy of total body irradiation retained normal NK cell function for short periods of time (Datta *et al.*, 1979). If mice are exposed to a high sublethal dose of ionising irradiation (700 cGy), NK cell function is maintained for 12 days if activity is reported on a per cell basis, i.e. frequency of NK cells (Hochman *et al.*, 1978). Later on, suppression was observed for about two weeks, and the mechanism appeared to be the emergence of suppressor cells capable of inhibiting NK cell function. Haller and Wigzell observed that chronic irradiation of the bone marrow by ^{89}Sr eliminated NK cell activity in the spleen (Haller and Wigzell, 1977). This bone-seeking isotope could have functioned by irradiating stem cells for NK cells and/or by irradiating immature NK cells which must sojourn through the marrow tissue in order to differentiate fully.

The stem cells for NK cells have many properties of other immature haemopoietic progenitor cells. If 10^5 to 10^7 bone-marrow cells are infused into syngeneic irradiated host mice, a graded increase in splenic NK cell function or clearance of YAC-1 tumour cells from the lung occurs 8 to 21 days later (Hackett *et al.*, 1985; Hackett *et al.*, 1986a; Hackett *et al.*, 1986b). Hackett observed that the stem cells for NK cells were different from myeloid stem cells, in that no defect was seen in NK stem cells of marrow taken from (WB × B6)F$_1$ W/W^b donor mice. Moreover, the stem cells differed from progenitor cells for T and B cells, since marrow from mice with severe combined immunodeficiency (SCID) generates NK cells normally but is unable to form B or T cells. Nevertheless, Hackett did observe that drugs, e.g. 5-fluorouracil, affect CFU-Ss and NK stem cells to a similar degree, and that 800 cGy of gamma rays destroys both CFU-Ss and NK stem cells. Evidence that NK cells form an independent lineage of lymphoid cells includes the following: (1) Purification of NK cells with Koo's monoclonal reagent, anti-NK-1.1, separates a unique population of cells with NK cell-surface markers (NK-1.1, NK-2.1, asialo GM1) but lacking T (L3T4, Lyt-2) or B (Ig) cell markers (Hackett *et al.*, 1986c). (2) Tutt propagated purified NK-1.1$^+$ NK cells in vitro using recombinant interleukin 2, and the cells so generated were 'pure' NK cells which did not express functional transcripts of the T cell receptor genes (Tutt *et al.*, 1986). Similar analyses of NK cells derived from SCID mice gave similar results (Tutt *et al.* 1987; Lauzon *et al.*, 1986). The investigators in the second study (Lauzon *et al.*, 1986) unfortunately misinterpreted their own data and concluded that two NK cell lineages exist, and that SCID mice have the non-T cell variety while normal mice have T and non-T cell NK cell types. There really is not an expanded NK cell pool in SCID mice; the frequency of NK cells is enriched because there are no T and B cells in the spleen. Normally 80–90% of spleen cells are T and B cells while about 3–7% are NK cells. Without other lymphocytes, it appears that NK cells have expanded. However, spleens of SCID mice have low numbers of total cells and the frequency of NK cells in the marrow is not increased to the point of calling the NK cell population 'expanded'. I have emphasised this controversial point because, when one talks about NK cells and the effects of radiation, one should know if one or two populations of cells are being considered.

In a study of human NK cells, which lyse K562 erythroleukaemia cells, doses of 400 of 1600 cGy X-irradiation only slightly decreased NK cell function (Rotstein *et al.*, 1983). Local irradiation of patients for carcinomas of the breast, prostate and urinary bladder (dose about 4500 cGy maximum at once, with total doses of 5400 cGy in six weeks) caused a moderate, but significant, decrease in NK cell function temporarily (Blomgren *et al.*, 1980).

Antibody-dependent cellular cytotoxicity (ADCC) directed against tumour cells can be effectively mediated by NK cells (Ojo and Wigzell, 1978). These effector cells were observed to be as radioresistant as NK cells (Hebermann *et al.*, 1979). ADCC was depressed in patients exposed to local irradiation for cancers, as with NK cell function, and the activity recovered between five and ten weeks of the commencing of irradiation (McCredie *et al.*, 1979).

E. Natural Cytotoxic (NC) Cells

Stutman described a type of 'null' lymphocyte capable of lysing adherent tumour cells in vitro, which was not a T, B or NK cell by the criteria used at the time (Stutman *et al.*, 1978). Eventually the WEHI-164.1 fibrosarcoma cell line became the prototyic target cell for these natural cytotoxic (NC) cells. The NC cells were resistant to elimination by the bone-seeking isotope, ^{89}Sr, indicating that marrow was not essential for their differentiation and that the stem cells were not greatly diminished (Lust *et al.*, 1981). If NC cells are all non-NK lymphocytes capable of lysing tumour cells spontaneously, they must be a heterogeneous group of cells. The cells which lyse the Friend erythroleukaemia cells FLD-3, are not eliminated by treatment with ^{89}Sr, as expected. However, if mice are lethally irradiated three days before spleen cells are harvested, the cells which lyse FLD-3 cells are absent or inactive (Lust *et al.*, 1984). The NK and NC cells capable of lysing YAC-1 and WEHI-164.1 cells respectively are present at normal or increased frequency. A greater difference was observed when anti-asialo-GM serum was used. This antiserum abrogates the ability of spleen cells to lyse FLD-3 or YAC-1 cells, but not WEHI-164.1 cells (Afifi *et al.*, 1986). The ability to resist grafts of FLD-3 cells is intact if animals are challenged immediately after irradiation (800–900 cGy), but the ability is diminished three days later (Afifi *et al.*, 1986). Thus, the immediate precursors of the anti-FLD-3 effector cells are more radiosensitive than the immediate precursors of NK cells and the NC cell which lyses WEHI-164.1 cells.

Recently, two new findings concerning NC cells have been reported. It appears that any haemopoietic cell population one can enrich for or can purify is capable of NC activity against WEHI-164.1 cells (Bykowsky and Stutman, 1986). The NC activity appears to be mediated by cachectin, or tumour necrosis factor alpha, since antibodies to cachectin can abolish NC activity (Ortaldo *et al.*, 1986). Similar antibodies did not affect NK cell function. Therefore, NC cell function appears to be a basic function of many types of haemopoietic cells, at least when tested in vitro. In vivo the cells which mediate NC function have not been determined, and could be primarily NK cells (Hackett *et al.*, 1986b).

F. B Cells

B cells are correctly considered in the context of acquired rather than natural immunity. However, B cells do secrete 'natural antibodies' which may function in marrow allograft responses (Warner and Dennert, 1985) and in tumour surveillance (Miller *et al.*, 1983). B cells can also present antigen to T cells (Frohman and Cowing, 1985). This ability to present antigen was least in resting B cells, which were about 1000 times less efficient than adherent cells. Lipopolysaccharide (LPS)-activated B cells were one-quarter as efficient as adherent cells. Antigen presentation by all three cell types was preserved after 1100 cGy irradiation. Resting B cells could not present antigen if exposed to 2200 or 3000 cGy. As early as three hours after LPS, B cells became more radioresistant and by 21 hours they were resistant to doses of 2200 and 3000 cGy, to the level of adherent cells.

Antibody synthesis itself is quite radioresistant. An ongoing IgE antibody response to ovalbumin was resistant to 800 to 1000 cGy of total body irradiation (Peeters and Carter, 1981). Exposure of mice to 400 cGy from one day before to eight days after immunisation enhanced the production IgE antibody responses (Tada *et al.*, 1971). Ongoing antibody responses in diffusion chambers implanted into the peritoneal cavities of mice were resistant to 10 000 cGy of X-rays (Sado, 1969; Vann and Makinoden, 1969).

Progenitor cells for B cells may be quite radiosensitive, since exposure of mice to 100 to 500 cGy of X-rays as long as one month prior to immunisation significantly inhibited antibody responses to sheep RBCs (Makidono *et al.*, 1978).

G. T Cells

T cells, like B cells, are principally involved in acquired immune responses. Nevertheless, T-cell-produced lymphokines, e.g. interferon gamma, can stimulate the functions of macrophages and NK cells involved in natural immunity. For example, mice injected with the T cell mitogen concanavalin A become more resistant to early stages of infection with *Listeria monocytogenes* (Masuda and Bennett, 1981). T cells exhibit a heterogeneous degree of sensitivity to irradiation. In one study, mice were exposed to 0 to 500 cGy prior to cannulation of the thoracic duct for enumeration of recirculating T cells. There was a dramatic drop-off of cells recoverable between 0 and 50 cGy, a plateau between 50 and 300 cGy, and another steep drop-off between 300 and 500 cGy (Anderson and Williams, 1977). The effect of irradiation increased with time from 6 to 48 hours after irradiation. The ability of T and B cells to migrate into lymphoid tissues after irradiation was studied (Anderson *et al.*, 1974). If the cells were infused immediately after irradiation, migration was near-normal. If the cells were incubated in vitro 1–7 hours before infusion, the cells failed to migrate, as many were dying rapidly. B cells were more sensitive to radiation than T cells, and 5–10 per cent of T cells were resistant even to 1000 cGy.

Thymocytes and lymph node cells were exposed to 10 to 10 000 cGy of X-rays, and were cultured in vitro for up to 30 hours, and viability was tested (Lowenthal and Harris, 1985). Some cells were activated by exposure to concanavalin A or LPS. The resting cells were very much more sensitive to the loss of viability with time than activated cells.

The loss of migratory properties of irradiated T cells may explain the finding that T cells responsible for delayed-type hypersensitivity responses, after exposure to 1500 cGy, could transfer that reaction only if injected locally into the test footpad (Kettman and Mathews, 1975). The type of activation of T cells can also affect radiosensitivity. T cells sensitised by glutaraldehyde-fixed RBCs were more radiosensitive than T cells sensitised with unfixed RBCs, for transfer of delayed-type hypersensitivity (Lathen and Kettman, 1979).

The radiosensitivty of pre-cytolytic T lymphocytes (pCTLs) was determined (Spellman and Anderson, 1982). A definite subset of pCTLs were susceptible to 10–25 cGy of X-rays. The effects of low-dose irradiation on pCTLs could be decreased by addition of interleukin 2 to the culture, suggesting that stimulation of growth of the cells enhanced radioresistance (Gerber, 1984). A dose of 500 cGy inhibited the subsequent secondary CTL response to alloantigens, but there was no effect on frequency of pCTLs. The addition of interleukin 2 to the culture allowed the pCTLs of the irradiated mice to reveal their numbers (Kanagawa *et al.*, 1983). If mice were exposed to 500 cGy and immunised with large numbers of allogeneic cells, there was an enhanced CTL response and a very depressed antibody response to H-2 antigens (Engers and Louis, 1979).

Mice exposed to lethal doses of irradiation can mount T-cell-mediated (including CTL) responses to H-2 semiallogeneic marrow cells (Aizawa *et al.*, 1980). In a more detailed study, these investigators observed that 850 cGy is required to suppress host T cells of C57BL/6 mice and 1100 cGy is required in C3H mice (Sado *et al.*, 1985). Evidence for the ability of radioresistant host T cells to inhibit stem cell function of H-2 allogeneic stem cells grafted into irradiated mice was presented in a fascinating series of experiments, involving spleen organ cultures (von Melchner and Bartlett, 1983). Finally, the ability of heavily irradiated rats to reject skin grafts was observed (Gassman *et al.*, 1986). Even after 1230 cGy of total-body irradiation RT-1 incompatible skin grafts were rejected by seven days if and only if the rats were immunised with 10^8 marrow cells of skin-donor origin. This result, in my opinion, dramatises the importance of consideration of time after exposure when cells are properly stimulated. In the above experiment, the immediate immunisation with marrow cells obviously led to the activation of host effector cells responsible for rejection in an accelerated fashion allowing rejection to occur before the effector cells manifested radiation damage. It may also have rendered them relatively more resistant to radiation.

III. SENSITIVITY OF A PARTICULAR NATURAL IMMUNE FUNCTION TO RADIATION: MARROW ALLOGRAFT REACTIVITY

The analysis of the radiosensitivity of a single immune cell type is difficult enough. To describe and analyse accurately the radiosensitivity of a complex multicellular and multifactorial biological response can be very difficult. Before we knew which cell types were involved in marrow allograft reactivity, we described the effect of irradiation on the 'whole response'.

The ability of mice to reject marrow allografts is relatively radio-resistant, since lethally irradiated mice are used to detect rejection. However, progressive increases in dose of irradiation do weaken resistance (Cudkowicz and Bennett, 1971). A high dose of sublethal irradiation (400–700 cGy) results in the weakening of allograft reactivity after seven days; recovery requires about three weeks (Cudkowicz and Bennett, 1971). If mice are irradiated and infusion of marrow is delayed by one to five days, a progressive loss of reactivity is observed (Cudkowisz, 1965).

In Trentin's laboratory, specific-pathogen-free mice were so well maintained that they could be exposed to doses of X-rays as high as 4000 cGy and survive for several days. This feat made it possible to determine just how much radiation was required to prevent marrow allograft reactivity (Rauchwerger *et al.*, 1977). Doses of 2000 cGy or higher were needed.

Chronic irradiation of the marrow by ^{89}Sr prevented marrow graft rejection (Bennett, 1973). This was interpreted to be due to the necessity for the effector cells to undergo critical stages of differentiation in the bone marrow. The subsequent studies of NK cells described above indicate that ^{89}Sr eliminated the critical cell type responsible for marrow allograft rejection.

Another form of irradiation which weakens marrow graft rejection (while also preventing graft-versus-host disease) is total lymphoid irradiation (Slavin *et al.*, 1978). Animals are exposed to 17 fractionated doses of 200 cGy (total 3400 cGy) to the lymphoid organs, shielding much of the marrow tissue. The mechanism of tissue non-reactivity appears to be the development of non-specific 'natural suppressor cells' followed by specific suppressor cells (Okada and Strober, 1982).

What is the cell type affected by radiation which inhibits marrow allograft reactivity? Cells with features of NK cells were derived from irradiated animals' spleens that could restore marrow allograft reactivity (Miller, 1983). Cloned cells with NK cell properties were capable of restoring marrow allograft reactivity to mice exposed to sublethal irradiation so as to inhibit marrow graft reactivity (Warner and Dennert, 1982). Nevertheless, since macrophages function in this response, primarily by secreting interferon (Afifi *et al.*, 1985), radiation may also weaken marrow graft rejection by inhibiting macrophages or macrophage function.

In summary, the cell types which contribute to natural immunity vary in their degree of radiosensitivity. Resting B and T cells are quite radiosensitive, some effects being seen at doses of 50 cGy or less. In general, the mature functional cells are radioresistant, since they perform their functions rapidly, e.g. secrete antibody or interferon or lyse target cells. Relative immediate precursor cells are of intermediate radio-sensitivity, and the D_0 value varies for the various cell types as detailed above. The transplantable stem cells are quite radiosensitive. The careful analysis of the effects of radiation on a given immune cell type or of a complex immune response can contribute to its characterisation in important ways and can help lead to the elucidation of new cell types.

ACKNOWLEDGMENTS

This work was supported in part by grants CA36921, CA36922 and A120451 from the National Cancer Institute, NIH, Bethesda, Maryland.

I wish to acknowledge the following colleagues in the lab, who have performed much of the work described in this chapter: Vinay Kumar, Michelle Tutt, John Hackett, Jr, William J. Murphy, Richard M. Rembecki and Charles Sentman. I thank Deborah Scott for typing the manuscript.

REFERENCES

Abruzzo, L. V. and Rowley, D. A. (1983). Homeostatis of the antibody response: immunoregulation by NK cells. *Science* 222: 581.

Adamson, I. Y. R. and Bowden, D. H. (1982). Effects of irradiation on macrophage response and transport of particles across the alveolar epithelium. *Am. J. Pathol.* 106: 40.

Afifi, M. S., Kumar, V. and Bennett, M. (1985). Stimulation of genetic resistance to marrow grafts in mice by interferon-alpha/beta. *J. Immunol.* 134: 3739.

Afifi, M. S, Bennett, M. and Kumar, V. (1986). Natural immunity to grafts of FLD-3 erythroleukemia cells by irradiated mice. *Nat. Immun. Cell Growth Regul.* 5: 200.

Aizawa, S., Sado, H., Kamisaka, H. and Kubo, E. (1980). Cellular basis of the immunohematologic defects observed in short-term semiallogeneic B6C3F1-C3H chimeras: evidence for host-versus-graft reaction initiated by radioresistant T cells. *Cell. Immunol.* 56: 47.

Anderson, R. E. and Williams, W. L. (1977). Radiosensitivity of T and B lymphocytes: V: Effects of whole-body irradiation on numbers of recirculating T cells and sensitization to primary skin grafts in mice. *Am. J. Pathol.* 89: 367.

Anderson, R. E., Sprent, J. and Miller, J. F. A. P. (1974). Radiosensitivity of T and B lymphocytes: I: Effect of irradiation on cell migration. *Eur. J. Immunol.* 4: 199.

Austen, K. F. (1982). Tissue mast cells in immediate hypersensitivity. *Hosp. Pract.* 17: 98.

Benacerraf, B., Kivy-Rosenberg, E., Sebestyen, M. M. and Zwifach, B. W. (1959). The effect of high doses of X-irradiation on the phagocytic, proliferative and metabolic properties of the reticuloendothelial system. *J. Exp. Med.* 110: 49.

Bennett, M. (1973). Prevention of marrow allograft rejection with radioactive strontium: evidence for marrow-dependent effector cells. *J. Immunol.* 110: 510.

Blomgren, H., Baral, E., Edsmyr, F., Strender, L.-D., Petrini, B. and Wasserman, J. (1980). Natural killer cell activity in peripheral lymphocyte population following local radiation therapy. *Acta Radiol. Oncol.* 19: 139.

Bogman, M. J. J. T., Cornelissen, I. M. H. A., Berden, J. H. M., DeJong, J. and Koene, R. A. P. (1984). A comparative study of total body irradiation as a method of inducing granulocyte depletion in mice. *J. Immunol. Meth.* 70: 31.

Bueschner, E. S. and Gallin, J. I. (1984). Radiation effects on cultured human monocytes and on monocyte-derived macrophages. *Blood* 63: 1402.

Bykowsky, M. J. and Stutman, O. (1986). The cells responsible for murine natural cytotoxic (NC) activity: a multilineage system. *J. Immunol.* 137: 1120.

Carter, B. G. (1977). Mast cell numbers and passive cutaneous anaphylaxis in irradiated mice. *Int. Arch. Allergy Appl. Immunol.* 54: 378.

Cosenza, H., Leserman, L. D. and Rowley, D. A. (1971). The third cell type required for the immune response of spleen cells in vitro. *J. Immunol.* 107: 414.

Cudkowicz, C. (1965). Hybrid resistance to parental hemopoietic cell grafts: implications for bone marrow chimeras. In G. Mathe, J. L. Amjel and L. Schwarzenbend (eds), *La greffe des cellules hematopoietiques allogeniques.* Paris: Centre Natl. Rech. Scientist: 207.

Cudkowicz, G. and Bennett, M. (1971). Peculiar immunobiology of bone marrow allografts. *J. Exp. Med.* 134: 83 and 1513.

Cudkowicz, G. and Stimpfling, J. H. (1964). Deficient growth of C57BL marrow cells transplanted in F1 hybrid mice: Associated with the histocompatibility-2 locus. *Immunology* 7: 291.

Datta, S. K., Gallagher, M. T., Trentin, J. J., Kiessling, R. and Wigzell, H. (1979). Apparent identity of mechanisms of genetic resistance to marrow transplantation and natural killer cell activity. *Biomedicine* 31: 62.

Doyle, T. F. and Strike, T. A. (1977). Radiation-induced histamine release in the rhesus monkey as modified by mast-cell depletion and antihistamine. *Experientia* 33: 1047.

Engers, H. D. and Louis, J. (1979). Dissociation of the humoral and cell-mediated responses to alloantigens in mice by sublethal whole-body irradiation. *Scand. J. Immunol.* 10: 509.

Evans, M. J., Shami, S. G. and Martinez, L. A. (1986). Enhanced proliferation of pulmonary alveolar macrophages after carbon instillation in mice depleted of blood monocytes by strontium-89. *Lab. Invest.* 54: 154.

Frohman, M. and Cowing, C. (1985). Presentation of antigen by B cells: functional dependence on radiation dose, interleukins, cellular activation and differential glycosylation. *J. Immunol.* 134: 2269.

Gallily, R. and Feldman, M. (1967). The role of macrophages in the induction of antibody in x-irradiated animals. *Immunology* 12: 197.

Gallin, E. K., Green, S. W. and Darden, J. (1984). Defective Fc-mediated phagocytes in γ-irradiated mouse peritoneal macrophages. *Int. J. Radiat. Biol.* 45: 459.

Gassman, W., Wattage, H. V., von Kolzynski, M. and Muller-Ruchholtz, W. (1986). Immune reactivity after high-dose irradiation. *Transplantation* 41: 380

Geiger, B. and Gallily, R. (1974). Effect of x-irradiation on various functions of murine macrophages. *Clin. Exp. Immunol.* 16: 643.

Gerber, M. (1984). Radiosensitivity of murine T-lymphocyte cytotoxicity. *Rad. Res.* 100: 365.

Hackett, J. Jr., Bennett, M. and Kumar, V. (1985). Origin and differentiation of natural killer cells: I: Characteristics of a transplantable NK cell precursor. *J. Immunol.* 134: 3731.

Hackett, J. Jr., Bosma, G. C., Bosma, M. J., Bennett, M. and Kumar, V. (1986a). Transplantable progenitors of natural killer cells are distinct from those of T and B lymphocytes. *Proc. Natl. Acad. Sci. USA* 83: 3427.

Hackett, J. Jr., Bennett, M., Koo, G. C. and Kumar, V. (1986b). Origin and differentiation of natural killer cells: III: Relationships between the precursors and effectors of natural killer and natural cytotoxic activity. *Surv. Immunol. Res.* 5: 16.

Hackett, J. Jr, Tutt, M., Lipscomb, M., Bennett, M., Koo, G. C. and Kumar, V. (1986c). Origin and differentiation of natural killer cells: II: Functional and morphologic studies of purified NK-1.1[+] cells. *J. Immunol.* 136: 3124.

Haller, O. and Wigzell, H. (1977). Suppression of natural killer cell activity with radioactive strontium: effector cells are marrow dependent. *J. Immunol.* 118: 1503.

Hamilton, L. D. (ed.) (1964). Physical factors and modification of radiation injury. *Ann. NY Acad. Sci.* 114: 1–716.

Hlavaty, V. (1978). Effect of gamma ray low doses on the system of the nonspecific defense of the organism. *Strahlentherapie* 154: 801.

Herberman, R. B., Nunn, M. E., Holden, H. T. and Lavrin, D. (1975). Natural cytotoxic reactivity of mouse lymphoid cells against syngeneic and allogeneic tumor: II: Characterisation of the effector cells. *Int. J. Cancer* 16: 230.

Herberman, R. B., Djeu, J. Y., Kay, H. D., Ortaldo, J. R., Riccardi, C., Bonnard, G. D., Holden, H. T., Fagnari, R., Santoni, A. and Puscetti, P. (1979). Natural killer cells: characteristics and regulation of activity. *Immunol. Rev.* 44: 43.

Hochman, P. S., Cudkowicz, G. and Dausset, J. (1978). Decline of natural killer cell activity in sublethally irradiated mice. *J. Natl. Cancer Inst.* 61: 265.

Holley, T. R., van Epps, D. E., Harvey, R. L., Anderson, R. E. and Williams, R. C. Jr (1974). Effect of high doses of radiation on human neutrophil chemotaxis, phagocytosis and morphology. *Am. J. Pathol.* 75: 61.

Hornstein, P., Wahren, B. and Esposti, P.-L. (1985). Granulopoietic precursor cells and regulatory factors in irradiated human bone marrow. *Int. J. Radiation Oncology Biol. Phys.* 11: 783.

Kanagawa, O., Louis, J. A., Engers, H. D. and Cerottini, J.-C. (1983). Effect of sublethal whole-body irradiation on subsequent secondary cytolytic T cell responses in vitro. *J. Immunol.* 130:24.

Kettman, J and Mathews, M. C. (1975). Radioresistance of cells responsible for delayed hypersensitivity reactions in the mouse. *J. Immunol.* 115: 606.

Kiessling, R., Klein, E., Pross, H., and Wigzell, H. (1975). Natural killer cells in the mouse: II: Cytotoxic cells with specificity for mouse Moloney leukemia cells: Characteristics of killer cells. *Eur. J. Immunol.* 5: 117.

Kitamura, Y., Yokayama, M., Sonoda, T. and Mori, K. J. (1983). Different radiosensitivities of mast cell precursors in the bone marrow and skin of mice. *Rad. Res.* 93: 147.

Klimpel, G. R., Fleischmann, W. R., Bannon, S. and Klimpel, K. D. (1982). Mouse bone marrow cells produce a different interferon than do spleen cells in the response to alloantigens. *J. Immunol.* 129: 1982.

Koo, G. C. and Manyak, C. L. (1986). Generation of cytotoxic cells from murine bone marrow by human recombinant IL-2. *J. Immunol.* 137: 1751.

Lathen, D. and Kettman, J. (1979). Activation of T cells by glutaraldehyde-fixed erythrocyte antigens: radiosensitivity of cells mediating delayed-type hypersensitivity reactions in the mouse. *Cell. Immunol.* 47: 170.

Lauzon, R. J., Siminovitch, K. A., Fulop, G. M., Phillips, R. A. and Roder, J. C. (1986). An expanded population of natural killer cells in mice with severe combined immunodeficiency (SCID) lack rearrangement and expression of T cell receptor genes. *J. Exp. Med.* 164: 1797.

Leong, G. F., Wisecup W. G. and Grisham, J. W. (1964). Effects of divided doses of X-ray on mortality and hematology of small and large domestic animals. *Ann. NY Acad. Sci. US* 114: 138.

Lotzová, E. (1981). Experimental radiation and immune defense interactions. In N. Prasad (ed.), *Radiotherapy and Cancer Immunology*, Boca Raton; Florida: CRC Press: 1.

Lotzová, E. and McCredie, K. B. (1978). Natural killer cells in mice and man and their possible biological significance. *Cancer Immunol. Immunother.* 4: 215.

Lotzová, E. and Savary, C. A. (1977). Possible involvement of natural killer cells in bone marrow graft rejection. *Biomedicine* 27: 341.

Lowenthal, J. W. and Harris, A. W. (1985). Activation of mouse lymphocytes inhibits induction of rapid cell death by X-irradiation. *J. Immunol.* 135: 1119.

Lust, J. A., Kumar, V., Burton, R. C., Bartlett, S. P. and Bennett, M. (1981). Heterogeneity of natural killer cells in the mouse. *J. Exp. Med.* 154: 306.

Lust, J. A., Bennett, M. and Kumar, V. (1984). Lysis of FLD-3 Friend erythroleukemia cells in vitro and in vivo: Effects of ^{89}Sr treatment and Friend virus infection. *Int. J. Cancer* 33:107.

McCredie, J. A., MacDonald, H. R. and Wood, S. B. (1979). Effect of operation and radiotherapy on antibody-dependent cellular cytotoxicity. *Cancer* 44: 99.

McCulloch, E. A. and Till, J. E. (1962). The sensitivity of cells from normal mouse bone marrow to gamma radiation in vitro and in vivo. *Rad. Res.* 166: 822.

Makidono, R, Nomoto, K. and Takeya, K. (1978). Immune responses in irradiated mice: I: Radiosensitivity of antibody response against sheep erythrocytes in C57BL/6 mice. *J. Radiat. Res.* 19: 115.

Masuda, A. and Bennett, M. (1981). Concanavalin A induced resistance to *Listeria monocytogenes* and activation of macrophages: defect in mice treated with [89]Sr. *Eur. J. Immunol.* 11: 556.

Mayhew, E. and Bennett, M. (1971). An in vitro reaction between lymphoid cells and target fibroblastic cells; a possible model for in vivo rejection of haemopoietic allografts. *Immunology* 21: 123.

Miller, S. C. (1983). Genetically determined resistance to foreign bone marrow transplantion in mice: characterization of the effector cells. *J. Immunol.* 131: 92.

Miller, V. E., Pohajdak, B. and Greenberg, A. H. (1983). Murine natural antitumor antibodies: II: Interferon treatment of a natural killer-resistant lymphoma: augmentation of natural antibody reactivity and susceptibility to in vivo natural resistance. *J. Natl. Cancer Inst.* 71: 377.

Norby, K., Abok, K. Adamson, P. and Forsberg, B. (1984). Radiation effects of mast cells: secretory ability, histamine release and recovery, and cell number. *Acta Path. Microbiol. Immunol. Scand.* Sect. A 92: 417.

Nothdurft, W., Steinbach, K. -H. and Fliedner, T. M. (1983). In vitro studies of the sensitivity of canine granulopoietic progenitor cells (GM-CFC) to ionizing radiation: Differences between steady state GM-CFC from blood and bone marrow. *Int. J. Radiat. Biol.* 43: 133.

Nothdurft, W., Steinbach, K. H. and Fliedner, T. M. (1984). Dose- and time-related quantitative and qualitative alterations in the granulocytic/macrophage progenitor cell (GM-CFC) compartment of dogs after total-body irradiation. *Rad. Res.* 98: 332.

O'Flaherty, J. T. (1982). Lipid mediators of inflammation and allergy. *Lab. Invest.* 47: 314.

Ojo, E. and Wigzell, H. (1978) Natural killer cells may be the only cells in normal mouse lymphoid cell populations endowed with cytotoxic ability for antibody coated tumour target cells. *Scand. J. Immunol.* 7: 297.

Okada, S. and Strober, S. (1982). Spleens from adult mice given total body irradiation (TBI) and from newborn mice have similar regulatory effects in the mixed lymphocyte reaction (MLR). *J. Exp. Med.* 156: 522.

Ortaldo, J. R., Mason, L. H., Mathieson, B. J., Liang, S. M., Flick, D. A. and Herberman, R. B. (1986). Mediation of mouse natural cytotoxic activity by tumour necrosis factor. *Nature* 321: 700.

Peeters, S. H. and Carter, B. G. (1981). Regulation of the IgE antibody response in mice: II: Radioresistance of established IgE antibody production. *Immunology* 43: 25.

Perkins, E. H., Nettesheim, P. and Morita, T. (1966). Radioresistance of the engulfing and degradative capacities of peritoneal phagocytes to kiloroentgen X-ray doses. *J. Reticuloendothel. Soc.* 3:71.

Rauchwerger, J. M., Gallagher, M. T., Monie, H. J. and Trentin, J. J. (1977). Relative radioresistance of xenogeneic and hybrid resistance to bone marow transplantation. *Transplantation* 23: 150.

Riccardi, C., Poccetti, P., Santoni, A. and Herberman, R. B. (1979). Rapid in vivo assay of mouse natural killer cell activity. *J. Natl. Cancer Inst.* 63: 1041.

Roseman, J. (1969). X-ray resistant cell required for the induction of in vitro antibody formation. *Science* 165: 1125.

Rotstein, S., Baral, E., Blomgren, H. and Johansson, B. (1983). In vitro radiosensitivity of the spontaneous cytotoxicity of blood lymphocytes in patients with untreated Hodgkin's Disease. *Eur. J. Cancer. Clin. Oncol.* 19: 1405.

Sadarangani, C., Skamene, E. and Kongshavn, P. A. L. (1980). Cellular basis for genetically determined enhanced resistance of certain mouse strains to Listeriosis. *Infect. Immun.* 28: 381.

Sado, T. (1969). Functional and ultrastructural studies of antibody-producing cells exposed to 10 000 R in millipore diffusion chambers. *Int. J. Radiat. Biol.* 15: 1.

Sado, T., Kamisaku, H. and Kubo, E. (1985). Strain difference in the radiosensitivity of immunocompetent cells and its influence on the residual host-vs-graft reaction in lethally irradiated mice grafted with semiallogenic bone marrow. *J. Immunol.* 134: 704.

Sawyer, R. T., Strausbauch, P. H. and Volkman, A. (1982). Resident macrophage proliferation in mice depleted of blood monocytes by strontium-89. *Lab. Invest.* 46: 165.

Schmidtke, J. R. and Dixon, F. J. (1972). The functional capacity of X-irradiated macrophages. *J. Immunol.* 108: 1624.

Schultz, R. M., Pavlidis, N. A., Chirigos, M. A. and Weiss, J. F. (1978). Effects of whole body x-irradiation and cyclophosphamide treatment on induction of macrophage tumoricidal function in mice. *Cell. Immunol.* 38: 302.

Senn. J. S. and McCulloch, E. A. (1970). Radiation sensitivity of human bone marrow cells measured by a cell culture method. *Blood* 35: 56.

Shah, P. D., Gilbertson, S. M. and Rowley, D. A. (1985). Dendritic cells which have interacted with antigen are targets for natural killer cells. *J. Exp. Med.* 162: 625.

Slavin, S., Fuks, Z., Kaplan, H. S. and Strober, S. (1978). Transplantation of allogeneic bone marrow without graft *vs* host disease using total lymphoid irradiation. *J. Exp., Med.* 147: 963.

Spellman, C. and Anderson, R. E. (1982). Low dose radiosensitivity of allo-immune cytotoxic T cells. *J. Exp. Med.* 155: 1858.

Stutman, O., Paige, C. J. and Feo Figarella, E. (1978). Natural cytotoxic cells against tumors in mice: I: Strain and age distribution and target cell susceptibility. *J. Immunol.* 121: 1819.

Tada, T., Taniguchi, M. and Okumura, K. (1971). Regulation of the homocytotropic antibody formation in the rat: II: Effect of X-irradiation. *J. Immunol.* 106: 1012.

Thompson, J. and van Furth, R. (1970). The effect of glucocorticoids on the kinetics of mononuclear phagocytes. *J. Exp. Med.* 131: 429.

Till, J. E. and McCulloch, E. A. (1961). A direct measurement of the radiation sensitivity of normal mouse bone marrow cell. *Rad. Res.* 14: 213.

Tutt, M. M., Kuziel, W., Hackett, J. Jr, Bennett, M., Tucker, P. and Kumar, V. (1986). Murine natural killer cells do not express functional transcripts of T cell receptor genes. *J. Immunol.* 137: 2998.

Tutt, M. M., Schuler, W., Kuziel, W. A., Tucker, P. W., Bennett, M. Bosma, M. J. and Kumar, V. (1987). T cell receptor genes do not rearrange or express functional transcripts in natural killer cells of *scid* mice. *J. Immunol.* 138: 2338.

Valerius, N. H., Johansen, K. S., Nielsen, O. S., Platz, P., Rosenkvist, J. and Sorensen, H. (1981). Effect of in vitro X-irradiation on lymphocyte and granulocyte function. *Scand. J. Haematol.* 27: 9.

van Furth, R. and Cohn, Z. A. (1968). The origin and kinetics of mononuclear phagocytes. *J. Exp. Med.* 128: 415.

Vann, D. C. and Makinoden, T. (1969). In vitro antibody synthesis by diffusion chamber cultures of spleen cells: I: Methods and effects of 10 000 R on antibody synthesis. *J. Immunol.* 102: 442.

Volkman, A. and Gowans. J. L. (1965). The origin of macrophages from bone marrow in the rat. *Br. J. Exp. Pathol.* 46: 62.

von Melchner, H. and Bartlett. P. F. (1983). Mechanisms of early allogeneic marrow graft rejection. *Immunol. Rev.* 71: 31.

Walker, F. Nicola, N. A., Metcalf, D. and Burgess, A. W. (1986). Hierarchial down-modulation of hemopoietic growth factor receptors. *Cell* 43: 269.

Warner, J. F. and Dennert, G. (1982). Effects of cloned cell line with NK activity on bone marrow transplants, tumour development and metastasis in vivo. *Nature* 300: 31.

Warner, J. and Dennert, G. (1985). Bone marrow graft rejection as a function of antibody-directed natural killer cells. *J. Exp. Med.* 161: 563.

Wood, P. R., Spanidis, V., Frangos, K. and Cheers, C. (1986). The in vitro bactericidal activity of peritoneal and spleen cells from Listeria-resistant and -susceptible mouse strains. *Cell. Immunol.* 99: 160.

16

Local Tissue Injury

SIGURD J. NORMANN

Box J-275, JHMHC
Department of Pathology
College of Medicine
University of Florida
Gainesville, Fla. 32610, USA

I. INTRODUCTION

The significance of local tissue injury to natural resistance has focused on this question: Does local injury interfere with cellular immunity or exert systemic restraint upon the inflammatory process? This question has been the continued subject of both clinical and experimental study because of its relevance to infection, cancer, and the control of inflammation. This chapter will examine the thesis that burns, accidental and surgical trauma, and local irritant injury impair host resistance mechanisms. A second proposition to be examined is that cancer subverts host defence either by conditions inherent in malignant transformation or by tissue injury consequent to cancer invasion.

506

NATURAL IMMUNITY
ISBN 0 12 5145551

II. THERMAL INJURY

Burns induce immunosuppression directed against T-cell-mediated events (Howard and Simmons, 1974; Howard, 1979; Munster, 1984). In many burn patients there is anergy to recall antigens (Casson *et al.*, 1966; Wolfe *et al.*, 1982; Stratta *et al.*, 1985), circulating lymphocyte mitogenic responses when tested in vitro are reduced (Wolfe *et al.*, 1982; Stratta *et al.*, 1985; Mahler and Batchelow; Daniels *et al.* 1971), and allograft survival is prolonged (Polk, 1968; Kay, 1957; Ninneman *et al.*, 1978). Most studies concur that immunosuppression correlates with the extent of burn injury, being nearly always present when injury is extensive and generally absent when injury is mild.

Burns may suppress delayed-type hypersensitivity (DTH) reactions to multiple antigens including mumps, purified protein derivative (PPD), diphtheria toxoid, and coccidioidin (Casson *et al.*, 1966). Patients with greater than 30 percent total surface burn generally are anergic to all recall antigens, and the duration of their DTH suppression may last several months (Wolfe *et al.*, 1982; Stratta *et al.*, 1985). Similar observations have been made in animals subjected to experimental burns. For instance, 81 percent of sensitised guinea pigs responded to PPD before thermal injury but only 10 percent responded two days after burning and 2 percent were positive at three weeks (Rapaport *et al.*, 1968). As measured by DTH to dinitrofluorobenzene, cell-mediated immunity in mice was markedly suppressed 14 days after burn injury; the degree of depression was equivalent to that obtained with high-dose immunosuppressive drugs (Hansborough *et al.*, 1984a). No immuno-suppression occurred with partial thickness burns or with burns of less than 10 percent body surface area. Transfer to normal mice of burned skin or homogenised burn eschar, but not unburned skin, also induced anergy to dinitrofluorobenzene (Hansborough *et al.*, 1984a). Suppression of T-cell-mediated immunity by burns has been documented also by prolongation in skin graft survival. Several reports indicate that allogeneic skin grafts have survival prolonged up to eight months in patients with extensive burns (Polk, 1968; Kay, 1957; Ninnemann *et al.*, 1978). In rats and mice subjected to thermal injury, skin graft survival also is prolonged in direct relationship to the severity of the burn (Munster *et al.*, 1973) and continued presence of the burnt skin (Fried and Munster, 1975).

Several studies have reported that peripheral blood lymphocytes from burn patients and animals have decreased reactivity to mitogens or alloantigens in vitro (Wolfe *et al.*, 1982; Stratta *et al.*, 1985; Mahler and Batchelow, 1971; Daniels *et al.*, 1971). However, normal lymphocytes display the same behaviour when placed in culture in the presence of serum drawn from patients with thermal injury (Stratta *et al.*, 1985; Constantian, 1978). Further, lymphocytes from burn patients may react normally to mitogen stimulation in vitro if they are washed prior to testing in normal serum (Munster *et al.*, 1973). Such data suggest that burn patients' serum contains immunosuppressive activity.

Serum from burned patients suppresses in vitro proliferation of normal peripheral blood lymphocytes in responses to phytohaemagglutiuin, (PHA) (Wolfe *et al.*, 1982; Constantian, 1978) and to alloantigens (Stratta *et al.*, 1985; Ninnemann *et al.*, 1982; Ninnemann and Stockland, 1984; Ninnemann and Ozkan, 1985; Ozkan and Ninnemann, 1985). Serum suppressive activity not only parallels, in degree and duration, the severity of the clinical course (Wolfe *et al.*, 1982; Stratta *et al.*, 1985; Constantian, 1978), but also correlates with both the presence of anergy (Wolfe *et al.*, 1982) and the prolongation of skin graft survival (Ninnemann *et al.*, 1978). Wolfe *et al.* (1982) noted a close correlation between the impairment of burned patients' lymphocyte activation by PHA or anergy and the presence of immunosuppressive activity in the serum. Ninnemann and co-workers (1978) reported that allograft skin survival was prolonged when a burn patient's serum suppressed PHA responsiveness of normal lymphocytes, and that the duration of graft survival was directly related to the continued presence of serum immunosuppressive activity. Immunosuppressive activity in serum appears to precede lymphocyte dysfunction.

The nature of the immunosuppressive factors in burn patients' serum has been the subject of several studies, with the following conclusions. First, the factors are not iatrogenically induced. Immunosuppression does not correlate with blood transfusions, antibiotics, or anaesthesia (Constantian, 1978) and may be present in patients who have received no therapy (Stratta *et al.*, 1985). Second, there is no correlation between immunosuppression and blood cortisol (Wolfe *et al.*, 1982; Constantian, 1978; Ninnemann *et al.*, 1982) or ACTH (Hansborough *et al.*, 1984b) levels. Third, serum fractionation has consistently demonstrated a low molecular weight (MW) immunosuppressive factor of about 3500 daltons (Constantian, 1978; Ninnemann, *et al.*, 1982; Ninnemann and Stockland, 1984; Ninnemann and Ozkan, 1985; Ozkan and Ninnemann, 1985) and the variable presence of other, and usually higher-MW, immunosuppressive factors (Ninnemann *et al.*, 1982). The low-MW factor was not cytotoxic to lymphocytes and did not inhibit fibroblast proliferation (Constantian, 1978). By radioimmunoassay of fractions separated by G-200 Sephadex, Ninnemann and coworkers (Ninnemann *et al.*, 1982) detected prostaglandin E (PGE) in the albumin fraction which was not immunosuppressive and in the low-MW fraction which was immunosuppressive. They suggested that interaction of PGE with a serum component may contribute to its persistence and stability in the circulation and that a specific carrier molecule may be involved in its immunological activity. Addition of radioactive PGE_2 to normal serum bound primarily to albumin and less so to a carrier molecule of approximately 5000 daltons while in burn serum the majority of added PGE_2 bound to the low-MW fraction (Ninnemann and Stockland, 1984). Although the concentration of PGE in burn serum is general high (up to 3 ng/mL), the concentration of PGE_2 required to suppress mixed lymphocyte proliferation in vitro approximates 100 ng/mL or 3×10^{-7} molar (Ninnemann and Stockland, 1984). Further, immunosuppressive activity did not correlate with total PGE levels (Wolfe *et al.*, 1982; Ninnemann and Stockland, 1984). However, Ninnemann and Stockland (1984) found that radioimmunoassay seriously underestimated the amount of PGE present in serum. Their contention that PGE is essential to the immunosuppressive activity of the low-MW fraction is supported by their findings that anti-PGE and delipidation significantly reduced the suppressive activity of the fraction (Ninnemann and Stockland, 1984; Ninnemann and Ozkan, 1985). Further, post-burn suppression of cell-mediated immunity in mice was partially prevented by treatment with the prostaglandin inhibitors indomethacin and ibuprofen (Hansborough *et al.*, 1984b). The immunosuppressive polypeptide is unaffected by treatment with DNase, RNase, or trypsin but is affected by pronase and, to a lesser extent, by neuraminidase (Ninnemann and Ozkan, 1985). It is rich in glycine, serine and alanine and contains a sialic acid carbohydrate component (Ozkan and Ninnemann, 1985).

Other immunosuppressive factors may exist in post-burn serum. Several high MW suppressive factors have been identified but not characterised. Lipopolysaccharide (LPS) has been suggested as one factor (Ninnemann *et al.*, 1982) but there is no correlation between suppression and LPS levels as measured by the *Limulus* test (Wolfe *et al.*, 1982), and immunosuppression of burned animals was unaltered by treatment with polymyxin B, which binds LPS (Hansborough *et al.*, 1984a). Although cortisol levels do not correlate with immunosuppression (Wolfe *et al.*, 1982; Constantian, 1978; Ninnemann, *et al.*, 1982), prolactin levels are markedly elevated and the elevation is more sustained (Brizio-Molteni *et al.*, 1984). This finding may be important in view of the recent demonstration of prolactin receptors on T and B lymphocytes and the accumulating evidence that prolactin may modulate humoral and cell-mediated immunity (Russell, *et al.*, 1985).

Burns appear to elicit suppressor cells (Miller and Baker, 1979; Winchurch and Munster, 1980; Wolfe *et al.*, 1981; Kupper *et al.*, 1984;

Hansborough *et al.*, 1984b). Splenocytes from thermally injured mice inhibited normal T lymphocyte responses in one-way mixed lymphocyte cultures (Winchurch and Munster, 1980). The generation of such suppressor cells was inhibited by cyclophosphamide, suggesting a T suppressor cell (Kupper *et al.*, 1984). In mice, thermal impairment of contact sensitivity to dinitrofluorobenzene could be prevented by the H-2 antagonists cimetidine or ranitidine, but not by the H-1 antagonist diphenhydramine (Hansborough *et al.*, 1985). The authors suggested that histamine produced by mast cells in response to burn injury activates a subset of T suppressor cells carrying H-2 receptors on their surfaces.

Burns decrease serum immunoglobulin levels and transiently depress complement levels. The decrease in immunoglobulins and complement may relate to the substantial loss of protein to the interstitial fluid that accompanies most burns and to fluid replacement (Howard and Simmons, 1974). There is no consistent evidence that the primary antibody response following burns is depressed.

Inflammatory responses following burns have not been adequately studied. One report indicates that the cellular response to a skin abrasion was reduced in burn patients (Balch, 1963). Warden *et al.* (1975) observed inhibition of polymorphonuclear leukocyte (PMN) chemotaxis within 72 hours of thermal injury, the probability of abnormality increasing with the extent of burn. Chemotactic responses may have prognostic significance, since patients with normal chemotactic activity were more likely to survive than those with abnormal responses (Grogan, 1976). However, the abnormality of chemotaxis is most likely not intrinsic to the neutrophil but rather due to the presence of chemotactic inhibitors in the serum (Fikrig *et al.*, 1977). Chemotaxis of normal neutrophils was inhibited by burn sera (Ninnemann and Ozkan, 1985; Ozkan and Ninnemann, 1985; Fikrig *et al.*, 1977) and one inhibitor of chemotaxis has been identified as a low-MW polypeptide similar to that which suppresses T lymphocyte blastogenesis in the mixed lymphocyte reaction (Ninnemann and Ozkan, 1985; Ozkan and Ninnemann, 1985). However, the chemotactic suppressor was more susceptible to neuraminidase and pronase treatment than was the inhibitor of blastogenesis. After thermal injury, phagocytosis by PMNs in vitro appears to be normal (van Dijk *et al.*, 1982) although bactericidal activity may be reduced (Alexander and Wixson, 1970). Finally, thermal injury may suppress large granular lymphocytes (LGLs), since spontaneous cytotoxic (NK) activity of burn patients' cells was only 30 percent of control levels (Stein *et al.*, 1984). Pre-treatment with interferon had no effect on the NK activity of burn patients. The defect in NK activity was not due to a deficiency of LGLs.

In conclusion, thermal injury inhibits delayed-type hypersensitivity and prolongs skin allograft survival. In addition, thermal injury may suppress the inflammatory response, including cell accumulation at inflammatory sites, chemotaxis and bactericidal activities. The presence of immunosuppression and possibly anti-inflammation enhances the probability of infection and presages a poor prognosis. However, restoration of immunocompetence can be achieved by complete wound closure or surgical excision and grafting procedures (Stratta *et al.*, 1985). Circulating factors responsible for post-burn immunodepression may be multiple, with one factor being a low-MW polypeptide that has affinity for PGE.

III. SURGICAL AND ACCIDENTAL TRAUMA[1]

Major surgical trauma often inhibits delayed-type hypersensitivity (Slade *et al.*, 1975; MacLean *et al.*, 1975; Meakins *et al.*, 1977; McLoughlin *et al.*, 1979; Riboli *et al.*, 1984; Meijer *et al.*, 1984). In a series of 100 consecutive laparotomies, Riboli *et al.*, (1984) found temporary immunosuppression in all patients when they were tested intradermally and simultaneously with seven standardised recall antigens. Suppression was maximal on day 3, with recovery seven to 10 days after operation. This series included 38 cancer patients whose Multitest score indicated a more severe and prolonged DTH depression. Inhibition in DTH has been reported also with major non-abdominal operations (McLoughlin *et al.*, 1979), but the incidence of depressed responses approximated 40 percent. The increased incidence of immunosuppression reported by Riboli *et al.* probably relates less to the operative site than to the type of skin test used. Nonetheless, inhibition of DTH is probably not a universal accompaniment of all surgical procedures since it is not readily demonstrable with minor surgical procedures such as inguinal hernia repair, dental extraction, or orthopaedic manipulations (McLoughlin *et al.*, 1979). Although patient pathology could affect DTH responses, surgical trauma itself appears to induce immunosuppression. First, the DTH response in the post-operative period is substantially decreased from the pre-operative response measured in the same patient as well as from control patients tested concurrently (Slade *et al.*, 1975; Meijer *et al.*, 1984). Second, Slade and co-workers (1975) found inhibition of DTH responses in 12 healthy donor patients following nephrectomy for renal transplantation. Third, hind-limb amputation in healthy mice inhibited the DTH response to dinitrochlorobenzene (Lundy and Ford, 1983).

Surgical operations transiently decrease circulating B and T lymphocytes while increasing the number of granulocytes. A temporal relationship exists between lymphocyte depletion and elevation in serum

---

[1] The term 'surgical trauma' is retained for convenience and is not to be taken as a reflection on the skills of our surgical colleagues. (Ed.)

cortisol, suggesting that lymphocytopoenia is related to adrenal cortical secretion (Slade *et al.*, 1975). However, lymphocytopoenia does not explain post-surgical inhibition in DTH. Lymphocyte levels are restored by 24 hours after the operation while maximal inhibition in DTH reactions generally does not occur until day 3.

Blast transformation of circulating lymphocytes in the post-operative period is inhibited when tested in vitro using PHA (McLoughlin *et al.*, 1979; Riddle and Berenbaum, 1967; Constantian *et al.*, 1977) or mixed lymphocyte cultures (MLC) (Slade *et al.*, 1975; Lundy and Ford, 1983). This effect has been observed following cancer operations and in healthy kidney donor patients. With the latter group, maximum suppression was observed nine hours after nephrectomy and persisted for up to five days (Slade *et al.*, 1975). Like DTH suppression, inhibition in lymphocyte transformation does not occur following minor surgical procedures such as inguinal hernia repair (Payne *et al.*, 1984). The inhibition of both mitogen response and MLC was greater when lymphocytes were cultured in post-operative than in normal serum (Slade *et al.*, 1975; Riddle and Berenbaum, 1967) suggesting that post-operative serum contains immunosuppressive factors. This conclusion is supported by the following observations. First, inhibition of PHA-induced blastogenesis did not occur when patient's lymphocytes were first washed and then incubated in normal serum, suggesting that there is no intrinsic defect in patient's lymphocytes (Christou and Meakins, 1979). Second, mitogen-induced blast transformation and the MLC response of normal lymphocytes are inhibited in post-operative serum (McLoughlin *et al.*, 1979; Constantian *et al.*, 1977). Third, serum from hind-limb-amputated mice when transferred to normal mice inhibited the DTH response of the recipients (Lundy and Ford, 1983). Fourth, human post-operative serum which inhibited in vitro human lymphocyte proliferation also inhibited antibody responses in mice to sheep red blood cell challenge as measured by the Jerne haemolytic plaque test (McLoughlin *et al.*, 1979). This experiment demonstrated that the immunosuppressive activity is not species-restricted.

Immunosuppressive activity is not found in all post-operative sera. The most extensive examination of this issue was reported by Constantian *et al.*, (1977), who examined 109 patients representing a wide variety of non-cancerous operations. Patients with minor surgical trauma did not have immunosuppressive sera (0/18 patients) but 42 percent of patients with major surgical trauma and an uncomplicated clinical course had immunosuppressive sera (25/60 patients). Nearly all patients with major surgical trauma with life-threatening complications had immunosuppressive sera (28/31 patients). Further, McLoughlin *et al.*, (1979) reported that 42 percent of cardio-thoracic surgical patients had depressed DTH responses which correlated with immunosuppressive activity in their sera.

Surgical trauma also induces suppressor cells but the relationship of this activity to circulating immunosuppressive factors is unknown. Wang and co-workers (1980, 1982) reported that, following surgical amputation of the right hind limb, murine splenocytes consistently had diminished proliferative capacity to alloantigens and failed to form alloreactive cytotoxic cells. Immune incompetence was observed from two hours to six days after surgery and could be reversed by removal of adherent cells. They characterised the suppressor cell as a Thy 1.2 negative, surface immunoglobulin negative, esterase positive cell and presumably a macrophage. Similar results were reported by Miyazaki *et al.*, (1983) using human peripheral blood mononuclear cells obtained after surgery. A decreased capacity to form cytotoxic T cells in mixed cultures could be abrogated by removal of adherent cells from the responder population. Cholecystectomy transiently increased the ratio of circulating OKT8 suppressor to OKT4 helper cells on the first but not subsequent post-operative days (Hansborough *et al.*, 1984c).

Major surgery is often followed by a generalised depression in non-specific host defence mechanisms as judged by an inability to remove blood-borne particulates (Saba and Cho, 1979). Further, NK cell activity may be compromised in the post-operative period, as murine splenic NK cell cytotoxicity against chromium-labelled YAC-1 cells was markedly depressed 24 hours after hind-limb amputation (Pollock *et al.*, 1984). Finally, major surgery may inhibit the inflammatory process itself.

Anti-inflammation has been reported in rats following amputation, unilateral nephrectomy, and partial hepatectomy but not following sham operations (Normann *et al.*, 1981). The anti-inflammatory effect was directed against macrophages, since the PMN response was normal. However, neutrophil chemotaxis may be depressed in surgical patients with anergy, and sera from anergic patients will inhibit chemotaxis of normal leukocytes (Christou and Meakins, 1979). Inhibition of macrophage inflammatory responses could be passively transferred with serum following amputation and partial hepatectomy but not with serum from normal or sham-operated animals (Normann *et al.*, 1981). Passive transfer to rats of serum obtained from humans two days after parotid extirpation or cholecystectomy inhibited the permeability phase of inflammation (Boers *et al.*, 1979). The responsible factor appeared to have an MW between 30 000 and 100 000.

Accidental trauma predisposes to infection, but the nature of the impairment in host defence that permits infection has not been adequately investigated. Evidence suggests that blunt trauma impairs phagocytosis. Animals subjected to Noble-Collip drum trauma have decreased particulate clearance from their circulation, the degree of phagocytic depression correlating with the degree of traumatic injury (Altura and Hershey, 1968). Neutrophils from patients following battle trauma have decreased in vitro phagocytosis for the first 24 hours after injury (Alexander *et al.*, 1968). Chemiluminescence indirectly measures bactericidal-related oxidative metabolism and is impaired when normal neutrophils are incubated in serum from patients with accidental trauma (Lanser *et al.*, 1985). This effect appears to be mediated by a non-albumin serum factor of MW 50 000 to 100 000. Since phagocytosis was not quantified, it is unclear whether the defective chemiluminescence related to impairment of reactive oxygen product generation or to impaired surface binding of the stimulator particles. A systematic examination of humoral and cell-mediated immunity or of inflammatory responsiveness following accidental trauma has not been reported.

In conclusion, surgical trauma induces a number of reversible abnormalities in host defence mechanisms. Among these effects are impairment of DTH, suppression of NK cell activities, generation of suppressor cells that inhibit development of T cytotoxic cells, and inhibition of inflammatory responses. Although less well studied, accidental trauma also alters host defence mechanisms as suggested by inhibition of granulocyte chemiluminesence and phagocytosis. Some of these abnormalities following surgical and accidental trauma appear to be mediated by circulating soluble factors which may contribute to post-operative and post-traumatic infection (McLoughlin *et al.*, 1979; McIrvine *et al.*, 1983). In the case of cancer surgery, abnormalities in host defence may increase the probability of metastasis despite adequate resection of the primary tumour (Alexander and Altemeier, 1964; Keller, 1981; Keller, 1985; Cole and Humphrey, 1985).

IV. ANAESTHESIA

Depression of lymphocyte transformation in response to mitogens or antigens has been documented following anaesthesia and operation. Before 1975, investigators examining the cause for immunosuppression failed to distinguish the effect of surgical trauma from that of anaesthesia. It now emerges that most of the inhibitory effect during operation is due to surgical trauma.

Studies in vitro concur that halothane (Cullen *et al.*, 1972a), ketamine (Cullen and Chretien, 1973), lidocaine (Cullen *et al.*, 1972b; Stewart *et al.*, 1980) and some barbiturates (Park and Brody, 1971) will depress lymphocyte transformation and inhibit granulocyte chemotaxis (Mondgil *et al.*, 1977). However, the concentration and duration of anaesthetic exposure necessary to achieve these results were in excess of clinical use (Cullen and van Belle, 1975). Therefore, the contribution of anaesthetic agents to intra- and post-operative immunodepression cannot be inferred from these studies. Kent and Geist (1975) observed that general anaesthesia was not required for immunosuppression since it occurred also when spinal anaesthesia was used for surgery. In a definitive analysis of the effects of anaesthesia and operation on lymphocyte transformation, Cullen and van Belle (1975) examined 77 patients, correlating the extent of surgical trauma with the type and duration of anaesthesia. They found no depression of lymphocyte transformation following regional anaesthesia solely for the relief of pain or general anaesthesia for examinational purposes or for minor operations. Regression analysis revealed that the highest correlation existed between lymphocyte depression and the extent of surgical trauma and not with the type or duration of anaesthesia used. From this and other studies (Constantian *et al.*, 1977; Bruce, 1980), it can be concluded that immunodeficiency apparent immediately after major operations is primarily the result of surgical trauma and not anaesthesia.

V. CANCER

In 1962, Lamb and co-workers (1962) reported that cancer patients were anergic with respect to DTH. Subsequent studies have both confirmed (Brown *et al.*, 1967; Solowey and Rapaport, 1965; Eilber and Morton, 1970) and disputed this observation (Nelson, 1969). The results appear to vary with the extent and type of tumour as well as the test employed. In their review, Burdick, Wells and Herberman (1975) concluded that lymphoid tumours generally impair DTH to recall antigens, noting a consistent inhibition with Hodgkin's disease and a cyclic inhibition with leukaemia corresponding to episodes of remission and relapse. With Hodgkin's disease, the probability of suppressed cell-mediated immunity increases with advanced disease and is associated with increased susceptibility to infection (Howard, 1983). With non-lymphoid tumours, anergy to recall antigens was observed inconsistently and the conclusions drawn were often dependent upon test criteria. However, general agreement exists that solid tumours impair contact sensitisation (Burdick *et al.*, 1975) and inhibit PHA responses of peripheral blood lymphocytes in vitro (Howard, 1983). Wanebo *et al.* (1975) reported that only 30 percent of patients with small, non-metastatic, lymph-node-negative squamous cell carcinoma of the head and neck had anergy to dinitrochlorobenzene (DNCB) but that the percentage of anergic patients increased with large primary tumours, when lymph nodes were involved or with distant metastasis. Such observations suggest that impairment of cell-mediated immunity is related to tumour burden.

Suppression of DTH has been observed in mice and rats bearing a variety of tumours and the probability of suppression increases with tumour growth (Eccles and Alexander, 1974). In an elegant series of experiments beginning in 1978 addressing the mechanism of DTH suppression, Nelson and Nelson (1978) demonstrated inhibition of DTH in mice when fibrosarcoma cells were mixed with sheep red blood cells (SRBCs) prior to injection into appropriately sensitised mice. Equivalent DTH suppression was obtained when cell-free culture supernatants of tumour but not normal cells were mixed with the challenge injection of SRBCs. Production of the inhibitory factor was blocked by cycloheximide but not by indomethacin. Fractionation by gel filtration or ultrafiltration of tumour supernatants produced in serum-free medium revealed maximum inhibitory activity in a fraction with MW range 1000 to 10 000. This low-MW inhibitor was susceptible to inactivation by pronase, trypsin, neuraminidase and RNase, suggesting that it was a glycopeptide associated with an RNA fragment. In mice more than 17 weeks of age (Nelson and Nelson, 1980), this low-MW fragment inhibited the early phase of the DTH response (24 hour measurement) without inhibiting the late phase (48 hour response). A larger fragment also was identified (>10 000 dalton) which inhibited the late phase (Nelson and Nelson, 1978; 1980). There is evidence that the active material is antigenically related to the retroviral envelope protein p15E (Nelson *et al.*, 1985).

The in vitro proliferative capacity of circulating human (Garrioch *et al.*, 1970; Dellon *et al.*, 1984) and murine splenic lymphocytes (Adler *et al.*, 1971; Whitney *et al.*, 1977) is depressed by the presence in the cell donor of a wide variety of different tumours. Inhibition of lymphocyte proliferation has been correlated with soluble inhibitors and with suppressor cells (Whitney *et al.*, 1977; Kirchner *et al.*, 1975) of T lymphocyte (Hersh *et al.*, 1980; Yu *et al.*, 1977) or macrophage origin (Varesio, 1983). Known macrophage-derived suppressors include prostaglandin E, thymidine monophosphate, and a glycoprotein of about 55 000 daltons (Krakauer, 1985; Tadakuma and Pierce, 1978). Production of the latter factor may be under control of a soluble immune response suppressor produced by T cells (Tadakuma and Pierce, 1978). This discussion will be limited to certain non-specific immunosuppressive factors which have been identified in sera and tumorous ascites fluids (Glasgow *et al.*, 1974; Baskies *et al.*, 1980; Badger *et al.*, 1977; McCarthy *et al.*, 1968; Badger *et al.*, 1981), tumour homogenates (Roth *et al.*, 1982; Roth, 1983) and tumour culture supernatants (Nelson and Nelson, 1978;

DeLustro and Argyris, 1976; Kamo *et al.*, 1975). Their activity has been demonstrated not only in vitro by inhibition of lymphocyte proliferation and cytotoxic responses (Glasgow *et al.*, 1974; Baskies, *et al.*, 1980; Badger *et al.*, 1977; Badger *et al.*, 1981; Roth *et al.*, 1982; Roth, 1983; DeLustro and Argyris, 1976; Kamo *et al.*, 1975) but also in vivo by their capacity to prolong skin allograft survival (McCarthy *et al.*, 1968), to inhibit plaque formation following RBC immunisation (Glasgow *et al.*, 1974; Badger *et al.*, 1977), and to suppress delayed-type hypersensitivity (Nelson and Nelson, 1978).

Certain retroviruses associated with cancer are immunosuppressive (Essex *et al.*, 1985). In 1979, Mathes *et al.* (1979) demonstrated that the active moiety in feline leukaemia virus (FeLV) was a 15 000 dalton polypeptide (p15E). Other virion proteins had no effect on Con-A-induced blast transformation. Addition of p15E to heat-killed virus vaccine decreased antibody titre, demonstrating that p15E was immuno-suppressive in vivo. Further, p15E derived from FeLV inhibited mitogen-induced proliferation of human lymphocytes. In exploring the mechanism of p15E immunosuppression, Copelan *et al.* (1983) reported that p15E had no effect on macrophage antigen presentation or IL-1 secretion and did not induce T suppressor cells. Rather, p15E blocked IL-2 induction of T cell proliferation as well as inhibiting IL-2 production by T helper cells. This effect of p15E was partially restored by addition of macrophages. Cianciolo and co-workers (1981) found p15E-related proteins in human cancerous effusions by cross-reactivity with mono-clonal antibodies made against murine leukaemia viral p15E. p15E is a hydrophobic transmembrane protein that has been conserved among feline and murine retroviruses as well as human retroviruses HTLV I and II. When Cianciolo and co-workers (1985) synthesised a 17-amino-acid polypeptide corresponding to this region of homology, they found that it inhibited murine splenocyte proliferation in a two-way mixed leukocyte reaction but did not inhibit proliferation of 3T3 fibroblasts. In order for the fragment to be inhibitory, it had to be coupled to a carrier protein (bovine serum albumin). These results suggests that a conserved se-quence of amino acids is responsible for immunosuppression attributed to retroviruses and that a particular molecular configuration is required. Since p15E is hydrophobic, it may aggregate or even bind to carrier molecules within the circulation or in cancerous effusions and present as inhibitory entities of MW greater than its constitutive weight.

p15E is not the only non-specific immunosuppressive molecule produced in tumour-bearers. For instance, P-815 mastocytomas, which lack antibody-reactive p15E (Jacquemin, 1982), induce an immuno-suppressive factor (DeLustro and Argyris, 1976; Kamo *et al.*, 1975). This factor is representative of a second category of immunosuppressors which have been identified in tumorous ascites fluid (DeLustro and Argyris, 1976; Watanabe *et al.*, 1978) and in human serum (Glasgow *et al.*, 1974) as a low-MW polypeptide (<10 000 dalton) which may bind to a carrier molecule. The complex has been designated immunoregulatory alpha-globulin despite the fact that the responsible factor may bind to albumin as well as to alpha globulin and be dissociated by high ionic strength and low pH buffers (Occhino *et al.*, 1973). The contention of Watanabe *et al.* (1978) that this factor accounts for the high-MW inhibitor described by DeLustro and Argyris (1976) in P-815 tumour culture supernatants containing serum is supported by the findings of Nakamura *et al.* (1980) of a 700 to 2000 dalton polypeptide in P-815 mastocytoma serum-free culture medium which inhibits lymphocyte proliferation. The low-MW inhibitor does not contain neutral sugars, sialic acid, RNA, DNA, cortisol or PGE, and its biological activity is destroyed by trypsin and chymotrypsin. This factor may be present in trace amounts in normal serum (Occhino *et al.*, 1973) but increases markedly in response to cancer. It inhibits mitogen-induced blastogenesis and induction of haemolytic plaque-forming cells; it prolongs allograft survival and interferes with cell-mediated tumour cytotoxicity (Cooperband *et al.*, 1976; Wang *et al.*, 1977). This factor may be related to the low-MW inhibitor of the early phase DTH reaction described by Nelson and Nelson (1978), although the latter factor appears to contain carbohydrate and RNA.

Prostaglandins are known to be produced by certain tumours (Goodwin *et al.*, 1980; Plescia *et al.*, 1975), to down-regulate Ia antigen expression on macrophages (thereby interfering with antigen presentation) (Snyder *et al.*, 1982), to inhibit lymphocyte proliferation (Ninnemann and Stockland, 1984; Ninnemann and Ozkan, 1985), and to inhibit macrophage-mediated cytotoxicity (Taffet and Russell, 1981; Schultz *et al.*, 1978). The source of prostaglandins may not always be the neoplastic cells. In Hodgkin's disease, the decreased PHA response of peripheral blood lymphocytes in vitro appears to be due largely to an adherent suppressor cell, presumably a macrophage, which produces copious amounts of PGE (Goodwin *et al.*, 1980). However, the in vivo importance of prostaglandins in cancer immunosuppression is less certain. While indomethacin treatment may retard growth of some tumours (Plescia *et al.*, 1975), the anti-tumour effect of such treatment does not correlate with enhanced assays of cellular immunity (Goodwin *et al.*, 1980). The level of immunosuppression in cancer patients does not relate to the concentration of circulating PGE. Further, the concentration of prostaglandins is greater in human non-cancerous compared to malignant effusions (Valone, 1983) and the latter are below the level of effective activity in vitro. Prostaglandins are not detectable by radio-immunoassay in semi-purified cancer-associated, low-MW immune inhibitors (Glasgow *et al.*, 1974; Nakamura *et al.*, 1980).

Acute-phase proteins rise with cancer and some have been implicated in immunosuppression. C-reactive protein binds to a small subset of lymphocytes and early reports suggested that it was immunosuppressive (Mortensen and Gewurz, 1976). However, this has not been substantiated and a recent report suggests that C-reactive protein actually may enhance cell-mediated immunity (Vetter *et al.*, 1986). An immuno-suppressive, 50 000 dalton acidic protein has been found in large quantities in human malignant ascites (Badger *et al.*, 1977). This factor is antigenically related to alpha-1-glycoprotein, an acute-phase reactant, but has a higher MW and contains more carbohydrate. While this factor probably complexes with the low-MW inhibitor described previously, the carrier molecule itself may have weak immunosuppressive activity.

The list of putative immunosuppressive factors in the tumour-bearing host is extensive. In addition to factors cited above, the list includes alpha feto-protein (Yachnin and Lester, 1976), fibrin degradation products (Girmann *et al.*, 1976; Edgington *et al.*, 1985), and various glycoproteins of 40 000 to 70 000 daltons (Roth *et al.*, 1982; Roth, 1983; Keller and Calvanico, 1985). The significance of these factors in vivo and the relationship between them is unclear. The latter problem relates to the fact that few of these factors have been isolated to homogeneity and their structure determined. The published amino acid sequence of the immunosuppressive domain of p15E indicates that factors isolated from different species and tumours may differ, yet retain a common basis for immunosuppression. It remains to be determined how many of the putative immune suppressors contain homologous sequences.

In addition to lymphocyte suppression, tumour growth often inhibits the acute inflammatory process. The importance of this anti-inflammatory effect and its relevance to human cancer is suggested by the following: (a) patients with cancer may have depressed monocyte chemotaxis (Boetcher and Leonard, 1974; Snyderman *et al.*, 1977; 1978; Israel *et al.*, 1982) and macrophage accumulation following skin abrasion (Sokol and Hudson, 1983); (b) abnormal monocyte chemotaxis has been correlated with disease severity and prognosis (Snyderman *et al.*, 1977; 1978; Israel *et al.*, 1982); and (c) cancerous effusions contain factors which alter macrophage polarisation (Cianciolo *et al.*, 1981). Abnormal chemotaxis does not typify the patient with minimal disease, but is present in about two-thirds of patients with advanced disease. When present, the defect will disappear with tumour excision but recur with metastasis (Snyderman *et al.*, 1977). In patients with breast and lung cancer, the inhibition of monocyte chemotaxis was most severe in patients with lymph node involvement as determined by pathologic examination (Israel *et al.*, 1982).

Tumour-induced anti-inflammation appears directed against macrophages and not granulocytes (Normann and Sorkin, 1976; Snyderman *et al.*, 1976). Accordingly, most human studies have concerned peripheral blood monocytes while animal studies have focused on intratumoral or exudate-elicited macrophages. Our group has conducted a series of experiments in animals wih autochthonous tumours (Normann *et al.*, 1979a; 1981b; 1984; 1985a), searching for an experimental equivalent to human cancer wherein we might examine the relationship of abnormal inflammation to tumour emergence and growth. We found inhibition of macrophage accumulation with small histiocytic lymphomas in SJL/J mice (Normann *et al.*, 1979a) and concurrently with or immediately following the onset of each leukaemic episode in AKR mice (1981b). With fibrosarcomas induced by 3-methylcholanthrene, depressed macrophage responses occurred prior to tumour emergence and the frequency of such defects increased the risk of developing cancer (1984). Emerging tumours had impaired macrophage responses in mice but not in rats, and large tumours in both species generally produced no abnormalities. However, abnormal inflammatory responses did develop upon serial transplantation, being evident by the second transplant. Virally induced mammary adenocarcinoma and ultraviolet-light-induced skin cancer failed to demonstrate depressed responses during tumour growth or upon serial transplantation (1985a). Table 16.1 summarises these results and compares them to the immunosuppression and inhibition in monocyte chemotaxis described for equivalent human cancers.

Macrophage defects have been described in animals bearing multiple transplanted tumours, and for a given tumour the phenomenon is reproducible. However, the defect is not sustained throughout tumour growth but is biphasic with an intervening period of normal responses between the two phases of anti-inflammation (Normann *et al.*, 1979b). The defect does not occur when the number of tumour cells transplanted is below the threshold number required for tumour take (Normann 1978). Accordingly, the requisite number of tumour cells varies with each tumour but may be as low as 1000 tumour cells. The early phase of anti-inflammation occurs within 48 hours of tumour transplantation and generally lasts three to five days. The late phase abnormality begins midway in the clinical course and progressively increases until death. During this latter phase, intratumoural macrophage accumulation is depressed concurrently with the impairment of systemic inflammation

Table 16.1: Comparison of immunosuppressive and anti-inflammatory effects of human and animal cancers

Type of cancer	Animal	Human
Leukaemia/lymphoma	Inflammation decreased in SJL/J lymphoma and AKR leukaemia (cyclical). Induction by RNA tumour virus. Viral homogenates containing p15E inhibit macrophage mobility and are immunosuppressive.	Inhibition of recall DTH and contact sensitisation. Cyclical effect with leukaemia.
Breast carcinoma	Inflammation normal in C3H/He mice. Mammary tumour virus homogenates do not inhibit macrophage mobility.	Variable inhibition of recall DTH but contact sensitisation depressed. Monocyte chemotaxis frequently decreased. Abnormalities increase with advanced disease.
Skin carcinoma	Inflammation increased in C57BL/6 and BALB/c mice. UV light exposure inhibits contact sensitisation, decreases antigen-presenting cells of epidermis, and usually induces immunogenic tumours requiring generation of Ts for autochthonous growth.	
Fibrosarcoma	Inflammation decreased with small murine tumours. 3-methylcholanthrene inhibits inflammation which correlates with tumour incidence. Transplanted tumours inhibit DTH and frequently inflammation.	Insufficient data

Data from references Howard (1983), Wanebo *et al.* (1975), Normann *et al.* (1979a, 1981b, 1984, 1985a).

(Normann and Cornelius, 1978). Anti-inflammation can be reproduced by soluble factors extracted from tumours or produced in culture by primary tumour explants (Normann, 1985). Two mediators have been implicated in this process. One factor shares antigenic identity with p15E and is probably identical to the factor which inhibits DTH (Dellon *et al.*, 1984; Snyderman and Ciancolo, 1984). In human cancerous effusions, however, these anti-inflammatory factors had apparent MWs of 21 000 and 46 000 (Ciancolo *et al.*, 1981). A second factor is a polypeptide of less than 1000 daltons which is not extractable by lipid solvents, is inactivated by carboxypeptidase A but not by RNase or DNase and is produced in culture in the presence of indomethacin but not cycloheximide (Normann and Cornelius, 1982; Nelson *et al.*, 1981). This anti-inflammatory factor is not produced by normal cells in culture. It is present in tumorous ascites fluid but not in non-cancerous effusions. This factor inhibits chemotaxis, presumably by interference with membrane phospholipid methylation involved in the transduction of the chemotactic signal (Warabi *et al.*, 1984).

Table 16.2 lists the biological activities of three low-MW anti-inflammatory and immunosuppressive tumour-associated polypeptides. The anti-inflammatory factor of MW <1000 inhibits a variety of biological activities associated with macrophages, including capillary tube migration, chemotaxis and phagocytosis in vitro, and inflammation in vivo (Nelson *et al.*, 1981). The range of these activities suggests that it may be a general regulator of macrophage functions. In contrast, the 1000 to 10 000 dalton immunosuppressive factor fails to inhibit these macrophage activities but does impair the early phase of DTH reactions and mitogen-induced blastogenesis. Finally, p15E inhibits the late-phase

Table 16.2: Biological activities of tumour-associated anti-inflammatory and immunosuppressive factors

Biological activity	Anti-inflammatory factor (<1000 MW)	Immunosuppressive factor (<10 000 MW)	Retroviral protein p15E
Inhibits macrophage			
inflammation	yes	no	yes
chemotaxis/polarisation	yes	no	yes
capillary tube migration	yes	no	?
phagocytosis	yes	no	?
colony formation	yes	no	?
IL-1 production	no	yes	no
Inhibits IL-2 production	?	?	yes
Inhibits DTH reactions	no	yes	yes
Inhibits mitogen-induced			
blastogenesis	no	yes	yes
Prolongs skin allografts	no	yes	yes
Inhibits antibody production	?	yes	yes

Data from references Cianciolo *et al.*, (1981, 1985); Copelan *et al.* (1983); Farram *et al.* (1982); Jacquemin (1982); Mathes *et al.* (1979); Nelson and Nelson (1978, 1980, 1982); Nelson *et al.* (1981, 1985); Normann (1985); Normann and Cornelius (1982); Snyderman and Cianciolo (1984); Warabi *et al.* (1984).

DTH response and appears to have a broad range of inhibitory activities encompassing not only lymphocyte but also macrophage responses.

Tumour transplantation and growth alter hormonal balance. The most comprehensive study of multiple hormones throughout tumour growth has been reported by Besedovsky and co-workers (Besedovsky *et al.*, 1985). Of particular interest, they found that corticosterone was elevated with some tumours both early and late after transplantation, insulin levels were generally decreased in a biphasic pattern consistent with periods of anti-inflammation, thyroxin progressively decreased throughout tumour bearing, and prolactin was elevated rapidly by tumour transplantation. Glucocorticoids are immunosuppressive as well as anti-inflammatory and inhibit production of IL-1 (Gillis *et al.*, 1979; Stosic-Grujicic and Simic, 1982), secretion of prostaglandins (Dannenberg, 1979) and tumour-cytotoxic cells (Chirigos *et al.*, 1981; Acero *et al.*, 1984). Low levels of thyroxin and insulin independently or in conjunction with elevated corticosterone might logically inhibit cellular and humoral immunity. However, it remains to be determined if any of these hormonal changes account for the depression in inflammation and immune responses associated with cancer.

Since macrophage accumulation is an integral part of a DTH response and whereas inhibition of inflammation and DTH often develop concurrently, Eccles and Alexander (1974) suggested that abrogation of DTH in tumour-bearers was due to suppression of macrophage mobility. However, anti-inflammation appears to be a contributing but not complete explanation for DTH suppression. As Table 16.2 shows, factors exist which inhibit macrophage mobility but not DTH and vice versa. The DTH response may be critical to the non-specific tumoricidal activity of thymus-independent cells since DTH is probably the most common mechanism for the recruitment and activation of macrophages and may be involved also in stimulating large granular lymphocyte (NK) cytotoxicity. On the other hand, the impairment of inflammation and microbicidal activities of macrophages may predispose cancer patients to infection. It is important to emphasise that this impairment arises from the presence of the cancer and may be aggravated by the immuno-suppressive effect of many chemotherapeutic agents.

VI. LOCAL IRRITATION

Before the advent of anti-inflammatory drugs in the 20th century, clinical control of inflammation often consisted of applying a counter-irritant at a secondary site. The mechanism for this type of anti-inflammation remains unknown. Since it occurs after adrenalectomy (Laden *et al.*, 1958; Robinson and Robson, 1964; Atkinson and Hicks,

1975; Lu and Williams, 1980; Truax, 1978) or hypophysectomy (Laden *et al.*, 1958), it is not dependent upon the anti-inflammatory effect of adrenal steroids. Similarly, it does not depend upon adrenal medullary catecholamines such as epinephrine, which inhibits vascular permeability by its beta-receptor agonist action on post-capillary endothelium (Marciniak *et al.*, 1978). Although its clinical use has subsided, the phenomenon remains important as a little understood but physiologically significant control mechanism of inflammation and because any injected substance or bodily injury may alter subsequent inflammation by local irritant action.

That local irritation will impede the inflammatory response at distant sites has been established in a number of animal models. Nearly all such studies concern changes in vascular permeability measured by oedema formation (Atkinson and Hicks, 1975; Truax, 1978; Atkinson, 1971; Marciniak *et al.*, 1978). Only a few reports have examined cellular emigration (Lu and Williams, 1980; Normann *et al.*, 1985b) or the formation of granulation tissue (Cygielman and Robson, 1963). In a recent study, Truax (1978) suggested that suppression of oedema formation occurred only when the primary and secondary inflammatory responses were sensitive to steroid or non-steroid anti-inflammatory drugs. It did not occur with agents sensitive to anti-histamine or anti-serotonin drugs. Thus, the phenomenon appears to involve cellular as well as vascular reactions and does not affect immediate-transient oedema formation induced by certain chemicals, such as histamine or bradykinin, that are primarily mediators of vascular permeability with direct action on post-capillary venules. Recent evidence suggests that immediate-sustained oedema formation is dependent upon granulocyte exudation (Wedmore and Williams, 1981; Lewis and Granger, 1986). Granulocytes may be essential to the oedema-promoting action of leukotrienes B_4 and D_4 as well as anaphylotoxins C3a or C5a (Lewis and Granger, 1986). It has now been shown that neutrophil accumulation in either the pleural or the peritoneal cavity is inhibited by a prior irritant injection (Lu and Williams, 1980; Truax, 1978; Normann *et al.*, 1985b). Further, the degree of neutrophil suppression was correlated with the degree of inhibition of oedema formation (Truax, 1978). Thus, the mechanism of oedema suppression by local irritant injection may be secondary to suppression of cellular emigration.

Irritant-induced anti-inflammation is not cell-selective, as it affects both granulocyte and macrophage accumulation. Anti-inflammation occurs despite adequate circulating leukocyte levels and continued accumulation of inflammatory cells at the primary site of inflammation (Normann *et al.*, 1985b). In vitro chemotactic activity of neutrophils and macrophages is normal, implying that the anti-inflammatory effect is probably not due to alterations in circulating cells (Schardt *et al.*, 1984). A temporal relationship exists between counter-irritant injection and the inhibition of leukocyte accumulation. The counter-irritant must be administered before, not after, induction of the measured inflammatory response (Normann *et al.*, 1985b). No reports have appeared on the effect of counter-irritant action on large granular lymphocyte (NK cell) accumulation. It is unclear whether the phenomenon is involved in the suppression of DTH induced by certain inert, non-infectious granulomatous agents such as dextran sulfate (Allred *et al.*, 1985).

Tolerance develops to the counter-irritant action of some but not all irritants upon repeat injection (Normann *et al.*, 1985b). Based upon the capacity to develop tolerance, two classes of irritants have been distinguished:

1. *Type 1.* These irritants readily induce tolerance, usually within three injections. Irritants with this type of behavior include many commonly used phlogistic agents: sodium caseinate, proteose peptone, thioglycollate, glycogen and kappa carrageenan. Most importantly, these agents exhibit cross-tolerance to each other.
2. *Type 2.* These irritants do not induce tolerance even after six injections. Irritants with this type of behviour include PHA, Con A, and LPS. These irritants do not produce cross-desensitisation among themselves. Desensitisation to Type I irritants does not desensitise to Type 2 irritants.

Such data support the proposition that a common mechanism of anti-leukocyte activity exists among Type I irritants. Further, Type 2 irritants induce a separate or additional mechanism of anti-inflammation distinguished from the former by a lack of tolerance induction.

Both cancer and major surgery can inhibit the inflammatory process. To determine if either of these conditions was caused by a mechanism in common with Type I irritants, Normann and co-workers (1985c) performed surgical amputation or tumour transplantation in rats after a series of irritant injections. The results were as follows:

1. *Surgical amputation:* The anti-inflammatory effect was corrected by prior desensitisation with Type I irritants. Prior injection of Type 2 irritants had no effect.
2. *Tumour transplantation:* The anti-inflammatory effect was unaffected by prior injection of either Type I or Type 2 irritants.

It was concluded that the anti-inflammatory effect of major surgery derived from the anti-leukocyte activity of local inflammation. In contrast, the anti-inflammatory effect of tumour bearing was not caused solely by this mechanism.

Certain non-infectious irritants injected locally inhibit DTH. Many of these agents induce chronic granulomatous inflammation, but not all granulomas are associated with anergy. For instance, dextran beads produce large granulomas which inhibit DTH but no suppression of DTH occurs with small granulomas induced by latex beads (Allred *et al.*, 1985). Partial inhibition of DTH has been achieved by passive transfer of aqueous extracts of pulmonary dextran granulomas but not normal lung, suggesting that cells within the granuloma produce a soluble suppressive factor. Anergy associated with BCG-induced pulmonary granulomas correlates with local production of migration inhibitory factor and interleukin 1 (Kobayashi *et al.*, 1985). However, it is uncertain whether these cytokines actually mediate anergy associated with either immunological infectious or non-immunological foreign body granulomas. Transient anergy often accompanies clinical granulomas of infectious aetiology (Bullock, 1975).

VII. SUMMARY

Impairment of host resistance occurs following thermal and accidental trauma, major surgery, cancer, and certain local inflammatory reactions. These abnormalities consist of DTH suppression, anti-inflammation, inhibition of in vitro lymphocyte blast transformation, and appearance of suppressor cells. Prolonged anaesthesia inhibits haemopoiesis and in vitro exposure to anaesthetic drugs impairs chemotaxis. However, operative anaesthesia probably does not contribute to immunosuppression or anti-inflammation associated with major surgery.

A systemic anti-inflammatory effect may be an inevitable accompaniment of intense local acute inflammation (Table 16.3). Although vascular permeability is inhibited, the probable major effect of the phenomenon is to limit cellular accumulation at secondary sites of injury. The initial inflammatory reaction does not appear to be compromised. Tolerance to anti-inflammation develops rapidly to certain irritants but not to others, suggesting that more than one mechanism of anti-inflammation is involved. This idea gains support from studies with cancer which implicate at least two factors in the anti-inflammatory effect. One mediator is less than 1000 daltons while the other is larger and antigenically related to p15E. Caution is necessary in interpreting the anti-inflammatory effect of passively transferred mediators to ensure that such factors are not themselves irritants. The purpose served for the host by an inhibition of inflammation at a second and subsequent site of injury is not known.

Transient immunosuppression often accompanies local tissue injury (Table 16.3). The effect appears directed against T-cell-mediated events

Table 16.3: Systemic effects of local tissue injury on host resistance

Measurement of host resistance	Type 1 irritants[a]	Type 2 irritants[b]	Burns	Major surgery	Cancer
Anti-inflammation	yes	yes	yes(?)	yes	yes
Self-tolerance	yes	no	?	?	no
Cross-tolerance to Type 1 irritants	yes	no	?	yes	no
DTH suppression	no	yes	yes	yes	yes
NK cell suppression	?	?	yes	yes	yes

[a] Type 1 irritants include sodium caseinate, glycogen, thioglycollate and proteose peptone.
[b] Type 2 irritants include concanavalin A, phytohaemagglutinin, lipopolysaccharide and probably Freund's adjuvant.

with a suppression of DTH which correlates temporally with inhibition of T cell mitogen responses. Suppression of antibody responses to T-dependent antigens may occur. It is unclear if the immunosuppression results from the injury itself or from the inflammatory reaction to injury. It is known that inflammation induces an acute-phase reaction mediated by local IL-1 release, and perhaps some of the acute-phase proteins are immunosuppressive. IL-1 has been implicated in the anergy associated with infectious granulomas (Kobayashi *et al.*, 1985). Then, too, the low-MW immunosuppressive factor with affinity for alpha-globulin found in the sera of patients with burns, major surgery, and cancer may be synthesised as part of the acute-phase response. If so, it is entirely possible that diverse injuries share a mechanism of immunosuppression. Cancer may have an additional mechanism involving retroviral products, but it is not entirely clear that such products are unique to cancer, since stimulation of normal human lymph nodes reportedly releases retroviral antigens (Cianciolo *et al.*, 1985). Such immunosuppression could compromise T-cytotoxic reactions and limit certain amplificational pathways leading to enhanced NK cell and macrophage microbicidal and tumoricidal effects. It is possible that this transient immunosuppression has evolved to limit immune reactivity to self antigens released by trauma. This concept implies that the evolutionary force to protect self has been as strong as that promoting cellular immune reactions to infection.

It is generally accepted that inhibition of cellular immunity and inflammation predisposes to infection. Thus, it is not surprising that certain cancer patients are likely to develop infection and that a correlation exists between anergy and the incidence of post-operative complications. An intriguing unanswered question concerns the effect that anti-inflammation and immunosuppression associated with cancer operation may have on metastasis. Experimentally, injury to normal tissue increases tumour incidence when cancer cells are injected into the circulation (Alexander and Altemeir, 1964). Excision of a primary tumour can accelerate progression of already established metastases (Keller, 1981). However, the actual effect of surgery is not clear, since amputation of a control limb without removal of the primary tumour does not affect metastasis. That local tissue injury suppresses natural resistance is well documented, but central questions remain, including conditions necessary for its expression, the mechanism of its mediation, strategies for its control, and its significance to homeostasis and disease.

ACKNOWLEDGMENTS

This work was supported by American Cancer Society Grant IM-441.

REFERENCES

Acero, R., Polentarutti, N., Bottazzi, B., Alberti, S., Ricci, M. R., Bizzi, A. and Mantovani, A. (1984). Effect of hydrocortisone on the macrophage content, growth and metastasis of transplanted murine tumours. *Int. J. Cancer* 33: 95–105.

Adler, W. H., Takiguchi, T. and Smith, R. T. (1971). Phytohemagglutin unresponsiveness in mouse spleen cells induced by methylcholanthrene sarcomas. *Cancer Res.* 31: 864–7.

Alexander, J. W. and Altemeier, W. A. (1964). Susceptibility of injured tissues to hematogenous metastases: an experimental study. *Ann. Surg.* 159: 933–44.

Alexander, J. W. and Wixson, D. (1970). Neutrophil dysfunction and sepsis in burn injury. *Surg. Gynecol. Obstetrics* 130: 431–8.

Alexander, J. W., Hegg, M. and Altemeier, W. A. (1968). Neutrophil function in selected surgical disorders. *Ann. Surg.* 168: 447–58.

Allred, D. C., Kobayashi, K. and Yoshida, T. (1985). Anergy-like immunosuppression in mice bearing pulmonary foreign-body granulomatous inflammation. *Am. J. Path.* 121: 466–73.

Altura, B. M. and Hershey, S. G. (1968). RES phagocytic function in trauma and adaptation to experimental shock. *Am. J. Physiology* 215: 1414–19.

Atkinson, D. C. (1971). A comparison of the systemic anti-inflammatory activity of three different irritants in the rat. *Arch. Int. Pharmacodyn. Ther.* 193: 391–6.

Atkinson, D. C. and Hicks, R. (1975). The anti-inflammatory activity of irritants. *Agents Actions* 5: 239–49.

Badger, A. M., Cooperband, S. R., Merluzzi, V. J. and Glasgow, A. H. (1977). Immunosuppressive activity of ascites fluid from patients with cancer metastatic to the peritoneum. *Cancer Res.* 37: 1220–6.

Badger, A. M., Oh, S. K. and Moolten, F. R. (1981). Differential effects of an immune suppressive fraction from ascites fluid of patients with ovarian cancer on spontaneous and antibody-dependent cytotoxicity. *Cancer Res.* 41: 1133–9.

Balch, H. H. (1963). Resistance to infection in burned patients. *Ann. Surg.* 157: 1–19.

Baskies, A. M., Chretien, P. B., Weiss, J. F., Makeich, R. W., Beveridge, R. A., Catalona, W. J. and Spiegel, H. E. (1980). Serum glycoproteins in cancer patients, first reports of correlations with in vitro and in vivo parameters of cellular immunity. *Cancer* 45: 3050–60.

Besedovsky, H. O., del Rey, A., Schardt, M., Sorkin, E., Normann, S., Baumann, J. and Girard, J. (1985). Changes in plasma hormone profiles after tumor transplantation into syngeneic and allogeneic rats. *Int. J. Cancer* 21: 209–16.

Boers, W., van Gool, J. and Zwart, N. A. (1979). Effect of human cord and postoperative serum on experimental inflammation in the rat. *Brit. J. Exp. Path.* 60: 239–45.

Boetcher, D. A. and Leonard, E. J. (1974). Abnormal monocyte chemotactic response in cancer patients. *J. Natl. Cancer. Inst.* 52: 1091–9.

Brizio-Molteni, L., Molteni, A., Warpeha, R. L., Angelats, J., Lewis, N. and Fors, E. M. (1984). Prolactin, corticotropin, and gonadotropin concentrations following thermal injury in adults. *J. Trauma* 24: 1–7.

Brown, R. S., Haynes, H. A., Foley, H. T., Godwin, H. A., Berard, C. W. and Carbone, P. P. (1967). Hodgkin's disease: immunologic, clinical and histologic features of 50 untreated patients. *Ann. Intern. Med.* 67: 291–302.

Bruce, D. L. (1980). Anesthesia, formed elements of the blood, and macrophages. *Fed. Proc.* 39: 1592–4.

Bullock, W. E. (1945). Anergy and infection. *Adv. Int. Med.* 21: 149–73.

Burdick, J. F., Wells, S. A. Jr. and Herberman, R. B. (1975). Immunologic evaluation of patients with cancer by delayed hypersensitivity reactions. *Surg. Gynecol. Obstet.* 141: 779–94.

Casson, P., Solowey, H. C. and Converse, J. M. (1966). Delayed hypersensitivity status of burned patients. *Surg. Forum* 17: 268–70.

Chirigos, M. A., Schultz, R. M. and Stylos, W. A. (1981). Interaction of interferon, macrophage and lymphocyte tumoricidal activity with prostaglandin effect. *Ann. New York Acad. Sci.* 350: 91–101.

Christou, N. V. and Meakins, J. L. (1979). Delayed hypersensitivity in surgical patients: a mechanism for anergy. *Surgery* 86: 78–84.

Cianciolo, G., Hunter, J., Silva, J., Maskill, J. S. and Snyderman, R. (1981). Inhibitors of monocyte responses to chemotaxis are present in human cancerous effusions and react with monoclonal antibodies to the p15E structural protein of retroviruses. *J. Clin. Invest.* 68: 831–44.

Cianciolo, G. J., Copeland, T. D., Orozlan, S. and Snyderman, R. (1985). Inhibition of lymphocyte proliferation by a synthetic peptide homologous to retroviral envelope proteins. *Science* 230: 453–5.

Cole, W. H. and Humphrey, L. (1985). Need for immunologic stimulators during immunosuppression produced by major cancer surgery. *Ann. Surg.* 202: 9–20.

Constantian, M. B. (1978). Association of sepsis with an immunosuppressive polypeptide in the serum of burn patients. *Ann. Surg.* 188: 209–15.

Constantian, M. B., Menzoian, J. O., Nimberg, R. B., Schmid, K. and Mannick, J. A. (1977). Association of a circulating immunosuppressive polypeptide with operative and accidental trauma. *Ann. Surg.* 185: 73–9.

Cooperband, S. R., Nimberg, R., Schmid, K. and Mannick, J. A. (1976). Humoral immunosuppressive factors. *Transplant. Proc.* 8: 225–42.

Copelan, E. A., Rinehart, J. J., Lewis, M., Mathes, L., Olsen, R. and Sagone, A. (1983). The mechanism of retrovirus suppression of human T cell proliferation in vitro. *J. Immunol.* 131: 2017–20.

Cullen, B. F. and Chretien, P. B. (1973). Ketamine and in vitro lymphocyte transformation. *Anesthe. and Analgia.* 52: 518–21.

Cullen, B. F. and van Belle, G. (1975). Lymphocyte transformation and changes in leukocyte count: effects of anesthesia and operation. *Anesthesiology* 43: 563–9.

Cullen, B. F., Sample, W. F. and Chretien, P. B. (1972a) The effect of halothane on phytohemagglutinin induced transformation of human lymphocytes in vitro. *Anesthesiology* 36: 206–11.

Cullen, B. F., Chretien, P. B. and Leventhal, B. G. (1972b). The effect of lignocaine on PHA-stimulated human lymphocyte transformation. *Br. J. Anesth.* 44: 1247–52.

Cygielman, S. and Robson, J. M. (1963). The effect of irritant substances on the deposition of granulation tissue in the cotton pellet test. *J. Pharm. Pharmacol.* 15: 794–7.

Daniels, J. C., Sakai, H., Cobb, E. K., Lewis, S. R., Larson, D. L. and Ritzmann, S. E. (1971). Evaluation of lymphocyte reactivity studies in patients with thermal burns. *J. Trauma* 11: 595–601.

Dannenberg, A. M. Jr (1979). The anti-inflammatory effects of glucocorticoids: A brief review of the literature. *Inflammation* 3: 329–43.

Dellon, A. L., Elfenbein, G. J. and Orlando, J. C. (1984). Impairment of thymus-derived lymphoid cell function in patients with basal cell carcinoma. *J. Surg. Oncol.* 25: 92–7.

DeLustro, F. and Argyris, B. F. (1976). Mastocytoma-mediated suppression of mixed-lymphocyte culture and mitogen responsiveness. *Cell. Immunol.* 21: 177–84.

Eccles, S. A. and Alexander, P. (1974). Sequestration of macrophages in growing tumors and its effect on the immunological capacity of the host. *Br. J. Cancer* 30: 42–9.

Edgington, T. S., Curtiss, L. K. and Plow, E. F. (1985). A linkage between the hemostatic and immune systems embodied in the fibrinolytic release of lymphocyte suppressive peptides. *J. Immunol.* 134: 471–7.

Eilber, F. R. and Morton, D. L. (1970). Impaired immunologic reactivity and recurrence following cancer surgery. *Cancer* 25: 362–7.

Essex, M., McLane, M. F., Kanki, P., Allan, J., Kitchen, L. and Lee, T-H. (1985). Retroviruses associated with leukemia and ablative syndrome in animals and in human beings. *Cancer Res.* 45: 4534s–4538s.

Farram, E., Nelson, M., Nelson, D. S. and Moon, D. K. (1982). Inhibition of cytokine production by a tumor cell product. *Immunology* 46: 603–12.

Fikrig, S. M., Karl, S. C. and Suntharalingam, K. (1977). Neutrophil chemotaxis in patients with burns. *Ann. Surg* 186: 746–8.

Fried, D. A. and Munster, A. M. (1975). Does immunosuppression by thermal injury depend on the continued presence of the burn wound? *J. Trauma* 15: 483–5.

Garrioch, D. B., Good, R. A. and Gatti, R. A. (1970). Lymphocyte response to PHA in patients with non-lymphoid tumours. *Lancet* 1: 618.

Gillis, S., Crabtree, G. R. and Smith, K. (1979). Glucocorticoid induced inhibition of T cell growth factor production: I: The effect on mitogen induced lymphocyte proliferation. *J. Immunol.* 123: 1624–31.

Girmann, G., Pees, H., Schwartz, G. and Scheurlen, P. G. (1976). Immunosuppression by micromolecular fibrinogen degradation products in cancer. *Nature* 259: 399–401.

Glasgow, A. H., Nimberg, R. B., Menzoian, J. O., Saporoschetz, I., Cooperband, S. R., Schmid, K. and Mannick, J. A. (1974). Association of anergy with an immunosuppressive peptide fraction in the serum of patients with cancer. *N. Engl. J. Med.* 291: 1263–7.

Goodwin, J. S., Husby, G. and Williams, R. C. Jr. (1980). Prostaglandin E and cancer growth. *Cancer Immunology and Immunotherapy* 8: 3–7.

Grogan, J. B. (1976). Altered neutrophil phagocytic function in burn patients. *J. Trauma* 16: 734–8.

Hansbrough, J. F., Zapata-Sirvent, R., Peterson, V., Wang, X., Bender, E., Claman, H. and Boswick, J. (1984a). Characterization of the immunosuppressive effect of burned tissue in an animal model. *J. Surg. Res.* 37: 383–93.

Hansbrough, J. F., Peterson, V., Zapata-Sirvent, R. and Claman, H. (1984b). Studies of post-burn immunosuppression using an animal model: II: Restoration of cell-mediated immunity by immunomodulating drugs. *Surgery* 95: 290–5.

Hansbrough, J. F., Bender, E. M., Zapata-Sirvent, R. and Anderson, J. (1984c). Altered helper and suppressor lymphocyte populations in surgical patients. *Am. J. Surg.* 148: 303–6.

Hansbrough, J. F., Zapata-Sirvent, R., Bender, E. M. and Peterson, V. (1985). Prevention of suppressed cell-mediated immunity in burned mice with histamine-2 receptor antagonist drugs. *J. Surg. Res.* 39: 150–6.

Hersh, E. M., Patt, Y. Z., Murphy, S. G., Dicke, K., Zander, A., Adegbite, M. and Goldman, R. (1980). Radiosensitive, thymic hormone-sensitive peripheral blood suppressor cell activity in cancer patients. *Cancer Res.* 40: 3134–40.

Howard, R. J. (1979). Effect of burn injury, mechanical trauma, and operation on immune defenses. *Surg. Clinics of N. America* 59: 199–211.

Howard, R. J. (1983). Nonspecific host defenses in surgical cancer patients. *Current Problems in Cancer* 7: 3–39.

Howard, R. J. and Simmons, R. L. (1974). Acquired immunologic deficiencies after trauma and surgical procedures. *Surg. Gynecology and Obstetrics* 139: 771–82.

Israel, L., Samak, R., Edelstein, R., Amouroux, J., Battesti, J.-P. and de Saint Florent, G. (1982). In vivo non-specific macrophage chemotaxis in cancer patients and its correlation with extent of disease, regional lymph node status and disease-free survival. *Cancer Research* 42: 2489–94.

Jacquemin, P. C. (1982). Expression of type C viral glycoproteins on P815 cells: higher expression of Mr 70 000 glycoprotein-containing glycoprotein on immunogenic variants. *Cancer Res.* 42: 3828–36.

Kamo, I., Petal, C., Kateley, J. and Friedman, M. (1975). Immunosuppression induced in vitro by mastocytoma tumor cells and cell free extracts. *J. Immunol.* 114: 1749–56.

Kay, G. D. (1957). Prolonged survival of a skin homograft in a patient with very extensive burns. *Ann. NY Acad. Science* 64: 767–74.

Keller, R. (1981). Induction of macroscopic metastases via surgery: The site of the primary tumour inoculum is critical. *Invasion and Metastasis* 1: 136–48.

Keller, R. (1985). Surgical intervention and metastasis. *Recent Results in Cancer Research* 98: 11–16.

Keller, R. H. and Calvanico, N. J. (1985). Suppressor macromolecules. *CRC Critical Rev. in Immunol.* 5: 149–99.

Kent, J. R. and Geist, S. (1975). Lymphocyte transformation during operations with spinal anesthesia. *Anesthesiology* 42: 505–8.

Kirchner, H. A., Muchmore, A. V., Chused, T. M., Holden, H. T. and Herberman, R. B. (1979). Inhibition of proliferation of lymphoma cells and T lymphocytes by suppressor cells from spleens of tumor bearing mice. *J. Immunol.* 114: 206–10.

Kobayashi, K., Allred, C., Castriotta, R. and Yoshida, T. (1985). Strain variation of Bacillus Calmette-Guerin induced pulmonary granuloma formation is correlated with anergy and the local production of migration inhibition factor and interleukin I. *Am. J. Path.* 119: 223–35.

Krakauer, T. (1985). A macrophage-derived factor that inhibits the production and action of interleukin 2. *J. Leukocyte Biol.* 38: 429–39.

Kupper, T. S., Green, D. R., Chaudry, I. H., Fox, A. and Baue, A. E. (1984). A cyclophosphamide-sensitive suppressor T cell circuit induced by thermal injury. *Surgery* 95: 699–705.

Laden, C., Blackwell, R. Q. and Fosdick, L. S. (1958). Anti-inflammatory effects of counter-irritants. *Am. J. Physiology* 195: 712–18.

Lamb, D., Pilney, F., Kelly, W. D. and Good, R. A. (1962). A comparative study of the incidence of anergy in patients with carcinoma, leukemia, Hodgkin's disease and other lymphomas. *J. Immunol.* 89: 555–8.

Lanser, M. C., Mao, P., Brown, G., Coleman, B. and Siegel, J. H. (1985). Serum-mediated depression of neutrophil chemiluminescence following blunt trauma. *Ann. Surg.* 202: 111–18.

Lewis, R. E. and Granger, H. J. (1986). Neutrophil-dependent mediation of microvascular permeability. *Fed. Proc.* 45: 109–13.

Lu, W. H. M. and Williams, D. M. (1980). The modulation of inflammatory response in the peritoneal cavity through stimulation of the pleural cavity: an experimental study in the rat. *Br. J. Exp. Path.* 61: 540–3.

Lundy, J. and Ford, C. (1983). Surgery, trauma and immune suppression: Evolving the mechanism. *Ann. Surg.* 197: 434–8.

McCarthy, R. E., Coffin, J. N. and Gates, S. L. (1968). Selective inhibition of the secondary immune response to mouse skin allografts by cell-free Ehrlich ascites carcinoma fluid. *Transplantation* 6: 737–43.

McIrvine, A. J., Wolfe, J. H. N., Collins, K. and Mannick, J. A. (1983). Fatal infection in mice after injection of immunosuppressive serum fractions from surgical patients. *Br. J. Surg.* 70: 558–61.

MacLean, L. D., Meakins, J. L., Taguchi, K., Duignan, J. P., Dhillon, K. S. and Gordon, J. (1979). Host resistance in sepsis and trauma. *Ann. Surg.* 182: 207–16.

McLoughlin, G. A., Wu, A. V., Saporoschetz, I., Nimberg, R. and Mannick, J. A. (1979). Correlation between anergy and a circulating immunosuppressive factor following major surgical trauma. *Ann. Surg.* 190: 297–304.

Mahler, D. and Batchelow, J. R. (1971). Phytohemagglutinin transformation of lymphocytes in burned patients. *Transplantation* 12: 409–11.

Marciniak, D. J., Dobbins, D. E., Maciejko, J. J., Scott, J. B., Haddy, F. J. and Grega, G. J. (1978). Antagonism of histamine edema formation by catecholamines. *Am. J. Physiology* 234: H180–H185.

Mathes, L. E., Olsen, R. G., Hebebrand, L. C., Hoover, E. A., Schaller, J. P., Adams, P. W. and Nichols, W. S. (1979). Immunosuppressive properties of a virion polypeptide, a 15 000 dalton protein, from feline leukemia virus. *Cancer Res.* 39: 950–5.

Meakins, J. L., Pietsch, J. B., Bubenick, O., Kelly, R., Rode, H., Gordon, J. and Maclean, L. D. (1977). Delayed hypersensitivity: Indicator of acquired failure of host defenses in sepsis and trauma. *Ann. Surg.* 186: 241–9.

Meijer, S., Bom-van Nooloos, A. A. and Visser, J. J. (1984). Phytohemagglutinin skin test for the immunological assessment of the surgical patient. *Eur. Surg. Res.* 16: 348–53.

Miller, C. L. and Baker, C. C. (1979). Changes in lymphocyte activity after thermal injury: The role of suppressor cells. *J. Clin. Invest.* 63: 202–10.

Miyazaki, S., Akiyoshi, T., Arinaga, S., Koba, F., Wada, T. and Tsuji, H. (1983). Depression of the generation of cell-mediated cytotoxicity by suppressor cells after surgery. *Clin. Exp. Immunol.* 54: 573–9.

Mondgil, G. C., Allan, R. B., Russell, R. J. and Wilkinson, P. C. (1977). Inhibition by anesthetic agents of human leukocyte locomotion towards chemical attractants. *Br. J. Anesthesia* 49: 97–105.

Mortensen, R. F. and Gewurz, H. (1976). Effects of C-reactive protein on the lymphoid system: II: Inhibition of mixed lymphocyte reactivity and generation of cytotoxic lymphocytes. *J. Immunol.* 116: 1244–50.

Munster, A. M. (1984). Immunologic response of trauma and burns: An overview. *Am. J. Med.* 76(3A): 142–5.

Munster, A. M., Eurenius, K., Katz, R. M., Canales, L., Foley, F. D. and Mortensen, R. F. (1973) Cell-mediated immunity after thermal injury. *Ann. Surg.* 177: 139–43.

Nakamura, M., Ishida, N. and Kamo, I. (1980). Immunosuppressive factors from mastocytoma cells cultured in serum-free medium. *J. Natl. Cancer Inst.* 65: 759–67.

Nelson, H. S. (1969). Delayed hypersensitivity in cancer patients: cutaneous and in vitro lymphocyte response to specific antigens. *J. Natl. Cancer Inst.* 42: 765–70.

Nelson, M. and Nelson, D. S. (1978). Macrophages and resistance to tumours: I: Inhibition of delayed-type hypersensitivity reactions by tumor cells and by soluble products affecting macrophages. *Immunology* 34: 277–90.

Nelson, M. and Nelson, D. S. (1980). Macrophages and resistance to tumors: IV: Influence of age on susceptibility of mice to anti-inflammatory and anti-macrophage effects of tumor cell products. *J. Natl. Cancer Inst.* 65: 781–9.

Nelson, M. and Nelson, D. S. (1982). Macrophages and resistance to tumors: 6: The effects of supernatants from cultures of normal and tumor cells on phagocytosis. *J. Reticuloendothelial Society* 31: 433–50.

Nelson, D. S., Nelson, M., Farram, E. and Inoue, Y. (1981). Cancer and subversion of host defenses. *Aust. J. Exp. Biol. Med. Sci.* 59: 229–62.

Nelson, M., Nelson, D. S., Spadbrow, P. B., Kuchroo, V. K., Jennings, P. A., Cianciolo, G. J. and Snyderman, R. (1985). Successful tumor immunotherapy: possible role of antibodies to anti-inflammatory factors produced by neoplasms. *Clin. Exp. Immunol.* 61: 109–117.

Ninnemann, J. L. and Ozkan, A. N. (1985). Definition of a burn injury-induced immunosuppressive serum component. *J. Trauma* 25: 113–7.

Ninnemann, J. L. and Stockland, A. E. (1984). Participation of prostaglandin E in immunosuppression following thermal injury. *J. Trauma* 24: 201–7.

Ninnemann, J. L., Fischer, J. C. and Frank, H. A. (1978). Prolonged survival of human skin allografts following thermal injury. *Transplantation* 25: 69–72.

Ninnemann, J. L., Condie, J. T., Davis, S. E. and Crockett, R. A. (1982). Isolation of immunosuppressive serum components following thermal injury. *J. Trauma* 22: 837–44.

Normann, S. J. (1978). Tumor cell threshold required for suppression of macrophage inflammation. *J. Natl. Cancer Inst.* 60: 1091–6.

Normann, S. J. (1985). Macrophage infiltration and tumor progression. *Cancer and Metastasis Rev.* 4: 277–91.

Normann, S. J. and Cornelius, J. (1978). Concurrent depression of tumor macrophage infiltration and systemic inflammation by progressive cancer growth. *Cancer Res.* 38: 3453–9.

Normann, S. J. and Cornelius, J. (1982). Characterization of anti-inflammatory factors produced by murine tumor cells in culture. *J. Natl. Cancer Inst.* 69: 1321–7.

Normann, S. J. and Sorkin, E. (1976). Cell-specific defect in monocyte function during tumor growth. *J. Natl. Cancer Inst.* 57: 135–40.

Normann, S. J., Schardt, M. and Sorkin, E. (1979a). Anti-inflammatory effect of spontaneous lymphoma in SJL/J mice. *J. Natl. Cancer Inst.* 63: 825–33.

Normann, S. J., Schardt, M. and Sorkin, E. (1979b). Cancer progression and monocyte inflammatory dysfunction: relationship to tumor excision and meta-stasis. *Int. J. Cancer* 23: 110–13.

Normann, S. J., Schardt, M., Cornelius, J. and Sorkin, E. (1981a). Post-operative inhibition of macrophage inflammatory responses. *J. Reticuloendothelial Soc.* 30: 89–97.

Normann, S. J., Schardt, M. and Sorkin, E. (1981b). Alteration of macrophage function in AKR leukemia. *J. Natl. Cancer Inst.* 66: 157–62.

Normann, S. J., Schardt, M. C. and Sorkin, E. (1984). Macrophage inflammatory responses in rats and mice with autochthonous and transplanted tumors induced by 3-methylcholanthrene. *J. Natl. Cancer Inst.* 72: 175–84.

Normann, S. J., Schardt, M. and Sorkin, E. (1985a). Autochthonous murine tumors: effects of viral or ultraviolet induction, immunogenicity and transplantation on intratumoral macrophages and systemic inflammatory responses. *Eur. J. Cancer* 21: 119–25.

Normann, S. J., Schardt, M. and Sorkin, E. (1985b). Anti-leukocyte activity: I: Systemic inhibition of cellular emigration following local inflammation. *J. Leuk. Biol.* 37: 319–30

Normann, S. J., Schardt, M. and Sorkin, E. (1985c). Anti-leukocyte activity: II: Induction of tolerance to systemic anti-inflammation associated with local irritation and major surgery. *J. Leukocyte Biol.* 37: 331–9.

Occhino, J. C., Glasgow, A. H., Cooperband, S. R., Mannick, J. A. and Schmid, K. (1973). Isolation of an immunosuppressive peptide fraction from human plasma. *J. Immunol.* 110: 685–94.

Ozkan, A. N. and Ninnemann, J. L. (1985). Suppression of in vitro lymphocyte and neutrophil responses by a low molecular weight suppressor active peptide from burn-patient sera. *J. Clin. Immunology* 5: 172–9.

Park, S. K. and Brody, J. I. (1971). Phenobarbital: suppression of immunity. *Nature (New Biology)* 233: 181–2.

Payne, J., Hayden, P., Meyer, H.-J. and Walls, R. S. (1984). Observed differences in postoperative lymphocyte transformation are explained by patient and population variations. *Ann. Surg.* 147: 237–42.

Plescia, O. J., Smith, A. H. and Grinwish, K. (1975). Subversion of immune system by tumor cells and role of prostaglandins. *Proc. Natl. Acad. Sci. USA* 72: 1848–51.

Polk, H. C. Jr. (1968). Prolongation of xenograft survival in patients with pseudomonas sepsis: a clarification. *Surg. Forum* 19: 514–5.

Pollock, R. E., Babcock, G. F., Romsdahl, M. M. and Nishioka, K. (1984). Surgical stress-mediated suppression of murine natural killer cell cytotoxicity. *Cancer Res.* 44: 3888–91.

Rapaport, F. T., Milgrom, F., Kano, K., Gesner, B., Solowey, A. C., Casson, P., Silvernam, H. I. and Converse, J. M. (1968). Immunologic sequelae of thermal injury. *Ann. NY Acad. Science* 150: 1004–8.

Riboli, E. B., Terrizzi, A., Arnulfo, G. and Bertoglio, S. (1984). Immunosuppressive effect of surgery evaluated by the multitest cell-mediated immunity system. *Canadian J. Surg.* 27: 60–3

Riddle, P. R. and Berenbaum, M. C. (1967). Post-operative depression of the lymphocyte response to phytohemagglutinin. *Lancet* 1: 746–8.

Robinson, B. V. and Robson, L. M. (1964). Production of an anti-inflammatory substance at a site of inflammation. *Brit. J. Pharmacol.* 23: 420–32.

Roth, J. A. (1983). Tumor induced immunosuppression. *Surg. Gynecol. Obstet.* 156: 233–40.

Roth, J. A., Grimm, E. A., Gupta, R. K. and Ames, R. (1982). Immunoregulatory factors derived from human tumors: I: Immunologic and biochemical characterization of factors that suppress lymphocyte proliferative and cytotoxic responses in vitro. *J. Immunol.* 128: 1955–62.

Russell, D. H., Kibler, R., Matrisan, L., Larson, D. F., Poulos, B. and Magun, B. E. (1985). Prolactin receptors on human T and B lymphocytes: Antagonism of prolactin binding by cyclosporine. *J. Immunol.* 134: 3027–31.

Saba, T. M. and Cho, E. (1979). Reticuloendothelial systemic response to operative trauma as influenced by cryoprecipitate or cold-insoluble globulin therapy. *J. Reticuloendothelial Soc.* 26: 171–86.

Schardt, M., Normann, S. and Sorkin, E. (1984). Dissociation of chemotactic and inflammatory leukocyte responses. *Int. Arch. Allergy and Appl. Immunol.* 75: 68–74.

Schultz, R. M., Pavlidis, N., Stylos, W. A. and Chirigos, M. A. (1978). Regulation of macrophage tumoricidal function: a role for prostaglandins of the E series. *Science* 202: 320–1.

Slade, M. S., Simmons, R. L., Yunis, E. and Greenberg, J. (1975). Immunodepression after major surgery in normal patients. *Surgery* 78: 363–72.

Sokol, R. J. and Hudson, G. (1983). Disordered function of mononuclear phagocytes in malignant disease. *J. Clin. Pathol.* 36: 316–23.

Solowey, A. C. and Rapaport, F. T. (1965). Immunologic responses in cancer patients. *Surg. Gynecol. Obstet.* 121: 756–60.

Snyder, D. S., Lu, C. Y. and Unanue, E. R. (1982). Control of macrophage Ia expression in neonatal mice — role of a splenic suppressor cell. *J. Immunol.* 128: 1458–65.

Snyderman, R. and Cianciolo, G. J. (1984). Immunosuppressive activity of the retroviral envelope protein p15E and its possible relationship to neoplasia. *Immunol. Today* 5: 240–4.

Snyderman, R., Pike, M. C., Blaylock, B. L. and Weinstein, P. (1976). Effect of neoplasms on inflammation: depression of macrophage accumulation after tumor implantation. *J. Immunol.* 116: 585–9.

Snyderman, R., Seigler, H.F. and Meadows, L. (1977). Abnormalities of monocyte chemotaxis in patients with melanoma: Effects of immunotherapy and tumor removal. *J. Natl. Cancer Inst.* 58: 37–41.

Snyderman, R., Meadows, L., Holder, W. and Wells, S. Jr. (1978). Abnormal monocyte chemotaxis in patients with breast cancer: Evidence for a tumor-mediated effect. *J. Natl. Cancer Inst.* 60: 737–40.

Stein, M. D., Gamble, D. N., Klimpel, K. D., Herndon, D. N. and Klimpel, G. R. (1984). Natural killer cell defects resulting from thermal injury. *Cellular Immunol.* 86: 551–6.

Stewart, G.J., Knight, L.C., Arbogast, B.W. and Stern, H.S. (1980). Inhibition of leukocyte locomotion by tocainide, a primary amine analog of lidocaine: A study with 111-indium-labeled leukocytes and scanning electron microscopy. *Lab. Invest.* 42: 302–9.

Stosic-Grujicic, S. and Simic, M. M. (1982). Modulation of interleukin 1 production by activated macrophages: In vitro action of hydrocortisone, colchicine and cytochalasin B. *Cellular Immunology* 69: 235–47.

Stratta, R.J., Saffle, J.R., Ninnemann, J.L., Weber, M.E., Sullivan, J.J. and Warden, G.D. (1985). The effect of surgical excision and grafting procedures on postburn lymphocyte suppression. *J. Trauma* 25: 46–52.

Tadakuma, T. and Pierce, C.W. (1978). Mode of action of a soluble immune response suppressor (SIRS) produced by concanavalin A-activated spleen cells. *J. Immunol.* 120: 481–6.

Taffet, S.M. and Russell, S.W. (1981). Macrophage-mediated tumor cell killing: Regulation of expression of cytolytic activity by prostaglandin E. *J. Immunol.* 126: 424–7.

Truax, J.F. (1978). Some quantitative, temporal characteristics of counter-irritation in the rat. Master's Thesis, Dept. of Physiology and Pharmacology, Durham, N.C. Graduate School of Duke University.

Valone, F.H. (1983). Quantitation of arachidonic acid lipoxygenase products in malignant and nonmalignant effusions. *Cancer Res.* 43: 5695–8.

van Dijk, W.C., Verbrugh, H.A., Ruud, E.N., van Rijswijk, R.E.N., Vos, A. and Verhoef, J. (1982). Neutrophil function, serum opsonic activity, and delayed hypersensitivity in surgical patients. *Surgery* 92:21–9.

Varesio, L. (1983). Suppressor cells and cancer: Inhibition of immune functions by macrophages. In R.B. Herberman and H. Friedman (eds), *The Reticuloendothelial System, A Comprehensive Treatise,* vol. 5, *Cancer.* New York: Plenum Press: 217–52.

Vetter, M.L., Gewurz, H. and Baum, L.L. (1986). The effects of C-reactive protein on human cell-mediated cytotoxicity. *J. Leukocyte Biol.* 39: 13–25.

Wanebo, H.J., Jun, M.Y., Strong, E.W. and Oettgen, H. (1975). T-cell deficiency in patients with squamous cell cancer of the head and neck. *Am. J. Surg.* 130: 445–51.

Wang, B.S., Badger, A.M., Nimberg, R.R., Cooperband, S.R., Schmid, K. and Mannick, J.A. (1977). Suppression of tumor-specific cell-mediated cytotoxicity by immunoregulatory α-globulin and by immunoregulatory α-globulin-like peptides from cancer patients. *Cancer Res.* 37: 3022–5.

Wang, B.S., Heacock, E.H., Wu, A.V. and Mannick, J.A. (1980). Generation of suppressor cells in mice after surgical trauma. *J. Clin. Invest.* 66: 200–9.

Wang, B.S., Heacock, E.H. and Mannick, J.A. (1982). Characterization of suppressor cells generated in mice after surgical trauma. *Clin. Immunol. Immunopathology* 24: 161–70.

Warabi, H., Venkat, K., Geetha, V., Liotta, L.A., Brownstein, M. and Schiffmann, E. (1984). Identification and partial characterization of a low molecular-weight inhibitor of leukotaxis from fibrosarcoma cells. *Cancer Res.* 44: 915–22.

Warden, G.D., Mason, A.D. Jr. and Pruitt, B.A. Jr (1975). Suppression of leukocyte chemotaxis in vitro by chemotherapeutic agents used in the management of thermal injuries. *Ann. Surg.* 181: 363–9.

Watanabe, M., Pan, S.-H. and Friedman, H. (1978). Serologic and immunochemical characterization of an immunosuppression soluble factor from mastocytoma bearing mice. *J. Natl. Cancer Inst.* 61: 249–54.

Wedmore, C.V. and Williams, T.J. (1981). Control of vascular permeability by polymorphonuclear leukocytes in inflammation. *Nature* 289: 646–50.

Whitney, R.B., Kelly, B.S. and Levy, J.G. (1977). Immunosuppression in mice bearing primary tumors. *Eur. J. Cancer* 14: 699–705.

Winchurch, R.A. and Munster, A.M. (1980). Post-traumatic activation of suppressor cells. *J. Reticuloendothelial Soc.* 27: 83–8.

Wolfe, J.H.N., Saporoschetz, I, Young, A.E., O'Connor, N.E. and Mannick, J.A. (1981). Suppressive serum, suppressor lymphocytes and death from burns. *Ann. Surg.* 193: 513–20.

Wolfe, J.H.N., Wu, A.V.O., O'Connor, N.E. Saporoschetz, I. and Mannick, J.A. (1982). Anergy, immunosuppressive serum and impaired lymphocyte blastogenesis in burn patients. *Arch. Surg.* 117: 1266–71.

Yachnin, S. and Lester, E. (1976). Inhibition of human lymphocyte transformation by human alphafetoprotein (HAFP); comparison of foetal and hepatoma HAFP and kinetic studies of in vitro immunosuppression. *Clin. Exp. Immunol.* 26: 484–90.

Yu, A., Watts, H., Jaffe, N. and Parkman, R. (1977). Concomitant presence of tumor-specific cytotoxic and inhibitor lymphocytes in patients with osteogenic sarcoma. *N. Engl. J. Med.* 297: 121–7.

17

Effectors and Modulators of Natural Immunity: Discussion

D. S. NELSON

Kolling Institute of Medical Research
Royal North Shore Hospital, Sydney, NSW 2065, Australia

MOLECULES

It is a truism that the present era of biomedical science is the era of molecular biology. In its own right, molecular biology has enhanced enormously our understanding of many fundamental processes and principles. Its applications to other branches of biology and medicine have been both illuminating and productive. This is especially so in immunology, where the elucidation of the genetic mechanisms for the generation of diversity provides a spectacular example of its success. The study of natural immunity has also been advanced by the application of molecular biological techniques, particularly through the availability of relatively large quantities of purified proteins as a result of recombinant DNA technology. So much, indeed, has this dominated many areas of research that many scientists look askance at studies *not* done with purified recombinant proteins. Few, if any, eyebrows will be raised at the decision by Smith and Wahl (Chapter 8) to restrict their discussion of cytokines to those that have been cloned and for which recombinant molecules are now available. Recombinant DNA technology has not only made the analysis of the actions of cytokines more precise, but it has also provided them in quantities sufficient for studies of their possible therapeutic effects, in humans as well as in much smaller experimental animals. Even those cell products that have not yet been cloned are often either purified or well characterised — the macrophage products listed by Ezekowitz (Chapter 1), like the 100 products listed by Nathan (1987), provide good examples.

540

NATURAL IMMUNITY
ISBN 0 12 5145551

Our concepts of cytokines have grown steadily more precise and more sophisticated since macrophage migration inhibition factor (MIF) was discovered (David, 1966; Bloom and Bennett, 1966), the term lymphokine was coined (Dumonde *et al.*, 1969) and standardisation of the nomenclature of cytokines was begun (Aarden *et al.*, 1979; Waksman, 1979). While the days of 'lympho-*Dreck*' and 'soup' are, however, virtually over, there remains some room for studies on unfractionated or unpurified cell products. There are two reasons for this. One is that new activities may be found (which then, of course, urgently require characterisation). Examples of this are the finding of macrophage-activating factors that are not interferon gamma (IFN-*γ*) (e.g., Meltzer *et al.*, 1987; Chapter 22) and mast cell products that stimulate tumour cells, fibroblasts and endothelial cells (see below). The second reason is the frequency with which two factors act either in sequence or synergistically to produce a particular effect.

Our broader understanding of cytokine biology and chemistry includes concepts of their generally pleiotropic actions, the frequent occurrence of synergism, ways in which their effects can be amplified, the autocrine effects of some, and some understanding of both positive and negative regulation. Much of this, is, of course, clear from the discussion of Smith and Wahl (Chapter 8) and others in this book, but I wish to re-emphasise some points.

LPS and Synergism

In 1955 Rowley reported a biphasic effect of endotoxin on the resistance of mice to infection: a decrease, followed by an increase (Rowley, 1955). For more than 30 years lipopolysaccharide (LPS) has been widely used experimentally as a macrophage stimulant. In 1978 Hibbs and his colleagues reported the quite alarming finding of unsuspected small amounts of LPS in a wide variety of laboratory reagents (Weinberg *et al.*, 1978). Since then, many workers have gone to considerable lengths to eliminate traces of LPS from their culture media and reagents.

I wish to make two general points. First, exogenous LPS is a potent signal for macrophage activation. In the well studied mouse macrophages, it is the most commonly used second signal of the two (at least) required, IFN-*γ* being a potent priming signal (reviewed by Adams and Hamilton, 1984, 1987). It is not always clear what the physiological counterpart of LPS in the intact animal may be. In the case of tumour cell killing, the tumour cells themselves may provide the signal. In other cases, it is difficult to imagine that the normal *milieu intérieur* contains enough LPS to provide this signal.

Second, unsuspected (and very small) amounts of LPS in media or other reagents may indeed influence the results of experiments in vitro. Haslett *et al.* (1985) found that contaminating LPS (10–100 ng/mL) in cell separation media affected the subsequent responses of neutrophils to formyl-methionyl-leucyl-phenylalanine. Newton (1986) isolated human blood monocytes under 'low-endotoxin' conditions and found that they did not produce intracellular or extracellular interleukin 1(IL-1). They were, however, highly sensitive to the presence of exogenous LPS, producing IL-1 after exposure to picogram or even femtogram amounts. He suggested that previously reported 'spontaneous' production of IL-1 might have been due to trace contamination with LPS. Sub-threshold (nanogram) amounts of LPS have been found to be synergistic with sub-threshold amounts of IFN-γ in the induction of tumour necrosis factor alpha (TNF-α) by mouse and human macrophages (Gifford and Lohmann-Matthes, 1987) and the induction of procoagulant activity by mouse macrophages (C. L. Geczy and D. K. Moon, personal communication).

Synergism and Amplification: Other Cytokines

There are now numerous examples of cytokines promoting the production, or potentiating the action, of other cytokines. For example, colony-stimulating factor 1 (CSF-1 or M-CSF) can potentiate the production by stimulated human monocytes of TNF-α, IFN and (unspecified) colony-stimulating activity (Warren and Ralph, 1986) and can potentiate mouse macrophage tumoricidal activity induced by other lymphokines (Ralph and Nakoinz, 1987). TNF-α and IFN-γ are also synergistic in direct cytotoxic effects in vivo (Dealtry *et al.*, 1987). GM-CSF can potentiate TNF-α production by human monocytes (Cannistra *et al.*, 1987). Conversely, IFN-γ can increase TNF-α secretion (Nedwin *et al.*, 1985) and, although not inducing, can potentiate the secretion of IL-1 in response to other stimuli (Gerrard *et al.*, 1987). TNF-α can also induce or promote IL-1 secretion (Dinarello *et al.*, 1986). (For other examples of synergism and amplification, see Chapter 8).

Synergism and Amplification: Other Cells

As Smith and Wahl point out, vascular endothelial cells and fibroblasts can be targets for several lymphokines and monokines. Both can respond by proliferation, the development of MHC (notably class II) antigens and the production of colony-stimulating activity. Endothelial cells can also respond by producing procoagulant and neutrophil adhesion molecules.

Even vascular smooth muscle cells can respond to IL-1 by producing more IL-1 (Warner *et al.*, 1987). IL-1 is also chemotactic for lymphocytes (Miossec *et al.*, 1984). The potential of these responses to amplify inflammatory reactions is obvious. Such amplification may be of benefit to the host in mobilising effectors of natural immunity and helping to localise them at sites where they are required. The potential for tissue damage is also present, however, especially in the form of tissue breakdown from the release of collagenase, and fibrosis from overstimulated fibroblasts.

Regulation

Although many possible amplification pathways are now known, much less is known of the endogenous control pathways by which the reactions are restricted and ultimately stopped, or at least resolved. There appears to be little evidence for pure negative feedback (i.e. inhibition by cytokines of their own production). It would seem that prostaglandin E2 (PGE2) production, by macrophages (Stenson and Parker, 1980) and fibroblasts (Elias *et al.*, 1987), would provide a strong negative signal to other macrophages and to lymphocytes (Stenson and Parker, 1980; Cahill and Hopper, 1984). IL-1 production is not, however, always susceptible to regulation by inhibitors of PGE2 production (Eden and Turino, 1986). Other molecules that might provide regulatory controls include acute-phase proteins produced in response to IL-1 (see Breit, Chapter 9) and inhibitors of IL-1 (Dinarello, 1985). IFN-γ can act synergistically with TNF-β to reduce responses to CSFs (Murphy *et al.*, 1986).

CELLS

Just as recombinant DNA technology has so greatly facilitated the study of cytokines, the combination of monoclonal antibodies and flow cytometry has allowed much more precise separation, identification and purification of cells. Perhaps the results are less clearcut than with cytokines, because families of cells are diverse, and even cloned or individual cells are enormously plastic. A cell can change dramatically with time but remain the same entity. Somewhat fancifully it may be likened to the philosopher's river: one cannot step into the same river twice. Leaving such notions aside, the principal practical considerations in relation to cells in natural immunity are: (1) that cells of any one family are diverse; (2) that somewhat different cells may perform fairly similar functions; and (3) that most cells can be activated.

Functional Diversity

The heterogeneity of macrophages has been known and discussed for some years, with only a modicum of progress (cf. Ezekowitz [Chapter 1] and Hopper *et al.* [1979]). The differences between macrophages in different sites and between resident, inflammatory and activated macrophages are somewhat better known, but the mechanistic determinants of these differences are still poorly understood. Some well-defined cytokines cause the functional changes grouped as activation, but it is not known whether similar, but less intense, stimuli account for other differences. Analysis of cloned populations of mouse macrophages suggests the possibility that functionally specialised populations may be derived from distinct progenitors (Walker, 1987). In a functional sense, different populations of macrophages can appear well adapted to their particular environments. For example, it seems eminently appropriate for lung macrophages to be poor antigen-presenting cells, or even suppressor cells, so as to minimise immunological responses, especially allergic responses, to inhaled antigens (Holt, 1986; Holt and Sedgwick, 1987). Although it seems unattainable, the goal of understanding macrophage diversity would be the ability to recruit, to sites of infection or tumour deposition, macrophages that would exert the appropriate effector function without the capacity for tissue damage.

Purified neutrophils and eosinophils, while capable of being activated (see below), appear to be much less diverse than macrophages. The same probably applies to natural killer (NK) cells and other naturally occurring cytotoxic cells.

Diverse Cell Types with Similar Functions

In this area most interest, and a certain amount of controversy, has centred on naturally occurring cytotoxic cells: NK cells and others. The chapters by Herberman, Patek and Collins, and Hersey now make it clear that there are diverse types of cells in this group, the differences between NK and natural cytotoxic (NC) cells being rather more subtle than the differences between those cells and non-MHC-restricted cytotoxic T cells. While the last class is clearly of T cell lineage and the others are not, it would be of interest to see whether NK and NC cells prove to be derived from a common precursor. While it is not strictly germane to this book, it might also be noted that effector cells of antibody-dependent cell-mediated cytotoxicity can also be diverse: neutrophils, eosinophils, certain lymphocytes, macrophages and now even platelets (see below).

Activation

Possibly because of their putative role in tumour immunity, activated macrophages have received far more attention than neutrophils or eosinophils. The latter two cell types can, however, be activated. Activated neutrophils and eosinophils can manifest increased adhesiveness and phagocytosis, increased capacity for intracellular killing, increased capacity for extracellular antibody-dependent cytotoxicity, and increased leukotriene synthesis (Hopper *et al.*, 1981; Vadas, 1984; Silberstein *et al.*, 1986). CSFs are potent activators of granulocytes (Vadas, 1984; Silberstein *et al.*, 1986). TNF-α (Shalaby *et al.*, 1987) and IFN-γ are also active, the latter acting additively or synergistically with other cytokines (Perussia *et al.*, 1987).

Macrophage activation has been extensively investigated and reviewed, but remains, even now, difficult to define (e.g. Ezekowitz, Chapter 1, North [1978], Morahan [1980], and reviews by Adams and Hamilton [1984, 1987] and Nathan [1987]). The term 'activation' describes a variety of functional, biochemical and morphological changes that can be induced in various ways. Morahan proposed the use of the descriptive expression 'activated by (stimulus) for (function)'. It is a great pity that this proposal has not been followed far more widely.

One of the problems in considering activation is the scarcity of clearcut antigenic or biochemical markers. Todd and his colleagues have described an antigen (Mo-3e) on human monocytes/macrophages and macrophage cell lines stimulated in various ways, but its relation to other functional parameters or activation is not altogether clear (Todd and Liu, 1986; Todd *et al.*, 1986,1987). Ewan *et al.* (1986) produced a monoclonal antibody, A1-3, which bound selectively to stimulated human monocytes; it was thought to be directed against macrophage surface procoagulant, probably identical with tissue factor. The functional antigen LFA-1 is induced on mouse macrophages during activation (Strassmann *et al.*, 1985) but is, of course, not restricted to them.

Extensive studies have been made of biochemical changes during the induction and expression of activation. Like other cells, macrophages utilise pathways involving inositol phosphatides, protein kinase C activation and calcium mobilisation (Adams and Hamilton, 1987). Although changes in the profiles of proteins and glycoproteins have been detected, these tend to be multiple and somewhat subtle, and their relationship to functional activation is not always clear (Grand-Perret *et al.*, 1986; Tannenbaum *et al.*, 1987; MacKay and Russell, 1987; Irimura *et al.*, 1987). Nor have the techniques of molecular biology provided definitive markers. A variety of oncogenes and 'competence' genes are expressed (or show reduced expression) during activation, but the changes are in many ways similar to those occcurring during differentiation and maturation (Adams and Hamilton, 1987; Introna *et al.*, 1987; Sariban *et al.*, 1987; Lee *et al.*, 1987). Measurement of mRNA for different macrophage products, in cells stimulated in different ways, has, however, lent weight to the idea that macrophage responses at this level are not stereotyped (Vermeulen *et al.*, 1987). IFN-γ has been found to increase transcription of the genes for TNF-α, IL-1 and plasminogen activator in mouse macrophages. Transcription could also be induced by cycloheximide, indicating the operation of short-lived repressors (Collart *et al.*, 1986). This finding may offer new insights into the mechanism of control of macrophage activation.

Other Cells

Cells other than the traditional effectors of natural immunity deserve brief mention.

Mast cells at high effector : target ratios can be cytotoxic to tumour cells (Farram and Nelson, 1980). At low effector : target ratios they potentiate tumour cell proliferation, and supernatants from disrupted mast cells potentiate both tumour cell and fibroblast proliferation. Heparin has been identified as the 'growth factor'. Differential distribution of subcutaneous mast cells was thought likely to explain the curious 'antero-posterior gradient' of increased subcutaneous tumour growth in the anterior half of rodent bodies (Roche, 1985a, 1986). Mast cells can promote angiogenesis, probably in part by a stimulating effect of histamine on capillary endothelial cell proliferation (Roche, 1985b; Marks *et al.*, 1986). Other roles for mast cells include stimulation of fibrosis (Beranek and Clevy, 1985) and possible roles in graft versus host disease (Choi *et al.*, 1987) and inflammatory arthritic disease (Gruber *et al.*, 1986; D. G. Malone *et al.*, 1986). (For a recent review, see Galli, 1987.)

Vascular endothelial cells have been mentioned above as responding to cytokines. They may themselves be a source of cytokines, e.g. IL-1, which can also be produced by vascular smooth muscle cells (Warner *et al.*, 1987). Cultured vascular endothelial cells have been reported to produce a macrophage chemotactic factor (Berliner *et al.*, 1986) and to stimulate eosinophils (Rothenburg *et al.*, 1987).

Platelets are a troublesome contaminant of monocytes isolated from peripheral blood (Perussia *et al.*, 1982; Hopper *et al.*, 1986). They have, however, recently moved from the class of nuisances to the class of cytotoxic effector cells, either alone after lymphokine stimulation (Auriault *et al.*, 1987; Pancré *et al.*, 1987) or in antibody-dependent cell-mediated cytotoxicity (Slezak *et al.*, 1987).

Large granular lymphocytes, in addition to natural killer activity, may also have suppressor cell activity (Maier *et al.*, 1986).

ORGANS, ANIMALS AND POPULATIONS

Discussion of the factors modulating natural immunity highlights the importance of studies in whole animals, or even populations, to complement highly reductionist approaches using model systems in vitro.

Organs and Organisms: Complex Entities

A few examples illustrate the potential difficulties and pitfalls of reliance on models in vitro. Bone marrow culture has provided vital and fascinating insights into haemopoiesis. It has, however, long been apparent that the marrow of the intact animal provides an environment that is significantly different, and possibly 'better', than tissue culture: witness, for example, the difficulties of culturing human myeloma cells. It is only recently that wide attention has been paid to the roles of bone marrow accessory cells other than macrophages (see, for example: Collins and Dorshkind, 1987; Dorshkind, 1987; Heinen and Tsunoda, 1987).

In culture, macrophages, NK cells and lymphokine-activated killer (LAK) cells can simply be added to target cells. In the body they must be delivered across vascular endothelium to tumour tissue. In animals that have made an appropriate cell-mediated immune response, a local delayed-type hypersensitivity (DTH) reaction will do this for macrophages (Nelson *et al.*, 1981) and perhaps for NK cells. In the absence of DTH some other mechanism must be found. It is of interest that labelled LAK cells have been found to localise at sites of macrophage stimulation in mice (Migliori *et al.*, 1987).

Another example is provided by TNF-α. Although the monokine is directly cytotoxic to some tumour cells in vitro, it causes haemorrhagic necrosis of a wider range of tumours in vivo. The additional effects in vivo are probably related to its effect on vascular endothelial cells, especially the induction of procoagulant activity (Old, 1985; Le and Vilček, 1987; Kawai *et al.*, 1987; Smith and Wahl, Chapter 8). Interferons may also act therapeutically in vivo by a combination of direct effects on target cells, enhancement of effector cell function and potentiation of other cytokines.

Stress, Hormones and the Whole Animal

The work of Riley and his colleagues, summarised by Landy in Chapter 14, has made many experimentalists aware of the profound effects of even modest stress on the resistance of animals to infection and cancer. At the same time, there has been an upsurge both of scientific interest in interactions between neurohumoral factors and immunity and of clinical and public interest in stress and disease, especially cancer. Many of the possible neurohumoral pathays have been discussed by Fabris (Chapter 10). It is worth emphasising that monocytes/macrophages and polymorphs are susceptible to the adverse effects of corticosteroids at levels that are physiologically attainable under conditions of stress. Furthermore, macrophages, as well as NK cells, can be targets for neuroendocrine factors (Koff and Dunegan, 1986; J. D. Malone *et al.*, 1986; Fóris *et al.*, 1986).

Paying the Price

The cost to the host of exercising powerful antimicrobial and antitumour defence mechanisms can be made painfully apparent in intact animals, human or otherwise. Reactive oxygen intermediates are now known or believed to be involved in a wide range of pathological changes. Although, for the most part, antioxidant defences operate to limit the potential damage, there is clearly the opportunity for local and even systemic tissue damage when reactive oxygen intermediates are formed in abundance (Clark *et al.*, 1985; Clark, 1986; Cross, 1987).

Studies of the effects of IL-2 in humans rapidly revealed major problems with toxicity. Though by no means universal, severe toxic effects included a vascular leak syndrome, interstitial pulmonary oedema, renal insufficiency and hepatic insufficiency (Rosenberg *et al.*, 1985, 1987). Some of these effects would not have been predicted from studies in vitro. Toxicity has been reported to be much reduced by the use of continous infusion rather than intermittent administration, without apparent loss of efficacy (West *et al.*, 1987).

Exogenous TNF-α also has toxic effects in vivo, both in mice and in humans. It is of some interest that the severe toxic effects were apparent in mice only when purified recombinant TNF-α became available and was used (Old, 1985). The vascular leak syndrome was apparent in mice (Remick *et al.*, 1987) but, despite a variety of toxic effects, TNF-α was said to be 'well tolerated clinically' (Blick *et al.*, 1987). Perhaps more to the point, however, is the growing evidence that some of the severe pathology associated with malaria is attributable to TNF-α (Clark and

Chaudhri, 1988; see Clark, Chapter 23). Some of the severe toxic effects of recombinant human TNF-α in growing rats were associated with a large increase in plasma PGE2 levels and could be prevented by treatment with the cyclooxygenase inhibitors indomethacin and ibuprofen (Kettelhut *et al.*, 1987). As TNF-α is, in another setting, cachectin (Cerami and Beutler, 1986) it would be surprising if its administration did not have some adverse longer-term nutritional effect.

Yet another physiologically important cytokine, IL-1, has also been reported to have a not altogether predictable adverse effect in vivo. Mice receiving exogenous IL-1 were found to have decreased DTH (contact sensitivity) responses. The decrease could be inhibited by treatment with indomethacin and was thus attributable to prostaglandin, presumably PGE2 (Robertson *et al.*, 1987).

Much attention has been focused on the role of (activated) macrophages as antitumour effector cells. Over many years, however, evidence has also been presented that macrophages can sometimes potentiate tumour growth, both in vivo and in vitro (Evans, 1977; reviews by: Nelson, 1987; Nelson and Nelson, 1987; Mantovani *et al.*, 1987). It has even been suggested that cancer might be a 'macrophage-mediated autoaggressive disease' (Munzarová and Kovařík, 1987) and that tumours grow more slowly in old people than in young people because their macrophages are less stimulatory to tumour cells (Ershler, 1986). The broader significance of tumour cell stimulation by macrophages remains unclear, as does the mechanism. In one study, a mouse tumour that was stimulated by macrophages was also rather radioresistant (Milas *et al.*, 1987). In our own work, mouse macrophages that had been activated but had decayed to a non-activated state were highly stimulatory, and stimulation appeared to require cell contact (Nelson and Nelson, 1985).

A very good case can also be made for the idea that macrophage-derived growth factors (IL-1, platelet-derived growth factor) are important in the pathological development of pulmonary fibrosis, e.g. in sarcoidosis (Hunninghake, 1984; Mornex *et al.*, 1986; Martinet *et al.*, 1987). That mast cells are a mixed blessing has long been known to students of, and sufferers from, acute allergic reactions. They too have been implicated in pathological fibrosis (Claman, 1985) as well as in the promotion of tumour growth (see above).

Genetics and Nutrition

A great deal of elegant investigation of the genetics of natural immunity has been carried out and is summarised by Lemieux *et al.* in Chapter 11.

Much is also known, clinically and experimentally, of the devastating effects of nutritional deprivation on the immune system, especially in young animals (Gershwin *et al.*, Chapter 13). There are, however, some interesting grey areas that deserve mention.

The relationship between ethnic origin and susceptibility to certain diseases is one such area. Japanese living in Japan were (at least until very recently) apparently resistant to certain prevalent Western diseases — breast cancer in women, bowel cancer and atherosclerosis. All three conditions have become much more common in Japanese living in the essentially Western environment of Hawaii (Wynder, 1975; Buell, 1973; Stemmermann *et al.*, 1986). Differences in dietary fat intake have been linked to changes in the incidence of all three conditions. In all these cases, it seems that any connection with the immune system is tenuous, but the involvement of macrophages in lipid metabolism and atherosclerosis (see Chapter 27, Discussion to Part II), as well as in resistance to cancer suggests that it might be well to keep at least a tiny chink of the mind open. A recent review suggests that the area of dietary fat and immunity may be an interesting and useful one for further studies (Erickson, 1986).

In the case of nasopharyngeal carcinoma, to which Southern Chinese are especially susceptible, there is evidence that susceptibility has a strong genetic component, since South Chinese immigrants to other countries retain their susceptibility. Furthermore, susceptibility to the tumour is MHC-linked (Clifford, 1970; Simons and Day, 1977). This provides a slightly less tenous connection with the immune system.

There have been numerous other population-based studies of the relationship between certain nutrients and the prevalence of cancer (reviewed by Willett and MacMahon, 1984). Many observations appear to be conflicting and it seems very difficult to draw firm conclusions about individual components of diet. Carotenoids and retinoids are, however, of interest immunologically because they give rise to retinol, the physiologically active form of vitamin A. Retinol and other retinoids are active as immunological adjuvants and this may contribute to their apparent antitumour effects (for a fairly recent discussion, see Malkovský *et al.*, 1983). Two recent studies indicating quite marked diet-related differences in cancer incidence within populations are those of Menkes *et al.* (1986) showing a strong inverse association (relative odds 4.30) between serum β-carotene and squamous cell carcinoma of the lung, and of Katsouyanni *et al.* (1986), showing a 10-fold greater risk of breast cancer in Greek women in the highest quintile, compared with those in the lowest quintile, for the consumption of vegetables, especially lettuce, cucumber and carrots. Thus, it seems, is the conventional dietary wisdom of generations of mothers and grandmothers supported by science.

REFERENCES

Aarden, L. A. and 33 others (1979). *J. Immunol.* 123: 2928–9.

Adams, D. O. and Hamilton, T. A. (1984). *Ann. Rev. Immunol.* 2: 283–318.

Adams, D. O. and Hamilton, T. A. (1987). *Immunol. Rev.* 97: 5–27.

Auriault, C., Pancré, V., Joseph, M., Damonneville, M., Falcoff, E. and Capron, A. (1987). *Ann. Inst. Pasteur Immunol.* 138: 585–97.

Beranek, J. T. and Clevy, J. P. (1985). *Immunol. Today* 3: 317.

Berliner, J. A., Territo, M., Almada, L., Carter, A., Shafonsky, E. and Fogelman, A. M. (1986). *Arteriosclerosis* 6: 254–8.

Blick, M., Sherwin, S. A., Rosenblum, M. and Gutterman, J. (1987). *Cancer Res.* 47: 2986–9.

Bloom, B. R. and Bennett, B. (1966). *Science* 153: 80–2.

Buell, P. (1973). *J. Natl. Cancer Inst.* 51: 1479–83.

Cahill, J. C. and Hopper, K. E. (1984). *Int. J. Immunopharmacol.* 6: 9–17.

Cannistra, S. A., Rambaldi, A., Spriggs, D. R., Herrmann, F., Kufe, D. and Griffin, J. D. (1987). *J. Clin. Invest.* 79: 1720–8.

Cerami, A. and Beutler, B. (1986). *Cold Spring Harbor Symp. Quant. Biol.* 51: 625–9.

Choi, K. L., Giorno, R. and Claman, H. N. (1987). *J. Immunol.* 138: 4093–4101.

Claman, H. N. (1985). *Immunol. Today* 6: 192–5.

Clark, I. A. (1986). *Pathology* 18: 181–6.

Clark, I. A. and Chaudhri, G. (1988). In *Tumor Necrosis Factor: Proceedings of a Meeting, Heidelberg, 1987.* In press.

Clark, I. A., Cowden, W. B. and Hunt, N. H. (1985). *Med. Res. Rev.* 5: 297–332.

Clifford, P. (1970). *Int. J. Cancer* 5: 287–309.

Collart, M. A., Belin, D., Vassalli, J. D., De Kossodo, S. and Vassalli, P. (1986). *J. Exp. Med.* 164: 2113–18.

Collins, L. S. and Dorshkind, K. (1987). *J. Immunol.* 138: 1082–7.

Cross, C. E. (1987). *Ann. Intern. Med.* 107: 526–45.

David, J. R. (1966). *Proc. Natl. Acad. Sci. USA* 56: 72–7.

Dealtry, G. B., Naylor, M. S., Fiers, W. and Balkwill, F. R. (1987). *Eur. J. Immunol.* 17: 689–93.

Dinarello, C. A. (1985). *J. Clin. Immunol.* 5: 287–97.

Dinarello, C. A., Cannon, J. G., Wolff, S. M., Bernheim, H. A., Beutler, B., Cerami, A., Figari, I. S., Palladino, M. A. and O'Connor, J. V. (1986). *J. Exp. Med.* 163: 1433–50.

Dorshkind, K. (1987). *Immunol. Today* 8: 191–3.

Dumonde, D. C., Wolstencroft, R. A., Panayi, G. S., Matthew, M., Morley, J. and Howson, W. T. (1969). *Nature* 224: 38–42.

Eden, E. and Turino, G. M. (1986). *Immunopharmacolgy* 12: 81–8.

Elias, J. A., Gustilo, K., Baeder, W. and Freundlich, B. (1987). *J. Immunol.* 138: 3812–16.

Erickson, K. L. (1986). *Int. J. Immunopharmacol.* 8: 529–43.

Ershler, W. B. (1986). *J. Natl. Cancer Inst.* 77: 837–9.

Evans, R. (1977). *Brit. J. Cancer* 35: 557–66.

Ewan, V. A., Cieplinski, W., Hancock, W. W., Goldschneider, I., Boyd, A. W. and Rickles, F. R. (1986). *J. Immunol.* 136: 2408–15.

Farram, E. and Nelson, D. S. (1980). *Cell. Immunol.* 55: 294–301.

Fóris, G., Medgyesi, G. A. and Hauck, M. (1986). *Mol. Cell. Biochem.* 69: 127–37.

Galli, S. J. (1987). *Fed. Proc.* 46: 1906–14.

Gerrard, T. L., Siegel, J. P., Dyer, D. R. and Zoon, K. C. (1987). *J. Immunol.* 138: 2535–40.

Gifford, G. E. and Lohmann-Matthes, M-L. (1987). *J. Natl. Cancer Inst.* 78: 121–4.

Grand-Perret, T., Petit, J-F. and Lemaire, G. (1986). *J. Leuk. Biol.* 40: 1–19.

Gruber, B., Poznansky, M., Boss, E., Partin, E., Gorevic, P. and Kaplan, A. P. (1986). *Arthr. Rheum.* 29: 944–55.

Haslett, C., Guthrie, L. A., Kopaniak, M. M., Johnston, R. B. Jr and Henson, P. M. (1985). *Am. J. Pathol.* 119: 101–10.

Heinen, E. and Tsunoda, R. (1987). *Immunol. Today* 8: 142–4.

Holt, P. G. (1986). *Clin. Exp. Immunol.* 63: 261–70.

Holt, P. G. and Sedgwick, J. D. (1987). *Immunol. Today* 8: 14–15.

Hopper, K. E., Wood, P. R. and Nelson, D. S. (1979). *Vox Sang.* 36: 257–74.

Hopper, K. E., Mehta, K., Subrahmanyam, D. and Nelson, D. S. (1981). *Clin. Exp. Immunol.* 45: 633–41.

Hopper, K. E., Semler, A. D., Chapman, G. V. and Davey, R. A. (1986). *Blood* 68: 167–72.

Hunninghake, G. W. (1984). *Am. Rev. Respir. Dis.* 129: 569–72.

Introna, M., Bast, R. C. Jr, Tannenbaum, C. S., Hamilton, T. A. and Adams, D. O. (1987). *J. Immunol.* 138: 3891–6.

Irimura, T., North, S. M. and Nicolson, G. L. (1987). *Eur. J. Immunol.* 17: 73–8.

Katsouyanni, K., Trichopoulos, D., Boyle, P., Xirouchaki, E, Trichopoulos, A., Lisseos, B., Vasilaros, S. and MacMahon, B. (1986). *Int. J. Cancer* 38: 815–20.

Kawai, T., Satomi, N., Sato, N., Sakurai, A., Haranaka, K., Goto, T. and Suzuki, M. (1987). *Virchows. Arch. (Cell Pathol.)* 52: 489–500.

Kettelhut, I. C., Fiers, W. and Goldberg, A. L. (1987). *Proc. Natl. Acad. Sci. USA,* 84: 4273–7.

Koff, W. C. and Dunegan, M. A. (1986). *J. Immunol.* 136: 705–9.

Le, J. and Vilček, J. (1987). *Lab. Invest.* 56: 234–48.

Lee, J., Mehta, K., Blick, M. B., Gutterman, J. U. and Lopez-Berestein, G. (1987). *Blood* 69: 1542–5.

MacKay, R. J. and Russell, S. W. (1987). *J. Leuk. Biol.* 42: 213–21.

Maier, T., Holda, J. H. and Claman, H. N. (1986). *Immunol. Today* 7: 312–15.

Malkovský, M., Doré, C., Hunt, R., Palmer, L., Chandler, P. and Medawar, P. B. (1983). *Proc. Natl. Acad. Sci. USA* 80: 6322–6.

Malone, D. G., Irani, A. M., Schwartz, L. B., Barrett, K. E. and Metcalfe, D. D. (1986). *Arthr. Rheum.* 29: 956–63.

Malone, J. D., Richards, M. and Kahn, A. J. (1986). *Proc. Natl. Acad. Sci. USA* 83: 3307–10.

Mantovani, A., Bottazzi, B., Allavena, P. and Balotta, C. (1987). In R. B. Herberman, R. H. Wiltrout and E. Gorelik (eds), *Immune Responses to Metastases,* vol. I. Boca Raton: CRC Press: 105–18.

Marks, R. M., Roche, W. R., Czerniecki, M., Penny, R. and Nelson, D. S. (1986). *Lab. Invest.* 55: 289–94.

Martinet, Y., Rom, W. N., Grotendorst, G. R., Martin, G. R. and Crystal, R. G. (1987). *N. Engl. J. Med.* 317: 202–9.

Meltzer, M. S., Gilbreath, M. J., Crawford, R. M., Schreiber, R. D. and Nacy, C. A. (1987). *Cell. Immunol.* 107: 340–7.

554   *Nelson*

Menkes, M. S., Comstock, G. W., Vuilleumier, J. P., Helsing, K. J., Rider, A. A. and Brookmeyer, R. (1986). *N. Engl. J. Med.* 315: 1250–4.

Migliori, R. J., Gruber, S. A., Sawyer, M. D., Hoffman, R., Ochoa, A., Bach, F. H. and Simmons, R. L. (1987). *Surgery* 102: 155–61.

Milas, L., Wike, J., Hunter, N., Volpe, J. and Basic, I. (1987). *Cancer Res.* 47: 1069–75.

Miossec, P., Yu, C.-L. and Ziff, M. (1984). *J. Immunol.* 133: 2007–11.

Morahan, P. S. (1980). *J. Reticuloendothelial Soc.* 27: 223–31.

Mornex, J-F., Martinet, Y., Yamauchi, K., Bitterman, P. B., Grotendorst, G. R., Chytil-Weir, A., Martin, G. R. and Crystal, R. G. (1986). *J. Clin. Invest.* 78: 61–6.

Munzarová, M. and Kovařík, J. (1987). *Lancet.* 1: 952–4.

Murphy, M., Loudon, R., Kobayashi, M. and Trinchieri, G. (1986). *J. Exp. Med.* 164: 263–79.

Nathan, C. F. (1987). *J. Clin. Invest.* 79: 319–26.

Nedwin, G. E., Svedersky, L. P., Bringman, T. S., Palladino, M. A. and Goeddel, D. V. (1985). *J. Immunol.* 135: 2492–7.

Nelson, D. S. (1987). In R. B. Herberman, R. H. Wiltrout and E. Gorelik (eds), *Immune Responses to Metastases,* vol. I. Boca Raton: CRC Press: 79–103.

Nelson, D. S. and Nelson, M. (1987). *Immunol. Cell Biol.* 65: 287–304.

Nelson, M. and Nelson, D. S. (1985). *J. Natl. Cancer Inst.* 74: 637–45.

Nelson, M., Nelson, D. S., McKenzie, I. F. C. and Blanden, R. V. (1981). *Cell. Immunol.* 60: 34–42.

Newton, R. C. (1986). *J. Leuk. Biol.* 39: 299–311.

North, R. J. (1978). *J. Immunol.* 121: 806–9.

Old, L. J. (1985). *Science* 230: 630–2.

Pancré, V., Joseph, M., Mazingue, C., Weitzerbin, J., Capron, A. and Auriault, C. (1987). *J. Immunol.* 138: 4490–5.

Perussia, B., Janckiewicz, J. and Trinchieri, G. (1982). *J. Immunol. Methods* 50: 269–76.

Perussia, B., Kobayashi, M., Ross, M. E., Anegon, I. and Trinchieri, G. (1987). *J. Immunol.* 138: 765–74.

Ralph, P. and Nakoinz, I. (1987). *Cell. Immunol.* 105: 270–9.

Remick, D. G., Kunkel, R. G., Larrick, J. W. and Kunkel, S. L. (1987). *Lab. Invest.* 56: 583–90.

Robertson, B., Gahring, L., Newton, R. and Daynes, R. (1987). *J. Invest. Dermatol.* 88: 380–7.

Roche, W. R. (1985a). *Am. J. Pathol.* 119: 57–64.

Roche, W. R. (1985b). *Int. J. Cancer* 36: 721–8.

Roche, W. R. (1986). *J. Pathol.* 148: 175–82.

Rosenberg, S. A., Lotze, M. T., Muul, L. M., Leitman, S., Chang, A. E., Ettinghausen, S. E., Matory, Y. L., Skibber, J. M., Shiloni, E., Vetto, J. T., Seipp, C. A., Simpson, C. and Reichert, C. M. (1985). *N. Engl. J. Med.* 313: 1485–92.

Rosenberg, S. A., Lotze, M. T., Muul, L. M., Chang, A. E., Avis, F. P., Leitman, S., Linehan, W. M., Robertson, C. N., Lee, R. E., Rubin, J. T., Seipp, C. A., Simpson, C. G. and White, D. E. (1987). *N. Engl. J. Med.* 316: 889–97.

Rothenburg, M. E., Owen, W. F. Jr, Silberstein, D. S., Soberman, R. J., Austen, K. F. and Stevens, R. L. (1987). *Science* 237: 645–7.

Rowley, D. (1955). *Lancet* 1: 232–4.

Sariban, E., Mitchell, T., Griffin, J. and Kufe, D. W. (1987). *J. Immunol.* 138: 1954–8.

Shalaby, M. R., Palladino, M. A. Jr, Hirabayashi, S. E., Eessalu, T. E., Lewis, G. D., Shepard, H. M. and Aggarwal, B. B. (1987). *J. Leuk. Biol.* 41: 196–204.

Silberstein, D. S., Owen, W. F., Gasson, J. C., DiPersio, J. F., Golde, D. W., Bina, J. C., Soberman, R., Austen, K. F. and David, J. R. (1986). *J. Immunol.* 137: 3290–4.

Simons, M. J. and Day, N. E. (1977). *Natl. Cancer Inst. Monograph* 47: 143–6.

Slezak, S., Symer, D. E. and Shin, H. S. (1987). *J. Exp. Med.* 166: 489–505.

Stemmermann, G. N., Heilbrun, L. K., Nomura, A., Yano, K. and Hayashi, T. (1986). *Int. J. Cancer* 38: 789–94.

Stenson, W. F. and Parker, C. W. (1980). *J. Immunol.* 125: 1–5.

Strassmann, G., Springer, T. A. and Adams, D. O. (1985). *J. Immunol.* 135: 147–51.

Tannenbaum C. S., Nurmi-McKernan, L. and Largen, M. T. (1987). *J. Leuk. Biol.* 41: 527–38.

Todd, R. F. III and Liu, D. Y. (1986). *Fed. Proc.* 45: 2829–36.

Todd, R. F. III, Bury, M. J., Alvarez, P. A., Brott, D. A. and Liu, D. Y. (1986). *Blood* 68: 1154–61.

Todd, R. F. III, Bury, M. J., Liu, D. Y. (1987). *J. Leuk. Biol.* 41: 492–9.

Vadas, M. A. (1984). *Aust. N. Z. J. Med.* 14: 71–4.

Vermeulen, M. W., David, J. R. and Remold, H. G. (1987). *J. Immunol.* 139: 7–9.

Waksman, B. H. (1979). In E. Pick, S. Cohen and J. J. Oppenheim (eds), *Biology of the Lymphokines.* New York: Academic Press: 585–616.

Walker, W. S. (1987). *Cell. Immunol.* 107: 417–32.

Warner, S. J. C., Auger, K. R. and Libby, P. (1987). *J. Exp. Med.* 165: 1316–31.

Warren, M. K. and Ralph, P. (1986). *J. Immunol.* 137: 2281–5.

Weinberg, J. B., Chapman, H. A. Jr and Hibbs, J. B. (1978). *J. Immunol.* 121: 72–80.

West, W. H., Tauer, K. W., Yannelli, J. R., Marshall, G. D., Orr, D. W., Thurman, G. B. and Oldham, R. K. (1987). *N. Engl. J. Med.* 316: 898–905.

Willett, W. C. and MacMahon, B. (1984). *New Engl. J. Med.* 310: 633–638, 697–703.

Wynder, E. L. (1975). *Cancer Res.* 35: 3388–94.

PART II NATURAL IMMUNITY IN DISEASE PROCESSES

18

Viral Infections

PAGE S. MORAHAN

DONNA M. MURASKO

Department of Microbiology and Immunology,
Medical College of Pennsylvania,
3300 Henry Avenue,
Philadelphia, PA 19129, USA

NATURAL IMMUNITY
ISBN 0 12 5145551

I. INTRODUCTION

Natural resistance to virus infections can be expressed by way of several different mechanisms. This chapter focuses on interactions between those mechanisms and on their relative roles in natural resistance. Several comprehensive reviews of individual resistance mechanisms have been written recently (Stanton and Baron, 1984; Cooper, 1984; Morahan *et al.*, 1985; Rager-Zisman and Bloom, 1985; Brinton, 1985; Faden and Ogra, 1986). The purpose of this chapter, therefore, is to summarise current concepts and point out unanswered questions.

II. EXPERIMENTAL APPROACHES USED TO DEFINE NATURAL RESISTANCE TO VIRUSES

The ability of effector cells and molecules to inhibit viruses in vivo is much more complex than cell culture or cell-free systems can reveal. The relative roles of individual immune mechanisms depend upon virus strain, genetics of the host, route of infection, kinetics of viral pathogenesis, and target tissues. For example, infection by the intraperitoneal or intranasal route determines whether polyomavirus becomes latent in the kidneys or lungs; the outcome involves an as yet undefined balance between tissue tropism and host immune responses in vivo (Dubensky and Villarreal, 1984).

Delineation of the interaction of antiviral resistance mechanisms in vivo (Table 18.1) has been aided by correlative kinetic studies performed simultaneously for virus (infective virions, nucleic acid or antigens) and different effector functions in various organs during viral infection. Investigation with genetically engineered virus mutants has also proved to be a useful tool (Sharpe and Fields, 1985; Oldstone *et al.*, 1985, LaMonica *et al.*, 1986; Naeve *et al.*, 1984; Offit *et al.*, 1986). This approach has established that the reovirus S1 gene determines selective viral binding and entry into neurones or ependymal cells, the M2 gene determines virus susceptibility to proteolytic enzymes and thus infectibility by the intestinal route, and the L2 gene determines the degree

Abbreviations

Mononuclear phagocyte (MP), natural killer (NK) cell, natural cytotoxic (NC) cell, interferon (IFN), antibody-dependent cell-mediated cytotoxicity (ADCC), herpes simplex virus (HSV), vesicular stomatitis virus (VSV), encephalomyocarditis virus (EMC), cytomegalovirus (CMV), mouse hepatitis virus (MHV), lymphocytic choriomeningitis virus (LCM), human immunodeficiency disease virus (HIV).

Table 18.1: Experimental approaches used in vivo to define natural resistance to virus infections

Kinetic correlation of effector mechanisms with viral pathogenesis
Exploitation of genetic differences in the host that provide selective defects in effector mechanisms
Exploitation of genetic differences in the virus
Exogenous depletion of selected effector mechanisms
Augmentation of selected effector mechanisms by transfer of effector cells or molecules

of viral shedding and transmissibility between litter-mates (Keroack and Fields, 1986). Thus, certain viral genes that are important at particular stages in pathogenesis have been identified; the precise interaction of these gene products with natural resistance effector mechanisms can now be established.

Selective genetic deficiencies have proved invaluable in delineating acquired resistance mechanisms important in viral infections. A recent study in congenitally athymic mice established that host defence against murine rotavirus required neither functional T lymphocytes nor specific antiviral antibody, implicating natural resistance as the predominant protective entity (Eiden *et al.*, 1986). Unfortunately, there are few known experimental or clinical syndromes with significant genetic deficiencies in *natural* resistance mechanisms. This may reflect the early phylogenetic development of natural resistance mechanisms. Some genetic deficiencies in natural immunity are associated with decreased resistance to certain micro-organisms, but there has not been extensive investigation of resistance to virus infections (Vogel *et al.*, 1980; Morahan *et al.*, 1982; Soldateschi *et al.*, 1985; Springer and Anderson, 1986; Katz *et al.*, 1984).

Selective depletion has also been useful, though no method is completely selective. Treatment with anti-asialo-GM1 antibody, for example, affects certain activated mononuclear phagocytes (MP) in addition to natural killer (NK) cells (Wiltrout *et al.*, 1985). Of the methods used to remove MPs (Morahan *et al.*, 1985, 1986; McGeorge and Morahan, 1978; Claassen *et al.*, 1986), only treatment with silica has been extensively explored in viral infections and it causes complicating inflammatory influxes of monocytes and granulocytes after the initial depletion of macrophages. Additional investigation in vivo is needed with more selective cytotoxic agents or monoclonal antibodies that are cytotoxic for either NK or MP populations or important soluble mediators such as interferons (IFN).

The limitation of the genetic deficiency or depletion approaches is that the antiviral action defined for the separated mechanism may not reflect the mechanisms combined naturally in the host. The relative roles of the individual natural resistance mechanisms vary during different phases of pathogenesis, depending upon the organ in which virus is replicating, and the kinetics by which local and systemic resistance mechanisms are activated and regulated. Thus, multi-faceted experimental approaches are obligatory, including detailed analysis of the separate components, as well as investigation of the interrelationships among them during the course of viral infections. Ultimately, natural resistance mechanisms will be defined by comprehensive descriptive cellular immunological studies that are extended to investigation of molecular mechanisms. Our understanding of the precise molecular mechanisms of natural resistance components remains rudimentary. In vitro studies are just now beginning to probe the mechanisms of antiviral action of NK cells, MPs, and IFNs at the level of host gene expression (Krug *et al.*, 1985; Staehell *et al.*, 1986; Brinton, 1985).

III. ROLE OF COMPONENTS OF NATURAL IMMUNITY TO VIRUS INFECTIONS

A. Initial Barriers

The first requirement for successful viral infection is attachment to cells permissive for viral replication, or cells that can transmit the virus to permissive cells in target organs. The virus-related factors involved in the attachment to cells in vivo are being defined at the molecular level (La Monica *et al.*, 1986; Love *et al.*, 1985); investigation is now needed to define the effects of selectively altering the initial host-related barriers. The importance of virus–host interaction is demonstrated by the myxovirus system, in which entry of virus into cells and its subsequent pathogenesis is determined by both a virus-related factor, sensitivity of the virus glycoprotein to a host proteolytic enzyme, and host factors, in the form of availability of the enzyme (Scheid and Choppin, 1984). Changes in host defences alone, however, can also alter pathogenesis; herpes simplex virus (HSV) infections are more severe on abnormal skin, such as found in patients with eczema, abrasions and burns (Kohl, 1985).

Other physiological mechanisms that provide resistance include such factors as: acidity in the stomach that destroys most viruses, increased temperature of the lower respiratory tract that inhibits replication of rhinoviruses, mucociliary flow that expels aerosolised viruses, and virus inhibitory factors bathing the cells lining the respiratory tract. The degree of protection provided by the initial anatomical and physiological barriers, and their relative importance in conjunction with other natural resistance mechanisms, remains to be elucidated.

B. Mononuclear Phagocytes

The importance of mononuclear phagocytes (MPs) in many, but not all (Lehmann-Grube *et al.*, 1987), viral infections has been accepted since the 1960s (see reviews by Morahan, 1984, Morahan *et al.*, 1985). Like most immunological components, MPs may play both beneficial and deleterious roles in viral infections, and are closely interregulated with other natural and acquired immune responses.

The interaction of viruses and MPs may be designated as either *intrinsic* — i.e. MPs are permissive or nonpermissive for virus replication — or *extrinsic* — i.e. MPs inhibit virus replication in other permissive cells. Both MP interactions may be modified by virus-specific antibody or T cells. Antibodies may modify intrinsic MP resistance by increasing virus uptake, and depressing or enhancing virus replication in MPs (Boere *et al.*, 1985; Knudsen *et al.*, 1987a; Gollins and Porterfield, 1985; Cardosa *et al.*, 1986). The outcome appears to be a balance between antibody-enhanced Fc-mediated phagocytic uptake of virus and viral neutralisation, and involves a complex interaction between MP type, antibody class, and complement (Porterfield, 1985; Hotta *et al.*, 1983; Inada *et al.*, 1985).

There has been considerable investigation of extrinsic antiviral action of MPs (reviewed by Morahan *et al.*, 1985). It is clear that early during viral infections MPs are activated and can exert potent antiviral activity; in vitro studies have suggested that IFN may be involved in this macrophage activation (Mak and Ada, 1984; Bielefelt Ohmann *et al.*, 1984). A variety of macrophage-mediated antiviral mechanisms have been demonstrated. IFN appears to play a role in some (Proietti *et al.*, 1986), but not all MP antiviral actions (Morse and Morahan, 1981; Soldateschi *et al.*, 1985; Amber and Hibbs, 1986). Extrinsic antiviral activity has also been correlated with cytotoxicity or cytostasis of tumour- or virus-infected target cells (Morahan *et al.*, 1985; Morse and Morahan, 1981; Mak and Ada, 1984; Amber and Hibbs, 1986; Natuk *et al.*, 1986), and macrophage production of arginase or tumour necrosis factor (TNF) (Bonina *et al.*, 1984; Koff and Fann, 1986). MPs can also exert potent cytolytic activities in conjunction with antibody in the antibody-dependent cell-mediated cytotoxicity reaction (ADCC) (Bielefelt Ohmann *et al.*, 1984; Ihara *et al.*, 1986). Clearly, the predominant antiviral mechanisms vary depending upon three interacting elements: virus replication strategy, host cell type, and macrophage cell type.

Abortive or semi-permissive infection is the general outcome of the intrinsic interaction of MPs and viruses. The degree of non-permissiveness, however, varies with different MP populations and with the particular virus (Morahan *et al.*, 1985; Domurat *et al.*, 1985; Roberts and Horan, 1985; Liprandi *et al.*, 1986; Rossiter and Wardley, 1985; Rice *et al.*, 1984; Keller *et al.*, 1985; Cardosa *et al.*, 1986; Kowalchyk and Plagemann, 1985; Inada and Mims, 1985; Howie *et al.*, 1986; Torpey *et al.*, 1988; Cottman *et al.*, 1987). For example, bone-marrow-derived macrophages and thioglycollate-elicited peritoneal macrophages are more susceptible to HSV than resident peritoneal macrophages (Leary *et al.*, 1985; unpublished data). Similarly, increased susceptibility is observed when the human macrophage-like U937 cell line or monocytes are differentiated to macrophages in vitro (Tenney *et al.*, 1986). Whether there is a consistent increase in sensitivity to HSV with MP differentiation remains to be established.

The mechanisms for the varying resistance to viral infection expressed by different MPs have not been elucidated at the molecular level. Unique interactions with IFN may be involved in some systems (Linnavuori and Hovi, 1983; Narayan *et al.*, 1985; Straub *et al.*, 1986; Vogel *et al.*, 1986b; Rose *et al.*, 1986; Domke *et al.*, 1985). The non-permissiveness of freshly harvested peritoneal macrophages for vesicular stomatitis (VSV) and encephalomyocarditis (EMC) viruses has been reported to be due to their extreme sensitivity to the action of endogenous IFN-α/β, because treatment of mice with anti-IFN-α/β antibody abolished the MP resistance (Gresser *et al.*, 1985; Proietti *et al.*, 1986). Similar treatment, however, did not alter intrinsic resistance of resident macrophages for HSV (unpublished results). It will be useful to explore at the molecular level the relationship between virus-permissiveness and the effect of IFN on cellular differentiation (Grossberg and Taylor, 1986; Hovi *et al.*, 1985; Moore *et al.*, 1985). It is intriguing to note that cellular differentiation appears to convey increased permissiveness to a variety of viruses (Levine, 1982); what role this may play in normal immunoregulation of natural resistance mechanisms remains to be defined.

Interest in the role of MPs in viral infections has been increased by reports that several clinically important viruses can persist and/or replicate in MPs in vitro. Replicating intermediates of hepatitis B virus have been found in monocytes (Yoffe *et al.*, 1986). Human immuno-deficiency disease virus (HIV) has recently been reported to infect human monocytes and MP cell lines, and was detected in or recovered from various MPs of patients with AIDS (Ho *et al.*, 1986; Nicholson *et al.*, 1986; Smith *et al.*, 1986a; Salahuddin *et al.*, 1986; Hammer *et al.*, 1986; Koenig *et al.*, 1986). The relationship of HIV and MPs may be similar to that exhibited by lentiviruses (Narayan and Cork; 1985). For example, visna virus persists in sheep in MPs by mechanisms including restriction by a unique IFN, altered response to neutralising antibody, and replication dependence upon MP differentiation (Gendelman *et al.*, 1986; Narayan *et al.*, 1985; Kennedy-Stoskopf and Narayan, 1986). Viral persistence or replication in MPs is also clearly involved in several other viruses causing diseases of animals — equine infectious anaemia retrovirus (Cheevers and McGuire, 1985), African swine fever virus (Casal *et al.*, 1984; Knudsen *et al.*, 1987b) and haemorrhagic fever virus with renal syndrome (Nagai *et al.*, 1985). Canine distemper virus appears to persist and be infectious for MPs when virus–antibody complexes enter macrophages other than by Fc receptors (Appel *et al.*, 1984). Viral antigen sequestration by macrophages is an immunopathological feature of Aleutian disease of mink, although the virus probably does not replicate in MPs (Race *et al.*, 1986; Porter, 1986). MPs may be a site for latent cytomegalovirus (CMV) infection, although the cellular site has not been clearly established (Hayashi *et al.*, 1985; Jordan, 1983; Osorio *et al.*, 1985).

It is now clear that although MPs can restrict virus infection within themselves or other cells and thus prevent overwhelming infection, MPs also can provide a reservoir for viral persistence and a mechanism for viral immunopathological effects. The use of macrophage-like cell lines may be a useful experimental approach to define mechanisms of viral persistence. Understanding the antiviral mechanisms and complex interplay of MPs with other elements of natural and acquired immune processes is complicated by the noted heterogeneity that exists within this cell system (Morahan *et al.*, 1986, 1985). A major current challenge is to establish the origin of MP heterogeneity, in order to be able to manipulate selectively the protective aspects of MPs for viral immunotherapy.

C. Granulocytes

The role of granulocytes in resistance to virus infections remains ambiguous. Most data link granulocytic inflammatory processes with pyogenic bacterial infections and MPs with viral and intracellular bacterial infections. This concept is being questioned, with evidence accumulating that granulocytes may be important in initial natural resistance to intracellular bacteria and tumours (Campbell, 1986; Lichtenstein, 1986), as well as viruses (Faden and Ogra, 1986). More use of granulocyte-deficient models is needed to establish the role granulocytes play in either resistance or immunopathological effects in viral

infections. We have found that severe depletion of circulating granulocytes, monocytes and NK cells had no marked effect on natural resistance
of CD-1 mice to HSV-2 or to EMC viruses (Morahan *et al.*, 1986).

The in vitro work that has been reported has focused on neutrophilic
granulocytes, with basophils, mast cells and eosinophils remaining
virtually unexplored. Rabbit neutrophils have been reported to contain
at least two small cationic polypeptides that inactivate several enveloped
viruses, indicating that intracellular molecules might mediate direct
inactivation of viruses (Lehrer *et al.*, 1985). Although viruses do not
appear to replicate in neutrophils, interaction with infectious murine
CMV decreases several granulocyte functions (Bale *et al.*, 1985). Whether
any granulocyte precursors are permissive for virus infection remains to
be established; CMV DNA has been detected in bone-marrow progenitor
cells (Bale *et al.*, 1987). The use of undifferentiated human HL-60 cells
and ones that have been differentiated to granulocytes (Harris and
Ralph, 1985) would be a useful experimental approach to probe this
point. A similar approach has indicated that CMV and HSV can
productively infect human megakaryocyte lines (Morgan *et al.*, 1985).

Granulocyte-mediated extrinsic antiviral activity has been described,
either mediated alone, or with antibody in the ADCC reaction (Ihara
et al., 1986), or with complement (Faden and Ogra, 1986). The mechanisms are not elucidated, but may involve factors similar to the rabbit
neutrophil cationic peptides (Lehrer *et al.*, 1985). More investigation is
warranted concerning the antiviral activity of inflammatory granulocytes
early in viral infections, as well as comparative investigation of the
differences in antiviral activities of granulocytes and MPs.

D. NK and Other Natural Cytotoxic Cells, Other than MPs

Most of the early data supporting the hypothesis that NK cells are
important in host defence were based on increases in NK cell mediated
cytotoxicity seen early during viral infections, and genetic data demonstrating an association between resistance to particular viruses and high
constitutive levels of NK cell cytotoxicity (reviews in Welsh, 1986,
Trinchieri and Perussia, 1984; see also Chapters 11 and 3). Not only did
these studies rely on associative data, but, in addition, assessments of NK
cell cytotoxicity were performed using spleen cells rather than cells from
the major site of viral infection. Recent data have addressed these
problems. Localisation of host resistance factors at the site of virus
replication is a critical aspect that is being increasingly recognised, and
NK cell activity has been found within the gut intraepithelial lining,
cerebrospinal fluid and lung in association with virus infections (Stein-

Streilein *et al.*, 1983; Carmen *et al.*, 1986; Griffin and Hess, 1986; Mann *et al.*, 1985). Also, NK cell mediated resistance has been studied in systems in which NK cell cytotoxicity is selectively depleted either genetically (i.e. beige mice) or exogenously by treatment with anti-asialo-GM1 or ^{89}Sr; these methods, however, still have some inherent problems (Morahan *et al.*, 1982; Wiltrout *et al.*, 1985).

Regardless of the shortcomings of these experimental systems, the recent data clearly demonstrate that NK cells are important in certain, but not all, virus systems. Depletion of mice with anti-asialo-GM1 prior to virus infection resulted in increased virus titres of MHV, murine CMV, influenza and vaccinia viruses, but had no effect on titres of LCM (Stein-Streilein and Guffee, 1986; Bukowski *et al.*, 1983 a, b; 1985). Subsequent studies confirmed that anti-asialo-GM1 not only decreased resistance to CMV in acute infection, but also increased the amount of persistent CMV (Bukowski *et al.*, 1984). When adult leukocytes were adoptively transferred to suckling mice, protection against CMV was also shown to be mediated by NK cells because depletion of the leukocytes with anti-asialo-GM1 abrogated the protection, and because cloned NK cells, but not cloned T cells, gave protection (Bukowski *et al.*, 1985). NK cell cytotoxicity may not be sufficient, however; removal of NK cells with ^{89}Sr decreased resistance, as expected, but both normal and ^{89}Sr-treated mice had comparable levels of NK cell cytotoxicity by day 3 after infection (Masuda and Bennett, 1981). Possibly, NK cell activity may be most important very early after infection.

The story is not as straightforward for HSV-1. While transfer of adult leukocytes increased resistance of suckling mice, protection was mediated by cloned T cells and cells depleted of NK cells by anti-asialo-GM1. Other experiments using anti-IFN serum suggested that IFN production by the adoptively transferred cells, and not the cells themselves, was the major mediator of protection (Bukowski and Welsh, 1986). These observations support earlier results that T cells, and not NK cells, were important, but differ in that the earlier studies found no role for IFN (Chmielarczyk *et al.*, 1985a, b). Both reports differ from that of Habu *et al.* (1984), who suggested that NK cells, not IFN, were the major mediators of resistance, since high doses of anti-asialo-GM1 decreased resistance. The reasons for the different results are not completely clear. All three studies used the same strain of mouse, but the ages of the mice, virus strains, and amounts of anti-asialo-GM1 differed.

The importance of virus and host genetic background in NK cell cytotoxicity has been demonstrated in the MHV system (Bukowski *et al.*, 1983a, b; Pereira *et al.*, 1984). Resistance to one strain of MHV was associated with induction of NK cell cytotoxicity and IFN in the susceptible, but not the resistant, mouse strain. These data are consistent with the possibilities either that NK cells could enhance MHV replication in MPs (one of its targets), or that NK cells could be the site of MHV infection themselves. NK cells have recently been reported to support VSV and Pichinde virus replication (Rosenthal and Prevec, 1986; Gee *et al.*, 1981). The intrinsic interaction of NK cells with viruses has been relatively little explored because of difficulty in isolating a sufficient number of pure cells.

The depletion studies assume — wrongly — that 'natural killer' cells are a homogeneous population, equally depleted by anti-asialo-GM1 and monitored by cytotoxicity against YAC-1 cells. The question of the role of natural cytotoxic (NC) cells, which have a unique target specificity and are not enhanced by IFN, is not generally addressed. The heterogeneity, however, of non-MHC-restricted cell-mediated cytotoxicity, particularly against virus-infected cells, is becoming more apparent. The effector cell responsible for lysis of HSV-1-infected mouse cells is determined not by the virus, but rather by the host cell (e.g. YAC-1 cells infected with HSV are lysed by NK cells, while WEHI-164 cells infected are lysed by NC cells) (Colmenares and Lopez, 1986). Moreover, certain host cells that are resistant to lysis prior to viral infection become sensitive after infection. Importantly, an individual can have NK cytotoxicity against virus-infected cells and not against 'standard' NK cell targets (Fitzgerald *et al.*, 1983, 1985). Other studies have suggested that lysis of virus-infected targets is performed by a subset of NK/NC cells (Borysiewicz *et al.*, 1985, 1986; Bishop *et al.*, 1986). Using the morphology of large granular lymphocytes as a marker of NK cells is also not a sufficient criterion; cytotoxic T lymphocytes can look similar during the course of a viral infection (Biron *et al.*, 1986). A new natural cytotoxic cell, with the phenotype of a B cell, has been described in the spleens of normal mice, that can lyse MHV-infected target cells (Holmes *et al.*, 1986; Welsh *et al.*, 1986). These cells are not present in mice that are genetically resistant to MHV; it has been proposed that lysis of virus-infected cells by these novel cells might actually facilitate spread of the virus in the host. Finally, the Langerhans cell has recently been proposed to be involved in resistance to intradermal HSV infection in the footpad of mice (Sprecher and Becker, 1986).

The heterogeneity of the natural cytotoxic cells is further emphasised by the postulated targets on the virus-infected cells that these cytotoxic cells recognise[1]. The target structure on HSV-1 infected cells has been

---

[1]See also Chapters 3, 4 and 5.

putatively identified as virus-coded glycoproteins (Bishop *et al.*, 1984; Tilden *et al.*, 1986). Limiting dilution analysis suggests that HSV-1 NK cells are clonally derived in their specificity, because some of the clones recognised only glycoprotein gB while others recognised only glyco-protein gC (Bishop *et al.*, 1986). Other studies supporting this concept are that NK cells may recognise a shared epitope on the neuraminidase of influenza virus (Houde and Arora, 1986) and early host antigens induced by CMV (Borysiewicz *et al.*, 1985).

E. Interferon and Other Soluble Mediators

IFN, a potent inducer of NK cell activity and MP activation, may be of major importance during viral infections. A formidable problem, how-ever, in delineating the role of IFN in modifying natural host defences is the inherent ability of IFN to inhibit viral replication. Studies using anti-IFN serum have clearly shown that the severity of a number of viral infections is increased when endogenous production of IFN is prevented (Gresser *et al.*, 1976; Blank and Murasko, 1981). Whether the effects are related to loss of direct antiviral IFN activity or to loss of IFN to activate natural effector cells remains to be resolved. Also, depletion of cell populations does not guarantee that IFN production will remain intact, since NK cells and MPs are responsible for some IFN production during viral infection (Bukowski *et al.*, 1985). Moreover, NK cells may require the presence of DR$^+$ accessory cells that produce IFN for maximum lytic activity (Bandyopadhyay *et al.*, 1986).

Investigators have turned to in vitro systems to resolve better the interaction of IFN with effector cells. The general conclusions are that IFN both up- and down-regulates NK cell mediated lysis. IFN can augment the lytic ability of NK cells, but, depending upon the virus, can also decrease the sensitivity of target cells to the action of NK cells (Munoz *et al.*, 1983). This differential effect of IFN on target suscep-tibility may actually be one of the factors that determines the role of NK cells in resistance to a particular virus in vivo. For example, CMV-infected cells are actually less susceptible than LCM-infected cells to NK cell lysis, but the CMV-infected cells remain at the low, but susceptible level of sensitivity after exposure to IFN, while LCM-infected cells become almost totally resistant to NK cell lysis (Bukowski and Welsh, 1985). This association of in vitro findings with the in vivo role of NK cells needs to be explored for other viruses.

In addition to IFN, virus infections produce other factors that can alter NK cell cytotoxicity, either increasing it as in HSV infection (Bishop *et al.*, 1983) or decreasing it as in CMV infection (Schrier *et al.*, 1986).

The use of anti-IFN serum showed that IFN was not responsible for these changes. In another HSV system, supernatants of peripheral blood leukocytes from patients with recurrent HSV lesions inhibited NK cell cytotoxicity; the suppression appeared to involve prostaglandins as a necessary but not sufficient factor (Sheridan *et al.*, 1985).

Other factors modifying non-specific viral immunity include components of the complement system, which clearly play both beneficial and immunopathological roles in virus infections (reviewed by Hirsch, 1982 and Cooper, 1984). Virus–antibody complexes, virus-infected cells coated with antibody, and certain viruses themselves can activate complement. Complement activation results in enhanced virus neutralisation, lysis of enveloped viruses (at high complement concentrations), facilitation of interaction of natural resistance effector cells, and inflammation. There has been limited investigation in mice genetically deficient in complement components, or exogenously treated with substances to deplete complement components, but these studies indicate that complement can play a dual role. Depleting complement increased susceptibility to influenza, Sindbis, rabies, fowlpox and feline leukaemia viruses, but increased resistance to LCM virus (Hirsch, 1982; Ohta *et al.*, 1986; Kraut *et al.*, 1985). The study with fowlpox virus demonstrated that complement helps protect the chicken embryo, and thus is a component of natural antiviral resistance in the absence of acquired immunity (Ohta *et al.*, 1986). Complement may also play a role in maintenance of the viral latent state, at least for feline leukaemia virus (Kraut *et al.*, 1985).

The antiviral activity of most cytokines other than IFN has not been explored. Tumour necrosis factor (TNF) is induced by MPs or MP cell lines infected with influenza or Sendai viruses (Aderka *et al.*, 1986; Beutler *et al.*, 1986), suggesting that TNF, like IFN, may be a natural product of virus infection. A recent report indicates that TNF pretreatment of cells in vitro protected them against infection with HSV, VSV and EMC viruses (Mestian *et al.*, 1986). In some instances, however, the antiviral activity of TNF appears to be due to induction of IFN in the target cells (Kohase *et al.*, 1986). The role of TNF, interleukin 1, macrophage and granulocyte colony-stimulating factors, and non-IFN-γ macrophage activating factors in the course of virus infections needs to be further explored.

IV. MODULATION OF NATURAL IMMUNE RESPONSES

Most factors known to effect natural resistance to virus infections (Table 18.2) have not been explored in depth. They undoubtedly play a role, but are technically difficult to isolate and identify.

Table 18.2: Modifiers of natural immune responses

Genetics
Stress
Pregnancy
Age
Sex
Intercurrent inapparent infections
Nutrition
Temperature
Immunomodulators

A. Genetic Factors

There are several examples of marked changes in resistance associated with a single or a few host genes (reviewed by Brinton, 1985; see also Chapter 11). Usually the genes are not associated with the major histocompatibility complex, appear to be independent of acquired and natural resistance mechanisms, and influence resistance to one or a single group of viruses by modifying virus-specific steps in intracellular virus replication. A few of the genes, however, appear to involve natural resistance. These include resistance to HSV, CMV, ectromelia, MHV 3, some of the RNA leukaemia viruses, and influenza (reviewed by Brinton *et al.*, 1984 and Mogensen, 1985; Dupuy *et al.*, 1984; O'Neill and Blanden, 1983; Smith *et al.*, 1984; Mercer and Spector, 1986).

The elegant work with the *Mx* gene in resistance to influenza virus, discovered by Lindenmann and colleagues in 1964, provides an example of the usefulness of combined approaches in delineating mechanisms involved in natural resistance. Today it is agreed that the *Mx* gene is located on mouse chromosome 16, that it codes for a unique protein (Mx protein) which is induced in Mx^+ cells upon exposure to IFN-α/β (but not IFN-γ), and that this protein confers selective resistance to influenza virus (Staehell *et al.*, 1986). The establishment of the role of the *Mx* gene was facilitated by its lack of expression in all cells except IFN-treated Mx^+ cells; the role of the *Mx* gene in the normal economy of cells is still not clear. The Mx protein apparently inhibits influenza virus replication at an early step, presumably by affecting primary transcription or translation of influenza-virus-specific mRNAs.

B. Environmental and Physiological Factors

The effect produced on natural resistance to viruses by changes in housing and handling, stress, pregnancy, body temperature, toxic chemicals and nutritional status has been addressed occasionally over the last two decades (reviewed by Dempsey and Morahan, 1985 and Rodbard, 1981; Riley, 1981; Cabral *et al.*, 1986; Krzystyniak *et al.*, 1985; see also Chapters 10, 13 and 14). However, few investigations have correlated the effect of the changes on resistance parameters and viral pathogenesis. Moreover, many of the interventions that have been used cause widespread physiological changes; these complications limit interpretation of the results. Investigators need to readdress the role of environmental and physiological factors with the better quality of inbred mice, controlled housing conditions, and specific mediating molecules now available. There are a few such promising approaches. Hypothermia produced with the neuropeptide neurotensin increased susceptibility of mice to VSV (Doll and Johnson, 1985). In vitro treatment of macrophages with certain stress-related neuroendocrine hormones blocked activation of extrinsic antiviral activity by IFN-γ (Koff and Dunegan, 1986).

C. Microbial Flora and Inapparent Viral Infections

Microbial flora and inapparent viral infections are increasingly recognised as important modifiers of natural resistance (Gut *et al.*, 1984). Inapparent infection of mice with MHV causes a transient increase in resistance to subsequent infection with EMC virus (Dempsey *et al.*, 1986) or viral respiratory infections (Carrano *et al.*, 1984). The mechanism may involve IFN induction by MHV. The endogenous presence in mice of low levels of IFN, present perhaps because of normal flora or chronic inapparent viral infections, has been reported to be involved in the resistance of freshly harvested macrophages to VSV and EMC viruses (Vogel *et al.*, 1986a and b; Proietti *et al.*, 1986).

D. Age[2] and Sex as Modifying Factors

The effects of age and sex have not been explored much in the last five years, and need to be readdressed with our current understanding of natural resistance against virus infections. Recent studies show that the IFN response of macrophages to HSV may be both genetically determined and sex-linked (Ellermann-Eriksen, 1986), and that natural resistance to CMV may be both genetically determined and age-related (Shellam and Flexman, 1986). Numerous investigations have documented the increase in resistance observed between birth and young

[2]See also Chapters 12 and 13.

adult life in mice (Morahan, 1984), but the mechanisms involved have not been completely elucidated. In most cases, it is not clear whether the predominant mechanism of age-related increased antiviral resistance involves changes in permissiveness of target cells for virus growth, maturation of natural resistance mechanisms, or maturation of acquired immune mechanisms.

The mechanism of increasing resistance with maturation is an important issue for continued exploration, because of the obvious implications for clinical medicine. While it is well documented that neonates and infants generally are more susceptible to virus infections, such as congenital herpesvirus and HIV infections, the mechanisms involved are not completely defined (Wilson, 1986). Kohl *et al.* (1984) reported defects in cord blood mononuclear cells for both NK cell cytotoxicity and ADCC against HSV-infected target cells, proposing a multistep defect in binding to and lysis of target cells. There have been several recent reports of selective deficiency in the ability of neonatal cells to produce or respond to IFN-γ, IL-1 and IL-2 (Wilson *et al.*, 1986; Leibson *et al.*, 1986; Oh *et al.*, 1986; Lewis *et al.*, 1986; Taylor and Bryson, 1985). One implication is that there is less IFN-γ in neonates for activation of NK cells and macrophages for antiviral activity.

Changes in virus resistance in the elderly have not been as extensively investigated. Clinically, there is increased susceptibility to a certain spectrum of virus infections, such as orthomyxovirus infection and herpes zoster. There have been very few systematic studies in aged animal models; both increased and decreased resistance have been observed, and the mechanisms underlying these changes are not well defined (Kay *et al.*, 1979).

E. Immunomodulators

It has long been known that treatment of mice with certain agents increases resistance to viruses; since many of these agents induce IFN, it was presumed that they increased antiviral resistance through IFN. In the past decade, it has become clear that immunomodulators may increase antiviral resistance by a variety of mechanisms other than, or in addition to, the direct antiviral action of IFN (reviewed by Breinig and Morahan, 1980; Gangemi *et al.*, 1983). For example, *Propionobacterium acnes* (formerly *Corynebacterium parvum*) enhances not only macrophage activity but also NK cell cytotoxicity, particularly in the lung (Wiltrout *et al.*, 1984). There has been a recent resurgence in interest in immunotherapeutic approaches to prophylactic or early therapeutic treatment for viral infections. These treatments involve single or combination treatment with immunomodulators that act through different mechanisms, or immunomodulators in combination with direct antiviral chemotherapeutic drugs (Morahan *et al.*, 1987).

Investigation of the mode of action of immunomodulators provides another experimental avenue to delineate the interacting roles of the various natural resistance factors in given viral infections. We have recently demonstrated, for example, that circulating monocytes, granulocytes and splenic NK cells are not required for the increased resistance to HSV-2 and EMC viruses that is induced by treatment of mice with various immunomodulators. This indicates that tissue macrophages, or other local natural cytotoxic cells or factors, may be pivotal in immunomodulator-enhanced resistance (Morahan *et al.*, 1986). An interesting report by Mastroeni *et al.* (1985) indicates that *C. granulosum* can restore macrophage extrinsic antiviral functions that are impaired in tumour-bearing rats. These results indicate it may be possible to have successful antiviral immunotherapy in immunocompromised individuals.

V. VIRAL EFFECTS ON NATURAL IMMUNE RESPONSES AND THE NEUROENDOCRINE SYSTEM

Certain virus infections can transiently but significantly decrease host resistance to subsequent microbial infection in humans and animal models, especially to secondary bacterial respiratory infections (reviewed by Mogensen, 1981; Morahan *et al.*, 1985; Gilmore and Wainberg, 1985). The decreased resistance has been correlated with a variety of changes in functions of granulocytes and MPs (Miller *et al.*, 1985; Bielefelt Ohman and Babiuk, 1986; Nickerson and Jakab, 1986). However, which (if any) of the changes observed in vitro (e.g. reduced chemotaxis, phagocytosis, oxidative metabolism) is responsible for decreased resistance in the lung in vivo remains unclear. Other physiological and anatomical changes undoubtedly play a role. It is also not yet clear whether alterations in phagocytic cell functions are due to direct viral effects on phagocytic cells, or infection-induced alterations in immunoregulatory mechanisms (Jakab, 1982; Bielefelt Ohman and Babiuk, 1986). For example, IFN-α/β can decrease the ability of antigen-pulsed MPs to induce T cell proliferation (Blank *et al.*, 1985).

The effects of CMV infection in vitro on leukocyte functions have been extensively studied because of the clinical immunosuppression that is observed. Generally, murine CMV infection of phagocytes causes dysfunction (Pesanti and Shanley, 1984; Bale *et al.*, 1985). Variable effects, however, have been observed with human CMV, perhaps related to CMV strains; infection of leukocytes in vitro with clinical isolates produces more defects than the laboratory strain (Schreir *et al.*, 1986; Einhorn and Ost, 1984; Smith *et al.*, 1986b). CMV infection of monocytes appears to produce imbalances in IL-1 and IL-1 inhibitor production, which have been postulated to be one mechanism for CMV-induced immunosuppression (Smith *et al.*, 1986b). Similar imbalances have been found with influenza and hepatitis B virus infection of leukocytes (Roberts *et al.*, 1986; Knudsen *et al.*, 1986). In contrast, the non-specific immunosuppression induced by dengue virus infection was reported to involve a cytotoxic factor produced by macrophages (Gulati *et al.*, 1986).

Other effects of virus infection have been observed that exemplify the complex interactions that exist between viruses and natural and acquired immune effector systems. Cell proliferation was suppressed by infection of human bone-marrow cells with hepatitis B virus, or mouse peritoneal cells by Pichinde virus (Zeldis *et al.*, 1986; Freidlander *et al.*, 1984), while infection of MPs with influenza virus induced fibroblast-stimulating factors, which could be involved in development of end-stage fibrotic lung disease (Jennings *et al.*, 1984). Moreover, infection of unstimulated lymphocytes with influenza virus required monocytes (Mock *et al.*, 1987). It is obvious that viruses may have multiple direct and indirect effects on various immune cell populations that can lead to imbalances in immunoregulatory circuits. Effects may occur without overt cytocidal effects, but perturb 'differentiation' or 'luxury' functions (Oldstone *et al.*, 1982) of immune cell populations; thus, virus infections may produce more subtle effects on host resistance than previously recognised.

Virus infections can also alter the neuroendocrine system. The recent report that infection of mouse splenic lymphocytes with Newcastle disease virus caused induction of mRNA for the precursor protein for β-endorphin and adrenocorticotropin is an elegant demonstration of the interaction of virus infections with the immune and neuroendocrine systems (Westly *et al.*, 1986). Other examples include the finding that neuropeptides can modulate macrophage extrinsic antiviral activity for HSV, and that ACTH can suppress IFN-γ production by lymphocytes (Johnson *et al.*, 1984; Koff and Dunegan, 1986). The interaction of natural immune mechanisms with the neuroendocrine system during viral infections in vivo needs to be established.

In regard to the immunopathological role of natural immunity, inflammatory processes in response to viral infections in certain target organs, such as the central nervous system and the eye, can be deleterious. Although evolution has protected these areas from acquired immune damage by limiting the expression of major histocompatibility antigens on cells of these organs, virus infections (through IFN or independently) may increase these antigens (Suzamura *et al.*, 1986). A major challenge in viral immunotherapy is to devise procedures that selectively damp the deleterious inflammatory processes without affecting the protective natural and acquired immune processes.

VI. ROLE OF NATURAL IMMUNITY IN VIRAL INFECTIONS IN HUMANS

The preceding sections have established that natural immune mechanisms can play both beneficial and immunopathological roles in viral infections. The data on MPs, NK cells and IFN for animals may not be conclusive, but they are far superior to any information we have regarding humans, where most data are merely associative. For example, in renal transplant patients there appears to be an association between NK cell activity and recovery from CMV infection (Starr *et al.*, 1984), but the association is not consistent (Quinnan and Rook, 1984).

One reason that the clinical relevance of natural immunity is lagging behind that established for animal systems is that there are few individuals with selective deficiency in one or more of the components of natural immunity, without deficiencies in acquired immune processes. Thus, dissecting out the contribution of natural as opposed to acquired immunity is difficult. Patients with deficiencies in T cell immunity, such as renal transplant patients, are clearly more susceptible to viral infections. It has not been definitively established, however, whether this susceptibility stems primarily from lack of acquired T cell responses, T cell amplification of natural immune responses, or other problems in natural immune processes. Another reason for our limited information is that most patients with congenital deficiencies in acquired immunity present with recurrent bacterial infections, and problems with viral infections have not usually been described (Springer and Anderson, 1986). The increased use of rapid diagnostic methods for virology may reveal that certain viral infections occur simultaneously with the bacterial infections, or increase susceptibility to the bacterial infections. Patients with the Chediak-Higashi syndrome have abnormally low constitutive levels of NK cell cytotoxicity, but they have normal inducible NK cell activity after Epstein-Barr virus infection (Katz *et al.*, 1984), and do not show an abnormal frequency or severity in viral infections. Therefore, either induced NK cell activity provides protection, or another compartment of host defence can compensate to provide protection (i.e. protective redundancy). It is interesting to note that patients on extensive chemotherapy, with substantial reductions in circulating leukocytes and marrow reserve, do not present overwhelming problems with viral infections. Their innate resistance may be related to preservation of function of local effector MPs and NK cells in important organs such as the liver and lung. Information about such local natural immune responses will probably have to be obtained from experimental animal systems.

VII. CONCLUDING REMARKS

It is evident that there are complex interactions between viruses, natural host defences and acquired immune responses. In the last five years, advances in molecular virology and hybridoma technology have begun to provide better methods to dissect the virulence factors of viruses, and the mechanisms of action of both natural and acquired immunity. However, as Notkins (1985) recently said, 'In this period of rightful enthusiasm for molecular biology, much will be lost if studies on the pathophysiologic response of the organism to the infection are neglected.'

We would like to expand this concern to investigation of isolated components of host defences, both in vitro and in vivo. The goal in viral disease research, therefore, must be defining the various *interactions* of host defence mechanisms and viral components that result in either clinical disease or control of viral pathogenic effects. Although one effector cell or mechanism may be dominant, either with a particular virus or in a particular stage of disease, there is always an interacting network that affects all compartments. Before designing the 'perfect' 'definitive' network experiments, however, it is obvious that more information regarding individual components of the natural immunity system is needed. Some of the more obvious unanswered questions are:

1. How does the heterogeneity of MPs and natural cytotoxic cells influence the experimental results we obtain? What is the origin of the heterogeneity? How does the differentiation/activation state of these cells affect their permissiveness for virus infection? Can individual subpopulations be defined that selectively inhibit or enhance viral replication, either intrinsically or extrinsically in other cells? More research is needed with selective cellular deficiencies and augmentation to answer these questions.

2. What interrelationships among the various IFNs control their suppressive and enhancing roles in viral infections? In addition to IFNs, what other polypeptide lymphokines or cytokines are involved in limiting or enhancing viral infections? What is the cellular source of these soluble

factors in uninfected and infected animals, and can they be modulated? What contribution do lipid or carbohydrate molecules — on viruses, on cells or as soluble factors — have in natural resistance to viral infections? Are the soluble mediators controlled in a cascade or interacting network? The recent availability of substantial quantities of highly purified materials and antibodies produced through recombinant DNA and hybridoma technology will help answer these questions.

3. What is the role of various host defences during 'natural' infection with a small viral inoculum, in contrast to the usual experimental system of large viral challenge by systemic routes? What is the role of 'local' versus systemic natural immune defences? Can host defences in the natural situation be augmented by therapeutic modalities?

4. Can the information obtained from animal models and from in vitro cellular or molecular virology experiments be used to allow more definitive investigation in humans? For example, can markers of MP and NK activation for antiviral activity be used as probes in kinetic correlative studies in human viral infections? What steps in viral replication, or virus-induced changes in cell membranes or metabolism, are likely targets for natural immune effector cells and soluble mediators? Considerable data are available concerning in vitro mechanisms of natural immune antiviral systems, but these need to be put into context with the clinical disease process.

ACKNOWLEDGMENTS

This work was partially supported by grants CA 35961 and CA 43386 from the National Cancer Institute, and by contracts N00014-82-K-0669 from the Office of Naval Research and DAMD 17-86-C-6117 from the Army Medical Development Command. We thank Dr Angelo Pinto and Dr Mark Cosentino for their critical comments.

REFERENCES

Aderka, D., Holtmann, H., Toker, L., Hahn, T. and Wallach, D. (1986). *J. Immunol.* 136: 2938–42.

Amber, I. J. and Hibbs, J. B. (1986). *Clin. Res.* 34: 100A.

Appel, M. J. G., Mendelson, S. G. and Hall, W. W. (1984). *J. Virol.* 51: 643–9.

Bale, J. F., O'Neil, M.E. and Greiner, T. (1985). *J. Leuk. Biol.* 38: 723–34.

Bale, J. F., O'Neil, M. E., Giller, R., Perlman, S. and Koszinowski, U. (1987). *J. Infec. Dis.* 155: 207–12.

Bandyopadhyay, S., Perussia, B., Trinchieri, G., Miller, D. S. and Starr, S. E. (1986). *J. Exp. Med.* 164: 180–95.

Beutler, B., Krochin, N., Milsark, I. W., Goldberg, A. and Cerami, A. (1986). *Clin. Res.* 34: 491A.

Bielefeldt Ohmann, H. and Babiuk, L. A. (1986). *Infect. Immun.* 51: 344–7.

Bielefeldt Ohmann, H., Gilchrist, J. E. and Babiuk, L. A. (1984). *J. Gen. Virol.* 65: 1487–95.

Biron, C. A., Natuk, R. J. and Welsh, R. M. (1986). *J. Immunol.* 136: 2280–6.

Bishop, G. A., Glorioso, J. C. and Schwartz, S. A. (1983). *J. Immunol.* 131: 1849–53.

Bishop, G. A., Marlin, S. D., Schwartz, S. A. and Glorioso, J. C. (1984). *J. Immunol.* 133: 2206–14.

Bishop, G. A., Kumel, G., Schwartz, S. A. and Glorioso, J. C. (1986). *J. Virol.* 57: 294–300.

Blank, K. J. and Murasko, D. M. (1981). *J. Interferon Res.* 1: 437–42.

Blank, K. J., McKernan, L. N. and Murasko, D. M. (1985). *J Interferon Res.* 5: 215–21.

Boere, W. A. M., Benaissa-Trouw, B. J., Harmsen, T., Erich, T., Kraaijeveld, C. A. and Snippe, H. (1985). *J Virol.* 54: 546–51.

Bonina, L., Nash, A. A., Arena, A., Leung, K. N. and Wildy, P. (1984). *Virus Res.* 1: 501–5.

Borysiewicz, L. K., Rodgers, B., Morris, S., Graham, S. and Sissons, J. G. (1985). *J. Immunol.* 134: 2695–2701.

Borysiewicz, L. K., Graham, S. and Sissons, J. G. P. (1986). *Eur. J. Immunol.* 16: 405–11.

Breinig, M. C. and Morahan, P. S. (1980). In D. A. Stringfellow (ed.), *Interferon and Interferon Inducers.* New York: Marcel Dekker: 239–61.

Brinton, M. A. (1985). In E. Skamene and P. Kongshavn (eds), *Genetic Control of Host Resistance to Infection and Malignancy.* N. Y: Alan R. Liss: 111–23.

Brinton, M. A., Blank, K. J. and Nathanson, N. (1984). In A. L. Notkins and M. B. A. Oldstone (eds), *Concepts in Viral Pathogenesis.* New York: Springer-Verlag: 71–8.

Bukowski, J. F. and Welsh, R. M. (1985). *J. Immunol.* 135: 3537–40.

Bukowski, J. F. and Welsh, R. M. (1986). *J. Immunol.* 136: 3481–5.

Bukowski, J. F., Biron, C. A. and Welsh, R. M. (1983a). *J. Immunol.* 131: 991–6.

Bukowski, J. F., Woda, B. A., Habu, S., Okumura, K. and Welsh, R. M. (1983b). *J. Immunol.* 131: 1531–8.

Bukowski, J. F., Woda, B. A. and Welsh, R. M. (1984). *J. Virol.* 52: 119–28.

Bukowski, J. F., Warner, J. F., Dennart, G. and Welsh, R. M. (1985). *J. Exp. Med.* 161: 40–52.

Cabral, G. A., Lockmuller, J. C. and Mishkin, E. M. (1986). *Proc. Soc. Exp. Biol. Med.* 181: 305–11.

Campbell, P. A. (1986). *Immunol. Today* 7: 70–2.

Cardosa, M. J., Gordon, S., Hirsch, S., Springer, T. A. and Porterfield, J. S. (1986). *J. Virol.* 57: 952–9.

Carmen, P. S., Ernst, P. B., Rosenthal, K. L., Clark, D. A., Befus, A. D. and Bienenstock, J. (1986). *J. Immunol.* 136: 1548–53.

Carrano, V. A., Barthold, S. W., Beck, D. S. and Smith, A.L. (1984). *Lab. Animal Sci.* 34: 573–8.

Casal, I., Enjuanes, L. and Vinuela, E. (1984). *J. Virol.* 52: 37–46.

Cheevers, W. P. and McGuire, T. C. (1985). *Rev. Infec. Dis.* 7: 83–8.

Chmielarczyk, W., Domke, I. and Kirchner, H. (1985a). *Antiviral Res.* 5: 55–9.

Chmielarczyk, W., Engler, H., Ernst, R., Opitz, U. and Kirchner, H. (1985b). *J. Gen. Virol.* 66: 1087–94.

Claassen, E., Kors, N. and van Rooijen, N. (1986). *Europ. J. Immunol.* 16: 492–7.

Colmenares, C. and Lopez, C. (1986). *J. Immunol.* 136: 3473–80.

Cooper, N. R. (1984). In A. L. Notkins and M. B. A. Oldstone (eds), *Concepts in Viral Pathogenesis.* New York: Springer-Verlag: 11–9.

Cottman, G. W., Westall, J., Corey, L. and Wilson, C. B. (1987). *Clin. Res.* 32: 108A.

Dempsey, W. L. and Morahan, P. S. (1985). In J. Dean *et al.* (eds), *Immunotoxicology and Immunopharmacology.* New York: Raven Press: 55–68.

Dempsey, W. L., Smith, A. L. and Morahan, P. S. (1986). *J. Leuk. Biol.* 39: 559–65.

Doll, S. C. and Johnson, T. C. (1985). *J. Virol.* 55: 583–7.

Domke, I., Straub, P., Jacobsen, H., Kirchner, H. and Panet, A. (1985). *J. Gen. Virol.* 66: 2231–6.

Domurat, F., Roberts, N. J., Walsh, E. E. and Dagan, R. (1985). *J. Infec. Dis.* 152: 895–901.

Dubensky, T. W. and Villarreal, L. P. (1984). *J. Virol.* 50: 541–6.

Dupuy, J-M., Dupuy, C. and Decarie, D. (1984). *J. Immunol.* 133: 1609–13.

Eiden, J., Lederman, H. M., Vonderfecht, S. and Yolken, R. (1986). *J. Virol.* 57: 706–8.

Einhorn, L. and Ost, A. (1984). *J. Infec. Dis.* 149: 207–14.

Ellermann-Eriksen, S., Liberto, M. C., Iannello, D. and Mogensen, S. C. (1986). *J. Gen. Virol.* 67: 1025–33.

Faden, H. S. and Ogra, P. L. (1986). *Pediatric Infec. Dis.* 5: 86–92.

Fitzgerald, P. A., Evans, R., Kirkpatrick, D. and Lopez, C. (1983). *J. Immunol.* 130: 1663–7.

Fitzgerald, P. A., Mendelsohn, M. and Lopez, C. (1985). *J. Immunol.* 134: 2666–72.

Friedlander, A. M., Jahrling, P. B., Merrill, P. and Tobery, S. (1984). *Infec. Immun.* 43: 283–8.

Gangemi, J. D., Hightower, J. A., Jackson, R. A., Maher, M. H., Welsh, M. G. and Sigel, M. M. (1983). *Infec. Immun.* 39: 726–35.

Gee, S. R., Chan, M. A., Clark, D. A. and Rawls, W. E. (1981). *Infec. Immun.* 31: 919–28.

Gendelman, H. E., Narayan, O., Kennedy-Stoskopf, S., Kennedy, P. G. E., Ghotbi, Z., Clements, J. E., Standley, J. and Pezeshipour, G. (1986). *J. Virol.* 58: 67–74.

Gilmore, N. and Wainberg, M. A. (1985). *Viral Mechanisms of Immuno-suppression.* New York: Alan R. Liss.

Glover, D. M., Browstein, D., Burchett, S., Larsen, A. and Wilson, C. B. (1987). *Immunology* 61: 195–201.

Gollins, S. W. and Porterfield, J. S. (1985). *J. Gen. Virol.* 66: 1969–82.

Gresser, I., Tovey, M. G., Maury, C. and Bandu, M. (1976). *J. Exp. Med.* 144: 1316–23.

Gresser, I., Vignaux, F., Belardelli, F., Tovey, M. G. and Maunaury, M-T. (1985). *J. Virol.* 53: 221–7.

Griffin, D. E. and Hess, J. L. (1986). *J. Immunol.* 136: 1841–5.

Grossberg, S. E. and Taylor, J. L. (1986). In R. Friedman *et al.* (eds), *Interferons as Cell Growth Inhibitors and Antitumor Factors.* New York: Alan R. Liss: 27–34.

Gulati, L., Chaturvedi, U. C. and Mathur, A. (1986). *Br. J. Exp. Path.* 67: 269–77.

Gut, J-P., Schmitt, S., Bingen, A., Anton, M. and Kirn, A. (1984). *J. Infec. Dis.* 149: 621–9.

Habu, S., Akamatsu, K-I., Tamaoki, N. and Okumura, K. (1984). *J. Immunol.* 133: 2743–7.

Hammer, S. M., Gilles, J. M., Groopman, J. E. and Rose, R. M. (1986). International Conference on AIDS.

Harris, P. and Ralph, P. (1985). *J. Leuk. Biol.* 37: 407–22.

Hayashi, K., Saze, K. and Uchida, Y. (1985). *Microbiol. Immunol.* 29: 625–34.

Hirsch, R. L. (1982). *Microbiol. Rev.* 46: 71–85.

Holmes, K. V., Welsh, R. M. and Haspel, M. V. (1986). *J. Immunol.* 136: 1446–53.

Ho, D. D., Rota, T. R. and Hirsch, M. S. (1986). *J. Clin. Invest.* 77: 1712–5.

Hotta, H., Hotta, S., Susumu, H., Takada, H., Kotani, S., Tanaka, S. and Ohki, M. (1983). *Infec. Immun.* 41: 462–9.

Houde, M. and Arora, D. J. S. (1986). *Abstracts Int. Congress Immunol., Toronto:* 559.

Hovi, T., Lehto, V-P. and Virtanen, I. (1985). *Exp. Cell Res.* 159: 305–12.

Howie, S., Norval, M., Maingay, J. and McBride, W. H. (1986). *Arch. Virol.* 87: 229–39.

Ihara, T., Ito, M. and Starr, S. E. (1986). *Clin. Exp. Immunol.* 63: 179–87.

Inada, T. and Mims, C. A. (1985). *J. Gen. Virol.* 66: 1469–77.

Inada, T., Chong, K. T. and Mims, C. A. (1985). *J. Gen. Virol.* 66: 871–8.

Jakab, G. J. (1982). *Am. Rev. Resp. Dis.* 126: 778–82.

Jennings, S. T., Ettensohn, D. B. and Roberts, N. J. (1984). *Am. Rev. Respir. Dis.* 130: 98–101.

Johnson, H. M., Torres, B. A., Smith, E. M., Dion, L. D. and Blalock, J. E. (1984). *J. Immunol.* 132: 246–50.

Jordan, M. C. (1983). *Rev. Infec. Dis.* 3: 205–15.

Katz, P., Zaytoun, A. M., Lee, J. H. and Fauci, A. S. (1984). *J. Immunol.* 132: 571–3.

Kay, M. M., Mendoza, J., Hausman, S. and Dorsey, B. (1979). *Mech. Aging Devel.* 11: 347–62.

Keller, F., Wild, M. T. and Kirn, A. (1985). *J. Leuk. Biol.* 38: 293–303.

Kennedy-Stoskopf, S. and Narayan, O. (1986). *J. Virol.* 59: 37–44.

Keroack, M. and Fields, B. N. (1986). *Science* 232: 1635–8.

Koenig, S., Gendelman, H. E., Orenstein, J. M., DalCanto, M. C., Pezeshkpour, G. H., Yungbluth, M., Janotta, F., Aksamit, A., Martin, M. A. and Fauci, A. S. (1986). *Science* 233: 1089–93.

Koff, W. C. and Dunegan, M. A. (1986). *J. Immunol.* 136: 705–9.

Koff, W. C. and Fann, A. V. (1986). *Lymphokine Res.* 5: 215–21.

Kohase, M., Henriksen-DeStefano, D., May, L. T., Vilcek, J. and Sehgal, P. B. (1986). *Cell* 45: 659–66.

Kohl, S. (1985). *J. Infec. Dis.* 152: 435–40.

Kohl, S., Loo, L. S. and Gonik, B. (1984). *J. Infec. Dis.* 150: 14–19.

Kowalchyk, K. and Plagemann, P. G. W. (1985). *Virus Res.* 2: 211–29.

Knudsen, P. J., Strom, T. B. and Zeldis, J. B. (1986). *Clin. Res.* 34: 670A.

Knudsen, R. C., Genovesi, E. V., Whyard, T. C. and Wool, S. H. (1987). *Vet. Microbiol.* 14: 15–24.

Knudsen, R. C., Genovesi, E. V. and Whyard, T. C. (1987b). *Am. J. Vet. Res.* 48: 1067–71.

Kraut, E. H., Rojka, J. L., Olsen, R. G. and Tuomari, D. L. (1985). *J. Virol.* 54: 873–5.

Krug, R. M., Shaw, M., Broni, B., Shapiro, G. and Haller, O. (1985). *J. Virol.* 56: 201–6.

Krzystyniak, K., Hugo, P., Flipo, D. and Fournier, M. (1985). *Tox. Appl. Pharm.* 80: 397–408.

Kurane, I., Hebblewaite, D., Brandt, W. E. and Ennis, F. A. (1984). *J. Virol.* 52: 223–30.

LaMonica, N., Meriam, C. and Racaniello, V. R. (1986). *J. Virol.* 57: 515–25.

Leary, K., Connor, J. R. and Morahan, P. S. (1985). *J. Gen. Virol.* 66: 1123–9.

Lehmann-Grube, F., Krenz, S., Krahnert, T., Schwachenwald, R., Moskophidis, D., Lohler, J. and Posada, C. J. V. (1987). *J. Immunol.* 138: 2282–9.

Lehrer, R. I., Daher, K., Ganz, T. and Selsted, M. E. (1985). *J. Virol.* 54: 467–72.

Leibson, P. J., Hunter-Laszlo, M. and Hayward, A. R. (1986). *J. Virol.* 57: 976–82.

Levine, A. J. (1982). *Curr. Topics Microb. Immunol.* 101: 1–30.

Lewis, D. B., Larsen, A. and Wilson, C. B. (1986). *J. Exp. Med.* 163: 1018–23.

Lichtenstein, A. K. (1986). *Blood* 63: 657–65.

Linnavuori, K. and Hovi, T. (1983). *Virology* 130: 1–9.

Liprandi, F., Gomez, B. and Walder, R. (1986). *Arch. Virol.* 87: 163–71.

Love, A., Rydbeck, R., Kristensson, K., Orvell, C. and Norrby, E. (1985). *J. Virol.* 53: 67–74.

McGeorge, M. B. and Morahan, P. S. (1978). *Infec. Immun.* 22: 623–6.

Mak, N. K. and Ada, G. L. (1984). *Immunobiol.* 166: 458–72.

Mann, D. W., Sonnenfeld, G. and Stein-Streilein, J. (1985). *Proc. Soc. Exp. Biol. Med.* 180: 224–30.

Mastroeni, P., Bizzini, B., Bonina, L., Iannello, D., Merendino, R. A., Delfino, D., Berlinghieri, M. C., Leonardi, M. S., Arena, A., Liberto, M. C. and Gazzara, D. (1985). *Immunopharmacology* 10: 27–34.

Masuda, A. and Bennett, M. (1981). *Infec. Immun.* 34: 970–9.

Mercer, J. A. and Spector D. H. (1986). *J. Virol.* 57: 497–504.

Mestian, J., Digel, W., Jacobsen, H. and Kirchner, H. (1986). *Abstracts International Immunology Congress*: 601.

Miller, S. A., Bia, R. J., Coleman, D. L., Lucia, H. L., Young, K. R. and Root, R. K. (1985). *Infec. Immun.* 47: 211–16.

Mock, D. J., Domurat, F., Roberts, N. J., Walsh, E. E., Licht, M. R. and Keng, P. (1987). *J. Clin. Invest.* 79: 620–4.

Mogensen, S. C. (1981). In F. O'Grady and H. Smith (eds), *Microbial Perturbation of Host Defenses.* New York: Academic Press: 165–84.

Mogensen, S. C. (1985). *Immunol. Lett.* 11: 219–24.

Moore, R. N., Pitruzzello, F. J., Deana, D. G. and Rouse, B. T. (1985). *Lymphokine Res.* 4: 43–50.

Morahan, P. S. (1984). In B. T. Rouse and C. Lopez (eds), *Immunobiology of Herpes Simplex Virus Infection.* Boca Raton: CRC Press: 71–89.

Morahan, P. S., Coleman, P. B., Morse, S. S. and Volkman, A. (1982). *Infec. Immun.* 37: 1079–85.

Morahan, P. S., Connor, J. R. and Leary, K. R. (1985). *Brit. Med. Bull.* 41: 15–21.

Morahan, P. S., Dempsey, W. L., Volkman, A., and Connor, J. (1986). *Infec. Immun.* 51: 87–93.

Morahan, P. S., Leake, E. R., Tenney, D. J. and Sit, M. (1987). In J. Majde, (ed.), *Immunopharmacology of Infectious Diseases: Vaccine Adjuvants and Modulators of Nonspecific Resistance.* New York: Alan R.Liss: 313–24.

Morgan, D. A., Soslau, G., Howett, M. K. and Brodsky, I. (1985). Herpevirus Workshop.

Morse, S. S. and Morahan, P. S. (1981). *Cell. Immunol.* 58: 72–84.

Munoz, A., Carraco, L. and Fresno, M. (1983). *J. Immunol.* 131: 783–7.

Naeve, C. W., Hinshaw, V. S. and Webster, R. G. (1984). *J. Virol.* 51: 567–9.

Nagai, T., Tanishita, O., Takahashi, Y., Yamanouchi, T., Domae, K., Kondo, K., Dantas, J. R., Takahashi, M. and Yamanishi, K. (1985). *J. Gen. Virol.* 66: 1271–8.

Narayan, O. and Cork, L. C. (1985). *Rev. Infec. Dis.* 7: 89–99.

Narayan, O., Sheffer, D., Clements, J. E. and Tennekoon, G. (1985). *J. Exp. Med.* 162: 1954–69.

Natuk, R. J., Byrne, J. A. and Holowczak, J. A. (1986). *Cancer Immunol. Immunother.* 22: 197–203.

Nicholson, J. K. A., Cross, G. D., Callaway, C. S. and McDougal, J. S. (1986). *J. Immunol.* 137: 323–9.

Nickerson, C. L., and Jakab, G. J. (1986). *Am. Rev. Resp. Dis.* 133: A68.

Notkins, A. L. (1985). *N. Eng. J. Med.* 312: 507–9.

Offit, P. A., Blavat, G., Greenberg, H. B. and Clark, H. F. (1986). *J. Virol.* 57: 46–9.

Oh, S. H., Gonik, B., Greenberg, S. B. and Kohl, S. (1986). *J. Infec. Dis.* 153: 791–3.

Ohta, H., Yoshikawa, Y., Kai, C., Kamanouchi, K., Taniguchi, H., Komine, K-I., Ishijuma, Y. and Okada, H. (1986). *J. Virol.* 57: 670–3.

Oldstone, M. B. A., Sinha, Y. N., Blaunt, P., Tishon, A., Rodriguez, M., von Wedel, R. and Lampert, P. W., (1982). *Science* 218: 1125–7.

Oldstone, M. B. A., Ahmed, R., Byrne, J., Buchmeier, M. J., Riviere, Y. and Southern, P. (1985). *Brit. Med. Bull.* 41: 70–4.

O'Neill, H. C. and Blanden, R. V. (1983). *Infec. Immun.* 41: 1391–4.

Osorio, F. A., Rock, D. L. and Reed D. E. (1985). *J. Gen. Virol.* 66: 1941–51.

Pereira, C. A., Mercier, G., Oth, D. and Dupuy, J. M. (1984). *Immunobiol.* 166: 35–44.

Pesanti, E. L. and Shanley, J. D. (1984). *J. Leuk. Biol.* 36: 133–41.

Porter, D. D. (1986). *Prog. Med. Virol.* 33: 42–60.

Porterfield, J. S. (1985). *Immunol. Lett.* 11: 213–7.

Proietti, E., Gessani, S., Belardelli, F. and Gresser, I. (1986). *J. Virol.* 57: 456–63.

Quinnan, G. V. and Rook, A. H. (1984). *Birth Defects* 20: 245–61.

Race, R. E., Chesebro, B., Bloom, M. E., Aasted, B. and Wolfinbarger, J. (1986). *J. Virol.* 57: 285–93.

Rager-Zisman, B. and Bloom B. R. (1985). *Brit. Med. Bull.* 41: 22–7.

Rice, G. P. A., Schrier, R. D. and Oldstone, M. B. A. (1984). *Proc. Nat. Acad. Sci. USA* 81: 6134–8.

Riley, V. (1981). *Science* 211: 1100–9.

Roberts, N. J. and Horan, P. K. (1985). *J. Infec. Dis.* 151: 308–13.

Roberts, N. J., Prill, A. H. and Mann, T. N. (1986). *J. Exp. Med.* 163: 511–9.

Rodbard, D. (1981). *N. Eng. J. Med.* 305: 808–13.

Rose, R. M., Wasserman, A. S., Weiser, W. Y. and Remold, H. G. (1986). *Cell. Immunol.* 97: 397–406.

Rosenthal, K. L. and Prevec, L. (1986). *Abstracts International Immunology Congress:* 599.

Rossiter, P. B. and Wardley, R. C. (1985). *J. Gen. Virol.* 66: 969–75.

Salahuddin, S. Z., Rose, R. M., Groopman, J. E., Markham, P. D. and Gallo, R. C. (1986). *Blood* 68: 281–4.

Scheid, A. and Choppin, P. W. (1984). In A. L. Notkins and M. B. A. Oldstone (eds), *Concepts in Viral Pathogenesis.* New York: Springer-Verlag: 26–31.

Schrier, B. D., Rice, G. P. A., and Oldstone, M. B. A. (1986). *J. Infec. Dis.* 153: 1084–91.

Sharpe, A. H. and Fields, B. N. (1985). *New. Eng. J. Med.* 312: 486–96.

Shellam, G. R. and Flexman, J. P. (1986). *J. Virol.* 58: 152–6.

Sheridan, J. F., Beck, M., Aurelian, L. and Radowsky, M. (1985). *J. Infec. Dis.* 152: 449–56.

Smith, M. S., Click, R. E. and Plagemann, P. G. W. (1984). *J. Immunol.* 133: 428–32.

Smith P. D., Koenig, S., Gendelman, H. E., Folks, T. M., Wahl, L. M., Wahl, S. M. and Fauci, A. S. (1986a). *Clin. Res.* 34: 507A.

Smith, P. D., Wahl, L. M., Liu, R. and Wahl, S. M. (1986b). *Gastroenterology* 90: 1640.

Soldateschi, D., Boraschi, D. and Tagliabue, A. (1985). *Antiviral Res.* 5: 217–27.

Sprecher, E. and Becker, Y. (1986). *Arch. Virol.* 91: 341–9.

Springer, T. A. and Anderson, D. C. (1986). *Ciba Foundation Symp.* 118: 102–26.

Staehell, P., Pratcheva, D., Lundin L.-G., Acklin, M., Ruddle, F., Lindenmann, J. and Haller, O. (1986). *J. Virol.* 58: 967–9.

Stanton, G. J. and Baron, S. (1984). In A. L. Notkins and M. B. A. Oldstone (eds), *Concepts in Viral Pathogenesis.* New York: Springer-Verlag: 3–10.

Starr, S. E., Smiley, L., Wlodaver, C., Friedman, H. M., Plotkin, S. A. and Barker, C. (1984). *Transplantation* 37: 161–4.

Stein-Streilein, J., Bennett, M., Mann, D. and Kumar, V. (1983). *J. Immunol.* 131: 2699–2704.

Stein-Streilein, J. and Guffee, J. (1986). *J. Immunol.* 136: 1435–41.

Straub, P., Domke, I., Kirchner, H., Jacobsen, H. and Panet, A. (1986). *Virology* 150: 411–18.

Suzamura, A., Lavi, E., Weiss, S. R. and Silberberg, D. H. (1986). *Science* 232: 991–3.

Taylor, S. and Bryson, Y. Z. (1985). *J. Immunol.* 134: 1493–7.

Tenney, D. J., Ockenhouse, C. F. and Morahan, P. S. (1986). *J. Leuk. Biol.* 40: 290.

Tilden, A. B., Cauda, R., Grossi, C. E., Balch, C. M., Lakeman, A. D. and Whitley, R. J. (1986). *J. Immunol.* 136: 4243–8.

Torpey, D., Lindsley, M. and Rinaldo, C. (1988). Submitted for publication.

Trinchieri, G. and Perussia, B. (1984). *Lab. Invest.* 50: 489–513.

Vogel, S. N., Winblatt, A. C. and Rosenstreich, D. L. (1980). In E. Gershwin and B. Merchant (eds), *Immunologic Defects in Laboratory Animals.* New York: Plenum Press: 327–357.

Vogel, S. N., Fertsch, D. and Falk, L. A. (1986a). In R. Friedman *et al.* (eds), *Interferons as Cell Growth Inhibitors and Antitumour Factors.* New York: Alan R. Liss: 223–234.

Vogel, S. N. Havell, E. A. and Spitalny, G. L. (1986b). *J. Immunol.* 136: 2917–23.

Welsh, R. M. (1986). *Nat. Immun. Cell Growth Regul.* 5: 169–99.

Welsh, E. M., Haspel, M. V., Parker, D. C. and Holmes, K. V. (1986). *J. Immunol.* 136: 1454–68.

Westly, H. J., Kleiss, A. J., Kelley, K. W., Wong, P. K. Y. and Yuen, P-H. (1986). *J. Exp. Med.* 163: 1589–94.

Wilson, C. B. (1986). *J. Pediatrics* 108: 1–12.

Wilson, C. B., Westall, J., Johnston, L., Lewis, D. B., Dower, S. K. and Alpert, A. R. (1986). *J. Clin. Invest.* 77: 860–7.

Wiltrout, R. H., Mathieson, B. J., Talmadge, J. E., Reynolds, C. W., Zhang, S-R., Herberman, R. B. and Ortaldo, J. R. (1984). *J. Exp. Med.* 160: 1431–49.

Wiltrout, R. H., Santoni, A., Peterson, E. S., Knott, D. C., Overton, W. R., Herberman, R. B. and Holden, H. T. (1985). *J. Leuk. Biol.* 37: 597–614.

Yoffe, B., Noonan, C. A., Melnick, J. L. and Hollinger, F. B. (1986). *J. Infec. Dis.* 153: 471–7.

Zeldis, J. B., Mugishima, H., Gale, R. P. and Steinberg, H. (1986). *Gastroenterology* 90: 1783.

19

Chlamydial and Rickettsial Infections

CAROL A. NACY

MONTE S. MELTZER

THOMAS R. JERRELLS

Walter Reed Army Institute of Research
Washington, DC 20307–5100, USA

GERALD I. BYRNE

Department of Medical Microbiology
University of Wisconsin, Madison, Wis., USA

I. INTRODUCTION

There is no more challenging dilemma than that presented to mammalian hosts by infection with chlamydiae and rickettsiae. These pathogens have adopted specialised mechanisms to assure satisfaction of

NATURAL IMMUNITY
ISBN 0 12 5145551

their metabolic deficiencies: bacterial replication, and therefore survival, can occur only within cells. Once inside the host, the intracellular infectious cycle is repeated as bacteria pass from infected cell to neighbouring cell, metabolically inert, and frequently disguised in host-derived material. Tissue destruction and pathology eventually follow, and are usually evident well before the host is immunologically aware of the invader. The dilemma for the host lies in the mechanisms at its disposal for elimination of sequestered intracellular parasites once awareness occurs. These mechanisms are few and, as we will discuss throughout the chapter, less than optimally effective.

The chlamydiae and rickettsiae are set apart from other prokaryotes by their exclusively intracellular habitat in infected experimental animals or incidental human hosts. The differences between these two taxonomic groups, however, are substantial, and necessitate a separate discussion of natural immunity based on the distinctive attributes of each.

II. CHLAMYDIAE

Chlamydia species are obligate intracellular prokaryotes that replicate exclusively within the confines of a membrane-bound cytoplasmic vesicle (inclusion) in susceptible eukaryotic host cells. The genus is comprised of two species, *C. psittaci* and *C. trachomatis*. Chlamydial cellular morphology and ultrastructure is identical for both species. The organisms possess an outer envelope similar to that observed for Gram-negative bacteria, and lipopolysaccharide (LPS) is a common genus antigen for the chlamydiae (Caldwell and Hitchcock, 1984; Nurminen *et al.*, 1983). Each species, and the strains or serovars within either species, can be distinguished by other outer envelope protein epitopes (Batteiger *et al.*, 1985).

The agent of psittacosis, *C. psittaci*, is widely distributed in nature, and causes acute disease and persistent infections in a variety of vertebrate and invertebrate hosts. Transmission of *C. psittaci* may occur via the respiratory route, by ingestion of infectious organisms, by direct contact with infectious organisms on mucosal surfaces, or transplacentally. *C. trachomatis* is host-restricted, in contrast, and humans are essentially the sole susceptible host species. Most *C. trachomatis* infections occur by direct contact of the organism with mucosal surfaces, either through sexual contact or by direct instillation into the conjunctival sac. Respiratory transmission has also been reported, but actually may involve nasopharyngeal colonisation followed by extension to the respiratory tree.

A. Intracellular Infection

Chlamydia psittaci infects a variety of host cell types, including mononuclear phagocytes and epithelial cells. This may contribute to the systemic spread of *C. psittaci* within the infected individual. *C. trachomatis*, in general, is much more host cell restricted; this organism causes productive infections only within mucosal epithelia. Thus, dissemination of *C. trachomatis* is more likely to occur by direct extension from an initial infectious focus. A notable exception is the lymphogranuloma venereum (LGV) biovar of *C. trachomatis*, which can cause productive infections within lymph-node macrophages. LGV infections also have the potential to cause systemic complications as a result of lymphatic dissemination.

1. Attachment of chlamydiae

The mechanism for attachment and uptake of chlamydiae into host cell cytoplasmic vesicles is similar for both chlamydial species. A specialised chlamydial developmental form (the elementary body, EB) mediates the initial interaction between chlamydiae and the host cell. Evidence for specific chlamydial ligands acting as adhesins for attachment to susceptible host cells has been reported (Byrne and Moulder, 1978), but a chlamydial adhesin molecule has not yet been identified (Hackstadt and Caldwell, 1985). The chlamydial adhesin binds to a host cell surface glycoprotein that has thus far been defined only on the basis of its sensitivity to protease (Byrne and Moulder, 1978) and neuraminidase treatment (Kuo *et al.*, 1973). This putative glycoprotein receptor may be localised to regions of the host cell membrane associated with coated pits (Hodinka and Wyrick, 1986), although this finding remains controversial (Ward and Murray, 1984). The attachment process requires no energy expenditure on the part of the chlamydiae. In fact, the EB is a metabolically inert particle. Host cell energy requirements also are not essential for attachment, since the process occurs both at lowered temperatures and in the presence of energy uncouplers (Moulder, 1985).

2. Entry of the chlamydiae

Entry of chlamydiae occurs rapidly after attachment, although the two steps can be temporally separated (Byrne, 1978). The process resembles phagocytosis, and requires energy expenditure by the host cell. Chlamydiae do not participate metabolically, yet they do direct the process; the putative chlamydial adhesin must initiate the circumscription of the tightly opposed host cell membrane about the chlamydial EB.

3. Intracellular localisation of the chlamydiae

Once the entry process has been effected, the chlamydiae remain within the endocytic vesicle and undergo differentiation from the sturdy, metabolically inert infectious EB to a larger, osmotically sensitive reticulate body, or RB (Hatch *et al.*, 1984; Newhall and Jones, 1983). Intracellular replication does not begin until differentiation of the EB to the RB is complete. In addition, chlamydiae inhibit the fusion of lysosomes with chlamydiae-containing endocytic vesicles, and are thereby protected from this potent host cell defence mechanism (Eissenberg and Wyrick, 1981; Friis, 1972).

RB growth and division proceeds by binary fission within the endocytic vesicle. Vesicle membrane is added as the replicating microcolony increases in size, but the mechanism for inclusion growth has not been well characterised. Chlamydial growth proceeds for a length of time that is dependent upon both the chlamydial strain and the host cell type. Eventually, nearly the entire host cell cytoplasm is filled by the growing inclusion body. At this point a second round of differentiation ensues, and RBs differentiate to infectious EBs. The signal that triggers this event is not known, but may depend upon either depletion of some essential nutrient or accumulation of toxic metabolic products. Soon after RB to EB differentiation, the inclusion membrane disrupts. This is followed by plasma membrane lysis: a new population of EBs are released, each one capable of initiating an infectious cycle. Under ideal conditions in vitro, an increase of about 3 logs of chlamydiae occurs over the input multiplicity, and the process takes from two to three days to complete.

4. Progressive infection

The chlamydial developmental cycle has been well characterised in cell-culture systems, and is believed to proceed in a similar manner during actual chlamydial infections. Infections of mucosal surfaces (oculogenital infections) tend to remain localised at the initial infectious focus, but may spread by direct extension. For example, infections of the endocervix may directly ascend the genital tract resulting in uterine (endometritis) and fallopian tube (salpingitis) infections. It is not clear if mononuclear phagocytes can serve as reservoirs for chlamydial persistance, but overt intracellular development of *C. trachomatis* has not been characterised in these cells.

B. Natural Immunity

Chlamydial growth and development, as detailed above, must proceed according to six well-defined steps: (a) attachment; (b) entry; (c) organisation of infectious to replicative forms; (d) multiplication; (e) reorganisation of replicative forms to infectious forms; and (f) release of infectious forms from the host cell. In addition, the chlamydiae, like all transmissible pathogens, must be effectively passed from one host to another. Interruption of any one of these essential functions by a host not previously exposed to chlamydiae would be considered natural immunity, a response that does not rely on acquired immune reactions such as development of chlamydia-specific antibodies. Natural immunity will be discussed under the broad headings of barrier mechanisms, acute-phase reactions (such as inflammation and complement activation), and non-specific cytokine-mediated defence mechanisms. Although the contribution of both non-specific and acquired immunity in the control of diseases caused by the chlamydiae has been demonstrated, it is important to recognise that immunity does not necessarily lead to eradication of the organisms. All chlamydial infections tend to persist if left untreated. The mechanisms involved are by no means clear, but certain changes that accompany resolution of acute chlamydial disease may contribute to persistent or chronic infections. Indeed, immune responses, both natural and acquired, may in large part be responsible for the pathology of acute disease, as well as progression to chronicity.

1. Barrier mechanisms

Most successful pathogens have evolved survival strategies to either penetrate through or avoid undamaged skin, a formidable natural protective barrier. Certain pathogens, like the staphylococci and other opportunists, gain entry into the host via breaks or lesions in the skin. The rickettsiae and many parasitic protozoans and nematodes are injected directly by the bite of an insect. Other potential pathogens are ingested, and either cause gastrointestinal disease or disseminate from an initial infectious focus in the gut. Chlamydiae, on the other hand, most frequently become associated with hosts at mucosal surfaces, and are often transmitted by the intimate, frequently prolonged contact between mucosae associated with sexual activity. Transmission of chlamydiae can also occur by direct instillation of organisms in the conjunctival sac or by droplet inhalation into the respiratory tree. In each instance, however, barrier mechanisms at the mucosal surface represent the initial obstacle that must be overcome for chlamydiae to survive and replicate. The ciliary flow of mucus is a powerful barrier to the establishment of an infectious focus. Specific attachment of chlamydiae to respiratory, conjunctival, or genital epithelia, and subsequently parasite-specified entry into susceptible host cells may overcome the natural barriers at mucosal surfaces. Nonetheless, transmission from infected individual to cohort is less than fully efficient, and these barrier mechanisms may play a role in natural resistance to chlamydiae by limiting successful transmission.

2. Acute-phase reactions

Several *C. trachomatis* strains activate complement by the alternate pathway (Megran *et al.*, 1985). High levels of C5a are found in normal plasma following exposure to chlamydial EBs, and chlamydiae-mediated activation of the complement cascade results in the stimulation of polymorphonuclear leukocyte (PMN) chemotaxis. The presence of PMNs is characteristic of the initial inflammatory response to virtually all chlamydial infections, and PMNs can ingest and kill chlamydial EBs in vitro by mechanisms apparently unrelated to the production of toxic oxygen metabolites (Yong *et al.*, 1982). It is not clear how effective the PMN and chlamydiae interaction is in vivo, however, since infectious foci are maintained even in the presence of a profound PMN-predominant inflammatory response. As infections proceed from acute to chronic stages, the cellular infiltrate matures from predominantly PMN to predominantly mononuclear in character. In this progression, chlamydiae may (1) be protected from immune reactive cells by virtue of their intracellular habitat within mucosal epithelia, (2) be taken up and either persist or be killed by PMNs or mononuclear phagocytes, or (3) be inhibited from replicating or killed by host cells altered directly by soluble mediators (cytokines) released from lymphocytes or other cells attracted to the initial focus of infection. It is in these host–chlamydia interactions that natural immunity can contribute to the resolution of acute chlamydial disease. The net result of these early events associated with chlamydial infections could be either eradication of the pathogens or development of persistent infections. Each of these outcomes may occur under different circumstances; unfortunately, the circumstances that govern eradication or persistence are not well understood at the present time.

3. Cytokine-mediated defence mechanisms

Chlamydiae are nonviral microbial inducers of interferon, and like many of the other intracellular pathogens, their growth is inhibited in cells treated with interferon (IFN), especially gamma interferon (IFN-γ). Spleen cells from experimental animals infected with chlamydiae secrete much higher levels of IFN when stimulated in vitro with either specific antigen or mitogens than do cells from control animals (Byrne and Faubion, 1982). The influence of interferons on intracellular chlamydial growth has been well studied in cell-culture systems, but it is not clear yet how interferons actually influence the course of naturally occurring chlamydial infections. The effects of cytokines on chlamydiae appear to be restricted to events that occur after entry into host cells: cytokines do not influence either the attachment or phagocytosis of chlamydia, but do interrupt chlamydial growth and development within treated cells (Byrne and Faubion, 1982). All classes of interferons inhibit the intracellular development of *C. trachomatis*, but the degree of inhibition is at least partially dependent on the interferon class, the particular chlamydial strain, and the host cell type (Byrne, 1986; Byrne and Rothermel, 1983; de la Maza *et al.*, 1985). The mechanism of interferon-mediated inhibition of growth is not known, but has been reported for IFN-treated monocytes, macrophages, fibroblasts and other somatic cell types (Byrne and Krueger, 1983; Shemer and Sarov, 1985). No evidence for oxygen-dependent killing has been found, and some reports suggest that oxygen-independent mechanisms result in curtailment of replication that promotes chlamydial persistence (Byrne and Faubion, 1983; Byrne *et al.*, 1986; Murray *et al.*, 1983). Although the precise mechanism for IFN-mediated inhibition of *C. trachomatis* replication is not well understood (de la Maza *et al.*, 1985), inhibition of *C. psittaci* replication in cells treated with IFN may be related to the induction of indoleamine-2, 3-dioxygenase, and the resultant depletion of tryptophan, an essential amino acid (Byrne *et al.*, 1986). This mechanism has been reported for IFN-mediated inhibition of intracellular *Toxoplasma gondii* replication in fibroblasts (Pfefferkorn, 1984): *T. gondii* is an obligate intracellular protozoan that also lives within membrane-bound cytoplasmic vesicles that do not fuse with lysosomes.

Thus, the cytokine system, an important natural immune defence mechanism against many intracellular pathogens, may serve to restrict intracellular chlamydial replication within a variety of host cells without actually eradicating the organisms. IFN-mediated cytostasis may, in fact, contribute to immune-mediated chlamydial persistence rather than non-specific protection.

The essential stages of chlamydial development and possible points at which various parameters associated with natural immunity could act to interrupt the infectious process are outlined in Table 19.1.

C. In vivo Infections

1. Experimental animal models

A variety of experimental animal models have been developed to study natural and acquired immunity to *C. psittaci*, but mice and guinea pigs have been widely used for analysis of both systemic and local mucosal infections (Howard *et al.*, 1976; Lammert and Wyrick, 1982; Meyer and Eddie, 1962; Rank *et al.*, 1985a). The route of *C. psittaci* inoculation into

Table 19.1: Essential stages of chlamydial growth and points where parameters of natural or acquired immunity may interrupt the infectious cycle

Growth stage	Natural immunity parameter	Acquired immunity parameter
Attachment of EB[a] to susceptible host cell	Barrier mechanisms, especially mucociliary flow	Neutralising or opsonic antibody
Endocytosis of EB	Complement, chemotactic induction of PMNs and other inflammatory cells resulting in ingestion by non-permissive host cell	Opsonisation
Differentiation of EB to RB[b]	?	?
Multiplication of RB	Cytokine system (IFN etc.); inhibition of RB growth in activated host cell	Cytotoxic cells if novel antigens expressed on infected cell surface; augmented cytokine system
Differentiation of RB to EB	?	?
Lysis of infected host cell and re-infection	?	Neutralising or opsonic antibody
Transmission to new host	Barrier mechanisms	Neutralising secretory antibody

[a] EB = elementary body, the infectious form of the organism.

[b] RB = reticulate body, the intracellular replicative form of the organism.

mice profoundly influences the course of subsequent disease: systemic introduction of a large inoculum of viable chlamydiae results in a rapidly lethal infection that is attributed to a putative chlamydial toxin. No toxic factor other than LPS has ever been associated with chlamydiae, however. Mouse toxicity is inhibited by immunisation either with killed organisms or with live organisms introduced subcutaneously in low numbers (Bell *et al.*, 1959). Since LPS is a genus-specific antigen, and prevention of toxicity is strain-specific, it is doubtful that LPS alone mediates this toxic response. Immediate toxicity may be the result of chlamydia-induced chemotaxis and degranulation of PMNs, with resulting vascular shock (Moulder *et al.*, 1976). Chlamydial inocula introduced locally, either at mucosal surfaces (conjunctiva, genital tract) or subcutaneously, can result in the induction of immunity. This acquired immunity may confer protection against subsequent infections, although in most experimental systems this protection is quite relative and short-lived.

Chlamydia trachomatis is much more difficult to study than *C. psittaci* in experimental animal model systems. The organism is primarily a human pathogen: with the exception of some primate systems (Harrison *et al.*, 1979), useful animal models that reproduce human disease have been a research area that has remained undeveloped. Recently, both systemic (Brunham *et al.*, 1985) and mucosal (Tuffrey *et al.*, 1982) murine models have been reported. Although disease spontaneously resolves in these infected mice, inapparent infection persists; infected animals treated with immunosuppressive drugs exhibited recrudescence of disease after apparent resolution of the primary infection (Stevens *et al.*, 1982). Since infections can be established with human chlamydial strains in both primates and mice, appropriate host cell receptors must be present on mucosal epithelia of these species. A murine chlamydial strain that shares DNA homology and species-specific antigens with *C. trachomatis* has also been used extensively (Barron *et al.*, 1984, 1981; Rank *et al.*, 1985b; Swenson *et al.*, 1983; Williams *et al.*, 1981, 1984a, 1984b).

2. Human infections

Chlamydia trachomatis is the most common sexually transmitted pathogen in both Great Britain and the United States. It is responsible for a significant portion of uncomplicated urethritis cases in males, and also has been associated with complications such as epididymitis and proctitis. In females, *C. trachomatis* causes cervicitis, but the major health risk associated with this organism is a result of ascending complications of cervical infections. These include endometritis and salpingitis (pelvic inflammatory disease) with the attendant risk of infertility. *C. trachomatis* is also transmissible to the neonate during passage through an infected cervix: inclusion conjunctivitis and a distinctive pneumonia are the major chlamydial diseases of the newborn. Trachoma, a result of repeated chlamydial ocular infections over a period of years, remains the leading cause of preventable blindness in the world today (Oriel and Ridgway, 1984; Schachter and Dawson, 1978). Undefined species-specific innate factors play a role in natural immunity to *C. trachomatis*, since humans are uniquely susceptible to infection by this organism. The nature of these factors, however, remains a mystery. *C. psittaci*, in contrast, is not host range restricted, although subspecies host range specificity cannot be excluded.

III. RICKETTSIAE

The individual rickettsial species within the order Rickettsiales are genetically (Schramek, 1972; Tyeryar *et al.*, 1973; Myers and Wisseman, 1980), morphologically (Plotz *et al.*, 1943; Silverman and Wisseman, 1978) and physiologically (Weiss, 1973) distinct. Nonetheless, as a group they share two major characteristics: (a) they are all symbionts or parasites of arthropods, which serve as vectors for transmission; and (b) they are all obligate intracellular parasites of eukaryotic cells of their incidental mammalian hosts. These characteristics provide the rationale for the presently accepted rickettsial taxonomy (Table 19.2 and

Table 19.2: Classification of the rickettsiae[a]

Organism	Vector	Natural host	Clinical syndrome
Tick-borne rickettsiae:			
R. rickettsii	tick	rodents/vertebrates	Rocky Mountain spotted fever
R. conorii	tick	rodents/vertebrates	Boutonneuse fever
R. siberica	tick	rodents/vertebrates	North Asia tick typhus
R. australis	tick	rodents/vertebrates	Queensland tick typhus
R. akari	tick	rodents	Rickettsialpox
Insect-borne rickettsiae:			
R. typhi	flea	rats/mice	Endemic (murine) typhus
R. prowazekii	louse	human	Epidemic typhus
Trombiculid-borne rickettsia:			
R. tsutsugamushi	chigger (mite larva)	mammals	Scrub typhus

[a] Classification according to vector (as in this table) is supported by both immunochemical and genetic relationships between individual species of rickettsiae pathogenic for humans within the vector groups (Marchette, 1982).

Marchette, 1982). The recent Class III biological safety classification of all the rickettsiae has restricted experimental analysis of these micro-organisms to a few research centres; each centre concentrates on one or a very few species. Although some trends have emerged, the more frequent striking differences between species caution against broad generalisation across the taxonomic group.

Transmission of the rickettsiae in nature is exclusively through bites of arthropod vectors, and epidemiology of the rickettsioses suggests that host range is determined by vector habitat. For example, *R. prowazekii*, aetiologic agent of epidemic typhus, is transmitted from person to person by the human body louse. To date, few non-human mammalian reservoirs for this particular strain of rickettsiae are reported (Bozeman *et al.*, 1975; Marchette, 1982). In contrast, *R. tsutsugamushi*, aetiologic agent of scrub typhus, is transmitted by the bite of the larvae of trombiculid mites. *R. tsutsugamushi* can be isolated from many different mammalian species in the natural environment of the mite, as well as from incidental intruders into the habitat (Marchette, 1982).

The probable target cell in vivo for all the rickettsiae is the endothelial cell: rickettsial invasion of endothelium appears to cause the initial pathology and symptoms of infection. Virtually every cultured cell type, however, will support replication of rickettsiae in vitro, including several reptile, insect, and avian cell lines. Experiments with infected animals suggest that inflammatory cells and cells of the immune system also become infected, and may provide the means for passage of rickettsiae to their vectors in the natural life cycle of these arthropods (Boese, 1972).

A. Intracellular Infection

The characteristic feature of rickettsiae that sets them apart from other free-living micro-organisms is the absolute requirement of these parasitic bacteria for an intracellular site of replication. Clearly, the satisfaction of such an important function, survival of the species, is an evolutionary imperative. Mammalian hosts have undergone a similar and parallel evolutionary pressure to assure homeostatic balance in their complex tissues that sustain life. The creativeness of the rickettsiae in their adaptation to the perils of intracellular existence is remarkable. The association of rickettsiae and humans is relatively young on an evolutionary scale, and only time will tell whether this association will stabilise into a symbiotic relationship that benefits survival of both populations. The measure of the instability of this relationship at present is the degree of pathology generated in the battle between host and parasite: in most instances, the rickettsiae appear to have the upper hand.

1. Attachment of rickettsiae

The ability of rickettsiae to infect a wide variety of cells, from the highly phagocytic neutrophil and macrophage to the barely phagocytic fibroblast and lymphocyte, argues against a specific receptor on cells for rickettsial attachment. In fact, studies with *R. prowazekii* suggest that the primary molecule to which rickettsiae adhere on red blood cells (RBCs) is cholesterol, or a complex of cholesterol and another unidentified molecule (Ramm and Winkler, 1976). Use of abundant membrane constituents for attachment would certainly explain the wide range of cells entered by rickettsiae. Despite the logic of such a ubiquitous attachment site, however, the idea that cholesterol is the receptor on cells other than RBCs has eluded confirmation (Winkler, 1986).

2. Penetration of rickettsiae

Entry of rickettsiae into cells is by 'induced phagocytosis', a process observed for many, if not all, obligately intracellular micro-organisms (see also Section II.A). Unlike that of chlamydiae, however, entry of rickettsiae requires the expenditure of energy by both the bacterium and the host cell (Cohn *et al.*, 1959; Walker and Winkler, 1978): for productive infection to occur, both the rickettsiae and the host cell must be metabolically active. Further, the host cell must be capable of phagocytosis: cells treated with cytocholasin B do not ingest attached rickettsiae (Ramm and Winkler, 1976; Winkler and Miller, 1982), nor do rickettsiae enter cells (RBCs) that are not phagocytic (Ramm and Winkler, 1976). Although the mystery of how rickettsiae facilitate their own uptake into cells remains unsolved, one interesting theory of the induction of phagocytosis is based on a phospholipase A_2 activity observed in the lysis of RBCs. Winkler (1986) has proposed a concerted process of induced phagocytosis in which attachment of rickettsiae to cells activates a phospholipase A activity (presumed to be on the rickettsiae) that releases fatty acids from the cell membrane, and signals the cell to internalise the damaged membrane for repair. The rickettsiae attached to this portion of the damaged cell membrane is phagocytosed as a bystander of the repair process, and continues the disruption of the membrane as it is internalised. As the process of phagocytosis is completed, so is membrane lysis at the distal end of the phagosome. Thus, theoretically at least, as the rickettsiae are being phagocytosed, they are simultaneously disrupting the phagocytic vacuole and releasing themselves into the cytosol of the cell. The host cell membrane retains its integrity since the phagocytic event has isolated the damaged portion of the membrane. This theory ties together several different observations, and takes into account the information that certain of the rickettsiae have never been observed in a phagocytic vacuole, even within minutes of attachment and entry. However, the majority of data that contribute to this theory are from studies with *R. prowazekii*. Observations with the phospholipase A activity of *R. rickettsii* have been less consistent (Walker, 1984; Silverman, 1986). Moreover, *R. tsutsugamushi* has a complex, but markedly different scenario of entry into cells (discussed in Section III. A.4).

3. Intracellular localisation of the rickettsiae

The rickettsiae are energy parasites that can satisfy their metabolic needs only by localising in intracellular compartments rich in nutrients of the energy cycles. The major metabolic deficiency of typhus and spotted fever rickettsiae may be the generation of sufficient quantities of adenosine triphosphate (ATP) to fulfil all of their energy-requiring functions (Bovarnick, 1956). Given an exogenous source of glutamate, the rickettsiae can synthesise ATP *de novo*, albeit relatively poorly compared with other free-living bacteria (Bovarnick and Allen, 1957). The rickettsiae can, however, transport preformed ATP across their cell membrane, a process unusual among the prokaryotes (Winkler, 1976). The requirement for preformed ATP may explain the localisation of certain rickettsial strains, notably *R. tsutsugamushi*, in the glycogen- and mitochondrion-rich region of cells (Rikihisa and Ito, 1980). Although synthesis of ATP is minimal in *R. prowazekii*, pathways for liberation of energy by conversion of ATP to ADP are intact. Rickettsia-generated ATP is undoubtedly used to maintain baseline metabolic levels during transport from cell to cell, and for the energy required to induce phagocytosis. Thus, the rickettsiae can survive for short periods of time in an extracellular environment. They must, however, gain access to the intracellular environment of a cell for the preformed ATP to fuel such energy-requiring events as replication.

The intracellular location of the rickettsiae is characteristic for each species: *R. tsutsugamushi* is found only within the cytoplasm of the cell, generally in the perinuclear region; *R. typhi* and *R. prowazekii* are found dispersed throughout the cytoplasm; and the spotted fever group rickettsiae are found in both the cytoplasm and the nucleus of infected cells (Burgdorfer *et al.*, 1968) (Table 19.2). All rickettsiae multiply freely in the cytosol of the cell, and, in contrast to the chlamydiae, are not bound by any host-cell-derived membranes. The replication of rickettsiae is that charcteristic of all bacteria: division by binary fission. The generation time for each of the rickettsiae is quite slow, 8–20 hours, and is influenced primarily by the nature of the host cell. Thus, a single rickettsial species will exhibit varying generation times in different cell lines (Wisseman *et al.*, 1976; Silverman and Bond, 1984).

4. Progressive infection

It is clear from studies on plaque formation by the different rickettsiae in tissue culture that all the rickettsiae spread from an initial infectious focus to adjacent cells. For certain of the rickettsiae, such as *R. prowazekii*, it is presumed that lysis of the originally infected cell precedes infection of neighbouring cells. The temporal residence of other rickettsiae within cells appears to be governed by internal signals within the micro-organism: shortly after the onset of intracellular replication (10–15 hours for *R. rickettsii*; 18–24 h for *R. tsutsugamushi*) one or more rickettsiae begin migrating from the original infected cell to establish infection in adjacent cells. The percentage of infected cells increases linearly with time in culture in the absence of any detectable cell loss (Wisseman *et al.*, 1976; Nacy and Meltzer, 1979; Silverman and Bond, 1984). The signals that regulate this early rickettsial migration are not known, but may confer an evolutionary advantage on the organism able to establish widespread infection without massive tissue destruction. How is migration of rickettsiae prior to cell lysis accomplished? For *R. rickettsii*, whose intracellular residence includes both the cytoplasm and the nucleus, there is little information. *R. tsutsugamushi* infection of mouse mesothelium in vivo, however, demonstrated an interesting, and possibly unique, mechanism by which this rickettsia passes from cell to cell (Ewing *et al.*, 1978). Egress from infected cells occurs by a budding process analogous to that of enveloped viruses, and the rickettsiae leave the cell surrounded by a host-derived plasma membrane. Ingestion by adjacent cells occurs by phagocytosis of this membrane-bound micro-organism, and rickettsiae are then found within the newly infected cell with two layers of host material. Within minutes of internalisation, the rickettsiae dissolve the two host membrane layers and are free in the cytoplasm to begin replication. Lysosomal fusion does not occur during this brief time. Thus, *R. tsutsugamushi* is not only protected from the potentially hostile extracellular environment by a coat of host cell membrane, but it is also protected from the major intracellular source of antimicrobial activity, the phagolysosome, by its rapid escape into the cytoplasm.

At some point late in the replication cycle of all rickettsiae, infected cells become so filled with bacteria that rupture occurs, releasing massive numbers of these micro-organisms, each one capable of initiating a new infectious cycle.

B. Natural Immunity

As with chlamydiae (see Section II.B), the interaction of rickettsiae and host cell proceeds in a well-defined, and logical sequence: (a) attachment; (b) entry; (c) replication; and (d) release from the cell. Unlike that of the chlamydiae, however, transmission of rickettsiae from the infected individual is *not* under the control of the host, but is accomplished almost exclusively through the natural life cycle of the various arthropods that serve as reservoirs and vectors. Natural immune parameters are most effective, therefore, during transmission of the rickettsiae from cell to cell, rather than from host to host. Despite powerful evidence in experimental animals that non-specific immunity plays a role in both the initiation of disease and the resolution of established infections, this area of host defence is relatively unexplored in humans. With the exception of rickettsialpox (aetiologic agent, *R. akari*), intervention by drugs such as tetracycline and chloramphenicol is recommended to reduce the mortality (20 to 60 per cent) of untreated rickettsial diseases. Even with drug treatment, there is ample evidence to suggest that rickettsial organisms persist in tissues for years in the absence of any clinical symptoms (Fox, 1948; Murray *et al.*, 1951). In these infected individuals a balance is achieved between factors that protect the host from overt disease and factors that favour survival of the rickettsiae: the regulation of this new homeostatic balance is as yet unclear. The concept of non-sterile immunity in rickettsioses, however, will be a fascinating intellectual challenge to unravel.

1. Barrier mechanisms

The integrity of skin is a major barrier used as natural protection against infection. Each of the rickettsiae successfully breaches this barrier by a vector mode of transmission, although introduction of the organism differs for the different rickettsial species. Scrub typhus and spotted fever rickettsiae are inoculated directly into extravascular spaces during the feeding cycle of the chigger and the tick, respectively. In contrast, participation of the host is required for infection by typhus rickettsiae: inoculation occurs by introduction of infected louse faeces when the host scratches the insect bite (Blanc and Baltazard, 1938). Hypersensitivity to the bite of arthropod vectors occurs with repeated exposure, and inflammatory cells which accompany hypersensitivity responses, rather than providing a second line of defence, appear to support survival and replication of the rickettsiae (Wisseman and Tabor, 1964; Gambrill and Wisseman, 1973a, b; Rikihisa and Ito, 1980; Nacy and Osterman, 1979; Turco and Winkler, 1984; Nacy and Meltzer, 1984).

2. Acute-phase reactions

The efficiency of rickettsiae for establishment of infections in vivo is astonishing. In experimental animal models, one lethal dose equals one infectious dose: that is, a single viable rickettsia is sufficient to establish a lethal infection in a susceptible host (Groves and Osterman, 1978). This incredible efficiency suggests that most of the interstitial barrier mechanisms available to the host (acute-phase proteins, alternate pathway complement activation, inflammatory cell infiltrates) will be less than effective in preventing establishment of an infectious focus. Once the rickettsiae are intracellular, the host is faced with a whole new set of problems. How then are rickettsial infections controlled? Mortality rates (considerably less than 100 per cent for each of the human rickettsial diseases), persistence of rickettsiae in tissues after resolution of primary infection, and experience with a number of experimental animal models, all suggest that unidentified innate host factors do contribute to the containment of rickettsial infections.

3. Cytokine-mediated defence mechanisms

Experimental evidence suggests that the resolution of primary disease is through the cell-mediated arm of the immune system: antigen-reactive lymphocytes, their soluble products (lymphokines), regulatory cytokines from non-immune cells, and non-specific effector cells such as activated macrophages and NK cells. The combination of cells and cytokines required to protect animals from each of the rickettsial species is likely to be different, but in each case, events that lead to eradication of rickettsiae or suppression of rickettsial growth can be divided into events that occur outside of cells, and events that occur inside.

a. Factors that affect attachment or entry of rickettsiae

Under certain well-defined experimental conditions, the interaction between rickettsiae and macrophages during evolution of an immune response regulates susceptibility to disease (Nacy and Groves, 1981; Nacy and Meltzer, 1984; Jerrells and Osterman, 1981, 1982a). An analysis in vitro of the factors that play a role in this non-specific macrophage-mediated resistance demonstrates that the events for acquisition of antirickettsial activity by macrophages can be temporally separated into two discrete phases: (1) macrophages exposed to lymphokines (the soluble products of antigen-stimulated lymphocytes) before interaction with rickettsiae develop the capacity to resist infection with the bacterium; and (2) macrophages exposed to lymphokines after rickettsiae establish an intracellular infection acquire the capacity to kill the intracellular parasite (Nacy and Meltzer, 1979). The lymphokine-induced decrease in the ingestion of rickettsiae is fascinating, and has now been documented with several different rickettsiae (Nacy and Meltzer, 1979; Nacy and Meltzer, 1982; Turco and Winkler, 1984), and a variety of other obligate and facultative intracellular parasites (Miller and Twohy, 1969; Salvin and Chang, 1971; Hoff, 1975; Nacy *et al.*, 1981; Horwitz and Silverstein, 1981; Pappas and Nacy, 1983). This antimicrobial activity is not simply an alteration in phagocytic capacity of macrophages, nor is it a reflection of toxicity of lymphokines for these parasites (Nacy *et al.*, 1981; Oster and Nacy, 1984). The actual mechanism behind this reduction in the number of infected macrophages is not known but, since it is not parasite-specific, it is likely to be associated with an extracellular killing mechanisms at the site of parasite attachment.

The regulation of macrophage resistance to infection is an example of an effector reaction that is induced by the co-operation of several distinct lymphokines: both IFN-γ and another non-IFN macrophage-activating lymphokine are required for the reaction to proceed; neither activating factor alone is effective (Meltzer *et al.*, 1986). That this effector reaction develops during in vivo infections has been documented with both *R. tsutsugamushi* and *R. akari* (Nacy and Meltzer, 1982, Nacy *et al.*, 1983; Nacy and Meltzer, 1984).

b. Factors that affect intracellular survival of rickettsiae

Macrophages treated with lymphokines after infection with rickettsiae develop the capacity to kill the intracellular bacterium (Nacy and Meltzer, 1979; Wisseman and Waddell, 1983; Turco and Winkler, 1984; Jerrells *et al.*, 1986). The lymphokines that induce this effector reaction are several, and may differ for the different rickettsial species (Nacy *et al.*, 1981): without question, IFN-γ is the major, and in some case the only, macrophage-activating agent. For *R. tsutsugamushi*, both IFN and non-IFN-γ activating factors are effective in induction of intracellular killing by macrophages (Nacy *et al.*, 1981): these lymphokines act independently, but may co-operate by affecting different macrophage subpopulations for maximal intracellular killing in vivo (Nacy *et al.*, 1985). For intracellular destruction of *R. conorii*, however, IFN-γ may be the only lymphokine that regulates this macrophage-mediated effector activity: cloned murine IFN-γ reproduced the activity of lymphokines for induction of rickettsiacidal activities against *R. conorii* in macrophage monolayers, and monoclonal antibodies prepared against IFN-γ abrogated lymphokine-induced intracellular killing activites (Jerrells *et al.*, 1986). As with *R. conorii*, the antirickettsial activities of macrophages against *R. prowazekii* appear to be regulated primarily by IFN-γ (Wisseman and Waddell, 1983; Turco and Winkler, 1984). More importantly for rickettsial infections, however, these investigators determined that IFN-γ can also restrict multiplication of *R. prowazekii* in several different types of non-immune cells (Turco and Winkler, 1983a, b, c; Wisseman and Waddell, 1983). The mechanism for IFN-induced inhibition of rickettsial replication in fibroblasts and endothelial cells is not known, but is apparently not due to the depletion of tryptophan, as is the case with toxoplasmas and *C. psittaci* (Pfefferkorn, 1984; Byrne *et al.*, 1986; Turco and Winkler, 1984). *R. prowazekii* is also a nonviral inducer of IFN-α and IFN-β during active infections in experimental animals (Kazar, 1966). Unlike the effects of IFN-γ, however, intracellular replication of *R. prowazekii* is not inhibited by IFN-α/β (Turco and Winkler, 1983b). In contrast to the results obtained with *R. prowazekii*, intracellular survival of *R. akari* in fibroblasts is affected by treatment of cells with non-immune IFNs (Kazar *et al.*, 1971).

C. In vivo Infections

1. Experimental animal models

Probably the most striking evidence for the inherent diversity of the rickettsiae is the susceptibility of experimental animals to infection with these agents. Guinea pigs and mice have been used extensively for isolation of rickettsial agents, but the availability of genetically inbred mice facilitated analysis of host factors that may be important in resolution of rickettsial diseases. It came as no surprise to rickettsiologists, who had grappled with rickettsial strain and intrastrain diversity for years, that different rickettsial species manifested different patterns of susceptibility in inbred mouse stocks: some rickettsiae (for example, Karp strain of *R. tsutsugamushi*) were uniformly lethal to mice when injected intraperitoneally (ip); other closely related rickettsiae (Gilliam strain of *R. tsutsugamushi*) induced a pattern of resistance to ip infection that suggested a genetically determined resistance trait (Groves and Osterman, 1978). In fact, the gene for natural resistance to ip infection by Gilliam *R. tsutsugamushi*, *Ric*, has been mapped to chromosome 5 of the mouse, and is linked to the gene for retinal degeneration (Groves *et al.*, 1980). The resistant allele of this gene has been grafted onto the susceptible C3H/He genetic background, creating a congenic C3H/RV mouse that differs from susceptible C3H/He mice in but a single genetic locus (Darnell *et al.*, 1974). Changing the route of *R. tsutsugamushi* inoculation, however, changes the whole picture of mouse strain susceptibility: both Karp and Gilliam strains administered subcutaneously (sc) produce no detectable disease in the ip-susceptible animals, and will, in fact, protect mice from lethal ip rickettsial challenge with either of the strains; mice given an intravenous (iv) inoculation of Gilliam are resistant to lethal disease (Groves and Osterman, 1978; Jerrells and Osterman, 1982b).

That these differences within rickettsial strains are not a peculiarity of *R. tsutsugamushi* is underscored by studies with a spotted fever group rickettsia, *R. akari*. Analysis of inbred mouse susceptibility to different strains of this rickettsia showed that most strains of *R. akari* did not produce lethal disease when inoculated by any route. Inoculation of the Kaplan strain did, however, produce an interesting pattern of susceptibility that suggested macrophage control of resistance (Anderson and Osterman, 1980; Meltzer and Nacy, 1980): each mouse strain susceptible to lethal *R. akari* disease had a characterised macrophage defect (Boraschi and Meltzer, 1979a, b and c). The route of inoculation of this rickettsia was not critical to the outcome of disease (Anderson and Osterman, 1980). Further analysis of innate resistance to *R. akari* demonstrated that the gene responsible for susceptibility in C3H mice was the *Lps* gene on chromosome 4, a locus that controls not only susceptibility to the lethal effects of bacterial LPS, but also the ability of macrophages to respond to activation agents for intra- and extra-cellular killing effector mechanisms (Anderson and Osterman, 1980; Watson *et al.*, 1977; Ruco *et al.*, 1978; Nacy and Meltzer, 1982). The observation that C3H/HeJ mice are susceptible to lethal infections with two other spotted fever group rickettsiae, *R. conorii* and *R. siberica*, suggests an underlying common mechanism of resistance to this group of micro-organisms (Eisemann *et al.*, 1984).

The A strain mice are also susceptible to the Kaplan strain of *R. akari*, and have a macrophage defect for extracellular killing that is not under *Lps* gene control (Meltzer and Nacy, 1980; Boraschi and Meltzer, 1979b, c). Although macrophages from *R. akari*-infected A/J mice do not develop the capacity to kill tumour cells, a characteristic of their macrophage defect, rickettsial susceptibility could be genetically dissociated from the expression of this macrophage effector activity (Meltzer *et al.*, 1982; Nacy and Meltzer, 1982). The gene(s) that regulate susceptibility to *R. akari* infections in A strain mice are presently being mapped using recombinant inbred mice: preliminary analysis of the data suggests multigenic control.

Despite the availability of congenic pairs of mice whose innate susceptibility to disease is regulated by single genes (C3H/He [Ric^s] and C3H/RV [Ric^r] for *R. tsutsugamushi*; C3H/He [Lps^n] and C3H/HeJ

[Lps^d] for *R. akari*), the host factors that influence resistance or susceptibility to any of the rickettsiae remain undefined. At best, we can say that inflammation and macrophages probably play a role, and that the induction of non-specific immunity early in infection influences the outcome of disease (Jerrells and Osterman, 1981, 1982a, 1982b; Jerrells, 1983; Nacy and Groves, 1981; Nacy and Meltzer, 1982, 1984). Resistance of certain mouse strains to iv-inoculated *R. tsutsugamushi* can be abolished by treatment of mice with agents which destroy tissue macrophages (Jerrells and Osterman, 1982b); at some level, then, expression of resistance is an innate capacity of tissue macrophages. In lethal animal models, however, factors that regulate development of specific antigen recognition by T lymphocytes are most likely to influence resistance: Ia antigen expression, essential for the presentation of antigens, is comparatively downregulated in macrophages of the susceptible animals (Jerrells, 1983), and cells that most efficiently respond to IFN-γ for expression of Ia antigens — the younger peroxidase granule-containing macrophages — are not a major component of inflammatory exudates during lethal rickettsial infections (Nacy and Groves, 1981). The importance of the induction of immune responses for resistance against rickettsial diseases is demonstrated with monoclonal antibodies prepared against IFN-γ. The administration of monoclonal anti-IFN antibodies to resistant animals before infection with *R. conorii* blocks IFN-γ activity and Ia antigen expression, and exacerbates disease: more than 50 per cent of normally resistant mice die of fulminant rickettsial infections (Li, *et al.*, 1987). Whether antibodies administered later in infection could affect development of macrophage killing activities rather than Ia antigen-induced inductive events was not studied. Macrophages from *R. conorii*-infected mice do develop the capacity to eliminate intracellular rickettsiae (Kokorin *et al.*, 1980). That non-specific macrophage-mediated immunity is important in development of resistance to infection with *R. tsutsugamushi* and *R. akari* as well is suggested by protection studies with non-specific macrophage-activating agents (Nacy *et al.*, 1983; Nacy and Meltzer, 1984). In these studies, susceptible animals pretreated with *Mycobacterium bovis* strain BCG or *Propionobacterium acnes* (*C. parvum*) could be protected from lethal disease as long as they were able to respond to the non-specific activation agent with rickettsiacidal macrophages; susceptible mice with additional genetic defects in capacity to generate activated macrophages were not protected. Thus, macrophages appear to play a pivotal role in both the induction of immunity and the performance of effector functions in the expression of innate resistance to rickettsial infections.

2. *Human infections*

The rickettsiae all cause febrile exanthems, a result of infection of endothelial cells and peripheral vasculitis. Clinical symptoms, morbidity and mortality vary with the different rickettsial strains. Little is known about factors that influence natural resistance or successful resolution of disease with any these organisms. In all cases, intervention by drugs is recommended to reduce mortality: tetracycline is the drug of choice.

IV. SUMMARY

For both the chlamydiae and rickettsiae, the host responses that suppress replication of the organism and the host responses that promote survival of the organism paradoxically overlap. Thus the classic non-specific host defences that facilitate elimination of bacteria in an extracellular environment (i.e. inflammation, phagocytosis) now supply these obligate intracellular parasites with more susceptible cells, and a greater chance for survival. Once inside the cell, the host must now induce extraordinary changes in the intracellular milieu of a number of cell types to eliminate, or at least suppress the replication of, the infecting bacterium. That mortality rates are frequently far less than might be expected is strong testimony to the innovative evolution of both innate and acquired immune responses. Despite evidence for these novel host responses that excite and fascinate the basic researcher, analysis of host defence mechanisms, unfortunately, takes second place to design of optimal drug therapy for any micro-organism susceptible to conventional antibiotics. For both the chlamydiae and rickettsiae, drug therapy works. Only when evidence emerges that therapy is less than completely effective will there be an increase in interest in the precise nature of host-derived factors that contribute to natural resistance. Natural immunity certainly plays a role in resistance to infection, but the mechanisms involved, and the balance between host and parasite-derived factors that influence this naturally occurring resistance, are yet to be determined.

REFERENCES

Anderson, G. W. Jr, and Osterman, J. V. (1980). *Infect. Immun.* 28: 132.

Barron, A. L., White, H. J., Rank, R. G. Soloff, B. L. and Moses, E. B. (1981). *J. Inf. Dis.* 143: 63.

Barron, A. L., Rank, R. G. and Moses, E. B. (1984). *Infect. Immun.* 44: 82.

Batteiger, B. E., Newhall, W. J. and Jones, R. B. (1985). *Infect. Immun.* 50: 488.

Bell, S. D. Jr, Snyder, J. C. and Murray, E. S. (1959). *Science* 130: 626.

Blanc, G. and Baltazard, M. (1938). *Bull. Acad. Natl. Med. Paris* 120: 109.

Boese, J. L. (1972). *J. Med. Entomol.* 9: 591.

Boraschi, D. and Meltzer, M. S. (1979a). *Cell. Immunol.* 45: 188.

Boraschi, D. and Meltzer, M. S. (1979b). *J. Immunol.* 122: 1587.

Boraschi, D. and Meltzer, M. S. (1979c). *J. Immunol.* 122: 1592.

Bovarnick, M. R. (1956). *J. Biol. Chem.* 220: 353.

Bovarnick, M. R. and Allen, E. G. (1957). *J. Bacteriol.* 74: 637.

Bozeman, F. M., Masiello, S. A., Williams, M. S. and Ellisberg, B. L. (1975). *Nature* 255: 545.

Brunham, R. C., Kuo, C. -C. and Chen, W. -J. (1985). *Infect. Immun.* 48: 78.

Burgdorfer, W., Anacher, R. L., Bird, R. G. and Bertram, D. S. (1968). *J. Bacteriol.* 96: 1415.

Byrne, G. I. (1978). *Infect. Immun.* 19: 607.

Byrne, G. I. (1986). *Microbiology* 6: 99–102.

Byrne, G. I. and Faubion, C. L. (1982). *J. Immunol.* 128: 469.

Byrne, G. I. and Faubion, C. L. (1983). *Infect. Immun.* 40: 464.

Byrne, G. I. and Krueger, D. A. (1983). *Infect. Immun.* 42: 1152.

Byrne, G. I. and Krueger, D. A. (1985). *J. Immunol.* 134: 4189.

Byrne, G. I. and Moulder, J. W. (1978). *Infect. Immun.* 19: 598.

Byrne, G. I. and Rothermel, C. D. (1983). *Infect. Immun.* 39: 1004.

Byrne, G. I., Lehmann, L. K. and Landry, G. L. (1986). *Infect. Immun.* 53: 347–51.

Caldwell, H. D. and Hitchcock, P. J. (1984). *Infect. Immun.* 44: 306.

Cohn, Z. A., Bozerman, F. M., Campbell, J. M., Humphries, J. W. and Sawyer, T. K. (1959). *J. Exp. Med.* 109: 271.

Darnell, M. B., Koprowski, H. and Lagerspetz, K. (1974). *J. Infect. Dis.* 129: 240.

de la Maza, L. M., Peterson, E. M., Goebel, J. M., Fennie, C. W. and Czanieki, C. W. (1985). *J. Immunol.* 135: 4198.

Eisemann, C. S., Nypaver, M. J. and Osterman, J. V. (1984). *Infect. Immun.* 43: 143.

Eissenberg, L. G. and Wyrick, P. B. (1981). *Infect. Immun.* 32: 889.

Ewing, E. P., Takeuchi, A., Shirai, A. and Osterman, J.V. (1978). *Infect. Immun.* 19: 1078.

Fox, J. P. (1948). *J. Immunol.* 59: 109.

Friis, R. R. (1972). *J. Bacteriol.* 110: 706.

Gambrill, M. R. and Wiseman, C. L. Jr (1973a). *Infect. Immun.* 8: 631.

Gambrill, M. R. and Wiseman, C. L. Jr (1973b). *Infect. Immun.* 8: 519.

Groves, M. G. and Osterman, J. V. (1978). *Infect. Immun.* 19: 583.

Groves, M. G., Rosenstreich, D. L., Taylor, B. A. and Osterman, J. V. (1980). *J. Immunol.* 125: 1395.

Hackstadt, T. and Caldwell, H. D. (1985). *Infect. Immun.* 48: 546.

Hackstadt, T., Todd, W. J. and Caldwell, H. D. (1985). *J. Bacteriol.* 161: 25.

Harrison, H. R., Alexander, E. R., Chiang, W. -T., Giddens, W. E. Jr, Boyce, J. T., Benjamin, D. and Gale, J. L. (1979). *J. Inf. Dis.* 139: 141.

Hatch, T. P., Allen, I. and Pearce, J. H. (1984). *J. Bacteriol.* 157: 13.

Hodinka, R. L. and Wyrick, P. B. (1986). *Microbiology* 6: 86–90.

Hoff, R. (1975). *J. Exp. Med.* 142: 299.

Horwitz, M. A. and Silverstein, S. C. (1981). *J. Exp. Med.* 154: 1618.

Howard, L. V., O'Leary, M. P. and Nichols, R. L. (1976). *Brit. J. Vener. Dis.* 52: 261.

Jerrells, T. R. (1983). *Infect. Immun.* 42: 549.

Jerrells, T. R. and Osterman, J. V. (1981). *Infect. Immun.* 31: 1014.

Jerrells, T. R. and Osterman, J. V. (1982a). *Infect. Immun.* 37: 117.

Jerrells, T. R. and Osterman, J. V. (1982b). *Infect. Immun.* 37: 1066.

Jerrells, T. R., Turco, J., Winkler, H. H. and Spitalny, G. L. (1986). *Infect. Immun.* 51: 355.

Kazar, J. (1966). *Acta Virol.* 10: 277.

Kazar, J., Krautwurst, P. A. and Gordon, F. B. (1971). *Infect. Immun.* 3: 819.

Kokorin, I. N., Kabanova, E. A. and Shirokova, E. M. (1980). *Acta Virol.* 137: 24.

Kuo, C. -C., Wang, S. -P., and Grayston, J. T. (1973). *Infect. Immun.* 8: 74.

Lammert, J. K. and Wyrick, P. B. (1982). *Infect. Immun.* 35: 537.

Li, H., Jerrells, T. R., Spitalny, G. L. and Walker, D. H. (1987). *Infect. Immun.* 55: 1252.

Marchette, N. J. (1982). *Ecological Relationships and Evaluation of the Rickettsiae,* vols 1 and 2. Florida: CRC Press.

Megran, D. W., Stiver, H. G. and Bowie, W. R. (1985). *Infect. Immun.* 49: 670.

Meltzer, M. S. and Nacy, C. A. (1980). *Cell. Immunol.* 54: 487.

Meltzer, M. S., Nacy, C. A., Stevenson, M. M. and Skamene, E. (1982). *J. Immunol.* 129: 1719.

Meltzer, M. S. Hoover, D. L., Gilbreath, M. J., Schreiber, R. D. and Nacy, C. A. (1986). *Ann. Inst. Pasteur/Immunology* 137C: 206.

Meyer, K. F. and Eddie, B. (1962). *Ann. NY Acad. Sci.* 98: 288.

Miller, H. C. and Twohy, D. W. (1969). *J. Parasitol* 55: 200.

Moulder, J. W. (1985). *Microbiol. Rev.* 49: 298.

Moulder, J. W., Hatch, T. P., Byrne, G. I. and Kellogg, K. R. (1976). *Infect. Immun.* 14: 277.

Murray, E. S., Psarn, T., Djakovic, P., Sielski, S., Broz, V., Ljupsa, F., Gaon, J., Pavlevic, R., and Snydes, J. C. (1951). *Am. J. Public Health* 41: 1359.

Murray, H. W., Byrne, G. I., Rothermel, C. D. and Cartelli, D. M. (1983). *J. Exp. Med.* 158: 234.

Myers, W. F. and Wisseman, C. W. Jr (1980). *Int. J. Syst. Bacteriol.* 30: 143.

Nacy, C. A. and Groves, M. G. (1981). *Infect. Immun.* 31: 1239.

Nacy, C. A. and Meltzer, M. S. (1979). *J. Immunol.* 123: 2544.

Nacy, C. A. and Meltzer, M. S. (1982). *Infect. Immun.* 36: 1096.

Nacy, C. A. and Meltzer, M. S. (1984). *J. Leukocyte Biol.* 4: 385.

Nacy, C. A. and Osterman, J. V. (1979). *Infect. Immun.* 26: 744.

Nacy, C. A., Leonard, E. J. and Meltzer, M. S. (1981). *J. Immunol.* 126: 204.

Nacy, C. A., Hockmeyer, W. T., Benjamin, W. R., Farrar, J. J., James, S. L. and Meltzer, M. S. (1983). In E. Pick, J. J. Oppenheim and M. Landy (eds), *Interleukins, Lymphokines, and Cytokines.* New York: Academic Press: 617.

Nacy, C. A., Meltzer, M. S., Fortier, A. H., Buchmeier, N. and Schreiber, R. D. (1985). *J. Immunol.* 135: 3505.

Newhall, W. J. and Jones, R. B. (1983). *J. Bacteriol.* 154: 998.

Nuriminen, M., Leinonen, M., Saikku, P. and Makela, P. H. (1983). *Science* 220: 1279.

Oriel, J. D. and Ridgway, G. L. (1984). *Genital Infections by Chlamydia trachomatis,* New York: Elsevier.

Oster, C. N. and Nacy, C. A. (1984). *J. Immunol.* 132: 1494.

Pappas, M. G. and Nacy, C. A. (1983). *Cell. Immunol.* 80: 222.

Pfefferkorn, E. R., (1984). *Proc. Natl. Acad. Sci. USA* 81: 908.

Plotz, H., Smadel, J. E., Anderson, T. F. and Chambers, L. A. (1943). *J. Exp. Med.* 77: 355.

Ramm, L. E. and Winkler, H. H. (1976). *Infect. Immun.* 13: 120.

Rank, R. G., Hough, A. J. Jr, Jacobs, R. F., Cohen, C. and Barron, A. L. (1985a). *Infect. Immun.* 48: 153.

Rank, R. G., Soderberg, L. S., and Barron, A. L. (1985b). *Infect. Immun.* 48: 847.

Rikihisa, Y. and Ito, S. (1980). *Infect. Immun.* 30: 231.

Rothermel, C. D., Rubin, B. Y. and Murray, H. W. (1983). *J. Immunol.* 131: 2542.

Ruco, L. P., Meltzer, M. S. and Rosenstreich, D. L. (1978). *J. Immunol.* 121: 543.

Salvin, S. B. and Chang, S.-L . (1971). *Infect. Immun.* 3: 548.

Schachter, J. and Dawson, C. R. (1978). *Human Chlamydial Infections.* Littleton, Mass.: PSG Publishing Company.

Schramek, S. (1972). *Acta Virol. Engl. ed.* 16: 447.

Shemer, Y. and Sarov, I. (1985). *Infect. Immun.* 48: 592.

Shirai, A., Chan, T. C. Ghan, E. and Huxsoll, D. L. (1979). *Jpn. J. Med. Sci. Biol.* 32: 179.

Silverman, D. J. (1986). *Ann. Inst. Pasteur/Microbiol.* 137A: 336.

Silverman, D. J. and Bond, S. B. (1984). *J. Infect. Dis.* 149: 545.

Silverman, D. J. and Wisseman, C. L. Jr (1978). *Infect. Immun.* 21: 1020.

Stevens, R. S., Chen, W. -J. and Kuo, C. -C. (1982). *Infect. Immun.* 35: 680.

Swenson, C. E., Donegan, E. and Schachter, J. (1983). *J. Inf. Dis.* 148: 1101.

Tuffrey, M., Falder, P. and Taylor-Robinson, D. (1982). *Br. J. Exp. Path.* 63: 539.

Turco, J. and Winkler, H. H. (1983a). *Infect. Immun.* 42: 27.

Turco, J. and Winkler, H. H. (1983b). *J. Exp. Med.* 157: 974.

Turco, J. and Winkler, H. H. (1983c). *J. Exp. Med.* 158: 2159.

Turco, J. and Winkler, H. H. (1984). *Infect. Immun.* 45: 303.

Tyeryar, F. J. Jr, Weiss, E., Millar, D. B., Bozeman, F. M. and Ormsbee, R. A. (1973). *Science* 180: 415.

Walker, D. H., Firth, W. T., Ballard, J. G. and Hegarty, B. C. (1983). *Infect. Immun.* 40: 840.

Walker, T. S. (1984). *Infect. Immun.* 44: 205.

Walker, T. S. and Winkler, H. H. (1978). *Infect. Immun.* 22: 200.

Ward, M. E. and Murray, A. (1984). *J. Gen. Micro.* 130: 1765.

Watson, J., Riblet, R. and Taylor, B. A. (1977). *J. Immunol.* 118: 2088.

Weiss, E. (1973). *Bacterial. Rev.* 37: 259.

Williams, D. M., Schachter, J., Drutz, D. J. and Sumaya, C. V. (1981). *J. Inf. Dis.* 143: 238.

Williams, D. M., Schachter, J., Coalson, J. J. and Grubbs, B. (1984a). *J. Inf. Dis.* 149: 630.

Williams, D. M., Schachter, J., Weiner, M. H. and Grubbs, B. (1984b). *Infect. Immun.* 45: 674.

Winkler, H. H. (1976). *J. Biol. Chem.* 134: 884.

Winkler, H. H. (1986). *Ann. Inst. Pasteur/Microbiol.* 137A: 333.

Winkler, H. H. and Miller, E. T. (1982). *Infect. Immun.* 38: 109.

Wisseman, C. L. Jr and Tabor, H. (1964). *J. Immunol.* 93: 816.

Wisseman, C. L. Jr and Waddell, A. (1983). *J. Exp. Med.* 157: 974.

Wisseman, C. L. Jr, Edlinger, E. H., Waddell, A. D. and Jones, M. R. (1976). *Infect. Immun.* 14: 1052.

Yong, E. C., Klebanoff, S. J. and Kuo, C. -C. (1982). *Infect. Immun.* 37: 422.

20

Bacterial Infections

CHRISTINA CHEERS

Department of Microbiology
University of Melbourne
Parkville Victoria 3052
Australia

I. INTRODUCTION

In order to gain access to the body, bacterial pathogens have to run the gauntlet of numerous defences: the physical barriers of the skin and mucous membranes, enzymes of the saliva and mucus, the low pH of the stomach and the eliminating actions of gut peristalsis and respiratory

NATURAL IMMUNITY
ISBN 0 12 5145551

cilia, to name only a few. They must compete with other organisms, the natural flora, to gain an initial foothold. Once past these obstacles, they encounter the natural immunity mechanisms which are the subject of this chapter.

Natural immunity has been classically divided into humoral and cellular, the relative importance of the two depending on whether the bacterium survives in the extracellular or intracellular environment. However, the division is by no means clearcut, with most organisms being killed by a combination of mechanisms, and the ultimate fate of all being elimination by the phagocytic cells.

This review will concentrate on animal models of infection, except where there is clearcut evidence of the antibacterial mechanisms in humans. This approach is justified by the degree of precise information afforded by experimental manipulation of animals, and the belief that results in animals give at least a strong indication of useful areas of investigation in humans. Given the breadth of the topic the choice of references must be selective and sometimes rather arbitrary.

II. HUMORAL MECHANISMS

A. Complement Fixation

There exist two admirable recent reviews of the interaction of bacteria and complement by both classical and alternative pathways (Joiner *et al.*, 1984; Taylor, 1983). Complement as a mechanism of natural immunity is also reviewed in this book (Chapter 7). The subject will therefore be surveyed here with special emphasis on aspects potentially affecting the outcome of bacterial infection.

A number of bacterial components have been shown to activate the complement cascade, either by the classical pathway or by the alternative pathway. Activation of the alternative pathway by lipopolysaccharide (LPS) in the absence of antibody was described by Pillemer and colleagues (1955) as the properdin system. It has since been shown that cell walls of Gram-positive bacteria also activate the alternative pathway (Brown *et al.* 1983; Winkelstein and Tomasz, 1978).

Some bacterial components activate the classical complement pathway without the aid of specific antibody. LPS from rough strains of bacteria can directly bind C1q (Clas and Loos, 1982). Smooth LPS is a great deal less efficient at this task. On the other hand, the presence of 'natural' antibodies, especially to Gram-negative bacteria following colonisation of the gut by commensals, and perhaps as a result of inapparent infections, may greatly augment the role of the classical pathway in natural immunity (Mason and Richardson, 1981). The majority of natural antibodies[1] are of the IgM class, which is particularly efficient, in combination with antigen, at initiating the classical pathway, and may be effective at extremely low concentration (Bjornson and Michael, 1970).

Protein A from *Staphylococcus aureus* complexed with IgG by its Fc end can also initiate the classical pathway. It is suggested that protein A actually increases the C3b-mediated phagocytosis of staphylococci (Peterson *et al.*, 1977), thus casting doubt on the role of protein A in protecting *S. aureus* from host defences.

Bacterial capsules, on the other hand, may inhibit complement activation by the alternative pathway (Brown *et al.*, 1983), as does the M protein of some streptococci (Horwitz, 1982). This prevention of complement activation may contribute to the survival value of these materials for the pathogen.

In deciding the relative importance of the classical and alternative pathways in resistance to infection, data from animals and humans genetically deficient in components of those pathways are useful. C4-deficient guinea pigs are not unusually susceptible to infection (Ellman *et al.*, 1971), nor are humans deficient in C2 or C4 (Ruddy *et al.*, 1970; Silverstein, 1960). Since a deficiency in C2 or C4 could be made good by an intact alternative pathway, it is tempting to conclude that this may be all that is required. However, the fact that patients with C1r deficiency are susceptible to infection (Pickering *et al.*, 1970) suggests that this may be an oversimplification.

The complement cascade makes a fourfold contribution to antibacterial resistance, as an opsonin, as a vasodilator, as a chemattractant and as a bactericidal agent. All four of these functions are elicited by activation of either the classical or the alternative pathway.

Opsonisation is a function of C3b complexed with the bacterium and binding to receptors on the surface of the phagocytes, either polymorphonuclear neutrophils or monocyte/macrophages. Three distinct receptors for C3 fragments have been identified. CR1, the receptor with greatest affinity for C3b, is found on all phagocytic cells, B lymphocytes and several other cell types (Beller *et al.*, 1982; Fearon and Wong, 1983). Its expression is up-regulated from its normal low level by C5a. The second receptor, CR3, has a higher affinity for iC3b than for C3b (Beller *et al.*, 1982). Both have been chemically characterised. A third complement receptor, CR2, is not found on phagocytic cells.

---

[1]See also Chapter 6.

The C3 receptors are mobile in the membrane of the phagocytic cell. It is believed that when the pseudopodia move to embrace the particle, the ability of the C3 receptors to move in the plane of the membrane allows the successive interaction of receptors with C3 on the surface of the particle, drawing the cell membrane about the phagocytosed particle like a three-dimensional zipper (Griffin and Mullinax, 1981). Binding of complement to C3 receptors alone may not be sufficient to initiate phagocytosis, depending on the state of activation of the phagocyte. A second signal may be required. This can be provided by a few molecules of IgG or deposition of fibronectin (Mantovani *et al.*, 1972; Pommier *et al.*, 1983).

Opsonisation is clearly important where the bacterium is otherwise not readily phagocytosed and where it cannot survive intracellularly. This is apparently so for such organisms as *Staph. aureus, Streptococcus pyogenes, Strep. pneumoniae, Neisseria meningitidis, N. gonorrhoeae* and *Haemophilus influenzae*, and numerous studies have confirmed the requirement for complement (or other opsonin) for in vitro phagocytosis of these organisms.

Confirmation of the opsonic role of complement in vivo comes from studies on blood clearance of various organisms in complement-depleted animals. Complement depletion by immune complexes or immunoglobulin aggregates led to decreased sequestration of bacteria by hepatic macrophages (Spiegelberg *et al.*, 1963). Depletion of C3 by cobra venom factor resulted in defective blood clearance of pneumococci in guinea pigs, with a consequent 4 log lowering of the LD_{50} (Brown *et al.*, 1981). On the other hand, guinea pigs genetically deficient in C4 showed normal clearance, again emphasising the importance of the alternative pathway which can bypass the C4 deficiency.

An elegant study of the role of C3 in experimental pneumococcal meningitis has recently been reported (Tuomanen *et al.*, 1986). While normal cerebrospinal fluid (CSF) is deficient in complement, immuno-globulin and leukocytes, all these appear in the CSF during bacterial meningitis. When rabbits treated with cobra venom factor to deplete C3 were inoculated intracisternally with encapsulated pneumococci there was at least a 100-fold decrease in LD_{50}. Although there was a short delay in the appearance of leukocytes, there was no effect on the final numbers, suggesting that chemotaxins other than complement were available. The rate of clearance of bacterial particles from the CSF was normal in the treated mice but the major effect of complement depletion was to diminish the efficiency of leukocyte killing. Thus, in this model, the most important role of complement was as an opsonin.

A dramatic demonstration of opsonisation in natural resistance in humans is provided by a number of reports of patients whose neutrophils and monocytes were deficient in the CR3 receptor for C3b (Anderson *et al.*, 1984; Crowley *et al.*, 1980; Ross *et al.*, 1985). The children were subject to repeated bacterial infections and their neutrophils were deficient in phagocytosis and possibly chemotaxis. Another report of a baby girl lacking CR3 describes much wider deficiencies in immune function, including chemotaxis, phagocytosis, natural killer (NK) cell deficiency, reduced cytotoxic T cell deficiency, impaired interferon production and no antibody response to thymus-dependent antigens (Fischer *et al.*, 1985). The child suffered severe recurrent bacterial infections and was unable to form pus.

Deficiency of C3 itself increases susceptibility to infection in humans (Alper *et al.*, 1973). This is presumably in part attributable to the importance of opsonisation and chemotaxis, but also to loss of the later steps in the complement cascade.

The direct chemotactic activity of complement has been assigned to C5a (Hugli and Müller-Eberhard, 1978). While chemotactic activity can be readily demonstrated in vitro, fewer examples exist in vivo. Perhaps the best demonstration of the importance of C5 arises in C5-deficient mice, which show increased susceptibility to *Corynebacterium kutcheri, Staph. aureus, Escherichia coli* and *Strep. pneumoniae* (Caren and Rosenberg, 1966; Easmon and Glynn, 1976, Glynn and Medhurst, 1967; Shin *et al.*, 1969). C5 deficiency in humans also is associated with repeated infections (Miller and Nilsson, 1970). Gervais *et al.* (1984) have convincingly shown, using recombinant inbred mice, that the inflammatory response to *Listeria monocytogenes* and to non-specific irritants is influenced by the *Hc* gene coding for C5.

Both the cleavage products C3a and C5a act on mast cells to release histamine and polymorph chemotactic activity (Hugli and Müller-Eberhard, 1978). Histamine, amongst other activities, is a vasodilator, an action which facilitates entry of cells and plasma to the tissues.

The bactericidal activity of complement is a function of the final steps of the cascade, when C5b to C9 are inserted into the bacterial membrane as the 'membrane attack complex' (MAC). Whether C9 is actually required for this activity remains controversial (Burger, 1986) The mechanism of bacterial killing is far from clear. Physical lysis of the bacterium is not a general feature of complement-mediated bactericidal activity *per se*, but can occur in the presence of lysozyme, which is available in serum (Schreiber *et al.* 1979). Complement-mediated damage to the bacterial cytoplasmic membrane allows the release of cytoplasmic components, presumably leading to cell death without necessarily involving lysis (Wright and Levine, 1981).

The importance of the direct bactericidal activity of complement is difficult to separate from earlier events in the cascade. However, where the infection occurs at a site relatively inaccessible to phagocytic cells, as in Gram-negative bacterial endocarditis, it has been shown experimentally that bacterial resistance to complement-mediated killing is an important factor in allowing persistance of the infection (Gutschik *et al.*, 1980). Furthermore, patients with deficiencies in C5, C6, C7 and C8 suffer from neisserial meningitis or bacteraemia (Brooks *et al.*, 1978; Haeney *et al.*, 1980; Petersen *et al.*, 1979). Deficiency in C9, described in a 78-year-old man, had no effect on his susceptibility to infection (Lint *et al.*, 1980). The prominence of neisserial infections in patients with deficiencies in the late components of complement is consistent with the observation that gonococci from localised genital infections are usually susceptible to serum bactericidal activity, whereas those invading the bloodstream to cause disseminated infection are resistant (Eisenstein *et al.* 1977). It is probable, however, that the directly bactericidal effects of complement are less important than its influence on phagocytosis.

B. Other Serum Factors

Lysozyme is present in serum at concentrations varying from 1 to 10 µg/mL. It can act alone against susceptible Gram-positive bacteria and, as mentioned above, acts together with complement to lyse Gram-negative bacteria. While complement-mediated killing can occur in the absence of lysozyme, removal of lysozyme reduces the rate of bactericidal action (Glynn and Milne, 1967; Taylor and Kroll, 1983). This reduced activity could be restored by adding egg-white lysozyme.

Properdin, a component of the alternative pathway of complement fixation, may be required for optimal killing by the classical pathway (Taylor and Kroll, 1983), although its role is undefined.

C-reactive protein (CRP) is a 115-kilodalton pentraxin whose synthesis is remarkably increased during infection. When it is administered to mice, it passively protects them from challenge by certain strains of encapsulated pneumococci (Mold *et al.*, 1981; Yother *et al.*, 1982). Its binding to the phosphorylcholine of the pneumococcal cell wall, or to any other phosphorylcholine, leads to activation of the classical pathway of complement fixation (Claus *et al.*, 1977).

There also exist in serum a number of less well defined bactericidal substances. So called Gram-positive bactericidins are possibly also active against Gram-negative bacteria (Donaldson *et al.*, 1974; Myrvik and Weisser, 1955). A heat-stable bactericide in rabbit serum has been defined and shown to kill *Bacillus subtilis*, *E. coli* and *Salmonella typhimurium* at remarkably low concentrations (Carroll and Martinez, 1981). Beta-lysins are relatively low molecular weight cationic proteins found in the serum of a variety of animal species, being released from platelets during coagulation. They are active against Gram-positive and Gram-negative bacteria (Donaldson *et al.*, 1974; Hirsch, 1960). The factor, as yet undefined, responsible for killing *Listeria monocytogenes* in rat serum, and said to account for that species' resistance to *Listeria* infection (Czuprynski and Balish, 1981; Davies *et al.*, 1981) may belong to this group.

III. CELLULAR MECHANISMS

It is already clear from the foregoing discussion of the influences of complement on phagocytes, that cellular and humoral mechanisms of antibacterial resistance are inextricably linked. However, let us now consider the problem primarily from the cellular viewpoint.

A. Inflammation

The process of acute inflammation has been reviewed by Ryan and Majno (1977). Some events are especially relevant to antibacterial immunity.

Once bacteria pass into the tissues, they are phagocytosed first by the resident tissue macrophages. Polymorphonuclear neutrophils, followed by monocytes, are next attracted to the scene, possibly by the effects of complement detailed above, possibly also by other chemotactic factors. Bacterial products are themselves chemotactic for both neutrophils and monocytes (Keller and Sorkin, 1967; Ward, 1968). Sometimes this chemotactic activity requires the intervention of complement (Baker *et al.*, 1977; Symon *et al.*, 1972). Substances produced during tissue injury and cell death can also generate chemotactic activity for neutrophils and monocytes. These substances include fibrin and collagen and their breakdown products (Barnhart *et al.*, 1971; Houck and Chang, 1971). Both macrophages and neutrophils are capable of releasing factors which are themselves chemotactic or which act on serum components producing chemotaxins (Adamson and Bowden, 1982; Snyderman *et al.*, 1972; Ward and Hill, 1970). The fact that neutrophils appear at the site of inflammation before monocytes probably reflects their more rapid response to chemotactic factors and the very large reserve of mature polymorphs in the bone marrow, about 20 times as many as are to be found in the bloodstream.

Having reached the site of infection, what is the relative role of these two cell types?

B. Polymorphonuclear Granulocytes

Studies abound documenting neutrophil phagocytosis and killing of Gram-positive and Gram-negative bacteria in vitro and presumably all these are potential targets for neutrophils in vivo.

Evidence for a protective role of polymorphs in vivo is available in a number of experimental models, although critical determination of this role is difficult, at least partly because there is no satisfactory means of selectively depleting granulocytes without affecting monocytes. An example of this is a rabbit model of bacterial endocarditis which has been exploited by Meddens and colleagues. They showed that granulocytes were influential in limiting the establishment and progress of *E. coli* endocarditis, based on the fact that depletion of monocytes with the drug VP 16-123 had no effect, whereas depletion of both granulocytes and monocytes by nitrogen mustard lowered the LD_{50} and increased bacterial numbers (Meddens *et al*., 1984). Interestingly, it was monocytes which protected against *S. epidermidis* endocarditis, while with *Strep. sanguis* neither cell influenced the progress of the disease.

Perhaps the most telling evidence of the vital importance of polymorphs comes from the condition of neutropenia. The most common causes of neutropenia are certain leukaemias and cytotoxic drugs. The condition can be rapidly fatal, due to overwhelming bacterial infection (Brown, 1984).

The plethora of other deficiencies in granulocyte function in humans seem to obey the dictum 'what can go wrong, will'.

Disorders of neutrophil chemotaxis include the graphically named 'lazy leukocyte syndrome', in which there is defective chemotaxis and random motion of leukocytes (Miller *et al.*, 1971), apparently due to abnormalities in the actin in the cells (Foroozanfar *et al.*, 1984); a familial defect in chemotaxis with normal random movement (Miller *et al.*, 1973); Job's syndrome, also a neutrophil actin abnormality, in which fair-skinned, red-haired girls with high serum IgE levels suffer from repeated 'cold' staphylococcal abscesses (Davis *et al.*, 1966); and Chediak-Higashi syndrome (Clark and Kimball, 1971), in which other abnormalities in the neutrophils may also contribute to morbidity. All these patients suffer repeated infections.

Deficiency of C3b receptors has been mentioned above as a familial trait leading to susceptibility to infection. It also seen in Job's syndrome and chronic granulomatous disease (Chen and Koren, 1985). This of course interferes with phagocytosis of any organisms requiring opsonisation by complement.

Impaired intracellular bactericidal activity occurs in a number of syndromes. The most important of these is chronic granulomatous disease, an inherited syndrome occurring typically in boys and commonly leading to death before the seventh year (Quie *et al.*, 1967). The children usually present with multiple recurrent granulomatous skin and lymph node infections, often developing pneumonia, liver abscesses and osteomyelitis. The major defect is failure to produce the usual metabolic burst which follows phagocytosis, leading to failure to make H_2O_2 and superoxide (Curnutte *et al.*, 1974; Johnson *et al.*, 1975). Lack of H_2O_2 means that the myeloperoxidase system is non-functional. Thus the patients are relatively resistant to the catalase-negative bacteria such as the streptococci which supply their own H_2O_2, but succumb to the catalase-positive bacteria like *Staph. aureus*, which presumably remove any vestige of H_2O_2 produced.

Some individuals lack myeloperoxidase itself (Miller *et al.*, 1971) and may suffer repeated infections. However most myeloperoxidase-deficient people have no ill effects, suggesting there may be a compensatory increase in the directly microbicidal H_2O_2 (Klebanoff, 1975).

Finally in Chediak-Higashi syndrome, giant azurophil (peroxidase-containing) granules in the leukocytes fail to fuse normally with phagosomes, resulting in decreased release of lysosomal contents into phagocytic vacuoles. The result is decreased bactericidal activity of the granulocytes (Root *et al.*, 1972). A murine analogue of this syndrome, the beige mutation, increases susceptibility of mice to experimental infection with *Strep. pneumoniae*, *Klebsiella pneumoniae*, *Staph. aureus* and *E. coli* (Elin *et al.*, 1974), all organisms normally destroyed by neutrophils, but not to *L. monocytogenes* (Cheers and Wood, 1984) which is generally associated with monocytes and macrophages. Interestingly, the beige mice have a normal life-span and do not seem to suffer inordinately from intercurrent infection in the laboratory.

C. Macrophages

The major role for macrophages in natural resistance to bacteria has generally been associated with the facultative intracellular bacteria, which include *Mycobacterium* species, *Brucella* species, those *Salmonella* species causing systemic infections (*Salm. typhi* in humans, *Salm.*

typhimurium, Salm. enteritidis in mice), *Legionella* species and *L. monocytogenes*, among others. It is possible that neutrophils may contribute to the initial resistance to establishment of these infections. Human and bovine neutrophils can phagocytose and kill *B. abortus* (Riley and Robertson, 1984; Young *et al.*, 1985), mouse neutrophils can kill *Listeria* (Czuprinski *et al.*, 1985), while even leprosy and tubercle bacilli are initially phagocytosed by neutrophils. Nevertheless these bacteria are by definition resistant to killing by any phagocytes, and so they outlast the acute neutrophil inflammatory response to survive within macrophages.

Their strategies for survival vary considerably, and although they are not completely understood, it is of interest to list some of the proposed mechanisms. *Mycobacterium tuberculosis* has been the subject of extensive study, and it was thought that the ability of virulent bacteria to inhibit fusion between phagosomes and lysosomes was the secret of their survival (Hart and Armstrong, 1974). However, it was later observed that coating the bacteria with antibody allowed fusion to occur but did not lead to bacterial death (Armstrong and Hart, 1975). Recent observations emphasise the disruption of phagosomal membranes by virulent *M. tuberculosis* and their growth free in the cytoplasm (Myrvik *et al.*, 1984). Living *Legionella pneumophila* also prevent fusion of lysosomes and phagosomes, at least for long enough to establish the characteristic replicative vacuole required for the multiplication of this organism (Horwitz, 1983). Fusion of lysosomes after phagocytosis of *Brucella suis* is relatively slow (Oberti *et al.*, 1981), and components have been isolated from *B. abortus* which delay fusion in both macrophages and neutrophils (Canning *et al.*, 1985; Frenchick *et al.*, 1985). *L. monocytogenes* is also said to delay fusion between phagosome and lysosome (De Heer *et al.*, 1980) and has been observed growing free in the cytoplasm of macrophages, having disrupted the phagosome membrane with enzymes (Armstrong and Sword, 1966). *M. lepraemurium* growing in mouse tissues does not prevent fusion of phagosomes and lysosomes, but is wrapped by parallel fibrils of peptidoglycolipid which is postulated to protect the bacteria from lysosomal enzymes (Draper and Rees, 1973). Similar fibrils have been described for *M. leprae* in human tissue, but their protective value can only be speculated upon. *Salmonella typhimurium* is also said not to inhibit phagosome–lysosome fusion, but to resist, by unspecified means, the action of lysosomal enzymes (Carrol *et al.*, 1979).

Despite the relative resistance of these organisms to killing by phagocytes, numerous studies describe the in vitro bactericidal or bacteriostatic activity of macrophages. A reasonably long time period is often required in the assays, and many studies have been flawed by the use of antibiotics to control extracellular growth. Unfortunately the assumption that antibiotics do not enter the cells is not justified (Cole and Brostoff, 1975). The use of induced peritoneal exudates as a source of cells can also cause confusion among the unwary as, depending on the inducing agent, they may show either increased or decreased activity compared with resident macrophages (Cohn, 1978; Spitalny, 1981). Furthermore, our knowledge of the bactericidal mechanisms of monocytes and macrophages is still not definitive. The mechanisms available include the many lysosomal enzymes and production of hydrogen peroxide and superoxide anions (Karnovsky and Lazdins, 1978). Monocytes, but not macrophages, possess the enzyme myeloperoxidase, which, with the help of H_2O_2, halogenates bacterial proteins. It is interesting to speculate that the greater bactericidal efficiency of monocytes in some instances (Klebanoff and Shepard, 1984; Wood et al., 1986) may be due to the presence of this enzyme. Nevertheless, it is extremely difficult to relate any one mechanism to the killing of a particular bacterium.

Indeed a proportion of injected bacteria do succumb on their first encounter with the resident macrophages. One of the most extensively studied is Listeria monocytogenes, admittedly the most susceptible of all the intracellular bacteria to macrophage killing. Infection of athymic nude mice with Listeria has been used to study natural resistance in the absence of T-cell-mediated acquired immunity. In a number of reports, nudes were found to be highly resistant to Listeria (Cheers and Waller, 1975; Zinkernagel and Blanden, 1975) or to develop chronic but controlled infection (Emmerling et al., 1977), depending apparently on the degree of activation of their macrophages by natural flora (Sharp and Colston, 1984). This is an interesting example of how normal flora can modify natural immunity, since germ-free nude mice showed less macrophage activation than conventional or defined-flora mice. Injection of dextran sulphate, which selectively damages macrophages, caused a rapid increase in bacterial numbers in both athymic nude mice and euthymic mice, indicating a role for resident macrophages (Emmerling et al., 1977). Newborg and North (1980) divided the resistance mechanisms of the nude mice into a radioresistant and a radiosensitive phase. The radioresistant phase, lasting the first 12 hours of infection and representing presumably resident macrophages, enabled nude mice to destroy a larger than normal proportion of the bacterial inoculum. The subsequent radiosensitive mechanism, presumably relating to the known influx of monocytes from the bone marrow (North, 1970a), controlled progression of bacterial multiplication over the next 24–48 hours. However in the absence of T cells the infection could not be eliminated and mice died sporadically over a period of six weeks.

The other intracellular bacteria show a similar sequence of control by resident macrophages and inflammatory monocytes, followed by specific cell-mediated immunity, albeit over a longer time scale than *Listeria*. In the case of the other intracellular bacteria, the macrophages, without the eventual help of T cells, are less successful in control. T-cell-deprived mice were unable to prevent progressive infection with *M. leprae, M. lepraemurium* or *M. bovis* (Collins *et al.*, 1975; Lancaster *et al.*, 1983; Lefford, 1985; Ueda *et al.*, 1978) although they were relatively resistant to *B. abortus* (Cheers and Waller, 1975; Duquesnoy *et al.*, 1969).

It is indicative of the importance of macrophages for defence against these bacteria that the virulence of a number of species correlates with their ability to survive or grow within these cells. Similarly, genetic resistance of the host can relate to the bactericidal efficiency of their macrophages.[2]

Mackaness and colleagues reported in 1954 on the growth of virulent and avirulent strains of *M. tuberculosis* in rabbit macrophages cultured in vitro. They found that the growth of H37RV, R1RV, H37Ra and BCG in macrophages correlated with the early rate of increase in livers and spleens of infected mice. Similarly, growth of virulent and avirulent strains of *B. abortus, B. suis* and *B. melitensis* in macrophages in vitro was shown to vary in proportion with their virulence (Holland and Pickett, 1958; Smith and Fitzgeorge, 1964). Virulent and avirulent *Salm. typhimurium* have also been tested and behaved as expected (Furness and Ferreira, 1959; Jenkin and Benacerraf, 1960), as did virulent and avirulent *Listeria* (Godfrey and Wilder, 1985).

The major example of host genetic resistance depending on macrophage bactericidal efficiency is the *Ity* gene of mice. Originally described as governing resistance to *Salm. typhimurium*, it was subsequently shown to be identical with the *Lsh* gene governing resistance to *Leishmania donovani* (Plant *et al.*, 1982). The resident macrophages of resistant (*Ity^r*) mice are 10–50 times more efficient at killing *Salm. typhimurium* in vitro (Lissner *et al.*, 1983). This difference in vitro translates into an LD_{50} for resistant mice which was greater than 10^5, compared with less than 10 for susceptibles. Resistance is expressed in vivo as a slower initial growth rate of *Salmonella* in the spleen and liver (Hormaeche, 1980). This difference in macrophage activity also affects to some degree the early growth of BCG (Forget *et al.*, 1981; Orme and Collins, 1984) and of intravenously injected *M. lepraemurium* (Brown *et al.*, 1982). In vitro studies with BCG- or *M. lepraemurium*-infected splenic macrophages showed that those from resistant mice spontaneously produced H_2O_2, whereas those from susceptible strains did not (Stach *et al.*, 1984).

---

[2] See Chapter 11.

Macrophages from resistant mice also had higher levels of superoxide dismutase, but there was no difference in production of superoxide anion. It is not yet clear whether this reflects the action of the *Ity* gene.

In a second, extensively studied model of the genetics of mouse resistance, it is the speed of the monocyte/granulocyte inflammatory response which is critical. This is the *Lsr* gene governing resistance to *Listeria* in mice (Cheers and McKenzie, 1978; Skamene *et al.*, 1979). Again there is a difference in the initial growth rate of the bacteria, measured 24 hours after infection (Cheers *et al.*, 1978; Mandel and Cheers, 1980). Resistant mice were characterised by an early influx of monocytes into the blood stream (Mandel and Cheers, 1980; Sadarangani *et al.*, 1980), although at the site of infection in the liver the major early inflammatory cell observed was the granulocyte, present in greater numbers in resistant than in susceptible mice (Mandel and Cheers, 1980). There was no difference in the bactericidal activity of resident peritoneal cells but, in response to intraperitoneal infection, highly bactericidal cells appeared in the peritoneal cavity earlier in resistant than in susceptible mice (Wood *et al.*, 1986). Generation of these cells was radiosensitive. Irradiation of resistant mice just prior to infection, with doses as low as 200 rads, increased their bacterial load 24–48 hours later (Sadarangani *et al.*, 1980; Cheers and Macgeorge, 1982), suggesting a requirement for a newly divided cell. Irradiation of susceptible mice did not increase bacterial counts. At a more fundamental level, it appears that the resistant mice have more macrophage precursors (colony-forming cells) in their bone marrow and spleen (Young and Cheers, 1986). Sluiter *et al.* (1984) found that *Listeria* induced, in both resistant and susceptible mice, a serum factor, 'factor inducing monocytosis' (FIM), which transferred to normal recipients of resistant but not susceptible strains, rapid blood monocytosis. It is probable that FIM was able to draw on the high number of monocyte precursors in the bone marrow of resistant mice.

It seems, therefore, that the primary influence on natural immunity to *Listeria* infection, and probably some other model infections, such as *Corynebacterium kutcheri* (Hirst and Campbell, 1977) and BCG (Allen *et al.*, 1977) is a rapid supply of newly formed monocytes arising from the reserve of macrophage precursors in C57B1-related strains of mice. This then points to the importance of haemopoiesis in natural resistance.

D. Haemopoiesis

Although those granulocytes taking part in the acute inflammatory response are largely drawn from the considerable pre-existing reserve of granulocytes in the bone marrow, there is no such reserve of already mature monocytes. Indeed monocytes appearing in the bloodstream within six hours of a stimulus have recently divided in the bone marrow (van Furth and Cohn, 1968). Moreover, monocytes appearing at the site of infection can be abolished by blocking cell division chemically (North, 1970b) or by irradiation (North, 1970a) just prior to infection, with resultant exacerbation of infection. Hence the ability to activate haemopoiesis can be critical in the early stages of infection.

Granulocytes and macrophages arise from precursor cells in the bone marrow, known as colony-forming cells because of their ability to form colonies of daughter cells when cultured with the appropriate growth factors in semi-solid medium. A number of these growth factors or colony-stimulating factors (CSFs) have been defined and extensively studied (Metcalf, 1986). They include, in the mouse, multipotential CSF (multi-CSF or interleukin 3), granulocyte–macrophage CSF (GM-CSF), macrophage CSF (M-CSF) and granulocyte CSF (G-CSF) and, in the human, CSF-α, CSF-β, pluripoietin and urinary CSF (M-CSF). Each acts on a somewhat different subset of colony-forming cells and has a different end product, as its name suggests.

It has long been observed in humans that the production of CSFs increases following infection (Metcalf and Wahren, 1968; Metcalf *et al.*, 1971) and it was known that bacterial products, especially Gram-negative and Gram-positive cell-wall components, could stimulate the production of CSFs (Metcalf, 1971; Staber and Metcalf, 1980).

Following infection of mice with a number of different pathogens, *Salm. typhimurium* (Trudgett *et al.*, 1973; Wilson *et al.*, 1982), *L. monocytogenes* (Wing *et al.*, 1984; Young and Cheers, 1986) and *B. abortus* (Cheers and Young, 1987), there was a rapid rise in serum colony-stimulating activity, measurable 6–24 hours after infection. The major CSFs in serum following *Listeria* infection were M-CSF and G-CSF, with low levels of GM-CSF (Cheers *et al.*, 1988). Multi-CSF was not detected. M-CSF, assayed in tissue extracts by RIA, was particularly high in the spleen (Cheers and Stanley, unpublished). It is noteworthy that splenectomy ablates the rise in serum CSF (Wood *et al.*, 1984).

The levels of CSF depended on infecting dose and bacterial load in the animal (Young and Cheers, 1986). The time of peak titre varied, but in all cases CSF titres returned to normal before the infection was eradicated. According to Quesenberry and colleagues (1978), studying a number of bacterial pathogens (*E. coli, Staph. aureus, Pseudomonas aeruginosa, Haemophilus influenzae* and *Strep. pneumoniae*), this fall coincided with the onset of tolerance to the CSF-elevating effect of purified bacterial endotoxin. The mechanism of this tolerance is unknown.

When the number of colony-forming cells in *Listeria*-infected mice was followed, it was found that their numbers in the spleen rose over a period of seven days (Wing *et al.*, 1984; Young and Cheers, unpublished), but their number in the bone marrow fell (Wing *et al.*, 1984), particularly in resistant mice (Young and Cheers, 1986). This might reflect the maturation of cells in the bone marrow and their movement into the bloodstream and to the site of infection. It was of particular interest that the number of colony-forming cells in resistant mice was higher than in susceptible, even before infection (Young and Cheers, 1986). Furthermore, the numbers of cells bearing receptors for the macrophage-specific growth factor M-CSF was higher in resistant than in susceptible mice (Cheers and Stanley, unpublished). Since genetic resistance in this model appears to depend on the speed with which newly formed monocytes reach the site of infection (Czuprynski *et al.*, 1985; Stevenson *et al.*, 1981; Wood *et al.*, 1986), the numbers of haemopoietic cells could well be of critical importance.

At just which level of haemopoietic precursor cells the burst of proliferation occurs during infection is not yet determined. These cells exist as a hierarchy, with primitive, normally non-proliferating, cells giving rise to multipotential colony-forming cells. These in turn differentiate into erythrocytes, eosinophils, megakaryocytes, mast cells, granulocytes or macrophages. The last two have an identifiable common precursor, the GM-CFC. Marchal and Milon (1981) found that after a high dose of BCG, granulocytes and macrophages were formed at the expense of erythrocytes, suggesting a diversion of cells into the phagocytic cell compartment.

The best illustration of the importance of haemopoiesis in humans occurs in cyclic neutropenia, where the deficiency in both granulocyte and monocyte production occurs as a result of a recurring deficiency of colony-stimulating factors (Guerry *et al.*, 1974; Moore *et al.*, 1974). An equivalent model exists in dogs (Dale *et al.*, 1971). The deficiency leads to repeated and severe infections.

IV. VARIATION IN NATURAL RESISTANCE TO BACTERIA

Many factors, some well defined, some not, can either increase or decrease natural resistance to bacteria. Consideration will be confined here to genetic factors, irradiation, age and nutrition, which are relatively well defined areas.

A. Genetic factors[3]

Genetic factors have been covered already where they throw light on the importance of various mechanisms of natural immunity. In humans they include well-defined deficiencies in various components of complement

---

[3] See also Chapter 11.

and in certain activities of phagocytic cells. In addition there are less well defined variations in familial or racial susceptibilities to disease. These have been particularly studied with respect to tuberculosis and leprosy. However, we have little knowledge as to the basis of these susceptibilities and perhaps too few clues as to where to look. Some clues can be provided by animal models, where the availability of inbred, congenic and mutant animals make genetic studies easier.

Genetic variation in resistance to *Salm. typhimurium* (*Ity* gene) has already been mentioned as reflecting the innate bactericidal activity of macrophages (Lissner *et al.*, 1983). However, other genes can also affect *Salmonella* resistance in mice. Deficiency in responsiveness to bacterial lipopolysaccharide (*Lps*^{d}) decreases resistance to *Salm. typhimurium* (O'Brien *et al.*, 1980). It is suggested that the macrophage inflammatory response to infection is defective in the LPS non-responder mice (MacVittie *et al.*, 1982). In addition, an X-linked deficiency in antibody production (*Xid*) abrogated late recovery from infection, presumably related to the low titres of antibody produced (O'Brien *et al.*, 1979). Eventual recovery from *Salmonella* may also be influenced by the H-2 haplotype of the mice, presumably also an effect on acquired immunity (Hormaeche *et al.*, 1985). Biozzi mice, which were originally bred for either high or low antibody responsiveness to sheep erythrocytes, show differences in resistance to all intracellular bacteria tested, including *Salmonella*. High-antibody responders are susceptible to infection. They apparently carry the *Ity*^{s} allele and an additional susceptibility factor, X^s (Plant and Glynn, 1982). This may or may not be the same as the susceptibility factor carried by C3HeB/FeJ mice, which distinguishes them from other LPS-responsive C3H strains (Eisenstein *et al.*, 1982; O'Brien and Rosenstreich, 1983). Yet another gene determines susceptibility of C57Bl and DBA/2 mice (O'Brien *et al.*, 1985). Thus there are at least five genes associated with *Salm. typhimurium* resistance or susceptibility in mice.

This pattern of a number of genes controlling resistance to a single infection is repeated in the case of *L. monocytogenes*. As noted above, the primary determinant of resistance is the *Lsr* gene (Cheers and McKenzie, 1978). This resistance/susceptibility is not a function of T cells and is expressed within 24 hours of infection (Cheers *et al.*, 1978; Cheers *et al.*, 1980). Mice of the *Lsr*^{r} genotype have higher numbers of haemopoietic cells in the bone marrow (Young and Cheers, 1986), and are able to rapidly mobilise highly bactericidal monocytes to the site of infection (Wood *et al.*, 1986). Their monocytes also have a shorter generation time following infection (Punjabi *et al.*, 1984). This response may be modified or reinforced by the *Hc* gene, governing C5 production. Absence of C5 leads to a poor chemotactic response of macrophages to *Listeria-*

activated T cells, so that C5-deficient B10D2/oSn (H_c^o, Lsr^r) show slower recovery from infection, although there is no difference in the LD_{50} of *Listeria* compared with congenic C5-sufficient B10D2/nSn (Lawrence and Schell, 1978; Petit, 1980). Absence of C5, together with an as yet unidentified second gene, also affects the chemotactic response of macrophages and granulocytes to a number of stimuli, and reinforces the susceptibility of mouse strains such as A/J (Gervais *et al.*, 1984). Nevertheless, many complement-sufficient strains (including BALB/cJ and CBA/H originally used to define the *Lsr* gene) are susceptible to *Listeria* (Cheers and McKenzie, 1978). Variation in resistance of sublines of BALB/c mice has recently been reported, but it is unclear whether these differences are genetic or physiological (Skamene, 1985). Biozzi high-antibody responders allow more rapid early growth of *Listeria* in livers and spleens than do low responders but show no difference in recovery or LD_{50} (Berche, 1985).

The mouse leprosy and tuberculosis models are of particular interest given the documented variation in human resistance to these mycobacteria. The mouse strain distribution of resistance or susceptibility to *M. lepraemurium* varies according to route of injection. Following intravenous injection, the *Ity* gene plays a major role (Brown *et al.*, 1982; Potter *et al.*, 1983; Skamene *et al.*, 1984), while subcutaneous injection leads to an altogether different pattern (Closs, 1975) which may reflect more than one gene and can be modified by the *H-2* haplotype of the mice (Curtis *et al.*, 1984; Douglas-Jones and Watson, 1985). Resistant C57Bl showed an earlier macrophage inflammatory response than susceptible BALB/c under the control of T cells (Adu *et al.*, 1983).

Resistance to *M. bovis* BCG in mice is also determined by a number of genes (Orme and Collins, 1984). The *Bcg* gene, again co-mapping with *Ity*, influences early growth within macrophages (Stach *et al.*, 1984; Gros *et al.*, 1983). A defect has also been identified in macrophage presentation of BCG antigen to T cells, leading to induction of suppressor T cells (Nakamura and Tokunaga, 1980), thus straddling natural and acquired immune systems. Other genetic influences on the course of BCG infection in mice have also been identified (e.g. Allen *et al.*, 1977; Kakinuma *et al.*, 1983).

Not only can a number of genes influence susceptibility to a single infection, but the converse situation also occurs, where a single gene can influence the response to a number of infections. For example it is apparent from the above discussion that the *Ity/Lsh* gene controls resistance, not only to *Salm. typhimurium*, but also to *Leishmania donovani*, *M. bovis* (BCG) and intravenously injected but not subcutaneously injected *M. lepraemurium*. The macrophages of *Ity^s* strains of mice are deficient in their ability to kill in vitro *Salm. typhimurium*, *M. bovis*,

E. coli, Staph. aureus and *Corynebacterium diphtheriae* (Lissner *et al.*, 1985; Stach *et al.*, 1984). Another study found that, although they are deficient in killing *Salm. typhimurium*, there was no deficiency in killing *Listeria* or *Staph. aureus*, implying that different mechanisms apply to different bacteria (van Dissel *et al.*, 1985).

This by no means exhausts the list of genetic defects, which are also discussed in Chapter 11. If such complexity exists in these defined mouse models, one almost despairs of unravelling the subtle defects in humans. However, the benefits to human medicine that should accrue from these studies are the elucidation of markers to identify potential susceptibility, and the ability to manipulate the response in order to overcome the problem.

B. Irradiation[4]

The effects of irradiation on bacterial infection have become relevant today, and some components of natural immunity to bacteria are very susceptible to irradiation. The early death due to infection of animals that are not specific-pathogen-free following irradiation is familiar to many a practising immunologist.

The main effect of ionising irradiation relevant to antibacterial resistance is on the haemopoietic system. Using experimental animals, it has been shown that very low doses of irradiation can markedly deplete the bone marrow of haemopoietic precursor cells (Chen and Schooley, 1970). Similarly low doses can increase the susceptibility to infection with *Salm. enteritidis, E. coli, Ps. aeruginosa, Yersinia pestis, Strep. zooedemicus, M. tuberculosis, M. leprae, M. marinum* and *Listeria* (Bennett and Baker, 1977; Hollingsworth and Beeson, 1955; Kambara *et al.*, 1970; Mor *et al.*, 1985; Nelson and Becker, 1959; Sadarangani *et al.*, 1980; Schechmeister *et al.*, 1952).

The effect of irradiation on the accumulation of efficiently bactericidal macrophages at the site of infection in the peritoneal cavity has been directly demonstrated in murine listeriosis (Wood *et al.*, 1986). Irradiation immediately before intraperitoneal infection stopped accumulation of efficiently bactericidal cells in the peritoneal cavity two days later. However, once that exudate was established, irradiation on day 2 (just before harvesting the cells for in vitro assay), did not diminish their bactericidal activity. Similarly Selvaraj and Sbarra (1966), using casein-induced neutrophil exudates in guinea pigs, found that as little as 50–100 rads given before casein injection, resulted in very poor cell yields, poor phagocytic activity and lower metabolic rates amongst those cells which

[4] See also Chapter 15.

were harvested 24 hours later. Reduced bactericidal activity against *E. coli* was also noted. Irradiation in vivo once exudates were already present, or irradiation in vitro with doses as high as 50 000 rads, had no effect on the cells. Most studies of irradiation of phagocytic cells in vitro have shown no effect on phagocytosis (e.g. Perkins *et al.*, 1966; Schmitke and Dixon, 1972) but Clarke and Wills (1980) showed increased lysosomal activity. Interestingly, Mukherjee and Sbarra (1968) found that when irradiation was given actually during the period of phagocytosis, there was increased bactericidal activity due to H_2O_2 production.

There have been occasional reports of an anomalous increase in phagocytic and bactericidal activity in irradiated conventional (non-SPF) animals (e.g. Cheers and Waller, 1975; Fred *et al.*, 1970), which was apparently due to the activating effects of the gut flora (Fred *et al.*, 1970). In addition, recovery of haemopoietic precursor cells following irradiation was more rapid in the presence of a normal gut flora, whose endotoxin stimulates the production of haemopoietic growth factors (Quesenberry *et al.*, 1978).

Incorporation of radioisotopes into the bone marrow is an effective means of decreasing the number of haemopoietic cells. Mice injected with ^{89}Sr show increased susceptibility to *Listeria* infection (Bennett and Baker, 1977).

The intestinal epithelium, also a rapidly turning over population, is extremely sensitive to irradiation (Hendry *et al.*, 1983). In humans, irradiation of the gut during cancer therapy can damage the integrity of the epithelium, leading to susceptibility to infection via the gut (Husseinzadeh *et al.*, 1984; Jadeja *et al.*, 1983). It is undoubtedly this effect on the permeability of the gut to bacteria and bacterial components which leads to the presence of endotoxin in the serum of mice following irradiation (Quesenberry *et al.*, 1978), with subsequent stimulation of haemopoiesis and perhaps direct activating effects on the macrophages and granulocytes.

C. Age[5]

Individuals at the extremes of age, either young or old, show increased susceptibility to bacterial infections. Although a component of this susceptibility can be attributed to deficiencies in specific acquired immunity, either humoral or cellular, there are deficiencies in natural immunity which contribute.

Young mice are extremely sensitive to infection with *L. monocytogenes* (Ohara *et al.*, 1985; Patel, 1981). This was related to an extremely

---

[5] See also Chapter 12.

low number of macrophages, poor macrophage chemotaxis both in vivo and in vitro, and defective intracellular killing of the pathogen (Ohara *el al.*, 1985). Acquired cell-mediated immunity was also defective in the young mice. Although Wilson (1986) attributes human neonatal suscepti-bility to overwhelming infection with *Listeria* and other facultative intracellular bacteria to deficiencies in acquired T-cell-mediated immu-nity, some of the above mechanisms may also contribute.

Human neonates are also highly susceptible to infection with Group B streptococci. This appears to be due to a combination of deficiencies in natural immunity (Wilson, 1986). There is a diminished influx of neutrophils to the site of infection because of the low reserve of mature neutrophils in neonatal bone marrow and chemotactic abnormalities in the cells. There is also a slight deficiency in complement and decreased microbicidal activity of the neutrophils.

At the other end of the age scale, the elderly also show increased susceptibility to infection. The evidence for depressed natural immunity in humans is slight and the picture is confused by other disease processes in the elderly (Schneider, 1983; Yoshikawa, 1984). Of the natural immune mechanisms, neutrophil and monocyte responses may be somewhat depressed or unchanged (Antonaci *et al.*, 1984; Palmblad and Herak, 1978; Schneider, 1983) but complement levels are the same (Nagaki *et al.*, 1980; Palmblad and Herak, 1978). The evidence for a depressed acquired immune response in the elderly is stronger (Smith *et al.*, 1983; Yoshikawa, 1984).

On an experimental level, evidence for changes in resistance to the intracellular bacterium, *L. monocytogenes* in aged mice is equally confused, with some reports showing a decreased resistance (Gardner and Remington, 1977; Patel, 1981) and others an increase (Løvik and North, 1985; Matsumoto *et al.*, 1982). The increased resistance in old mice was apparently due to greater macrophage and monocyte activity early in infection, depressing bacterial numbers. It was suggested that this led to lower antigenic load to activate the T cells for acquired immunity, giving as a secondary effect a poor acquired response (Løvik and North, 1985). This study, then, emphasises some of the traps in studying the components of the immune response which may change with age, or indeed in other circumstances.

D. Nutrition[6]

Reports of increased susceptibility to bacterial infection associated with malnutrition abound (e.g. Chandra, 1983; Watson and Petro, 1983). Malnutrition does not have to be advanced for deficiencies in resistance

[6] See also Chapter 13.

to occur (Watson and Petro, 1983; Gross and Newberne, 1980). It is, however, difficult to relate susceptibility to infection to particular effects on the immune response, since these are so diverse.

Protein-malnourished patients have depressed haemolytic complement activities and depressed levels of all complement components except C4 (Sirisnha *et al.*, 1973; Smythe *et al.*, 1971; Suskind *et al.*, 1976). The complement deficiency which is a primary effect of protein malnutrition is probably worsened by the activation of the complement cascade as a result of accompanying infection (Chandra, 1975). In view of the importance of complement in defence against bacteria, it would seem that these effects must contribute to increased susceptibility.

Reports on the effects of malnutrition on phagocytosis and killing of bacteria are numerous but contradictory (Gross and Newberne, 1980). One is left with the impression that the effects of protein malnutrition on the acquired immune response may be more important in determining susceptibility to bacteria than the effects on natural immunity.

At the other end of the nutritional scale, obese dogs are less able to resist *Salmonella* infections while obese babies are more subject to lower respiratory tract infections (Gross and Newberne, 1980).

The effects of vitamins on phagocytes and antibacterial resistance are equally complex. Retinol deficiency appears to increase susceptibility to infection via a defect in serum opsonins and in phagocytosis (Dionigi, 1982). Shilotri (1977) found that the leukocytes of vitamin-C-deficient guinea pigs were deficient at killing *E. coli*, being markedly impaired in their glycolytic and hexose monophosphate shunt pathways. Ganguly *et al.* (1976) reported that scorbutic guinea pigs were susceptible to infection due to impaired mobility of phagocytic cells. It seems that supranormal levels of vitamin C increase the hexose monophosphate shunt in phagocytic cells, as well as enhancing random mobility and chemotaxis (Shilotri and Bhat, 1977; Smith *et al.*, 1975). Nevertheless there is no increase in bactericidal activity (McCall *et al.* 1971; Smith *et al.* 1975). There is little comfort here for the proponents of high doses of vitamin C, at least with respect to antibacterial resistance.

V. CONCLUSION

It should be obvious from the foregoing discussion that the division of immunity to bacteria into humoral and cellular is a highly artificial one, since the two are intimately interdependent. This interaction is summarised in Figure 20.1. In any one infection, it is probable that a number of immune mechanisms are operative. Genetic variation in resistance, where it leads to a deficiency in a single mechanism, can give important clues as to the contribution of that mechanism.

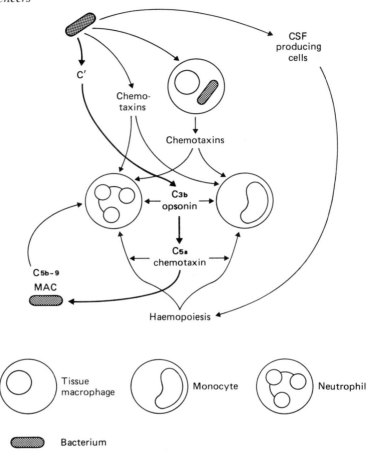

Fig. 20.1: Schematic representation of natural immune response to bacteria. When the bacterium invades the tissues it may be phagocytosed by resident macrophages. Chemotaxins are released from the bacteria themselves, by interaction with complement or from damaged tissue cells, including macrophages. Neutrophils and monocytes appear at the site of infection. Phagocytosis may be aided by complement-mediated opsonisation. Meanwhile the cells producing colony-stimulating factors (CSF) have been triggered and haemopoiesis stimulated. The end result of complement activation is killing of the bacteria by the membrane attack complex (MAC) and the dead bacteria are disposed of by the phagocytes.

ACKNOWLEDGMENTS

The author thanks Ms Angela Haigh and Ms Anne Young for their help in preparing the manuscript and Professor D. O. White for his constructive comments.

REFERENCES

Adamson, I. Y. R and Bowden, D. H. (1982). *Am. J. Path.* 106: 40–6.

Adu, H. O., Turk, J. L. and Curtis, J. (1983). *J. Pathol.* 139: 275–90.

Allen, E. M, Moore, V. L. and Stevens, J. O. (1977). *J.Immunol.* 119: 343–7.

Alper, C. A., Bloch, K. J., and Rosen, F. S. (1973). *N. Engl. J. Med.* 288: 601–6.

Anderson, D. C., Schmalsteig, F. C., Arnaout, M. A., Kohl, S., Tosi, M. F., Dana, N., Buffone, G. J., Hughes, B. J., Brinkley, B. R., Dickey, W. D., Abramson, J. S., Springer, T. A., Boxer, L. A., Hollers, J. M. and Smith, C. W. (1984). *J. Clin. Invest.* 74: 536–51.

Antonaci, S., Jirillo, E., Ventura, M. T., Garofalo, A. R. and Bonomo, L. (1984). *Mech. Ageing Dev.* 24: 367–75.

Armstrong, B. A. and Sword, C. P. (1966). *J. Bacteriol.* 91: 1346–55.

Armstrong, J. A. and Hart, P. D. (1975). *J. Exp. Med.* 142: 1–16.

Baehner, R. L. (1974). *J. Pediatr.* 84: 317–27.

Baker, L. A., Campbell, P. A. and Hollister, J. R. (1977). *J. Immunol.* 119: 1723–6.

Barnhart, M. I., Sulisz, L. and Bluhm, G. B. (1971). In B. K. Forscher and J. C. Houck (eds), *Immunopathology of Inflammation.* Amsterdam: Excerpta Medica: 59–65.

Beller, D. I., Springer, T. A. and Schreiber, R. D. (1982). *J. Exp. Med.* 156: 1000–9.

Bennett, M. and Baker, E.E. (1977). *Cell. Immunol.* 33: 203–10.

Berche, P. A. (1985). *Immunology* 56: 707–16.

Birmingham, J. R. Tabatabai, L. B., Deyoe, B. L., Jeska, E. L. and Nuessen, M. E. (1982). *Immunology* 46: 17–22.

Bjornson, A. B. and Michael, J. G. (1970). *Infect. Immun.* 2: 453–61.

Brooks, G. F., Ingwer, I. and Peterson, B. H. (1978). In G. F. Brooks and F. E. Young (eds), *Immunobiology of Neisseria gonorrhoeae.* Washington D. C.: American Society for Microbiology: 199–203.

Brown, A. E. (1984). *Amer. J. Med.* 76: 421–8.

Brown, E. J., Hosea, S. W. and Frank, M. M. (1981). *J. Clin. Invest.* 67: 975–82.

Brown, E. J., Joiner, K. A., Gaither, T. A., Hammer, C. H. and Frank, M. M. (1983). *J. Immunol.* 131: 409–15.

Brown, I. N., Glynn, A. A. and Plant, J. (1982). *Immunology* 47: 149–56.

Burger, R. (1986). *Immunol. Today* 7: 27–9.

Canning, P. C., Roth, J. A., Tabatabai, L. B. and Deyoe, B. L. (1985). *J. Infect. Dis.* 152: 913–21.

Caren, L. D. and Rosenberg, L. T. (1966). *J. Exp. Med.*124: 689–99.

Carrol, M. E., Jackett, P. S., Aber, V. R. and Lowrie, D. B. (1979). *J. Gen. Microbiol.* 110: 421–9.

Carroll, S. F. and Martinez, R. J. (1981). *Biochemistry* 20: 5981–7.

Chandra, R. K. (1975). *Arch. Dis. Child.* 50: 225–9.

Chandra, R. K. (1983). *Lancet* 1: 688–91.

Cheers, C. and Macgeorge, J. (1982). In R. B. Herberman (ed.), *NK Cells and other Natural Effector Cells.* New York: Academic Press: 1521–6.

Cheers, C. and McKenzie, I. F. C. (1978). *Infect. Immun.* 19: 755–62.

Cheers, C. and Waller, R. (1975). *J. Immunol.* 115: 844–7.

Cheers, C. and Wood, P, (1984). *Immunology* 51: 711–17.

Cheers, C. and Young, A. M. (1987). *Microbial Path.* 3: 185–194.

Cheers, C,. McKenzie, I. F. C., Pavlov, H., Waid, C. and York, J. (1978). *Infect. Immun.*19: 763–70.

Cheers, C., McKenzie, I. F. C., Mandel, T. E. and Chan, Y. Y. (1980). In E. Skamene, P. A. L. Kongshavn and M. Landy (eds), *Genetic Control of Natural Resistance to Infection and Malignancy.* New York: Academic Press: 141–7.

Cheers, C., Haigh, A. M., Kelso, A., Metcalf, D., Stanley, E. R. and Young, A. M. (1988). *Infect. Immun.* 56: 247–251.

Chen, A. R. and Koren, H. S. (1985). *J. Immunol.* 134: 1909–13.

Chen, M. G. and Schooley, J. C. (1970). *Radiat. Res.* 41: 623–36.

Clark, R. A. and Kimball, H. R. (1971). *J. Clin. Invest.* 50: 2645–52.

Clarke, C. and Wills, E. D. (1980). *Int. J. Radiat. Biol.* 38: 21–30

Clas, F. and Loos, M. (1982). *Infect. Immun.* 37: 935–9.

Claus, D. R., Siegel, J. Petras, K., Osmond, A. P. and Gewurz, H. (1977). *J. Immunol.* 119: 187–92.

Closs, O. (1975). *Infect. Immun.* 12: 480–9.

Cohn, Z. A. (1978). *J. Immunol.* 121: 813–16.

Cole, P. and Brostoff, J. (1975). *Nature* 256; 515–17.

Collins, F. M., Congdon, C. C. and Morrison, N. E. (1975). *Infect. Immun.* 11: 57–64.

Crowley, C. A., Curnutte, J. T., Rosin, R. E., Andre-Schwartz, J., Gallin, J. I., Klempner, M., Snyderman, R., Southwick, F. S., Stossel, T. P. and Bablior, B. M. (1980) *N. Engl. J. Med.* 302: 1163–8.

Curnutte, J. T., Whitten, D. M. and Bablior, B. M. (1974). *N. Engl. J. Med.* 290: 593–7.

Curtis, J., Akuffo-Adu, H. and Turk, J. L. (1984). *Infect. Immun.* 46: 635–8.

Czuprynski, C. J. and Balish, E. (1981). *Infect. Immun.* 33: 348:54.

Czuprynski, C. J., Henson, P. M. and Campbell, P. A. (1984). *J. Leukocyte Biol.* 35: 193–208.

Czuprynski, C. J., Canono, B. P., Henson, P. M. and Campbell, P. A. (1985). *Immunology* 55: 511–18.

Dale, D. C., Brown, C. H., Charbone, P. and Wolff, S. M. (1971). *Science* 173: 152–3.

Davies, W. A., Ackerman, V. P. and Nelson, D. S. (1981). *Infect. Immun.* 33: 477–81.

Davis, S. D., Schaller, J. and Wedgwood, R. J. (1966). *Lancet* 1: 1013–15.

De Heer, E., Kersten, M. C., Van der Meer, C., Linnemans, W. A. and Willers, J. M. (1980). *Lab. Invest.* 43: 449–55.

Dionigi, R. (1982). *Proc. Nutr. Soc.* 41: 355–71.

Donaldson, D. M., Roberts, R. R., Larsen, H. S. and Tew, J. G. (1974). *Infect. Immun.* 10: 657–66.

Douglas-Jones, A. G. and Watson, J. D. (1985). *J. Immunol.* 135: 2824–8.

Draper, P. and Rees, R. J. W. (1973). *J. Gen. Microbiol.* 77: 79–87.

Duquesnoy, R. J., Jeunet, F. S., Meuwissen, H. J. and Good, R. A. (1969). *Int. Arch. Allerg.* 35: 514–18.

Easmon, C. S. F. and Glynn, A. A. (1976). *Infect. Immun.* 13: 399–406.

Eisenstein, B. I., Lee, T. J. and Sparling, P. F. (1977). *Infect. Immun.* 15: 834–41.

Eisenstein, T. K., Deakins, L. W., Killar, L., Saluk, P. H. and Sultzer, B. M. (1982). *Infect. Immun.* 36: 696–703.

Elin, R. J., Edelin, J. B. and Wolff, S. M. (1974). *Infect. Immun.* 10: 88–91.

Ellman, L., Green, I., Judge, F. and Frank, M. M. (1971). *J. Exp. Med.* 134: 162–75.

Emmerling, P., Finger, H. and Hof, H. (1977). *Infect. Immun.* 15: 382–5.

Fearon, D. T. and Wong, W. W. (1983). *Ann. Rev. Immunol.* 1: 243–71.

Fischer, A., Seger, R., Durandy, A., Grospierre, B., Virelizier, J. L., Le Deist, F. Griscelli, C., Fischer, E., Kazatchkine, M. and Bohler, M. C. (1985). *J. Clin. Invest.* 75: 2385–92.

Forget, A., Skamene, E., Gros, P., Miailhe, A. C. and Turcotte, R. (1981). *Infect. Immun.* 32: 42–7.

Foroozanfar, N., Grohmann, T. H. and Hobbs, J. R. (1984). *Diagn. Immunol.* 2: 25–9.

Fred, R. K., Dobson, E. L., Kelly, L. S. and Shore, M. L. (1970). *J. Reticuloendothel. Soc.* 7: 453–70.

Frenchick, P. J., Markham, R. J. and Cochrane, A. H. (1985). *Am. J. Vet. Res.* 46: 332–5.

Furness, G. and Ferreira, I. (1959). *J. Infect. Dis.* 104: 203–6.

Ganguly, R., Durieux, M. F. and Waldman, R. H. (1976). *Amer. J. Clin. Nutr.* 29: 762–5.

Gardner, I. D. and Remington, J. S. (1977). *Infect. Immun.* 16: 593–8.

Gervais, F., Stevenson, M. and Skamene, E. (1984). *J. Immunol.* 132: 2078–83.

Glynn, A. A. and Medhurst, F. A. (1967). *Nature* 213: 608–10.

Glynn, A. A. and Milne, C. M. (1967). *Immunology* 12: 639–53.

Godfrey, R. W. and Wilder, M. S. (1985). *Infect. Immun.* 47: 837–9.

Griffin, F. M. and Mullinax, P. J. (1981). *J. Exp. Med.* 154: 291–305.

Gros, P., Skamene, E. and Forget, A. (1983). *J. Immunol.* 131: 1966–72.

Gross, R. L. and Newberne, P. M. (1980) *Physiol. Rev.* 60: 188–302.

Guerry, D., Adamson, J. W., Dale, D. C. and Wolff, S. M. (1974). *Blood* 44: 257–62.

Gutschik, E., Norwood, R. S., Møller, S. and Olling, S. (1980). *Acta. Pathol. Microbiol. Scand.* Sect. B. 88: 269–76.

Haeney, M. R., Thompson, R. A., Faulkner, J., Mackintosh, P. and Ball, A. P. (1980). *Clin. Exp. Immunol.* 40: 16–24.

Hart, P. D' A. and Armstrong, J. A. (1974). *Infect. Immun.* 10: 742–6.

Hendry, J. H., Potten, C. S. and Roberts, N. P. (1983). *Radiat. Res.* 96: 100–12.

Hirsch, J. G. (1960). *J. Exp. Med.* 112: 15–22.

Hirst, R. G. and Campbell, R. (1977). *Infect. Immun.* 17: 319–24.

Holland, J. J. and Pickett, M. J. (1958). *J. Exp. Med.* 108: 343–60.

Hollingsworth, J. W. and Beeson, P. B. (1955). *Yale J. Biol. Med.* 28: 56–62.

Hormaeche, C. E. (1980) *Immunology* 41: 973–9.

Hormaeche, C. E., Harrington, K. A. and Joysey, H. S. (1985). *J. Infect. Dis.* 152: 1050–6.

Horwitz, M. A. (1982). *Rev. Infect. Dis* 4: 104–23.

Horwitz, M. A. (1983). *J. Exp. Med.* 158: 2108–26.

Houck, J. and Chang, C. (1971). *Proc. Soc Exp. Biol Med.* 138: 69–75.

Hugli, T. E. and Müller-Eberhard, H. J. (1978). *Adv. Immunol.* 26: 1–53.

Husseinzadeh, N., Nahhas, W. A., Manders, E. K. and Whitney, C. W. (1984). *Obstet. Gynecol.* 63: 859–62.

Inoue, K., Yonemasu, K., Takamizawa, A and Amano, T. (1968). *Biken J.* 11: 203–6.

Jadeja, L., Kantarjian, H. and Bolivar, R. (1983). *South. Med. J.* 76: 1588–9.

Jenkin, C. and Benacerraf, B. (1960). *J. Exp. Med.* 112: 403–17.

Johnson, R. B., Keele, B. B. Misra, H. P., Lehmeyer, J. E., Webb, L. S., Baehner, R. L. and Rajagopalan, K. V. (1975). *J. Clin. Invest.* 55: 1357–72.

Joiner, K. A., Brown, E. J. and Frank, M. M. (1984). *Ann. Rev. Immunol.* 2: 461–91.

Kakinuma, M., Onoe, K., Yasumizu, R. and Yamamoto, K. (1983). *Immunology* 50: 423–31.

Kambara, T., Chandrasekhar, S., Dannenberg, A. M. and Meyer, O. T. (1970). *J. Reticuloendothel. Soc.* 7: 53–78.

Karnovsky, M. L. and Lazdins, J. K. (1978). *J. Immunol.* 121: 809–13.

Keller, H. U. and Sorkin, E. (1967). *Int. Arch. Allerg.* 31: 575–86.

Klebanoff, S. J. (1975). In J. A. Bellanti and D. H. Dayton (eds). *The Phagocytic Cell in Host Resistance.* New York: Raven Press: 45–9.

Klebanoff, S. J. and Shepard, C. C. (1984). *Infect. Immun.* 44: 534–6.

Klemperer, M. R., Woodworth, H. C., Rosen, F. S. and Austen, K. F. (1966). *J. Clin. Invest.* 45: 880–90.

Lancaster, R. D., Hilson, G. R. F., McDougall, A. C. and Colston, M. J. (1983). *Infect. Immun.* 39: 865–72.

Lawrence, D. A. and Schell, R. F. (1978) *Cell. Immunol.* 39: 336–44.

Lefford, M. J. (1985). *Infect. Immun.* 49: 190–6.

Lint, T. F., Zeitz, H. J. and Gewurz, H. (1980). *J. Immunol.* 125: 2252–7.

Lissner, C. R., Swanson, R. N. and O'Brien, A. D. (1983). *J. Immunol.* 131: 3006–13.

Lissner, C. R., Weinstein, D. L. and O'Brien, A. D. (1985). *J. Immunol.* 135: 544–7.

Løvik, M., and North, R. J. (1985). *J. Immunol.* 135: 3479–86.

McCall, C. E., De Chatelet, L. R., Cooper, M. R. and Ashburn, P. (1971). *J. Infect. Dis.* 124: 194–8.

MacVittie, T. J., O'Brien, A. D., Walker, R. I. and Weinberg, S. R. (1982). *Adv. Exp. Med. Biol.* 155: 325–34.

Mandel, T. E. and Cheers, C. (1980). *Infect. Immun.* 30: 851–61.

Mantovani, B., Rabinovitch, M. and Nussenzweig, V. (1972). *J. Exp. Med.* 135: 780–92.

Marchal, G. and Milon, G. (1981). *Br. J. Haematol.* 48: 551–60.

Mason, T. G. and Richardson, G. (1981) *J. Appl. Bact.* 51: 1–16.

Matsumoto, T., Miake, S., Mitsuyama, M., Takeya, K. and Nomoto, K. (1982). *J. Clin. Lab. Immunol.* 8: 51–4.

Meddens, M. J. M., Thompson, J., Bauer, W. C. and van Furth, R. (1984). *Infect. Immun.* 43: 491–6.

Metcalf, D. (1971). *Immunology* 21: 427–36.

Metcalf, D. (1986). *Blood* 67: 257–67.

Metcalf, D. and Wahren, B. (1968). *Brit. Med. J.* 3: 99–101.

Metcalf, D., Chan, S. H., Gunz, F. W., Vincent, P. and Ravich, R. B. M. (1971). *Blood* 38: 143–52.

Miller, M. E. and Nilsson, U. R. (1970). *N. Engl. J. Med.* 282: 354–8.

Miller, M. E., Oski, F. A. and Harris, M. B. (1971). *Lancet* 1: 665–9.

Miller, M. E., Norman, M. E., Koblenzer, P. J. and Schonauer, T. (1973). *J. Lab. Clin. Med.* 82: 1–8.

Mold, C., Nakayama, S., Holzer, T. J., Gewurz, H. and du Clos, T. W. (1981). *J. Exp. Med.* 154: 1703–8.

Moore, M. A., Spitzer, G., Metcalf, D. and Penington, D. G. (1974). *Br. J. Haematol.* 27: 47–55.

Mor, N., Lutsky, I., Weiss, L., Morecki, S. and Slavin, S. (1985). *Int. J. Radiat. Oncol. Biol. Phys.* 11: 79–85.

Murkherjee, A. K. and Sbarra, A. J. (1968). *J. Reticuloendothel. Soc.* 5: 134–46.

Myrvik, Q. N. and Weisser, R. S. (1955). *J. Immunol.* 74: 9–16.

Myrvik, Q. N., Leake, E. S. and Wright, M. J. (1984). *Am. Rev. Respir. Dis.* 129: 322–8.

Nagaki, K., Hiramatsu, S., Inai, S. and Sasaki, A. (1980). *J. Clin. Lab. Immunol.* 3: 45–50.

Nakamura, R. M. and Tokunaga, T. (1980). *Infect. Immun.* 28: 331–5.

Nelson, E. L. and Becker, J. R. (1959). *J. Infect. Dis.* 104: 20–3.

Newborg, M. F. and North, R. J. (1980) *J. Immunol.* 124: 571–6.

North, R. J. (1970a). *J. Exp. Med.* 132: 521–34.

North, R. J. (1970b). *J. Exp. Med.* 132: 535–45.

Oberti, J., Caravano, R. and Roux, J. (1981). *Ann. Immunol. Inst. Pasteur* 132D: 201–6.

O'Brien, A. D. and Rosenstreich, D. L. (1983). *J. Immunol.* 131: 2613–15.

O'Brien, A. D., Scher, I., Campbell, G. H., MacDermott, R. P. and Formal, S. B. (1979). *J. Immunol.* 123: 720–4.

O'Brien, A. D., Rosenstreich, D. L., Scher, I., Campbell, G. H., MacDermott, R. P. and Formal, S. B. (1980). *J. Immunol.* 124: 20–4.

O'Brein, A. D., Weinstein, D. A., Soliman, M. Y. and Rosenstreich, D. L. (1985). *J. Immunol.* 134: 2820–3.

Ohara, R., Mitsuyama, M., Miyata, M. and Nomoto, K. (1985). *Infect. Immun.* 48: 763–8.

Orme, I. M. and Collins, F. M. (1984). *Clin. Exp. Immunol.* 56: 81–8.

Palmblad, J. and Herak, A. (1978). *Gerontology* 24: 381–5.

Patel, P. J. (1981). *Infect. Immun.* 32: 557–62.

Perkins, E. H., Nettesheim, P. and Morita, T. (1966). *J. Reticuloendothel. Soc.* 3: 71–82.

Petersen, B. H., Lee, T. J., Snyderman, R. and Brooks, G. F. (1979). *Ann. Intern. Med.* 90: 917–20.

Peterson, P. K., Verhoff, J., Sabath, L. D. and Quie, P. G. (1977). *Infect. Immun.* 15: 760–4.

Petit, J–C. (1980). *Infect. Immun.* 27: 61–7.

Pickering, R. J., Naff, G. B., Stroud, R. M., Good, R. A. and Gewurz, H. (1970). *J. Exp. Med.* 131: 803–15.

Pillemer, L., Schoenberg, M. D., Blum, L. and Wurz, L. (1955). *Science* 122: 5453–7.

Plant, J. E. and Glynn A. A. (1982). *Clin. Exp. Immunol.* 50: 283–90.

Plant J. E., Blackwell, J. M., O'Brien, A. D., Bradley, D. J. and Glynn A. A. (1982). *Nature* 297: 510–11.

Pommier, C. G., Inada, S., Fries, L. F., Takahashi, T., Frank, M. M. and Brown, E. J. (1983). *J. Exp. Med.* 157: 1844–54.

Potter, M., O'Brien, A. D., Skamene, E., Gros, P., Forget, A., Kongshavn, P. A. and Wax, J. S. (1983). *Infect. Immun.* 40: 1234–1235.

Punjabi, C. J., Galsworthy, S. B. and Kongshavn, P. A. L. (1984). *Clin. Invest,. Med.* 7: 165–72.

Quesenberry, P., Cohen, H., Levin, J., Sullivan, R., Bealmear, P. and Ryan, M. (1978). *Blood* 51: 229–44.

Quie, P. G., White, J. G., Holmes, B. and Good, R. A. (1967). *J. Clin. Invest.* 46: 668–79.

Riley, L. K. and Robertson, D. C. (1984). *Infect. Immun.* 46: 224–30.

Root, R. K., Rosenthal, A. S. and Balestra, D. (1972). *J. Clin. Invest.* 51: 649–65.

Ross, G. D., Thompson, R. A., Walport, M. J., Springer, T. A., Watson, J. V., Ward, R. H., Lida, J., Newman, S. L., Harrison, R. A. and Lachman, P. J. (1985). *Blood* 66: 882–90.

Ruddy, S., Klemperer, M. R. , Rosen, F. S., Austen, K. F. and Kumate, J. (1970). *Immunology* 18: 943–54.

Ryan, G. B. and Majno, G. (1977). *Am. J. Path.* 86: 185–276.

Sadarangani, C., Skamene, E. and Kongshavn, P. A. L. (1980). *Infect. Immun.* 28: 381–6.

Schechmeister, I. L., Bond, V. P. and Swift, M. N. (1952). *J. Immunol.* 68: 87–95.

Schmidtke, J. R. and Dixon, F. J. (1972). *J. Immunol.* 108: 1624–30.

Schneider, E. L. (1983). *Ann. Int. Med.* 98: 395–400.

Schreiber, R. D., Morrison, D. C., Podack, E. R. and Müller-Eberhard, H. J. (1979). *J. Exp. Med.* 149: 870–82.

Selvaraj, R. J. and Sbarra, A. J. (1966). *Nature* 210: 158–61.

Sharp, A. K. and Colston, M. J. (1984). *Eur. J. Immunol.* 14: 102–5.

Shilotri, P. G. (1977). *J. Nutr.* 107: 1507–12.

Shilotri, P. G. and Bhat, K. S. (1977). *Am. J. Clin. Nutr.* 30: 1077–81.

Shin, H. S., Smith, M. R. and Wood, W. B. (1969). *J. Exp. Med.* 130: 1229–41.

Silverstein, A. M. (1960). *Blood* 16: 1338–41.

Sirisnha, S., Edelman, R., Suskind, R., Charupatana, C. and Olsen, R. E. (1973). *Lancet* 1: 1016–20.

Skamene, E. (1985). *Curr. Top. Microbiol. Immunol.* 122: 128–33.

Skamene, E., Kongshavn, P. A. L. and Sachs, D. H. (1979). *J. Infect. Dis.* 139: 228–31.

Skamene, E., Gros, P., Forget, A., Patel, P. J. and Nesbitt, M. N. (1984). *Immunogenetics* 19: 117–24.

Sluiter, W., Elzenga-Claasen, I., van der Voort van der Kley - van Andel, A., and van Furth, R. (1984). *J. Exp. Med.* 159: 524–36.

Smith, D. J., Ebersole, J. L. and Taubman, M. A. (1983). *Immunology* 50: 407–13.

Smith, H. and Fitzgeorge, R. B. (1964). *Br. J. Exp. Path.* 45: 672–4.

Smith, W. B., Shohet, S. B., Zagajeski, E. and Lubin, B. H. (1975). *Ann. N Y Acad. Sci.* 258: 329–38.

Smythe, P. M., Brereton-Stiles, G. G., Grace, H. J., Mafoyane, A., Schonland, M., Coovadia, H. M., Loening, W. E. K., Parent, M. A. and Vos, G. H. (1971). *Lancet* 2: 939–43.

Snyderman, R., Shin, H. S. and Dannenberg, A. M. (1972). *J. Immunol.* 109: 896–8.

Spiegelberg, H. L., Miescher, P. A. and Benacerraf, B. (1963). *J. Immunol.* 90: 751–9.

Spitalny, G. L. (1981). *Infect. Immun.* 34: 274–84.

Staber, F. G. and Metcalf, D. (1980). *Proc. Natl. Acad. Sci.* 77: 4322–5.

Stach, J. L., Delgado, G., Tchiboza, V., Strobel, M. and Legrange, P. H. (1984). *Ann. Immunol. (Inst. Pasteur)* 135D: 25–37.

Stevenson, M. M., Kongshavn, P. A. L. and Skamene, E. (1981). *J. Immunol.* 127: 402–7.

Suskind, R., Edelman, R., Kulapongs, P., Pariyanonda, A. and Sirisinha, S. (1976). *Am. J. Clin. Nutr.* 29: 1089–92.

Symon, D. N. K., Mckay, I. C. and Wilkinson, P. C. (1972). *Immunology* 22: 267–76.

Taylor, P. W. (1983). *Microbiol. Rev.* 47: 46–83.

Taylor, P. W. and Kroll, H–P. (1983). *Infect. Immun.* 39: 122–31.

Trudgett, A., McNeill, T. A. and Killen, M. (1973). *Infect. Immun.* 8: 450–5.

Tuomanen, E., Hengstler, B., Zak, O. and Tomasz, A. (1986). *Microbial Pathogenesis* 1: 15–32.

Ueda, K., Yamazaki, S., Saegusa, J. and Sameya, S. (1978). *Jap. J. Exp. Med.* 48: 533–43.

Van Dissel, J. T., Leijh, P. C. and van Furth, R. (1985). *J. Immunol.* 134: 3404–10.

Van Furth, R. and Cohn, Z. A. (1968). *J. Exp. Med.* 128: 415–33.

Ward, P. A. (1968). *J. Exp. Med.* 128: 1201–21.

Ward, P. A. and Hill, J. H. (1970). *J. Immunol.* 104: 535–43.

Watson, R. R. and Petro, T. M. (1983). *CRC Critical Reviews in Microbiology* 10: 297–315.

Wilder, M. S. and Edburg, J. C. (1973). *Infect. Immun.* 7: 409–15.

Wilson, B. M., Rosendaal, M. and Plant, J. E. (1982). *Immunology* 45: 395–9.

Wilson, C. B. (1986). *J. Pediatr.* 108: 1–12.

Wing, E. J., Waheed, A. and Shadduck, R. K. (1984). *Infect. Immun.* 45: 180–4.

Winkelstein, J. A. and Tomasz, A. (1978). *J. Immunol.* 120: 174–8.

Wood, R. R., Young, A. M., McKimm-Breschkin, J. L. and Cheers, C. (1984). *Infect. Immun.* 46: 860–861.

Wood, P. R., Spanidis, V., Frangos, K. and Cheers, C. (1986). *Cell. Immunol.* 99: 160–9.

Wright, S. D. and Levine, R. P. (1981). *J. Immunol.* 127: 1146–51.

Young, A. M. and Cheers, C. (1986). *Cell. Immunol.* 97: 227–37.

Young, E. J., Borchet, M., Kretzer, F. L. and Musher, D. M. (1985). *J. Infect. Dis.* 151: 682–90.

Yoshikawa, T. T. (1984). *Gerontology* 30: 275–8.

Yother, J., Volankis, J. E. and Briles, D. E. (1982). *J. Immunol.* 128: 2374–6.

Zinkernagel, R. M. and Blanden, R. V. (1975). *Experientia* 31: 591–3.

Fungal Infections

TANIA C. SORRELL

Department of Medicine
The University of Sydney
and
Department of Infectious Diseases and Microbiology
Westmead Hospital
Sydney

I. INTRODUCTION

Diseases caused by fungi are uncommon in the normal human host. Mammalian tissue provides an effective barrier to entry and subsequent

NATURAL IMMUNITY
ISBN 0 12 5145551

fungal growth. The major physiological factors which modify fungal growth include temperature and redox potential (Rippon, 1982).

Fewer than 0.2 per cent of the known species of fungi are pathogenic in humans (Rippon, 1982). Such pathogenic fungi exhibit adaptive changes in human tissue. True pathogens are characterised by their ability to undergo critical metabolic and morphological changes in vivo (dimorphism). However, determinants of pathogenicity in these tissue forms are not known (Bulmer and Fromptling, 1985). Fungi of lesser virulence, for example *Cryptococcus neoformans*, *Candida* species and *Aspergillus* species are thermotolerant, though metabolically inefficient in mammalian tissue. *Candida albicans* is the only species which colonises the immediate human environment, being a commensal in the alimentary tract and vagina. The fungi of lesser virulence cause deep-seated infections in patients with compromised host defences.

The purpose of this chapter is to review host aspects of the host–fungal interaction, with particular reference to species of *Candida*. For a discussion of fungal virulence factors and of host defences to other fungi the reader is referred to recent reviews by Domer and Carrow (1983), Bulmer and Fromptling (1985) and Fleischmann and Lehrer (1985).

II. EPITHELIAL HOST DEFENCE AGAINST *CANDIDA ALBICANS* AND OTHER SPECIES

The mechanical barriers of the skin and mucous membranes comprise the primary host defence against invasive candidiasis. Suppression of fungal growth and prevention of fungal adherence to epithelial surface cells have been implicated as major components of this host defence (Wain *et al.*, 1976; Helmstrom and Balish, 1979; Kennedy and Voltz, 1985; Rotrosen *et al.*, 1986).

A. Skin and Respiratory Tract

Candida albicans does not colonise normal skin (Winner and Hurley, 1964) despite its ability to adhere readily to freshly isolated, human epidermal corneocytes in vitro (Ray *et al.*, 1984). When applied experimentally to rodent or guinea pig skin, inocula of *C. albicans* are cleared without the induction of an inflammatory response (Sohnle *et al.*, 1976; Fader *et al.*, 1985), by a mechanism which in the guinea pig model includes profuse scaling of the keratinised layer of the epidermis (Sohnle *et al.*, 1976). In human studies, the rate of clearance of *C. albicans* is decreased by pre-treatment of the skin with acetone, suggesting a protective role of acetone-soluble material, presumptively skin lipids (Aly *et al.*, 1972). It was not established in this study whether this material prevented adherence, exhibited fungistatic activity or otherwise modified the environment to inhibit fungal growth, although antifungal activity was demonstrated in a subsequent study (Aly *et al.*, 1975). Interference with the skin surface, for example by thermal burns or maceration of the skin under occlusive dressings, is associated with the establishment of infection in animal models (Sohnle *et al.*, 1976; Fader *et al.*, 1985) and, in the case of burns, dissemination of disease (Fader *et al.*, 1985). *Candida albicans* fails to colonise the normal respiratory tract. Even in neutropenic patients in the presence of oral infection, aspiration pneumonitis due to *C. albicans* is uncommon. This may reflect the large size of the yeast-phase organisms (3–4 µm) and of *C. albicans* pseudohyphae (5–10 µm) (Roberts, 1985). Studies of respiratory tract defences have shown that 90 per cent of particles more than 2–3 µm in size fail to reach the alveoli and are removed by the mucociliary 'escalator' and the coughing mechanism, usually within one hour (Green, 1970). Those yeasts which do enter the lung may be phagocytosed by resident alveolar macrophages. Immunoglobulins and other opsonins in the alveolar lining fluid undoubtedly aid this process (Green, 1970).

B. Gastrointestinal Tract and Vagina

Experimental studies have shown that the ability of the intact intestinal mucosa to prevent entry of *C. albicans* into the bloodstream is inoculum-dependent. *C. albicans* was cultured from blood and urine within three hours of ingestion of 10^{12} colony-forming units (cfu) by a human volunteer (Krause *et al.*, 1969). Twenty-four hours after intragastric administration of a single inoculum of 10^7 cfu of *C. albicans* to conventionally reared hamsters, the organism was recovered from the liver and spleen of 5 per cent of animals, compared with 53 per cent of those given three inocula of *C. albicans* over a sixteen hour period. Human studies of oral candidiasis have also suggested that a certain threshold concentration of the yeasts must be attained to initiate invasive disease (Wain *et al.*, 1976). Factors which allow a symbiotic relationship to be established between *C. albicans* and the human gastrointestinal tract or vagina include adherence and regulation of fungal growth.

C. Adherence of *Candida* Species to Mucosal Surfaces

Adherence via surface components of yeast particles and epithelial cells appears to be a prerequisite for the establishment of colonisation and invasive disease. Studies using techniques of competitive inhibition by purified *Candida* cell wall products, blocking by antibody of lectin and partial degradation of the yeast cell wall (reviewed by Rotrosen *et al.*, 1986), suggest that surface mannoproteins are an important component of the *Candida* adhesin. The epithelial cell receptors or sites of adherence are poorly defined. In fact a recent study suggested that candidal adherence occurs in the absence of a specific epithelial cell receptor (Reinhart *et al.*, 1985). Binding of *C. albicans* to exfoliated human epithelial cells is dependent on pH (King *et al.*, 1980; Sobel *et al.*, 1981) and temperature (Kimura and Pearsall, 1978) and is unaffected by conditions of high ionic strength, the addition of divalent cations such as Mg^{2+} and Mn^{2+} or incubation with the metal chelator EDTA (Lee and King, 1983). Adherence is decreased by pre-treatment of epithelial cells with proteolytic enzymes (Sobel *et al.*, 1981; Lee and King, 1983), but *C. albicans* can bind efficiently to non-viable cells. For example, binding of *C. albicans* to HeLa cells is increased by pre-treatment of cell monolayers with formalin (Samaranayake and MacFarlane, 1981).

In studies of oral and vaginal candidiasis, observations both in vitro and in vivo indicate that the extent of adherence is also influenced by the metabolic state and species of *Candida* and the epithelial surface chosen for study. The adherence of *C. albicans* blastospores to vaginal and oral exfoliated epithelial cells is consistently greater than that of other *Candida* species (King *et al.*, 1980). High inocula of *C. albicans* germ tubes adhere more readily than blastospores (Kimura and Pearsall, 1978; Kimura and Pearsall, 1980; Sobel *et al.*, 1981). However, human cells have the limitation that a non-uniform population is being tested and the viability of the cells is usually not defined. Other workers have shown by using vital stains that the majority of exfoliated cells are probably non-viable (Albright *et al.*, 1978). In addition, the adherence of *C. albicans* to exfoliated vaginal epithelial cells is subject to marked variation between individuals and in the same individual when tested repeatedly (King *et al.*, 1980).

The extent of keratinisation of the surface cells may also be relevant to adherence. Organisms such as *Gardnerella vaginalis* adhere better to desquamating epithelial cells than to cells in mitosis (Sobel *et al.*, 1982) and keratinisation of oral epithelial cells strongly enhances adherence of certain oral streptococci to these cells (Sklavounou and Germaine, 1980).

D. Regulation of Candidal Growth in the Normal Gastrointestinal Tract and Vagina

Anti-candidal activity has been identified in extracts of calf conjunctivae and tissue explants. This material is stable to heating at 42°C and is not removed by dialysis (Kozinn *et al.*, 1964). Inhibitory activity has not been identified in stimulated human saliva, even after concentration (Bartels *et al.*, 1967). However, growth of *C. albicans* in sterile human saliva is dependent upon the presence of glucose (Knight and Fletcher, 1971).

The complex indigenous microflora of the bowel also regulates fungal growth and the development of invasive disease. Broad-spectrum antimicrobial therapy is a well-established risk factor for gastrointestinal colonisation and disseminated infection in humans (Seelig, 1966; Stone, 1973; Edwards, 1985). Studies in vitro and in experimental animals have shown that certain intestinal bacteria are inhibitory to growth and gastrointestinal colonisation by *C. albicans* (Paine, 1958; Balish and Phillips, 1966; Hummel *et al.*, 1973; Helmstrom and Balish, 1979; Kennedy and Volz, 1985). Adherence of *C. albicans* to epithelial (HeLa) cells is inhibited competitively by certain oral bacteria, including *Streptococcus salivarius* and *Streptococcus mitior* but not *Streptococcus mutans* (Samaranayake and MacFarlane, 1982); *S. mutans* has a relatively low affinity for epithelial cell receptors (Marsh, 1980). Similar findings have been reported in vivo with a murine model of oral candidal colonisation (Liljemark and Gibbons, 1973).

There is indirect evidence that intestinal anaerobes are important in regulating gastrointestinal colonisation with *C. albicans*. Pre-treatment of hamsters with penicillin has been associated with a decrease in gastrointestinal anaerobes and increase in facultative anaerobes in parallel with increased adhesion, colonisation and dissemination of infection by *C. albicans* (Kennedy and Volz, 1985). Wingard *et al.* (1980) failed to detect disseminated infection after suppression of aerobic intestinal flora in mice pre-treated with gentamicin. Colonisation of the gastrointestinal tract of infant mice, which follows intragastric challenge with *C. albicans*, persists for approximately three weeks (Field *et al.*, 1981) and declines during the period of acquisition of an anaerobic gut microflora (Davis *et al.*, 1973).

The study of Kennedy and Volz (1985) indicated that, in the large bowel, the predominant effect of the indigenous microflora was to prevent adhesion of *C. albicans* to mucosal sites in the hamster caecum, apparently by competitive inhibition of binding to cells, by prevention of penetration by *C. albicans* through the overlying mucous barrier and by production of volatile fatty acids. The latter were found to reduce adhesion of *C. albicans* to mucosal tissue explants in vitro. In the same assay secondary bile acids, which are known to be produced by bacterial metabolism in vivo, also reduced adhesion of *C. albicans* to mucosal explants. Reduction of the redox potential of the bowel as a result of bacterial metabolism is also unfavourable to fungal growth (Helmstrom and Balish, 1979).

The role of an intact mucosal surface in the prevention of candidal penetration is illustrated in human patients by the association of candidiasis with gastrointestinal surgery, perforation of colonised areas of the gastrointestinal tract, and loss of integrity of the gastrointestinal mucosa due to disease and its therapy in patients with acute leukaemia (Edwards, 1985).

Of relevance to the pathogenesis of vaginal candidiasis is the clinical observation that counts of vaginal lactobacilli are reduced during and immediately after the menses (Saigh *et al.*, 1978), a time when vaginal candidiasis occurs with increased frequency. In vitro pre-incubation of exfoliated vaginal epithelial cells with lactobacilli of vaginal origin decreased the mean count of adherent *C. albicans* per cell by 35 per cent (Sobel *et al.*, 1981). Continual exfoliation of epithelial cells apparently also assists in reducing the number of colonising micro-organisms.

E. Modulation of Superficial Host–fungal Interactions

Modification of the host environment which is favourable to the growth of *Candida* species is seen in patients with diabetes and those treated with corticosteroids or broad-spectrum antibiotics. In each of these groups there is evidence that the underlying factor which promotes fungal growth in the oral cavity is the concentration of salivary glucose (Knight and Fletcher, 1971). The prevalence of yeast colonisation is known to increase in diabetics in proportion to the elevation of blood glucose concentrations (Odds *et al.*, 1978). In addition, excess dietary sucrose stimulates yeast growth in mixed saliva (Knight and Fletcher, 1971) and sucrose rinses have been shown to initiate and aggravate chronic atrophic candidosis in humans (Olsen and Birkeland, 1976). In vitro, pre-incubation of *C. albicans* in 100 to 400 millimolar sucrose solutions facilitates adhesion of *C. albicans* to HeLa cells and buccal epithelial cells (Samaranayake and MacFarlane, 1981). In addition to sucrose and glucose, galactose promotes adherence of *C. albicans*, obtained from patients with active oral infection, to buccal epithelial cells (McCourtie and Douglas, 1984). Enhancement of the adhesion of *C. albicans* to epithelial cells in the presence of saliva results from initiation of blastospore germination and production of the more adherent hyphal phase (Kimura and Pearsall, 1978; Samaranayake and MacFarlane, 1982).

Diabetic and pregnant females have high levels of vaginal glycogen, which can be converted to glucose by enzymes present in tissue or produced by normal flora (Rogosa and Sharpe, 1960). Pre-incubation of *C. albicans* with glucose also causes a modest increase in adherence to exfoliated vaginal epithelial cells in vitro (Sobel *et al.*, 1981).

McCourtie and Douglas (1984) showed that the effect of pre-incubating *C. albicans* with sugars was to modify the surface composition of the yeast in a strain-dependent fashion. Seven strains of *C. albicans* isolated from patients with active infection and incubated in high concentrations of galactose were observed to synthesise a fibrillar surface layer, which promoted adherence of exfoliated epithelial cells and was associated with increased virulence of the strain for mice. In contrast, two strains of *C. albicans* from asymptomatic carriers failed to undergo these changes in vitro or in vivo. Phenotypic variation in *C. albicans* has been demonstrated by other workers in vivo and in vitro (Poulain *et al.*, 1983), possibly involving the production of mannoprotein (Douglas and McCourtie, 1983).

In studies on adherence of *Candida* species to vaginal epithelial cells, a consistent influence of hormonal status has not been demonstrated. For example, the adherence of *C. albicans* to cells obtained at different phases of the menstrual cycle showed no significant variation in attachment (Sobel, 1979). These results may have been influenced by poor reproducibility of the test. Progesterone-binding activity has been observed in the cytosol of *C. albicans* but not *C. tropicalis* or *C. pseudotropicalis*, raising the possibility of a relationship between the increased progesterone levels found in pregnancy and the increased incidence of vaginal candidiasis (Powell and Drutz, 1983). The binding activity is of high affinity, is extractable and competes with mammalian progesterone-binding sites. It appears to be the same as the corticosteroid-binding site identified by Loose and Feldman (1982), although the natural ligand is not yet known.

F. Penetration of Epithelial Surfaces by *Candida* Species

Natural barriers to invasion of the deeper layers of the skin and mucous membranes are poorly defined. Penetration appears to depend on both fungal and host factors. In an organ culture model of candidiasis using rat tongue mucosa, Howlett (1975) observed initial penetration of the superficial keratinised layer by *C. albicans* with minimal local cell damage (Howlett and Squier, 1980), followed by extension of yeast into subdermal connective tissue. In contrast, the less pathogenic species *C. tropicalis* and *C. krusei* failed to penetrate the stratum corneum, despite luxuriant growth on the epithelial cell surface (Howlett, 1975). Paracellular passage of large inocula *C. albicans* through intact epithelium has been reported to occur in the jejunum of dogs and Rhesus monkeys (reviewed by Stone *et al.*, 1974); indirect evidence of intestinal persorption has also been obtained in humans after ingestion of a very high inoculum of *C. albicans* (Krause *et al.*, 1969).

The observations of Howlett are consistent with the presence of an intercellular barrier to movement of substances into the epithelium from both surface and from deeper tissues, such as has been demonstrated for other materials in oral mucosa (Squier, 1973) and in skin (Schriener and Wolff, 1969). The presence of *C. albicans* in the epidermis is also associated with activation of complement, mobilisation of an inflammatory response (Sohnle *et al.*, 1976) and increased desquamation of keratinised epithelium from skin (Sohnle *et al.*, 1976) and oral mucosa (Montes and Wilborn, 1968).

III. CLEARANCE OF *CANDIDA* FROM THE BLOOD

Candida albicans most commonly enters the blood stream via the gastrointestinal tract (Lehrer, 1978) and in animal models is cleared efficiently by liver and kidney after portal vein inoculation. Afferent to efferent blood ratios of *C. albicans* reach 10 000:1 for hepatic clearance and 100:1 for renal clearance in dogs and monkeys (Stone *et al.*, 1974).

Several species of *Candida*, including *C. albicans*, *C. tropicalis* and *C. parapsilosis* may be introduced through indwelling intravenous or intra-arterial catheters (Edwards, 1985), an observation which has been related to the propensity of these strains to adhere to plastic (Rotrosen *et al.*, 1983). Intravenous inoculation of radiolabelled *C. albicans* blastospores into mice (Trnovec *et al.*, 1978) and guinea pigs (Gelfand *et al.*, 1978) is followed by rapid clearance from the circulation in the lung, with subsequent accumulation of radioactivity in other sites. In the guinea pig, 99.8 per cent of an inoculum of *C. albicans* is cleared within 30 minutes. The mechanism of clearance is independent of complement and of the accumulation of inflammatory cells (Gelfand *et al.*, 1978). In rabbits, approximately 99 per cent of organisms are removed from the circulation within 10 minutes, followed by a longer period of low-grade fungaemia (Baine *et al.*, 1974).

IV. METASTATIC CANDIDAL INFECTION

The kidney is the most common site of metastatic infection in humans, with less frequent involvement of the eye, the heart and the brain. The tropism of *C. albicans* for the kidney is well established in experimental models including mice, rabbits and guinea pigs (Louria, 1977) and is apparently associated with germ tube formation and growth in the tubular lumen, protected from the inhibitory effect of phagocytic cells (Louria, 1977). Additional factors may be involved, as homogenates of renal tissue support the growth of *C. albicans* preferentially compared with other tissues. In this context hyperosmolality and inactivation of complement in the renal medulla have been shown to be important (Kernbaum, 1975).

The clinical association of *C. albicans* endophthalmitis with intravenous inoculation or haematogenous spread from other sites (Edwards, 1982, 1985; Sorrell *et al.*, 1984) has been reproduced experimentally by Edwards *et al.* (1975) in a rabbit model. Induction of chorioretinitis and vitreal infection were noted in this model with *C. albicans* but not *C. stellatoidea* or *C. tropicalis* (Edwards *et al.*, 1977). Factors responsible for the apparent tropism of *C. albicans* for the eye have not been studied.

The rabbit has also been used to study *Candida* endocarditis following induction of platelet–fibrin clots by abrasion of the aortic valve. Inocula of *Candida* are trapped and multiply in the resultant vegetations. Host factors may contribute to fungal multiplication at this site. It is known that germination of yeast cells occurs readily in the presence of serum. Germination is also stimulated by heat-stable, trypsin-sensitive, cationic component(s) of platelet origin (Skerl *et al.*, 1981). Cell wall fragments of *Candida* cause platelet aggregation and may promote further clotting on the valve surface (Skerl *et al.*, 1981). Fungal growth may then continue in the protective site of the vegetation (Calderone *et al.*, 1978).

The pathogenesis of metastatic infections appears to require an initial adherence step. Experimentally, spontaneous mutants of *C. albicans* which are unable to adhere to a fibrin–platelet clot in vitro are avirulent in the rabbit model of endocarditis (Calderone *et al.*, 1985). *Candida albicans* adheres readily to fibrin–platelet clots in vitro, produces endocarditis in 50 per cent of rabbits at an inoculum of 10^5 (Scheld *et al.*, 1981) and is the most common cause of fungal endocarditis in humans. In contrast, *C. krusei* adheres poorly to fibrin–platelet clots, requires much higher inocula to produce endocarditis in the rabbit model (Scheld *et al.*, 1981) and is a rare cause of infection in humans. The fibrin-platelet 'receptor' for *C. albicans* has not yet been characterised, although fibronectin, a major surface glycoprotein produced by mammalian cells, is found within and on the surface of the fibrin–platelet clot (Scheld, 1984). *C. albicans*, but not *C. krusei*, adheres to fibronectin in vitro, provided that the fibronectin is fixed to a surface (Skerl *et al.*, 1984). Adherence to vascular endothelium is also dependent on the species of *Candida*, being greatest with *C. albicans* and *C. tropicalis* when incubated in vitro with porcine aortic and vena caval vascular strips (Klotz *et al.*, 1983). These findings reflect the known capacity of different candidal species for haematogenous dissemination of infection. In this study small differences were noted in the number of *C. albicans* adherent to epithelium harvested from aorta or inferior vena cava. The authors speculated that receptor density varies in endothelium derived from different sites (Klotz *et al.*,1983), a possible explanation for the apparent tropism of *Candida* for different body tissues.

In addition, Calderone *et al.* (1985) recently isolated a cerulenin-resistant mutant of *C. albicans* which exhibited properties of reduced adherence to fibrin–platelet clots *in vitro*, relative avirulence in the rabbit model of endocarditis, pathogenicity for the rabbit kidney and virulence similar to wild strains of *C. albicans* in a murine model of systemic candidiasis. These observations are consistent with the presence of different receptors for *Candida* in different tissues. Data on the renal tropism of *C. albicans*, however, suggest that the ability of *C. albicans* to invade and multiply in sites of metastatic infection is determined primarily by the local tissue environment and its relative degree of protection from the body defences (Louria, 1977).

V. THE INTERACTION OF *CANDIDA* SPECIES WITH PHAGOCYTIC CELLS

Clinical observation and studies in animal models suggest that the polymorphonuclear leucocyte or neutrophil is the major host defence against invasive candidiasis.

In experimental animals, control of systemic infection is associated with brisk mobilisation of neutrophils, which, if delayed, for example, by administration of corticosteroids, results in marked augmentation of infection (Louria *et al.*, 1960). In clinical practice, severe deficiencies of phagocyte function, such as chronic granulomatous disease (CGD), are associated with an increased incidence of fungal infection. Leukopenia, due to haematological malignancy or therapeutic agents, also reduces resistance to *Candida* infection in humans and in experimental animals. In experimental animals cyclophosphamide-induced susceptibility to candidiasis can be prevented by administration of granulocyte trans-fusions prior to challenge with *C. albicans* (Ruthe *et al.*, 1978). Disseminated candidiasis is not characteristic of patients with B-lymphocyte deficiencies, or T-lymphocyte deficiencies including the acquired immunodeficiency syndrome and the syndrome of mucocutaneous candidiasis.

The extent to which circulating phagocytes contribute to the initial clearance of *Candida* species from the circulation is uncertain. Nevertheless, studies in vitro have confirmed that anticoagulated human blood is candidacidal for both blastospores and pseudohyphal forms of *C. albicans* (Davies and Denning, 1972; Roth and Goldstein, 1961). Despite early claims to the contrary (Roth and Goldstein, 1961; Louria and

Brayton, 1964a), the candidacidal activity of whole blood is now known to reside within the phagocytic cells (Lehrer, 1978). Neutrophils (Lehrer, 1970; Leijh *et al.*, 1977), monocytes (Lehrer, 1975; Leijh *et al.*, 1977) and eosinophils (Lehrer, 1971a; Ishikawa *et al.*, 1972) all ingest and kill *C. albicans*.

A. The Role of Complement in Chemotaxis, Phagocytosis and Killing of *Candida* Species

Actively metabolising *C. albicans* (Cutler, 1977), sonicates of *C. albicans*, and relatively low molecular weight, heat-stable material released by *C. albicans* grown under certain conditions (Cutler, 1977), are directly chemotactic. *C. albicans* is also chemotaxigenic (Denning and Davies, 1973; Ray and Wuepper, 1976; Sohnle *et al.*, 1976), apparently via activation of the alternative complement pathway by the mannan component of the yeast cell wall (Ray *et al.*, 1979). Thus, incubation of *Candida* blastospores in fresh non-immune human serum is associated with deposition on the yeast surface of C3 and factor B (Denning and Davies, 1973; Ray and Wuepper, 1976) without demonstrable IgG, IgA or IgM. In a guinea pig model of cutaneous candidiasis, C3 but not C4 or immunoglobulin can be identified on the surface of yeast-phase organisms and pseudomycelia at the keratinised surface of the infected skin (Sohnle *et al.*, 1976). Receptors for iC3b and C3d have been identified on several strains of *C. albicans* and on *C. stellatoidea* but not *C. tropicalis*, *C. parapsilosis* and *C. krusei* (Heidenreich and Dierich, 1985). Adherence of *Candida* species to complement-labelled, indicator erythrocytes was inhibited by D-glucose and D-mannose in the incubation medium, suggesting a lectin-like interaction (Heidenreich and Dierich, 1985). These sites are different from the stable binding site of C3 (Law and Levine, 1977) which attaches C3b covalently to acceptors on the *Candida* cell surface. Deposition of C3 and factor B on *C. albicans* blastospores may initiate changes in surface components, as suggested by the observation of decreased adherence of such blastospores to epithelial cells (Ray *et al.*, 1979).

Both heat-stable and heat-labile serum factors enhance the ingestion of *C. albicans* blastospores by human peripheral blood neutrophils (Lehrer and Cline, 1969; Schmid and Brune, 1974; Solomkin *et al.*, 1978), monocytes (Leijh *et al.*, 1977) and eosinophils (Ishikawa *et al.*, 1972). Preopsonisation (Solomkin *et al.*, 1978) or incubation of *C. albicans* with neutrophils in medium containing low concentrations of serum, results in completion of phagocytosis within one to 15 minutes (Schmid and Brune, 1974; Leijh *et al.*, 1977; Solomkin *et al.*, 1978). Studies employing serum from animals or humans with inherited deficiencies of C4 or C5 and normal serum depleted of complement factors by chemical or physical techniques, have shown that complement is opsonic for *C. albicans*. The relative importance of components of the classical or alternative pathways is, however, disputed (Miller and Nilsson, 1970; Morelli and Rosenberg, 1971; Root *et al.*, 1972; Kernbaum, 1975; Solomkin *et al.*, 1978). In vitro, complement has been reported either to enhance intracellular killing of *C. albicans* (Schmid and Brune, 1974; Yamamura and Valdimarsson, 1977) or to exert no effect (Lehrer and Cline, 1969; Morelli and Rosenberg, 1971; Kernbaum, 1975). Methodological differences may contribute to these discrepancies; for example serum components may persist on the surface of washed leukocytes (Ishikawa *et al.*, 1972) and the effect of serum components varies with the morphological state of the yeast (Cockayne and Odds, 1984). In vivo, an intact alternative pathway of complement activation appears to be of particular importance in containing candidal infection in organs with relatively few fixed phagocytic cells, for example, the guinea pig kidney (Gelfand *et al.*, 1978).

1. Complement deficiencies in humans

Although Miller and Nilsson (1970) noted defective phagocytosis of *C. albicans* in the proband of a family with C5 deficiency, the clinical spectrum of recurrent infection in this patient included only bacterial infections (Miller *et al.*, 1968). In contrast, opsonisation of *C. albicans* by serum from a C5-deficient family described by Rosenfeld *et al.* (1976) was normal. In this family, the proband suffered recurrent bacterial infections. Chronic oral and vaginal candidiasis were observed only when the patient was receiving corticosteroid therapy (Rosenfeld *et al.*, 1976). Deficiencies in other complement components have not been associated with recurrent fungal infection (Day and Good, 1980).

2. Non-complement-dependent functions of serum in Candida–phagocyte interactions

Specific antibodies to *C. albicans* are found in normal serum and are effective opsonins (Ishikawa *et al.*, 1972; Lehrer, 1978), although they are not strictly components of natural immunity.

B. Candidacidal Activity of Blood Leukocytes

Candida albicans is ingested rapidly by neutrophils in mixed leukocyte preparations. At high yeast to neutrophil ratios of 10:1, a maximum of 4 or 5 yeasts per neutrophil is ingested within one minute (Solomkin *et al.*, 1978). Using ratios of one yeast per neutrophil, Lehrer and Cline (1969) observed that all *Candida* blastospores were ingested within 10 minutes, with more than 90 per cent of ingested organisms being found within neutrophils. Ingestion of *Candida* is similarly rapid in preparations enriched for granulocytes or for monocytes (Leijh *et al.*, 1977) although Lehrer (1975) found a slightly more rapid rate of ingestion by human neutrophils compared with blood monocytes. Others have reported that phagocytosis by monocytes is poor (Solomkin *et al.*, 1978) or better than that by neutrophils (Schuit, 1979).

Leijh *et al.* (1977) observed that the initial rate of killing of *C. albicans* was faster in human neutrophils than in monocytes. Lehrer (1975) showed that purified preparations of peripheral blood neutrophils consistently kill a higher proportion of ingested blastospores of *C. albicans* than purified preparations of peripheral blood monocytes. By a method of specific staining, after 2½ hours, 37 per cent of ingested *C. albicans* were found to be killed within neutrophils, compared with 25 per cent within monocytes. Notably, the extent of monocyte killing was enhanced significantly in mixed populations of neutrophils and monocytes, from 31 per cent in the neutrophil-poor preparations to 47 per cent in the mixed blood leukocyte preparations. The reason for the apparent synergy of killing effect could not be determined, but was not related to procedures involved in the purification of cell types, and killing by purified monocytes was not enhanced by addition of lysates of intact neutrophils, neutrophil cytoplasmic granules or supernatants of cultures containing *C. albicans* phagocytosed by neutrophils. Similarly, the effect was not due to differences in the number of ingested candida per phagocyte. Of particular interest in this regard is the observation by Lehrer, that in mixed leukocyte preparations from patients with chronic granulomatous disease (CGD) killing of *C. albicans* was similar to that observed in purified monocyte preparations (9.5 per cent compared with 10 per cent of ingested *C. albicans*). These data suggest that the extracellular damage to *C. albicans* by oxidase-dependent oxygen metabolites of phagocyte origin may render the fungi more susceptible to killing after ingestion by monocytes (see below).

C. Candidacidal Activity of Macrophages

Intracellular killing by macrophages is less well studied than that by neutrophils. Much of the available information has been derived from studies on animal cells and was reviewed recently by Fleischmann and

Lehrer (1985). Anti-candidal activity of macrophages varies with the anatomical site and species of origin (Lehrer *et al.*, 1980; Sorrell *et al.*, 1985). Freshly isolated resident macrophages from rabbit lung (Arai *et al.*, 1977; Peterson and Calderone, 1977; Lehrer *et al.*, 1980) kill *C. albicans* as measured by a variety of techniques. Rabbit peritoneal macrophages are significantly less candidacidal (Lehrer *et al.*, 1980). Resident murine peritoneal macrophages (Sasada and Johnston, 1980) and bone-marrow-derived macrophages (Baccarini *et al.*, 1985) have poor killing efficiency against *C. albicans*, although in an experimental mouse model, hepatic macrophages appeared to kill *C. albicans* administered intravenously, within 48 hours (Meister *et al.*, 1977). *C. krusei* is killed by mouse alveolar macrophages in vitro (Warr and Jakab, 1979) but not by 24-hour cultures of peritoneal macrophages (Fleischmann and Lehrer, 1985), in contrast to *C. parapsilosis*, which is killed effectively by fresh mouse peritoneal macrophages (Sasada and Johnston, 1980). In limited studies of human alveolar macrophages, candidacidal activity was recorded against *C. pseudotropicalis* (Territo and Golde, 1979) but not *C. albicans* (Cohen and Cline, 1971). Macrophages derived by cultivating human blood monocytes in vitro retain their ability to phagocytose and digest heat-killed *C. albicans* but lose their ability to kill viable *C. albicans* yeast cells (Fleischmann and Lehrer, 1985).

D. Candidacidal Mechanisms of Phagocytic cells

Candidacidal activity of neutrophils and mononuclear phagocytes includes both oxygen-dependent and oxygen-independent mechanisms. The relative importance of the different mechanisms depends on the type of phagocyte and species of *Candida* selected for study.

1. Oxygen-dependent candidacidal activity of phagocytic cells

In normal neutrophils, *C. albicans* is killed predominantly by oxygen-dependent pathways. Strong evidence for this has been obtained from in vitro studies using neutrophils from patients with two inherited disorders of oxygen metabolism, chronic granulomatous disease (CGD) and myeloperoxidase (MPO) deficiency. The membrane-bound NAD(P)H oxidase of neutrophils and monocytes of patients with CGD is usually unresponsive to activation by microbial stimuli, including fungi. The normal increase in oxygen consumption and generation of reactive oxygen metabolites (e.g. superoxide, hydrogen peroxide, hydroxyl radicals) observed during phagocytosis therefore fails to occur. Myeloperoxidase, a constituent of the primary (azurophil) granule, augments the antimicrobial effect of hydrogen peroxide through a halide-dependent mechanism (Klebanoff and Clark, 1978). Hypochlorite and monochloramine are potentially fungicidal products of this pathway (Grisham *et al.*, 1984; Wagner *et al.*, 1986). Myeloperoxidase is also found in monocytes (Nichols *et al.*, 1971). A distinct peroxidase enzyme occurs in eosinophils (Dri *et al.*, 1982).

Granulocytes, monocytes and eosinophils of patients with CGD fail to kill *C. albicans* effectively, despite normal levels of MPO in granules, presumably due to failure of production of hydrogen peroxide (Lehrer and Cline, 1969; Lehrer, 1971a; Leijh *et al.*, 1977). Similarly, killing of *C. albicans* by neutrophils and monocytes of patients with MPO deficiency is defective.

The importance of oxygen-dependent candidacidal mechanisms is further supported by studies showing decreased killing by neutrophils incubated under hypoxic conditions (Lehrer and Cline, 1969), or with myeloperoxidase inhibitors, for example, sulfonamide, (Lehrer, 1971b), azide, cyanide, thiocyanate, methimazole and thiourea (Lehrer, 1975; Klebanoff and Clark, 1978) or substances which quench hypochlorous acid and chloramines (Wagner *et al.*, 1986). In addition, catalase, which inhibits the MPO-mediated antimicrobial system, partially protects micro-organisms which contain it from the effects of this system (Klebanoff and Clark, 1978).

Despite these observations and the known efficacy of MPO in catalysing bactericidal activity in cell-free systems (Lehrer, 1972), several findings raise doubts about the relative importance of MPO in oxygen-dependent killing. The pH optimum for the enzyme in vitro is 4.5 to 5.0. During phagocytosis, peak superoxide anion and hydrogen peroxide production by neutrophils occurs during the respiratory burst, when the pH approximates 7.0 (Segal *et al.*, 1981). Thus the importance of MPO as a primary mechanism for amplification of intraphagosomal anti-microbial activity is uncertain. A less important role is suggested by the clinical observation that recurrent infections are uncommon in patients with hereditary MPO deficiency, despite impaired killing in vitro. However, the discrepancy can also be explained if compensatory fungicidal mechanisms were to exist in congenitally MPO-deficient phagocytes, by the presence of incomplete MPO deficiency (Parry *et al.*, 1981), or by the fact that lower levels of MPO activity are sufficient for the presumed smaller number of fungi presented to phagocytes in vivo compared with in vitro. An additional observation has been that the duration of the respiratory burst is prolonged in MPO-deficient granulo-cytes, possibly because of decreased inactivation of NAD(P)H oxidase activity, which is responsible for the burst (reviewed by McPhail and Snyderman, 1984). The increased persistence of reactive oxygen metab-olites may therefore contribute to the killing of micro-organisms. In addition, MPO can convert hydrogen peroxide and chloride to non-ionised hypochlorous acid and hypochlorite ion at physiological pH, substances which may constitute a major toxic product of neutrophils (Albrich *et al.*, 1981) either directly, or via conversion of neutrophil constituents to chloramines (Root and Cohen, 1981; Test *et al.*, 1984).

Iodination of bacteria has been reported to comprise a mechanism of MPO-mediated microbicidal activity (reviewed by Klebanoff and Clark, 1978). As a result, several studies have used iodination as an index of MPO-mediated killing. The validity of their conclusions must be questioned by the observation that iodination of *Candida* phagocytosed by normal monocytes can be inhibited by pre-treatment with agents such as aminotriazole, methimazole and isoniazid without impairment of killing ability (Lehrer, 1975).

Oxygen-dependent candidacidal activity of human monocytes can occur independently of myeloperoxidase-mediated pathways. Thus, while monocytes from CGD-deficient patients are impaired in their ability to kill *C. parapsilosis* and *C. pseudotropicalis*, monocytes from MPO-deficient patients are highly effective in doing so (Lehrer, 1975). Limited studies with peroxidase inhibitors suggest that candidacidal activity in rabbit macrophages is peroxidase-independent (Lehrer *et al.*, 1980). The existence of peroxidase in rabbit macrophages has been debated (Klebanoff, 1980; Lehrer *et al.*, 1980).

Other workers have suggested that macrophage-mediated killing of *C. albicans* is dependent on energy provided by both glycolytic and oxidative metabolism (Cohen and Cline, 1971) and that in mouse peritoneal macrophages, oxygen-dependent killing mechanisms are paramount (Sasada and Johnston, 1980).

2. *Oxygen-independent candidacidal activity of phagocytic cells*

The observation by Lehrer that neutrophils from patients with CGD and MPO deficiency retain the ability to kill *C. parapsilosis* and *C. pseudotropicalis* (Lehrer, 1975), despite marked reduction in activity against *C. albicans* (Lehrer, 1972), provided early evidence for the existence of oxygen-independent killing mechanisms. Several potentially microbicidal components have been identified within the granules of phagocytic cells. Lysozyme, lactoferrin, high concentrations of H^+, neutral proteases, cationic proteins and peptides and other small peptides are all microbicidal in vitro (reviewed by Spitznagel, 1984).

a. Cationic proteins and peptides. The existence of intravacuolar, cationic, microbicidal proteins was postulated at the turn of the century (reviewed by Spitznagel, 1984). In animal models of bacterial abscess formation, Spitznagel and Chi (1963) used histochemical methods to confirm that intravacuolar *E. coli* was coated with arginine-rich cationic proteins. These proteins were shown to originate from neutrophil granules and to prevent multiplication of bacteria to which they had bound (Spitznagel and Chi, 1963). Subsequent electron microscopic studies showed that cationic proteins were transferred into phagocytic vacuoles from a specific set of cytoplasmic granules (MacRae and Spitznagel, 1975). Several cationic proteins with varying molecular weights and antimicrobial spectra have now been characterised. Human neutrophil granules contain arginine-rich peptides (MW 35 kD) with antifungal, antibacterial and antiviral activity (Ganz *et al.*, 1985a), arginine-rich peptides (MW 36 kD) with predominant activity against Gram-negative bacilli (Modrzakowski and Spitznagel, 1979) and a lysine-rich protein (MW 57 kD) (Spitznagel, 1984) similar to the BPI protein identified by Weiss *et al.* (1978), with predominant activity against Gram-negative bacilli. Chymotrypsin-like cationic proteins (CLCP) (Odeberg and Olsson, 1975; Drazin and Lehrer, 1977), one of which is cathepsin G, with broad-spectrum antibacterial activity (Odeberg and Olsson, 1975) and activity against *C. parapsilosis*, have also been identified (Drazin and Lehrer, 1977).

Granules of human eosinophils contain arginine-rich proteins (MW 9–12 kD) which are toxic to parasites (Wassom and Gleich, 1979). Similar proteins (Gleich *et al.*, 1976) from guinea pig eosinophils are only weakly bactericidal (Gleich *et al.*, 1974, Wassom and Gleich, 1979). Antimicrobial cationic proteins or peptides have not yet been identified in human mononuclear phagocytes, but are abundant in rabbit alveolar macrophages (Lehrer *et al.*, 1981). Microbicidal cationic proteins have also been found in chicken (Brune and Spitznagel, 1973), rat (Hodinka and Modrzakowski, 1983), guinea pig and rabbit granulocytes (Zeya and Spitznagel, 1963; Zeya and Spitznagel, 1966; Lehrer *et al.*, 1975; Selsted *et al.*, 1984).

Cationic peptides isolated from guinea pig granulocytes (Lehrer *et al.*, 1975), rabbit granulocytes (Lehrer *et al.*, 1975; Selsted *et al.*, 1985c) and rabbit alveolar macrophages (Patterson-Delafield *et al.*, 1980, 1981) are candidacidal in vitro, at concentrations calculated to be exceeded within phagocytic cells. Lehrer's group has now characterised nine homologous peptides rich in arginine and hydrophobic amino acids, with a highly conserved region containing six cysteine groups linked by disulphide bonds. Two peptides have been identified in rabbit alveolar macrophages (Patterson-Delafield, 1980; Selsted *et al.*, 1983), six in rabbit granulocytes (Selsted *et al.*, 1984; Selsted *et al.*, 1985a) and three in human neutrophils (Selsted *et al.*, 1985b), but none or negligible amounts in adult rabbit monocytes, peritoneal macrophages and neonatal rabbit alveolar macrophages (Ganz *et al.*, 1985b). The human peptides, located in azurophil granules by immunogold staining, are less cationic than the rabbit peptides (Ganz *et al.*, 1985a). Sequence data on the human and rabbit neutrophil peptides suggest that the cysteine-containing infrastructure is more critical to their function than cationicity (Selsted *et al.*, 1985b).

The peptides from rabbit alveolar macrophages, which are identical to two of the six rabbit neutrophil peptides, exhibit greater activity against *C. albicans* and more broad-spectrum antibacterial activity than the four related neutrophil peptides (Selsted *et al.*, 1985c).

The candidacidal activity of NP-1, one of the most active rabbit granulocyte peptides, is initiated by a reversible, ionic binding step, followed by post-binding events which are temperature-dependent and inhibitable by millimolar concentrations of calcium (Lehrer *et al.*, 1985). Early indices of yeast cell well damage include release of ^{86}Rb from pre-labelled *C. albicans* and *C. parapsilosis* and decreased oxygen consumption (Patterson-Delafield *et al.*, 1980).

Several observations are consistent with an antimicrobial role of cationic peptides in vivo. Homologous peptides have been isolated from rabbit and human granulocytes and rabbit macrophages (Lehrer *et al.*, 1981; Selsted *et al.*, 1985a, b). These peptides comprise a substantial proportion of the protein content of phagocytes. For example, antimicrobial peptides comprise 1.7 per cent of the total cell protein in rabbit alveolar macrophages elicited by prior intravenous injection of Freund's complete adjuvant, representing an increase in MCP-1 of 2.8 times and in MCP-2 of 4.1 times that of resident alveolar macrophages (Lehrer *et al.*, 1981). Alveolar macrophages kill *C. albicans* blastospores more effectively than do rabbit peritoneal macrophages, which are devoid of the peptides (Lehrer *et al.*, 1980; Ganz *et al.*, 1985b; Sorrell *et al.*, 1985). The fungicidal activity of elicited alveolar macrophages is increased in comparison with that of resident alveolar macrophages, commensurate with the increased cationic peptide content (Lehrer *et al.*, 1980; Sorrell *et al.*, 1985). Although enhancement of oxygen-dependent killing in elicited macrophages was not explored in these studies, killing was azide-insensitive — evidence against peroxidase mediation (Lehrer *et al.*, 1980). It has also been shown that ^{35}S-cysteine is incorporated by cationic peptides in explanted alveolar macrophages from young rabbits, indicating active peptide synthesis (Ganz *et al.*, 1985b).

It has been argued that macrophages acquire cationic proteins or peptides by scavenging them from effete neutrophils (Spitznagel, 1984).

The observations noted above make this unlikely. In addition, Heifets *et al.* (1980) found that although several products of effete neutrophils, including myeloperoxidase (MPO), could be phagocytosed by resident mouse peritoneal macrophages, subsequent macrophage fungicidal activity was not augmented. The exogenously acquired MPO remained functional as evidenced by increased fixation of iodine during phagocytosis of zymosan. These authors postulated that the scavenged material was not accessible to phagolysosomal sites of fungicidal action.

On a weight basis, CLCP in neutrophil granules is approximately one-third as abundant as myeloperoxidase, elastase and lysozyme (Odeberg *et al.*, 1976). At an ionic strength approximating that of serum, however, adsorption and killing of *C. parapsilosis* is minimal, suggesting that CLCP is unlikely to be fungicidal in the extracellular environment (Drazin and Lehrer, 1977). Although the ionic strength within the phagocytic vacuole is unknown, binding of CLCP does occur within the appropriate pH range. Drazin and Lehrer (1977) were not able to demonstrate binding of CLCP to the surface of yeasts contained within phagolysosomes, but binding of CLCP to *Staphylococcus aureus* has been demonstrated in chicken granulocyte phagolysosomes (MacRae and Spitznagel, 1975).

b. Other agents involved in oxygen-independent killing. Oxygen-independent killing by neutrophils has been reviewed recently by Spitznagel (1984). Lactoferrin has been of particular interest, although controversies remain about its putative mode of action. A simplistic view has been that iron-free (apo) lactoferrin forms complexes with iron, rendering the iron unavailable for fungal growth, as demonstrated in vitro (Kirkpatrick *et al.*, 1971). It is believed that lactoferrin within the neutrophil is iron-poor (Klebanoff and Clark, 1978). Lactoferrin is also known to be released both into the phagocytic vacuole and outside the cell during phagocytosis (Leffell and Spitznagel, 1975). However, the importance of iron binding within the phagocytic vacuole is unclear, as lactoferrin binds iron strongly at low pH and releases it at pH 5–6, (Lestas, 1976); pH levels of 6–6.5 have been measured in the phagocytic vacuole after ingestion of heat-killed *C. albicans* (Mandell, 1970). Recently it has been shown that lactoferrin can interact with H_2O_2 to enhance hydroxyl radical generation by human neutrophils and particulate fractions thereof, through the Haber-Weiss reaction (Ambruso and Johnston, 1981) and that this source of iron in vitro is more efficient than the use of ferric chloride. However the efficiency of the Haber-Weiss reaction in biological systems has been questioned (Klebanoff and Clark,

1978) and differentiated HL-60 promyelocytic leukaemia cells, which lack lactoferrin, can generate hydroxyl radicals or similar reactive oxygen metabolites normally (McPhail and Snyderman, 1984).

Leukocytes also contain phospholipases that cleave membrane-bound free fatty acids, including arachidonic acid. Arachidonic acid metabolism is stimulated in neutrophils and macrophages during phagocytosis and substantial amounts of free arachidonic acid and its products are released to the extracellular environment (Higgs *et al.*, 1976; Goetzl and Sun, 1979; Hsueh, 1979; Stenson and Parker, 1980; Walsh *et al.*, 1981). In high concentrations (5×10^{-6} M), arachidonic acid is toxic to certain Gram-positive and Gram-negative bacteria (Knapp and Melly, 1986). In addition it may undergo auto-oxidation and create an additional antimicrobial effect (Gutteridge *et al.*, 1981).

3. Interactions between fungicidal mechanisms

There are few data published on the additive or synergistic activity that may exist between different killing mechanisms within phagocytes. In 1976, Odeberg and Olsson proposed that CLCP, because of its activity on cell surfaces and on the metabolism of micro-organisms, may act synergistically with other microbicidal mechanisms, including elastase and MPO (Odeberg and Olsson, 1976).

Lehrer *et al.* (1986) showed recently that NP-5, a relatively non-fungicidal component of the family of rabbit granulocyte defensins, potentiates in vitro the candidacidal effect of NP-1, NP-2 and NP-3A. Thorne *et al.* (1976) also suggested that granule proteases may exert a synergistic antibacterial effect with each other or with lysozyme.

Evidence has been presented that the dismutation of superoxide produced following the activation of NAD(P)H oxidase is responsible for the alkalinising effect seen in the phagolysosome during the respiratory burst (Segal *et al.*, 1981) and hence maintains the pH optimum for the function of intralysosomal enzymes and cationic peptides. Failure of alkalinisation in the neutrophils of patients with chronic granulomatous disease results in a rapid fall in pH to 6.0 or less during phagocytosis (Segal *et al.*, 1981) and may contribute to the intracellular killing defect in these neutrophils.

4. Clinical disorders of oxygen-dependent and oxygen-independent killing

CGD is classically associated with recurrent bacterial and fungal infections caused by catalase-positive micro-organisms, including *C. albicans* (Johnston and Newman, 1977). MPO deficiency is associated infrequently with recurrent candidal infections, despite impaired killing of *C. albicans* by affected phagocytes in vitro (Fleischmann and Lehrer, 1985). In a recent report, Parry *et al.* (1981) noted that five of 29 patients with hereditary MPO deficiency suffered from recurrent infections, four of them systemic candidiasis. Of these four, diabetes mellitus was a concomitant illness in three. As discussed earlier in this chapter, the candidal load is significantly increased in patients with diabetes mellitus, due to increased concentrations of glucose in tissues and secretions. In combination with the killing defect noted in vitro in MPO-deficient patients, clinical evidence of systemic fungal infection appears more likely. In a single patient with severe acquired MPO deficiency and refractory megaloblastic anaemia, neutrophil killing of *C. albicans* and *C. tropicalis* was remarkably impaired and the patient eventually died from systemic infections with *C. albicans* and *Aspergillus fumigatus* (Lehrer *et al.*, 1972).

Isolated deficiencies of cationic proteins have not been described in humans, raising the possibility that such deficiencies are not compatible with life. However the neutrophils of one patient with acute granulocytic leukaemia described by Odeberg *et al.* (1976) retained normal bactericidal activity against *E. coli* and *S. aureus* despite very low levels of lactoferrin, elastase, collagenase, CLCP and myeloperoxidase. Antifungal activity was not assessed in this patient, although decreased fungicidal activity has been reported in acute granulocytic leukaemia (Lehrer and Cline, 1971; Rosner *et al.*, 1970).

Lactoferrin deficiency has been described in association with specific granule deficiency and partial lysozyme deficiency (reviewed by Spitznagel, 1984). In the six patients summarised by Spitznagel, recurrent bacterial infections were present in all, in association with *C. albicans* in one. Interpretation of the results is complicated by the observation that additional phagocyte function defects can occur in these patients (Gallin *et al.*, 1982). In vitro intraleukocytic killing of *C. albicans* was normal in the patient in whom it was tested. Nevertheless, the case studies suggest that specific granules and lactoferrin are necessary for normal granulocyte-mediated killing.

No compromise in host resistance has yet been associated with genetically determined deficiencies of lysozyme.

5. Modulation of fungicidal activities of phagocytes

Fungicidal activity of macrophages can be enhanced by mechanisms which non-specifically activate macrophages, usually through a lymphokine-dependent mechanism. Thus candidacidal activity in explanted mouse peritoneal macrophages is enhanced by prior intraperitoneal administration of BCG or lipopolysaccharide (Sasada and Johnston, 1980), intravenous administration of BCG (Maiti *et al.*, 1980) or in vitro pre-incubation with recombinant interferon gamma (Brummer *et al.*, 1985). In one study, however, pre-incubation of mouse peritoneal macrophages with lipopolysaccharide in vitro did not enhance their candidacidal activity (Brummer *et al.*, 1985). Candidacidal activation of rabbit alveolar and peritoneal macrophages can be achieved by prior intravenous and intraperitoneal injection of Freund's complete adjuvant (Lehrer *et al.*, 1980; Sorrell *et al.*, 1985).

In vivo activation of murine macrophages by BCG did not influence the course of renal candidiasis in Swiss-Webster white mice (Rogers and Balish, 1977) in one study, but in A/J mice, prior activation with glucan was protective (Williams *et al.*, 1978). The relevance of these observations to human candidiasis is uncertain.

VI. THE EXTRACELLULAR ENVIRONMENT IN ANTIFUNGAL ACTIVITY

Diamond *et al.* demonstrated that extracellular hyphal and pseudo-hyphal forms of *C. albicans* are damaged following contact with human neutrophils in the absence of serum in vitro (Diamond *et al.*, 1978; Diamond and Krzesicki, 1978). This contact was associated with the preferential release of enzymes from specific granules (Diamond *et al.*, 1978). Substantial release of lysosomal contents has also been noted during phagocytosis of other yeast particles (Baggiolini and Dewald, 1984).

Several lines of evidence support the supremacy of oxygen-dependent killing mechanisms, particularly MPO, in the extracellular killing of hyphae of *C. albicans*. Thus chemiluminescence was increased during *Candida*–neutrophil interactions, and iodination of hyphal proteins was noted, suggesting activation of the $MPO-H_2O_2$–halide system (Diamond *et al.*, 1978). In contrast, extracellular contact of *Candida* hyphae with neutrophils from patients with chronic granulomatous disease failed to affect the uptake of [14]cytosine by *C. albicans* or to cause morphological damage (Diamond and Krzesicki, 1978; Diamond *et al.*, 1980). Similarly, contact between *C. albicans* hyphae and neutrophils of patients with MPO deficiency did not result in inhibition of [14]cytosine uptake by the yeasts (Diamond *et al.*, 1980). In the presence of normal neutrophils, inhibitors of peroxidase, catalase, superoxide dismutase and singlet oxygen were protective (Diamond and Krzesicki, 1978). In a cell-free system, myeloperoxidase, hydrogen peroxide and halide were all required for toxic fungal damage (Diamond *et al.*, 1980), which was confirmed by electron microscopy. A possible mechanism via generation of singlet oxygen was suggested by the observation that partial protection was afforded by incubation with singlet oxygen quenchers but not with superoxide dismutase. Data obtained using putative hydroxyl radical scavengers were conflicting, DMSO being effective, but not mannitol or sodium benzoate (Diamond and Krzesicki, 1978; Diamond *et al.*, 1980).

Active MPO has been shown to be released extracellularly during phagocytosis of *Staphylococcus aureus* by human neutrophils (Bradley *et al.*, 1982) and has been identified extracellularly in a rat model of staphylococcal intradermal abscess, in concentrations which are sufficient to cause inactivation of chemoattractants (Clark and Klebanoff, 1979) and which allow participation in other relevant iodination reactions (Bradley *et al.*, 1982). Wright *et al.* (1984), using mannan derived from *Saccharomyces cerevisiae*, reported binding of MPO to mannan by an ionic interaction with phosphate groups on the mannan outer chain. MPO has been found to bind to *Candida* yeast forms (Wright *et al.*, 1983) rendering them more susceptible to killing by the $MPO-H_2O_2$-halide system. In addition, intraperitoneal injection of MPO was noted to decrease mortality in a mouse model of renal candidiasis; the effect was abrogated by pre-incubation of MPO with soluble *C. albicans* cell wall mannan (Wright and Nelson 1985). The candidacidal activity of MPO is inhibited when the enzyme is complexed with soluble mannan (Wright *et al.*, 1983), an interaction which does not affect the catalytic activity of MPO (Wright *et al.*, 1981). The MPO–mannan complex may subsequently bind to neutrophils (Wright *et al.*, 1984). Oxygen-dependent mechanisms also appear to be of primary importance in the extracellular killing of *Candida* hyphae by human monocytes (Diamond and Haudenschild, 1981).

Cationic proteins are known to be released from neutrophils and may result in activation of the complement system with generation of chemotactic factors (Venge and Olsson, 1975). However, the ionic strength of the extracellular milieu is not likely to be appropriate for an antifungal effect of CLCP (Drazin and Lehrer, 1977) or the cationic peptides purified by Lehrer's group (Selsted *et al.*, 1984). This conclusion is supported by the observation of Cech and Lehrer that 40 per cent of granulocyte phagocytic vacuoles maintain continuity with the external environment after ingestion of *C. albicans* blastospores, thereby providing a means of egress of phagolysosomal contents and ingress of components from the external milieu. Notably, only 14.5 percent of ingested fungi in 'unsealed' vacuoles are killed within 60 minutes, compared with 71.8 percent of blastospores in sealed vacuoles (Cech and Lehrer, 1984).

Potentially fungicidal activities of extracellular lactoferrin, arachidonic acid and other materials released during phagocytosis have not been determined.

VII. MODULATION OF HOST DEFENCES BY *CANDIDA ALBICANS*

Although the purpose of this chapter is to focus on host defences against *C. albicans*, a number of studies have demonstrated that the fungus itself exerts a toxic effect on phagocytic cells. It has been known for several years that not all intracellular blastospores of *C. albicans* are killed by neutrophils, monocytes (Lehrer, 1970, 1975) or macrophages (Lehrer *et al.*, 1980). A proportion of the *Candida* are killed and disintegrate, some remain viable although apparently inactive (based on vital staining) and others form intracellular germ tubes. Germ tube formation may result in growth of the yeast beyond the confines of the phagocyte, resulting in phagocyte rupture (Stanley and Hurley, 1969; Louria and Brayton, 1964b). The response of phagocytes to yeasts is also determined by the morphological and metabolic state of the yeast at the time of ingestion. In one study, when standardised on the basis of ATP concentration, intracellular killing of hyphae of *C. albicans* was greater than that of yeasts or germ tubes in the presence of normal serum. Inactivation of complement by heating resulted in reduced intracellular killing of all three candidal forms. Because of large standard deviations, reduced killing was statistically significant only with the yeast and hyphal forms (Cockayne and Odds, 1984). It has been suggested that after ingestion, yeast cells resistant to intracellular killing are selected from a heterogeneous population and that such selection is relevant to the maintenance of infection in vivo (Richardson and Smith, 1981). An alternative explanation is provided by the observation that 40 per cent of blastospores ingested by human neutrophils remain in contact with the external environment and are relatively resistant to neutrophil candidacidal mechanisms (Cech and Lehrer, 1984).

Diamond and Haudenschild (1981) suggested that human monocytes are susceptible to disruption by *C. albicans*. They noted that under serum-free conditions, monocytes with attached hyphae in vitro exhibited swollen and disrupted membranes on electron microscopy. Hyphae were coated with surface-adherent vesicles, thought to originate from the monocyte. Similar anomalies were not noted during neutrophil–hyphal interactions. With both cell types, however, damage to hyphae was apparent (Diamond *et al.*, 1978; Diamond and Haudenschild, 1981).

In the presence of serum, germlings of *C. albicans* produced measurable amounts of hydrogen peroxide and caused early release of ^{51}Cr from prelabelled human monocytes but not neutrophils. In mixed leukocyte cultures, the extent of ^{51}Cr release was influenced by the test strain of *C. albicans* (Danley and Polakoff, 1986). In contrast to these findings with mature leukocytes, bone-marrow-derived monocyte precursors exhibit extracellular candidacidal activity without evidence of leukocyte damage (Baccarini *et al.*, 1985). The mechanism of the relative susceptibility of monocytes to toxic effects of *C. albicans* is unknown.

REFERENCES

Albrich, J. M., McCarthy, C. A. and Hurst, J. K. (1981). *Proceedings of National Academy of Sciences (USA)* 78: 210–14.

Albright, B. L., Selinger, D. S. and Reed, W. P. (1978). *Stain Technology* 54: 347–9.

Aly, R., Maibach, H. I., Shinefield, H. R. and Strauss, W. G. (1972). *Journal of Investigative Dermatology* 58: 205–10.

Aly, R., Maibach, H. I., Rahman, R. Shinefield, H. R. and Mandel, A. D. (1975). *Journal of Infectious Diseases* 131: 579–83.

Ambruso, D. R. and Johnston, R. B. (1981). *Journal of Clinical Investigation* 67: 352–60.

Arai, T., Mikami, Y. and Yokoyama, K. (1977). *Sabouraudia* 15: 171–8.

Baccarini, M. Bistoni, F. and Lohmann-Matthes, M-L. (1985). *Journal of Immunology* 134: 2658–65.

Baggiolini, M. and Dewald, B. (1984). Ch. 8 in R. Snyderman (ed.), *Contemporary Topics in Immunobiology: 14: Regulation of Leukocyte Function*. New York: Plenum Press.

Baine, W. B., Koening, M. G. and Goodman, J. S. (1974). *Infection and Immunity* 10: 1420–5.

Balish, E. and Phillips, A. W. (1966). *Journal of Bacteriology* 91: 1736–43.

Bartels, H. A., Blechman, H. and Mori, M. (1967). *Nature (London)* 213: 830.

Bradley, P. P., Christensen, R. D. and Rothstein, G. (1982). *Blood* 60: 618–22.

Brummer, E., Morrison, C. J. and Stevens, D. A. (1985). *Infection and Immunity* 49: 724–30.

Brune, K. and Spitznagel, J. K. (1973). *Journal of Infectious Diseases* 127: 84–94.

Bulmer, G. S. and Fromptling, R. A. (1985). Chapter 1, The fungi pathogenic for humans and animals, in D. H. Howard (ed), *Pathogenic Mechanisms of Mycotic Agents*, part B. New York, Marcelle Decker Inc.

Calderone, R. A., Rotondo, M. F. and Sande, M. A. (1978). *Infection and Immunity* 20: 279–89.

Calderone, R. A., Cihlar, R. L., Lee, D. D.-S., Hoberg, K. and Scheld, W. M. (1985). *Journal of Infectious Diseases* 152: 710–15.

Cech, P. and Lehrer, R. I. (1984). *Blood* 64: 147–51.

Clark, R. A. and Klebanoff, S. J. (1979). *Journal of Clinical Investigation* 64: 913–20.

Cockayne, A. and Odds, F. C. (1984). *Journal of General Microbiology* 130: 465–71.

Cohen, A. B. and Cline, M. J. (1971). *Journal of Clinical Investigation* 50: 1390–8.

Cutler, J. E. (1977). *Infection and Immunity* 18: 568–73.

Danley, D. L. and Polakoff, J. (1986). *Infection and Immunity* 51: 307–13.

Davies, R. R. and Denning, T. J. V. (1972). *Sabouraudia* 10: 301–12.

Davis, C. P., McAllister, J. S. and Savage, D. C. (1973). *Infection and Immunity* 7: 666–72.

Day, N. K. and Good, R. A. (1980). Chapter 3 in M. H. Grieco (ed.), *Infections in The Abnormal Host* New York: Yorke Medical Books.

Denning, T. J. V. and Davies, R. R. (1973). *Sabouraudia* 11: 210–21.

Diamond, R. D. and Haudenschild, C. C. (1981). *Journal of Clinical Investigation* 67: 173–82.

Diamond, R. D. and Krzesicki, R. (1978). *Journal of Clinical Investigation* 61: 360–9.

Diamond, R. D., Krzesicki, R. and Jao, W. (1978). *Journal of Clinical Investigation* 61: 349–59.

Diamond, R. D., Clark, R. A. and Haudenschild, C. C. (1980). *Journal of Clinical Investigation* 66: 908–17.

Domer, J. E. and Carrow, E. W. (1983). *Advances in Experimental Medicine and Biology* 162: 383–408.

Douglas, L. J. and McCourtie, J. (1983). *FEMS Microbiology Letter* 16: 199–202.

Drazin, R. E. and Lehrer, R. I. (1977). *Infection and Immunity* 17: 382–8.

Dri, P., Cramer, R., Soranzo, M. R., Comin, A., Miotti, V. and Patriacha, P. (1982). *Blood* 60: 323–7.

Edwards, J. E. Jr (1982). Candida endophthalmitis. In J. S. Remington and M. N. Swartz (eds), *Current Clinical Topics in Infectious Diseases*, no. 3. New York: McGraw Hill: 381–97.

Edwards, J. E. Jr (1985). Ch. 216. Candida species. In G. L. Mandell, R. D. Douglas Jr and J. E. Bennett (eds), *Principles and Practice of Infectious Diseases*, 2nd edn. New York: John Wiley and Sons.

Edwards, J. E. Jr, Montgomerie, J. Z., Foos, R. Y., Shaw, V. K. and Guze, L. B. (1975). *Journal of Infectious Diseases* 131: 649–57.

Edwards, J. E. Jr, Montgomerie, J. Z., Ishida, K., Morrison, J. O. and Guze, L. B. (1977). *Journal of Infectious Diseases* 135: 294–7.

Fader, R. C., Nunez, D., Unbehagen, J. and Linares, H. A. (1985). *Infection and Immunity* 49: 780–4.

Field, L. H., Pope, L. M., Cole, G. T., Guentzel, M. N. and Berry, L. J. (1981). *Infection and Immunity* 31: 783–91.

Fleischmann, J. and Lehrer, R. I. (1985). Phagocytic mechanisms in host response. Chapter 4 in D. H. Howard (ed.), *The Fungi Pathogenic for Humans and Animals*, part C. New York: Marcelle Decker Inc.

Gallin, J. I., Fletcher, M. P., Seligmann, B. E., Hoffstein, S., Cehrs, K. and Mounessa, N. (1982). *Blood* 59: 1317–29.

Ganz, T., Selsted, M. E., Szklarek, D., Harwig, S. S. L., Daher, K., Bainton, D. F. and Lehrer, R. I. (1985a). *Journal of Clinical Investigation* 76: 1427–35.

Ganz, T., Sherman, M. P., Selsted, M. E. and Lehrer, R. I. (1985b). *American Review of Respiratory Diseases* 132: 901–4.

Gelfand, J. A., Hurley, D. L., Fauci, A. S. and Frank, M. M. (1978). *Journal of Infectious Diseases* 138: 9–16.

Gleich, G. J., Loegering, D. A., Kueppers, F., Bojoj, S. P. and Mann, K. G. (1974). *Journal of Experimental Medicine* 140: 313–32.

Gleich, G. J., Loegering, D. A., Mann, K. G. and Maldonado, J. E. (1976). *Journal of Clinical Investigation* 57: 633–40.

Goetzl, E. J. and Sun, F. F. (1979). *Journal of Experimental Medicine* 150: 406–11.

Green, G. (1970). *American Review of Respiratory Diseases* 102: 691–703.

Grisham, M. B., Jefferson, M. M. and Thomas, E. G. (1984). *Journal of Biological Chemistry* 259: 6766–72.

Gutteridge, J. M. C., Paterson, S. K., Segal, A. W. and Halliwell, B. (1981). *Biochemical Journal* 199: 259–61.

Heidenreich, F. and Dierich, M. P. (1985). *Infection and Immunity* 50: 598–600.

Heifets, L., Imai, K. and Goren, M. B. (1980). *Journal of the Reticuloendothelial Society* 28: 391–404.

Helmstrom, P. B. and Balish, E. (1979). *Infection and Immunity* 23: 764–74.

Higgs, G. A., Bunting, S., Moncada, S. and Vane, J. R. (1976). *Prostaglandins* 12: 749–57.

Hodinka, R. L. and Modrzakowski, M. C. (1983). *American Society for Microbiology Annual Meeting Abst.* 91: 74.

Howlett, J. A. (1975). *Journal of Medical Microbiology* 9: 309–16.

Howlett, J. A. and Squier, C. A. (1980). *Infection and Immunity* 29: 256–60.

Hsueh, W. (1979). *American Journal of Pathology* 97: 137–47.

Hummel, R. P., Oestreicher, E. J., Maley, M. P. and MacMillan, B. G. (1973). *Journal of Surgical Research* 15: 53–8

Ishikawa, T., Condon Dalton, A. and Arbesman, C. E. (1972). *Journal of Allergy and Applied Immunology* 49: 311–15.

Johnston, R. B. and Newman, S. L. (1977). *Pediatric Clinics of North America* 24: 365–76.

Kennedy, M. J. and Volz, P. A. (1985). *Infection and Immunity* 49: 654–63.

Kernbaum, S. (1975). *Annales Microbiologie (Institut Pasteur)* 126A: 75–81.

Kimura, L. H. and Pearsall, N. N. (1978). *Infection and Immunity* 21: 64–8.

Kimura, L. H. and Pearsall, N. N. (1980). *Infection and Immunity* 28: 464–8.

King, R. D., Lee, J. C. and Morris, A. L. (1980). *Infection and Immunity* 27: 667–74.

Kirkpatrick, C. H., Green, I., Rich, R. R. and Schade, A. L. (1971). *Journal of Infectious Diseases* 124: 539–44.

Klebanoff, S. J. (1980). Oxygen intermediates and the microbicidal event. Ch. 43 in R. van Furth (ed.), *Mononuclear Phagocytes: Functional Aspects*, part II. The Hague: Martinus Nijhoff.

Klebanoff, S. J. and Clark, R. A. (1978). *The Neutrophil: Function and Clinical Disorders.* Amsterdam: North-Holland.

Klotz, S. A., Drutz, D. J., Harrison, J. L. and Huppert, M. (1983). *Infection and Immunity* 42: 374–84.

Knapp, H. R. and Melly, M. A. (1986). *Journal of Infectious Diseases* 154: 84–94.

Knight, L. and Fletcher, J. (1971). *Journal of Infectious Diseases* 123: 371–7.

Kozinn, P. J., Caroline, L. and Taschdjian, C. L. (1964). *Science* 146: 1479–80.

Krause, W., Matheis, H. and Wulf, K. (1969). *Lancet* 1: 598–9.

Law, S. K. and Levine, R. P. (1977). *Proceedings of the National Academy of Sciences (USA)* 74: 2701–5.

Lee, J. C. and King, R. D. (1983). *Infection and Immunity* 41: 1024–30.

Leffell, M. S. and Spitznagel, J. K. (1975). *Infection and Immunity* 12: 813–20.

Lehrer, R. I. (1971a). *Infection and Immunity* 3: 800–2.

Lehrer, R. I. (1971b). *Journal of Clinical Investigation* 50: 2498–2505.

Lehrer, R. I. (1972). Ch. 10. In R. C. Williams Jr and H. H. Fudenberg (eds), *Phagocytic Mechanisms of Health and Disease*. New York: Intercontinental Medical Book Corporation: ch. 10.

Lehrer, R. I. (1975). *Journal of Clinical Investigation* 55: 338–46.

Lehrer, R. I. (1978). UCLA Conference. *Annals of Internal Medicine* 89: 91–106.

Lehrer, R. I. and Cline, M. J. (1969). *Journal of Bacteriology* 98: 996–1004.

Lehrer, R. I. and Cline, M. L. (1969). *Journal of Bacteriology* 98: 996–1004.

Lehrer, R. I. and Cline, M. J. (1971). *Cancer* 27: 1211–17.

Lehrer, R. I., Goldberg, L. S., Apple, M. A. and Rosenthal, N. P. (1972). *Annals of Internal Medicine* 76: 447–53.

Lehrer, R. I., Ladra, K. M. and Hake, R. B. (1975). *Infection and Immunity* 11: 1226–34.

Lehrer, R. I., Ferrari L. G., Patterson-Delafield, J. and Sorrell, T. C. (1980). *Infection and Immunity* 28: 1001–8.

Lehrer, R. I., Szklarek, D., Selsted, M. E. and Fleischmann, J. (1981). *Infection and Immunity* 33: 775–8.

Lehrer, R. I., Szklarek, D., Ganz, T. and Selsted, M. E. (1985). *Infection and Immunity* 49: 207–11.

Lehrer, R. I., Szklarek, D., Ganz, T. and Selsted, M. (1986). *Infection and Immunity* 52: 902–4.

Leijh, P. C. J., van den Barselaar, M. T. and van Furth, R. (1977). *Infection and Immunity* 17: 313–18.

Lestas, A. N. (1976). *British Journal of Haematology* 32: 341–50.

Liljemark, W. F. and Gibbons, R. J. (1973). *Infection and Immunity* 8: 846–9.

Loose, D. S. and Feldman, D. (1982). *Journal of Biological Chemistry* 257: 4925–30.

Louria, D. B. (1977). Experimental infections with fungi and yeasts. In A. M. Beemer, A. Ben-David, M. A. Klingberg and E. S. Kuttin (eds), *Contributions to Microbiology and Immunology*, vol. 3, *Host–Parasite Relationships in Systemic Mycoses: Part 1: Methodology, Pathology and Immunology*. Basel: S. Karger: 31–47.

Louria, D. B. and Brayton, R. G. (1964a). *Nature (London)* 201: 309.

Louria, D. B. and Brayton, R. G. (1964b). *Proceedings of the Society for Experimental Biology and Medicine* 115: 93–9.

Louria, D. B., Fallon, N. and Browne, H. G. (1960). *Journal of Clinical Investigation* 39: 1435–49.

McCourtie, J. and Douglas, J. (1984). *Infection and Immunity* 45: 6–12.

McPhail, L. C. and Snyderman, R. (1984). Ch. 9 In R. Snyderman (ed), *Contemporary Topics in Immunobiology*, vol. 14, *Regulation of Leukocyte Function*. New York: Plenum Press.

MacRae, E. K. and Spitznagel, J. K. (1975). *Journal of Cell Science* 17: 79–94.

Maiti, P. K., Kumar, R. and Mohapatra, L. N. (1980). *Infection and Immunity* 29: 477–82.

Mandell, G. L. (1970). *Proceedings of the Society for Experimental Biology and Medicine* 134: 447–9.

Marsh, P. (1980). *Oral Microbiology*. London: Nelson: 32.

Meister, H., Heymer, B., Schäfer, H. and Haferkamp, O. (1977). *Journal of Infectious Diseases* 135: 235–42.

Miller, M. E. and Nilsson, U. R. (1970). *New England Journal of Medicine* 282: 354–8.

Miller, M. E., Seals, J., Kaye, R. and Levitsky, L. C. (1968). *Lancet* 2: 60–3.

Modrzakowski, M. C. and Spitznagel, J. K. (1979). *Infection and Immunity* 25: 597–602.

Montes, L. F. and Wilborn, W. H. (1968). *Journal of Bacteriology* 96: 1349–56.

Morelli, R. and Rosenberg, L. T. (1971). *Journal of Immunology* 107: 476–80.

Nichols, B. A., Bainton, D. F. and Farquhar, M. G. (1971). *Journal of Cell Biology* 50: 498–515.

Odds, F. C., Evans, E. G. V., Taylor, M. A. R. and Wales, J. K. (1978). *Journal of Clinical Pathology* 31: 840–4.

Odeberg, H. and Olsson, I. (1975). *Journal of Clinical Investigation* 56: 1118–24.

Odeberg, H. and Olsson, I. (1976). *Infection and Immunity* 14: 1269–75.

Odeberg, H., Olofsson, T. and Olsson, I. (1976). *Blood Cells* 2: 542–51.

Olsen, I. and Birkeland, J. M. (1976). *Scandinavian Journal of Dental Research* 84: 94–7.

Paine, T. F. Jr (1958). *Antibiotics and Chemotherapy* 8: 273–81.

Patterson-Delafield, J., Martinez, R. J. and Lehrer, R. I. (1980). *Infection and Immunity* 30: 180–92.

Patterson-Delafield, J., Szklarek, D., Martinez, R. J. and Lehrer, R. I. (1981). *Infection and Immunity* 31: 723–31.

Parry, M. F., Root, R. K., Metcalf, J. A., Delaney, K. K., Kaplow, L. S. and Richar, W. J. (1981). *Annals of Internal Medicine* 95: 293–301.

Peterson, E. M. and Calderone, R. A. (1977). *Infection and Immunity* 15: 910–15.

Poulain, D., Tronchin, G., Vernes, A., Popeye, R. and Biguet, J. (1983). *Sabouraudia* 21: 99–112.

Powell, B. L. and Drutz, D. J. (1983). *Journal of Infectious Diseases* 147: 359.

Ray, T. L. and Wuepper, K. D. (1976). *Journal of Investigative Dermatology* 67: 700–3.

Ray, T. L., Hanson, A., Ray, R. F. and Wuepper, K. D. (1979). *Journal of Investigative Dermatology* 73: 269–74.

Ray, T. L., Digre, K. B. and Payne, C. D. (1984). *Journal of Investigative Dermatology* 83: 37–41.

Reinhart, H., Muller, G. and Sobel, J. D. (1985). *Annals of Clinical Laboratory Science* 15: 406–13.

Richardson, M. D. and Smith, H. (1981). *Journal of Infectious Diseases* 144: 557–64.

Rippon, J. W. (1982). *Medical Mycology: The Pathogenic Fungi and the Pathogenic Actinomycetes.* New York: W. B. Saunders Co.

Roberts, G. D. (1985). Chapter 47 in *Manual of Clinical Microbiology*, 4th edn. Washington, DC: American Society for Microbiology: 502.

Rogers, T. J. and Balish, E. (1977). *Journal of the Reticuloendothelial Society* 22: 309–18.

Rogosa, M. and Sharpe, M. E. (1960). *Journal of General Microbiology* 23: 197–201.

Root, R. K. and Cohen, M. S. (1981). *Reviews of Infectious Diseases* 3: 565–98.

Root, R. K., Ellman, L. and Frank, M. M. (1972). *Journal of Immunology* 109: 477–86.

Rosenfeld, S. I., Kelly, M. E. and Leddy, J. P. (1976). *Journal of Clinical Investigation* 57: 1626–34.

Rosner, F., Valmont, I., Kozinn, P. J. and Caroline, L. (1970). *Cancer* 25: 835–42.

Roth, F. J. and Goldstein, M. I. (1961). *Journal of Investigative Dermatology* 36: 383–7.

Rotrosen, D., Gibson, T. R. and Edwards, J. E. Jr (1983). *Journal of Infectious Diseases* 147: 594.

Rotrosen, D., Calderone, R. A. and Edwards, J. E. Jr (1986). *Reviews of Infectious Disease* 8: 73–85.

Ruthe, R. C., Anderson, B. L., Cunningham, B. L. and Epstein, R. B. (1978). *Blood* 52: 493–8.

Saigh, J. H., Sanders, C. C. and Sanders, W. E. Jr (1978). *Infection and Immunity* 19: 704–10.

Samaranayake, L. P. and MacFarlane, T. W. (1981). *Archives of Oral Biology* 26: 815–20.

Samaranayake, L. P. and MacFarlane, T. W. (1982). *Archives of Oral Biology* 27: 869–73.

Sasada, M. and Johnston, R. B. Jr (1980). *Journal of Experimental Medicine* 152: 85–98.

Scheld, W. M. (1984). Pathogenesis and pathophysiology of infective endocarditis. In M. A. Sande, D. Kaye and R. K. Root (eds), *Contemporary Issues in Infectious Diseases*, vol. 2. New York: Churchill Livingstone: 14.

Scheld, W. M., Calderone, R. A., Alliegro, G. M. and Sande, M. A. (1981). *Proceedings of the Society for Experimental Biology and Medicine* 168: 208–13.

Schmid, L. and Brune, K. (1974). *Infection and Immunity* 10: 1120–6.

Schriener, E. and Wolff, K. (1969). *Archiv für Klinische und Experimentelle Dermatologie (Berlin)* 235: 78–88.

Schuit, K. E. (1979). *Infection and Immunity* 24: 932–8.

Seelig, M. S. (1966). *Bacteriological Reviews* 30: 442–59.

Segal, A. W., Geisow, M., Garcia, R., Harper, A. and Miller, R. (1981). *Nature (London)* 290: 406–9.

Selsted, M. E., Brown D. M., DeLange, R. J. and Lehrer, R. I. (1983). *Journal of Biological Chemistry* 258: 14485–9.

Selsted, M. E., Szklarek, D. and Lehrer, R. J. (1984). *Infection and Immunity* 45: 150–4.

Selsted, M. E., Brown D. M., DeLange, R. J., Harwig, S. S. L. and Lehrer, R. I. (1985a). *Journal of Biological Chemistry* 260: 4579–84.

Selsted, M. E., Harwig, S. S. L., Ganz, T., Schilling, J. W. and Lehrer, R. I., (1985b). *Journal of Clinical Investigation* 76: 1436–9.

Selsted, M. E., Szklarek, D., Ganz, T. and Lehrer, R. I., (1985c). *Infection and Immunity* 49: 202–6.

Skerl, K. G., Calderone, R. A. and Sreevalsan, T. (1981). *Infection and Immunity* 34: 938–43.

Skerl, K. G., Calderone, R. A., Segal, E., Sreevalsan, T. and Scheld, W. M. (1984). *Canadian Journal of Microbiology* 30: 221–7.

Sklavounou, A. and Germaine, G. R. (1980). *Infection and Immunity* 27: 686–9.

Sobel, J. D. (1979). *Clinical Research* 27: 357A.

Sobel, J. D., Myers, P. G., Kaye, D. and Levison, M. E. (1981). *Journal of Infectious Diseases* 143: 76–82.

Sobel, J. D., Myers, P., Leveson, M. E. and Kaye, D. (1982). *Infection and Immunity* 34: 697–701.

Sohnle, P. G., Frank, M. M. and Kirkpatrick, C. H. (1976). *Journal of Immunology* 117: 523–30.

Solomkin, J. S., Mills, E. L., Giebink, G. S., Nelson, R. D., Simmons, R. L. and Quie, P. G. (1978). *Journal of Infectious Diseases* 137: 30–7.

Sorrell, T. C., Dunlop, C., Collignon, P. J. and Harding, J. A. (1984). *British Journal of Ophthalmology* 68: 841–5.

Sorrell, T. C., Lehrer, R. I., Ferarri, L. G., Müller, M. and Selsted, M. E. (1985). *Australian Journal of Experimental Biology and Medical Science* 63: 53–63.

Spitznagel, J. K. (1984). Ch. 10. In R. Snyderman (ed), *Contemporary Topics in Immunobiology*, vol. 14, *Regulation of Leukocyte Function*. New York: Plenum Press.

Spitznagel, J. K. and Chi, H.-Y. (1963). *American Journal of Pathology* 43: 697–708.

Squier, C. A. (1973). *Journal of Ultrastructural Research* 43: 160–77.

Stanley, V. C. and Hurley, R. (1969). *Journal of Pathology* 97: 357–66.

Stenson, W. F. and Parker, C. W. (1980). *Journal of Immunology* 125: 1–5.

Stone, H. H. (1973). *Journal of Surgical Research* 14: 273–6.

Stone, H. H., Kolb, L. D., Currie, C. A. Geheber, C. E. and Cussell, J. Z. (1974). *Annals of Surgery* 179: 697–710.

Territo, M. C. and Golde, D. W. (1979). *Journal of the Reticuloendothelial Society* 25: 111–20.

Test, S. T., Lampert, M. B., Ossanna, P. J., Thoene, J. G. and Weiss, S. J. (1984). *Journal of Clinical Investigation* 74: 1341–9.

Thorne, K. J. I., Oliver, R. C. and Barrett, A. J. (1976). *Infection and Immunity* 14: 555–63.

Trnovec, T., Sikl, D., Zemanek, M., Fabernova, S., Bezek, S., Gadjosik, A. and Koprda, V. (1978). *Sabouraudia* 16: 239–306.

Venge, P. and Olsson, I. (1975). *Journal of Immunology* 115: 1505–8.

Wagner, D. K., Collins-Lech, C. and Sohnle, P. G. (1986). *Infection and Immunity* 51: 731–5.

Wain, W. H., Price, M. F. and Cawson, R. A. (1976). *Sabouraudia* 14: 149–54.

Walsh, C. E., Moseley Waite, B., Thomas, M. J. and De Chatelet, L. R. (1981). *Journal of Biological Chemistry* 256: 7228–34.

Warr, G. A. and Jakab, G. J. (1979). *Infection and Immunity* 26: 492–7.

Wassom, D. L. and Gleich, G. J. (1979). *American Journal of Tropical Medicine and Hygiene* 28: 860–3.

Weiss, J., Elsbach, P., Olsson, I. and Odeberg, H. (1978). *Journal of Biological Chemistry* 253: 2664–72.

Williams, D. L., Cook, J. A., Hoffman, E. O. and Di Luzio, N. R. (1978). *Journal of the Reticuloendothelial Society* 23: 479–90.

Wingard, J. R., Dick, J. D., Merz, W. G., Sanford, G. R., Saral, R. and Burns, W. H. (1980). *Infection and Immunity* 29: 808–13.

Winner, H. I. and Hurley, R. (1964). *Candida albicans,* Ch. 8. London: Churchill: 76.

Wright, C. D. and Nelson, R. D. (1985). *Infection and Immunity* 47: 363–5.

Wright, C. D., Herron, M. J., Gray, G. R., Holmes, B. and Nelson, R. D. (1981). *Infection and Immunity* 32: 731–8.

Wright, C. D., Bowie, J. U., Gray, G. R. and Nelson, R. D. (1983). *Infection and Immunity* 42: 76–80.

Wright, C. D., Bowie, J. U. and Nelson, R. D. (1984). *Infection and Immunity* 43: 467–71.

Yamamura, M. and Valdimarsson, H. (1977). *Scandinavian Journal of Immunology* 6: 591–4.

Zeya, H. I. and Spitznagel, J. K. (1963). *Science* 142: 1085–7.

Zeya, H. I. and Spitznagel, J. K. (1966). *Science* 154: 1049–51.

22

Protozoan Infections

DAVID L. HOOVER

*Infectious Disease Service, Walter Reed Army Medical Center,
Washington, DC, USA*

MONTE S. MELTZER

CAROL A. NACY

*Department of Immunology, Walter Reed Army Institute of Research,
Washington, DC, USA*

I. INTRODUCTION
II. CLINICAL DESCRIPTION AND IMMUNOPATHOPHYSIOLOGY
III. INTERACTIONS OF PARASITIC PROTOZOA WITH NON-SPECIFIC
     DEFENCES
IV. IMMUNOTHERAPEUTIC APPROACHES
V. CONCLUSION
REFERENCES

I. INTRODUCTION

Numerous genera of protozoa infect humans. These multiform organisms are responsible for remarkably diverse infections. Route of parasite entry, location of infection, clinical manifestations, and antiparasitic host defences vary tremendously. It is impossible to describe in detail the contributions of natural immunity to resistance to infection or recovery

---

The views of the authors do not purport to reflect the position of the
Department of the Army or the Department of Defense

NATURAL IMMUNITY
ISBN 0 12 5145551

from infection with each of this complex group of organisms. In this chapter, we emphasise interactions of *Leishmania* with non-specific defences, and illustrate principles of these interactions using other parasites.

II. CLINICAL DESCRIPTION AND IMMUNOPATHOPHYSIOLOGY

Leishmania species are important aetiologic agents of human disease in tropical and subtropical regions. Small animals serve as reservoirs of infection; the organism is transmitted between animals and humans by inoculation of the promastigote form of the parasite into skin by sandfly vectors as they ingest a blood meal. Cutaneous leishmaniasis, caused by *L. major* or *L. tropica* in the Old World and *L. mexicana* or *L. braziliensis* in the New, consists of skin ulcers at the sites of sandfly bites. Lesions begin several weeks after inoculation of the parasite, and may persist for many months before they resolve without antimicrobial therapy. Systemic manifestations are usually absent, but metastasis of viable parasites to regional lymph nodes has been repeatedly demonstrated. A more severe form of disease, mucocutaneous leishmaniasis, initially resembles cutaneous disease. After apparent spontaneous healing, however, lesions reappear in the nasal and oral mucosa and other structures of the face. Disease progresses to enlarging local lesions with mutilating destruction of cartilage and soft tissue. Mucocutaneous leishmaniasis eventually causes death by respiratory compromise, superinfection, or inanition. It is possible that characteristics of the parasite rather than of the host most forcefully determine whether cutaneous or mucocutaneous disease occurs as a consequence of infection: disease expression differs depending on the species of infecting organism. Moreover, skin responses to leishmanial antigens and lymphocyte mitogenic responses to lectins or antigens are similar in both conditions (Castes *et al.*, 1983). Delayed cutaneous hypersensitivity to leishmanin, a preparation of formalinised promastigotes, is generally present concurrently with the lesions, and persists during and after convalescence.

In contrast to patients with cutaneous or mucocutaneous disease, patients with diffuse cutaneous leishmaniasis do not manifest delayed hypersensitivity to intradermal injection of leishmanin; nor do their lymphocytes divide in response to stimulation with leishmanial antigen in vitro (Castes *et al.*, 1983). These patients have numerous, widely distributed skin lesions that contain abundant parasites. In many ways, this disease form resembles lepromatous leprosy. It is thought that failure to mount an appropriate cellular immune response underlies the heavy parasite burden of diffuse cutaneous disease (Convit *et al.*, 1972). Whether this failure is attributable to characteristics of the leishmanial species or of the host is not yet known. *L. mexicana amazonensis*, which causes diffuse cutaneous leishmaniasis, also causes localised cutaneous disease. The relative contributions of host and parasite factors to disease manifestations are particularly difficult to determine in this instance because taxonomy of *Leishmania* is still based largely on clinical grounds. As yet, there is little general agreement on classification of these organisms by the numerous biochemical and molecular approaches that have been suggested (Lainson, 1983).

In contrast to cutaneous leishmaniasis, visceral leishmaniasis is caused by only three species of *Leishmania; L. donovani* or *L. donovani infantum* in the Old World and *L. chagasi* in the New (Wirth *et al.*, 1986). A nodular lesion develops at the site of parasite injection by sandflies. The parasite then disseminates to infect macrophages throughout the reticuloendothelial system. Macrophages in spleen, liver and bone marrow may be heavily parasitised. Clinically uninvolved skin may also contain large numbers of infected cells. As in diffuse cutaneous disease, the leishmanin skin test in visceral leishmaniasis is negative initially, but may become positive when patients recover from disease (Rees *et al.*, 1981). Similarly, patient lymphocytes stimulated with leishmanial antigens in vitro respond poorly during acute infection. Response improves, however, with treatment (Carvalho *et al.*, 1981; Haldar *et al.*, 1983).

The diagnosis of leishmanial infection is confirmed by demonstration of the organism in tissues, either by biopsy, culture, or recently by hybridisation with radiolabelled DNA probes (Wirth and McMahon-Pratt, 1982). All forms of leishmaniasis respond to treatment with antimony compounds. Mucocutaneous and diffuse cutaneous disease, however, may relapse or respond poorly to antimicrobial therapy.

Organisms closely related to *Leishmania* include *Trypanosoma cruzi*, which causes American trypanosomiasis (Chagas' disease) and *T. gambiense* and *T. rhodesiense*, which cause African sleeping sickness. The trypomastigote form of *T. cruzi* is deposited on the skin by infected reduviid bugs when they defecate after eating a blood meal. Parasites enter the circulation through breaks in the skin and disseminate widely. They enter macrophages or smooth or cardiac muscle cells, where they transform into amastigotes. The amastigotes multiply, burst their host cell, and circulate as trypomastigotes. In this acute phase of the disease, parasites are easily demonstrable in blood and other tissues. Symptoms are those of acute infection with local findings at the site of inoculation. Acute myocarditis or meningoencephalitis may occur during the acute phase. In survivors, a quiescent period ensues. Years later, chronic disease (cardiomyopathy or megaoesophagus or megacolon) may develop. Few parasites are evident at this time. Late disease may be a consequence of autoantibodies directed against cardiac muscle, but conclusive evidence for this hypothesis is lacking. A number of studies indicate that cellular immunity plays a role in destruction of *T. cruzi*, presumably during early stages of disease (Kierszenbaum, 1979). In vitro, lymphokines induce intracellular killing of *T. cruzi* by macrophages. These findings suggest that lymphocyte–macrophage co-operation provides the basis for control of acute Chagas' disease. Whether continued lymphocyte-mediated cytotoxic activity plays a role in late-stage disease is presently unknown.

In contrast to Chagas' disease, African trypanosomiasis is overwhelmingly characterised by interactions of parasites with specific antibody. After a period of systemic complaints, the disease is manifest as progressive central nervous system impairment, characterised initially by inattention, and finally by stupor, coma and death in untreated patients. African trypanosomiasis is immunologically fascinating because the organisms continuously change their surface antigens in response to selective pressure by host antibody. As a consequence of these changes, successive waves of parasitaemia with different antigenic types of trypanosomes occur until the host dies. Natural immunity plays little role in the unsuccessful defence against these organisms. Although phagocytic cells are primarily responsible for destruction of the parasite, they act fundamentally in concert with specific, opsonising antibody. The host's inability to match parasite antigenic variation and the immunological consequences of antigen–antibody interactions, especially perivascular mononuclear infiltration and vasculitis, eventually lead to the patient's demise.

Toxoplasma gondii infects a wide range of animals, including humans. The parasite undergoes sexual reproduction only in felines, the definitive hosts. Felines are required to maintain the life cycle in nature, since incidental hosts do not excrete the parasite in their faeces. Humans, an incidental host, acquire toxoplasmosis transplacentally, by ingestion of oocysts excreted by felines, or by ingestion of tissue cysts from undercooked meat of infected animals, especially sheep and pigs. *Toxoplasma* infects one-third to one-half of normal humans by age 40, but causes recognisable disease in only a few of these individuals. After ingestion, the parasite excysts in the human digestive tract. Trophozoites disseminate to virtually all organs, where they parasitise a wide range of cell types, including skeletal and cardiac muscle, fibroblasts, and macrophages. In normal individuals, the most common symptoms of primary infection include fever and generalised or localised (usually cervical) lymphadenopathy. This phase generally subsides without treatment as replication of trophozoites is controlled and encystment occurs. The organism rarely causes recurrent disease. In individuals who have been immunosuppressed by haemopoietic malignancy, cytotoxic chemotherapy, or other acquired cellular immunodeficiency conditions, (including acquired immunodeficiency syndrome, AIDS), the organisms may excyst, recommence replication, and cause illness. Encephalitis is the most common manifestation of acute toxoplasmosis in such individuals (Ruskin and Remington, 1976). The most significant consequence of *Toxoplasma* infection may lie in its effect on the fetus of infected mothers. Of mothers who acquire primary infection with *Toxoplasma* in the first trimester, 30–50 per cent deliver an obviously affected infant. Congenital infection is associated with hydrocephalus, chorioretinitis, hepatosplenomegaly, and rash. In survivors, mental retardation, deafness, and cardiac malformations may be noted. Chorioretinitis may also appear in adulthood as a sequela of congenital infection.

Although control of *Toxoplasma* infection clearly requires participation of components of cell-mediated immunity (Frenkel, 1967), the mechanistic basis for inhibition of parasite replication remains unknown. Present in vitro models are most germane to control of the initial infectious episode. Most published work examines the ability of lymphokine-treated macrophages to destroy parasites immediately after infection of its target cell (Anderson and Remington, 1974; McLeod *et al.*, 1980). In these in vitro systems, however, the parasite rapidly escapes the cytotoxic efforts of the activated macrophage, and begins to replicate even in the face of lymphokine treatment. These observations indicate that those mechanisms that effectively prevent parasite replication in immunologically normal, chronically infected hosts are fundamentally different from the mechanisms that underlie the transient cytotoxic phenomena observed in present in vitro systems. Further work to investigate the means by which cellular immune mechanisms prevent excystment and replication of *Toxoplasma* in mononuclear phagocytes and non-phagocytic cells will be necessary to elucidate this problem.

Two categories of amoebae cause disease in humans. The enteric pathogen, *Entamoeba histolytica*, primarily coexists with human hosts as an asymptomatic infection. Trophozoites live in the lumen of the large intestine, encyst there, and are passed in the stool as either trophozoites or cysts to infect other humans. Occasionally, *Entamoeba* may invade the bowel wall and cause amoebic dysentery; from there they travel through the portal system to the liver and cause amoebic liver abscess. Free-living amoebae, *Naegleria* and *Acanthamoeba*, cause amoebic meningoencephalitis. These organisms inhabit warm freshwater lakes. Amoebae penetrate the nasal mucosa of swimmers, infect the paranasal sinuses, and invade the brain. The resulting meningoencephalitis is fatal despite antiamoebic chemotherapy. Acanthamoebae may also cause destructive ocular infection in wearers of contact lenses.

Amoebae pose an interesting challenge to immunocytes. Since the invader is itself phagocytic and possesses cytotoxins and digestive enzymes, it can ingest and destroy the cells that would eliminate it. Early studies, which investigated the antiamoebic role of antibody, complement and phagocytic cells, have failed to outline conclusively the crucial components of host defence against either free-living or enteric amoebae (Trissl, 1982). Recent investigations, however, suggest that lymphocytes and macrophages are the major protective effectors (Salata *et al.*, 1986; Salata *et al.*, 1985; Ghadirian and Meirovitch, 1981; Cleary and Marciano-Cabral, 1986a, b).

Pneumocystis carinii is among the most fascinating and enigmatic of protozoa that cause significant infection of extraluminal tissues (Walzer *et al.*, 1980). Asymptomatic pulmonary infection is common, but disease almost never occurs in immunologically normal individuals. Circumstances associated with T lymphocyte defects are generally associated with infection. Thus, patients who have lymphoid malignancies, who have received corticosteroids or cytotoxic chemotherapy, or who have congenital or acquired immunodeficiency syndromes, especially AIDS, are peculiarly susceptible to *Pneumocystis* pneumonia. Indeed, *Pneumocystis* pneumonia is the most significant infectious disease associated with AIDS. The disease may result from reactivation of long-standing latent infection or from recent acquisition of the organism. Despite the clear association of susceptibility to disease with impairment of cell-mediated immunity, the immunological mechanisms that control the parasite under most circumstances are unknown. In contrast to many organisms controlled by non-specific cellular immune processes, *Pneumocystis* is found exclusively extracellularly in alveolar fluid. Although the cellular response of immunodeficient patients to the organism is characterised by infiltration of monocytes and lymphocytes, the precise role of these cells in the destruction of the parasite in normal hosts is unknown. Alveolar macrophages cultured for less than two days in vitro fail to ingest *Pneumocystis* in the absence of specific antibody. In the presence of specific antiserum, however, macrophages ingest and kill the parasites (von Behren and Pesanti, 1978; Masur and Jones, 1978). Lack of a suitable animal model and inability to cultivate the organism axenically have hampered efforts to characterise further interactions of *Pneumocystis* with immune cells or their products. Elucidation of the factors that inhibit extracellular replication or enhance ingestion and destruction of this parasite will require considerable ingenuity, but should prove to be an engrossing area for study.

Other protozoal infections are caused by luminal parasites. Of these, *Giardia lamblia, Crytosporidium* and *Trichomonas vaginalis* are the most significant. Despite their prevalence as human pathogens, they have received little attention from cellular immunologists. Evidence suggests, however, that co-operation between T cells and macrophages is important in defence against *Giardia*. Resistance to murine giardiasis requires participation of thymus-dependent cells; monocytes ingest and destroy the organisms (Roberts-Thompson and Mitchell, 1978; Smith *et al.*, 1982; Stevens *et al.*, 1978). The details of cell-mediated resistance, however, are not yet known.

III. INTERACTIONS OF PARASITIC PROTOZOA WITH NON-SPECIFIC DEFENCES

Host defence can be conveniently analysed by layers. Parasites must first overcome mucosal or integumentary barriers. They must resist soluble cytotoxic factors in extracellular fluid, and must avoid destruction by phagocytes or other killer cells. Obligate intracellular parasites must also avoid further obstacles to replication in their target cells. The course of infection with *Leishmania* illustrates the interplay of host defences and parasite avoidance mechanisms that result in disease, resistance to disease, or cure.

The skin is the first defensive layer encountered by *Leishmania*, which must eventually reach an intracellular environment within macrophages to survive. Sandflies bypass this defence by injecting the promastigote form of the parasite subepidermally. In the inflammatory environment of a bite, the parasite is exposed to serum-derived mediators of inflammation and components of the complement system. Promastigotes of *L. donovani* are killed by complement. Killing is mediated primarily by the classical pathway via absorbable factors, presumably cross-reacting antibody (Pearson and Steigbigel, 1981). The alternative complement pathway also participates in promastigote killing, without requirement for participation of antibody (Mosser and Edelson, 1984). Promastigotes grown to maximum cell concentration in vitro are more resistant to complement-mediated lysis than promastigotes in a logarithmic phase of growth (Franke *et al.*, 1985). These maturational or differentiative changes in parasite susceptibility to complement-mediated lysis may explain how sufficient promastigotes survive to infect host cells at the site of inoculation. This notion is supported by infectivity studies: stationary-phase promastigotes not only resist lysis by complement, but also infect animal hosts more readily than do log-phase parasites (Gianini, 1974; Sacks and Perkins, 1984). Even after promastigotes have infected macrophages and transformed into amastigotes, serum factors may play a further role in host defence. To infect additional macrophages, amastigotes must be released extracellularly. There, like promastigotes, they are exposed to complement-rich inflammatory extracellular fluid (Ridley and Ridley, 1984). Amastigotes are killed by complement via the alternative pathway (Hoover *et al.*, 1984). Destruction of amastigotes does not require participation of antibody: serum adsorbed extensively with amastigotes remains fully cytotoxic. Indeed, *Leishmania major* amastigotes are extraordinarily sensitive to complement-mediated lysis: unlike most other targets, they are readily killed by serum deficient in components of the complement membrane attack complex (Hoover *et al.*, 1985a). These and other data suggest that complement-mediated defence may be important in control of the early stages of *Leishmania* infection. *Leishmania major*, which causes cutaneous leishmaniasis, is at least five-fold more sensitive to serum-mediated cytotoxicity than *L. donovani*, which causes disseminated, visceral disease (Hoover *et al.*, 1984). The importance of this phenomenon depends upon the mechanism by which *Leishmania* disseminate from the initial focus to distant sites of infection. Parasites may be protected from complement if they circulate within monocytes and macrophages, as described in patients with established visceral disease (Chulay *et al.*, 1985). If they travel extracellularly early in infection, however, they may be exposed to complement-mediated cytotoxicity. Complement may then preferentially destroy *L. major* so that visceral infection caused by that species dose not occur. In contrast, the relative resistance of *L. donovani* to complement-mediated cytotoxicity may favor its dissemination. Non-specific complement-mediated cytotoxicity is buttressed later in infection by specific antibody. Antibody enhances complement-mediated killing of *L. donovani* at least five-fold (Hoover *et al.*, 1985b). Specific humoral immunity does not, however, appear to play a role in recovery from leishmanial infection: visceral disease progresses despite high titres of antibody (Rezai *et al.*, 1978), and adoptive transfer of serum does not prevent infection of non-immune animals (Turk and Bryceson, 1971). Not only *Leishmania*, but also other flagellates are susceptible to antibody-independent complement-mediated killing. African trypanosomes and *Giardia lamblia*, for example, are killed by action of the alternative complement pathway (Flemmings and Diggs, 1978; Ferrante and Allison, 1983; Hill *et al.*, 1984).

Fundamental to establishment of intracellular infection is parasite entry into the host cell. Conceptually, entry may occur by effort of the parasite, of the host cell, or both. Susceptibility to infection and, conversely, resistance to infection, then may depend in part on the efficiency with which infection of individual cells occurs. For *Leishmania*, which replicate only in macrophages in the mammalian host, intracellular infection may require participation of both macrophage and parasite. Infection begins with parasite attachment to macrophages. Promastigotes preferentially attach by the flagellum, with a limited number of discrete contact points along the body of the organism (Chang, 1979; Pearson *et al.*, 1983a). Attachment is not a random phenomenon, but requires interaction of parasite membrane structures to specific receptor sites on macrophages (Chang, 1981). Promastigotes bind to both the mannose/fucose receptor and the CR3 receptor for C3bi (Blackwell, 1985). For effective internalisation, the promastigote must bind both receptors simultaneously (Blackwell *et al.*, 1985). Attachment of both promastigotes and amastigotes requires effort on the part of the parasite: it is inhibited by pre-treatment of parasites with cytochalasin B, which interferes with monofilament function (Aikawa, 1982; Wyler, 1982). This observation suggests that binding requires active maintenance by the parasite of some specific membrane structure. Cytochalasin treatment of macrophages, in contrast, prevents internalisation but not binding (Wyler, 1982). Other inhibitors of phagocytosis also inhibit internalisation of parasites. In sum, these findings indicate that leishmanial infection of macrophages is a co-operative activity initiated by the parasite but finally accomplished by the host cell (Silverstein, 1977). In effect, the parasite subverts macrophage defences to bring itself to an intracellular environment suitable for its replication.

To fully realise their goal of intracellular infection, parasites not only must bind to and enter the host cell, but must arrive at their destination alive. To do so, they must overcome the potent cytotoxicity of macrophage oxygen products. For *Leishmania*, the survival mechanisms are not apparent. *Leishmania* promastigotes are deficient in catalase and glutathione peroxidase, which scavenge H_2O_2 (Murray, 1981). Because of this deficiency, promastigotes are readily killed by H_2O_2. They do, however, resist destruction by other potentially toxic oxygen products (O_2^-, $OH\cdot$, and $^1O_2$) (Murray, 1981; Reiner and Kazura, 1983). Peroxide-mediated killing is markedly enhanced by the addition of lactoperoxidase and halide. Promastigotes of *L. major* are three-fold more sensitive than those of *L. donovani* to H_2O_2 (Murray, 1981). Not only are promastigotes extremely sensitive to H_2O_2, but they also induce its generation by mononuclear phagocytes upon association with the host-cell membrane

(Pearson *et al.*, 1983b). As a consequence of these phenomena, at least 80 per cent of promastigotes are destroyed when incubated with monocytes or macrophages cultured in vitro (Pearson *et al.*, 1983b; Murray, 1981). Given this great susceptibility to oxygen-mediated destruction by macrophages from non-immune animals, it is surprising that infection occurs at all! Other, unknown mechanisms must operate in vivo to prevent parasite destruction at the site of a bite. Other protozoans, for example, the trypomastigote and epimastigote forms of *T. cruzi*, are also highly susceptible to H_2O_2 (Nathan *et al.*, 1979). Nevertheless, *T. cruzi* also establishes intracellular infection of myocytes in vivo and mononuclear phagocytes in vitro (Nogueira and Cohn, 1976).

Other intracellular parasites do not share this marked susceptibility to oxygen-mediated cytotoxicity. *Leishmania* amastigotes, for example, are seven times as resistant as promastigotes to the lethal effects of H_2O_2, and survive macrophage contact to replicate intracellularly (Pearson *et al.*, 1983b). Similarly, *Toxoplasma* tachyzoites, which are endowed with plentiful scavengers (superoxide dismutase, catalase and glutathione peroxidase) of oxygen intermediates, resist H_2O_2 and O_2^- mediated killing (Murray and Cohn, 1979; Murray *et al.*, 1980). Moreover, *Toxoplasma* tachyzoites do not trigger the macrophage oxidative burst during ingestion (Wilson *et al.*, 1980).

The fate of intraphagocytic parasites depends not only on their susceptibility to oxygen-mediated cytotoxicity, but also on their ability to evade other potentially destructive macrophage products. For example, *Toxoplasma*, like *Leishmania*, replicates intracellularly in macrophages cultured in vitro. *Toxoplasma*, like *Leishmania*, enters the macrophage via phagocytosis (Nichols and O'Connor, 1981). The subsequent fate of these two intracellular organisms, however, is quite different. *Toxoplasma* inhibits fusion of parasitophorous vesicles and lysosomes in macrophages of non-immune animals (Jones and Hirsch, 1972). In the phagosome, protected from hostile lysosomal enzymes, tachyzoites replicate and eventually disrupt the host cell. Lysosome–phagosome fusion occurs normally if dead parasites are ingested, if viable parasites are ingested by macrophages from immune animals, or if immune serum is present during ingestion (Jones *et al.*, 1975). Under these conditions, viable tachyzoites are destroyed by intracellular microbicidal mechanisms. The mechanisms by which *Toxoplasma* prevents phagolysosomal fusion are not known. Similarly, the molecular basis for restoration of normal fusion by antibody or immune macrophages has not been elucidated. In contrast to *Toxoplasma, Leishmania* does not inhibit fusion of lysosomes and phagosomes, but replicates in the phagolysosome of macrophages from non-immune animals (Alexander and Vickerman, 1975; Chang and Dwyer, 1978). *Trypanosoma cruzi* also does not inhibit phagolysosomal fusion, but escapes from the parasitophorous vacuole to replicate in the cytoplasm (Nogueira and Cohn, 1976).

The fate of intracellular *Leishmania* depends on the state of macrophage microbicidal capability. In general, the events that lead to macrophage activation for leishmanicidal activity parallel those elucidated by Mackaness (1962) in his pioneering work on resistance to infection with *Listeria monocytogenes*. Thus, *Leishmania* infect and replicate in resident macrophages harvested from the peritoneal cavity of non-immune, susceptible animals (Chang and Dwyer, 1978; Nacy and Diggs, 1981). In contrast, macrophages from immune animals previously infected with *Leishmania* destroy the parasites (Miller and Twohy, 1969). Macrophage cytotoxicity in cultures of cells from immune animals is related to the number of immune lymphocytes present with macrophages in peritoneal cell cultures (Mauel *et al.*, 1978). Induction of leishmanicidal activity in infected macrophages, however, is not entirely antigen-specific: lymphocytes from *Toxoplasma*-infected animals, for example, can substitute for lymphocytes from *Leishmania*-infected animals if *Toxoplasma* antigen is present in the culture. Conversely, lymphocytes from *Leishmania*-infected animals induce macrophage cytotoxicity for *Listeria* if *Leishmania* antigen is present in the culture (Behin *et al.*, 1975). These findings indicate that lymphocytes sensitive to one pathogen induce macrophage cytotoxicity for other, unrelated pathogens. This immunologically non-specific induction of cytotoxicity is mediated by lymphokines, factors secreted by stimulated lymphocytes that alter macrophage function. In a manner analogous to activation of complement or blood-clotting systems, lymphokine-induced macrophage activation involves participation of a number of molecules in a definite series of reactions. This process has been extensively analysed in C3H/HeN mouse peritoneal macrophages cultured in vitro as a nonadherent cell pellet. The amastigote form of *L. major* readily infects these cells, and replicates 5–10-fold over 72 hours of culture (Nacy and Diggs, 1981). In contrast, macrophages treated in vitro with lymphokines (supernatant fluids from cultures of PPD-stimulated spleen lymphocytes from BCG-immune mice or of concanavalin-A-stimulated cells from non-immune mice) develop potent antileishmanial activity (Nacy *et al.*, 1981; Pappas and Nacy, 1983). This activity has two distinct components. The first component, resistance to infection, occurs in macrophages treated with lymphokines for at least four hours prior to exposure to amastigotes. Lymphokine pre-treatment reduces leishmanial infection of macrophages by 30–50 per cent compared with untreated cells (Oster and Nacy, 1984). Following the pre-treatment period, macrophages retain their resistance to infection with amastigotes for at least 24 hours. The mechanistic explanation of this phenomenon is not yet known; it is not

due to generalised depression of phagocytic activity, for treated macrophages ingest latex beads and sheep erythrocytes in a normal fashion
(Nacy *et al.*, 1981). It may reflect extracellular killing of parasites,
perhaps through the oxidant-mediated mechanisms discussed later.
Alternatively, it may be due to alterations in specific receptor-mediated
ingestion of parasites or to alterations in other, as yet undefined,
mechanisms of parasite entry. Whatever its mechanism, resistance to
infection is an intriguingly unique response to an obligate intracellular
organism: denied its essential environment, the parasite may fall prey to
humoral defence mechanisms in the extracellular milieu.

Lymphokines also induce another, far more potent, antileishmanial
activity in resident macrophages. This activity, intracellular killing,
occurs in macrophages treated with lymphokines after infection with
amastigotes. After culture for 72 hours, the percentage of infected cells in
lymphokine-treated cultures is reduced by 80–100 per cent compared to
the percentage of infected cells in medium-treated cultures. Leishmanicidal activity is induced in macrophages by a number of lymphocyte-
derived factors (Meltzer *et al.*, 1986). Most of the antileishmanial
macrophage-activating activity in crude lymphokine preparations is due
to gamma interferon (IFN-γ). As little as 5 IU/mL of IFN-γ induces
maximal microbicidal activity in murine macrophages (Nacy *et al.*,
1985). Non-glycosylated IFN-γ produced by recombinant DNA technology and glycosylated forms of the molecule secreted by T cell hybridomas have equivalent activity. Most antileishmanial activity in crude
lymphokine is removed by treatment with anti-IFN-γ. Anti-IFN-γ is
effective both when added as soluble antibody to the culture fluids, and
when affixed to a solid support matrix to remove IFN-γ from solution.
Approximately one-third of antileishmanial activity remains, however,
when lymphokine preparations are treated with anti-IFN (Nacy *et al.*,
1985). Thus, non-IFN molecules induce murine leishmanicidal activity.
The scope of functions mediated by these agents is not yet known. It is
possible that multiple factors are required to achieve maximal cytotoxicity in vivo. Alternatively, different factors may be secreted preferentially
to fine-tune macrophage responses at different phases of the host
response to infection. This concept, that multiple lymphokine factors
participate in the regulation of macrophage leishmanicidal activity, leads
to the prediction that inhibitory factors should also exist. In fact, at least
one such lymphokine has been described in the leishmanicidal system.
This factor, secreted by the EL-4 mouse thymoma cell line, abrogates
macrophage microbicidal activity in response to IFN or non-IFN
activation factors, but does not by itself enhance amastigote replication

in macrophages (Nacy, 1984). Although this molecule has so far proven difficult to characterise and purify by biochemical means, it has provided intriguing information on mechanisms of control of the antileishmanial activity induced by IFN and non-IFN macrophage activation factors. Purification of non-IFN macrophage activation factors will provide important reagents for further analysis of interactions between *Leishmania* and macrophages.

Although the cytotoxic response of lymphokine-treated macrophages is dramatic, it requires rather precise conditions for optimal effect. Timing, for example, is crucial. Macrophage responsiveness for lymphokine-induced cytotoxicity decays rapidly with time of culture. After culture for eight hours prior to lymphokine treatment, macrophages develop only two-thirds maximal leishmanicidal activity. They are completely unresponsive if cultured for 24 hours prior to treatment (Oster and Nacy, 1984). These findings indicate that some as yet undefined factors present in vivo but absent from in vitro culture systems maintain the macrophage in a receptive state for the action of macrophage activation factors.

Certain aspects of this 'priming' phenomenon can be recapitulated by experiments with brief pulses of lymphokine in vitro (Fig. 22.1) (Nacy *et al.*, 1984). Treatment of macrophages with high concentrations of lymphokine for 4–8 hours elicits microbicidal activity at 72 hours equivalent to that induced by treatment with lymphokine throughout the entire culture period. Macrophages pulsed with lymphokine for less than four hours fail to develop microbicidal activity. During this crucial four-hour time period of continuous exposure to low or high concentrations of lymphokine, the resting macrophage is 'primed': it becomes receptive to 'triggering' by a short pulse (15 minutes) of high-dose lymphokine or immunologically non-specific stimuli such as lipopolysaccharide (LPS) or certain plant lectins. The requirement for several hours of priming is crucial. Administration of fully microbicidal concentrations of lymphokine for 15–60 minutes at the beginning of the experiment will not prime macrophages to respond to a subsequent 15 minute lymphokine pulse. The order of treatment with priming and triggering agents is also important. Agents such as LPS, though capable of triggering the microbicidal response, do not prime the macrophage for triggering by LPS or lymphokine. These findings suggest that intervention by lymphokine may provide specificity to the microbicidal response. Further specificity is provided by distinct pathways for non-IFN lymphokine and IFN during the priming and triggering sequence. Non-IFN lymphokine does not prime macrophages to respond to IFN, and IFN does not prime

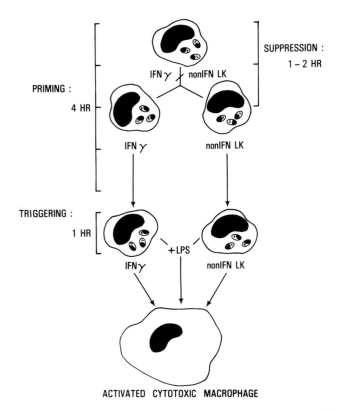

PRIMING :

4 HR

IFN γ   nonIFN LK

IFN γ   nonIFN LK

SUPPRESSION :
1 – 2 HR

TRIGGERING :

1 HR

+ LPS

IFNγ   nonIFN LK

ACTIVATED CYTOTOXIC MACROPHAGE

Fig. 22.1: Sequential steps in the activation of macrophages for intracellular killing. IFN = interferon; LK = lymphokine; LPS = lipopolysaccharide

macrophages to respond to non-IFN lymphokine. Interestingly, the suppressor lymphokine produced by EL-4 cells inhibits priming by both IFN and non-IFN lymphokine (Nacy, 1984).

One should emphasise that these interpretations depend heavily on the nature of the in vitro system used to analyse interactions among *Leishmania*, macrophages, and mediators. This caveat is clearly demonstrated in findings with human monocytes. Freshly harvested human monocytes cultured as a non-adherent cell pellet, as in the preceding experiments with mouse peritoneal macrophages, respond to IFN and to at least one other non-IFN lymphokine to kill *L. donovani* (Hoover *et al.*, 1986). Expression of microbicidal activity requires only a brief pulse with lymphokine or IFN immediately before or within a few hours of infection in vitro (Hoover *et al.*, 1985c). In another system, developed by

Murray and others, adherent monocytes are cultured for 7–10 days prior to lymphokine treatment (Murray and Cartelli, 1983). During this period of culture, monocyte production of oxidative products declines dramatically (Nakagawara *et al.*, 1981). It can, however, be boosted back to levels of freshly harvested cells by treatment with lymphokine. Lymphokine must be administered for three days prior to infection to induce optimum oxidative and microbicidal effect (Murray and Cartelli, 1983). Oxidative killing may occur primarily during parasite entry into the cell. It is also possible that killing occurs intracellularly by oxidative and non-oxidative mechanisms. In contrast to the non-adherent cell system, microbicidal activity in the adherent cell system occurs only in response to IFN. Non-IFN molecules are without effect (Murray *et al.*, 1983b; Nathan *et al.*, 1984).

Lymphokine-stimulated macrophages also kill *Toxoplasma gondii* and *Trypanosoma cruzi*. A number of studies have indicated that destruction of these two organisms is associated with increased secretion of oxidative products by lymphokine-stimulated macrophages (Murray *et al.*, 1979; Murray and Cohn, 1980; Murray *et al.*, 1980; Locksley *et al.*, 1982; Wilson *et al.*, 1980). It is not yet known which oxygen products mediate the cytotoxic event. *T. gondii* is more resistant than *T. cruzi* to H_2O_2, perhaps due to its higher concentration of catalase (Nathan *et al.*, 1979; Murray and Cohn, 1979). For *T. gondii*, metabolites of H_2O_2 such as $OH \cdot$ or $1O_2$ may be more effective agents of cytotoxicity (Murray and Cohn, 1979). In contrast to these findings, other observations indicate that antitoxoplasma activity by lymphokine-stimulated human monocytes does not require production of reactive oxygen metabolites (Wilson and Haas, 1984). These data suggest that non-oxygen-mediated microbicidal mechanisms may be more important than oxidative mechanisms for destruction of *Toxoplasma*. One should note that *T. cruzi* and *T. gondii*, unlike *Leishmania*, replicate in cells other than macrophages. Indeed, the majority of parasites in infected animals may reside in non-phagocytes. Interestingly, IFN inhibits replication of *Toxoplasma* in human fibroblasts cultured in vitro. This antitoxoplasma effect is associated with enhanced degradation of tryptophan by host cells (Pfefferkorn and Guyre, 1983). The effects of lymphokine and other immune mediators on non-phagocytic cells that support parasite growth will be an intriguing area of investigation for the future (Murray *et al.*, 1983a).

Expression of lymphokine-induced microbicidal activity depends not only on several signals delivered to macrophages in a precise order, it also depends on the state of maturation and/or differentiation of the macrophage. Inflammatory peritoneal macrophages that have recently emigrated from the blood express less microbicidal activity in response to lymphokine than do mature, resident cells (Hoover and Nacy, 1984). Murine blood monocytes respond even more poorly than inflammatory macrophages for leishmanicidal activity. These observations suggest that macrophages that arrive early at a site of leishmanial infection may be readily infected with amastigotes, but may be unable to kill them. Recent data lend support to this hypothesis. Adoptive transfer of T cells that mediate delayed-type hypersensitivity to *Leishmania* causes increased lesion size in normally leishmania-resistant animals (Titus *et al.*, 1984). These large lesions contain more macrophages that are more heavily infected than cells in lesions of control animals. Chemotaxis of large numbers of immature macrophages that are incapable of leishmanicidal activity might be responsible for this paradoxically detrimental effect of sensitised lymphocytes.

Other adoptive transfer experiments have demonstrated remarkably complex interactions between suppressive and enhancing cell populations in control of leishmanial infection. A number of investigators have analysed infection of CBA or BALB/c mice with *L. major* (Preston and Dumonde, 1976; Howard *et al.*, 1980; Scott and Farrell, 1981; Mitchell *et al.*, 1981). This species causes localised cutaneous disease in humans, but results in extensive local necrotic lesions, disseminated infection, and eventually death in BALB/c mice. Susceptibility to fatal infection can be abrogated by sublethal irradiation of mice 10 days prior to infection. These irradiated mice heal their infection in a manner similar to other, resistant strains of mice (Howard *et al.*, 1981). Interestingly, susceptibility can be conferred on irradiated BALB/c mice by adoptive transfer of T cells from non-irradiated susceptible animals (Howard *et al.*, 1982). These suppressor T cells paradoxically express a Lyt 1^+2^- IJ$^-$ phenotype. The mechanism by which suppressor cells enhance susceptibility is not yet known. Reduced lymphokine production by lymph-node cells from infected, susceptible animals may be one component of impaired host response (Sadick *et al.*, 1986).

Other cell-mediated suppressive influences have also been described in severe leishmanial infections. For example, monocytes suppress antigen-induced blastogenesis of lymphocytes from the blood of patients with diffuse cutaneous leishmaniasis (Petersen *et al.*, 1984). Similarly, adherent cells in spleens of BALB/c mice infected with *L. major* inhibit spleen lymphocyte proliferation in response to mitogens or leishmanial antigens (Scott and Farrell, 1981). Other reports indicate that reduced lymphocyte responses to mitogens or antigens may not require the action of suppressor cells (Carvalho *et al.*, 1981; Castes *et al.*, 1983). Blood mononuclear cells from patients with untreated American visceral leishmaniasis showed impaired proliferation to antigens, but not to non-specific mitogens (Carvalho *et al.*, 1981). With successful therapy, however, antigen-induced proliferation was restored. Monocyte-enriched cell fractions did not mediate suppression in these studies. Antigen-specific lymphocyte proliferation and IFN production in vitro may also be reduced before treatment of extensive cutaneous leishmaniasis, but return to normal with treatment (Murray *et al.*, 1984). Studies in *L. donovani*-infected mice reached similar conclusions: reduced interleukin 2 (IL-2) production by lymphocytes of infected animals was not mediated by macrophages or suppressive factors in supernatant fluids of cell cultures (Reiner and Finke, 1983). These findings indicate that during the course of leishmaniasis, numerous influences regulate production of lymphokines and lymphocyte proliferative responses. The interplay of these influences may result in prolongation of the disease state, but also terminates host response as infection is successfully resolved.

IV. IMMUNOTHERAPEUTIC APPROACHES

With the recognition that natural immunity inhibits progression of disease caused by a number of protozoa have come efforts to enhance resistance to infection by administration of 'non-specific' immunomodulating agents. Administration of BCG to BALB/c mice prior to infection with *L. donovani* reduced the number of organisms found in spleen or liver, but was not curative (Smrkovski and Larson, 1977). Similarly, administration of glucan, a polyglucose derivative from yeast cell walls, reduced the number of parasites in the livers and spleens of CF1 mice infected with *L. donovani* (Holbrook *et al.*, 1981). Glucan also reduced parasite numbers in hamsters infected with *L. donovani* (Cook *et al.*, 1982). Moreover, macrophages from these glucan-treated hamsters inhibited replication of *Leishmania*. The pathway by which glucan treatment induces antileishmanial activity in macrophages in vitro, and presumably in vivo, is unknown. Further study of non-specific potentiators of macrophage function for defence against intracellular organisms will be of great interest. Other non-specific factors produced by specifically sensitised immune cells have also been tested for therapeutic efficacy in vivo. Administration of liposome-encapsulated lymphokines, for example, reduced parasite burdens in *L. chagasi*-infected mice (Reed *et al.*, 1984). Survival of *Toxoplasma*-infected mice was also improved by treatment with IL-2 or IFN (Sharma *et al.*, 1985; McCabe *et al.*, 1984). In vitro studies of cells from IL-2-treated mice indicated no enhancement of macrophage antitoxoplasma activity, but demonstrated enhanced natural killer cell cytotoxicity against the parasite (Sharma *et al.*, 1985).

V. CONCLUSION

As this brief review indicates, interactions of protozoan parasites with natural immune mechanisms are exceedingly complex. As a consequence, we presently understand these events at a phenomenologic level, rather than at a molecular level. It is likely that, as our understanding deepens, we will perceive more specificity in the mechanisms that enhance or diminish antiprotozoal responses. Recognition of this specificity may provide tools for rational immunotherapy or immunoprophylaxis of disease caused by this fascinating and diverse group of organisms.

REFERENCES

Aikawa, M., Hendricks, L. D., Ito, Y. and Jagusiak, M. (1982). *American Journal of Pathology* 108: 50–9.

Alexander, J. and Vickerman, K. (1975). *Journal of Protozoology* 22: 502–8.

Anderson, S. E. and Remington, J. S. (1974). *Journal of Experimental Medicine* 139: 1154–74.

Behin, R., Mauel, J., Biroum-Noerjasin and Rowe, D.S. (1975). *Clinical and Experimental Immunology* 20: 351–8.

Blackwell, J. M. (1985). *Transactions of the Royal Society of Tropical Medicine and Hygiene* 79: 606–12.

Blackwell, J. M., Ezekowitz, R. A. B., Roberts, M. B., Channon, J. Y., Sim, R. B. and Gordon, S. (1985). *Journal of Experimental Medicine* 162: 324–31.

Carvalho, E. M., Teixeira, R. S. and Johnson, W. D. (1981). *Infection and Immunity* 33: 498–502.

Castes, M., Agnelli, A., Verde, O. and Rondon, A. J. (1983). *Clinical Immunology and Immunopathology* 27: 176–86.

Chang, K. -P. (1979). *Experimental Parasitology* 48: 175–89.

Chang, K. -P. (1981). *Molecular and Biochemical Parasitology* 4: 67–76.

Chang, K. -P. and Dwyer, D. W. (1978). *Journal of Experimental Medicine* 147: 515–30.

Chulay, J. D., Adoyo, M. A. and Githure, J. I. (1985). *Transactions of the Royal Society of Tropical Medicine and Hygiene* 79: 218–22.

Cleary, S. F. and Marciano-Cabral, F. (1986a). *Cellular Immunology* 98: 125–36.

Cleary, S. F. and Marciano-Cabral, F. (1986b). *Cellular Immunology* 101: 62–71.

Convit, J., Pinardi, M. E. and Rondon, A. J. (1972). *Transactions of the Royal Society of Tropical Medicine and Hygiene* 66: 603–6.

Cook, J. A., Holbrook, T. W. and Dougherty, W. J. (1982). *Infection and Immunity* 37: 1261–9.

Ferrante, A. and Allison, A. C. (1983). *Parasite Immunology* 5: 491–8.

Flemmings, B. and Diggs, C. (1978). *Infection and Immunity* 19: 928–33.

Franke, E. D., McGreevy, P. B., Katz, S. P. and Sacks, D. L. (1985). *Journal of Immunology* 134: 2713–18.

Frenkel, J. K. (1967). *Journal of Immunology* 98: 1309–19.

Ghadirian, E. and Meirovitch, E. (1981). *Infection and Immunity* 31: 571–6.

Gianini, M. S. (1974). *Journal of Protozoology* 21: 521–30.

Haldar, J. P., Ghose, S., Saha K. C. and Ghose, A. C. (1983). *Infection and Immunity* 42(2): 702–7.

Hill, D. R., Burge, J. J. and Pearson, R. D. (1984). *Journal of Immunology* 132: 2046–52.

Holbrook, T. W., Cook, J. A. and Parker, B. W. (1981). *American Journal of Tropical Medicine and Hygiene* 30: 762–8.

Hoover, D. L. and Nacy, C. A. (1984). *Journal of Immunology* 132: 1487–93.

Hoover, D. L., Berger, M., Nacy, C. A., Hockmeyer, W. T. and Meltzer, M. S. (1984). *Journal of Immunology* 132: 893–7.

Hoover, D. L., Berger, M., Hammer, C. H. and Meltzer, M. S. (1985a). *Journal of Immunology* 135: 570–4.

Hoover, D. L., Berger, M., Oppenheim, M. H., Hockmeyer, W. T. and Meltzer, M. S. (1985b). *Infection and Immunity* 47: 247–52.

Hoover, D. L., Nacy, C. A. and Meltzer, M. S. (1985c). *Cellular Immunology* 99: 500–11.

Hoover, D. L., Finbloom, D. S., Crawford, R. M., Nacy, C. A., Gilbreath, M. and Meltzer, M. S. (1986). *Journal of Immunology* 136: 1329–33.

Howard, J. G., Hale, C. and Liew, F. Y. (1980). *Journal of Experimental Medicine* 152: 594–607.

Howard, J. G., Hale, C. and Liew, F. Y. (1981). *Journal of Experimental Medicine* 153: 557–68.

Howard, J. G., Nicklin, S., Hale, C. and Liew, F. Y. (1982). *Journal of Immunology* 129: 2206–12.

Jones, T. C. and Hirsch, J. G. (1972). *Journal of Experimental Medicine* 136: 1173–94.

Jones, T. C., Len, L. and Hirsch, J. G. (1975). *Journal of Experimental Medicine* 141: 466–82.

Kierszenbaum, F. (1979). *American Journal of Tropical Medicine and Hygiene* 28: 965–8.

Lainson, R. (1983). *Transactions of the Royal Society of Tropical Medicine and Hygiene* 77: 569–96.

Locksley, R. M., Wilson, C. B. and Klebanoff, S. J. (1982). *Journal of Clinical Investigation* 69: 1099–1111.

McCabe, R. E., Luft, B. J. and Remington, J. S. (1984). *Journal of Infectious Diseases* 150: 961–2.

Mackaness, G. B. (1962). *Journal of Experimental Medicine* 116: 381–406.

McLeod, R., Bensch, K. G., Smith, S. M. and Remington, J. S. (1980). *Cellular Immunology* 54: 330–50.

Masur, H. and Jones, T. C. (1978). *Journal of Experimental Medicine* 147: 157–170.

Mauel, J., Buchmuller, Y. and Behin, (1978). *Journal of Experimental Medicine* 148: 393–407.

Meltzer, M. S., Hoover, D. L., Gilbreath, M. J., Schreiber, R. D. and Nacy, C. A. (1986). *Annals of the Institute Pasteur (Immunology)* 137c: 206–11.

Miller, H. C. and Twohy, D. W. (1969). *Journal of Parasitology* 55: 200–6.

Mitchell, G. F., Curtis, J. M., Scollay, R. and Handman, E. (1981). *Australian Journal of Experimental Biology and Medicial Science* 59(5): 539–54.

Mosser, D. M. and Edelson, P. J. (1984) *Journal of Immunology* 132: 1501–5.

Murray, H. W. (1981). *Journal of Experimental Medicine* 153: 1302–15.

Murray, H. W. and Cartelli, D. M. (1983). *Journal of Clinical Investigation* 72: 32–44.

Murray, H. W. and Cohn, Z. A. (1979). *Journal of Experimental Medicine* 150: 938–49.

Murray, H. W. and Cohn, Z. (1980). *Journal of Experimental Medicine* 152: 1596–1609.

Murray, H. W., Juangbach, C. W., Nathan, C. and Cohn, Z. (1979). *Journal of Experimental Medicine* 150: 950–64.

Murray, H. W., Nathan, C. F. and Cohn, Z. A. (1980). *Journal of Experimental Medicine* 152: 1610–24.

Murray, H. W., Bryne, G. J., Rothermel C. D. and Cartelli, D. M. (1983a). *Journal of Experimental Medicine* 158: 234–9.

Murray, H. W., Rubin, B. Y. and Rothermel, C. D. (1983b). *Journal of Clinical Investigation* 72: 1506–10.

Murray, H. W., Rubin, B. Y., Carriero, S. and Acosta, A. M. (1984). *Journal of Immunology* 133: 2250–4.

Nacy, C. A. (1984). *Journal of Immunology* 133: 448–53.

Nacy, C. A. and Diggs, C. L. (1981). *Infection and Immunity* 34: 310–13.

Nacy, C. A., Meltzer, M. S., Leonard, E. J. and Wyler, D. J. (1981). *Journal of Immunology* 127: 2381–6.

Nacy, C. A., Oster, C. N., James, S. L. and Meltzer, M. S. (1984). *Contemporary Topics in Immunobiology* 13: 147–70.

Nacy, C. A., Fortier, A. H., Meltzer, M. S., Buchmeier, N. A. and Schreiber, R. D. (1985). *Journal of Immunology* 135: 3505–11.

Nakagawara, A., Nathan, C. F. and Cohn, Z. A. (1981). *Journal of Clinical Investigation* 68: 1243.

Nathan, C., Noguiera, N., Juangbhanich, C. Ellis, J. and Cohn, Z. (1979). *Journal of Experimental Medicine* 149: 1056–68.

Nathan, C.F., Prendergast, T. J., Wiebe, M. E., Stanley, E. R., Platzer, E., Remold, H. G., Welte, K., Rubin, B. Y. and Murray, H. W. (1984). *Journal of Experimental Medicine* 160: 600–5.

Nichols, B. A. and O'Connor, G. R. (1981). *Laboratory Investigation* 44: 324–35.

Nogueira, N. and Cohn, Z. (1976). *Journal of Experimental Medicine* 143: 1402–20.

Oster, C. N. and Nacy, C. A. (1984). *Journal of Immunology* 132: 1494–1500.

Pappas, M. G. and Nacy, C. A. (1983). *Cellular Immunology* 80: 217–22.

Pearson, R. D., Steigbigel, R. T. (1981). *Journal of Immunology* 127: 1438–43.

Pearson, R. D., Sullivan, J. A., Roberts, D., Romito, R. and Mandell, G. L. (1983a). *Infection and Immunity* 40: 411–16.

Pearson, R. D., Harcus, J. L., Roberts, D. and Donowitz, G. R. (1983b). *Journal of Immunology* 131: 1994–9.

Petersen, E. A., Neva, F. A., Barral, A., Correa-Coronas, R., Bogaert-Diaz, H., Martinez, D. and Ward, F. E. (1984). *Journal of Immunology* 132: 2603–6.

Pfefferkorn, E. R. and Guyre, P. M. (1983). *Federation Proceedings* 42: 964–71.

Preston, P. M. and Dumonde, D. C. (1976). *Clinical and Experimental Immunology* 23: 126–38.

Reed, S. G., Barral-Netto, M. and Inverso, J. (1984). *Journal of Immunology* 132: 3116–19.

Rees, P. H., Kager, P. A., Murhthi, M. R., Wambua, P. P., Shah, S. D. and Butterworth, A. E. (1981). *Transactions of the Royal Society of Tropical Medicine and Hygiene* 75: 630–1.

Reiner, N. E. and Finke, J. H. (1983). *Journal of Immunology* 131: 1487–91.

Reiner, N. E. and Kazura, J. W. (1983). *Infection and Immunity* 36: 1023–7.

Rezai, H. R., Ardehall, S. M., Amirhakimi, G. and Kharazmi, A. (1978). *American Journal of Tropical Medicine and Hygiene* 27: 1079–83.

Ridley, M. J. and Ridley, D. S. (1984). *British Journal of Experimental Pathology* 65: 327–36.

Roberts-Thompson, I. C. and Mitchell, G. E. (1978). *Gastroenterology* 75: 42–6.

Ruskin, J. and Remington, J. (1976). *Annals of Internal Medicine* 84: 193–9.

Sacks, D. L. and Perkins, P. V. (1984). *Science* 223: 1417–9.

Sadick, M. D., Locksley, R. M., Tubbs, C. and Raff, H. V. (1986). *Journal of Immunology* 136: 655–61.

Salata, R. A., Pearson, R. P. and Ravdin, J. I. (1985). *Journal of Clinical Investigation* 76: 491–9.

Salata, R. A., Martinez-Palomo, A., Murray, H. W., Conales, L., Trevino, N., Segovia, E., Murphy, C. F. and Radvin, J. I. (1986). *Journal of Immunology* 136: 2633–9.

Scott, P. A. and Farrell, J. P. (1981). *Journal of Immunology* 127: 2395–2400.

Sharma, S. D., Hofflin, J. M. and Remington, J. S. (1985). *Journal of Immunology* 135: 4160–3.

Silverstein, S. C. (1977). *American Journal of Tropical Medicine and Hygiene* 26 (suppl. 6): 161–8.

Smith, P. D., Elson, C. O., Keister, D. B. and Nash, T. E. (1982). *Journal Immunology* 128: 1372–6.

Smith, P. D., Keister, D. B. and Elson, C. O. (1983). *Cellular Immunology* 82: 308–15.

Smrkovski, L. L. and Larson, C. L. (1977). *Infection and Immunity* 16: 249–57.

Stevens, D. P., Frank, D. M. and Mahmoud, A. A. F. (1978). *Journal of Immunology* 120: 680–5.

Titus, R. G., Lima, G. C., Engers, H. D. and Louis, J. A. (1984). *Journal of Immunology* 133: 1594–1600.

Trissl, D. (1982). *Reviews of Infectious Diseases* 4: 1154–84.

Turk, J. L. and Bryceson, A. D. M. (1971). *Advances in Immunology* 13: 200–66.

Von Behren, L. A. and Pesanti, E. L. (1978). *American Review of Respiratory Disease* 118: 1051–9.

Walzer, P. D., Powell, R. D., Yoneda, K., Rutledge, M. E. and Milder, J. E. (1980). *Infection and Immunity* 27: 928–37.

Wilson, C. B. and Haas, J. E. (1984). *Journal of Clinical Investigation* 73: 1606–16.

Wilson, C. B., Tsai, V. and Remington, J. S. (1980). *Journal of Experimental Medicine* 151: 328–46.

Wirth, D. F. and McMahon-Pratt, D. M. (1982). *Proceedings of the National Academy of Science USA* 79: 6999–7003.

Wirth, D. F., Rogers, W. O., Barker, R., Dourado, H., Suesebang, L. and Albuquerque, B. (1986). *Science* 234: 975–9.

Wyler, D. J. (1982). *Journal of Clinical Investigation* 70: 82–8.

Wyler, D. J., Weinbaum, F. I. and Herrod, H. R. (1979). *Journal of Infectious Diseases* 140: 215–21.

23

Malaria

I. A. CLARK

Zoology Department, Australian National University
Canberra, ACT 2601, Australia

W. B. COWDEN

N. H. HUNT

John Curtin School of Medical Research
Australian National University
Canberra, ACT 2601, Australia

I. INTRODUCTION

Although previous exposure to *Plasmodium* spp., the causative organisms of malaria, is undoubtedly the biggest influence on the outcome of

NATURAL IMMUNITY
ISBN 0 12 5145551

infection with this disease, other factors also influence the course of infection, and the amount of tissue damage that accompanies it; all these can conveniently be regarded as natural immunity, and form the subject of this chapter. This type of immunity is, by definition, unrelated to the host's past experience of malaria. As will be seen, these phenomena are not insignificant, since they can determine whether a host survives the infection. While mostly discussing the asexual erythrocytic forms of the parasite (ring forms, trophozoites and schizonts, in order of maturity) it must not be forgotten that sporozoites (the forms injected by mosquitoes), the stages in the liver, and the sexually differentiated forms (gametocytes) are also potential targets for natural immunity.

A brief synopsis of the main malarias is warranted. Mammals, birds, and reptiles all harbour *Plasmodium* spp., and four species, *P. falciparum, P. vivax, P. malariae* and *P. ovale,* infect humans. Virtually all of the research effort is directed towards *P. falciparum,* since it is the only one of the four likely to be fatal and to have become resistant to the main antimalarial drugs. Originally bird malaria was the laboratory model, but has been supplanted by four species exclusive to rodents, *P. berghei, P. yoelii, P. vinckei* and *P. chabaudi.* The first two are closely related and prefer to inhabit reticulocytes, making them susceptible to influences that alter the availability of these cells. *P. knowlesi* infection in Rhesus monkeys *(Macaca mulatta)* is another traditional laboratory model. *P. falciparum* is sometimes studied in *Aotus trivirgatus,* the owl monkey, and *Saimiri sciureus,* the squirrel monkey. Neither is a natural host, and the parasite needs careful adaptation before it will infect these animals.

At present no other malaria parasite except *P. falciparum* can be continously cultured in vitro. This is a slow process with distinct limitations, as only the asexual erythrocytic forms can be cultured, and in low concentrations. Thus our current knowledge of the detailed interaction of host effector cells and malaria parasites is very much in its infancy compared with that of most infectious agents. So too is the contribution of host cells, and their secretions, to processes that can confidently be described as natural immunity, as distinct from the specific immune response, in this disease. We will therefore treat this section with corresponding caution.

Other aspects of malaria have, in contrast, been closely studied. It is unique among the infectious diseases in the way it has dominated most tropical rural communities: historically, no one escaped repeated infection, and it took years to acquire a functional immunity. If not fatal it was chronically debilitating. It seems clear that this has led to scores of millions of people, whose genes evolved in malarial areas, possessing genetic traits that would be rare if they did not provide some measure of natural immunity against *P. falciparum.* A large body of literature describes this interaction, and we will concentrate on this aspect accordingly.

Natural immunity is expressed independently of the host's previous experience of malaria, and is, in this sense, nonspecific. We should note, however, that the mechanism itself may be quite specific, a clear-cut example being the need for Duffy antigen to be present for *P. vivax*, but not *P. falciparum*, to enter red cells.

Our choices in this review were to cover most of the known non-immunological influences on malaria, handling each briefly, or to expand on a relative few of importance, particularly those for which a mechanism can be discussed. We have chosen the latter course.

II. HOST CELLS AND THEIR SOLUBLE MEDIATORS

The literature on mechanisms of immunity to erythrocytic forms of malaria now has several main streams. Earlier it was dominated by phagocytosis, but references to antibody began to emerge some decades ago (Coggeshall and Kumm, 1938; Cohen *et al.*, 1961). This work was crystallised in elegant in vitro studies (Cohen *et al.*, 1969) showing that antibody could prevent merozoites entering red cells. With some variation this is still an active field of study, and this principle of antibody acting alone is currently used by various groups (for example Brown *et al.*, 1985; Berzins *et al.*, 1986) to help define possible protective antigens. As these processes depend entirely on a host's prior experience of malaria, they are clearly outside the scope of natural immunity.

Phagocytosis has the potential to participate in natural immunity, since it can function without priming by antibody. Its involvement in the immune response is still uncertain, the course of *P. berghei* reportedly being identical throughout the infection in two strains of rats with very different phagocytic capacities (Cantrell and Elko, 1976). In vitro studies, however, still attribute an antibody-assisted immune function to this process (Khusmith *et al.*, 1982), particularly in the presence of an activating lymphokine (Ockenhouse and Shear, 1983).

Of more relevance to this chapter is the literature on the type of cell-mediated killing that leads not to phagocytosis, but to the degeneration of parasites inside circulating red cells (Taliaferro and Taliaferro, 1934; Clark *et al.*, 1976a). This depends on T cells, but not antibody (Grun and Weidanz, 1981). A central role for macrophages as a secretory cell (Clark, 1976, 1978) and mediation by either tumour necrosis factor (TNF) (Clark, 1978; Clark *et al.*, 1981; Taverne *et al.*, 1981) or reactive oxygen species (Clark and Hunt, 1983; Dockrell and Playfair, 1983) have been proposed. The in vitro evidence is now against direct killing by TNF

(Carlin *et al.*, 1985; Jensen, 1986), but recent information that TNF can activate neutrophils to secrete superoxide (Larrick *et al.*, 1985; Klebanoff *et al.*, 1986), and that hyperimmune serum from subjects from endemic malarial areas readily triggers these cells into chemiluminescence (Salmon *et al.*, 1986), will doubtlessly stimulate a reappraisal of its role in vitro. Natural killer cells have also been invoked (Eugui and Allison, 1979), but several different approaches have produced contrary evidence (Wood and Clark, 1982; Skamene *et al.*, 1983).

Whatever the effector cell, evidence is mounting that gamma inter-feron (IFN-γ) is likely to be the activating lymphokine contributed by T cells (Ockenhouse *et al.*, 1984; Troye-Blomberg *et al.*, 1985), as in parallel circumstances with intra-macrophage protozoa (Nathan *et al.*, 1983; Murray *et al.*, 1985; see also Chapter 22). Arguments for IFN-γ working unaided against malaria parasites, this time by inhibiting development of the sporozoite form inside hepatocytes, has also recently been presented (Ferreira *et al.*, 1986). IFN-γ, which is found in serum in acute falciparum malaria (Rhodes-Feuillete *et al.*, 1985), also enhances expression of TNF receptors on various cells (Aggarwal *et al.*, 1985; Tsujimoto *et al.*, 1986). Thus synergy between IFN-γ and TNF in malaria is conceivable. This warrants investigation in experimental infections, since it has impli-cations both for immunopathology and for antiparasitic immunity.

There are two clear links between this type of acquired immunity and natural immunity to malaria: one is the nonspecificity of the putative toxic mediators (perhaps focused by specific antibodies linking the effector cell and the parasitised red cell, as proposed by Brown and Smalley (1980); the other is an inability to distinguish between IFN-γ secreted by T cells stimulated by a specific malarial antigen and that released from T cells exposed to other agents, infectious or otherwise. Presumably the same would apply in the action of IFN-γ against sporozoites (Ferreira *et al.*, 1986). The influence of these other agents is discussed in the next section of this chapter.

III. CONCOMITANT INFECTIONS

There is much evidence that animals infected with various organisms are more resistant to malaria. An early example is from Adler (1954), who found that *Leishmania infantum* would protect hamsters against *P. berghei*. He noted that the parasites were destroyed inside circulating red cells, an observation given little prominence then or since, but very relevant to current thinking. Subsequently *Eperythrozoon coccoides* was reported to protect mice against *P. berghei* (Peters, 1965) and *P. chabaudi*

(Ott and Stauber, 1967), findings that explained many a frustration in inadvertently *Eperythrozoon*-infected mouse colonies! The first serious attempt to understand this phenomenon was made by Cox (1970a, b) who, in a comprehensive study of *Plasmodium* spp. and *Babesia* spp. in mice, made the intriguing observation that cross-protection between genera could be far better than within the one genus. Cross-reacting antibody titres did not fit the pattern of protection (Cox, 1970b), and the end result of protection between genera was intra-erythrocytic death of parasites (Cox, 1978).

In seeking to understand why certain rodent malaria and babesia infections are normally terminated by disintegration of parasites inside circulating red cells (Clark *et al.*, 1976a), we found that prior infection with the Bacillus Calmette Guérin (BCG) strain of *Mycobacterium bovis* (Clark *et al.*, 1976b) or with *Brucella abortus* strain 19 (Herod *et al.*, 1978) protected mice from these parasites in the same fashion. These and other agents were selected because they had a history of protecting animals against tumours or intra-macrophage protozoa (see references in Clark, 1978). They did not need to be infectious: killed *Corynebacterium parvum* (Clark *et al.*, 1977) or an extract of *Coxiella burneti* (Clark, 1979a) worked very well.

A pattern began to emerge when we noted that *Eperythrozoon coccoides,* BCG and *Brucella* sp. were known to sensitise animals to the harmful effects of bacterial endotoxin (reviewed in Suter, 1962) and could establish this to be true of our other protectants (Clark, 1978, 1979a, b), including the cross-protecting protozoa (Cox, 1970a). As with BCG (Peavy *et al.*, 1979), the sensitivity of malaria- and babesia-infected mice to endotoxin reflects the in vitro sensitivity of their macrophages to be provoked, by endotoxin, to release monokines (Wood and Clark, 1984). In addition, *P. vinckei*-infected mice (Clark *et al.*, 1981) proved to be equally primed for endotoxin-triggered release of TNF as were are those treated with BCG or *C. parvum* (Carswell *et al.*, 1975): so too are those pretreated with *Coxiella burneti* extract (Carswell and Clark, unpublished data).

Thus, although all the details are yet to be established, it appears that the concomitant infections discussed here protect against certain malarias because, like malaria itself, these agents systemically activate macrophages. This apparently sensitises these cells to release protective monokines, the malarial parasitaemia required to trigger this event reflecting the animal's heightened sensitivity to endotoxin. Those malarias that parasitise reticulocytes are least susceptible to this type of protection, and also to alloxan-induced oxidant stress, a model for superoxide release by macrophages (Cox, 1983). As discussed in the next section, this concept of endotoxin sensitivity determining the outcome of a malarial infection can be developed into an explanation of malarial tolerance, whether innate and species-determined, or acquired by repeated, untreated exposure to the disease.

IV. MALARIAL TOLERANCE

A. Acquired Tolerance

Someone who has falciparum or vivax malaria for the first time starts to feel ill when each microlitre of their blood contains about 100 parasites (Kitchen, 1949). This is about 0.002 per cent parasitaemia, an astoundingly low density to those used to dealing with experimental models. In contrast, young children who live where malaria is very common, and have had many past episodes of clinical malaria, may harbour several thousand times more parasites than this without apparent harm (Hill *et al.*, 1943; McGregor *et al.*, 1956). This is the phenomenon of malarial tolerance, not to be confused with immunological tolerance, an unrelated term coined several decades later. Malarial tolerance is a useful acquisition for these children, since without it their life would be one continuous bout of malaria until, if they were still alive after some years of exposure, acquired immunity was finally established. Evidently this tolerance begins to develop during even a single exposure: Kitchen (1949) reported that in 100 consecutive untreated cases of vivax malaria (used in past decades as a surprisingly successful treatment for neurosyphilis) the mean parasite density at spontaneous termination of illness was over five times as great as the density at its onset. Likewise, it can take many times more parasites to make a patient ill when an infection relapses than it did for onset of the initial illness (Sinton *et al.*, 1931).

We have suggested how this tolerance might operate by proposing a link between the sensitivity of people to the harmful effects of endotoxin and their individual pyrogenic threshold (the parasitaemia required to trigger fever) for malaria (Clark, 1982). Since endotoxicity acts through macrophages, and is caused mainly by the soluble factors that endotoxin triggers these cells to release (Michalek *et al.*, 1980), we reasoned that this might indicate that some material of parasite origin could initiate the same processes. This would be consistent with reports that people who have recently recovered from malaria are tolerant to the pyrogenic effect of injected endotoxin (Heyman and Beeson, 1949; Rubenstein *et al.*, 1965). It would also fit with the observation that malarial tolerance extends to aspects of malarial illness other than fever, since these changes, when seen in endotoxicity, are also mediated by monokines. The main culprit appears to be tumour necrosis factor (TNFα or cachectin). This monokine, recently reviewed by Beutler and Cerami

(1986), is, in our view, also likely to explain much of the pathology of severe falciparum malaria. Nonetheless, the most compelling argument that macrophages are central to the mechanism of malarial tolerance comes from comparing the natural tolerance of different host species to malaria, as discussed below.

B. Innate Tolerance

The parasite density required for onset of illness in malaria and babesiosis (similar to malaria and caused by *Babesia* spp.) in a first infection is a fixed characteristic of the host species, not of the parasite. Thus, as with *P. falciparum*, people become ill when very few *Babesia microti* are present in their blood (Healy and Ruebush, 1980). Yet owl monkeys or mice remain oblivious to *P. falciparum* or *B. microti* (respectively) until much higher parasitaemias are reached: indeed, monkeys and rodents are invariably much more tolerant to these haemoprotozoa than are humans, and birds or reptiles need even higher densities to trigger illness (reviewed by Clark, 1982). Cattle are at the other end of the scale, being sensitive to very low densities of *Babesia* spp.

As with acquired malarial tolerance in humans, we have argued that the innate tolerance of a species to haemoprotozoa is also linked with readiness of macrophages to release harmful monokines, since the species ranking of innate tolerance to haemoprotozoa correlates with their innate tolerance to endotoxin (Clark, 1982). We know of no exceptions to this pattern, although some extreme cases emerge. We found, for instance, that small lizards are unperturbed by enough endotoxin to make 10^7 people severely ill! Small wonder, from our reasoning, that they can withstand 100 per cent parasitaemia (i.e., a malaria parasite in every red cell) without apparent harm (Goodwin and Stapleton, 1952).

For these reasons we suggest that acquired malarial tolerance in humans most probably operates through macrophages, and is controlled by events at the macrophage surface, as is endotoxin tolerance (Larsen and Sullivan, 1984). It could have evolved because it provides a mechanism to limit the harm done by the parasite during the years it takes acquired immunity to develop.

V. GENETIC FACTORS

The most dramatic evidence that natural immunity to malaria can have very real consequences can be gained by comparing the gene products controlling red cell chemistry in the malarial world and elsewhere.

A. Haemoglobin Variants and Enzyme Deficiencies

One would expect the genetic abnormalities that produce aberrant haemoglobins and lead to deficiencies of such key enzymes as glucose-6-phosphate dehydrogenase (G-6-PD) to be rare, but in tropical areas they can be very common indeed. Over the past 35 years the concept has arisen that someone carrying one or several of these mutations has more chance than usual of surviving an attack of falciparum malaria. Thus these traits are believed to have developed their present stable polymorphisms in these areas because of selection by this tropical disease.

It appears to have been J. B. S. Haldane who first published the argument that infectious diseases could have been an important evolutionary agent (Haldane, 1949a). In the same year (Haldane, 1949b) he proposed that falciparum malaria had been particularly effective, reasoning that thalassaemia was preserved because the loss of mutant genes through early death of unfit homozygotes was more than compensated for by an increased likelihood of heterozygotes (compared to the normals) surviving infection. This concept was developed (Raper, 1949; Brain, 1952; Allison, 1954; Luzzatto et al., 1969) with sickle cell disease, and then extended to encompass other haemoglobinopathies, including persistent fetal haemoglobin, and haemoglobin E. Excellent reviews of this area have been written by Livingstone (1971) and Luzzatto (1979).

Although geographic correlations can always be criticised as merely circumstantial, and not addressing cause and effect, they have become much more powerful tools since it has been realised just how polymorphic are the alleles that govern these functions. For instance nearly 300 distinct mutations that have led to G-6-PD deficiency are now described (Luzzatto and Battistuzzi, 1985), and they have arisen independently in many geographically separated areas. These mutations are related only in their functional end result — giving rise to G-6-PD deficiency. The same telling argument can be made for thalassaemia, which is really a complex of associated congenital haemolytic diseases, not a single entity. Again the shared feature of this group of closely related but distinct mutations is functional, in this case an imbalance of the globin chains that form normal haemoglobin (reviewed by Neinhuis et al., 1984).

When it became possible to grow P. falciparum in vitro (Trager and Jensen, 1976) other workers soon designed studies intended to help understand the basis of this apparent protection. It can be shown, for instance, that, provided oxygen tensions are altered, P. falciparum grows poorly in red cells from homozygous sickle cell patients (Pasvol et al., 1978) and in G-6-PD-deficient or thalassaemic red cells (Friedman, 1979). The same principle has been demonstrated for red cells containing fetal haemoglobin (Pasvol et al., 1976) and, more controversially, haemoglobin E (Nagel *et al.*, 1981; Santiyanont and Wilairat, 1981). All of these processes can be linked in terms of the toxic effects of reactive oxygen species (reviewed in Clark and Hunt, 1983). Even in normal red cells oxidative stress is finely balanced against the cell's antioxidant capacities, and unstable haemoglobins, which convert to methaemoglobin (generating superoxide in the process; Misra and Fridovich, 1972) more readily than does normal haemoglobin, appear to tip this balance against *P. falciparum.* This parasite is very prone to free-radical-induced damage (Clark *et al.*, 1983), perhaps via oxidatively denatured haemoglobin (Orjih *et al.*, 1985) or aldehydic products of lipid peroxidation (Butcher *et al.*, 1986).

The in vitro case for sickle cell disease needs close examination: it is insufficient to base arguments on red cells from homozygous individuals, since they invariably die too young to have contributed to the gene pool. Newer work, in which the red cells of heterozygotes generated more superoxide than those from normals (Schacter, 1986) sits more comfortably with the proposed mechanism, since it provides a means for the selected gene to carry over to the next generation.

However precise, such in vitro data cannot substitute for field studies on populations actually exposed to endemic malaria. The earlier work on sickle cell trait seems to have weathered well, but it is only recently that such studies have provided field evidence in favour of thalassaemia being protective against falciparum malaria (Willcox *et al.*, 1983). The link between G-6-PD deficiency and malaria may be more complex. Since first proposed (Motulsky, 1960) its universality has been questioned many times, with evidence being presented for (Allison and Clyde, 1961; Luzzatto, 1979) and against (Kidson and Gorman, 1962; Martin *et al.*, 1979) a sufficiently close regional correlation for malaria to have been a strong enough pressure to select this otherwise disadvantageous trait. The story becomes much more plausible if one takes dietary oxidative stress into account. This has been elucidated with favism, the severe haemolytic state sometimes affecting G-6-PD-deficient individuals after eating fava beans *(Vicia faba).* Historically this is a staple food of the Mediterranean and Middle East countries, the area where G-6-PD deficiency is most severe and common. This seems paradoxical, since favism haemolysis, caused by H_2O_2 generated by agents in fava beans (Chevion *et al.*, 1982), should be more dramatic in G-6-PD deficients, tending to *lower* the gene frequency.

Huheey and Martin (1975) resolved this problem by proposing that malaria *plus* regular intake of fava beans, not malaria alone, had selected for G-6-PD deficiency in these areas. This was based on the prediction that an active principle in fava beans would prove toxic to *P. falciparum,* particularly if the parasite was in G-6-PD-deficient red cells. Evidence for this has now been provided in vitro (Golenser *et al.*, 1983) and in an in vivo model (Clark *et al.*, 1984). Thus variable dietary oxidant stress may help explain the patchy geographic correlation between G-6-PD deficiency and falciparum malaria, and give us grounds for formally including this mutation among those that confer natural immunity to this infection.

B. Duffy Antigen

In 1929 Barber and Komp reported that while American Blacks were just as susceptible to *P. falciparum* as were Caucasians, they had a much lower incidence of infection with *P. vivax*. It was then recognised that vivax malaria was very rare in West Africa, and Bray (1958) was able to demonstrate that Liberians were almost completely refractory to infection. Subsequently it was shown that pre-entry attachment to red cells by *P. knowlesi* or *P. vivax* occured at the Duffy antigen, a component of the erythrocytic surface, since without access to this antigen the relevant parasite could not enter rhesus (Miller *et al.*, 1975) or human (Miller *et al.*, 1976) red cells. Field studies on populations that lack the gene for Duffy antigen have completed the story. One community in Honduras, studied by Spencer (1978), had both vivax and falciparum malaria, and a 59% incidence of Duffy antigen. All the vivax infections proved to be in Duffy-positives, while the falciparum cases were equally divided between the two groups. Similarly, Welch *et al.* (1977) documented a population in The Gambia that was entirely Duffy-negative (i.e., all homozygous for its absence) and had no vivax malaria, but much falciparum.

Absence of Duffy antigen on the red cell coat is therefore an interesting and extreme example of genetically induced natural immunity to an infectious agent. It demonstrates how a mutation that does not reduce the fitness of the homozygote will not lead to a balanced polymorphism, but can take over entirely, resulting in a population homozygous for this trait. Evidently *P. vivax* has provided sufficient selection pressure for this to occur in this region.

VI. NUTRITION

Malnutrition is clearly more common in those parts of the world where malaria is rife than elsewhere. This has real significance for understanding malaria as a disease, since host nutrition influences the severity of the infection. Diets of no apparent harm to the host, such as those high in milk, may also alter the outcome of the disease. Some important examples of nutritional influences on malarial immunity are given below.

A. Kwashiorkor

In Africa cerebral malaria is predominately a disease of well-nourished children, rarely affecting those with kwashiorkor (Edington, 1967). Kwashiorkor is not simple starvation, but a complex syndrome seen when children are weaned on to low-protein diets (see Trowell *et al.*, 1954). An early explanation for its association with malaria was that the parasites, as well as the child, suffered from protein deficiency, but the story is evidently much more complex than this. Children with kwashiorkor have thymic atrophy (Vint, 1937; Trowell *et al.*, 1954). This prompted Wright (1968) to investigate the effect of neonatal thymectomy on the outcome of *P. berghei*-induced cerebral malaria in hamsters. It protected them completely, and from this he reasoned that these animals, and kwashiorkor children, were protected from the worst excesses of malaria by being immunodeficient. While he was the first to show the T-cell-dependence of cerebral malaria, his argument on kwashiorkor would have been strengthened had the hamsters been thymectomised somewhat later in life, since kwashiorkor, and presumably its associated thymic atrophy, usually do not occur until some time after weaning. While there is ample confirmation that neonatal thymectomy affects the course of rodent malaria (Brown *et al.*, 1968; Hansen and Chapman, 1974), thymectomy at 6–8 weeks of age does not do so (Sheagren and Monaco, 1969).

As reviewed by Waterlow (1984), kwashiorkor is evidently not a simple protein deficiency, as first proposed (Williams, 1933), so it is still unresolved just how it influences malaria. One compounding factor could be aflatoxins from fungus-contaminated food, which have been argued to contribute to kwashiorkor and also to suppress experimental malaria infections (Hendrickse, 1984).

B. Iron Deficiency

Instinctively we might think that, being inside red cells, malaria parasites have access to ample iron for their needs even if the host as a whole is iron-deficient. This may not be so, since treating clinical iron deficiency gives the parasite more of a boost than it does the host, and converts sub-clinical to clinical malaria (Masawe *et al.*, 1974; Murray *et al.*, 1978a; Oppenheimer *et al.*, 1984). Nurse (1979) has argued that in practice malaria parasites have limited access to red cell iron, and that it is easy to tip the scales against it. Indeed, *P. falciparum* has proved very susceptible to the iron chelator desferrioxamine in vitro (Raventos-Suarez *et al.*, 1982) and iron deficiency protects mice against *P. chabaudi* (Harvey *et al.*, 1985). In parallel to field experience, these authors reported that no recrudescences occurred for as long as an iron-deficient diet was fed, but all of a group returned to normal diet exhibited parasitaemias.

The broader picture suggests that mechanisms other than poor access to intra-erythrocytic iron may operate in vivo. Iron excess is well known to contribute to peroxidative damage of red cells (Smith and Mengel, 1968), most likely through catalytically reducing the oxygen in hydrogen peroxide to a more reactive species (reviewed by Halliwell and Gutteridge, 1984). It is less well recognised, however, that iron deficiency can affect erythrocytes in essentially the same way. Red cells from iron-deficient patients have been shown to have various membrane abnormalities consistent with peroxidative injury, exhibiting reduced deformability (Hutton, 1979; Yip *et al.*, 1983) reduced surface-to-volume ratio (Tillmann and Schroter, 1980), decreased filterability (Hutton, 1979; Linderkamp *et al.*, 1979) and decreased sodium transport (Yoshimoto and Yawata, 1983). In addition, the red cell membrane barrier to calcium is defective (Shimoda and Yawata, 1985). Possible mechanisms for these changes include reduced levels of vitamin E, glutathione peroxidase, or catalase, all of which have been reported in iron deficiency (Macdougall, 1972; Rodvien *et al.*, 1974; Cellerino *et al.*, 1976). It is not difficult to visualise how penetration of red cells by merozoites, a complex process, could be jeopardised by these membrane changes, and the slowed infection re-vitalised when the iron deficiency is corrected.

C. All-Milk Diet

Following up a fortuitous observation, Maegraith *et al.* (1952) reported that all-milk (human or cow) diets suppressed *P. berghei* infections in rats. The following year this was confirmed in *P. cynomolgi*-infected rhesus monkeys, infections initiated either with blood forms (the earlier group's method) or with mosquitoes being equally suppressed (Bray and Garnham, 1953). Hawkings (1953) offered a mechanism by showing that supplementing the all-milk diet of *P. berghei*-infected rats with para-aminobenzoic acid (PABA) restored normality. This was based on the concept that milk is particularly low in PABA, which protozoa, but not mammals, need in order to synthesise folic acid. Mammals depend on dietary folic acid. Field trials eventually showed the same phenomenon in PABA-supplemented human infants (Kretschmar, 1966).

This principle has been shown to apply to older children by Murray *et al.* (1978b), who reported, from a famine relief station in West Africa, that cerebral malaria was common in those fed grain without milk but did not occur in those who, because of their nomadic life, were more easily supplemented with milk products only. Thus anyone whose diet is predominately milk, be they herd-keeping nomad or very young infant, can expect to have a degree of natural immunity to malaria because they are starving the parasites of PABA, with no harm to themselves.

D. Riboflavin Deficiency

Riboflavin (vitamin B_2) functions as a cofactor for various enzymes, including glutathione reductase. A deficiency of this vitamin thus reduces cycling of glutathione, thereby reducing red cell survival in vivo as a consequence of decreased capacity to inactivate peroxides (Powers and Thurnham, 1981). Riboflavin deficiency is common in the tropics, and when prolonged its systemic effects can be severe, including interference with iron metabolism and erythropoiesis (Alfrey and Lane, 1970). In 1944 Seeler and Ott reported that diets low in riboflavin inhibited multiplication of a bird malaria, but this work was not confirmed until the experiments of Kaikai and Thurnham (1983) in *P. berghei*-infected rats. Although the parasites were suppressed, in each case the riboflavin-deficient hosts, previously unexposed to malaria, lived no longer than those on normal diets.

Nevertheless, the case has been put (Thurnham *et al.*, 1983) that riboflavin deficiency might help protect against human malaria in circumstances where the host can be expected to be partially immune. In a series of malaria-infected infants, from an area of Papua New Guinea where maternal immunity would have been passively transferred, these workers found lower riboflavin levels to be associated with lower parasite loads. Thurnham (1985) has carefully distinguished the partially immune and the non-immune in this context, contrasting the expected influence of riboflavin deficiency on malaria in each group. He has thus cautioned against optimism on the development of riboflavin antagonists as possible antimalarial drugs (Divo *et al.*, 1985; Geary *et al.*, 1985; Dutta *et al.*, 1985). Even so, the relative sensitivity of host and parasite biochemistry to the loss of this coenzyme may be sufficiently different to warrant close inspection of this possibility.

VII. PREGNANCY

It has been recognised for some 70 years (reviewed by McGregor, 1984) that pregnancy seems to interfere with immunity to malaria, since the disease is more common, and worse, in pregnant women (Bruce-Chwatt, 1952). This has been explained in terms of lowered antimalarial antibody titres (Williams and McFarlane, 1970; Bray and Anderson, 1979), but others have not found this association (Giles *et al.*, 1969). The uncertainty surrounding this phenomenon reflects the general confusion on the precise mechanism of protective immunity to malaria in the normal individual.

Pregnancy also exacerbates malaria in rodents (Van Zon and Eling, 1980), so an in vivo experimental approach is possible. As discussed earlier, the protective response that leads to intra-erythrocytic death of malaria parasites in certain rodent malarias appears to depend on macrophage activation, and behaves, for practical purposes, as if the parasites were inside macrophages. Thus the observation that pregnancy markedly reduces resistance of mice to *Listeria monocytogenes* and *Toxoplasma gondii* (Luft and Remington, 1982) may have something to teach us about the interplay of malaria and pregnancy. When they measured cellular capacity to kill *T. gondii* in vitro, these authors found that *Corynebacterium parvum* activates macrophages less effectively in pregnant than in normal animals (Luft and Remington, 1984). Since *C. parvum* protects in vivo both against blood forms of malaria (Clark *et al.*, 1977) and *T. gondii* (Swartzberg *et al.*, 1975), the parallel experiments with *C. parvum* and malaria in pregnant and normal mice could be informative. Serum from pregnant women will inhibit the chemotactic responsiveness and phagocytic activity of human peripheral blood monocytes (Björksten, 1980), but whether it reduces their capacity to secrete the monokines that injure intra-erythrocytic *P. falciparum* (Ockenhouse *et al.*, 1984) is as yet unexplored.

Furthermore, the capacity of lymphocytes to proliferate in response to a mitogen or alloantigen is diminished by the *a*2-glycoprotein in pregnancy serum (Stinson, 1980). This molecule, not found in normal serum, appears to inhibit interleukin-2 production (Nicholas *et al.*, 1984). An additional mechanism by which pregnancy may influence malarial immunity is by the increased plasma corticosteroid that occurs in this condition. Van Zon *et al.* (1985) found that when plasma corticosteroid was maintained in mice at the level to which it normally rises in pregnancy the loss of malarial immunity was close to that observed in pregnant animals.

VIII. SUMMARY

As this brief review summarises, the relationship between the malarial parasite and its host does not exist in a vacuum, and is influenced by much besides acquired immunity. The host may be harbouring other infections, or have aberrant biochemistry stemming from mutant genes or unusual diet, that makes life harder for the parasite. Other host states, such as pregnancy, temporarily give the parasite the upper hand. We have reviewed the mechanisms through which the more important of these influences are thought to operate, stressing both the practical consequences and the uncertainties that still exist.

ACKNOWLEDGMENTS

We wish to acknowledge the financial support of the UNDP/World Bank/WHO Special Programme for Research and Training in Tropical Diseases and the National Health and Medical Research Council of Australia. We also thank Wendy Sharp for skilful assistance in preparing this manuscript.

REFERENCES

Adler, S. (1954). *Transactions of the Royal Society of Tropical Medicine and Hygiene* 48: 431.

Aggarwal, B. B., Eessula, T. E. and Hass, P. E. (1985). *Nature* 318: 665.

Alfrey, C. P. and Lane, M. (1970). *Seminars in Haematology* 7: 49.

Allison, A. C. (1954). *British Medical Journal* 1: 290.

Allison, A. C. and Clyde, D. F. (1961). *British Medical Journal* 1: 1346.

Barber, M. A. and Komp, W. H. W. (1929). *United States Public Health Report* 44: 2048.

Berzins, K., Perlmann, H., Wahlin, B., Carlson, J. and Perlmann, P. (1986). *Proceedings of the National Academy of Science, USA* 83: 1065.

Beutler, B. and Cerami, A. (1986). *Nature* 320: 584.

Björksten, B. (1980). *Immunology Today* 1: 55.

Brain, P. (1952). *British Medical Journal* 2: 880.

Bray, R. S. (1958). *Journal of Parasitology* 44: 371.

Bray, R. S. and Anderson, M. J. (1979). *Transactions of the Royal Society of Tropical Medicine and Hygiene* 73: 427.

Bray, R. S. and Garnham, P. C. C. (1953). *British Medical Journal,* 1953, 1: 1200.

Brown, G. V., Culvenor, J. G., Crewther, P. E., Bianco, A. C., Coppel, R. L., Saint, R. B., Stahl, H. -D., Kemp, D. J. and Anders, R. F. (1985). *Journal of Experimental Medicine* 162: 774.

Brown, I. N., Allison, A. C. and Taylor, R. B. (1968). *Nature* 219: 292.

Brown, J., and Smalley, E. (1980). *Clinical and Experimental Immunology* 41: 423.

Bruce-Chwatt, L. J. (1952). *Annals of Tropical Medicine and Parasitology* 46: 173.

Butcher, G. A., Buffinton, G. D., Cowden, W. B., Hunt, N. H. and Clark, I. A. (1986). *Journal of Cellular Biochemistry* suppl. 10A: 159.

Cantrell, W. and Elko, E. E. (1976). *Experimental Parasitology* 40: 281.

Carlin, J. M., Jensen, J. B. and Geary, T. G. (1985). *American Journal of Tropical Medicine and Hygiene* 38: 668.

Carswell, E. A., Old, L. J., Kassel, R. L., Green, S., Fiore, N. and Williamson, B. (1975). *Proceedings of the National Academy of Science, USA* 72: 3666.

Cellerino, R., Guidi, G. and Perona, G. (1976). *Scandinavian Journal of Haematology* 17: 111.

Chevion, M., Navok, T., Glaser, G. and Mager, J. (1982). *European Journal of Biochemistry* 127: 405.

Clark, I. A. (1976). Ph. D. thesis, University of London: 141

Clark, I. A. (1978). *Lancet* 2: 75.

Clark, I. A. (1979a). *Infection and Immunity* 24: 319.

Clark, I. A. (1979b). *Parasite Immunology* 1: 179.

Clark, I. A. (1982). *Transactions of the Royal Society of Tropical Medicine and Hygiene* 76: 4.

Clark, I. A. and Hunt, N. H. (1983). *Infection and Immunity* 39: 1.

Clark, I. A., Wills, E. J. and Richmond, J. E. (1976a). *Transactions of the Royal Society of Tropical Medicine and Hygiene* 70: 12.

Clark, I. A., Allison, A. C. and Cox, F. E. G. (1976b). *Nature* 259: 309.

Clark, I. A., Cox, F. E. G. and Allison, A. C. (1977). *Parasitology* 74: 9.

Clark, I. A., Virelizier, J. -L., Carswell, E. A. and Wood, P. R. (1981). *Infection and Immunity* 32: 1058.

Clark, I. A., Cowden, W. B. and Butcher, G. A. (1983). *Lancet* 1: 234.

Clark, I. A., Cowden, W. B., Hunt, N. H., Maxwell, L. E. and Mackie, E. J. (1984). *British Journal of Haematology* 57: 479.

Coggeshall, L. T. and Kumm, H. W. (1938). *Journal of Experimental Medicine* 68: 17.

Cohen, S., McGregor, I. A. and Carrington, S. (1961). *Nature* 192: 733.

Cohen, S., Butcher, G. A. and Crandall, R. B. (1969). *Nature* 233: 368.

Cox, F. E. G. (1970a). *Bulletin of the World Health Organization* 43: 325.

Cox, F. E. G. (1970b).*Bulletin of the World Health Organization* 43: 337.

Cox, F. E. G. (1978). *Parasitology* 76: 55.

Cox, F. E. G. (1983). *Bulletin de la Societé de Pathologie Exotique* 76: 503.

Divo, A. A., Geary, T. G. and Jensen, J. B. (1985). *Antimicrobial Agents and Chemotherapy* 27: 21.

Dockrell, H. M. and Playfair, J. H. L. (1983). *Infection and Immunity* 39: 456.

Dutta, P., Pinto, J. and Rivlin, R. (1985). *Lancet* 2: 1040.

Edington, G. (1967). *British Medical Journal* 1: 715.

Eugui, E. M. and Allison, A. C. (1979). *Bulletin of the World Health Organization* 57 (suppl.): 231.

Ferreira, A., Schofield, L., Enea, V., Schellekens, H., Van der Meide, P., Collins, W. E., Nussenzweig, R. S. and Nussenzweig, V. (1986). *Science* 232: 881.

Friedman, M. J. (1979). *Nature* 280: 245.

Geary, T. G., Divo, A. A. and Jensen, J. B. (1985). *Journal of Protozoology* 32: 65.

Giles, H. M., Lawson, J. B., Sibelas, M., Voller, A. and Allan, N. (1969). *Annals of Tropical Medicine and Parasitology* 63: 245.

Golenser, J., Miller, J., Spira, D. T., Navok, T. and Chevion, M. (1983). *Blood* 61: 507.

Goodwin, M. H. and Stapleton, T. K. (1952). *American Journal of Tropical Medicine and Hygiene* 1: 773.

Grun, J. L. and Weidanz, W. P. (1981). *Nature* 290: 143.

Haldane, J. B. S. (1949a). *La Ricerca Scientifica* 19 (suppl. 1): 68.

Haldane, J. B. S. (1949b). Proceedings of the VIIIth International Congress on Genetics. *Hereditas* suppl. 35: 367.

Halliwell, B. and Gutteridge, J. M. C. (1984). *Biochemical Journal* 219: 1.

Hansen, W. L. and Chapman, W. L. (1974). *Zeitschrift für Parasitenkunde* 44: 227.

Harvey, P. W. J., Bell, R. G. and Nesheim, M. C. (1985). *Infection and Immunity* 50: 932.

Hawkings, F. (1953). *British Medical Journal* 1: 1201.

Healy, G. R. and Ruebush, T. K. (1980). *American Journal of Clinical Pathology* 73: 107.

Hendrickse, R. G. (1984). *Transactions of the Royal Society of Tropical Medicine and Hygiene* 78: 427.

Herod, E., Clark, I. A. and Allison, A. C. (1978). *Clinical and Experimental Immunology* 31: 518.

Heyman, A. and Beeson, P. B. (1949). *Journal of Laboratory and Clinical Medicine* 34: 1400.

Hill, R. B., Cambournac, F. J. C. and Simoes, M. P. (1943). *American Journal of Tropical Medicine and Hygiene* 23: 147.

Huheey, J. E. and Martin, D. L. (1975). *Experientia* 31: 1145.

Hutton, R. D. (1979). *British Journal of Haematology* 43: 191.

Jensen, J. B. (1986). *Journal of Cellular Biochemistry* suppl. 10A: 121.

Kaikai, P. and Thurnham, D. I. (1983). *Transactions of the Royal Society of Tropical Medicine and Hygiene* 77: 680.

Khusmith, S., Druihle, P. and Gentilini, M. (1982). *Infection and Immunity* 35: 874.

Kidson, C. and Gorman, J. G. (1962). *Nature* 196: 49.

Kitchen, S. F. (1949). In M. F. Boyd (ed.), *Malariology*. Philadelphia: W. B. Saunders: 966–94.

Klebanoff, S. J., Vadas, M. A., Harlan, J. M., Sparks, L. H., Gamble, J. R., Agosti, J. M. and Waltersdorph, A. M. (1986). *Journal of Immunology* 136: 4220.

Kretschmar, W. (1966). *Zeitschrift für Tropenmedizin und Parasitologie* 17: 301.

Larrick, J. W., Fendly, B. M., Gray, O., Toy, K. and Senyk, G. (1985). *Blood* 66 (suppl. 1): 892.

Larsen, N. E. and Sullivan, R. (1984). *Proceedings of the National Academy of Science, USA* 81: 3491.

Linderkamp, O., Klose, H. J., Betke, K., Kelson, S. and Sengespeik, C. (1979). *Journal of Pediatrics* 95: 567.

Livingstone, F. B. (1971). *Annual Review of Genetics* 5: 33.

Luft, B. J. and Remington, J. S. (1982). *Infection and Immunity* 38: 1164.

Luft, B. J. and Remington, J. S. (1984). *Cellular Immunology* 85: 94.

Luzzatto, L. (1979). *Blood* 54: 961.

Luzzatto, L. and Battistuzzi, G. (1985). *Advances in Human Genetics* 14: 217.

Luzzatto, L., Usanga, E. A. and Reddy, S. (1969). *Science* 164: 839.

Macdougall, L. G. (1972). *Journal of Pediatrics* 80: 775.

McGregor, I. A. (1984). *American Journal of Tropical Medicine and Hygiene* 33: 517.

McGregor, I. A., Gilles, H. M., Walters, J. H., Davies, A. H. and Pearson, F. A. (1956). *British Medical Journal* 2: 686.

Maegraith, B. G., Deegan, T. and Sherwood Jones, E. (1952). *British Medical Journal* 2: 1382.

Martin, D. K., Miller, L. H., Alling, D., Okoye, V. C., Esan, G. J. F., Osunkoya, B. O. and Deane, M. (1979). *Lancet* 1: 524.

Masawe, A. E. J., Muindi, J. M. and Swai, G. R. B. (1974). *Lancet* 2: 314.

Michalek, S. M., Moore, R. N., McGhee, J. R., Rosenstreich, D. L. and Mergenhagen, S. E. (1980). *Journal of Infectious Diseases* 141: 55.

Miller, L. H., Mason, S. J., Dvorak, J. A., McGinnis, M. H. and Rothman, I. K. (1975). *Science* 189: 561.

Miller, L. H., Mason, S. J., Clyde, D. F. and McGinnis, M. H. (1976). *New England Journal of Medicine* 295: 302.

Mizra, H. P. and Fridovich, I. (1972). *Journal of Biological Chemistry* 247: 6960.

Motulsky, A. G. (1960). *Human Biology* 32: 28.

Murray, M. J., Murray, A. B. and Murray, C. J. (1978a). *British Medical Journal* 2: 1113.

Murray, M. J., Murray, A. B., Murray, N. J. and Murray, M. B. (1978b). *American Journal of Clinical Nutrition* 31: 57.

Murray, H. W., Spitalny, G. L. and Nathan, C. F. (1985). *Journal of Immunology* 134: 1619.

Nagel, R. L., Raventos-Suarez, C., Fabry, M. E., Tanowitz, H., Sicard, D. and Labie, D. (1981). *Journal of Clinical Investigation* 68: 303.

Nathan, C. F., Murray, H. W., Wiebe, M. E. and Rubin, B. Y. (1983). *Journal of Experimental Medicine* 156: 670.

Neinhuis, A. W., Anagnau, N. P. and Ley, T. J. (1984). *Blood* 63: 738.

Nicholas, N. S., Panayi, G. S. and Nouri, A. M. E. (1984). *Clinical and Experimental Immunology* 58: 587.

Nurse, G. T. (1979). *Lancet* 2: 938.

Ockenhouse, C. F. and Shear, H. L. (1983). *Infection and Immunity* 42: 733.

Ockenhouse, C. F., Schulman, S. and Shear, H. L. (1984). *Journal of Immunology* 133: 1601.

Oppenheimer, S. J., Gibson, F. D., MacFarlane, S. B., Moody, J. B. and Hendrickse, R. G. (1984). *Lancet* 1: 389.

Orjih, A. U., Chevli, R. and Fitch, C. D. (1985). *American Journal of Tropical Medicine and Hygiene* 34: 223.

Ott, K. J. and Stauber, L. A. (1967). *Science* 155: 1546.

Pasvol, G., Weatherall, D. J., Wilson, R. J. M., Smith, D. H. and Gilles, H. M. (1976). *Lancet* 1: 1269.

Pasvol, G., Weatherall, D. H. and Wilson, R. J. M. (1978). *Nature* 274: 701.

Peavy, D. L., Baughn, R. E. and Musher, D. M. (1979). *Infection and Immunity* 24: 59.

Peters, W. (1965). *Experimental Parasitology* 16: 158.

Powers, H. J. and Thurnham, D. I. (1981). *British Journal of Nutrition* 46: 257.

Raper, A. B. (1949). *East African Medical Journal* 26: 281.

Raventos-Suarez, C., Pollack, S. and Nagel, R. L. (1982). *American Journal of Tropical Medicine and Hygiene* 31: 919.

Rhodes-Feuillete, A., Bellosguardo, M., Druihle, P., Ballet, J. J., Chousterman, S., Canivet, M. and Peries, P. (1985). *Journal of Interferon Research* 5: 169.

Rodvien, R., Gillum, A. and Weintraub, L. R. (1974). *Blood* 43: 281.

Rubenstein, M., Mulholland, J. H., Jeffery, G. M. and Wolff, S. (1965). *Proceedings of the Society for Experimental Biology and Medicine* 118: 283.

Salmon, D., Vilde, J. L., Andrieu, B., Simonovic, R. and Lebras, J. (1986). *Infection and Immunity* 51: 801.

Santiyanont, R. and Wilairat, P. (1981). *American Journal of Tropical Medicine and Hygiene* 30: 541.

Schacter, L. P. (1986). *European Journal of Clinical Investigation* 16: 204.

Seeler, A. O. and Ott, W. H. (1944). *Journal of Infectious Diseases* 75: 175.

Sheagren, J. N. and Monaco, A. P. (1969). *Science* 164: 1423.

Shimoda, M. and Yawata, Y. (1985). *American Journal of Hematology* 19: 55.

Sinton, J. A., Harbhagivan, S. and Singh, J. (1931). *Indian Journal of Medical Research* 18: 871.

Skamene, E., Stevenson, M. M. and Lemieux, S. (1983). *Parasite Immunology* 5: 557.

Smith, K. A. and Mengel, C. E. (1968). *Journal of Laboratory and Clinical Medicine* 72: 505.

Spencer, H. C., Miller, L. H., Collins, W. E., Knud-Hansen, C., McGinnis, M. H., Shiroishi, T., Lobos, R. A. and Feldman, R. A. (1978). *American Journal of Tropical Medicine and Hygiene* 27: 664.

Stinson, W. H. (1980). *Clinical and Experimental Immunology* 40: 157.

Suter, E. (1962). *Transactions of the New York Academy of Science* 24: 281.

Swartzberg, J. E., Krahenbuhl, J. L. and Remington, J. S. (1975). *Infection and Immunity* 12: 1037.

Taliaferro, W. H. and Taliaferro, L. G. (1934). *American Journal of Hygiene* 20: 1.

Taverne, J., Dockrell, H. M. and Playfair, J. H. L. (1981). *Infection and Immunity* 33: 83.

Thurnham, D. I. (1985). *Lancet* 2: 1310.

Thurnham, D. I., Oppenheimer, S. J. and Bull, R. (1983). *Transactions of the Royal Society of Tropical Medicine and Hygiene* 77: 423.

Tillmann, W. and Schroter, W. (1980). *Blut* 40: 179.

Trager, W. and Jensen, J. B. (1976). *Science* 193: 673.

Trowell, H. C., Davies, J. N. P. and Dean, R. F. A. (1954). *Kwashiorkor.* London: Edward Arnold.

Troye-Blomberg, M., Anderson, G., Stoczkowska, M., Shabo, P., Romero, P., Patarroya, E. and Perlmann, P. (1985). *Journal of Immunology* 135: 3498.

Tsujimoto, M., Yip, Y. K. and Vilček, J. (1986). *Journal of Immunology* 136: 2441.

Van Zon, A. A. J. C. and Eling, W. M. C. (1980). *Infection and Immunity* 28: 630.

Van Zon, A. A. J. C., Eling, W. M. C., Schetters, T. P. M. and Hermsen, C. C. (1985). *Parasite Immunology* 7: 107.

Vint, F. W. (1937). *East African Medical Journal* 13: 332.

Waterlow, J. C. (1984). *Transactions of the Royal Society of Tropical Medicine and Hygiene* 78: 436.

Welch, S. G., McGregor, I. A. and Williams, K. (1977). *Transactions of the Royal Society of Tropical Medicine and Hygiene* 71: 295.

Willcox, M., Björkman, A. and Brohult, J. (1983). *Annals of Tropical Medicine and Parasitology* 77: 335.

Williams, A. I. O. and McFarlane, H. (1970). *African Journal of Medical Science* 1: 369.

Willams, C. D. (1933). *Archives of Disease in Childhood* 8: 423.

Wood, P. R. and Clark, I. A. (1982). *Parasite Immunology* 4: 319.

Wood, P. R. and Clark, I. A. (1984). *Parasite Immunology* 6: 309.

Wright, D. H. (1968). *British Journal of Experimental Pathology* 49: 379.

Yip, R., Mohandas, N., Clark, M. R., Jain, S., Shohet, S. B. and Dallman, P. R. (1983). *Blood* 62: 99.

Yoshimoto, M. and Yawata, Y. (1983). *Acta Haematologica Japonica* 46: 814.

24

Metazoan Infections

DAVID I. GROVE

Department of Medicine, University of Western Australia
Queen Elizabeth II Medical Centre, Nedlands, WA 6009, Australia

I. INTRODUCTION AND DEFINITIONS

"Eggs of . . . *A. lumbricoides* develop outside the body of man, but the embryo only hatches when it is brought into the intestine by food or drink . . . In whichever animal supplies these conditions, the egg

NATURAL IMMUNITY
ISBN 0 12 5145551

hatches if it remains in the intestine long enough; however, the embryo does not linger if the animal is not of the kind where the worm can acquire its final form." (Davaine, 1862)

With these words, Casimir Davaine in 1862 highlighted the phenomenon of natural resistance to helminth parasites. Davaine had taken ova of the common roundworm of humans, *Ascaris lumbricoides*, and had fed them, first to a cow, then to rats. He failed subsequently to find adult worms in the intestine of these animals and concluded that, in contrast to humans, they were not susceptible hosts to this parasite. Despite over 100 years of investigation since that time, we are little wiser about why these tremendous variations in responsiveness of vertebrate hosts to different worms occur, or about the mechanisms by which such responses are generated. At one extreme, for example, stands *A. lumbricoides* which infects humans only (although there are very debatable claims that pigs are also susceptible), while at the other is *Trichinella spiralis* which infects a wide range of mammals.

The accumulation of such data has led to the development of two important concepts in parasitology — the host specificity of a parasite, and the parasite fauna characteristic of a given host species. Both of these aspects interact and ultimately are determined genetically, the first reflecting the genetic constitution of the parasite and the second controlled by the genetic background of the host. When the resultant phenotypes are compatible, infection occurs. When they are incompatible, infection does not occur. Parasitologists call this phenomenon host–parasite specificity and immunologists label it natural resistance.

Before any attempt can be made to understand natural resistance in worm infections, some basic biological facts need to be kept in mind. The severity of disease in helminth infections generally depends upon the intensity of infection, although in some circumstances, location of the parasite (e.g. hydatid cyst) or the reaction of the host (e.g. in strongyloidiasis) may be important. Unlike all other infectious agents, most worms are unable to multiply, i.e. complete their life cycle, within the definitive host. This means that the worm burden is a function of the number of infective forms (eggs or larvae) encountered and is inversely proportional to the resistance of the host. Thus, one *Ascaris* can become only one *Ascaris* adult and one hookworm larva can become only one hookworm adult. The most notable exception to this rule is *Strongyloides stercoralis* which is able to complete its life cycle and replicate. A few other worms, such as *Echinococcus* species, have a limited ability to multiply in that the larval forms are able to multiply asexually, but maturation of the parasite and sexual reproduction do not occur.

In terms of helminth infections, resistance means the ability of a host both to prevent the maturation of larvae into adult worms (such as the development of hookworm larvae into hookworm adults) and to inhibit asexual multiplication of larvae (such as the growth of echinococcal cysts). In resistant animals, the invading worms may either be killed by the host defences or be prevented from maturing, although the parasites evade these defences and live as long as the intrinsic lifespan of the worm (see section on intestinal nematodes). Resistance of a host may be acquired, i.e. the result of previous exposure to the parasite, and effected by humoral and cell-mediated immune mechanisms. The extent to which immunity is acquired in many human helminth infections is debatable (Grove, 1982). What is clear is that humans are not susceptible to many helminth parasites of lower animals and vice versa. Furthermore, some individuals of a host species are more resistant to a particular worm than are other individuals of the same species. These variations are a consequence of natural immunity. Natural immunity, therefore, can be defined as the resistance of a host to a parasite on first exposure to that organism as a consequence of the host's pre-existing anatomical, biochemical and physiological constitution (Wakelin, 1978). Natural immunity has been further classified as 'passive' or 'active' (Mauel, 1982). The former obtains when no manipulations whatever have been made. The latter occurs when protection against an infectious agent results from prior exposure to antigenically unrelated organisms, microbial extracts or certain synthetic products (Mahmoud, 1982). In this chapter, passive natural immunity will be called 'innate immunity' and active natural immunity will be labelled 'non-specific acquired resistance'.

One caveat should be made, however. At times, the distinction between natural immunity and specific acquired immunity may be blurred, especially in those infections in which several weeks or more are required for the infection to become manifest. In such situations, the apparent success or otherwise of a primary infection may really reflect a race between the worm and the acquisition of specific, acquired, protective immunity.

Parasitic worms have widely varying life cycles which greatly influence the possibilities which a host has for mounting natural immunity, and the mechanisms by which this achieved. The life cycles of some of the more important parasites will be summarised, then the evidence for innate immunity and non-specific acquired resistance in various metazoan parasitic infections will be reviewed. An attempt will then be made to provide a synthesis of the mechanisms by which these phenomena occur.

II. INTESTINAL NEMATODE INFECTIONS

Most intestinal nematodes do not require the services of an intermediate host and are acquired either by ingestion of eggs or by penetration of the skin by infective larvae. The subsequent development of these worms may be categorised in two groups. In some species, such as *Enterobius vermicularis* and *Trichuris trichiura*, ingestion of ova is followed by hatching of the eggs and moulting of larvae several times to become adult worms, all of these events taking place within the lumen of the bowel. In other infections in which eggs are ingested, such as *A. lumbricoides* in humans and *Toxocara canis* in dogs, however, the eggs hatch and the larvae migrate through the tissues before returning to the bowel to continue their development. In worms in this latter group, as well as in helminths which penetrate the skin, a phenomenon known as arrested development or diapause may occur. Arrested development may be considered as a manifestation of natural immunity and occurs with many nematode infections of veterinary importance (Michel, 1974) and in humans.

Arrested development is seen in two distinct situations. The first occurs when infective forms enter an unnatural host. For example, *T. canis* is usually transmitted directly from dog to dog. Should the ova be ingested by a rodent, however, the eggs hatch and the larvae migrate to the tissues where they remain, failing to follow the normal circuit to the small intestine and so to mature. If the rodent is eaten by a dog subsequently, maturation of the parasites occurs in the small intestine of the new host. The rodent may therefore be considered as a paratenic (i.e. carrier or transport) host. Clearly, either a signal from the paratenic host stimulating development of the worm is missing, or the paratenic host in some unknown way inhibits the maturation of the parasite. Examples of this type of arrested development in human infections are with *T. canis* (visceral larva migrans or ocular toxocariasis) and *Angiostrongylus cantonensis* (eosinophilic meningitis).

The second form of arrested development occurs within the usual host. Instead of the larvae completing the migratory phase of the life cycle, their transit and maturation is delayed. After a variable period, the larvae either follow the normal pathway or take another route and mature (Schad, 1977). It has been suggested that the former is designed to allow the parasite to take advantage of propitious external environmental circumstances, thus facilitating transmission, but how the parasite or the host is programmed to effect this event are unknown. Alteration of route is exemplified by transmammary transmission. In mature female dogs infected with *Ancylostoma caninum* or *Toxocara canis*, many larvae become arrested in the tissues, but then migrate to the mammary gland during lactation and appear in the milk, especially during the first week of parturition. Both forms of emergence from diapause have been postulated for human infections.

A. Ancylostomiasis — Hookworm Infection

Infections with *Ancylostoma duodenale* and *Necator americanus* in humans are acquired by infective larvae penetrating the skin; they then pass via the bloodstream to the lungs, ascend the airways to the mouth, are swallowed, and mature in the small intestine.

1. Innate immunity

The most substantive evidence for the existence of natural immunity is provided by dogs infected with related hookworms. Dogs become progressively resistant to infection with *A. caninum* with advancing age. This age resistance is more marked in female than in male animals (Miller, 1965). As mentioned earlier, arrested development occurs in abnormal hosts. Larvae of this species persist in the tissues of mice for up to one year and are able to complete their development when the mice are killed and fed to dogs (Miller, 1970).

The human clinical counterpart to this situation is cutaneous larva migrans; when infective larvae of the cat and dog hookworm, *A. braziliense*, penetrate human skin, they migrate slowly through the subcutaneous tissues (Kirby-Smith *et al.*, 1926, 1929) and possibly the lungs (Mühleissen, 1953) without being able to complete their development. Another form of arrested development of the human parasite *A. duodenale* has also been described in humans. An Indian strain of this parasite has been shown to have an extended prepatent period so that the worms do not mature and the eggs are not excreted until the next monsoon (Schad *et al.*, 1973). Furthermore, this phenomenon occurred in an infected individual who travelled around the world to an entirely different seasonal area, and was then reproduced in a volunteer living in that area (Nawalinski and Schad, 1974). The mechanisms of this phenomenon are uncertain but the observations suggest that there may be some form of biological clock in either the parasite or the host.

The role of genetic factors in producing variations in innate immunity in the normal host is uncertain. It has been suggested that racial factors may influence resistance to hookworms. Black people in the southern United States were observed to be less susceptible to *N. americanus* compared to poor white people when living under similarly insanitary conditions. It has been postulated that this may have been due to the thicker negroid skin inhibiting passage of infective larvae (Smillie and Augustine, 1925). Alternatively, it has been proposed that this effect was mediated by a greater nutritional deficiency in white subjects lowering innate resistance (Ahmann and Bristol, 1933). It seems more likely, however, that if this difference was real, it was due to ecological factors influencing the degree of exposure to infective larvae.

Hookworm infection and nutritional deficiency go hand in hand in many regions of the world. It is unproven whether poor nutrition lowers resistance to hookworm infection in humans (Variyam and Banwell, 1982), but it has been shown that nutritional deficiency leads to heavier worm burdens in dogs infected with *A. caninum* (Foster and Cort, 1935).

Epidemiological studies in humans have shown that hookworm burdens rise rapidly in the first 10 years of life, remain constant or are reduced over the next few decades, then sometimes increase again in old age (Miller, 1979). Whether this is due to variations in age resistance, the acquisition of specific protective immunity or variations in exposure to reinfection as a consequence of epidemiological factors is unknown.

Little information is available concerning non-specific acquired resistance in hookworm infection.

B. Strongyloidiasis

Strongyloides stercoralis has a complex life cycle. Initially, it parallels that of hookworm with infective larvae penetrating the skin, passing to the lungs, ascending the airways to the mouth, being swallowed, and maturing in the small intestine. The adult worms are parthenogenetic and they release rhabditiform larvae which are excreted in the faeces. Some worms, however, may autoinfect; they presumably moult twice then penetrate either the large bowel mucosa or the perianal skin. In immunosuppressed hosts, massive multiplication and widespread dissemination of larvae occur. In contrast, the rodent parasite *S. ratti* does not have this capacity to autoinfect.

1. Innate immunity

It has been shown that age confers some resistance of laboratory rats to infection with *S. ratti* (Sheldon, 1937). *S. ratti* is not a natural parasite of mice, and the susceptibility to infection varies enormously among different inbred strains of mice, thus indicating that genetic influences are of major importance in controlling innate immunity (Dawkins *et al.*, 1980).

Genetic factors also appear to determine the resistance of dogs, monkeys and humans to *S. stercoralis*, but whether these variations are mediated by innate or acquired immunity is unknown. These effects are seen most plainly in relation to the presence or absence of autoinfection. For example, in one study of Australian ex-servicemen living in a non-endemic area but who had acquired the infection while prisoners-of-war 35 years earlier, only one-third of them were still infected (Grove, 1980). It could reasonably be expected that most of them had been exposed to infection with *Strongyloides*, and indeed most of them were infected with hookworm which follows a similar epidemiological pattern. Similarly, only a small proportion of dogs develop chronic infections with *S. stercoralis*. The majority of animals eliminate infection spontaneously (Grove and Northern, 1982), although this rejection can be overcome by immunosuppression (Grove *et al.*, 1983). Finally, patas monkeys may evidence the other side of the coin, i.e. profound innate susceptibility; when infected with small numbers of *S. stercoralis*, some animals are extremely susceptible and develop fatal, disseminated infections in the absence of immunosuppression (Harper *et al.*, 1984).

Parasite factors also relate to innate immunity. Galliard (1967) considered that there are 'geographical races' of *S. stercoralis* which differ in their infectivity for different hosts. For example, *S. stercoralis* from humans in Indochina infects dogs easily whereas the African and West Indian strains are relatively avirulent for these animals.

Little is known about non-specific acquired resistance in strongyloidiasis.

C. Other Intestinal Worms

Almost nothing is known concerning either innate immunity or non-specific acquired resistance to the other three common intestinal roundworm infections of human — ascariasis, trichuriasis and enterobiasis — despite the fact that *Ascaris* infection is the most common helminth infection of humans, with over one thousand million people being infected. For all practical purposes, humans are the only definitive host of *A. lumbricoides*, *T. trichiura* and *E. vermicularis*, and no vector is required, infection being acquired by ingestion of ova.

Wakelin (1975) has shown that some mice are genetically incapable of expelling *Trichuris muris*. The ability to achieve expulsion is a dominant characteristic involving a small number of genes, but resistance, when it occurs, is mediated by specific acquired resistance, not natural immunity.

Brindley and Dobson (1983) have attempted to dissect the contributions of natural and acquired immunity to *Nematospiroides dubius* in mice. They bred mice relatively refractory or susceptible to infection with this worm, then assessed the effect on challenge infection of transfer of immune serum from these animals to naive animals. No differences were seen in immunity transferred by these sera, as assessed by quantifying the numbers of adult worms in the intestines three weeks later. The authors concluded that the differences seen between refractory and susceptible mice were due to variations in innate immunity; this seems quite unwarranted, for the differences could equally well reflect variations in the effectiveness of cell-mediated immune processes.

Haemonchus contortus is a parasite of sheep and cattle which sucks blood from the stomach of these animals; eggs are passed in the faeces and hatch and moult to form infective larvae on the pasture, then these are ingested and develop into adult worms. Heritable resistance of sheep to this parasite occurs, and this resistance is associated with haemoglobin type. Sheep with haemoglobin A have a greater resistance to clinical disease as measured by haemoglobin concentration, as well as a lower worm burden. Haemoglobin type is not the only factor, however, as susceptibility varies among sheep even when the haemoglobin type is the same. Both immune and non-immune mechanisms are thought to contribute to these differences, but this view has not been well sub-stantiated (Whitlock and Georgi, 1968; Altaif and Dargie, 1978).

III. TISSUE NEMATODE INFECTIONS

A. Trichinosis

Trichinosis is both an intestinal and a tissue nematode infection. When meat containing infective cysts is ingested, the larvae excyst in the small intestine, penetrate into the epithelial layer and mature. Adult worms mate and newborn larvae are produced; these pass via the bloodstream to the skeletal muscle where they encyst and develop into infective larvae. Resistance against *Trichinella spiralis* can be measured by quantifying adult worm expulsion from the gut and by enumerating the numbers of larvae in the muscles.

1. *Innate immunity*

A wide range of mammals is susceptible to infection with *T. spiralis*, but fish, amphibians, reptiles and birds do not support this parasite. Not only are there variations in susceptibility between species, but the genetic background of a particular host is important. For example, Wassom *et al.* (1979) measured worm burdens in different strains of inbred mice and found that susceptibility varied not only between strains, but also between mice of the same strain but with different H-2 haplotypes (congenic mice). When muscle worm burdens were measured, it was found that strains of mice possessing the H-2^k gene were the most resistant. Nevertheless, genes outside the major histocompatibility complex were also shown to be associated with the degree of innate immunity.

2. Non-specific acquired resistance

Exposure to a number of unrelated organisms alters host reactivity to *T. spiralis*. Prior infection with *Toxoplasma gondii* has a dual effect; elimination of adult worms from the gut is impaired, but resistance against the migratory phase of the parasite is increased (Copeland and Grove, 1979). Similar observations have been made with *Mycobacterium bovis* strain BCG (Grove and Civil, 1978). Non-specific acquired resistance induced by intracellular organisms such as these is presumably related to their ability to stimulate macrophage activity, although similar effects were not seen with another phagocyte stimulant, *Listeria mono-cytogenes* (Franco-Loayza, 1979).

B. Filariasis

Filarial parasites are transmitted by insects. When infective larvae of the two major causes of lymphatic filariasis, *Wuchereria bancrofti* and *Brugia malayi*, penetrate the skin following a mosquito bite, the larvae migrate through the lymphatics to near the lymph nodes, where they mature. Adult worms produce microfilariae which circulate in the peripheral blood and may be ingested by a mosquito during its blood meal.

1. Innate immunity

A number of factors including species, age and sex of the host affect innate susceptibility to various filarial parasites. Different host species vary considerably in their susceptibility to these worms. The subperiodic strain of *B. malayi* develops fully in a number of mammalian hosts including humans, monkeys, cats, dogs and gerbils. In contrast, the periodic strain (i.e. one in which microfilariae appear in the blood only at night) of *B. malayi* and *W. bancrofti* have a much more limited host range. When rats are inoculated with infective larvae of *W. bancrofti*, morphogenesis is arrested and the final moult does not occur (Ash and Schacher, 1971). A number of rodents are innately susceptible to *B. pahangi*, but this susceptibility can be modified by selective breeding (Sucharit and MacDonald, 1973).

Older rats are more resistant to infection with *Litomosoides carinii* (Siddiqui and Kershaw, 1976). Sex is sometimes important; male gerbils are more susceptible to *B. pahangi* than are female animals (Ash, 1971), but sex does not affect patency rates in cats infected with this parasite (Denham, 1974).

Familial clustering of patients with filariasis has often been noted. In one recent study, the data were said to best fit a model of Mendelian inheritance by a recessive gene, but the rather more likely hypothesis that the prevalence of filariasis was determined environmentally was not excluded. Certainly, there was no linking of susceptibility to infection with the patients' HLA-A or -B locus genes (Ottesen *et al.*, 1981).

Attempts have been made to break down innate immunity with a variety of techniques. Splenectomy and immunosuppression with irradiation or 6-mercaptopurine all fail to alter the resistance of guinea pigs, rabbits and mice to infection with *B. malayi* and *B. pahangi*, although patent infections do develop in a small number of splenectomised rats inoculated with *B. malayi* (Ahmed 1967a, b). Patent infections have been produced experimentally in some Taiwan monkeys (*Macaca cyclopis*) which were splenectomised or treated with various immunosuppressants, but the effects were erratic (Cross *et al.*, 1979). In animals in which patent infections with *Dirofilaria immitis*, *D. repens*, *D. vitiae* or *L. carinii* normally occur, splenectomy does not alter microfilarial levels (Hawking, 1962).

Little is known about non-specific acquired resistance in filariasis.

C. Other Tissue Nematode Infections

Apart from a mere recitation of host specificities, little can be said about natural resistance to other tissue-dwelling nematodes. The three major species infecting humans, *Onchocerca volvulus*, *Loa loa* and *Dracunculus medinensis*, are primarily parasites of humans.

IV. TREMATODE INFECTIONS

A. Schistosomiasis

Schistosomes have life cycles which involve vertebrate definitive hosts and snail intermediate hosts. When eggs are released into the environment from the definitive host, they hatch and the emergent miracidia invade certain species of snail in which they develop and multiply, forming first sporocysts then cercariae. The cercariae are released into water, then penetrate the integument of the definitive host, losing their tails in the process. The resultant schistosomula migrate via the bloodstream through the lungs to the portal venous system where they mature. Adult male and female worms copulate and produce eggs, some of which are excreted in the faeces or urine, depending upon the species of schistosome.

1. *Innate immunity*

Of the three schistosomes commonly infecting humans, *Schistosoma japonicum* is the least host-specific, meeting little innate resistance in a wide variety of vertebrate animals. *S. haematobium* is not so well adapted to non-human hosts, but a number of rodent and other primate species are susceptible. The range of host specificities of *S. mansoni* lies somewhere between those of the other schistosomes. Although many mammals can be infected with schistosomes, the degree of susceptibility among host species varies considerably, when measured in terms of the percentage of parasites developing, the growth and maturation of worms, their fecundity, the viability of eggs and the infectivity of the miracidia (Smithers and Doenhoff, 1982). Furthermore, there are intra-specific differences in these parasites in host susceptibility. For example, humans and some other primates are innately resistant to the Formosan strain of *S. japonicum*; the cercariae penetrate the skin but adult worms do not develop (Hsu and Hsu, 1956). Similarly, different strains of *S. japonicum* (Hsu and Hsu, 1960) and *S. mansoni* (Warren, 1967) vary in their virulence for mice. On the other hand, different strains of inbred mice vary in their susceptibility to the same worm (Stirewalt *et al.*, 1965, Stirewalt, 1963).

A number of other factors influence the degree of susceptibility of innately susceptible hosts. Very young mice are more susceptible to *S. mansoni* than are older animals (Lewert and Mandlowitz, 1963). Age resistance is associated with an increased mortality of schistosomula in the skin (Ghandour and Webbe, 1973). Likewise, female rodents are more resistant to *S. mansoni* and *S. haematobium* than are male animals (Purnell, 1966).

Whereas humans are innately susceptible to most strains of *S. mansoni*, *S. japonicum* and *S. haematobium*, they are naturally resistant to avian schistosomes. These organisms penetrate human skin but the cercariae fail to develop. Conversely, *S. mansoni* cercariae penetrate the skin of birds in the same proportion as they do in susceptible mammals, but again fail to develop (Warren and Peters, 1967). Nevertheless, it has been found that the viability of cercariae in the skin of naturally resistant animals is greatly reduced when compared with those in the skin of susceptible hosts (Clegg and Smithers, 1968).

Penetration of cercariae through the skin is largely dependent upon enzymatic lysis of tissues. It has been suggested that innate immunity may be determined by the ability or inability of cercarial enzymes to break down the acellular glycoprotein barriers, especially in the region of the basement membrane, which may be strengthened with age (Lewert and Mandlowitz, 1963). Death of schistosomula in the skin of resistant hosts often occurs within 10 minutes and happens in the epidermis rather than the dermis. Explanations of this phenomenon have been that some reserve material in the worm is exhausted, or that a toxic substance is present in the epidermis. Certainly, the thickness of the stratum corneum seems to be of little importance. It has also been claimed that there is a correlation between the cercaricidal activity of unheated serum and the susceptibility of a host to infection, but this has not stood up to critical review (Smithers and Terry, 1969).

There is a marked similarity between the cellular reaction of naive abnormal hosts to invading schistosomula in the skin and that seen in susceptible hosts that have been immunised (Lichtenberg *et al.*, 1962). It may be that migration of parasites is inhibited in resistant hosts, rendering them more susceptible to attack by cells of the inflammatory reaction. If this is indeed the case, then the factors responsible for slowing migration remain a mystery.

Innate immunity may dovetail with enhanced specific acquired immunity in some hosts, or at least with the ability of the parasite to evade the immune responses of those hosts. Such a dual response is seen in rats infected with *S. mansoni*: (1) greater numbers of schistosomula die in the more effective skin barrier and (2) sterilising immunity against the survivors develops within a few weeks of exposure (Smithers and Terry, 1965; Clegg and Smithers, 1968). When stunted worms from a rat are transferred to a permissive host such as a hamster, they increase in size, migrate to the mesenteric veins (rather than accumulate in the liver) and produce eggs. The converse also applies when mature worms are transferred from a susceptible host to rats (Cioli *et al.*, 1977). Thus, the physiological and reproductive status of the worm is influenced strongly by the host, but the effect is reversible. These effects seem to be mediated non-immunologically, for worms still fail to mature in immunosuppressed rats (Knopf and Soliman, 1980).

On the other hand, there is some evidence to show that mononuclear phagocytes play a role in species-related innate resistance, for such cells obtained from innately resistant hosts are more efficient at killing schistosomula in vitro than are those obtained from permissive hosts (Peck *et al.*, 1983).

An association has been noted between the severity of schistosomiasis and both the ABO blood group (Pereira *et al.*, 1979) and the HLA type (Salam *et al.*, 1979) of infected persons. It seems much more likely, however, that any linkage between the histocompatibility system and disease is mediated through specific acquired immunity rather than natural resistance.

2. Non-specific acquired resistance

Non-specific immunity can be induced in a number of ways. Inflammation in the skin prior to exposure to *S. mansoni* kills many invading worms (Gysin and Le Coroller, 1976). Similarly, prior exposure of mice to killed *Escherichia coli* (Smith *et al.*, 1975), *Mycobacterium bovis* strain BCG (Civil *et al.*, 1978), cord factor (Olds *et al.*, 1980a), *Toxoplasma gondii* (Mahmoud *et al.*, 1976) and *Corynebacterium parvum* (Mahmoud *et al.*, 1979) may stimulate a high degree of protection against *S. mansoni*. The degree of such protection, however, is dependent upon the genetic background of the host. Thus, the degree of protection induced in mice by BCG against *S. mansoni* varies markedly among different inbred strains. The ability to acquire non-specific resistance is inherited dominantly and does not segregate with the major histocompatibility complex (Civil and Mahmoud, 1978). The relevance of such observations in experimental animals is exemplified by the finding that monocytes obtained from people with active pulmonary tuberculosis have an enhanced ability to kill *S. mansoni* schistosomula (Olds *et al.*, 1980c).

Such resistance is mediated by activated macrophages. Macrophages obtained from mice treated with the agents mentioned earlier, but not those taken from mice exposed to proteose–peptone or thioglycollate, when grown in monolayers will kill schistosomula. Worm killing is T-lymphocyte-dependent, and the killing is mediated by soluble substances released from the macrophages which come in contact with the parasites. The nature of these substances is under investigation; they may include arginase (Olds *et al.*, 1980b) and hydrogen peroxide (Kazura *et al.*, 1981). Finally, in vitro studies with macrophages obtained from various inbred strains of mice indicate that the degree of worm killing parallels the degree of resistance induced in vivo by BCG in these mice.

B. Other Trematode Infections

There are a number of other important flukes that infect humans, including *Clonorchis sinensis, Fasciola hepatica, Fasciolopsis buski, Opisthorchis* species and *Paragonimus* species. In addition to humans, a number of other vertebrate species also act as definitive hosts to these parasites. These worms have snail intermediate hosts, then the released cercariae encyst either on plants (e.g. *Fasciola, Fasciolopsis*) or in animal second intermediate hosts such as crustaceans (*Paragonimus*) or fish (*Clonorchis, Opisthorchis*). Apart from information on which species are the preferred definitive and intermediate hosts, very little is known about natural immunity to these parasites.

V. CESTODE INFECTIONS

Cestodes have complex life cycles. Cyclophyllidean tapeworms such as *Taenia solium, T. saginata* and *Echinococcus granulosus* have an alternation of generations and an alternation of hosts in which the adult tapeworm is found in the small intestine of one mammal species and the cystic larval forms are found in the tissues of another mammal. Pseudophyllidean tapeworms such as *Diphyllobothrium latum* have a more complicated life cycle: adult tapeworms are found in crustacean first intermediate hosts and the later larval forms develop in the fish second intermediate hosts.

Around the middle of the last century, a tremendous argument raged as to whether cystic worms were dropsically degenerated tapeworms that had strayed into unsuitable hosts, or whether there was a cycle of transmission involving cystic worms and adult tapeworms which needed to occur between defined but different species of intermediate hosts. The latter postulate won the day and it became clear that there was natural immunity of many host species to one or both stages in the life history of cestode worms. Thus, dogs are host to the adult but not the cystic stages of *E. granulosus*, while hydatid cysts are found in sheep, cattle and humans. Similarly, *T. solium* and *T. saginata* adult worms are found only in humans whereas the cystic forms of the species are found only in pigs and cattle, respectively.

A. Adult Worm (Tapeworm) Infections

Apart from our knowledge of which definitive hosts will harbour the adult tapeworm form of various cestodes, almost nothing is known of the mechanisms controlling natural resistance in non-permissive hosts. Further, there are few data available concerning any factors which might influence the susceptibility of different individuals within a given species to a particular tapeworm when measured in terms of the numbers of worms that develop, whether growth is stunted, and whether fecundity is impaired. One exception is a study which has shown that resistance to *E. granulosus* adult worms is induced in some dogs inoculated with *Bordetella pertussis* and Freund's adjuvant; it was suggested that potent, non-immunological, perhaps genetically determined, resistance mechanisms operated in these animals (Herd, 1977).

B. Larval Cestode Infections

1. Innate immunity

Many variables which influence immunity to the larval stages (metacestodes) of species of *Taenia* and *Echinococcus* have been identified. These include a number of host factors and differences in infectivity among strains of parasites.

Different inbred strains of rodents vary in their susceptibility to infection with *T. taeniaeformis* (Dow and Jarrett, 1960; Mitchell *et al.*,

1977; Williams *et al.*, 1981) and *E. multilocularis* (Lubinsky, 1964). Both very young (less than three weeks) and older laboratory mice and rats have a marked increase in resistance to the cysticerci of *T. taeniaeformis* (Greenfield, 1942; Dow and Jarrett, 1960). Similarly, older rabbits are more resistant to *T. pisiformis* (Potseleuva, 1958), but conflicting findings have been reported with *T. saginata* in cattle (Rickard and Williams, 1982). Age resistance of mice to *E. granulosus* (Schwabe *et al.*, 1959) and *E. multilocularis* (Kamiya, 1972) has been recorded but there is little evidence to support the existence of such a phenomenon in humans infected with *E. granulosus* (Beard, 1978). Although there are divergent reports on the effects of sex on resistance to infection, the consensus is that males are more susceptible than females to *T. taeniaeformis*, but there appear to be interactions between sex, age and strain of host (Campbell and Melcher, 1940; Mitchell *et al.*, 1977; Rickard and Williams, 1982). Similarly, male cattle are more susceptible to *T. saginata* (Froyd, 1960) and male mice are more susceptible to *T. multiceps* (Esch, 1967) and to *T. crassiceps* (Freeman, 1962). Administration of corticosteroids increases the susceptibility of mice to *T. taeniaeformis* (Olivier, 1962).

There is also a clear interaction between egg dose of *T. taeniaeformis* and success of infection, suggesting that a more vigorous host response induced by a large quantity of worm products may militate against survival of larvae (Mitchell *et al.*, 1980).

A number of mechanisms have been proposed by which these effects may be mediated. The insusceptibility of young rats to *T. taeniaeformis* could be due to a deficiency in proteolytic enzymes necessary for hatching of eggs. The composition of host bile has a marked influence on the survival of *E. granulosus* protoscolices (Smyth and Haselwood, 1963). It has been shown that a high proportion of cestode oncospheres fail to penetrate the gut of innately resistant animals (Heath, 1971; Turner and McKeever, 1976). Furthermore, there is a greatly accelerated, non-specific cellular response in the livers of older Swiss albino mice infected with *T. taeniaeformis* which could kill those larvae that do penetrate (Turner and McKeever, 1976). It has also been suggested that genetic control of susceptibility may be partly mediated via the efficiency of complement activation (Mitchell *et al.*, 1977).

2. Non-specific acquired resistance

Injection of *Mycobacterium bovis* BCG stimulates considerable protection of cotton rats, gerbils and mice against growth of *E. multilocularis* (Rau and Tanner, 1975), *E. granulosus* (Thompson, 1976) and *T. taeniaeformis* (Thompson *et al.*, 1982) larvae, respectively. This non-specific acquired resistance is presumably effected by enhanced reactivity of macrophages.

VI. ARTHROPOD ECTOPARASITIC INFESTATIONS

A number of arthropods parasitise the human skin, and many more species infest other vertebrate animals. Such arthropods include ticks, mites, lice and fleas. In addition to direct irritation (often immunologically mediated), these parasites may transmit important pathogens such as *Babesia*, *Borrelia*, *Rickettsia* and *Yersinia* as well as various viruses. Each ectoparasite has its preferred host or hosts, presumably as a result of natural resistance. With some parasites, the situation is complex. For example, some ticks undergo all stages of development on the same host ('one-host' ticks) while others suck blood and fluid from one host, then drop onto the ground and infect another host ('two-host' and 'three-host' ticks), on which they moult in order to complete their development. It is possible that this is a reflection of natural immunity, but it is perhaps more likely due to a specific, acquired immune response.

Information on natural immunity in ectoparasitic infestations is so sparse that one commentator, in briefly reviewing 'innate resistance' in tick infestations, was moved to ask concerning this term: 'What does it mean?' (Willadsen, 1980). He concluded that the use of the term to describe host specificity added little and emphasised that previous exposure to the same or related organisms needed to be rigorously excluded before any claims could be made that variation of intensity of infestation within a particular host species was due to natural resistance. Such studies are in their infancy but a beginning is being made. For example, Brahman cattle (*Bos indicus*) are much more resistant to the cattle tick, *Boophilus microplus*, than are European cattle (*B. taurus*). These resistance levels are affected by stress such as lactation and malnutrition and fluctuate with the season, cattle becoming less resistant in autumn and more resistant in spring. Furthermore, resistance can be selected for by crossing Brahman with European cattle (Wharton and Norris, 1980). Although some of this resistance is thought be innate in origin (Riek, 1956, 1962), it is now believed that most resistance is generated by a more efficient specific acquired immune response in Brahman cattle (Wagland, 1980). Acquired immunity and immuno-modulation of host responses in tick and other ectoparasitic infestations have been reviewed recently (Wikel, 1984).

Another phenomenon which might be considered a manifestation of natural resistance is the long-recognised rapid departure of lice from the bodies of humans with fever (whether coincidental or as a result of a louse-borne infection such as typhus or relapsing fever). Likewise, the sex and physiological status of the host may influence the intensity of infection with the mite, *Demodex folliculorum*. This mite lives in the hair follicles, feeding on sebum and depositing eggs in the sebaceous glands. The number of parasites present is dependent upon the number of sebum-rich hair follicles available for occupation; this is influenced by hormones, for greater numbers are found in males and at puberty (Spickett, 1961).

VII. MECHANISMS OF RESISTANCE

The mechanisms involved in natural resistance to metazoan parasites clearly vary with the location or route of migration of the organism. Ectoparasites may drop off the skin and endoparasites may be expelled from the gut. Worms in the tissues either undergo arrested development or are killed. Natural resistance has been ascribed to varying combinations of anatomical barriers, baseline phagocytosis by mononuclear cells, digestion by neutrophils, and the effects of various expressor mechanisms, such as complement, all being determined by the genetic constitution of the host and modulated by its nutritional and hormonal status (Frenkel and Caldwell, 1975; Albright and Albright, 1984). The final modus operandi of worm destruction or expulsion may in large part be common to both natural non-specific resistance and resistance generated by specific acquired immunological means.

Experiments with inbred mice have shown that in many cases, major control of resistance seems to reside in relatively few genes. Moreover, although there are exceptions, genes associated with the 'immune response' region or any other region of the major histocompatibility complex do not appear to be primarily responsible for regulating susceptibility to parasites (Albright and Albright, 1984; Wakelin, 1985).

Attempts have been made to differentiate the influence of natural resistance from that of immunologically mediated resistance by studying host–parasite relationships in immunodeficient animals. Albright and Albright (1984) have reviewed studies of protozoal and helminth infections in hypothymic mice and mice with B lymphocyte defects. Although these authors have proposed a number of complicated hypotheses, it seems premature to attempt to define the interrelationships between natural resistance and humoral and cell-mediated immunity in worm infections.

A. Resistance in the Skin

Larvae attempting to infect via the skin face the mechanical barrier of the acellular stratum corneum and must find a way of penetrating the integument, whether directly through the stratum corneum or through the openings of the hair follicles or sweat glands. Consequently, the thickness of the epidermis, the presence or absence of hairs, and the density of the sweat glands might all influence the innate susceptibility or resistance of a host to a particular parasite. For example, penetration through the skin of nude mice (which are hairless and have disorientated follicles and clogging of the follicular orifices with sebum) by *Strongyloides ratti* is reduced by about 90 per cent when compared with normal litter-mates (Dawkins *et al.*, 1982). Similarly, fewer *Schistosoma mansoni* cercariae penetrate the thick, tough skin of beige mice (Stirewalt *et al.*, 1965).

If larvae do penetrate the skin, they may be destroyed by non-specific inflammatory responses. For example, Gysin and Le Coroller (1976) heated tails of mice before exposure to *S. mansoni* cercariae and found that infections failed to develop. Similarly, inflammation in the skin induced by the subcutaneous injection of talc and calcium phosphate gave some protection against *Schistosoma* infection (Fauve and Dodin, 1976). The cellular processes responsible for destruction of worms in such situations are described in the next section.

B. Resistance During Migration Through the Tissues

The ability of worms to migrate through the body depends upon anatomical factors such as the size of the parasite and the nature of the tissue or vessel through which it is migrating. Lysis of parasites by complement in the absence of antibodies has been demonstrated for some hosts against protozoa, but has not yet been shown against metazoa, although antibody-independent binding of guinea pig C3 complement to *Ascaris suum* infective larvae has been observed (Leventhal and Soulsby, 1977).

Smaller forms of worms such as infective larvae may be attacked by phagocytic cells. The stimuli to such attack may be both immunological and non-immunological. Worms differ from most other pathogenic organisms in that they are much larger than the defending phagocytes. Consequently, some potential effector cells such as cytotoxic lymphocytes are relatively inactive in mediating damage compared with eosinophils, neutrophils and cells of the macrophage series (Ellner and Mahmoud, 1982; Butterworth, 1984).

Damage of helminths by eosinophils depends upon binding of the cells to the worm by ligands such as IgG, IgE and the third component of complement (C3). Once bound to the target worm, eosinophils release their granular contents, which include various enzymes as well as other toxic, non-enzymatic substances such as major basic protein and eosinophil cationic protein, onto the surface of the worm. This results in disruption of the tegument or cuticle and may culminate in destruction of the parasite. These effects may be mediated by both oxidative and non-oxidative mechanisms.

Neutrophils may also have some activity against helminths, but the role of antibody and complement in such killing is controversial. It has been suggested that neutrophils may kill some worms only when the parasite is not functionally intact or when the cells are able to exert massive toxicity very early during the interaction (Butterworth, 1984). In contrast to eosinophils, neutrophils do not degranulate extensively on contact with antibody- or complement-coated helminths, but they do mount a strong respiratory burst which leads to release of toxic superoxide anions, hydrogen peroxide, and other oxygen radicals.

Macrophages bear receptors for IgG, IgE and C3 which may serve as ligands but, unlike eosinophils and neutrophils, macrophages may bind to worms in the absence of ligands. More important is a change in the functional properties of macrophages induced by various activating agents such as BCG, cord factor, *Listeria monocytogenes*, *Corynebacterium parvum* and *Toxoplasma gondii* via T cell mediators, polymeric IgE, or other uncertain mechanisms. Once activated, macrophages attach to the worms and eventually breach the cuticle, possibly by oxidative and non-oxidative mechanisms, then phagocytose disintegrating worm material.

Since helminths show marked differences in their surface structure, depending upon both the species of worm and the stage of the parasite, the relative efficacies of the various cellular effector mechanisms vary according to the species and stage of the worm.

C. Resistance in the Gastrointestinal Tract

Worms in the intestines are influenced by local, non-immunological factors as well as by immunologically mediated events. Larvae entering the alimentary tract must run the gauntlet of acidity, enzymes, bile and changes in oxygen and carbon dioxide tension. The intestinal milieu must be propitious for the parasite to remain in its niche and to enable appropriate physiological signals to stimulate maturation of larvae. These requirements are ill-understood, and their absence would lead to natural resistance.

The mechanisms of immunologically mediated resistance against worms in the vicinity of the gastrointestinal mucosa have been difficult to study, but are now beginning to be defined. The mechanisms of natural resistance are less well comprehended, but they may include some of the final effector processes of immunologically generated resistance. The consensus of opinion is that worms are usually expelled from the gut as a consequence of inflammatory reactions, incorporating interactions of many cell types and various molecular mediators, which create an environment unsuitable for the parasite (Befus and Bienenstock, 1982). In addition to these protective events, there are also diverse host responses that are designed to return the intestinal milieu to normal as quickly as possible after the parasites have been eliminated or reduced in number. The differentiation of these two functions with respect to certain cell types is sometimes difficult to achieve.

When inflammatory reactions are generated by immunological means in specific acquired resistance, it is believed that parasite antigens from the lumen of the gut are transported by the lymphoepithelium of the gut-associated lymphoid tissue to lymphocytes and macrophages lying below the epithelial surface. In the case of parasites which invade the mucosa, antigens have direct access to the immune system. Macrophages process antigen and interact with various lymphocytes which migrate to the lymph nodes where they proliferate and differentiate into cells such as IgA- and IgE-secreting plasma cells and specific T cell populations. These latter cells orchestrate tissue eosinophilia, hyperplasia of mucosal mast cells and goblet cells, and acute-phase reactions.

Some intraepithelial lymphocytes appear to have natural killer activity. Mucosal mast cells release a variety of vasoactive amines which may affect worm expulsion either directly or indirectly. As discussed earlier, eosinophils may be concerned with destruction of worms. Macrophages undoubtedly have an important role in accessory cell function, immunomodulation, cytokine release, cytotoxicity, and phago-cytosis. Goblet cell hyperplasia occurs in some intestinal parasitic infections (Ackert *et al.*, 1939). These cells secrete mucus and it has been shown that duodenal mucus from resistant hosts differs qualitatively from that obtained from susceptible hosts; this may be one mechanism of age-related natural resistance (Frick and Ackert, 1948). More recent studies have confirmed that goblet cell hyperplasia and mucus secretion serve a protective function in certain parasitic infections. Copious amounts of mucus may be secreted in response to many factors including bacterial toxins, immune complexes, and vasoactive amines, trapping worms and preventing them from becoming established in the intestine (Miller and Huntley, 1982). Paneth cells (which may share a common lineage with goblet cells) also increase in number in some parasitic infections (Roberts-Thomson *et al.*, 1976); these cells release lysozyme and may be phagocytic. The role of complement in mucosal resistance is controversial and the significance of increases in certain acute-phase reactants such as alpha-1-antitrypsin and C-reactive protein in the gut are unclear.

Some of these responses may be utilised in non-specific natural resistance. A number of studies of concurrent intestinal infections have revealed that when one species of parasite is being expelled from the gut, an 'innocent bystander' species is often expelled concurrently, or at least is inhibited in some way (Behnke *et al.*, 1977; Bruce and Wakelin, 1977; Dineen *et al.*, 1977; Kennedy, 1980). In none of these instances has antigenic cross-reactivity been identified. This suggests that non-specific inflammatory events generated by other means, and which include the activation of macrophages, marshalling of neutrophils, eosinophils, mast cells and goblet cells, the production of mucus and enzymes, and the release of prostaglandins affecting vascular permeability and intestinal motility, culminate in the non-specific expulsion of parasites from the gut. One caveat must be added, however. There are variations from one host–parasite system to another, for some worms are expelled efficiently with little apparent inflammatory reaction in the intestine, whereas in other helminth infections expulsion is associated with pronounced inflammation.

VIII. CONCLUSION

There is no doubt that natural immunity makes a far greater contribution to freedom from infection with worms than does resistance generated by acquired immune responses. The latter reactions, however, have been studied far more extensively and rigorously, and our understanding of their mechanisms is correspondingly greater. The mechanisms of natural resistance are poorly understood, but if they could be discerned and harnessed to advantage, they would provide tremendous potential for controlling helminth infections. Unfortunately, such a desirable outcome seems far distant.

REFERENCES

Ackert, J. E., Edgar, S. A. and Frick, L. P. (1939). *Transactions of the American Microscopical Society* 58: 937–46.

Ahmann, C. F. and Bristol, L. M. (1933). *Southern Medical Journal* 26: 959–62.

Ahmed, S. S. (1967a). *Annals of Tropical Medicine and Parasitology* 61: 93–100.

Ahmed, S. S. (1967b). *Annals of Tropical Medicine and Parasitology* 61: 432–6.

Albright, J. F. and Albright, J. W. (1984). *Contemporary Topics in Immunobiology* 12: 1–52.

Altaif, K. I. and Dargie, J. D. (1978). *Parasitology* 77: 161–75.

Ash, L. R. (1971). *Journal of Parasitology* 57: 777–80.

Ash, L. R. and Schacher, J. F. (1971). *Journal of Parasitology* 57: 1043–51.

Beard, T. C. (1978). *Lancet* 2: 30–2.

Befus, D. and Bienenstock, J. (1982). *Progress in Allergy* 31: 76–177.

Behnke, J. M., Bland, P. W. and Wakelin, D. (1977). *Parasitology* 75: 79–88.

Brindley, P. J. and Dobson, C. (1983). *International Journal for Parasitology* 13: 503–7.

Bruce, R. G. and Wakelin, D. (1977). *Parasitology* 74: 163–73.

Butterworth, A. E. (1984). *Advances in Parasitology* 23: 143–235.

Campbell, D. H. and Melcher, L. R. (1940). *Journal of Infectious Diseases* 66: 184–8.

Cioli, D., Knopf, P. M. and Senft, A. W. (1977). *International Journal for Parasitology* 7: 293–7.

Civil, R. H. and Mahmoud, A. A. F. (1978). *Journal of Immunology* 120: 1070–2.

Civil, R. H., Warren, K. S., Mahmoud, A. A. F. (1978). *Journal of Infectious Diseases* 137: 550–1.

Clegg, J. A. and Smithers, S. R. (1968). *Parasitology* 58: 111–29.

Copeland, D. and Grove, D. I. (1979). *International Journal for Parasitology* 9: 205–11.

Cross, J. H., Partono, F., Hsu, M. K., Ash, L. R. and Oemijati, S. (1979). *American Journal of Tropical Medicine and Hygiene* 28: 56–66.

Davaine, C. J. (1862). *Comptes Rendus Hebdomadaires des Séances de l'Académie des Sciences*, series 3, 4: 261–5. Translated in B. H. Kean, K. E. Mott and A. J. Russell (eds), *Tropical Medicine and Parasitology: Classic Investigations*. Ithaca: Cornell University Press, 1978.

Dawkins, H. J. S., Grove, D. I., Dunsmore, J. D. and Mitchell, G. F. (1980). *International Journal for Parasitology* 10: 125–9.

Dawkins, H. J. S., Mitchell, G. F. and Grove, D. I. (1982). *Australian Journal of Experimental Biology and Medical Science* 60: 181–6.

Denham, D. A. (1974). *Journal of Parasitology* 60: 642.

Dineen, J. K., Gregg, P., Windon, R. D., Donald, A. D. and Kelly, J. D. (1977). *International Journal for Parasitology* 7: 211–15.

Dow, C. and Jarrett, W. F. (1960). *Experimental Parasitology* 10: 72–4.

Ellner, J. J. and Mahmoud, A. A. (1982). *Reviews of Infectious Diseases* 4: 698–714.

Esch, G. W. (1967). *Parasitology* 57: 175–9.

Fauve, R. M. and Dodin, A. (1976). *Comptes Rendus Hebdomadaires de l'Académie des Sciences* 282: 131–4.

Foster, A. O. and Cort, W. W. (1935). *American Journal of Hygiene* 21: 302–18.

Franco-Loayza, A. (1979). Master's Thesis, Case Western Reserve University.

Freeman, R. S. (1962). *Canadian Journal of Zoology* 40: 969–90.

Frenkel, J. K. and Caldwell, S. A. (1975). *Journal of Infectious Diseases* 131: 201–9.

Frick, L. P. and Ackert, J. E. (1948). *Journal of Parasitology* 34: 192–206.

Froyd, G. (1960). *Journal of Parasitology* 46: 491–6.

Galliard, H. (1967). *Helminthological Abstracts* 36: 247–60.

Ghandour, A. M. and Webbe, G. (1973). *International Journal for Parasitology* 3: 789–94.

Greenfield, S. H. (1942). *Journal of Parasitology* 28: 207–11.

Grove, D. I. (1980). *British Medical Journal* 280: 598–601.

Grove, D. I. (1982). In L. E. A. Symons, A. D. Donald and J. K. Dineen (eds), *Biology and Control of Endoparasites*. Sydney: Academic Press: 375–400.

Grove, D. I. and Civil, R. H. (1978). *Experimental Parasitology* 44: 181–9.

Grove, D. I. and Northern, C. (1982). *Transactions of the Royal Society of Tropical Medicine and Hygiene* 76: 833–8.

Grove, D. I., Heenan, P. J. and Northern, C. (1983). *International Journal for Parasitology* 13: 483–90.

Gysin, J. and Le Coroller, Y. (1976). *Journal of Parasitology* 62: 697.

Harper, J. S. III, Genta, R. M., Gam, A., London, W. T. and Neva, F. (1984). *American Journal of Tropical Medicine and Hygiene* 33: 431–43.

Hawking, F. (1962). *Annals of Tropical Medicine and Parasitology* 56: 168–72.

Heath, D. D. (1971). *International Journal for Parasitology* 1: 145–52.

Herd, R. P. (1977). *International Journal for Parasitology* 7: 135–8.

Hsu, H. F. and Hsu, S. Y. (1956). *American Journal of Tropical Medicine and Hygiene* 5: 521–8.

Hsu, S. Y. and Hsu, H. F. (1960). *American Journal of Tropical Medicine and Hygiene* 9: 195–8.

Kamiya, H. (1972). *Japanese Journal of Veterinary Research* 20: 69–76.

Kazura, J. W., Fanning, M. M., Blumer, J. T. and Mahmoud, A. A. (1981). *Journal of Clinical Investigation* 67: 93–102.

Kennedy, M. W. (1980). *Parasitology* 80: 61–72.

Kirby-Smith, J. L., Dove, W. E. and White, G. F. (1926). *Archives of Dermatology and Syphilology* 13: 137–73.

Kirby-Smith, J. L., Dove, W. E. and White, G. F. (1929). *American Journal of Tropical Medicine* 9: 179–93.

Knopf, P. M. and Soliman, M. (1980). *International Journal for Parasitology* 10: 197–204.

Leventhal, R. and Soulsby, E. J. (1977). *Experimental Parasitology* 41: 423–31.

Lewert, R. M. and Mandlowitz, S. (1963). *Annals of the New York Academy of Science* 113: 54–62.

Lichtenberg, F. von, Sadun, E. H. and Bruce, J. I. (1962). *American Journal of Tropical Medicine and Hygiene* 11: 347–56.

Lubinsky, G. (1964). *Canadian Journal of Zoology* 42: 1099–1103.

Mahmoud, A. A. (1982). In S. Cohen and K. S. Warren (eds), *Immunology of Parasitic Infections*, 2nd edn. Oxford: Blackwell Scientific Press: 99–115.

Mahmoud, A. A. F., Warren, K. S. and Strickland, G. T. (1976). *Nature* 263: 56–7.

Mahmoud, A. A., Peters, P. A., Civil, R. H. and Remington, J. S. (1979). *Journal of Immunology* 122: 1655–7.

Mauel, J. (1982). *Progress in Allergy* 31: 1–75.

Michel, J. F. (1974). *Advances in Parasitology* 12: 279–366.

Miller, H. R. and Huntley, J. F. (1982). *Advances in Experimental Medicine and Biology* 144: 243–5.

Miller, T. A. (1965). *Journal of Parasitology* 51: 701–4.

Miller, T. A. (1970). *Journal of Parasitology* 56 (supplement): 238.

Miller, T. A. (1979). *Advances in Parasitology* 17: 315–84.

Mitchell, G. F., Goding, J. W. and Rickard, M. D. (1977). *Australian Journal of Experimental Biology and Medical Science* 55: 165–86.

Mitchell, G. F., Rajasekariah, G. R. and Rickard, M. D. (1980). *Immunology* 39: 481–9.

Mühleisen, J. P. (1953). *Annals of Internal Medicine* 38: 595–600.

Nawalinski, T. A. and Schad, G. A. (1974). *American Journal of Tropical Medicine and Hygiene* 23: 894–8.

Olds, G. R., Chedid, L., Lederer, E. and Mahmoud, A. A. (1980a). *Journal of Infectious Diseases* 141: 473–8.

Olds, G. R., Ellner, J. J., Kearse, L. A., Kazura, J. W. and Mahmoud, A. A. (1980b). *Journal of Experimental Medicine* 151: 1557–62.

Olds, G. R., Ellner, J. J., El Kholy, A. and Mahmoud, A. A. (1980c). *Journal of Immunology* 127: 1538–42.

Olivier, L. (1962). *Journal of Parasitology* 48: 373–8.

Ottesen, E. A., Mendell, N. R. and MacQueen, J. M. (1981). *Acta Tropica* 38: 205–16.

Peck, C. A., Carpenter, M. D. and Mahmoud, A. A. (1983). *Journal of Clinical Investigation* 71: 66–72.

Pereira, F. E. Z., Bortolini, E. R., Carneiro, J. L. A., da Silva, C. R. M. and Neves, R. C. (1979). *Transactions of the Royal Society of Tropical Medicine and Hygiene* 73: 238.

Potseleuva, V. A. (1958). In *Contributions to Helminthology, Israel Program for Scientific Translations, Jerusalem*: 304–10.

Purnell, R. E. (1966). *Annals of Tropical Medicine and Parasitology* 60: 94–9.

Rau, M. E. and Tanner, C. E. (1975). *Nature* 256: 318–9.

Rickard, M. D. and Williams, J. F. (1982). *Advances in Parasitology* 21: 229–96.

Riek, R. F. (1956). *Australian Veterinary Journal* 32: 204–8.

Riek, R. G. (1962). *Australian Journal of Agricultural Research* 13: 532–50.

Roberts-Thomson, I. C., Grove, D. I., Stevens, D. P. and Warren, K. S. (1976). *Gut* 17: 953–8.

Salam, A. E., Ishaac, S. and Mahmoud, A. A. (1979). *Journal of Immunology* 123: 1829–31.

Schad, G. A. (1977). In G. W. Esch, (ed), *Regulation of Parasite Populations.* New York: Academic Press: 111–167.

Schad, G. A., Chowdhury, A. B., Dean, C. G., Kockar, V. K., Nawalinski, T. A., Thomas, J. and Tonascia, J. A. (1973). *Science* 180: 500–1.

Schwabe, C. W., Schinazi, L. A. and Kilejian, A. (1959). *American Journal of Tropical Medicine and Hygiene* 8: 29–36.

Sheldon, A. J. (1937). *American Journal of Hygiene* 25: 53–65.

Siddiqui, M. A. and Kershaw, W. E. (1976). *Annals of Tropical Medicine and Parasitology* 70: 313–22.

Smillie, W. G. and Augustine, D. L. (1925). *Journal of the American Medical Association* 85: 1958–63.

Smith, M. A., Clegg, J. A., Kusel, J. R. and Webbe, G. (1975). *Experientia* 31: 595–7.

Smithers, S. R. and Doenhoff, M. J. (1982). In S. Cohen and K. S. Warren (eds), *Immunology of Parasitic Infections*, 2nd edn. Oxford: Blackwell Scientific Publications: 527–607.

Smithers, S. R. and Terry, R. J. (1965). *Parasitology* 55: 711–17.

Smithers, S. R. and Terry, R. J. (1969). *Advances in Parasitology* 7: 41–93.

Smyth, J. D. and Haselwood, G. A. (1963). *Annals of the New York Academy of Sciences* 113: 234–60.

Spickett, S. G. (1961). *Parasitology* 51: 181–92.

Stirewalt, M. A. (1963). *Experimental Parasitology* 13: 18–44.

Stirewalt, M. A., Shepperson, J. R. and Linicome, D. R. (1965). *Parasitology* 55: 227–35.

Sucharit, S. and MacDonald, W. W. (1973). *Southeast Asian Journal of Tropical Medicine and Public Health* 4: 71–7.

Thompson, R. C. (1976). *Veterinary Record* 99: 273.

Thompson, R. C., Penhale, W. J., White, T. R. and Pass, D. A. (1982). *Parasite Immunology* 4: 93–9.

Turner, H. M. and McKeever, S. (1976). *International Journal for Parasitology* 6: 483–7.

Variyam, E. P. and Banwell, J. G. (1982). *Reviews of Infectious Diseases* 4: 830–5.

Wagland, B. M. (1980). *Proceedings of the 56th Annual Conference of the Australian Veterinary Association, 1979*: 55–60.

Wakelin, D. E. (1975). *Parasitology* 71: 377–84.

Wakelin, D. (1978). *Advances in Parasitology* 16: 219–308.

Wakelin, D. (1985). *Parasitology Today* 1: 17–23.

Warren, K. S. (1967). *Transactions of the Royal Society of Tropical Medicine and Hygiene* 61: 795–802.

Warren, K. S. and Peters, P. A. (1967). *American Journal of Tropical Medicine and Hygiene* 16: 718–22.

Wassom, D. L., David, C. S. and Gleich, G. J. (1979). *Immunogenetics* 9: 491–6.

Wharton, R. H. and Norris, K. R. (1980). *Veterinary Parasitology* 6: 135–64.

Whitlock, J. H. and Georgi, J. R. (1968). *Cornell Veterinarian* 58: 90–110.

Wikel, S. K. (1984). *Veterinary Parasitology* 14: 321–39.

Willadsen, P. (1980). *Advances in Parasitology* 18: 293–313.

Williams, J. F., Shearer, A. M. and Ravitch, M. M. (1981). *Journal of Parasitology* 67: 540–7.

25

Cancer

OSIAS STUTMAN

*Immunology Program, Memorial Sloan-Kettering Cancer Center
1275 York Avenue, New York, NY, 10021, USA*

I. INTRODUCTION

Natural immunity is a concept which usually implies the detection of responses (or activities) in normal individuals in the absence of a known or deliberate immunisation. Thus, 'natural' will be used here to denote a spontaneous response detected without known prior elicitation. The response may be of the immunology textbook type (such as antibodies) or may include less conventional types which have been termed para-immunological (Woodruff, 1980) and comprise mostly cytotoxic or cytostatic cell-mediated activities, with natural killer (NK) cells being among the better studied agents (Herberman, 1980, 1982). The definition can be expanded to include elicited responses with broad reactivities (the so-called non-specific responses) mediated by macrophages and polymorphs, which lack true immunological memory, as well as the

749

NATURAL IMMUNITY
ISBN 0 12 5145551

various in vitro activated killer (AK) cells, which are thus non-adaptive in the sense used by Greenberg and Greene, (1976). In some studies, natural resistance is equated with T-independent mechanisms (Greenberg *et al.*, 1984).

Based on the effectors (and some of the modulators) listed in Part I of this volume, it is apparent that only the conventional T cells (except as producers of some of the cytokines discussed in Chapter 8) have been left out from the effector listing. However, since B cells can display natural cytotoxicity for virus-infected or tumour targets (Welsh *et al.*, 1986; Bykowsky and Stutman, 1986), mast cells can kill NK- and NC-susceptible targets (Ghiara *et al.*, 1985) and even platelets can act as effective natural killers of schistosomes (Bout *et al.*, 1986; Joseph *et al.*, 1983), it may be argued that the armamentarium of natural immunity is still being catalogued.

Natural immunity may represent either the antigen-independent internal activity of the immune system itself needed for homeostatic control (Stutman, 1986), the spontaneous response to endogenous antigens (Dighiero *et al.*, 1986) or the responses to unknown antigens in the environment (or a combination of all three). Whatever the mechanism(s), natural immunity in all its manifestations represents the host's background activity on which clinical and experimental studies are superimposed. Most definitions of natural immunity also include some distinction between such innate functions and the adaptive specific responses which are the most recognisable qualities of the immune system (specificity and memory). However, my task is not to define natural immunity or the internal repertoire that it may be detecting, but rather to discuss its possible role in a particular disease process: cancer.

The expression 'original antigenic sin' (Francis, 1953; East *et al.*, 1980) has been used to denote a defined phenomenon (the production of antibodies to a specific antigen, elicited by boosting with a related antigen), but could be loosely applied to some of the phenomena related to natural immunity. For example, natural antibodies and NK cells may each represent a special type of primed response to unknown antigenic sins of the individual or the species, which may be elicited by inappropriate (but cross-reacting) determinants. It is clear that antigens in the diet and the intestinal flora can modulate overall levels of NK activity (Bartizal *et al.*, 1984). However, most of the cells mediating natural cell-mediated cytotoxicity (NCMC) follow different rules in vivo and in vitro than do the specific cytotoxic T cells (and to some extent also different rules from those for macrophages activated via T-dependent mechanisms), in spite of the fact that the ultimate killing mechanism of T and NK effectors could be very similar (Henkart, 1985; Podack, 1985). The determinants recognised by NCMC effectors on malignant or infected target cells are still undefined, but are probably not related to the traditional tumour-associated (transplantation) antigens of the rodent tumour models (Stutman, 1981, 1983a; Stutman and Lattime, 1985, 1986). However, one of the properties of NCMC effectors in general is that they do not follow the MHC restrictions of specific cytotoxic T cells in target recognition (summarised in Stutman and Lattime, 1986; see also Chapters 3, 4 and 5). On the other hand, natural antibodies are usually conventional responses to a variety of endogenous (Boiocchi and Colnaghi, 1983; Greenberg *et al.*, 1983) and autologous antigens (Dighiero *et al.*, 1986; see also Chapters 6 and 26). Based on the experience of this author, this essay will concentrate mostly on the interaction of NCMC (as an example of natural immunity) with cancer development and progression.

II. NATURAL IMMUNITY AND CANCER

'Teleology' is defined in *Webster's* as the study of evidences of design in nature. The title of this section was selected on purpose, to avoid the unfortunate teleological idea that natural immunity (or any immunity) acts 'against' (or 'for') the cancer as it is developing in the host. I have indicated more than once that there appears to be no evolutionary need for a defence mechanism against cancer as such, whether mediated by conventional or unconventional branches of the immune system (Stutman, 1975a, 1977, 1981, 1983a–c, 1985). Basically I will try to avoid the voluntaristic view so well expressed in the news, by titles such as 'Arming Cancer's Natural Enemies' (*Time,* December 16, 1985, p. 58). Although the levels of scepticism have slowly risen, the first paragraph of the 'News and Views' in *Nature* on 'Cancer and Immunity' written 15 years ago (Anonymous, 1971), is still paraphrased in various forms in present-day publications, especially those proposing NCMC as a critical regulator of tumour development and behaviour (no references will be given here). The text indicates that it is hard 'to find a cancer researcher who would these days deny that the state of an animal's immune defence system' critically affects its responses to carcinogens and cancer cells, or that the growth of the tumour correlates 'with at least a partial failure of the immune system' (Anonymous, 1971). However, such unanimity was certainly not absolute (for more on this see Stutman, 1975a). For example, at approximately that time the immunostimulation theory of tumour development was presented (Prehn and Lappe, 1971) and this author published experiments showing that the genetic resistance to chemical carcinogenesis with 3-methylcholanthrene (MC) in certain mouse strains was not affected by profound and lasting im-munodepression (Stutman, 1972), although previously showing that the carcinogen at high dosages was immunosuppressive only in the suscep-tible mouse strain (Stutman, 1969). Subsequently it was shown that the resistance to MC was under polygenic control (Stutman, 1973) and could only be partially explained by aryl hydrocarbon hydroxylase inducibility controlled by the *Ah* locus (Thomas *et al.*, 1973; Kouri and Nebert, 1977). The complexities of the mechanisms of resistance to chemical carcino-genesis will be further discussed below. These examples were presented only to show that it was not too hard to find researchers with different views on the immune responses and cancer (summarised also in Stutman, 1975a).

Cancer development as a multi-step process. There is agreement that cancer development is a multi-step (Foulds, 1954; Klein and Klein, 1985), usually clonal (Nowell, 1976; Fialkow, 1976) process which includes several independent events leading to progression from a normal to a malignant state. This view is based on considerations of the time course and age-incidence of cancer in humans (Peto, 1977), the exposure to environmental hazards (Doll, 1977), fixation of chromoso-mal changes (Rowley, 1984), two-oncogene concepts (Land *et al.*, 1983), dependency on growth factors (Goustin *et al.*, 1986) and activation of genes suppressing tumour formation (Harris, 1971; Sager, 1986). Such a multi-step process implies inheritable phenotypic alterations which lead to the appearance of cells which show independence from most types of homeostatic control (Foulds, 1954; Nowell, 1986). However, a good deal of tumour immunology in its most general scope, whether natural or not, has remained fixed on the actual response to the established tumour, rather than being adapted to the growing knowledge regarding malignant transformation. For example, it may be speculated that: (1) an autoim-mune antibody response against growth-factor receptors could be benefi-cial for the host and interfere with tumour development (not tested yet); (2) anti-idiotypic antibody responses against such autoantibodies (or other natural responses) may provide mirror images of the antigenic sites and could activate responses (Koprowski *et al.*, 1984; Raychaudhuri *et al.*, 1986); (3) NCMC effectors may affect local tumour behaviour by interfering with cells producing growth factors, rather than by actually killing tumour cells (not tested yet); (4) single-step cell variants within the multi-step progression should be studied regarding how they are per-ceived by the host (Collins *et al.*, 1980; Wortzel *et al.*, 1986; see also Chapter 5); (5) interactions of tumour cells with NCMC effectors or natural antibodies may activate the expression of genes which suppress malignant change (not tested yet) and so on. I do not wish to labour the issue, but this introduction helps to put in perspective the extremely narrow window through which the immunological aspects of the tumour–host interaction are usually viewed. The 'established local tumour' bias is conceptually derived from the long-standing use of large numbers of antigenic tumour cells transplanted into a predetermined subcutaneous site as the preferential model for tumour immunology (see Hewitt, 1978, 1982, 1983; Hewitt *et al.*, 1976; Herberman, 1983a, b; Klein and Klein, 1977a, b; Stutman, 1975a, 1977, 1983a for various views on this problem), and is still attached to the idea that cells are 'good' and antibodies are 'bad' in the host–tumour balance (Hellstrom and Hellstrom, 1974).

Two final points. Firstly, it is unrealistic to assume that a single effector mechanism will be involved in the anti-tumour responses of the host (more about this below). And secondly, in spite of the comments above, almost the only experimental test available on the possible anti-tumour responses of the host is the study of tumour development (and behaviour) during spontaneous or induced deficiencies of the putative effector arm of the immune system under scrutiny (as proposed by Burnet, 1970b). Thus, the call to replace the 'all or none' discussions about the role of immune surveillance mechanisms in the protection against tumour development by a case-by-case evaluation of the biologic history of each system under consideration (Klein, 1980), is appropriate. However, theories that apply only to particulars should not be generalised.

A. The Tumour–host Interaction

Although a vast number of studies on the immunology of experimental and clinical tumours had been published since the beginning of the century (the review by Woglom, 1929, on 'Immunity to transplantable tumours' has a few hundred references), it was only in 1973 that 'Tumour Immunology' was enthroned as a section (separate from 'Cellular Immunology') in the *Journal of Immunology*. It is also worth noting that the word 'lymphocyte' did not appear in the index of the *Journal of Immunology* until 1948 (Talmadge, 1979).

Three levels of tumour-host interaction. Regardless of the host responses to the oncogenic agent (whether it be chemical or viral) which may affect its fate as a carcinogen (Stutman, 1975a, 1977; Kouri and Nebert, 1977) and some of the possibilities discussed above regarding the process of malignant transformation and progression, at least three types of potential interactions may take place between the tumour and the natural and/or conventional immunological mechanisms of the host (Stutman, 1983b, c, 1985):

1. The possible early recognition of the malignant change in situ, and some form of reaction to it, which, it is hoped, will eliminate such abnormal cells (i.e. immunological surveillance proper, preventing tumour development as discussed by Burnet, 1970a, b; Thomas, 1959, 1982; and some selected cases considered by Klein, 1980).
2. The complex responses of the host to the developing tumour, once it has attained a certain critical mass in situ; with all the putative effector and regulatory circuits (Stutman, 1982a), involving different types of activities, some of which seem to benefit the host and some of which appear to be beneficial for the tumour (i.e. the perplexing domain of tumour immunology proper [Hellstrom and Hellstrom, 1974]; many times confused with immunological surveillance [Herberman, 1983a,b]) and;
3. The mechanisms which affect metastatic spread of the tumour, which also include interactions between different components of the host's defence mechanisms and possible selection of tumour cell variants (Fidler and Hart, 1982).
4. A fourth interaction, and perhaps the only important one from the clinical standpoint, could be the responses to the residual tumour after reductive therapies (Stutman, 1983a).

As I have said before (Stutman, 1983b, c), the appearance of 'tumour immunity' as in (2) above means that 'surveillance' as in (1) has failed. Similarly, the appearance of actual metastases as in (3), means that in spite of the ongoing responses as in (2), such responses were ineffective in preventing the progression of the tumour to its clinically dangerous stage (Stutman, 1983b).

Defence mechanisms are multifactorial. In previous reviews (Stutman 1981, 1983a, b, c, 1985; Stutman and Lattime, 1985, 1986) I have commented on the 'simplification fallacy' which is the assumption that a single effector mechanism would be operative as defence against parasites, bacteria or tumours. While this fact is consistently taken into account by scientists studying immune responses to parasites and other infectious agents, even when using experimental modes in which single variables are manipulated (see Taverne *et al.* [1982] on malaria and Hatcher and Kuhn [1982] on *Trypanosoma cruzi* as instructive examples), it is not usually taken into account in most studies of tumour immunology, especially in its surveillance aspect (see below, and any of the references which discuss the various mechanisms of immunological surveillance or tumour immunity; see also Stutman and Lattime, 1986).

The function of cellular immunity. Two general views have dominated the whole subject of tumour immunity, whether natural or acquired (including immunological surveillance). The first is the idea that the cellular branch of the immune system has evolved primarily as a defence mechanism against cancer, rather than as the instrument for the rejection of surgical artifacts such as organ transplants (Thomas, 1959, 1982; Burnet, 1970a, b; Good, 1972). The second is the reverse view which suggests that functions such as the capacity to reject allografts (a nuisance for organ replacement) are simply by-products of an efficient system of defence against bacterial, viral and parasitic invaders (Brent, 1958). This last view is the one we have supported (Stutman, 1975a, 1977, 1981, 1983a, 1985) to 'justify' the existence of the immune system and more specifically of cell-mediated immunity; we have proposed that the whole area of tumor immunity may be simply a by-product of an efficient defence system against infectious invaders. The same argument can be made about the functions of the various NCMC effector cells (see below). Suffice it to remember that the main causes of mortality in patients with primary or acquired immunological deficiencies are infections with a variety of opportunistic invaders, including otherwise poorly pathogenic organisms, rather than opportunistic malignancies (Stutman, 1975a, 1985).

B. Immunological Surveillance and Natural Immunity

Mechanisms. Several mechanisms of immune surveillance (and tumour immunity) have been proposed, in a progression which has followed our understanding of cell-mediated immunity and has usually been of the 'all or none' type (Klein, 1980): (1) the allograft rejection mechanism (Thomas, 1959; Burnet, 1970a, b); (2) thymus-dependent mechanisms and T cells (Burnet, 1970a, b); (3) macrophages (Alexander, 1976; Hibbs *et al.*, 1978; Chow *et al.*, 1979; Adams and Snyderman, 1979; Keller, 1983); and (4) NK and similar effector cells, encompassed under the NCMC category (Baldwin, 1977, who uses the unfortunate term 'normal killers'; Klein and Klein, 1977b; Herberman and Holden, 1978; Kiessling and Wigzell, 1979; Mitchison and Kinlen, 1980; Roder *et al.*, 1981; Bloom, 1982; Herberman, 1983c, d, Chapters 3, 4 and 5). See also Stutman (1975a, b, 1981, 1983a, 1984a, 1985) for comments on other putative effector mechanisms of immunological surveillance and on the possibilities of complex interactive mechanisms. The components under

(3) and (4) would fall under the category of non-adaptive (Greenberg and Greene, 1976) or natural cellular immunity. One variation of these arguments has been to consider NCMC as a first line of defence, which allows the T-dependent responses to develop later (e.g. Roder *et al.*, 1981).

Experimental testing. The single testable prediction of the surveillance theory (or of natural immunity 'against' tumours) is that spontaneous or induced immunodeficiencies of the putative defence mechanism(s) should increase the risk for tumour development and/or alter the behaviour of the developing tumours towards a more aggressive pattern (as in Burnet, 1970a, b). Almost all of the experimental tests of surveillance or of any other form of host's response to the tumour have used models of this type (although many use transplanted tumours into the immunocompromised host; more on this below). The usual conclusion is that the single deficiency is or is not responsible for the observed response (the 'all or none' discussion by Klein, 1980). In some selected cases, a reverse approach based on the restoration of the defective putative mechanisms has been attempted (see Stutman, 1983a for more on this). This last approach has been the conceptual basis for the ambiguous notion of biological response modifiers (Oldham, 1982, 1985). The ambiguity is derived from the fact that it is not very clear what response should be modified and how it should be modified. The purely empirical nature of some of these studies, especially those related to therapeutic procedures, may explain the puzzling situation in which protocols, such as intrapleural BCG in lung cancer patients, could give results ranging from clear benefit (McKneally *et al.*, 1981) to no detectable effect (Bakker *et al.*, 1981, 1986; Mountain and Gail, 1981; Law *et al.*, 1982; Ludwig Lung Cancer Study Group, 1984), or even enhancement of tumour growth (Bakker *et al.*, 1981, 1986). In summary, we are faced with the intrinsic problem of testing multifactorial defence mechanisms in single-variable models, and with the transfer of such information back to the complex clinical situations.

Escape mechanisms. There is agreement among the supporters of immunological surveillance and other antitumour host responses, that the actual development of a local tumour represents an escape from surveillance, due to some cunning of the tumour itself which bypasses the host's defensive responses, whatever such mechanism(s) may be (Klein 1975, 1980; Nelson *et al.*, 1981, North *et al.*, 1978). Words like 'subversion' were used to denote such behaviour of transplanted murine tumours (Plescia *et al.*, 1975; North *et al.*, 1978). For more on the peculiar terminology used in relation to cancer see Sontag (1978). The fact that most tumours are indeed clonal (Fialkow, 1976) would argue for 'subversion' of the hosts' defence mechanisms mediated by a single transformed cell, or would argue conversely that such mechanisms do not act as a true surveillance system (Stutman 1975a, 1977, 1981; Möller and Möller, 1979).

Function(s) of natural immunity. As commented above, it is most probable that true 'defence mechanisms' are not mediated by a single effector arm, but are multifactorial and interactive (Stutman, 1983a; Stutman and Lattime, 1985, 1986). It may be worth revisiting immunological surveillance, mainly in the few experimental cases where it seems to be operative, with this concept in mind, as we proposed some time ago for polyoma oncogenesis (Stutman, 1975b), especially considering that the murine polyoma model has been termed an example of 'complete watertight protection' of tumour development (Klein, 1980).

Consequently, if we would rephrase the definition of immunological surveillance as the multifactorial natural defence mechanism against bacterial–viral–parasitic invasion (rather than as against cancer), it becomes apparent that the prediction of increased risk of infection when any of the effector mechanisms is depressed or absent, would be fulfilled (Stutman 1983a, 1985). Natural and adaptive anti-infectious immunological surveillance would then be a generalised theory which applied to most infectious agents (including polyoma in mice and Epstein-Barr virus in humans) and to all branches of the immune system. I would strongly argue that this 'defence' function is a sufficient teleological justification for the existence of the immune system, as well as of cellular immunity and NCMC in mice and humans. From an evolutionary standpoint, it makes sense to have defence mechanisms that prevent direct transmission of infectious agents between mature individuals and their developing progeny. This view has certainly more heuristic value than to argue that immunological surveillance as a natural defence against cancer simply 'ought to exist' (Thomas, 1982). It is worth noting that tumour necrosis factor (TNF) is also quite active against malaria parasites (Taverne *et al.*, 1982), in addition to its known direct effects on tumours (Carswell *et al.*, 1975) or the mediation of the tumour-killing activity of NC cells (Ortaldo *et al.*, 1986). Alternative hypotheses for the appearance of a narrow spectrum of opportunistic tumours in patients with immunological deficiencies (Stutman, 1985), would also have more heuristic value than to ascribe such pathology simply to the lack of the putative surveillance mechanisms in those patients (see Stutman 1981, 1983c, 1985 for more on this). This is particularly so when the tumours are derived from the immune system itself, as is the case in most of the tumours occurring in the primary and acquired immunodeficiencies in humans (Stutman, 1975a, 1985), in feline leukaemia (Essex *et al.*, 1975) and in other models. The highly emotional charge that cancer brings to our present-day society, transforming it into one of the main metaphors for 'evil' (Sontag, 1978), is also an important component of what I termed the 'voluntarism' behind the enthusiastic acceptance of every shred of evidence supporting any kind of response which might indicate an active immunological defence of the host against cancer (Stutman 1975a, 1977, 1981, 1983a, 1985).

C. Comparison with Parasite–host Interactions

Comparisons between tumour immunity and immunity to infection (Nelson, 1974; Stutman, 1975a, 1981) have proved useful in defining the possibilities and limitations of conventional and non-conventional immune responses.

Six levels. If the comparison is expanded to include the 'six levels' of parasite–host interactions (Playfair, 1978), a potential picture of cancer development and host responses can be presented in which good examples of every category except level 2 can be identified in spontaneous or induced tumour systems. The Playfair (1978) levels, in free paraphrases, are:

1. No invasion = natural resistance (with oncogenic viruses, resistance may or may not include a immunologically dependent step; more on this below).
2. Colonisation with mutual benefit (symbiosis; see also Thomas [1975] for more on the paradox of successful symbiosis versus traditional non-self immunology). No clear example in tumour systems; remember that the intestinal flora seems to modulate NK levels in mice (Bartizal *et al.*, 1984).
3. Colonisation with no disease = commensalism. In the tumour systems this level may explain dormancy and long latency periods for detectable tumour development.
4. Invasion followed by disease and cure. This is the recognisable achievement of immunology which allows prevention by vaccination of infectious diseases, already observed by Thucydides during the plague in Athens around 430 BC — he indicated that those surviving the disease never caught it again, or if they did it was mild and never fatal (*Pelopennesian Wars* II, 52). In tumour models and clinical situations this level is usually obtained by surgical cure and rarely by immunological means. Vaccinations against infection with oncogenic viruses, such as the agent of Marek's disease in fowl, have been successful (Nazerian, 1980).
5. Invasion followed by disease without cure which, however, produces resistance to reinfection usually described as concomitant immunity.

In tumours this phenomenon was observed by Ehrlich in 1906; was defined as immunological by Bashford *et al.*, in 1908, who coined the term; and was rediscovered almost 60 years later (Mikulska *et al.*, 1966; Gershon *et al.*, 1967). It is not clear whether it may control tumour spread in vivo, although one study showed decreased spontaneous hepatoma development in mice after temporary growth of transplanted hepatomas (Becker, 1981); on the other hand, concomitant immunity has been observed even with non-antigenic tumours (Ruggiero *et al.*, 1985).

6. Invasion followed by disease with no resistance or cure, usually described as ineffective immunity; also includes a variety of escape mechanisms and subversion of defences by the parasite to avoid the protective host responses (Nelson, 1974; Playfair, 1978; Bloom, 1979; Keusch, 1982; to cite but a few). This seems to be the usual level in most experimental and clinical cancer studies.

Levels 5 and 6 have been those most studied in tumour models.

D. Conventional Versus Natural Tumour Immunity

One of the problems of specific tumour immunity, including immunological surveillance, is that it requires antigens for its triggering; and not all tumours have unique determinants that can be detected by immunological methods (Hewitt *et al.*, 1976; Klein and Klein, 1977a, b; Old, 1981). In addition, as I have discussed in previous reviews (Stutman, 1975a, 1977, 1981, 1983a,b), and drawing upon the similarities of the responses to highly antigenic infectious agents, it seems that the specific T cell immune component is incapable of detecting small numbers of such agents, only recognising the invaders once they attain a critical mass (Nelson, 1974), and may even indulge in 'immunological complaisance' (Gray and Cheers, 1967). From the standpoint of immunological surveillance proper, the conventional cellular immunity mediated by T cells has the additional inconvenience of requiring priming. Such a time-consuming step certainly does not fulfil the criteria for a surveillance mechanism; since by definition, such a mechanism should detect small numbers of abnormal cells as they develop, which means almost instantaneously. This delay is also a problem that applies to the activation of macrophages for cytotoxicity (Meltzer *et al.*, 1982; see also Stutman, 1981, 1983b for further discussion).

NCMC. On the other hand, NCMC, which in mice includes NK cells (Herberman and Holden, 1978; Kiessling and Wigzell, 1979; Roder *et al.*, 1981) and natural cytotoxic (NC) cells (Stutman, 1982b), appears to be ideally fit for mediating surveillance in situ in a true Burnetian sense, based on the following properties: (1) these cells do not need time-consuming priming for function; (2) they exist in relatively high frequencies in normal hosts; (3) they are present in circulation; (4) their cytotoxic capacity does not require the presence of conventional tumour-associated transplantation antigens, although the NK–NC effector cells seem to recognise particular surface structures in the target cells (Herberman and Holden, 1978; Kiessling and Wigzell, 1979; Roder *et al.*, 1981; Stutman, 1982b) and (5) they can handle small numbers of tumour cells (see below).

While there is good evidence that NK–NC cells may be involved in preventing the growth of small inocula of transplanted tumour cells and that NK cells may be active in clearing intravascular and lung metastases, their actual in vivo function in surveillance of tumour development is not well established (see below). However, the current interpretation of the normal incidence of spontaneous and induced tumours in nude mice (Stutman, 1974, 1978, 1979) is that nudes have normal or high levels of NK–NC cells (Herberman and Holden, 1978; Roder *et al.*, 1981). It is worth noting that the 'sneaking through' phenomenon by which small numbers of antigenic tumour cells can grow, while larger numbers are rejected (Old *et al.*, 1962), has also been seen with tumours which are highly susceptible to NK lysis in vitro (Bonmassar *et al.*, 1974); thus, point (5) above needs better definition.

Models. The reasons for our insistence on tumour development studies rather than the use of transplanted tumours as a test for surveillance (or natural immunity) have been voiced in previous reviews (Stutman 1975a, 1977, 1981, 1983a–c, 1985), and I would certainly stay clear of the argument regarding good or bad tumour models (Hewitt, 1978, 1982, 1983; Herberman, 1983a,b). Suffice it to indicate two problems: (1) site selection, since marked regional variations of tumour growth are well documented in mice (Auerbach and Auerbach, 1982); and (2) that tumour transplantation per se can affect the function under study, as is the case with the augmentation of NK activity in mice after tumour transplantation (Herberman *et al.*, 1977). The latter point is important because it is assumed that the transplanted tumours usually subvert or suppress the putative defence mechanisms under study (Kamo and Friedman, 1977; Nelson *et al.*, 1981). Thus, tests of antitumour responses using transplanted tumours, whether giving positive or negative results, will be sparsely discussed in this essay. I have made similar comment on suppressor cells appearing after tumour transplantation, especially of models in which the tumour had to reach a size of 10 per cent or more of the animal's body weight for the expected supression to be detectable (Stutman, 1982a).

Comments on NK and NC cells. Extensive activity has marked the NCMC field since the acceptance of the phenomenon as worthy of study and the coining of the NK terminology (Kiessling *et al.*, 1975). Once it was accepted, a vast amount of information was generated in a short time (i.e. two volumes on NCMC with a total of 2855 pages compiled during 1980–82: Herberman 1980, 1982). However, in spite of the amount of published material, important questions on NCMC remain unanswered, such as: effector cell lineage, recognition structures and overall function. On the other hand, progress has been made recently in the characterisation of the lytic event, in which the rapid killing by NK (and T) cells is predominantly mediated by cytolysin (Henkart, 1985)/perforin (Podack, 1985), while the slow killing by the NC effectors is mediated by tumour necrosis factor (Ortaldo *et al.*, 1986). The demonstration that NK activity could be augmented in vivo in mice (Herberman *et al.*, 1977) and that the interferons were the mediators of such augmentation in humans (Trinchieri and Santoli, 1978) and mice (Gidlund *et al.*, 1978), and the discovery of the role of other lymphokines such as IL-2 and IL-3 in NCMC regulation (Henney *et al.*, 1981; Lattime *et al.*, 1983a) were important events in the analysis of NCMC regulation and function.

A minimal NCMC terminology can be agreed upon in which two main categories of NCMC effectors are defined: (1) Natural killer (NK) cells are freshly obtained cells, with spontaneous cytotoxicity against a variety of target cells, which are lymphoid in appearance, are different from granulocytes, macrophages, monocytes and cytotoxic T cells and show no MHC-related restriction for killing. This group includes other subclasses of effectors, such as NK subsets, NC cells and NK cells killing virus-infected targets in addition to the classical NK cells (summarised in Stutman and Lattime, 1986); and (2) Activated killer (AK) cells are a more heterogeneous group which includes the agents of any type of non-MHC-restricted cell-mediated killing produced after culture in vitro, ranging from T cells to the popular LAK (lymphokine-activated killer) cells, and it may include in vitro activated NK cells (summarised in Stutman and Lattime, 1986). Neither NK nor AK effectors show immunological memory as observed after priming in conventional responses. Finally, the initial dichotomy of NK = lymphoid and NC = non-lymphoid tumour targets is no longer tenable, now that appropriate numbers of tumour targets have been tested (Lattime *et al.*, 1983b, Stutman and Lattime, 1986).

In our view, the main intrinsic problem in animal and human NCMC studies is that a certain activity — such as the capacity to kill some selected tumour targets in vitro — has been equated with the specific function of NCMC in vivo. Thus, cells which kill YAC-1 targets in mice and K-562 in humans are NK cells by definition. From this conceptual problem, two unfortunate conclusions have been drawn: (1) that the properties of the cells which kill YAC-1/K-562 are the prototypic features of NK effector cells; and (2) that NCMC effectors, especially of the NK type, must have some antitumour function in vivo, since they kill tumour cells in vitro. A third conclusion, arrived at to some extent as a reaction to the strictures of (1), was that the NCMC effectors that did not fulfill the characteristics of the classical NK cells represented either a special subset or a distinct but related effector cell (summarised by Stutman and Lattime, 1985, 1986). From these distinct but apparently NK-related effectors, the concept of heterogeneity of NCMC effectors has emerged (Stutman *et al.*, 1978, Burton, 1980, Lust *et al.*, 1981, Minato *et al.*, 1981, Hercend *et al.*, 1983, Ortaldo and Herberman, 1984), and this still remains an unresolved issue.

Two possible levels of heterogeneity can be defined: (1) the finding of several types of NCMC effectors capable of killing different targets in a non-MHC-restricted manner, suggesting a family of distinct but related effectors as we originally proposed (Stutman *et al.*, 1978); and (2) a spurious heterogeneity derived from the killing of NK-susceptible targets by a variety of other, unrelated, effector cells. Good examples of the latter case are: (1) the murine promonocyte-versus-NK situation, where both cell types can readily kill YAC-1 target cells, although it is evident that they represent distinct populations (Roder *et al.*, 1979), and (2) the evidence of both T and non-T human cloned cell lines with NK activity (Hercend *et al.*, 1983).

Thus, the central problem is that almost all of the properties of the NCMC system have been defined by utilising the in vitro killing of a selected tumour target cell line as the final read-out, and it is conceivable that such killing activity is not representative of the actual function of NCMC. It is possible that NCMC effectors are important in homeostasis and regulation of normal cells, especially of the haemopoietic system (Hansson and Keissling, 1983), and could be involved in the control of some conventional immune functions (Nabel *et al.*, 1982; Abruzzo and Rowley, 1983; Shah *et al.*, 1985), or could act as part of the early defence mechanisms against a variety of parasitic, viral, fungal or bacterial invaders (Biron and Welsh, 1982). In many of the early responses to infectious agents, the effector cells do not seem to be 'classical' NK cells, but are certainly different from conventional T or B cells or macrophages (Campbell, 1976; Bennett and Baker, 1977; Biron and Welsh, 1982). Thus, and paraphrasing our previous comments on cellular immunology, the antitumour activities of NCMC effectors may be simply the by-product of a system which deals primarily with normal dividing cells or with infected cells and parasites.

In summary, and returning to NCMC, it is possible that: (1) the capacity to kill certain tumour targets may merely reflect but a single in vitro activity of a system possessing other biological functions in vivo; (2)

that such in vitro activity of killing tumour targets may represent only one compartment of NCMC rather than defining the general character- istics of NCMC as a whole; and (3) in all probability none of these defence responses, whether directed against tumours or not, is actually mediated by a single protagonist (Stutman and Lattime, 1986).

E. Experimental Studies

In this section I will discuss five types of experimental studies, mostly in rodents, on possible natural defences affecting tumour development or behaviour. These are: (1) studies of immunosuppression of the putative defence mechanism(s) by the carcinogen proper, (2) studies of effects on tumour growth (these use transplanted tumours), (3) studies of effects on spontaneous or artificial metastases, (4) studies of genetic aspects of resistance–susceptibility to tumour development and (5) studies of effects on spontaneous or induced tumour development. In some cases I will discuss papers which do not fit the predictions of antitumour natural immunity or simply some recent data on these subjects which were not discussed in the most recent of our series of detailed papers on immunological surveillance (Stutman 1983a, completed 22 December 1982).

1. Immunosuppression by the Carcinogen

The concept states that the direct action of the carcinogen on the immune system of the host is a necessary but not sufficient factor for its carcinogenic action (Prehn, 1964, 1976). This is a persistent concept which, however, has little relevance to cancer development by most chemical carcinogens (Stutman, 1975a, 1977, 1983a), for three reasons. First, for most chemical carcinogens, the immunosuppressive effect can be dissociated from its oncogenic effect simply by adjusting dosages, regardless of the immune function studied (Stutman, 1972, 1973, 1979, 1984b,c). Second, it is highly improbable that the injection of a single massive dose of a carcinogen such as polycyclic aromatic hydrocarbons (or any other of the environmental carcinogens), usually several thou- sand-fold the LD50 for the rodent species, has any clinical counterpart (the effects of chronic low-dose carcinogen exposure on immune func- tions have not been studied). Third, most of the experiments showing suppressive effects have used such large doses or have shown effects only at the higher doses, regardless of the immune function studied (Dean *et al.*, 1983, 1986; Alfred and Wojdani, 1983; Alfred *et al.*, 1983; Wojdani and Alfred, 1983, 1984; Ward *et al.*, 1984; White and Holsapple, 1984; Lyte and Bick, 1985; Urso *et al.*, 1986).

The corollary of the first reason is that suppression of any branch of the immune system will be consistently found in most experimental models if a sufficiently high dose of carcinogen is administered, regardless of its participation in the multi-step process of tumour development and progression. Furthermore, the complex temporal interactions between environmental chemicals and other variables with immune or other functions make the studies on 'mechanisms versus effects' quite difficult (Sharma and Zeeman, 1980; Porter *et al.*, 1984). The fact that the expected results can always be obtained reduces the heuristic value of these models. The immunosuppressive effect of the carcinogen has been a long-standing conceptual component of the immunological surveillance theory and one of the proposed mechanisms of subversion of surveillance (Burnet, 1970a,b). The main, and almost single example of a situation where modification of the host immune responses by the carcinogen proper seems to play a role in the appearance and progression of tumours is the UV-light-induced cancers in mice (Kripke, 1981). In the polyoma model in its natural murine host, the other example of a natural and adaptive immune response mediating resistance to oncogenesis (Law, 1966; Allison, 1980), it is worth noting that no detectable immunodepression induced by the virus has been detected (Stutman, 1975a,b). A variety of oncogenic viruses (Dent, 1972), but not all of them (Stutman, 1975a), as well as various non-oncogenic viruses and other infections (Salaman, 1970) are immuno-depressive, especially at high infectivity dosages. However, in most cases it is not clear whether such immunodepressive effects participate in tumour development and progression (Stutman, 1975a). Causality versus concomitance is a long-standing problem in biology. For example, the deficient NK activity observed in patients with the X-linked lymphoproliferative syndrome was proclaimed as an example of high risk for lymphoma development due to the low NK activity (Sullivan *et al.*, 1980), thus fulfilling the criteria for NK as a surveillance mechanism in humans. However, a more detailed study of those patients showed that the NK deficiency was the consequence of the lymphoproliferation, rather than its permissive factor (Seeley *et al.*, 1982). It is unfortunate that the paper by Sullivan *et al.* (1980) was published in a widely read journal, while the refutation by Seeley *et al.* (1982) appeared in a specialised multi-author book.

Some of the studies with chemical carcinogens which diverge from the expected are worth citing: (1) While transplacental administration of benzo(a)pyrene to mice produces a depression of humoral and cellular immunity (Urso and Gengozian, 1980, 1982, 1984), transplacental administration of urethane has only marginal effects on antibody production and no effect on NK cells (Luebke *et al.*, 1986), in spite of the fact that both transplacental regimes produce increased number of tumours in the progeny; (2) The presence of natural antitumour antibodies (which kill tumour cells in the presence of complement) showed an inverse correlation with the development of primary lung adenomas after urethane administration (Witz *et al.*, 1984); (3) Dimethylnitrosamine (DMN), a potential environmental carcinogen, at various dosages, increased NK and macrophage antitumour activities and actually decreased the number of artificial lung metastases in mice (Duke *et al.*, 1985); on the other hand, DMN at the same dose schedules depressed a variety of T cell functions and decreased the resistance of the mice to *Listeria* infection (Holsapple *et al.*, 1985); (4) While high doses of 7,12-dimethylbenz(a)anthracene produced 95 per cent and 55 per cent reductions respectively of T- and NK-mediated killing of targets, with no clear effect on macrophage functions, such dosages had no effect on the capacity of the mice to eliminate intravenously injected tumour cells from their lungs (Dean *et al.*, 1986); (5) Diethylstilbestrol (DES) is a powerful immunodepressant (Ablin *et al.*, 1979; Kalland, 1980a; Luster *et al.*, 1980; Morahan *et al.*, 1984) with marked depressive effects on the NK compartment (Kalland, 1980b; Kalland and Forsberg, 1981) and a limited carcinogenic effect (Andervont *et al.*, 1960; Walker, 1983); in a parallel study, however, where high doses of cyclophosphamide markedly increased the number of artificial lung metastases, treatment with DES decreased the incidence and number of lung metastases in mice (Morahan *et al.*, 1984); (6) The pattern of resistance (CBA) and susceptibility (BALB/c) to DES-induced interstitial testicular tumours was retained in spite of profound NK deficiencies induced in both strains by the DES treatment (Stutman, 1983a and unpublished data); and finally (7) The depressive effect of urethane on NK activity is markedly strain-dependent and has no clear correlation with risk for tumour development (Gorelik and Herberman, 1981a, 1982; see also Stutman, 1983a for discussion of this issue).

2. Effects on Tumour Growth

The increased local growth of transplanted tumours in NK-deficient animals has been cited as suggestive of an in vivo role for NK cells (Herberman and Holden, 1978; Kiessling and Wigzell, 1979; Haller *et al.*, 1979; Roder *et al.*, 1981; Herberman, 1983c,d; Pollack, 1983; to cite but a few review papers; see also articles on pages 1105 and 1121 in Herberman [1980] and on pages 1323, 1331, 1339, 1347, 1353, 1359, 1369 in Herberman [1982]; for criticisms on conclusions reached with transplanted tumours see Stutman [1981, 1983a,b, 1985]). These studies include mostly experiments with homozygous beige mice and some other low-NK strains of mice with NK deficiency induced by various treatments (irradiation, cyclophosphamide, oestrogens, anti-asialo-Gm1 antibodies, etc.). Subcutaneous growth of transplanted syngeneic tumours in 24-month-old mice was less than that of tumours transplanted in three-month-old animals (Ershler *et al.*, 1984); this would have not been predicted by those who accept the age-dependent decline of NK activity in spleen as support of its antitumour activities (Herberman and Holden, 1978; Kiessling and Wigzell, 1979; Haller *et al.*, 1979; Roder *et al.*, 1981; Herberman, 1983c,d). It may be argued that the effect observed in the aged mice is due to participation of NC cells, which do not show any age-related decline in activity (Stutman *et al.*, 1978), although it is also possible to propose non-immunological hypotheses (Stutman, 1979). See below for further comments on the effect of age.

3. Effects on Metastases

The conventional murine NK cells, as well as other NK/NC-like cells, appear to play an important role in the control of blood-borne metastatic spread and organ-restricted local tumour growth, whether one uses artificially induced or spontaneous metastatic lung (see below) or liver models (Wiltrout *et al.*, 1984; Cohen *et al.*, 1985; Malter *et al.*, 1986). The consistent finding is a higher incidence of lung colonies (or metastases) or impairment in the lung clearance of radiolabelled tumour cells in animals with spontaneous or induced NK deficencies (Riccardi *et al.*, 1979, 1980; Gorelik *et al.*, 1979, 1982; Karre *et al.*, 1980; Hanna, 1980, 1983; Hanna and Fidler, 1981; Hanna and Burton, 1981; Talmadge *et al.*, 1980, 1981; Pollack and Hallenbeck, 1982). NK cells appear to be operative in the control of lung metastasis of lymphoid or non-lymphoid tumours (see above references), while metastasis to other sites, such as lymph nodes, do not seem to be affected by NK deficiencies such as those seen in beige mice (Talmadge *et al.*, 1980, 1981; Stutman and Cuttito, 1981). In the case of the lung studies, the role of local NK-like cells needs further study, especially since the lung NCMC compartment does not follow some of the same rules as NK cells in spleen (Puccetti *et al.*, 1980; Stein-Streilein *et al.*, 1983). No correlation between the NK activity of the host and subcutaneous growth of various human tumour or mouse tumour cells (including YAC-1) as well as lung, liver or spleen clearance of human or mouse tumour cells (including YAC-1 and B16-F10) was observed in a study using adult nude mice (with high NK activity), 2–3-week-old nude mice (with lower NK activity, as in Hanna and Fidler, 1981), nude–beige mice (with low NK activity) and B-cell-defective nude mice (with normal NK activity); the study questions strongly any role for NK cells in the in vivo handling of tumour cells (Fodstad *et al.*, 1984).

Another problem is that in almost all studies the status of NK activity is measured in the spleen, which may not reflect the total picture of NK activity in the host, especially in other compartments. For example, the age-associated decay of conventional NK activity in murine spleen (Herberman and Holden, 1978; Kiessling and Haller, 1978; Kiessling and Wigzell, 1979; Cudkowicz and Hochman, 1979) is not correlated with the persistence of normal-high level of NK activity in blood for most of the life-span of the animal (Lanza and Djeu, 1982; Stutman, 1983a) or with a lack of age-decay of NC activity (Stutman *et al.*, 1978). However, some studies have shown increased subcutaneous tumour growth in the older mice at 4–6 months of age, when they have low splenic NK activity with normal NK activity in blood and other tissues (Kiessling and Haller, 1978; Haller *et al.*, 1979; Roder *et al.*, 1981; Riccardi *et al.*, 1980; see also Stutman 1983a for more on this paradox). Even the lung clearance of injected tumour cells was impaired in the older (3–5-month-old) mice (Riccardi *et al.*, 1980), at a time in which NK activity in blood is perfectly normal (Lanza and Djeu, 1982; Stutman, 1983a). As we indicated in a previous review, it is difficult to understand why the clearance of intravenously injected tumour cells by the lung should correlate with spleen rather than with blood NK activity (Stutman, 1983a). Similarly, as discussed above, the higher dose of 7,12-dimethylbenz[a]anthracene which produced a decrease of NK activity in spleen had no detectable effect on artificial lung metastases measured as clearance or as tumour foci (Dean *et al.*, 1986) and the treatment with DES, which depresses splenic NK activity, actually augmented lung clearance of tumour cells (Morahan *et al.*, 1984). Furthermore, the clearance of labelled tumour cells from other sites, such as foot-pads (Gorelik and Herberman, 1981b), seems to be mediated and regulated by NCMC effectors different from conventional (splenic) NK cells, even in adoptive transfer experiments (Gorelik *et al.*, 1981). On the other hand, the antimetastatic effects of heparin (Gasic *et al.*, 1973) appear to have a component which is mediated by host NK cells (Gorelik *et al.*, 1984). These topics are mentioned only as examples of the difficulties in arriving at generalisations concerning the in vivo correlates of the in vitro NCMC activity.

A caveat. Intravascular death of labelled tumour cells is a complex phenomenon, and in many instances the injected cells die spontaneously in vivo, rather than being killed by some host-mediated mechanism (Bishop and Donald, 1979; Bishop *et al.*, 1982; Bishop and Whiting,

1983). These authors questioned the role of any host cell type, whether T or NK, and recently showed that most of the pulmonary cell death detected a few hours after intravenous injection of labelled tumour cells (as used in most of the studies above) is of the coagulative necrosis type (i.e. the spontaneous death which takes place in extreme non-physiological conditions) rather than of the apoptosis type which could be attributed to killing by other cells, such as NK cells (Bishop and Whiting, 1983; it is interesting to note that the complexities of lung clearance of tumour cells in relation to NK cells was already noted by Talmadge *et al.* [1980], in a paper usually quoted as strong support for the role of NK cells in the control of intravascular tumour cells; for more on apoptosis and cell death see Wyllie *et al.*, [1980]).

A comment on the effects of age. The number of lung colonies after intravenous injection of the B16-F10 melanoma (a commonly used tumour for lung metastasis studies, see Hanna and Fidler, 1980, 1981; Hanna, 1980; Fidler and Hart, 1982) in syngeneic C57BL/6 mice was markedly diminished in old (24-month-old) when compared with young (three-month-old) animals (Ershler *et al.*, 1984). This finding would have not been predicted either by the supporters of NK surveillance of metastases (see above and Herberman and Holden, 1978; Haller *et al.*, 1979; Roder *et al.*, 1981; Herberman, 1983d; which mostly include the age-dependent decline of NK activity in murine spleen as further support) or by those who include the association of neoplasia and age-dependent immunological deficiencies as support of the immunological surveillance hypothesis (Burnet, 1970a,b; Good, 1972). It is obvious that studies on the pulmonary NK compartment in aged mice are necessary (Ershler *et al.* [1984] include only tumour transplantation studies), especially considering that lung clearance of labelled tumour cells has been found to be diminished in older mice (3–5-month-old) of various strains (Riccardi *et al.*, 1980).

Tumour development by chemical carcinogens is depressed in mice older than one year, whether normal (Saxen, 1953; Franks and Carbonell, 1974) or nude (Stutman, 1979). Various non-immunological interpretations can be made (see Stutman, 1975a, 1977, 1979, 1981, 1983a) and will not be repeated here; suffice it to indicate that the trivial explanation regarding carcinogen metabolism does not apply, since the older mice have increased hydroxylase activities (Stutman, 1979). More on tumour development models below.

A second caveat. Many in vivo studies define the mechanism by the selective removal of the cells (or factors) of interest by some in vivo procedure. For example, the antitumour effects of intraperitoneal

Corynebacterium parvum could be abrogated by whole-body irradiation or repeated injections of silica (Lichtenstein *et al.*, 1984). These authors conclude that the experiment indicated a role for neutrophils in the *C. parvum*-mediated response (Lichtenstein *et al.*, 1984). It is clear that alternative interpretations regarding the cell type involved could also be considered (Cudkowicz and Hochman, 1979).

4. Resistance–susceptibility to Tumour Development

Regardless of the complexities of overall resistance–susceptibility to tumour development in rodents (see below), one has to keep in mind that practically every branch of the putative antitumour mechanisms (whether natural or not), and their regulatory influences (such as interferon production) shows strain variation and in some cases well-defined genetic control (see especially Chapter 9 of this book). The influences of these complex levels of genetic control on the in vivo models used for the study of natural antitumour responses are difficult to evaluate at present. Suffice to cite the example in which the differences between two laboratories in the capacity of gamma interferon to activate murine cytotoxic macrophages directly were actually due to the strain of mice used (Pace *et al.*, 1983).

Even with 'single-gene' models, other host components may influence the overall type of response measured. For example, the homozygous beige (*bg/bg*, on chromosome 13) mice on C57Bl/6 and other backgrounds have an NK deficiency which can be partially restored by interferon and interferon-inducers, while beige on other backgrounds, such as SJL, is totally refractory to augmentation by interferon or its inducers (summarised by Stutman and Lattime, 1986). As a matter of fact, low-NK mouse strains can be grouped into those which are augmentable by interferon and interferon-inducers (such as A/J and sublines, C57Bl/6 beige, etc.) versus those which are non-augmentable by interferon and interferon-inducers (such as SJL/J, PL/J, 129/J, I/StUmc or mice homozygous for the motheaten mutation (*me/me*) on chromosome 6; summarised in Stutman 1983a; see also Lattime *et al.*, 1982a,b, 1986). Thus, experiments with transplanted tumours in various low-NK strains may have different results depending on whether the NK deficiency is augmentable or not, especially since tumour transplantation can augment NK activity in augmentable low NK strains (Herberman *et al.*, 1977).

Some marked differences in mouse strain distribution of basal activity as well as possible genetic control have been described for NK and NC cells which, although having complex genetics, also show a strong influence of genes distal to the D-end of H2 (on chromosome 17) for both NK and NC activity (Petranyi *et al.*, 1976; Klein *et al.*, 1978b; Kiessling and Wigzell, 1979; Stutman *et al.*, 1978; Stutman and Cuttito, 1980, 1981, 1982; Clark and Harmon, 1980). So far, all the mouse strains and mutations with absent or low NK activity have a normal NC compartment (Stutman and Cuttito, 1980, 1981, 1982; Clark *et al.*, 1981; Lattime *et al.*, 1982a,b, 1986). Single mutations which affect NK activity, regardless of their intrinsic effect, include: beige (*bg*, chromosome 13), motheaten (*me*, 6), obese (*ob*, 6) but not diabetes (*db*, 4), steel (*Sl*, 10) and hairless (*hr*, 14); while yellow (*Ay* on chromosome 2, see below) had no effect on NK activity (Clark *et al.*, 1980, 1981). Mice with low NK activity may or may not include strains with deficiencies of macrophage tumoricidal capacity (Boraschi and Meltzer, 1979a,b; Ruco and Meltzer, 1978a,b). Although we have detected mouse strains with low NC activity for some selected targets (Stutman and Cuttito, 1980, 1982), we have not been able to define a true low NC strain, comparable with the low NK strains. A possible exception is (WB-*W/*+ × C57Bl/6-*Wv/*+)F$_1$ mice with the *W/Wv* (on chromosome 5) genotype. These mice consistently have 50 per cent of the splenic NC activity of the heterozygous *W/*+, *Wv/*+ and +/+ controls, which can, however, be normalised in vitro by short pulses with IL-2 (Lattime *et al.*, 1986). *W/Wv* mice have deficiencies of myeloid precursors (McCulloch *et al.*, 1964), mast cells (Kitamura *et al.*, 1978), and hair pigmentation, and are sterile; however, most studies show normal NK activity in spleen (Clark *et al.*, 1980, 1981; Seaman and Talal, 1981; Tanooka *et al.*, 1982) and intestinal lamina propria (Tagliabue *et al.*, 1984) as well as normal T and B functions (Mekori and Phillips, 1969; Tanooka *et al.*, 1982; Landreth *et al.*, 1984). *W/Wv* mice also seem to have a deficiency of NC precursors in marrow (Hackett *et al.*, 1986). The *W/Wv* mice will be discussed further in the next section.

In a review on the genetics of cancer, it was indicated that, based on studies of spontaneous and induced tumours in inbred mouse strains, as yet 'none of the ... tumours have shown clear-cut single factor inheritance' (Heston, 1944). This view was intact 30 years later (Heston, 1974) and is still intact today. As a matter of fact, the description by Wright (1934) of inheritance of a complex trait (polydactyly) as influenced by multiple genes and non-genetic factors, producing alternative expression due to a threshold above or below which the summation effect of these factors may fall, could certainly be appropriate for the multi-step process of cancer development discussed at the beginning of this essay. It could also explain the incomplete dominance in the studies of genetic influences in polyoma resistance in mice (Chang and Hildemann, 1964) or the complex effects augmenting incidence of various types of spontaneous and induced tumours by the viable yellow gene (Ay in chromosome 2; see Heston [1972] for review on Ay) which do not seem to include an immunological component (Stutman, 1978).

The multigenic influence on tumour incidence and behaviour in various mouse strains and their crosses has been seen for spontaneous subcutaneous tumours (Dunn *et al.*, 1956), spontaneous lung tumours (Heston, 1940), tumours, including subcutaneous tumours and tumours at other sites, after subcutaneous administration of methylcholanthrene (Burdette and Strong, 1943; Burdette, 1943, 1948; Strong, 1952; Lilly, 1966; Stutman, 1972, 1973) or dibenzanthracene (Andervont, 1940), tumours after percutaneous application of methylcholanthrene (Andervont and Edgcomb, 1956; Duran-Reynals and Cook, 1974; Duran-Reynals *et al.*, 1978; Mayer *et al.*, 1980; Goodenow and Lilly, 1984), oestrogen-induced testicular tumours (Andervont *et al.*, 1960; Stutman 1978, 1983a, 1984a), bladder tumours induced by nitrosamines (Diwan *et al.*, 1977a), plasmacytoma induced by mineral oils (Potter *et al.*, 1975), intestinal tumours induced by dimethylhydrazine (Evans *et al.*, 1974; Diwan *et al.*, 1977b), transplacental effects of nitrosourea (Diwan *et al.*, 1973), Rous sarcoma virus induced tumorigenesis (Whitmore and Houghton, 1975; Whitmore *et al.*, 1978), polyoma virus induced runting syndrome and tumorigenesis (Chang and Hildemann, 1964; Chang *et al.*, 1968) and lung tumour development induced by urethane (Malkinson and Beer, 1983); to cite but a few without including the complex genetics of resistance–susceptibility to murine leukaemia virus (see Lilly and Mayer [1980] or Rowe [1982] for reviews) or to the murine mammary tumour virus (Bentvelzen and Hilgers, 1980; Stutman, 1982c). The examples cited above were selected because in most instances they show that macrophage deficiences (such as in C3H/HeJ or A/J), as well as low NK activities (A/J, I, beige) or T deficiencies (nude mice) did not seem to be of importance in determining the genetic pattern of susceptibility–resistance to a given carcinogen. Only in the polyoma and Rous sarcoma models was there a suggestion of immune responses being part of the complex resistance patterns (Chang *et al.*, 1968; Whitmore *et al.*, 1978). On the other hand, leukaemia-prone wild mice did not show deficiencies of their NK compartment (Scott *et al.*, 1981) and our own studies on spontaneous and induced leukaemias in low NK strains showed no clear correlation with NK levels or type of NK deficiency (Stutman 1983a,b,c; 1984a,c).

Complex interactions between carcinogens and other modulator drugs show marked strain variation in their effects. For example, butylated hydroxytoluene can completely inhibit lung tumour induction by urethane in adult A/J mice, but acts as a strong co-carcinogen with 48 to 655 per cent increases in lung tumour number in other strains such as SWR/J, C57Bl/6J and 129/J (Malkinson and Thaete, 1986). Neither the mechanism nor the formal genetics of this phenomenon have been defined.

A final comment on Friend leukaemia. The resistance regulated by the *Fv-1* and *Fv-2* loci in mice (Lilly and Mayer, 1980) showed two patterns. Some strains became susceptible after effective immunodepression, while some strains remained resistant in spite of effective immunodepression (Stutman and Dupuy, 1972; Stutman, 1973; confirmed by Raikow *et al.*, 1985 using cyclophosphamide). However, the nature of such an immunological compartment seems to be related more to the complex effects of the *Rfv* genes (Chesebro and Wehrly, 1978, 1979; Lilly and Mayer, 1980) than to NK cells. Although Friend virus can induce some changes in NK activity after infection (increasing activity from day 1 to 10 after infection, followed by depression at days 14–21; Migliorati *et al.*, 1983), no differences in NK reactivity between susceptible (DBA/2) and resistant (C57Bl/6) mice were observed and, furthermore, Friend-resistant beige mice remained resistant (Hertenstein *et al.*, 1984). Conversely, injection of endotoxin, which makes C57Bl/6 mice susceptible to Friend virus, was followed by an increase in NK activity (Hertenstein *et al.*, 1984).

5. Studies on Tumour Development

In this section I will discuss some examples of the role of various murine deficiencies of natural immunity on tumour development and behaviour. I will not repeat here the comments made in previous sections regarding single-variable models and the study of multiple variable phenomena. Based on my comments in the Introduction, I will discuss the studies using nude mice or other types of T-cell-depleted animals (see Stutman 1974, 1975a,b, 1977, 1978, 1979, 1981, 1982c, 1983a,b, 1984a) only as they relate to possible functions of NCMC effectors.

It is worth noting that in neither of the two watertight examples of immunological control of tumour development in mice (UV carcinogenesis and polyoma virus oncogenesis; see Klein, 1980), is there any good evidence for natural immunities being critical. The main defence mechanism against UV-light tumours seems to be mediated by conventional T cells and the main carcinogen-induced defect seems related to antigen presentation and suppressor T cell generation (Kripke, 1981; Urban and Schreiber, 1983; Wortzel *et al.*, 1986). Similarly, in the polyoma model, the main defence during the susceptible periods in infant mice is mediated by maternal specific antibodies, while the resistance of the adults is dependent on conventional T cell responses (Law, 1966, 1972; Stutman, 1975b; Allison, 1980; Schatten *et al.*, 1984). It is only under special conditions of T cell deficiency, such as in nude mice, that natural non-adaptive mechanisms of resistance can be detected (Stutman, 1975b, 1984a). Furthermore, the non-T pathway of polyoma resistance seems to include a B cell component as well as a NCMC component, since it is partially abrogated by chronic treatment with anti-mu antibodies (Stutman, 1984a); anti-mu treatment does not affect either the NK or the NC compartment (Gidlund *et al.*, 1979; Brodt and Gordon, 1982; Stutman, 1984a,b). Similarly, the complex immune responses to the murine mammary tumour virus, which in some cases seem to be necessary for tumour development, are all mediated by conventional T and B responses, although such responses appear spontaneously in the virus-infected animals (Stutman, 1982c).

Macrophages. The susceptibility of tumour cells to lysis by activated macrophages in long-term cultures seems to be a universal property which cannot be modulated (resistant variant lines cannot produced) and is independent of growth rate, invasiveness, metastasis formation, resistance to lysis by other cells (NK, etc.) and conventional antigenicity (Fogler and Fidler, 1985). As we have discussed in the past (Stutman, 1981), with the exception of the time-consuming steps for activation (especially T-dependent activation), macrophages could be efficient mediators of a surveillance function. Absolute macrophage deficiencies cannot be found in mice, although strains with selected macrophage deficiencies, including antitumour cytotoxicity, have been described (Ruco and Meltzer, 1978a,b; Boraschi and Meltzer, 1979a,b). The macrophages from some of these strains do not produce tumour necrosis factor in response to endotoxin (Beutler *et al.*, 1986) and the cytotoxic activity is controlled by the same gene which regulates overall reactivity to endotoxin in mice (Ruco *et al.*, 1978). However, the deficiency is not absolute, since tumour cytotoxicity can be activated by other means (Ruco and Meltzer, 1978b) although there is variation among the various macrophage-defective strains in their capacity to produce cytotoxicity in response to some inducers such as gamma interferon (Boraschi *et al.*, 1984). For further comments on the endotoxin–LPS-unresponsive mice see Vogel and Rosenstreich (1981). As we indicated in a previous review (Stutman, 1981), and with the proviso that methical comparative studies have not been actually made, there is abundant literature on spontanous and induced tumour development and tumour behaviour in macrophage-deficient mice, showing no major differences from normal strains (nine references by several authors are cited in Stutman [1981], for C3H/HeJ and A/J; see also Stutman [1983a]; see Storer [1966] for P/J). C3H/HeJ and macrophage-normal C3H sublines showed the same degree of resistance to lung tumour development after urethane (Malkinson and Beer, 1983). This is certainly an area that needs systematic research before firm conclusions can be reached.

NC and mast cells. In the previous section I commented on the *W/Wv* mutants, which among their several deficiencies have severe depletion of tissue mast cells and lower levels of NC cells (Lattime *et al.*, 1986). One study has shown that subcutaneous injection of 0.5 or 0.05 mg/mouse of 3-methylcholanthrene in *W/Wv* and +/+ mice resulted in a significant increase in local tumour incidence in the *W/Wv* group, with no differences in tumour type or growth rate; injection of +/+ marrow to the *W/Wv* mice normalised tumour incidence (Tanooka *et al.*, 1982). The conclusion of the study was that mast cells are involved in tumour suppression in mice (Tanooka *et al.*, 1982), but it is tempting to speculate that NC cells may also be involved in this phenomenon. Mast cells have been shown to kill tumour targets in vitro (Farram and Nelson, 1980; Ghiara *et al.*, 1985). One study also showed that tumour takes of a chemically induced fibrosarcoma and the 3LL lung carcinoma, both of C57Bl/6 origin, as well as spontaneous metastases of the 3LL tumour, were increased in the *W/Wv* and *Wv*/+ animals, when compared to the +/+ hosts (Burtin *et al.*, 1985). Thus, the *W* gene seems to affect the mechanisms of F_1 hybrid resistance to transplanted parental tumours (Klein *et al.*, 1978a), although the mechanism needs clarification. NK cells have been proposed as effectors of F_1 hybrid resistance (Kiessling and Wigzell, 1979; Cudkowicz and Hochman, 1979; Roder *et al.*, 1981), although we have previously indicated that the *W* gene has no clear effects on NK activity. Tumour growth and metastases in the study by Burtin *et al.* (1985) showed an inverse correlation with the content of tissue histamine.

NK cells. Several studies on tumour development have been performed with either the NK-deficient beige mice or mice in which NK activity was depressed by other procedures (such as treatments with anti-NK antibodies, etc.; such studies have been reviewed in Stutman [1983a] and will not be repeated here). Due to the high expectations generated by the discovery that beige mutation affected levels of NK activity (Roder and Duwe, 1979) and the prediction that the beige mice would clarify the in vivo role of NK cells (Mitchison and Kinlen, 1980; Roder *et al.*, 1981), the observations that beige mice did not show an increased risk for tumour development after exposure to different carcinogens (see below) were interpreted in a rather morose way by stating that the beige mice were not such a good model, since they had some NK activity left. The studies with transplanted tumours in beige-nude mice (Fodstad *et al.*, 1984) discussed in Section II.E of this essay also argued strongly against an in vivo role for NK cells.

Beige mice. A brief summary of tumour development studies in beige mice shows mostly negative results: (1) similar incidence of tumours in beige and control C57Bl/6 mice after intragastric administration of 9, 10-dimethyl-s,2-benzanthracene (DMBA) (Argov *et al.*, 1981; Karre *et al.*, 1982); (2) similar incidence of local tumours in eight beige and eight control mice after subcutaneous injection of 100 μg of 3-methyl-cholanthrene (Salomon *et al.*, 1980); (3) lower susceptibility to local tumour induction by low doses of Moloney sarcoma virus (M-MSV) in C57Bl/6 beige mice than in control animals (Truesdale *et al.*, 1982), a situation reminiscent of that observed in nude mice (Stutman, 1975c); however, while the tumours which actually appeared in the nudes did not regress, no differences in regression time or tumour size were observed in the beige study; a second study did not show differences in tumour development or regression patterns in beige and controls (Karre *et al.*, 1982); (4) similar resistance to Friend leukaemia virus in normal and beige C57Bl/6 mice (Hertenstein *et al.*, 1984); (5) no differences in resistance to urethane-induced lung tumours in normal and beige C57Bl/6 mice (Gorelik and Herberman, 1982; Malkinson and Beer, 1983); (6) no differences in leukaemia development in suckling beige and controls, or in the age-dependent resistance in adult beige and controls after Moloney leukaemia virus injection (Karre *et al.*, 1982); (7) no difference between C57Bl/6 beige and controls in tumour development after subcutaneous injection of DMBA or after four weekly doses of 160 rads of gamma irradiation and a marginal increase in tumours after subcutaneous injection of benzo(a)pyrene (Haliotis *et al.*, 1982, 1985); (8) no clear difference in spontaneous tumour development in C57Bl/6 beige and controls (Haliotis *et al.*, 1982, 1985) and (9) no difference in tumour incidence or tumour type after transplacental carcinogenesis with ethylnitrosourea in C57Bl/6 beige and controls (Stutman, 1984c).

Low-NK strains and other models. Before discussing some of our own work, I will comment on four studies which do not support a role of NK activities in affecting tumour development: (1) no correlation between NK activity in spleen and risk for leukaemia development was observed in leukaemia-prone wild mice (Scott *et al.*, 1981); (2) in a longitudinal study of spontaneous tumour development in C57Bl/6 mice chronically treated with crude mouse alpha interferon (weekly injections from five months of age until death), which actually decreased NK activity in the treated animals, no major differences in lymphoma development were observed between groups, except for a slight increase in animals receiving mock-interferon (Bruley-Rosset and Rappaport, 1983); (3) no clear effects on NK activity in spleen were observed by lifelong dietary restriction which prolongs life and reduces the incidence of spontaneous tumours in mice (Weindruch *et al.*, 1983) and (4) no correlation between NK levels and tumour incidence or type was observed after intragastric administration of DMBA to four H-2 congenic strains on the C57Bl/10 background (Gronberg *et al.*, 1983).

Several examples from our own studies also do not support the view that NK cells are operative in the control of tumour development (Stutman, 1983a–c, 1984a–c). These examples include: (1) no effect of NK deficiencies on genetic susceptibility or resistance to diethylstilbestrol (DES)-induced interstitial testicular tumours in mice, in spite of profound and lasting depression of NK activity (Stutman, 1978, 1983c); (2) high incidence of B-cell lymphomas in anti-mu-treated nude mice, in the presence of normal or high levels of NK activity (Stutman, 1983c; 1984a,b); (3) lack of correlation between resting levels of NK activity and risk for spontaneous tumours of different types (Stutman, 1983a); (4) lack of correlation between spontaneous development of leukaemia in seven low-NK strains (including some which are non-augmentable by interferon or interferon-inducers; Stutman, 1983a,b; 1984d); (5) lack of correlation between NK activity and susceptibility or resistance to T cell leukaemia development after percutaneous administration of 3-methylcholanthrene (following the model of Duran-Reynals *et al.* [1978]) to mice which included seven low-NK strains (Stutman 1983a, 1984d); (6) lack of correlation between tumour development (lymphoma, lung adenomas and hepatomas) in high-NK (CBA/H) and low-NK (A/J) mouse strains after exposure to 1-ethyl-1-nitrosourea (ENU) at birth (low NK activity in both strains) or at 45 days of age (normal NK activity for each strain type); especially pertinent since ENU treatment has no depressive effects on NK activity (Stutman, 1983c; 1984c) and (7) no correlation between NK activity and risk for lung tumour or lymphoma development in either normal C57Bl/6 (B6), B6 carrying the *Ay* dominant gene, B6 *bg*/+ and B6 *bg*/*bg* mice after transplacental carcinogenesis with ENU (Stutman, 1984c). In summary, the experimental evidence in mice with spontaneous and induced tumours does not support the idea that NK cells affect tumour development in mice. In a previous paper discussing the possible role of NK cells in immunological surveillance we indicated that surveillance in its strict definition either is not mediated by NK cells or is a very restricted phenomenon which, 'by a stroke of chance, does not apply to any of the experimental models selected' (Stutman, 1983c). The same could be said of NK cells as mediators of natural immunity against developing tumours in mice.

A comment on our ENU experiments. In these experiments we explored two aspects: (1) the effect of ENU on lymphoma and lung tumour development in A/HeJ (low-NK) and CBA/H (high-NK) strains (Stutman, 1983c) and in normal or homozygous beige C57Bl/6 mice (Stutman, 1984c) and (2) tumour development in the absence of any detectable effect of ENU on NK activity of the treated hosts (Stutman, 1983c, 1984c). Whether ENU was given at the 16th day of gestation, at birth (a time in which NK activity is still undeveloped in all strains, see Herberman and Holden, 1978; Kiessling and Wigzell, 1979), or at 45 days of age (when NK activity is fully developed), the incidence of lung tumours and lymphomas (and hepatomas in males) was similar (Stutman 1983c, 1984c). The prediction of an NK-mediated immunological surveillance model would have been to find more tumours in the low-NK strains, especially when the carcinogen was given early in life. We selected ENU not only because it is a powerful carcinogen active transplacentally as well as when administered after birth, but because ENU, at a variety of dosages and schedules of administration, does not affect NK activity in spleen in any of the mouse strains so far studied (Stutman, 1984c). Thus, the lack of differences in tumour incidence after ENU in high- and low-NK strains could not be attributed to differential immunodepressive effects of the carcinogen on NK activities (Gorelik and Herberman, 1982).

A comment on the anti-mu-induced lymphomas. During experiments aimed at determining the role of B cells in the partial resistance of nude CBA/H mice to polyoma virus oncogenesis (Stutman, 1975b), nude and normal mice received chronic anti-mu treatment from birth, and some of the mu-treated nudes developed lymphomas which could not be attributed to polyoma virus (Stutman, 1983a,c; 1984a,b). The incidence of B-cell lymphomas ranged from 30 to 50 per cent in CBA/H or BALB/c nudes when the experiments were terminated at 12 months (Stutman, 1983a,c; 1984a,b). Lymphoma incidence in the different controls ranged from 2 to 9 per cent, which is similar to that observed in untreated nudes or normal CBA/H and BALB/c mice (Stutman, 1978). All of the lymphomas appearing in the anti-mu-treated nudes were surface and/or cytoplasmic Ig positive and expressed murine leukaemia virus antigens (Stutman, 1983a,c; 1984a,b). Most of the lymphomas in the controls were 'null', not expressing either Ig or Thy 1 (Stutman 1983a,c; 1984a,b).

Similar results were obtained independently in another laboratory (Gershwin *et al.*, 1983). It is tempting to speculate on the pathogenesis of this particular model of B lymphoma induction, which certainly bears some resemblance to the lymphomas appearing in immunodepressed patients (Klein and Purtilo, 1981). The B cell maturational arrest, the mitogenic effects of anti-mu, the lack of regulatory T cells and the activation of endogenous retrovirus could be operative in the development of these tumours. Oncogene activation (c-*myc*?), chromosomal translocations or other changes and mono- versus polyclonality of the B lymphomas remain to be defined. Our unpublished studies show that the incidence of B lymphomas can be drastically reduced by injection of mature T Lyt1⁻ L3T4⁺ cells in the anti-mu-treated nudes. One point worth noting is that these lymphomas appear in the presence of an intact NK compartment (Stutman, 1983c; 1984a,b) and in one of the murine strains (CBA) which is the prototype of high NK activity (Kiessling and Wigzell, 1979; Roder *et al.*, 1981). Treatment with anti-mu either does not affect (Gidlund *et al.*, 1979) or actually augments (Brodt and Gordon, 1981) NK activity in mice. Although these studies do not support a role for NK cells in this model, they certainly suggest a possible regulatory role in lymphoma development for T cells, which, however, were the only cell category left out from the list of natural effectors in Part I of this book.

A final comment. The main support for some of the criticisms voiced in the previous sections is provided by actual experiments aimed at finding a correlation between levels of the putative natural immunity effector system and spontaneous or induced tumour development in experimental animals. Such experiments were strongly recommended as the most desirable test of the surveillance theory, especially if the incidence of spontaneous tumours in the 'surveillance-deficient' mice was examined during the whole life-span of the animal; the prediction being increased risk for tumour development in the deficient animals (Burnet, 1970a,b). At present it is fair to say that there is no clear evidence for a natural defence mechanism against tumour development in mice, if we accept that in the few models in which such defence mechanisms can be detected (UV-light carcinogensis, polyoma), they seem to be mediated by conventional immune responses, beyond the scope of the present book.

III. CONCLUSION

In *Tusculanae Disputationes* (Book I, iii, 6) Cicero asserts (in my rather loose translation): 'For a man [Cicero is talking about Latin authors] to commit his thoughts to writing when he can neither put them in [new] order nor bring any new light [to bear on them], and when he also has no attraction whatsoever to offer to his reader, is a senseless waste of time, and of paper, too.' It is probable that if I had had Cicero's advice in mind I would have declined to write this essay, since it brings neither new order nor new light to the issue of the immunological interface between the tumour and the host, and as a text it is certainly not attractive to the reader.[1] However, the text was completed, falls within the page limitations suggested and describes certain aspects of natural immunity and tumour development and behaviour in mice about which I feel comfortable in providing opinions and facts. I will not repeat here the arguments used at the beginning of this essay, but regardless of the vast amount of information available in clinical and animal models, and regardless of the mechanism(s) invoked for the antitumour responses, we still do not have a good answer to the experiments showing that only after the attention of the immune system is attracted by some manipulation (such as auto-grafting the carcinogen-treated skin) is there any evidence of the tumour being detected by the immune system (Andrews, 1974). The paradox of the frustrating invisibility of most tumours to the immune system of the host, even during their incipient development (as discussed in this essay) versus the clear evidence of selection of variant clones which are resistant to the specific T cell responses of the host (as is the case in UV-light carcinogenesis in mice; Urban and Schreiber, 1983; Wortzel *et al.*, 1986; or in Epstein-Barr virus positive Burkitt's lymphoma; Rooney *et al.*, 1985) is still unanswered. It may, however, be argued that resistant variant selection may occur only in the few tumour systems in which an active immune response of the host is usually detected. It is easy to understand in evolutionary terms why the species *Mus musculus*, from which the inbred mouse strains are derived, would develop an efficient immune mechanism to prevent the spread and the activity of an endemic oncogenic virus such as polyoma virus. On the other hand, it is not easy to understand in evolutionary terms why the members of this same species, which in their natural state are active only at night, would develop such an efficient immune mechanism against the transforming effects of UV-light.

To summarise, the following conclusions can be drawn about natural immunity and its interactions with cancer:

1. Immunological surveillance is operative in a limited number of systems (especially in systems which involve natural occurring oncogenic viruses) and in most of those cases it seems to be mediated by

[1] The author is unduly modest. (Ed.)

conventional T cells, with only a questionable involvement of the natural immunity effectors listed in Part I of this book.

2. Tumour progression in the cases discussed in (1) above seems to imply variant selection of tumour clones which are resistant to the effector cells of surveillance.

3. Successful metastasis formation seems to be controlled, to some extent and in special experimental models, by natural immunity, especially by NK-like effectors.

4. In some selected cases of opportunistic tumours of the immune system (non-Hodgkin lymphomas) associated with immunodeficiency (see Stutman, 1985), there may be the possibility that the tumours arise as a consequence of the loss of normal homeostatic control, a control which may be mediated by some of the natural immunity effectors.

5. In this author's view, any other generalisations are not warranted by the facts.

ACKNOWLEDGMENTS

This experimental work described in this text was supported by National Institutes of Health grants CA-08748 and CA-15988. I would like to thank Ms Kristin Barnet for preparing the manuscript, and to acknowledge the patience of the Editor during the preparation of this text. The reference list is extensive but not exhaustive. This text was completed 6 October 1986.

REFERENCES

Ablin, R. J., Bhatti, R. A., Guinan, P. D. and Khin, W. (1979). *Clin. Exp. Immunol.* 38: 83.

Abruzzo, L. V. and Rowley, D. A. (1983). *Science* 222: 581–5.

Adams, D. O. and Snyderman, R. (1979). *JNCI* 62: 1341.

Alexander, P. (1976). *Br. J. Cancer* 33: 344.

Alfred, L. J. and Wojdani, A. (1983). *Int. J. Immunopharmac.* 5: 123.

Alfred, L. J., Wojdani, A., Nieto, M., Perez, R. and Yoshida, G. (1983). *Immunology* 50: 207.

Allison, A. C. (1980). In G. Klein (ed.), *Viral Oncology.* New York: Raven Press: 481–7.

Ames, I. H., Garcia, A. M., John, P. A., Litty, C. A., Farrell, M. A. and Tomar, R. (1986). *Clin. Immunol. Immunopathol.* 38: 265.

Andervont, H. B. (1940). *JNCI* 1: 135.

Andervont, H. B. and Edgcomb, J. H. (1956). *JNCI* 17: 481.

Andervont, H. B., Shimkin, M. B. and Canter, H. Y. (1960). *JNCI* 25: 1069.

Andrews, E. J. (1974). *JNCI* 52: 729.

Anonymous (1971). News and Views, *Nature* 233: 302.

Argov, S., Cochran, A. J., Karre, K., Klein, G. O. and Klein, G. (1981). *Int. J. Cancer* 28: 739.

Auerbach, R. and Auerbach, W. (1982). *Science* 205. 127.

Bakker, W., Nijhuis-Heddes, J. M. A., Wever, A. M. J., Brutel de la Riviere, A., van der Velde, E. A. and Dijkman, J. H. (1981). *Thorax* 36: 870.

Bakker, W., Nijhuis-Heddes, J. M. A. and van der Velde, E. A. (1986). *Cancer Immunol. Immunother.* 22: 155.

Baldwin, R. W. (1977). *Nature* 270: 557.

Bartizal, K. F., Salkowski, C., Pleasants, J. R. and Balish, E. (1984). *J. Leuk. Biol.* 36: 739.

Bashford, E. F., Murray, J. A., Haaland, M. and Bowen, W. H. (1908). *Third Scientific Report, Imperial Cancer Res. Fund London* 3: 262.

Becker, F. F. (1981). *Cancer Res.* 41: 3320.

Bennett, M. and Baker, E. E. (1977). *Cell. Immunol.* 33: 203.

Bentvelzen, P. and Hilgers, J. (1980). In G. Klein (ed.), *Viral Oncology.* New York: Raven Press: 311–55.

Beutler, B., Krochin, N., Milsark, J. W., Luedke, C. and Cerami, A. (1986). *Science* 232: 977.

Biron, C. A. and Welsh, R. A. (1982). *Med. Microbiol. Immunol.* 170: 155.

Bishop, C. J. and Donald, K. J. (1979). *Br. J. Exp. Pathol.* 60: 29.

Bishop, C. J. and Whiting, V. A. (1983). *Br. J. Cancer* 48: 441.

Bishop, C. J., Sheridan, J. W., Ablett, G. and Donald, K. J. (1982). *Aust. J. Exp. Biol. Med. Sci.* 60: 55.

Bloom B. R. (1979). *Nature* 279: 21.

Bloom, B. R. (1982). *Nature* 300: 214.

Boiocchi, M. and Colnaghi, M. I. (1983). *Clinics in Immunology and Allergy.* 3: 365.

Bonmassar, E., Menconi, E., Goldin, A. and Cudkowicz, G. (1974). *JNCI* 53: 475.

Boraschi, D. and Meltzer, M. A. (1979a). *Cell. Imunol.* 45: 188.

Boraschi, D. and Meltzer, M. A. (1979b). *J. Immunol.* 122: 1587.

Boraschi, D., Censini, S. and Tagliabue, A. (1984). *Eur. J. Immunol.* 14: 1061.

Bout, D., Joseph, M., Pontent, M., Vorng, H., Deslee, D. and Capron, A. (1986). *Science* 231: 152.

Brent, L. (1958). *Prog. Allergy* 5: 271.

Brodt, P. and Gordon, J. (1981) *Cell. Immunol.* 65: 20.

Brodt, P. and Gordon, J. (1982). *Cancer Immunol. Immunother.* 13: 125.

Brodt, P., Kongshavn, P., Vargas, F. and Gordon, J. (1981). *J. Reticuloendothel. Soc.* 30: 283–9.

Bruley-Rosset, M. and Rappaport, H. (1983). *Int. J. Cancer.* 31: 381.

Burdette, W. J. (1943). *Cancer Res.* 3: 318.

Burdette, W. J. (1948). *JNCI* 9: 105.

Burdette, W. J. and Strong, J. C. (1943). *Cancer Res.* 3: 13.

Burnet, F. M. (1970a). *Prog. Exp. Tumor Res.* 13: 1.

Burnet, F. M. (1970b). *Immunological Surveillance.* Oxford: Pergamon Press.

Burtin, C., Ponvert, C., Fray, A., Scheinmann, P., Lespiants, G., Loridon, B., Canu, P. and Paupe, J. (1985). *JNCI* 74: 671.

Burton, R. C. (1980). In R. B. Herberman (ed.), *Natural Cell-Mediated Immunity Against Tumors.* New York: Academic Press: 19–35.

Bykowsky, M. J. and Stutman, O. (1986). *J. Immunol.* 137: 1120.

Campbell, P. A. (1976). *Bacteriological Reviews* 40: 284.

Carswell, W. A., Old, L. J., Kassel, R. L., Green, S., Fiore, N. and Williamson, B. (1975). *Proc. Natl. Acad. Sci. USA* 72: 3666.

Chang, S. S. and Hildemann, W. H. (1964). *JNCI* 33: 303.

Chang, S. S., Hildemann, W. H. and Rasmussen, A. F. Jr (1968). *JNCI* 40: 363.

Chesebro, B. and Wehrly, K. (1978). *J. Immunol.* 120: 1081.

Chesebro, B. and Wehrly, K. (1979). *Proc. Natl. Acad. Sci. USA* 76: 425.

Chow, D. A., Greene, M. and Greenberg, A. H. (1979). *Int. J. Cancer* 23: 788.

Clark, E. A. and Harmon, R. C. (1980). *Adv. Cancer Res.* 31: 227.

Clark, E. A., Windsor, N. T., Sturge, J. C. and Stanton, T. H. (1980). In R. B. Herberman (ed.), *Natural Cell-Mediated Immunity to Tumours*. New York: Academic Press: 417–29.

Clark, E. A., Shultz, L. D. and Pollack, S. B. (1981). *Immunogenetics* 12: 601.

Cohen, S. A., Salazar, D., von Muenchhausen, W., Werner-Wasik, M. and Nolan, J. P. (1985). *J. Leuk. Biol.* 37: 559.

Collins, J. L., Patek, P. Q. and Cohn, M. (1980). *Contemp. Topics Immunobiol.* 11: 1.

Cudkowicz, G. and Hochman, P. S. (1979). *Immunol. Rev.* 44: 13.

Dean, J. H., Luster, M. I., Boorman, G. A. Lauer, L. D., Leubke, R. W. and Lawson, L. (1983). *Clin. Exp. Immunol.* 52: 199.

Dean, J. H., Ward, E. C., Murray, M. J., Lauer, L. D., House, R. V., Stillman, W., Hamilton, T. A. and Adams, D. O. (1986). *Int. J. Immunopharmac.* 8: 189.

Dent, P. B. (1972). *Prog. Med. Virol.* 14: 1.

Dighiero, G., Lymberi, P., Guilbert, B., Ternynck, T. and Avrameas, S. (1986). *Ann. NY Acad. Sci.* 475: 135.

Diwan, B. A., Meier, H. and Huebner, R. J. (1973). *JNCI* 51: 1965.

Diwan, B. A., Fox, A. and Blackman, K. B. (1977a). *Naturwissenschaften* 64: 647.

Diwan, B. A., Meier, H. and Blackman, K. E. (1977b). *JNCI* 59: 455.

Djeu, J. Y., Lanza, E., Pastore, S. and Hapel, A. J. (1983). *Nature* 306: 788.

Doll, R. (1977). *Nature* 265: 589.

Duke, S. S., Schook, L. B. and Holsapple, M. P. (1985). *J. Leuk. Biol.* 37: 383.

Dunn, T. B., Heston, W. E. and Derringer, M. K. (1956). *JNCI* 17: 639.

Duran-Reynals, M. L. and Cook, C. (1974). *JNCI* 52: 1001.

Duran-Reynals, M. L., Lilly, F., Bosch, A. and Blank, K. J. (1978). *J. Exp. Med.* 147: 459.

East, I. J., Todd, P. E. E. and Leach, S. J. (1980). *Mol. Immunol.* 17: 1539.

Ehrlich, P. (1906). *Arb. Inst. Exp. Ther. Frankfurt* 1: 65.

Emmelot, P. and Bentveltzen, P. (eds) (1972). *RNA Viruses and Host Genome in Oncogenesis*. Amsterdam: North-Holland Publ. Co.

Ershler, W. B., Stewart, J. A., Hacker, M. P., Moore, A. L. and Tindle, B. H. (1984). *JNCI* 72: 161.

Essex, M., Sliski, A., Cotter, S. M., Jakowaki, R. M. and Hardy, W. D. Jr (1975). *Science* 190: 790.

Evans, J. T., Hauschka, T. S. and Mittelman, A. (1974). *JNCI* 52: 999.

Farram, E. and Nelson, D. S. (1980). *Cell. Immunol.* 55: 294.

Fialkow, P. J. (1976). *Biochim. Biophys. Acta* 458: 283.

Fidler, I. J. and Hart, I. R. (1982). *Science* 217: 998.

Fodstad, O., Hansen, C. T., Cannon, G. B., Statham, C. N., Lichtenstein, G. R. and Boyd, M. R. (1984). *Cancer Res.* 44: 4403.

Fogler, W. E. and Fidler, I. J. (1985). *Cancer Res.* 45: 14.

Foulds, L. (1954). *Cancer Res.* 14: 327.

Francis, T. Jr (1953). *Ann. Int. Med.* 39: 203.

Franks, L. M. and Carbonell, A. W. (1974). *JNCI* 52: 565.

Gasic, G., Gasic, T., Galanti, N., Johnson, T. and Murphy, S. (1973). *Int. J. Cancer* 11: 704.

Gershon, R. K., Carter, R. L. and Kondo, K. (1967). *Nature* 213: 674.

Gershwin, M. E., Ohsugi, Y., Castles, J. J., Ikeda, R. M. and Ruebner, B. (1983). *J. Immunol.* 131: 2069

Ghiara, P., Boraschi, D., Villa, L., Scapigliati, G., Tadei, C. and Tagliabue, A. (1985). *Immunology* 55: 317.

Gidlund, M., Orn, A., Wigzell, H., Senik, A. and Gresser, I. (1978). *Nature* 273: 759.

Gidlund, M., Ojo, E. A., Orn, A., Wigzell, H. and Murgita, R. A. (1979). *Scand. J. Immunol.* 9: 167.

Good, R. A. (1972). *Proc. Natl. Acad. Sci. USA* 69: 1026.

Goodenow, M. M. and Lilly, F. (1984). *Proc. Natl. Acad. Sci. USA* 81: 7612.

Gorelik, E. and Herberman, R. B. (1981a). *JNCI* 66: 543.

Gorelik, E. and Herberman, R. B. (1981b). *Int. J. Cancer* 27: 209.

Gorelik, E. and Herberman, R. B. (1982). *JNCI* 69: 89–93.

Gorelik, E. and Herberman, R. B. (1982). R. B. Herberman (ed.), *NK Cells and Other Effector Cells*, New York: Academic Press: 1415–1421.

Gorelik, E., Fogel, M., Feldman, M. and Segal, S. (1979). *JNCI* 63: 1397.

Gorelik, E., Kedar, E., Sredni, B. and Herberman, R. B. (1981). *Int. J. Cancer* 28: 157.

Gorelik, E., Wiltrout, R. H., Okumura, J., Habu, S. and Herberman, R. B. (1982). *Int. J. Cancer* 30: 107.

Gorelik, E., Bere, W. W. and Herberman, R. B. (1984). *Int. J. Cancer* 33: 87.

Goustin, A. S., Leof, E. B., Shipley, G. D. and Moses, H. L. (1986). *Cancer Res.* 46: 1015.

Gray, D. F. and Cheers, C. (1967). *Aust. J. Exp. Biol. Med. Sci.* 45: 417.

Greenberg, A. H. and Greene, M. (1976). *Nature* 264: 356.

Greenberg, A. H., Chow, D. A. and Wolosin, L. B. (1983). *Clinics in Immunology and Allergy* 3: 389.

Greenberg, A. H., Dyck, D. G., Sandler, L. S., Pohajdak, B., Dressel, K. M. and Grant, D. (1984). *JNCI* 72: 653.

Gronberg, A., Cochran, A. J., Karre, K., Klein, G., Klein, G. O. and Kiessling, R. (1983). *Int. J. Cancer.* 32: 247.

Hackett, J. Jr, Bennett, M., Koo, G. C. and Kumar, V. (1986). *Immunol. Res.* 5: 16.

Haliotis, T., Roder, J. and Dexter, D. (1982). In R. B. Herberman (ed.), *NK Cells and Other Natural Effector Cells.* New York: Academic Press: 1399–1404.

Haliotis, T., Ball, J. K., Dexter, D. and Roder, J. C. (1985). *Int. J. Cancer.* 35: 505.

Haller, O., Kiessling, R., Gidlund, M. and Wigzell, H. (1979). In F. Spreafico and R. Arnon (eds), *Tumor-associated Antigens and Their Specific Immune Response.* New York: Academic Press: 151–66.

Hanna, N. (1980). *Int. J. Cancer* 26: 675.

Hanna, N. (1983). *Surv. Synth. Path. Res* 2: 68.

Hanna, N. and Burton, R. C. (1981). *J. Immunol.* 127: 1754.

Hanna, N. and Fidler, I. J. (1980). *JNCI* 65: 801.

Hanna, N. and Fidler, I. J. (1981). *JNCI* 66: 1183.

Hansson, M. and Kiessling, R. (1983). *Clinics in Immunology and Allergy* 3: 495.

Harris, H. (1971) *Proc. R. Soc. Lond.* (Ser. B) 179: 1.

Hatcher, F. M. and Kuhn, R. E. (1982). In R. B. Herberman (ed.), *NK Cells and Other Natural Effector Cells.* New York: Academic Press: 1091–7.

Hellstrom, K. E. and Hellstrom, I. (1974). *Adv. Cancer Res.* 18: 209.

Henkart, P. A. (1985). *Ann. Rev. Immunol.* 3: 31.

Henney, C. S., Kuribayashi, K., Dern, D. E. and Gillis, S. (1981). *Nature* 291: 335.

Herberman, R. B. (ed.) (1980). *Natural Cell-Mediated Immunity Against Tumors.* New York: Academic Press.

Herberman, R. B. (ed.) (1982). *NK Cells and Other Effector Cells.* New York: Academic Press.

Herberman, R. B. (1983a). *J. Biol. Resp. Mod.* 2: 39.

Herberman, R. B. (1983b). *J. Biol. Resp. Mod.* 2: 217.

Herberman, R. B. (1983c). In Y. Yamamura and T. Tada (eds), *Progress in Immunology*, vol. 5. Tokyo: Academic Press: 1157–67.

Herberman, R. B. (1983d). In J. I. Galin and A. S. Fauci (eds), *Advances in Host Defense Mechanisms,* vol. 2. New York: Raven Press: 241–73.

Herberman, R. B. and Holden, H. T. (1978). *Adv. Cancer Res.* 27: 305.

Herberman, R. B., Nunn, M. E., Holden, H. T., Saal, S. and Djeu, J. (1977). *Int. J. Cancer* 19: 555.

Hercend, T., Reinherz, E. L., Meuer, S., Schlossman, S. F. and Ritz, J. (1983). *Nature* 301: 158.

Hertenstein, B., Kreja, L. and Seidel, H. J. (1984). *Exp. Hematol.* 12: 603.

Heston, W. E. (1940). *JNCI* 1: 105.

Heston, W. E. (1944). *JNCI* 5: 161.

Heston, W. E. (1972). In P. Emmelot and P. Bentvelzen (eds), *RNA Viruses and Host Genome in Oncogenesis.* Amsterdam: North-Holland: 13–24.

Heston, W. E. (1974). *J. Heredity* 65: 262.

Hewitt, H. B. (1978). *Adv. Cancer Res.* 27: 149.

Hewitt, H. B. (1982). *J. Biol. Resp. Mod.* 1: 107.

Hewitt, H. B. (1983). *J. Biol. Resp. Mod.* 2: 210.

Hewitt, H. B., Blake, E. R. and Walder, A. S. (1976). *Br. J. Cancer* 33: 241.

Hibbs, J. B., Chapman, H. A. and Weinberg, J. B. (1978). *J. Reticuloendothel. Soc.* 24: 549.

Holsapple, M. P., Bick, P. H. and Duke, S. S. (1985). *J. Leuk. Biol.* 37: 367.

Joseph, M., Auriault, C., Capron, A., Vorng, H. and Viens, P. (1983). *Nature* 303: 810.

Kalland, T. (1980a). *J. Immunol.* 124: 194.

Kalland, T. (1980b). *J. Immunol.* 124: 1297.

Kalland, T. and Forsberg, J. G. (1981). *Cancer Res.* 41: 5134.

Kamo, I. and Friedman, H. (1977). *Adv. Cancer Res.* 25: 271.

Karre, K., Klein, G. O., Kiessling, R., Klein, G. and Roder, J. C. (1980). *Nature* 284: 624.

Karre, K., Klein G. O., Kiessling, R., Argov, S. and Klein, G. (1982). In R. B. Herberman (ed.), *NK Cells and Other Natural Effector Cells.* New York: Academic Press: 1369–78.

Keller, R. (1983). *Clinics in Immunology and Allergy* 3: 523.

Keusch, G. T. (1982). *Rev. Infect. Dis.* 4: 751.

Kiessling, R., and Haller, O. (1978). *Contemp. Topics Immunobiol.* 8: 171.

Kiessling, R., Klein, E. and Wigzell, H. (1975). *Eur. J. Immunol.* 5: 112.

Kiessling, R., and Wigzell, H. (1979). *Immunol. Revs.* 44: 165.

Kitamura, Y., Go, S. and Hatanaka, K. (1978). *Blood* 52: 447.

Klein, G. (1975). *Harvey Lect. Ser.* 69: 71.

Klein, G. (1980). *Cancer* 45: 2486.

Klein, G. and Klein, E. (1977a). *Transplant. Proc.* 9: 1095.

Klein, G. and Klein, E. (1977b). *Proc. Natl. Acad. Sci. USA* 74: 2121.

Klein, G. and Klein, E. (1985). *Nature* 315: 190.

Klein, G., and Purtilo D. T. (1981). *Cancer Res.* 41: 4209.

Klein, G., Klein, G. O., Karre, K. and Kiessling, R. (1978a). *Immunogenetics* 7: 391.

Klein, G. O., Klein, G., Kiessling, R. and Karre, K. (1978b). *Immunogenetics* 6: 561.

Koprowski, H., Herlyn, D., Lubeck, M., DeFreitas, E. and Sears, H. F. (1984). *Proc. Natl. Acad. Sci. USA* 81: 216.

Kouri, R. E. and Nebert, D. W. (1977). In H. H. Hiatt, J. D. Watson and J. A. Winsten (eds), *Origins of Human Cancer*. Cold Spring Harbor: Cold Spring Harbor Laboratories: 811–35.

Kripke, M. L. (1981). *Adv. Cancer Res.* 34: 69.

Land, H., Parada, L. F. and Weinberg, R. A. (1983). *Nature* 304: 596.

Landreth, K. S., Kincade, P. W., Lee, G. and Harrison, D. E. (1984). *J. Immunol.* 132: 2724.

Lanza, E. and Djeu, J. Y. (1982). In R. B. Herberman (ed.), *NK Cells and Other Natural Effector Cells*. New York: Academic Press: 335–40.

Lattime, E. C., Pecoraro, G. A. and Stutman, O. (1982a). *Int. J. Cancer* 30: 471.

Lattime, E. C., Pecoraro, G. A. and Stutman, O. (1982b). In R. B. Herberman (ed.), *NK Cells and Other Natural Effector Cells*. New York: Academic Press: 179–86.

Lattime, E. C., Pecoraro, G. A. and Stutman, O. (1983a). *J. Exp. Med.* 157: 1070.

Lattime, E. C., Pecoraro, G. A., Guttito, M. J. and Stutman, O. (1983b). *Int. J. Cancer* 32: 523.

Lattime, E. C., Bykowsky, M. J. and Stutman, O. (1986). *Immunol. Res.* 5: 15.

Law, L. W. (1966). *Cancer Res.* 26: 551.

Law, L. W. (1972). In P. Emmelot and P. Bentvelzen (eds), *RNA Viruses and Host Genome in Oncogenesis.* Amsterdam: North-Holland: 25–47.

Law, M. R., Lam, W. K., Studdy, P. R., Pugsley, W. B. and Hodson, M. E. (1982). *Br. J. Dis. Chest* 76: 151.

Lichtenstein, A. K., Berek, J., Kahle, J. and Zighelboim, J. (1984). *Cancer Res.* 44: 5118.

Lilly, F. (1966). *Natl. Cancer Inst. Monog.* 22: 631.

Lilly, , F. and Mayer, A. (1980). In G. Klein (ed.), *Viral Oncology.* New York: Raven Press: 89–108.

Ludwig Lung Cancer Study Group (1984). *Dtsch. Med. Wochenschr.* 109: 935.

Luebke, R. W., Riddle, M. M., Rogers, R. R., Rowe, D. G., Garner, R. J. and Smialowicz, R. R. (1986). *J. Immunopharmacol.* 8: 243.

Lust, J. A., Kumar, V., Burton, R. C., Bartlett, S. P. and Bennett, M. C. (1981). *J. Exp. Med.* 154: 306.

Luster, M. I., Boorman, G. A., Dean, J. H., Luebke, R. W. and Lawson, L. D. (1980). *J. Reticuloendothel. Soc.* 28: 561.

Lyte, M. and Bick, P. H. (1985). *Mech. Ageing Dev.* 30: 333.

McCulloch, E. A., Siminovitch, L. and Till, J. E. (1964). *Science* 144: 866.

McKneally, M. F., Maver, C., Liniger, L., Kausel, H. W., McIlduff, J. B., Older, T. M., Foster, E. D. and Alley, R. D. (1981). *J. Thorac. Cardiovasc. Surg.* 81: 485.

Malkinson, A. V. and Beer, D. S. (1983). *JNCI* 70: 931.

Malkinson, A. V. and Thaete, L. G. (1986). *Cancer Res.* 46: 1694.

Malter, M., Friedrich, E. and Suss, R. (1986). *Cancer Res.* 46: 3055.

Mayer, A., Lilly, F. and Duran-Reynals, M. L. (1980). *Proc. Natl. Acad. Sci. USA* 77: 2960.

Mekori, T. and Phillips, R. A. (1969). *Proc. Soc. Exp. Biol. Med.* 132: 115.

Meltzer, M. S., Occionero, M. and Ruco, L. P. (1982). *Federation Proc.* 41: 2198.

Migliorati, G., Jezzi, T., Frati, L., Bonmassar, E., Rossi, G. B., Garaci, E. and Riccardi, C. (1983). *Int. J. Cancer* 31: 81.

Mikulska, Z. B., Smith, C. and Alexander, P. (1966). *JNCI* 36: 29.

Minato, N., Reid, L. and Bloom, B. R. (1981). *J. Exp. Med.* 154: 750.

Mitchison, N. A. and Kinlen, L. J. (1980). In M. Fougereau and J. Dausset (eds), *Immunology 80, Progress in Immunology IV.* New York: Academic Press: 641–50.

Möller, G. and Möller, E. (1979). *Transplant. Rev.* 11: 1041.

Morahan, P. S., Gaylen Pradley, S., Munson, A. E., Duke, S., Fromtling, R. A. and Marciano-Cabral, F. (1984). *J. Leuk. Biol.* 35: 329.

Mountain, C. F. and Gail, M. H. (1981). *J. Thorac. Cardiovasc. Surg.* 83: 649.

Nabel, G., Allard, W. J. and Cantor, H. (1982). *J. Exp. Med.* 156: 658.

Nazerian, K. (1980). In G. Klein (ed.), *Viral Oncology.* New York: Raven Press: 665–82.

Nelson, D. S. (1974). *Transplant. Rev.* 19: 226.

Nelson, D. S., Nelson, M., Farram, E. and Inoue, Y. (1981). *Aust. J. Exp. Biol. Med. Sci.* 59: 229.

North, R. J. (1982). *J. Exp. Med.* 155: 1063.

North, R. J., Spitalny, G. L. and Kirstein, D. P. (1978). In H. Waters (ed.), *The Handbook of Cancer Immunology*, vol. 2. New York: Garland STPM Press 187–223.

Nowell, P. C. (1976). *Science* 194: 23.

Nowell, P. C. (1986). *Cancer Res.* 46: 2203.

Old, L. J. (1981). *Cancer Res.* 41: 361.

Old, L. J., Boyse, E. A., Clarke, D. A. and Carswell, E. A. (1962). *Ann. NY Acad. Sci.* 101: 80.

Oldham, R. K. (1982). *J. Biol. Resp. Mod.* 1: 81.

Oldham, R. K. (1985). *Cancer Investigation* 3: 53.

Ortaldo, J. R. and Herberman, R. B. (1984). *Annual Rev. Immunology* 2: 359.

Ortaldo, J. R., Mason, L. H., Mathieson, B. J., Liang, S. M., Flick, D. A. and Herberman, R. B. (1986). *Nature* 321: 700.

Pace, J. L., Russell, S. W., Torres, B. A., Johnson, H. M. and Gray, P. W. (1983). *J. Immunol.* 130: 2011–3.

Peto, R. (1977) in H. H. Hiatt, J. D. Watson and J. A. Winsten (eds), *Origins of Human Cancer.* Cold Spring Harbor: Cold Spring Harbor Laboratories: 1403–28.

Petranyi, G., Kiessling, R., Povey, S., Klein, G., Herzenberg, L. and Wigzell, H. (1976).*Immunogenetics* 3:15.

Playfair, J. H. L. (1978). *Curr. Topics Microbiol. Immunol.* 80: 37.

Plescia, O., Smith, A. H. and Grinwich, K. (1975). *Proc. Natl. Acad. Sci. USA* 72: 1848.

Podack, E. R. (1985). *Immunol. Today* 6: 21.

Pollack, S. B. (1983). *Surv. Synth. Path. Res.* 2: 93.

Pollack, S. B. and Hallenbeck, L. A. (1982). *Int. J. Cancer* 29: 203.

Porter, W. R., Hindsill, R., Fairbrother, A. E., Olson, L. J., Jaeger, J., Yuill, J., Bisgaard, S., Hunter, W. G. and Nolan, K. (1984). *Science* 224: 1014.

Potter, M., Pumphrey, J. G. and Bailey, D. W. (1975). *JNCI* 54: 1413.

Prehn, R. T. (1964). *JNCI* 32: 1.

Prehn, R. T. (1976). *Adv. Cancer Res.* 23: 203.

Prehn, R. T. and Lappe, M. A. (1971). *Transplant. Rev.* 7: 26.

Puccetti, P., Santoni, A., Riccardi, C. and Herberman, R. B. (1980). *Int. J. Cancer* 25: 153.

Raikow, R. B., Okunewick, J. P., Buffo, M. J. and Kociban, D. L. (1985). *Cancer Res.* 45: 555.

Raychaudhuri, S., Sakei, Y., Fuji, H. and Kohler, H. (1986). *J. Immunol.* 137: 1743.

Riccardi, C., Puccetti, P., Santoni, A. and Herberman, R. B. (1979). *JNCI* 63: 1041.

Riccardi, C., Santoni, A., Barlozzari, T., Puccetti, P. and Herberman, R. B. (1980). *Int. J. Cancer* 25: 475.

Roder, J. and Duwe, A. K. (1979). *Nature* 278: 451.

Roder. J. C., Lohmann-Matteś, M. L., Domzig, W. and Wigzell, H. (1979). *J. Immunol.* 123: 2174.

Roder J. C., Karre, K. and Kiessling, R. (1981). *Prog. Allergy* 28: 66.

Rooney, C. M., Rowe, M., Wallace, L. E. and Rickinson, A. B. (1985). *Nature* 317: 629.

Rowe, W. P. (1982). *Cancer* 49: 1958.

Rowley, J. D. (1984). *Cancer Res.* 44: 3159.

Ruco, L. P. and Meltzer, M. S. (1978a). *J. Immunol.* 120: 329.

Ruco, L. P. and Meltzer, M. S. (1978b). *Cell. Immunol.* 41: 35.

Ruco, L. P., Meltzer, M. S. and Rosenstreich, D. L. (1978). *J. Immunol.* 121: 543.

Ruggiero, R. A., Bustoabad, O. D., Bonfil, R. D., Meiss, R. P. and Pasqualini, C. D. (1985). *Br. J. Cancer* 51: 37.

Sager, R. (1986). *Cancer Res.* 46: 1573.

Salaman, M. H. (1970). *Proc. Roy. Soc. Med.* 63: 11.

Salomon, J. C., Creau-Goldberg, N. and Lynch, N. R. (1980). *Cancer Immunol. Immunother.* 8: 67.

Saxen, E. A. (1953). *JNCI* 41: 547.

Schatten, S., Drebin, J. A., Granstein, R. D. and Greene, M. I. (1984). *Federation Proc.* 43: 2460.

Scott, J. L., Pal, B. K., Rasheed, S. and Gardner, M. B. (1981). *Int. J. Cancer* 28: 241.

Seaman, W. E. and Talal, N. (1981). *Exp. Hematol.* 9: 691.

Seeley, J. K., Bechtold, T., Purtillo, D. T. and Lindsten, T. (1982). In R. B. Herberman (ed.), *NK Cells and Other Natural Effector Cells.* New York: Academic Press: 1211–18.

Shah, P., Gilbertson, S. M. and Rowley, D. A. (1985). *J. Exp. Med.* 162: 625.

Sharma, R. P. and Zeeman, M. G. (1980). *J. Immunopharmacol.* 2: 285.

Sontag, S. (1978). *Illness as Metaphor.* New York: Farrar, Strauss & Giroux.

Stein-Streilen, J., Bennett, M., Mann, D. and Kumar, V. (1983). *J. Immunol.* 131: 2699.

Storer, J. B. (1966). *J. Gerontol.* 21: 404.

Strong, L. C. (1952). *Yale J. Biol. Med.* 25: 34.

Stutman, O. (1969). *Science* 166: 620.

Stutman, O. (1972). *Natl. Cancer Inst. Monogr.* 35: 107.

Stutman, O. (1973). *Isr. J. Med. Sci.* 9: 217.

Stutman, O. (1974). *Science* 183: 534.

Stutman, O. (1975a). *Adv. Cancer Res.* 22: 261.

Stutman, O. (1975b). *J. Immunol.* 144: 1213.

Stutman, O. (1974c). *Nature* 253: 142.

Stutman, O. (1977). In H. H. Hiatt, J. D. Watson and J. W. Winsten (eds), *Origins of Human Cancer.* Cold Spring Harbor: Cold Spring Harbor Laboratories: 729–50.

Stutman, O. (1978). In J. Fogh and B. C. Giovanella (eds), *The Nude Mouse in Experimental and Clinical Research.* New York: Academic Press: 411–35.

Stutman, O. (1979). *JNCI* 62: 353.

Stutman, O. (1981). In H. Waters (ed.), *The Handbook of Cancer Immunology,* vol. 7. New York: Garland STPM Press: 1–25.

Stutman, O. (1982a). In E. Mihich (ed.), *Biological Responses in Cancer: Progress Toward Potential Application.* New York: Plenum Press: 23–87.

Stutman, O. (1982b). In B. Serrou, C. Rosenfeld and R. B. Herberman (eds), *Natural Killer Cells.* Amsterdam: Elsevier Biomedical: 205–23.

Stutman, O. (1982c). *Springer Semin. Immunopathol.* 4: 333.

Stutman, 0. (1983a). In R. B. Herberman (ed.), *Clinical and Basic Tumor Immunology.* The Hague: Martinus Nijhoff: 1–81.

Stutman, O. (1983b). In E. A. Mirand, W. B. Hutchinson and E. Mihich (eds), *13th International Cancer Congress*, part B, *Biology of Cancer* 1. New York: A. R. Liss Inc.: 311–23.

Stutman, O. (1983c). In Y. Yamamura and T. Tada (eds), *Progress in Immunology*, vol. 5. Tokyo: Academic Press: 1195–1207.

Stutman, O. (1984a). In B. Sordat (ed.), *Immune-deficient Animals.* Basel: S. Karger: 30–9.

Stutman, O. (1984b). In T. Hoshino, H. S. Koren and A. Uchida (eds), *Natural Killer Activity and its Regulation*, International Congress Series No. 641. Amsterdam: Excerpta Medica: 384–8.

Stutman, O. (1984c). In T. Hoshino, H. S. Koren and A. Uchida (eds), *Natural Killer Activity and its Regulation*, International Congress Series No. 641. Amsterdam: Excerpta Medica: 389–94.

Stutman, O. (1984d). *Exp. Cell Biol.* 52: 30–9.

Stutman, O. (1985). In A. E. Reif and M. S. Mitchell (eds), *Immunity to Cancer.* Orlando: Academic Press: 323–42.

Stutman, O. (1986). *Immunol. Rev.* 81: 159.

Stutman, O. and Cuttito, M. J. (1980). In R. B. Herberman (ed.), *Natural Cell-Mediated Immunity Against Tumors.* New York: Academic Press: 431–42.

Stutman, O. and Cuttito, M. J. (1981). *Nature* 290: 254.

Stutman, O. and Cuttito, M. J. (1982). In R. B. Herberman (ed.), *NK Cells and Other Natural Effectors.* New York: Academic Press: 281–9.

Stutman, O. and Dupuy, J. M. (1972). *JNCI* 49: 1283.

Stutman, O. and Lattime, E. C. (1985). *Lymphokines* 12: 107.

Stutman, O. and Lattime, E. C. (1986). In M. L. Kripke and P. Frost (eds), *M. D. Anderson Symposium on Fundamental Cancer Research*, vol. 38, *Immunology and Cancer.* Austin: University of Texas Press: 221–58.

Stutman, O., Paige, C. J. and Feo Figarella, E. (1978). *J. Immunol.* 121: 1819.

Sullivan, J. L., Byron, K. S., Brewster, F. E., and Purtilo, D. T. (1980). *Science* 210: 543.

Tagliabue, A., Befus, A. D., Clark, D. A. and Bienenstock, J. (1982). *J. Exp. Med.* 155: 1785.

Talmadge, D. W. (1979). *J. Immunol.* 123: 1.

Talmadge, J. E., Meyers, K. M., Prieur, D. G. and Starkey, J. R. (1980). *JNCI* 65: 929.

Talmadge, J. E., Meyers, K. M., Prieur, D. J. and Starkey, J. R. (1981). *Nature* 284: 622.

Tanooka, H., Kitamura, Y., Sado, T., Tanaka, K., Nagase, M. and Kondo, S. (1982). *JNCI* 69: 1305.

Taverne, J., Depledge, P. and Playfair, J. H. L. (1982). *Infect. Immun.* 37: 972.

Thomas, L. (1959). In H. S. Lawrence (ed.), *Cellular and Humoral Aspects of the Hypersensitivity State.* New York: Hoeber-Harper: 529–32.

Thomas, L. (1975). In F. Milgron (ed.), *The Immune System and Infectious Diseases, 4th Int. Conv. Immunol.* Basel: S. Karger: 2–11.

Thomas, L. (1982). *Yale J. Biol. Med.* 55: 329.

Thomas, P. E., Hutton, J. J. and Taylor, B. A. (1973). *Genetics* 74: 655.

Trinchieri, G. and Santoli, D. (1978). *J. Exp. Med.* 148: 1314.

Truesdale, A. T., Johnson, D. A., Bedigian, H. G., Outzen, H. C. and Carlson, G. A. (1982). *Cell. Immunol.* 74: 120.

Urban, J. L. and Schreiber, H. (1983). *J. Exp. Med.* 157: 642.

Urso, P. and Gengozian, N. (1980). *J. Toxicol. Environ. Health* 6: 569.

Urso, P. and Gengozian, N. (1982). *J. Toxicol. Environ. Health* 10: 817.

Urso, P. and Gengozian, N. (1984). *J. Toxicol. Environ. Health* 14: 569.

Urso, P., Gengozian, N., Rossi, R. M. and Johnson, R. A. (1986). *J. Immunopharmacol.* 8: 223.

Vogel, S. N. and Rosenstreich, D. L. (1981). *Lymphokines* 3: 149.

Walker, B. E. (1983). *J. Natl. Cancer Inst.* 70: 477.

Ward, E. C., Murray, M. J., Lauer, L. D., House, R. V., Irons, R. and Dean, J. H. (1984). *Toxic. Appl. Pharmac.* 75: 299.

Weindruch, R., Devens, B. H., Raff, H. V. and Walford, R. L. (1983). *J. Immunol.* 130: 993.

Welsh, R. M., Haspel, M. V., Parker, D. C. and Holmes, K. V. (1986). *J. Immunol.* 136: 1454.

White, K. L. Jr and Holsapple, M. P. (1984). *Cancer Res.* 44: 3388.

Whitmore, A. C. and Haughton, G. (1975). *Immunogenetics* 2: 379.

Whitmore, A. C., Babcock, G. F. and Haughton, G. (1978). *J. Immunol.* 121: 213.

Wiltrout, R. H., Mathieson, B. J., Talmadge, J. E., Reynolds, C. W., Zhang, S. R., Herberman, R. B. and Ortaldo, J. R. (1984). *J. Exp. Med.* 160: 1431.

Witz, I. P., Yaakubowicz, M., Gelernter, I., Hochberg, Y., Anavi, R. and Ran, M. (1984). *Immunobiol.* 166: 131.

Woglom, W. H. (1929). *Cancer Reviews* 4: 129.

Wojdani, A. and Alfred, L. J. (1983). *Cell. Immunol.* 77: 132.

Wojdani, A. and Alfred, L. J. (1984). *Cancer Res.* 44: 942.

Woodruff, M. F. A. (1980). *The Interaction of Cancer and Host: Its Therapeutic Significance.* New York: Grune & Stratton.

Wortzel, R. D., Strauss, H. J., Van Waes, C. and Schreiber, H. (1986). In M. L. Kripke and P. Frost (eds), *M. D. Anderson Symposium on Fundamental Cancer Research,* Vol. 38, *Immunology and Cancer.* Austin: University of Texas Press: 161–82.

Wright, S. (1934). *Genetics* 19: 537.

Wyllie, A. H., Kerr, J. F. R. and Currie, A. R. (1980). *Int. Rev. Cytol.* 68: 251.

26

Autoimmune Inflammatory Diseases

ELIE GERTNER

Department of Medicine, Division of Clinical Immunology
The University of Texas Health Science Center
7703 Floyd Curl Drive, San Antonio, Tex. 78284, USA

NORMAN TALAL

Clinical Section, Audie L. Murphy Memorial Veterans Hospital,
and Department of Medicine, Division of Clinical Immunology
The University of Texas Health Science Center
7703 Floyd Curl Drive, San Antonio, Tex. 78284, USA

I. INTRODUCTION

The autoimmune inflammatory diseases are considered multifactorial disorders of immune regulation in which a genetic predisposition related

NATURAL IMMUNITY
ISBN 0 12 5145551

to immune response genes and a possible infectious (? viral) agent play major roles.

It is only recently that natural immunity has become a subject of interest and study in these diseases. The discovery of autoantibodies such as rheumatoid factor made immunoglobulins and B cells an early focus of attention. A decade later, with the discovery of T cells as the primary mediators of immunoregulation, attention turned towards this major lymphocyte population in peripheral blood. More recently, natural immunity and the importance of immunomodulators such as interferon have received considerable attention. Since natural killer (NK) cells are highly dependent upon immunomodulators such as interleukin 2 and interferon, these topics will be discussed together in this chapter.

II. INTERFERON

The interferons are a large number of distinct proteins and glycoproteins that have antiviral, antiproliferative and immunoregulatory properties. Interferons (IFNs) were initially described in 1957 by Isaacs and Lindenmann, who found antiviral activity in the supernatant fluid of chick chorioallantoic membrane pieces that had been incubated with heat-inactivated influenza virus (Isaacs and Lindenmann, 1957). Although the initial paper referred to 'the interferon', studies over the last 25 years have shown that interferon is a family of many proteins and glycoproteins. In addition to their antiviral activity, they also have effects on cellular proliferation and expression of cell-surface antigens, as well as potent immunoregulatory effects.

A. The Interferon System

Today we classify human IFN into three distinct groups. IFN-α is produced when leukocytes are exposed to viruses, whereas IFN-β is produced primarily by fibroblast-like cells. Mixtures of IFN-α and IFN-β were studied in early experiments and are often called type I or 'classical' IFN. IFN-γ (type II) or 'immune IFN' is produced by T lymphocytes that have been stimulated by mitogens in vitro, antigens in vitro or in vivo, or phorbol esters. Recombinant DNA technology has shown that more than a dozen different human IFN-α genes exist on chromosome 9 with about 85 per cent homology in their base sequence (Allan and Fantes, 1980; Shows *et al.*, 1982). Different subsets of IFN-α may have differing biological properties although it is unclear why so many alpha interferons exist. The gene for IFN-β also resides on chromosome 9 and has 50 per cent homology with the IFN-α genes. Only one gene for IFN-γ has thus far been found and cloned and it resides on chromosome 12 (Gray *et al.*, 1982). The molecular weights of IFN-α and IFN-β range from 18 000 to 25 000. IFN-β is a glycoprotein whereas most alpha interferons do not appear to have carbohydrate components. IFN-γ is also a glycoprotein sensitive to pH 2. IFN-γ can potentiate the activity of both IFN-α and IFN-β in a synergistic manner (Fleischmann *et al.*, 1979).

Other IFN subtypes include the unusual IFN with antigenic reactivity of IFN-α but physicochemical properties of IFN-γ (acid lability) described below (Balkwill *et al.*, 1983), and IFN-δ (Wilkinson and Morris, 1983).

IFNs act by binding to specific cell-surface receptors. IFN-α and IFN-β share one class of receptors whereas interferon-γ utilises a different receptor (Branca and Baglioni, 1981).

Viruses are among the best inducers of IFN although they differ in potency. A wide variety of non-viral substances can also induce IFN. IFN-α/β may be induced by double-stranded (ds) RNAs, organisms such as *Brucella abortus, Listeria monocytogenes, Haemophilus influenzae, Nocardia, Rickettsia, Mycoplasma* and *Chlamydia*; by protozoans; by bacterial products such as lipopolysaccharides; and by organic polymers and low molecular weight substances (Epstein, 1979; Preble and Friedman, 1983). T lymphocytes produce IFN-γ after stimulation by mitogens or antigens (Preble and Friedman, 1983). Interleukin 2 is a potent stimulator of IFN-γ (Torres *et al.*, 1982; Kawase *et al.*, 1983). Many cell types including fibroblasts, epithelial cells, lymphocytes, macrophages and NK cells can be stimulated to produce IFN, given the appropriate inducers.

B. Antiviral Effects of Interferons

The antiviral effects of IFN were the first effects recognised. Of the numerous mechanisms involved, the best-characterised are those involving enzymes important in protein synthesis. These include 2',5' -oligoadenylate synthetase, which mediates the synthesis of 2',5'-linked adenylate oligomers from ADP (Lengyel, 1982). This oligonucleotide activates an endogenous ribonuclease which causes inactivation of viral and host cell messenger RNA, leading to diminished synthesis of viral protein in infected cells. Clinically, quantitation of 2',5'-oligo-A synthetase levels in cells has been proposed as a diagnostic aid in viral diseases (Schattner *et al.*, 1981). Viral infections, but not bacterial infections, lead to elevated levels of 2',5'-oligo-A synthetase, suggesting that this assay may be useful in confirming or excluding a viral aetiology in acute disease. Others, however, have observed that there is some increase in enzyme concentration in patients with bacterial infections as well (Chousterman *et al.*, 1983). Since local production of IFN may be more important than high levels of circulating IFN, levels of this enzyme may provide evidence of local production even in the absence of systemic elevation of IFN levels. It should be noted that autoimmune diseases also have elevated levels of 2',5'-oligo-A synthetase (as discussed below). A comprehensive review of enzymes induced by IFN has been written by Lengyel (1982).

C. Immunological Role of Interferon

In addition to antiviral and cellular effects, IFNs-α, β and γ have immunoregulatory properties that affect antibody production, cell-mediated immunity and other functions of the immune system (Preble and Friedman, 1983). IFN-α/β can enhance or inhibit antibody formation depending on the dose and time of exposure to IFN relative to the antigenic challenge in vivo (Broduer and Merigan, 1974; Chester *et al.*, 1973). IFNs may inhibit antibody synthesis by activating suppressor T cells (Aune and Pierce, 1982) or by activating NK cells which suppress immunoglobulin production by B cells (Abruzzo and Rowley 1983). IFN-γ is more immunosuppressive of primary antibody responses in vitro than the other IFNs (Sonnenfeld *et al.*, 1977; Virelizier *et al.*, 1977) but suppression is also time- and dose-dependent (Sonnenfeld *et al.*, 1978). Interestingly, in one study, IFN-α enhanced in vitro production of pokeweed-mitogen-driven IgG and IgM including IgM rheumatoid factor (Rodriguez *et al.*, 1983).

IFN treatment produces an increase in the expression of cell-surface antigens. Lymphoid cells treated with IFN-α/β had increased expression of histocompatibility antigens (Lindahl *et al.*, 1976). Similarly IFN-α produces increased expression of β-2 microglobulin and HLA antigens on human peripheral blood lymphocytes in vitro (Heron *et al.*, 1978; Hokland *et al.*, 1981; Fellous *et al.*, 1979). IFN-γ is more potent than IFN-α/β in inducing expression of class I antigens. Furthermore, only IFN-γ induces the expression of class II major histocompatibility antigens, both Ia in the mouse and DR in humans, in a highly preferential and selective manner (Steeg *et al.*, 1982; Basham and Merigan, 1983; Virelizier *et al.*, 1984) and at remarkably low doses. New messenger RNA is required for this Ia expression which occurs on macrophages, melanoma cells, B cell lines and even vascular endothelium (Wong *et al.*, 1983; Pober *et al.*, 1983). There are, however, some reports of human and murine IFN-α and IFN-β stimulating class II antigen expression (Kim *et al.*, 1983; Dolei *et al.*, 1983). In summary, all three IFNs stimulate expression of class I antigen, with IFN-γ being the most efficient. IFN-γ

also induces class II antigens, although it seems that IFN-α/β may do so under certain conditions. Treatment with IFN leads to increased expression of IgG Fc receptors on lymphocytes in vitro and in vivo in the mouse, as well as in humans (Friedman *et al.*, 1980; Auget *et al.*, 1981; Itoh *et al.*, 1980).

IFNs are important regulators of NK cells. Enhanced cytotoxic activity of NK cells results following exposure to IFN (Djeu *et al.*, 1982). This is due to at least two mechanisms: (1) IFN enhances the differentiation of NK precursor cells so that they become cytotoxic cells, and (2) IFN also increases the recycling activity of existing NK cells, resulting in an increase in the number of target cells lysed by a given number of NK cells. This in effect increases the functional life of the NK cell. Further, the ability of NK cells themselves to produce IFN (Trinchieri *et al.*, 1978) suggests that in the body's response to a foreign agent such as viral infection, not only will augmentation of NK activity result from the production of IFN but the NK cells themselves may produce local IFN to magnify the response further.

Macrophages also play an important role in host defences, and are one of the cell classes regulated by IFN. IFN enhances Fc receptor expression on macrophages and phagocytosis (Fertsch and Vogel, 1984). There is substantial evidence implicating IFN-γ as a major macrophage-activating factor (see chapters 1 and 8).

IFN-γ-treated macrophages demonstrate an increase in messenger RNA coding for I-region cell-surface molecules and have immuno-enhancing capability on antibody formation (Nakamura *et al.*, 1984). Therefore, IFN-γ together with other lymphokines plays a central role in the defence against organisms (Virelizier and Arenzana-Seisdedos, 1985). Macrophages themselves can also produce IFN. It has been hypothesised that a basal endogenous secretion of IFN regulates the level of macrophage activation and is a requisite for normal monocyte/macrophage function. Finally, as noted previously, IFN can enhance cell-surface antigen expression on macrophages. IFN-γ, but not IFN-α or IFN-β, increased the expression of class II HLA antigens (Virelizier *et al.*, 1984).

In summary, it should be evident that all three IFNs are potent immunomodulators. For some activities (for example, modulation of class II MHC antigens), IFN-γ is more potent than IFN-α/β, whereas for other activities IFNs α and β are more efficient.

D. Interferon in Autoimmune Diseases

The observation that lymphocytes produce IFN in response to antigenic stimulation, and the close involvement of IFN with the immune system, suggested a search for IFN in autoimmune disease. Numerous investigators have reported elevated levels of IFN in rheumatoid arthritis (RA) and systemic lupus erythematosus (SLE) (Skurkovich and Eremkina, 1975; Hooks *et al.*, 1979; Osial *et al.*, 1981; Hooks *et al.*, 1982; Preble *et al.*, 1982; Ytterberg and Schnitzer, 1982). Table 26.1 presents data on patients with various diseases as reported by Moutsopoulos and Hooks (1983). IFN can also be detected in Sjögren's syndrome, vasculitis and Behçet's syndrome, but not such disorders as Wegener's granulomatosis or drug-induced SLE. Although it is not confirmed by all, many investigators find that IFN levels correlate with overall disease activity and serological abnormalities (Hooks *et al.*, 1979; Osial *et al.*, 1981; Preble *et al.*, 1982; Ytterberg and Schnitzer, 1982; Hooks *et al.*, 1982). IFN was found more commonly in patients with active disease and correlated positively with serum anti-DNA antibodies (Hooks *et al.*, 1979; Ytterberg and Schnitzer, 1982).

This IFN, initially thought to be IFN-γ because of its lability at pH 2.0, has been shown to be an unusual acid-labile IFN-α (Preble *et al.*, 1982). Since natural IFN-α is a mixture of many subtypes, it is likely that a normally minor subtype of IFN-α is produced out of proportion in patients with SLE (Preble and Friedman, 1983). Indeed, a normal human IFN with antigenic properties of α and physicochemical properties of γ is produced by normal peripheral blood mononuclear cells during an immune response (Balkwill *et al.*, 1983). Anti-IFN antibodies are infrequent.

As mentioned above, 2'5'-oligo-A synthetase is an enzyme that is induced by IFN and can reflect exposure to interferon. Mononuclear cells

Table 26.1: Interferon in sera of patients with autoimmune disease[a]

	Interferon	
Disease	No. positive/ No. tested	Percent positive
Systemic lupus erythematosus	25/49	51
Rheumatoid arthritis	6/11	55
Scleroderma	6/10	60
Sjögren's syndrome	4/15	27
Vasculitis	7/12	33
Behçet's disease	30/58	51
Aphthous stomatitis	0/13	0
Normal	1/34	3

[a] From data of Moutsopoulos and Hooks (1983).

from patients with SLE and high levels of IFN contained elevated levels of 2′5′-oligo-A synthetase, as did those from half of those patients who were serum IFN negative (Preble and Friedman, 1983; Schattner *et al.*, 1981). Possibly local production of IFN occurs in lymphoid organs (but is not detectable in serum) and may have profound effects on the immune system. Elevated 2′5′-oligo-A synthetase levels can be found in several other connective tissue diseases including RA and Behçet's syndrome (Hylton *et al.*, 1986) although these authors found no correlation with disease activity. There was pronounced elevation of 2′5′-oligo-A synthetase in lymphocytes from patients with SLE, and a less pronounced elevation in patients with RA and Behçet's disease. Thus, induction of 2′5′-oligo-A synthetase is a potential means of screening cells for exposure to IFN (Hylton *et al.*, 1986), and may be a more sensitive indicator of endogenous IFN production than is assay of serum IFN.

IFN is also an inducer of tubuloreticular inclusions (TRIs) in normal lymphocytes. TRIs are often present in the endoplasmic reticulum and lymphocytes of lupus patients. Lymphocytes from SLE patients with elevated IFN levels have more inclusions than patients without elevated IFN levels. Thus, patients with SLE frequently have elevated IFN levels, elevated levels of 2′5′-oligo-A synthetase, and increased inclusions in their lymphocytes.

Several studies have shown that lymphocytes from some SLE patients have a diminished capacity to produce IFN in response to some IFN-inducers (Neighbour and Grayzel, 1981; Tsokos *et al.*, 1982; Preble *et al.*, 1983). When defects of IFN-γ production occur, they may be associated with concomitant abnormalities in production of interleukin 2 (IL-2) (Sibbitt *et al.*, 1984a). The production of IFN-γ was severely depressed, particularly in patients with active SLE, upon in vitro stimulation of peripheral blood mononuclear cells (PBMCs) with IL-2 and these patients showed an absence of IFN-γ specific messenger RNA in their mononuclear cells (Tsokos *et al.*, 1986). Interestingly, it has also been shown that immunoglobulin fractions from patients with SLE are capable of inducing synthesis and release of IFN-γ when cultured with normal human PBMCs.

Insensitivity of PBMCs to IFN-γ is another aspect of deranged immunoregulation by IFN in SLE. This is particularly manifest in the NK system and will be discussed in detail later.

As mentioned, anti-IFN antibodies are relatively uncommon in SLE despite the propensity for antibody formation. Panem *et al.* (1982) suggested that IFN-α might occur in association with immune complex deposition and further reported finding IFN-α by indirect immuno-fluorescence in kidneys of three patients with SLE. The immuno-fluorescence resembled that of human IgG (Panem *et al.*, 1983). However, this has not been confirmed. Husby *et al.* (1986) found no evidence of IFN-α or -γ in nine biopsy sections, although all had striking deposits of IgG, IgA, IgM and C3. Levels of serum IFN did not correlate with renal tissue IFN. Further, components of SLE serum showed no direct binding to, or significant interaction with, IFN by ELISA assay. A distinct role for IFNs in SLE nephritis could thus not be confirmed.

What is the role of IFN in SLE? Is IFN involved in the pathogenesis of the disease or are elevated levels of IFN merely an epiphenomenon? IFN can accelerate the onset and severity of disease in autoimmune mice (Heremans *et al.*, 1978; Engleman *et al.*, 1981) and can induce glomerulonephritis in newborn mice (Gresser *et al.*, 1976). Clinically, fever, alopecia, and muscle pain occur in patients who have received IFN treatment (Gutterman *et al.*, 1982). Given the wide range of disorders in which IFN is elevated, it would appear that high levels of IFN may contribute to the state of disordered immunoregulation underlying generalised autoimmune diseases.

Why might there be elevated levels of IFN in autoimmune diseases such as SLE? In a multifactorial disease of disordered immunoregulation in which a genetic predisposition and an infectious agent may play a role, it has been suggested that the presence of IFN points to an underlying chronic viral infection, to a certain genetic predisposition to produce deficient or the 'wrong' IFN, or to an abnormal cellular response to IFN. Hyperinterferonaemia may contribute to pathology as part of the disordered immunoregulation present in the disease (DeMaeyer-Guignard and DeMaeyer, 1985; Preble and Friedman, 1983; Gresser, 1982).

Finally, further reason to implicate IFN comes from recent observations in homosexual and haemophiliac patients with AIDS whose serum often contains acid-labile IFN (Preble *et al.*, 1982; Eyster *et al.*, 1983; DeStefano *et al.*, 1982). Approximately 12 per cent of patients with generalised lymphadenopathy and 71 per cent of patients with Kaposi's sarcoma and/or opportunistic infection had elevated serum IFN titres. Acid-labile IFN was also present in 10 per cent of asymptomatic homosexual men. Furthermore, lymphocytes from AIDS patients had elevated levels of 2'5'-oligo-A synthetase as well as characteristic TRIs, suggesting that AIDS patients, like those with SLE, respond to endogenously produced IFN (Preble and Friedman, 1983).

III. NATURAL KILLER CELLS[1]

A. Systemic Lupus Erythematosus (SLE)

Numerous laborates have documented diminished NK cell activity in SLE (Silverman and Cathcart, 1980; Goto *et al.*, 1980; Katz *et al.*, 1982;

---

[1] See Chapters 3, 4 and 5 for descriptions of NK and related cells and of their regulation.

Sibbitt *et al.*, 1983c; Sibbitt *et al.*, 1985; Hoffman, 1980; Fitzharris *et al.*, 1982; Tsokos *et al.*, 1982). Active or untreated disease may be associated with lower cytotoxicity (Silverman and Cathcart, 1980; Katz *et al.*, 1982; Sibbitt *et al.*, 1983c) and in serially studied patients, further reductions in NK activity occurred with disease exacerbation (Sibbitt *et al.*, 1983c). Other investigators do not find a consistent correlation (Goto *et al.*, 1980; Hoffman, 1980; Sibbitt *et al.*, 1985), probably reflecting a different patient population.

Much effort has been directed to identifying the basis of the defect in NK function. A decreased NK activity due to a decreased NK cell population has been suggested (Egan *et al.*, 1983) although it appears that defect is an inability to lyse the target cell after binding (Katz *et al.*, 1982). The functional NK cells cycle from target to target normally. Abnormal NK cell activity has been associated with anti-lymphocyte antibodies and immune complexes (Goto *et al.*, 1980; Silverman and Cathcart, 1980; Rook *et al.*, 1982; Sibbitt *et al.*, 1983; Karsh *et al.*, 1981). Sibbitt *et al.* (1984b) demonstrated impaired release of natural killer cell derived cytolytic factor (NKCF) in patients with SLE. As discussed in Chapter 3, the NK cell recognises its target, binds to it and releases NKCF. Effector–target cell conjugate formation was not impaired but the decreased NKCF activity correlated with the impairment of NK cell function.

Sibbitt *et al.* (1985) have also demonstrated a potential role of IFN in the pathogenesis of impaired cytotoxicity in SLE. IFN levels are elevated in SLE serum. In normal peripheral blood, continued exposure to circulating endogenous IFN may result in defective baseline NK cell activity and an insensitivity to IFN. This may be occurring in SLE. Possibly NK cells are constantly primed by high levels of IFN, resulting in a decreased response to further IFN. Alternatively, prolonged incubation with IFN decreases the number of IFN receptors with a decrease in response to IFN or may lead to depletion of factors such as NKCF with resultant decreased NK activity. IFN-γ antibodies, although reported in SLE, do not appear to play an important role in NK dysfunction in SLE. Prostaglandins have not been implicated in the suppression of NK cell activity (Sibbitt *et al.*, 1983c), and the defect in NK cell function is independent of IL-2 production (Sibbitt *et al.*, 1983b), which usually augments NK function in normals.

B. Rheumatoid Arthritis

Studies examining peripheral blood NK activity in rheumatoid arthritis (RA) have been numerous and conflicting. NK activity has been reported to be normal (Neighbour *et al.*, 1982), decreased in patients with active disease but not those with inactive disease (Karsh *et al.*, 1981), decreased in patients with sero-positive but not sero-negative RA (McDaniel *et al.*, 1983), or increased in females but not males with RA, especially those being treated with gold (Goto *et al.*, 1981). Several other investigators have found NK activity to be similar in RA patients and controls (Doblough *et al.*, 1982; Silver *et al.*, 1982). We have observed a significant impairment in peripheral NK activity in RA patients with active disease and joint effusions which correlated inversely with the erythrocyte sedimentation rate (Combe *et al.*, 1984b). It would seem that those patients with more active severe disease and joint effusions are more likely to have reduced NK activity. Since patients who are sero-positive are more likely to have active disease, this may also explain the findings of McDaniel *et al.* (1983).

Normally indomethacin inhibits prostaglandins, resulting in increased NK activity. Treatment of RA peripheral blood mononuclear cells with indomethacin augmented NK activity, suggesting normal regulation of NK activity by prostaglandins (Combe *et al.*, 1984a). Removal of macrophages, which are a major source of prostaglandins, increased NK activity in normals and patients with RA (Combe *et al.*, 1984a).

Large granular lymphocytes (LGLs) are present in synovial fluid. Several investigators have demonstrated decreased NK activity in rheumatoid synovial fluid (Armstrong and Panayi, 1983; Silver *et al.*, 1982). We have also shown that NK activity in rheumatoid synovial fluid is diminished even in comparison to RA peripheral blood. In contrast to peripheral blood, addition of indomethacin to mononuclear cells from the rheumatoid joint has no effect on NK activity. Removal of macrophages resulted in a reduction of NK activity rather than the increase seen in peripheral blood. The addition of synovial macrophages increased NK activity of the synovial non-adherent cells to a level similar to that of unseparated mononuclear cells. Peripheral blood macrophages also increased the NK activity of synovial fluid non-adherent cells, where they decreased NK activity of peripheral blood non-adherent cells. This suggests that there is defective NK activity in the joint and that macrophages modulate NK activity differently in the rheumatoid joint compared to normal or rheumatoid peripheral blood (Combe *et al.*, 1984b). Finally one study did find an increase in synovial fluid NK activity (Reinitz *et al.*, 1982). However, this study used a conjugate-binding cytotoxicity assay, rather than ^{51}Cr release from the NK target cell line K562. It has been suggested that some of these differences between synovial fluid and peripheral blood may relate to the presence of a unique population of cytotoxic cells present in synovial fluid. While able to lyse a variety of targets, these cells have the phenotype $OKT11^+$ Leu7 $(HNK1)^-$ $OKM1^-$ Fc^- (Goto and Zvaifler, 1985).

NK cells have the ability to down-regulate the production of immuno-globulin. Synovial fluid NK cells continue to modulate the spontaneous production of Ig in synovial fluid. Thus, despite the low NK activity in the rheumatoid joint, down-regulation of immunoglobulin production does occur, and depletion of NK cells leads to increased immunoglobulin production (Tovar *et al.*, 1986). In summary, NK activity in peripheral blood of patients with quiescent RA appears to be normal but in patients with active aggressive disease it may be depressed. NK activity in the rheumatoid joint is decreased. The significance of other cytotoxic cells with NK-like activity in the blood and synovial fluid of patients with RA remains unclear.

Finally, it should be noted there have been recent reports of patients with expanded populations of LGLs who had polyarthritis, neutropenia, splenomegaly, and recurrent infections and were considered to be atypical cases of Felty's syndrome or patients with RA. Surface markers showed that these LGLs generally belonged to the T cell lineage (Wallis *et al.*, 1985; Barton *et al.*, 1986).

C. Sjögren's Syndrome

There are several reports on NK activity of peripheral blood mono-nuclear cells in patients with Sjögren's syndrome (SS). Two studies have reported diminished activity (Goto *et al.*, 1981; Miyasaka *et al.*, 1983) both in patients with primary SS and in those with secondary SS. Multiple mechanisms were thought to be involved in the defective NK activity. Sera from SS with decreased NK activity resulted in decreased NK activity of normal lymphocytes, suggesting the presence of a serum factor although there was no correlation with levels of immune com-plexes or with anti-lymphocyte antibodies. Some patients had adherent cells that inhibited NK function. NK activity could be partially restored by the addition of indomethacin or catalase. The authors suggested that lower NK activity might be involved in the increased incidence of pseudolymphoma and lymphoma, which are recognised complications of SS. The number of NK cells was not found to be decreased (Miyasaka *et al.*, 1983).

Two other reports, however, have not found decreased NK function in patients with SS. Minato *et al.* (1982) reported a reduction in the expected augmentation of NK activity in response to administered IFN in patients with SS. Ichikawa *et al.* (1985), while finding normal NK cell activity, reported fewer circulating NK cells in patients than in healthy controls.

Finally, in a larger study of more than 20 patients with primary SS, Pedersen *et al.* (1986) found a normal proportion of LGLs but decreased baseline NK activity and decreased IFN-enhanced NK activity. Interestingly, IL-2 enhanced NK cell activity to a level similar to that found in controls. Thus, defective NK cell activity may be secondary to a deficiency of IL-2.

IV. INTERLEUKIN 2[2]

A. Systemic Lupus Erythematosus

It was initially shown that autoimmune susceptible strains of mice such as NZB/NZW and MRL/lpr mice share as a common feature defective production of, and response to, IL-2. This IL-2 deficiency correlates with disease expression in these murine models of SLE. For example, the abnormality is more severe in MRL/lpr mice than in NZB/NZW mice, corresponding to the earlier onset and more fulminant course of autoimmune disease in the MRL/lpr strain (Dauphinee *et al.*, 1981; Wofsy *et al.*, 1981).

In human SLE the findings reported with respect to IL-2 production and response to IL-2 have been conflicting. Alcocer-Varela and Alarcon-Segovia (1982) reported that SLE T cells activated by phytohaemagglutinin (PHA) or the autologous mixed lymphocyte reaction produced low levels of IL-2, exhibited a decreased response to IL-2 and absorbed IL-2 poorly. Miyasaka *et al.* (1984) found that PHA-stimulated lymphocytes from patients with SLE demonstrated decreased ability to produce IL-2, but SLE lymphocytes responded normally to exogenous IL-2. Linker-Israeli *et al..* (1985) also showed decreased in vitro production of IL-2, but Sibbitt *et al.* (1983a) found decreased IL-2 production in relatively few patients even in the face of co-existing severe NK abnormalities. Generally, decreased IL-2 activity does not correlate with disease activity, although Alcocer-Varela and Alarcon-Segovia (1982) and Alcocer-Varela *et al.* (1984) did find that patients with active disease had less IL-2 activity than those with inactive disease.

Linker-Israeli *et al.*, (1985) have demonstrated that one important mechanism of decreased IL-2 production appears to be active inhibition. Removal of OKT8[+] cells increased the IL-2 production to normal or above normal levels in SLE patients, particularly in patients with inactive disease. The inhibition was active, rather than being due to passive absorption of lymphokine. Removal of Leu-7 (HNK-1) cells,

---

[2] For a discussion of the basic properties and physiology of IL-2, see Chapter 8.

however, also enhanced IL-2 production. Further, since 30 per cent of their OKT8$^+$ cell population was also found to bear the HNK-1 marker, it was postulated that this may be one of the subsets responsible for the suppression. Thus, one or more circulating mononuclear cell subsets may be responsible for the defect in IL-2 production.

B. Rheumatoid Arthritis

Alcocer-Varela *et al.* (1984) reported decreased IL-2 production in a group of patients with RA but a normal response to, and absorption of, IL-2. Miyasaki *et al.* (1984) found that PHA-stimulated lymphocytes from RA patients produced less IL-2 than normals and also responded poorly to exogenous IL-2. There was no correlation with disease activity.

Three aspects of IL-2 biology (production, induction of proliferation and induction of IFN-γ) were found to be diminished, employing synovial and peripheral blood lymphocytes from patients with RA, by Combe *et al.* (1985). RA lymphocytes from synovial fluid and peripheral blood all produced less IL-2. Activated RA cells had a defective response to exogenous IL-2 when compared with normals. The latter defect was greater in the synovial compartment than in peripheral blood. Rheumatoid lymphocytes from both peripheral blood and synovial fluid also produced less IFN-γ after treatment with IL-2 than normal controls despite the enhancement of NK activity. This defect was not corrected by removal of adherent cells. No spontaneous IL-2 activity in culture supernatants of unstimulated RA cells was detected, although others have reported IL-2 activity in synovial fluid of rheumatoid patients (Wilkins *et al.*, 1983; Nouri *et al.*, 1984).

In keeping with the decreased IL-2 described in RA, Husby and Williams (1985), using monoclonal antibodies, noted surprisingly faint staining for IL-2 in rheumatoid tissue rather than the massive amounts one might expect with the intensity of tissue inflammation and lymphocytic infiltration seen in RA.

C. Sjögren's Syndrome

As with the other autoimmune diseases, conflicting results have been reported in Sjögren's syndrome. Alcocer-Varela *et al.* (1984) found decreased production of and response to IL-2 in patients with SS. Miyasaka *et al.* (1984) found a wide variation of production and response to IL-2 among patients with SS but these were no different from controls. In a later study, however, Miyasaka *et al.* (1984) did find decreased IL-2 production by peripheral blood lymphocytes in patients with SS.

V. CONCLUSION

In this chapter, we have discussed the role of IFN, IL-2 and NK cells in three autoimmune diseases. Further investigation of these abnormalities may lead to the development of an immunoregulatory approach to the treatment of rheumatic diseases.

ACKNOWLEDGMENT

We would like to thank Ms Ann Kirkland for her excellent assistance in the preparation of this manuscript.

REFERENCES

Abruzzo, L. V. and Rowley, D. A. (1983). Homeostasis of the antibody response: immunoregulation by NK cells. *Science* 222: 581.

Alcocer-Varela, J. and Alarcon-Segovia, D. (1982). Decreased production of and response to interleukin-2 by cultured lymphocytes in patients with systemic lupus erythematosus. *J. Clin. Invest.* 69: 1388.

Alcocer-Varela, J., Laffon, A. and Alarcon-Segovia, D. (1984). Differences in the production of and/or the response to interleukin-2 by T lymphocytes from patients with the various connective diseases. *Rheumatol. Int.* 4: 39.

Allan, G. and Fantes, K. H. (1980). A family of structural genes for human lymphoblastoid interferon (Leukocyte-type) interferon. *Nature* 287: 408.

Armstrong, R. D. and Panayi, G. S. (1983). Natural killer cell activity in inflammatory disease. *Clin. Rheumat.* 2: 243.

Auget, M., Vignaux, F., Friedman, W. H. and Gresser, I. (1981). Enhancement of Fc receptor expression in interferon-treated mice. *Eur. J. Immunol.* 11: 926.

Aune, T. M. and Pierce, C. W. (1982). Activation of suppressor T-cell pathway by interferon. *Proc. Natl. Acad. Sci. USA* 79: 3808.

Balkwill, F. R., Griffin, D. B., Band, H. A. and Beverley, P. C. L. (1983). Immune lymphocytes produce an acid-labile α-interferon. *J. Exp. Med.* 157: 1059.

Barton, J. C., Prasthofer, E. F., Egan, M. L., Heck, L. W. Jr, Koopman, W. J. and Grossi C. E. (1986). Rheumatoid arthritis associated with expanded populations of granular lymphocytes. *Ann. Intern. Med.* 104: 314.

Basham, T. Y. and Merigan, T. C. (1983). Recombinant interferon-gamma increases HLA-DR expression. *J. Immunol.* 130: 1492.

Birron, C. A., Turgiss, L. R. and Welsh, R. M. (1983). Increase in NK cell number and turnover rate during acute viral infection. *J. Immunol.* 131: 1539.

Branca, A. A. and Baglioni, C. (1981). Evidence that type I and II interferons have different receptors. *Nature* 294: 768.

Brodeur, B. R. and Merigan, T. C. (1974). Suppressive effect of interferon on the humoral immune response to sheep red blood cells in mice. *J. Immunol.* 113: 1319.

Chester, T. J., Paucker, K. and Merigan, T. C. (1973). Suppression of mouse antibody producing spleen cells by various interferon preparations. *Nature* 246: 92.

Chousterman, S., Chousterman, M., Reinert, P. and Thang, M. N. (1983). Clinical value of the determination of an interferon-induced enzyme activity: Studies of the 2'5' oligoadenylate synthetase activity in peripheral blood lymphocytes of patients. *Biomed. Pharmacother.* 37: 176.

Combe, B., Pope, R., Darnell, B. and Talal, N. (1984a). Modulation of natural killer cell activity in the rheumatoid joint and peripheral blood. *Scand. J. Immunol.* 20: 551.

Combe, B., Pope, R., Darnell, B., Kincaid, W. and Talal, N. (1984b). Regulation of natural killer cell activity by macrophages in the rheumatoid joint and peripheral blood. *J. Immunol.* 133: 709.

Combe, B., Pope, R. M., Fischbach, M., Darnell, B., Baron, S. and Talal, N. (1985). Interleukin-2 in rheumatoid arthritis: production of and response to interleukin-2 in rheumatoid synovial fluid, synovial tissue and peripheral blood. *Clin. Exp. Immunol.* 59: 520.

Dauphinee, M. J., Kipper, S. B., Wofsy, D. and Talal, N. (1981). Interleukin-2 deficiency is a common feature of autoimmune mice. *J. Immunol.* 127: 2483.

DeMaeyer-Guignard, J. and DeMaeyer, E. (1985). In I. Gresser (ed.), *Interferon*, vol. 6. New York: Academic Press: 69.

DeStefano, E., Friedman, R. M., Friedman-Kien, A. E., Goedert, J. J., Henricksen, D., Preble, O.T., Sonnanbend, J. A. and Vilcek, J. (1982). Acid-labile human leukocyte interferon in homosexual men with Kaposi's sarcoma and lymphadenopathy. *J. Infec. Dis.* 146: 451.

Djeu, J. Y., Stocks, N., Zoon, K., Stanton, G. J., Timonen, T. and Herberman, R. B. (1982). Positive cell regulation of cytoxicity in human natural killer cells by production of interferon upon exposure to influenza and herpes virus. *J. Exp. Med.* 156: 1222.

Doblough, J. H., Forre, O., Kvien, T. A., Egland, T. and Degre, M. (1982). Natural killer (NK) cell activity of peripheral blood synovial fluid and synovial tissue lymphocytes from patients with rheumatoid arthritis and juvenile rheumatoid arthritis. *Ann. Rheum. Dis.* 41: 490.

Dolei, A., Capobianchi, M. R. and Ameglio, F. (1983). Human interferon-γ enhances the expression of class I and class II major histocompatibility complex products in neoplastic cells more effectively than interferon-α and interferon-β. *Infect. Immun.* 40: 172.

Egan, M. L., Mendelsohn, S. L., Abo, T. and Balch, C. M. (1983). Natural killer cells in systemic lupus erythematosus: abnormal numbers and functional immaturity of HNK-1$^+$ cells. *Arthritis Rheum.* 26: 623.

Engleman, E. G., Sonnenfeld, G., Dauphinee, M., Greenspan, J. S. and Talal, N. (1981). Treatment of NZB/NZW Fl hybrid mice with Mycobacterium bovis strain BCG or type II interferon preparations accelerates autoimmune disease. *Arthritis Rheum.* 24: 1396.

Ennis, F. A., Meager, A., Beare, A. S., Yi-Hua, Q., Riley, D., Schwartz, G., Schild, G. C., Rook A. H. (1981). Interferon induction and increased natural killer cell activity in influenza infections in man. *Lancet* 2: 891.

Epstein, L. B. (1979). In S. Cohen, E. Pick and J. J. Oppenheim (eds), *Biology of the Lymphokines*. New York: Academic Press: 443.

Eyster, M. E., Goeder, J. J., Poon, M. C. and Preble, O. T. (1983). Acid-labile alpha interferon: A possible pre-clinical marker for the acquired immuno-deficiency syndrome in hemophilia. *N. Engl. J. Med.* 309: 583.

Fellous, M., Kamoun, M., Gresser, I. and Bono, R. (1979). Enhanced expression of HLA antigen and beta-2 microglobulin on interferon treated human lymphoid cells. *Eur. J. Immunol.* 9: 446.

Fertsch, D. and Vogel, S. N. (1984). Recombinant interferons increased macrophage Fc receptor capacity. *J. Immunol.* 132: 2436.

Fitzharris, P., Alcocei, J., Stephens, H. A. F., Knight, R. A. and Snaith, M. L. (1982). Insensitivity to interferon of NK cells from patients with systemic lupus erythematosus. *Clin. Exp. Immunol.* 47: 110.

Fleischmann W. R., Georgiades J. A., Osborne L. C., Johnson H. M. (1979). Potentiation of interferon activity by mixed preparations of fibroblasts and immune interferon. *Infect. Immun.* 26: 248.

Friedman, W. H., Gresser, I., Bandeu, M. T., Auget, M. and Neauport-Sautes, C. (1980). Interferon enhances expression of Fc γ receptors. *Cell. Immunol.* 124: 2436.

Goto, M. and Zvaifler, N. J. (1985). Characterization of the natural killer-like lymphocytes in rheumatoid synovial fluid. *J. Immunol.* 134: 1483.

Goto, M., Tanimoto, K. and Horiuchi, Y. (1980). Natural cell mediated cytoxicity in systemic lupus erythematosus. Suppression by anti-lymphocyte antibody. *Arthritis Rheum.* 23: 1274.

Goto, M., Tanimoto, K., Chihara, T. and Horiuchi, Y. (1981). Natural cell-mediated cytotoxicity in Sjogren's syndrome and rheumatoid arthritis. *Arthritis Rheum:* 24: 1377.

Gray, P. W., Leung, D. W., Pennica, D., Yelverton, E., Najarian, R., Simonsen, C. C., Derynck, R., Sherwood, P. J., Wallace, D. M., Berger, S. L., Levinson, A. D. and Goeddel, D. V. (1982). Expression of human immune interferon cDNA in *E. coli* and monkey cells. *Nature* 295: 503.

Gresser, I. (1982). In I. Gresser (ed.), *Interferon*, vol. 4. New York: Academic Press: 95.

Gresser, I., Maury, C., Tovey, M., Morel-Maroger, L. and Pontillon, F. (1976). Progressive glomerulonephritis in mice treated with interferon preparations at birth. *Nature* 263: 420.

Gupta, S. (1985). In S. Gupta and N. Talal (eds), *Immunology of Rheumatic Diseases*. New York: Plenum Publishing Corporation: 109–39.

Gutterman, J. U., Fine, S., Quiesada, J., Horning, S. J., Levine, J. F., Alexanian, R., Bernhardt, L., Kramer, M., Speigel, H., Colburn, W., Trown, P., Merigan, T. and Dziewanowski, Z. (1982). Recombinant leukocyte A interferon: pharmacokinetics, single-dose tolerance, and biologic effects in cancer patients. *Ann. Intern. Med.* 96: 549.

Heremans, H., Billiau, A., Colombatti, A., Hilgers, J. and De Sommer, P. (1978). Interferon treatment of NZB mice: accelerated progression of autoimmune disease. *Infect. Immunol.* 21: 925.

Heron, I., Hokland, M. and Berg, K. (1978). Enhanced expression of β-2 microglobulin and HLA antigen on human lymphoid cells by interferon. *Proc. Natl. Acad. Sci. USA* 75: 6215.

Hoffman, T. (1980). Natural killer function in systemic lupus erythematosus. *Arthritis Rheum.* 23: 30.

Hokland, M., Heron, I. and Berg, K. (1981). Increased expression of β-2 microglobulin and histocompatibility antigens on human lymphoid cells induced by interferon. *J. Interferon Res.* 1: 483.

Hooks, J. J., Moutsopoulos, H. M., Geis, S. A., Stahl, N. I., Decker, J. L. and Notkins, A. L. (1979). Immune interferon in the circulation of patients with autoimmune diseases. *N. Engl. J. Med.* 301: 5.

Hooks, J. J., Jordan, G. W., Cupps, T., Moutsopoulos, H. M., Fauci., A. S. and Notkins, A. L. (1982). Multiple interferons in the circulation of patients with systemic lupus erythematosus and vasculitis. *Arthritis Rheum.* 25: 396.

Husby, G. and Williams, R. C. Jr (1985). Immunohistochemical studies of interleukin-2 and γ-interferon in rheumatoid arthritis. *Arthritis Rheum.* 28: 174.

Husby, G., Williams, R. C. Jr, Ramirez, F. and Tung, K. S. K. (1986). Absence of interferons-α and -β in renal lesions of systemic lupus erythematosus and membranous glomerulonephritis. *Clin. Immunol. Immunopathol.* 39: 68.

Hylton, W., Cayley, J., Dore, C. and Denman, A. M. (1986). 2′, 5′ Oligoadenylate synthetase induction in lymphocytes of patients with connective tissue diseases. *Ann. Rheum. Dis.* 45: 220.

Ichikawa, Y., Yoshida, M., Takaya, M., Uchiyama, M., Shimizu, H. and Arimori, S. (1985). Circulating natural killer cells in Sjogren's syndrome. *Arthritis Rheum.* 28: 182.

Isaacs, A. and Lindenmann, J. (1957). Virus interference: I: The interferon. *Proc. R. Soc. Lond.* (Biol.) 147: 258.

Itoh, K., Inoue, M., Kataoka, S. and Kumagai, K. (1980). Differential effect of interferon on expression of IgG- and IgM-receptor on human lymphocytes. *J. Immunol.* 125: 2589.

Karsh, J., Dorval, G. and Osterland, C. K. (1981). Natural cytotoxicity in rheumatoid arthritis and systemic lupus erythematosus. *Clin. Immunol. Immunopathol.* 19: 437.

Katz, P., Zaytoun, A. M., Lee, J. H. Jr., Panush, R. S. and Longley, S. (1982). Abnormal natural killer cell activity in systemic lupus erythematosus: an intrinsic defect in the lytic event. *J. Immunol.* 129: 1966.

Kawase, I., Brooks, C. G., Kuribayashi, K., Olabuenaga, S., Newman, W., Gillis, F. and Henney, C. S. (1983). Interleukin-2 induces gamma-interferon production; participation of macrophages and NK-like cells. *J. Immunol.* 131: 288.

Kim, K. J., Chaouat, G., Leiserson, W. M., King, J. and DeMaeyer, E. (1983). Characterization of T-cell-soluble factors modulating expression of Ia and H2 antigens on BALB/c B lymphoma cell lines. *J. Cell. Immunol.* 76: 253.

Lengyel, P. (1982). The biochemistry of interferons and their actions. *Ann. Rev. Biochem.* 51: 251.

Lindahl, P., Gresser, I., Leray, P. and Tovey, M. (1976). Interferon treatment of mice: enhanced expression of histocompatibility antigens on lymphoid cells. *Proc. Natl. Acad. Sci. USA* 73: 1284.

Linker-Israeli, M., Bakke, A. C., Quismorio, F. P. Jr and Horwitz, D. A. (1985). Correction of interleukin-2 production in patients with systemic lupus erythematosus by removal of spontaneously activated suppressor cells. *J. Clin. Invest.* 75: 762.

McDaniel, D. O., Barger, B. O., Alarcon, G. F. and Acton, R. T. (1983). NK activity in rheumatoid arthritis and its association with HLA DR antigen. *Clin. Res.* 31: 652A.

Minato, N., Takeda, A., Kano, S. and Takaku, S. (1982). Studies of the functions of natural killer-interferon system in patients with Sjogren syndrome. *J. Clin. Invest.* 69: 581.

Miyasaka, N., Seaman., W., Bakshi, A., Sauvezie, B., Strand, Z., Pope, R. and Talal, N. (1983). Natural killing activity in Sjogren syndrome: an analysis of defective mechanisms. *Arthritis Rheum.* 26: 954.

Miyasaka, N., Nakamura, T., Russell, I. J. and Talal, N. (1984). Interleukin deficiencies in rheumatoid arthritis and systemic lupus erythematosus. *Clin. Immunol. Immunopathol.* 31: 109.

Moutsopoulos, H. M. and Hooks, J. J. (1983). Interferon and autoimmunity. *Clin. Exp. Rheumatol.* 1: 81.

Nakamura, M., Manser, T., Pearson, G. D. N., Daley, M. J. and Gefter, M. L. (1984). The effect of interferon-γ on the immune response *in vivo* and on gene expression *in vitro*. *Nature* 307: 381.

Neighbour, P. A. and Grayzel, A. I. (1981). Interferon production *in vitro* by leucocytes from patients with systemic lupus erythematosus and rheumatoid arthritis. *Clin. Exp. Immunol.* 45: 576.

Neighbour, P. A., Grayzel, A. I. and Miller, A. E. (1982). Endogenous and interferon-augmented natural killer cell activity of human peripheral blood mononuclear cells *in vitro*. Studies of patients with multiple sclerosis, systemic lupus erythematosus or rheumatoid arthritis. *Clin. Exp. Immunol.* 49: 11.

Nouri, A. M. E., Panayi, G. S. and Goodman, S. M. (1984). Cytokines and the chronic inflammation of rheumatic disease: II: The presence of interleukin-2 in synovial fluid. *Clin. Exp. Immunol.* 58: 402.

Ortaldo, J. R., Sharrow, S. O., Timonen, T. and Herberman, R. B. (1981). Analysis of surface antigens on highly purified human NK cells by flow cytometry with monoclonal antibody. *J. Immunol.* 127: 2401.

Osial, T. A. Jr, Pazin, G. J., Ho, M., Armstrong, J. A., Breinig, M. C., Medsger, T. A. Jr. and Rodnan G. P. (1981). Serum interferon (if) levels in connective tissue disease. *Clin. Res.* 29: 160A.

Panem, S., Check, I. J., Henriksen, D. and Vilcek, J. (1982). Antibodies to α-interferon in a patient with systemic lupus erythematosus. *J. Immunol.* 129: 1.

Panem, S., Ordonez, N. and Vilcek, J. (1983). Renal deposition of alpha-interferon in systemic lupus erythematosus. *Infect. Immun.* 42: 368.

Pedersen, B. K., Oxholm, P., Manthorpe, R. and Andersen, V. (1986). Interleukin 2 augmentation of the defective natural killer cell activity in patients with primary Sjogren's syndrome. *Clin. Exp. Immunol.* 63: 1.

Pober, J. S., Gimbrone, M. A., Catron, R. S., Reiss, C. S., Burakoff, S. J., Friers, W. and Ault, K. A. (1983). Ia expression by vascular endothelium is induced by activated T cells and by human γ-interferon. *J. Exp. Med.* 157: 1339.

Preble, O. T. and Friedman, R. M. (1983). Interferon-induced alterations in cells: relevance to viral and non-viral diseases. *Lab. Invest.* 49: 4.

Preble, O. T., Black, R. J., Friedman, R. M., Klippel, J. H. and Vilcek, J. (1982). Systemic lupus erythematosus: presence in human serum of an unusual acid-labile leukocyte interferon. *Science* 216: 429.

Preble, O. T., Rothko, K., Klippel, J. H., Friedman, R. M. and Johnston, M. I. (1983). Interferon-induced 2'5' adenylate synthetase *in vivo* and interferon production *in vitro* by lymphocytes from systemic lupus erythematosus patients with and without circulating interferon. *J. Exp. Med.* 157: 2140.

Ramirez, F., Williams, R. C. Jr, Sibbit, W. L. Jr and Searles, R. P. (1986). Immunoglobulin from systemic lupus erythematosus serum induces interferon release by normal mononuclear cells. *Arthritis Rheum.* 29: 326.

Reinitz, E., Neighbour, P. A. and Grayzel, A. I. (1982). Natural killer cell activity of mononuclear cells from rheumatoid patients measured by a conjugate binding cytotoxicity assay. *Arthritis Rheum.* 25: 1440.

Robb, R. J. (1984). Interleukin-2: the molecule and its function. *Immunology Today* 5: 203.

Rodriguez, M. A., Prinz, W. A., Sibbitt, W. L., Bankhurst, A. D. and Williams, R. C. Jr (1983). Human alpha-interferon enhances *in vitro* IgM rheumatoid factor synthesis by lymphocytes from normal subjects and rheumatoid arthritis patients. *Arthritis Rheum.* 26: 1091.

Rook, A. H., Tsokos, G. C., Quinnan, G. V. Jr, Balow, J. E., Ramsey, K. M., Stocks, N., Phelan, M. A. and Djeu, J. Y. (1982). Cytotoxic antibodies to natural killer cells in systemic lupus erythematosus. *Clin. Immunol. Immunopathol.* 24: 179.

Schattner, A. N. and Duggan, D. B. (1986). Natural killer cells and the pathogenesis of systemic lupus erythematosus (Letter). *Arthritis Rheum.* 27: 1072.

Schattner, A., Wallach, D., Merlin, G., Hahn, T., Levin, S. and Revel, M. (1981). Assay of an interferon-induced enzyme in white blood cells as a diagnostic aid in viral diseases. *Lancet* 2: 497.

Shows, T. B., Sakaguchi, A. Y., Naylor, F. L., Goeddel, D. V. and Lawn, R. M. (1982). Clustering of leucocyte and fibroblast interferon clones on human chromosome 9. *Science* 218: 373.

Sibbitt, W. L., Froelich, C. J. and Bankhurst, A. D. (1983a). Natural cytotoxicity in systemic lupus erythematosus: mechanisms of suppression by inhibitory serum factors. *Clin. Exp. Immunol.* 53: 363.

Sibbitt, W. L. Jr, Likar, L, Spellman, C. W. and Bankhurst, A. D. (1983b). Impaired natural killer cell function in systemic lupus erythematosus: relationship to interleukin-2 production. *Arthritis Rheum.* 26: 1316.

Sibbitt, W. L. Jr, Mathews, P. M. and Bankhurst, A. D. (1983c). The natural killer cell in systemic lupus erythematosus: defects in effector lytic activity and response to interferon and interferon inducers. *J. Clin. Invest.* 71: 1230.

Sibbitt, W. L. Jr, Froelich, C. J. and Bankhurst, A. D. (1984a). Interferon-α regulation of lymphocyte function in systemic lupus erythematosus. *Clin. Immunol. Immunopathol.* 32: 70.

Sibbitt, W. L. Jr, Matthews, P. M. and Bankhurst, A. D. (1984b). Impaired release of a soluble natural killer cytotoxic factor in systemic lupus erythematosus. *Arthritis Rheum.* 27: 1095.

Sibbit, W. L. Jr, Gibbs, D. L., Kenny, C., Bankhurst, A. D., Serales, R. P. and Ley, K. D. (1985). Relationship between circulating interferon and anti-interferon antibodies and impaired natural killer cell activity in systemic lupus erythematosus. *Arthritis Rheum.* 28: 624.

Silver, R. M., Redelman, V., Zvaifler, N. J. and Naides, F. (1982). Studies of rheumatoid synovial fluid lymphocytes: I: Evidence of activated natural killer (NK) like cells. *J. Immunol.* 128: 1758.

Silverman, S. L. and Cathcart, E. S. (1980). Natural killing in systemic lupus erythematosus: inhibitory effects of serum. *Clin. Immunol. Immunopathol.* 17: 219.

Skurkovich, S. V. and Eremkina, E. I. (1975). The probable role of interferon in allergy. *Ann. Allergy* 35: 356.

Sonnenfeld, G., Mandel, A. D. and Merigan, T. C. (1977). The immunosuppressive effect of type II interferon preparations on antibody production. *Cell. Immunol.* 34: 193.

Sonnenfeld, G., Mandel, A. D. and Merigan, T. C. (1978). Time and dosage dependence of immunoenhancement by immune type II interferon preparation. *Cell. Immunol.* 40: 285.

Steeg, P. S., Moore, R. N., Johnson, H. W. and Oppenheim, J. J. (1982). Regulation of murine macrophage Ia antigen by lymphokine with immune interferon activity. *J. Exp. Med.* 156: 1780.

Timonen, T. and Saksela, E. (1980). Isolation of human natural killer cells by discontinuous gradient centrifugation. *J. Immunol. Methods* 36: 285.

Timonen, T., Ortaldo, J. R. and Herberman, R. B. (1982). Analysis by a single cell cytotoxicity assay of natural killer (NK) cell frequencies among human large granular lymphocytes and of the effects of interferon on their activity. *J. Immunol.* 128: 2514.

Torres, B. A., Farrar, W. L. and Johnson, H. M. (1982). Interleukin 2 regulates immune interferon (IFNγ) production by normal and suppressor cell cultures. *J. Immunol.* 128: 2217.

Tovar, Z., Pope, R. M. and Talal, N. (1986). Modulation of spontaneous immunoglobulin production by natural killer cells in rheumatoid arthritis. *Arthritis Rheum.* 29: 1435–9.

Trinchieri, G., Santoli, D., Dee, R. and Knowles, B. B. (1978). Antiviral activity induced by culturing lymphocytes with tumor-derived or virus-transformed cells: identification of the anti-viral activity as interferon and characterization of the human effector lymphocyte subpopulation. *J. Exp. Med.* 147: 1299.

Tsokos, G. C., Rook, A. H., Djeu, J. Y. and Balow, J. E. (1982). Natural killer cells and interferon responses in patients with systemic lupus erythematosus. *Clin. exp. Immunol.* 50: 239.

Tsokos, G. C., Boumpas, D. T., Smith, P. L., Djeu, J. Y., Balow, J. E. and Rook, A. H. (1986). Deficient γ-interferon production in patients with systemic lupus erythematosus. *Arthritis Rheum.* 29: 1210.

Virelizier, J. L. and Arenzana-Seisdedos, F. (1985). The immunological functions of macrophages and the regulation by interferons. *Med. Biol.* 63: 149.

Virelizier, J. L., Chan, E. L. and Allison, A. C. (1977). Immunosuppressive effects of lymphocyte (type II) and leukocyte (type I) interferon on primary antibody responses *in vivo* and *in vitro. Clin. Exp. Immunol.* 30: 299.

Virelizier, J. L., Perez, N., Arenzana-Seisdedos, F. and Devos, R. (1984). Pure interferon gamma enhances class II HLA antigens on human monocyte cell lines. *Eur. J. Immunol.* 14: 106.

Wallis, W. J., Loughran, T. P., Kaddin, M. E., Clark, E. A. and Starkebaum, G. A. (1985). Polyarthritis and neutropenia associated with circulating large granular lymphocytes. *Ann. Intern. Med.* 103: 357.

Wilkins, J. A., Warrington, R. J., Sigurdson, S. L. and Rutherford, W. J. (1983). The demonstration of an interleukin-2 like activity in the synovial fluids of rheumatoid arthritis patients. *J. Rheumatol.* 10: 109.

Wilkinson, M. N. and Morris, A. (1983). Interferon with novel characteristics produced by human mononuclear leukocytes. *Biochem. Biophys. Res. Commun.* 111: 498.

Wofsy, D., Murphy, E. D., Roths, J. B., Dauphinee, M. J., Kipper, S. B. and Talal, N. (1981). A deficient interleukin-2 activity in MRL/Mp and C57BL/6J mice bearing the lpr gene. *J. Exp. Med.* 154: 1671.

Wong, G. H. W., Clark-Lewis, I., McKinn-Breschkin, J. L., Harris, A. W. and Schrader, J. W. (1983). Interferon-γ induces enhanced expression of Ia and H-2 antigens on B lymphoid, macrophage, and myeloid cell lines. *J. Immunol.* 131: 788.

Yamamoto, J. K., Farrai, W. L. and Johnson, H. M., (1982). Interleukin-2 regulation of mitogen induction of immune interferon (IFN-γ) in spleen cells and thymocytes. *Cell Immunol.* 66: 333.

Ytterberg, S. R. and Schnitzer, T. J. (1982). Serum interferon levels in patients with systemic lupus erythematosus. *Arthritis Rheum.* 25: 401.

Natural Immunity in Disease Processes: Discussion

D. S. Nelson

Kolling Institute of Medical Research, Royal North Shore Hospital
St Leonards, NSW 2065, Australia

INTRODUCTION

The chapters in Part II of this book have dealt, in depth, with the operation of natural immune mechanisms in many settings of health and disease. Some other conditions, however, while less obviously related to natural immunity, deserve brief attention. In an age of great pragmatism in biomedical sciences it is also of interest to look briefly at opportunities for immunological intervention in certain diseases, by way of the effectors and modulators of natural immunity.

OTHER CONDITIONS AND DISEASES

Pregnancy and related conditions

In all but highly inbred strains of animal, the mammalian fetus is an allograft, and its survival as such has long intrigued immunologists. Numerous explanations have been put forward (see: Jones, 1978; Jacoby *et al.*, 1984). Among them is the idea of non-specific depression of maternal immune responsiveness. This has received some support from studies of lymphocyte transformation in vitro. It is, however, essentially untenable because immune responses, both cell-mediated and humoral, are not really impaired in pregnant women (Larsen and Galask, 1978; Jones, 1978; Sargent and Redman, 1985). Furthermore, it is a common observation that, whatever the discomforts of the early and late stages of

NATURAL IMMUNITY
ISBN 0 12 5145551

pregnancy, most women are extremely healthy for the remainder (hence the term 'bloom of pregnancy'). The picture is probably clouded for two reasons. First, certain infections (notably rubella) can have devastating effects on the fetus. They have achieved prominence for this reason, rather than for a marked increase in prevalence among pregnant women. Second, some infections have been claimed to be more severe in pregnant women (e.g. infectious hepatitis, smallpox, varicella, pneumococcal pneumonia). In at least some of these cases the observations have been made on populations among which nutritional deprivation is not uncommon (see: D'Cruz *et al.*, 1968; Thong *et al.*, 1973; Larsen and Galask, 1978) and it is quite conceivable that the additional demands of the fetuses have left the mothers even more nutritionally deprived.

Eclampsia and severe pre-eclampsia (toxaemia of pregnancy), are important, interesting and puzzling diseases in which the possible operation of immunological mechanisms has often been discussed. Predisposition appears to have a genetic component, in that women whose mothers or sisters were affected are more at risk than other women. There is a high degree of 'acquired immunity', in that the diseases rarely recur in previously affected women having a second pregnancy by the same father. Strong arguments have been put forward both for inheritance by way of a simple recessive gene and for an immunological basis for severe pre-eclampsia (Redman, 1980; Cooper, 1982). The translation of observations — genetic, immunological and pathological — into likely mechanisms has, however, proved very difficult. Autoimmunity, immune complex deposition and other immunologically induced vascular lesions have been suggested as possibilities.

Disordered immunity has been proposed as one cause of recurrent spontaneous abortion in some cases in which other causes are unlikely (e.g. endocrine, infectious, or genetic) (Rock and Zacur, 1983; Harger *et al.*, 1983; Mowbray and Underwood, 1985). In such cases the husband and wife tend to have an *increased* frequency of shared HLA antigens and reduced husband–wife mixed lymphocyte reactivity, and the wives/ mothers have less (or no) antibody to paternal antigens. In some cases deliberate systemic immunisation with paternal leukocytes has apparently allowed the successful establishment of pregnancy (Taylor and Faulk, 1981; Beer *et al.*, 1981). The underlying immunological mechanisms are by no means clear, but it is suggested that 'protective' antibody to paternal or trophoblastic antigens is an important factor in normal pregnancy, and that its absence predisposes to abortion. Very recently, several monokines and lymphokines have been reported to damage mouse embryos (Hill *et al.*, 1987). Conceivably, a local cell-mediated immune reaction could cause cytokine release and damage to the embryo, such reactions being prevented if embryonic antigens are masked by antibody. It is, however, not easy to reconcile this with reduced reactivity of wives/mothers to paternal antigens in mixed lymphocyte cultures.

Non-specific factors may also play a part in the infertility of endometriosis and other pelvic inflammatory diseases, and perhaps in other cases of infertility and in the action of contraceptive intrauterine devices. Human peritoneal macrophages can phagocytose sperm, apparently in the absence of antibody, and peritoneal macrophages from women with pelvic inflammatory disease were found to be more active than normal. There was also a more general association between peritoneal macrophage numbers and infertility (Haney *et al.*, 1981; Muscato *et al.*, 1982; Olive *et al.*, 1985). Interestingly, pregnancy may occur more readily after pelvic radiological investigations (hysterosalpingography). Ethiodol, a contrast agent used in such studies, has been found to inhibit phagocytosis of sperm and of *Candida* by human pelvic macrophages (Boyer *et al.*, 1986).

Atherosclerosis

Cardiovascular disease is the commonest cause of death in the Western world and the lesions of atherosclerosis, in the coronary and cerebral arteries, are the commonest form of underlying pathology. The typical lesion is an intimal plaque having a lipid core and a fibrous cap. This is preceded by simpler fatty streaks, which can be found even in young children. The fatty streaks consist essentially of lipid-filled macrophages and smooth muscle cells. In the fully developed lesions increased intimal smooth muscle cells are prominent and the cap consists of further smooth muscle and connective tissue. Observations both in experimental animals and in humans have shown the involvement of macrophages, endothelial cells, platelets and smooth muscle cells in the development of lesions (Ross, 1986).

Numerous epidemiological studies, notably the Framinghan study, have revealed that there are certain factors — risk factors — that greatly increase the likehood of atherosclerosis-related diseases. These include an increase in total to high density plasma lipoprotein cholesterol ratio, hypertension, elevated blood sugar, obesity, cigarette smoking and lack of exercise (Castelli, 1984). In recent years there has been a decline in mortality in coronary artery disease which has been attributed, in part, to medical and social intervention aimed at reducing the risk factors (Castelli, 1984; Goldman and Cook, 1984; Hardes *et al.*, 1985).

In a sense, there has been a epidemic of atherosclerosis-related heart disease, which is now showing signs of declining in the Western world. It is probably no more than a play on words to say that a degree of 'natural immunity' is conferred on those who eliminate or avoid risk factors. There are, however, two reasons for looking more closely at natural immunity and atherosclerosis. The first is the possibility that infectious agents may play a part in triggering the development of atherosclerosis. The second is the involvement of cells (notably macrophages) and cellular interactions in which immunologists have a strong interest.

One of the most popular and fruitful hypotheses about atheroscelerosis is the response-to-injury hypothesis (Ross and Glomset, 1976; Ross, 1986). Ross postulated that the initial event is injury to the endothelium. Possible causes of injury could include not only low-density lipoproteins and mechanical factors, but also viruses, immunological reactions or toxins. The likely sequence of events, then, is that monocytes adhere to the endothelium, migrate beneath it, and accumulate lipids, including cholesteryl ester. They also secrete growth factors and chemotactic factors, leading both to proliferation of smooth muscle and fibroblasts, and to the further immigration of inflammatory cells. Endothelial cells may both respond to and produce growth factors, and platelets may contribute further growth factors.

From a totally different viewpoint, Cliff and Schoefl (1983) have also suggested that infectious agents could play a part in the genesis of coronary artery disease. They demonstrated neovascularisation of the intima of coronary arteries, both in patients who had died from sudden cardiac arrest, and in patients who had died from other causes. They revived the idea that neovascularisation is an important feature of intimal pathology. They suggested that the triggers to intimal inflammatory reactions, of which the neovascularisation was part, could be common virus infections. Perhaps more importantly, they suggested that such reactions, like inflammation generally, usually undergo resolution. When resolution did not occur, or when there were repeated local episodes of inflammation, the more severe pathological changes of atherosclerosis might result. In experimental animals, removal of the atherogenic stimulus is frequently followed by resolution or 'cure' of the atheromatous lesions. This has been more difficult to demonstrate in humans, but there is evidence that it can and does occur (Malinow, 1984). The occurrence of regression and resolution does not, of course, shed light on the aetiology of atherosclerosis. It is, however, consistent with the ideas of Cliff and Schoefl and it offers more hope for successful intervention.

Possible microbial and immunological factors in the pathogeneis of atherosclerosis have been reviewed by Lopes-Virella and Virella (1985). Circumstantial evidence consistent with virus involvement includes the occurrence of atherosclerosis in chickens infected with the herpesvirus causing Marek's disease (Minick *et al.*, 1979), the presence of mRNA for this virus in the chicken lesions, and the presence of herpes simplex virus mRNA in some human arteries (Benditt *et al.*, 1983).

Whatever the ultimate aetiology of atherosclerosis may be, there is ample evidence of interactions between macrophages, endothelial cells and smooth muscle cells (Ross, 1986; Setiadi *et al.*, 1986). When monocytes are added to endothelial cell cultures there is always some adherence, but this is increased by low-density lipoproteins, raised levels of which are a risk factor for atherosclerosis (Alderson *et al.*, 1986; Endemann *et al.*, 1987). Both endothelial cells (Berliner *et al.*, 1986) and smooth muscle cells (Schwartz *et al.*, 1986) can produce, in culture, factors that are chemotactic for macrophages/monocytes. In a pigeon model, chemotactic factors have been extracted from atheromatous and atheroma-prone parts of the aorta (Denholm and Lewis, 1987). Human vascular smooth muscle cells can respond to interleukin 1 by producing more interleukin 1, a process which could aggravate the inflammatory component of atherosclerosis and other vascular lesions (Warner *et al.*, 1987). Amplification could also be achieved by way of the scavenger receptor, which mediates the uptake of altered low density lipoproteins (Goldstein *et al.*, 1979). Occupation of the scavenger receptor was found to trigger the biochemical and functional changes of activation (Johnston *et al.*, 1987). Conversely, macrophage activation led to increased cholesteryl ester synthesis and accumulation (Lopes-Virella *et al.*, 1987).

Extensive and elegant studies on the uptake and disposition of low density lipoproteins by macrophages (Goldstein *et al.*, 1985) have proceeded for years in parallel with studies by immunologists of phagocytosis. They have, however, apparently impinged little on immunological thinking. There is now clearly a considerable community of interest between immunologically and cardiologically oriented cell biologists. Both dietary cholesterol in vivo (Rogers *et al.*, 1986) and low density lipoproteins in vitro (Paragh *et al.*, 1986) have demonstrable effects on immunologically relevant activities of macrophages. Such findings should stimulate interest in dietary fat and immunity (Erickson, 1986).

Hypertension

Interest is expressed from time to time in the possible involvement of the immune system in the pathogenesis of hypertension. It is clearly involved, though indirectly, in the hypertension associated with immunologically mediated renal disease. It may be involved, again perhaps indirectly, in the hypertension of pre-eclampsia and eclampsia (see above). In essential hypertension there may be increased serum immunoglobulin levels, and increased frequency of anti-nuclear antibodies and rheumatoid factor, and an increased prevalence of the C3F gene (Mackay, 1979; Kristensen, 1984). Evidence for the involvement of, or disturbance of, mechanisms of natural immunity appears, however, to be lacking.

Rheumatic and Arthritic Diseases

It is now thoroughly established that immunoregulation is disordered in the common rheumatic diseases, including rheumatoid arthritis, systemic lupus erythematosus, and Sjögren's syndrome. In Chapter 26 Gertner and Talal focused on the involvement of interferon, NK cells and interleukin 2. Although advances are now being made in understanding these abnormalities in molecular terms, their consequences in terms of resistance to infection are not clear. More importantly, the basic inciting events in these diseases are unknown. Perhaps the most popular general hypothesis, at least for rheumatoid arthritis, is that such events involve microbial agents and that, once initiated, the pathological processes become self-perpetuating because of disordered immunity (see March, 1987). The role of natural resistance mechanisms in determining either the occurrence of, or consequences of, such postulated infections is utterly unclear. The same can be said even of reactive arthritides that follow defined infections, e.g. Reiter's syndrome after urethritis or enteric infections (Edmonds, 1984). In patients with reactive arthritis the presence of the MHC class I antigen HLA-B27 is increased. It is increased even more in ankylosing spondylitis, which has been linked (though not unequivocally) with *Klebsiella* infection (see Ebringer and Shipley, 1983). Geczy and his colleagues reported that certain antisera to *Klebsiella* antigens were cytotoxic to the lymphocytes of HLA-B27-positive patients with ankylosing spondylitis. These findings proved controversial and difficult to reproduce, though ultimately they were confirmed in a blind study (Geczy *et al.*, 1986). Again, however, their aetiologic and pathogenetic significance, and the role of natural resistance mechanisms, are not clear (van Rood, 1986).

One of the commonest and most severe consequences of infection is rheumatic fever, following streptococcal infection. This disease, and the glomerulonephritis which can also follow streptococcal infection, almost certainly have an immunological pathogenesis, but the mechanisms that determine why these sequelae develop in only a minority of patients are, yet again, unknown.

INTERVENTION

A growing understanding of the immunological factors involved in various disease processes should allow new forms of intervention — prophylactic or therapeutic — to be devised. Some of the humoral factors that influence natural immunity are now readily available in pure form as a result of recombinant DNA technology. This both expands and highlights the possibilities for novel forms of immunological intervention.

Cancer

The forms of biotherapy that show the most effectiveness or promise at present are interferon and interleukin 2 plus lymphokine-activated killer (LAK) cells (Oldham *et al.*, 1984; Fauci, 1987; Fahey, 1987). Interferon (currently alpha and possibly gamma in the future) has proved most effective clinically against hairy cell leukaemia, with modest response rates in leukaemia, lymphoma, Kaposi's sarcoma, renal cell carcinoma, myeloma and melanoma (Goldstein and Laszlo, 1986). It seems likely, however, that it is the anti-proliferative, rather than the immunomodulatory, effect of interferon that is critical.

Interleukin 2, with or without LAK cells, has produced impressive responses in some patients with disseminated cancer. Rosenberg *et al.* (1987) reported eight complete and 15 partial responses in 106 patients treated with interleukin 2 plus LAK cells, and one complete and five partial responses in 46 patients treated with interleukin 2 alone. The complete responses were in patients with renal cell cancer or lymphoma. West *et al.* (1987) reported partial responses in 13 of 40 patients who received interleukin 2 plus LAK cells. Three of these were in melanoma (among eight patients), three in renal cancer (among six patients) and two in lymphoma. As already discussed in Chapter 17, quite severe toxic effects could occur. Studies in mice suggest that it is possible for both NK-related lymphocytes and T lymphocytes to take part in the response (Mulé *et al.*, 1987). A finding that may well be of future importance is the susceptibility of tumour cells with multiple drug resistance to the cytotoxic effects of LAK cells (and of activated macrophages) (Allavena *et al.*, 1987).

The use of TNF-α is still in its infancy (Blick *et al.*, 1987). Its synergy with other cytokines, notably interferon-γ, may offer better prospects for cancer biotherapy.

A totally different form of immunotherapy may depend on reducing the susceptibility of animals to the immunosuppressive or anti-inflammatory effects of tumour cell products. Bovine ocular squamous cell carcinoma (BOSCC) can be treated by immunisation with phenol–saline extracts of the tumour. If an adequate dose of an extract of an allogeneic tumour is injected into affected cattle, slow partial or complete regression occurs in about 50 per cent. Regression of the tumour is accompanied by a mononuclear cell infiltrate (Spradbrow *et al.*, 1977). Phenol–saline extracts of BOSCC were found to immunise mice against immunosuppressive/anti-inflammatory effects of tumour cell products, as manifested by the depression of delayed-type hypersensitivity (DTH) reactions. Immunised mice were resistant to the depressive effects not only of BOSCC cell products, but also of products of a variety of mouse, rat and human tumours. Furthermore, when BOSCC extracts were fractionated, the fractions that had immunotherapeutic activity in cattle were also those that rendered mice resistant to the depression of DTH (Nelson *et al.*, 1985, 1987).

Reference has been made in Chapter 17 to the possible roles of dietary retinoids as immunomodulators. Retinoids are also potent differentiation-inducing agents. Limited experience with individual patients with leukaemia has been encouraging, in terms of induction of remission and lack of severe side effects (Fontana *et al.*, 1986; Daehner *et al.*, 1986; Abrahm *et al.*, 1986). The patients were selected on the basis of the response of their leukaemic cells to retinoids in vitro, and it is likely that this effect, rather than an adjuvant effect, was the basis of the good clinical response. 'Impressive results' were also recorded in four patients with advanced squamous cell carcinoma of the skin treated with retinoids (Lippman and Meyskens, 1987). Synergism between TNF and retinoic acid in differentiation induction of leukaemic cells in vitro suggests another potentially useful therapeutic strategy (Trinchieri *et al.*, 1987). The possible therapeutic role of CSFs as differentiation inducers remains to be defined.

Leucopenias and Radiation

Leucopenias, either iatrogenic or as part of a disease, are now among the commonest causes of reduced resistance to infection. CSFs might be expected to be useful in the management of some leucopenias, provided that there are responsive haemopoietic precursor cells. Limited experience suggests that this may be so (Groopman *et al.*, 1987; Nathan, 1987). CSFs have direct stimulating effects on granulocytes and macrophages which may also promote resistance to infection in abnormally susceptible hosts (Chapters 8, 17 and 20 and Lee and Warren, 1987).

Interleukin 1 has a radioprotective effect (Neta *et al.* (1986) as does TNF (Urbaschek *et al.*, 1987). Interleukin 1 has also been found to enhance the resistance of non-irradiated animals to bacterial infections (Ozaki *et al.*, 1987). It is likely that many individual actions of these pleiotropic monokines contribute to such effects. Their role, if any, in the management of irradiated patients remains to be explored — very carefully, in view of their side effects (Chapter 17). It is possible that agents such as glucan, which act broadly and indirectly by stimulating cytokine production and macrophage activity, may ultimately have a therapeutic role (Patchen *et al.*, 1987; Sherwood, 1987).

Stress and Ageing

Major surgery is a clearly defined stressful stimulus which can depress natural immunity (see Chapter 16). It is conceivable that modulators of natural immunity will prove useful, at least in selected high-risk patients, in mitigating this depression.

The depression of immunity, natural and acquired, that occurs with advancing age (see Chapter 12) also seems to invite the possibility of therapeutic intervention. As mortality is inescapable, the best that might be expected in general terms is prolongation of good health. It is quite possible that means can be devised to improve natural immunity in old age. At present any such intervention would be expensive and perhaps fraught with unpredictable consequences. It will be interesting to see whether ageing individuals and an ageing society will judge the expense and the risks to be worthwhile.

REFERENCES

Abrahm, J., Besa, E. C., Hyzinski, M., Finan, J. and Nowell, P. (1986). *Blood* 67: 1323–7.

Alderson, L. M., Endemann, G., Lindsey, S., Pronczuk, A., Hoover, R. L. and Hayes, K. C. (1986). *Am. J. Pathol.* 123: 334–42.

Allavena, P., Grandi, M., D'Incalci, M., Geri, O., Giuliani, F. C. and Mantovani, A. (1987). *Int. J. Cancer* 40: 104–7.

Beer, A. E., Quebbeman, J. F., Ayers, J. W. T. and Haines, R. F. (1981). *Am. J. Obstet. Gynecol.* 141: 987–97.

Benditt, E. P., Barrett, T. and McDougall, J. K. (1983). *Proc. Natl. Acad. Sci. USA* 80: 6836–9.

Berliner, J. A., Territo, M., Almada, L., Carter, A., Shafonsky, E. and Fogelman, A. M. (1986). *Arteriosclerosis* 6: 254–8.

Blick, M., Sherwin, S. A., Rosenblum, M. and Gutterman, J. (1987). *Cancer Res.* 47: 2986–9.

Boyer, P., Territo, M. C., de Ziegler, D. and Meldrum, D. R. (1986). *Fertil. Steril.* 46: 715–7.

Castelli, W. P. (1984). *Am. J. Med.* 76(2A): 4–12.

Cliff, W. J. and Schoefl, G. I. (1983). In M. O'Connor and J. Nugent (eds), *Development of the Vascular System* (Ciba Foundation Symposium 100). London: Pitman: 207–21.

Cooper, D. W. (1982) *Oxford Rev. Reprod. Biol.* 3: 127–55.

Daehner, S., Vellenga, E., van Dobbenburgh, O. A. and Halie, M. R. (1986). *Blood* 67: 559–61.

D'Cruz, I. A., Balani, S. G. and Iyer, L. S. (1968). *Obstet. Gynecol.* 31: 449–55.

Denholm, E. M. and Lewis, J. C. (1987). *Am. J. Pathol.* 126: 464–75.

Ebringer, A. and Shipley, M. (eds) (1983). *Brit. J. Rheumatol.* 22: Suppl. 2.

Edmonds, J. (1984). *Aust. N. Z. J. Med.* 14: 81–8.

Endemann, G., Pronczuk, A., Friedman, G., Lindsey, S., Alderson, L. and Hayes, K. C. (1987). *Am. J. Pathol.* 126: 1–6.

Erickson, K. L. (1986). *Int. J. Immunopharmac.* 8: 529–43.

Fahey, J. L. (1987). *Ann. Intern. Med.* 106: 257–74.

Fauci, A. (1987). *Ann. Intern. Med.* 106: 421–33.

Fontana, J. A., Rogers, J. S. III and Durham, J. P. (1986). *Cancer* 57: 209–17.

Geczy, A. F., van Leeuwen, A., van Rood, J. J., Ivanyi, P., Breur, B. S. and Cats, A. (1986). *Hum. Immunol.* 17: 239–245.

Goldman, L. and Cook, E. F. (1984). *Ann. Intern. Med.* 101: 825–36.

Goldstein, D. and Laszlo, J. (1986). *Cancer Res.* 46: 4315–29.

Goldstein, J. L., Ho, Y. K., Basu, S. K. and Brown, M. S. (1979). *Proc. Natl. Acad. Sci. USA* 76: 333–7.

Goldstein, J. L., Brown, M. S., Anderson, R. G. W., Russell, D. W. and Schneider, W. J. (1985). *Ann. Rev. Cell Biol.* 1: 1–39.

Groopman, J. E., Mitsuyasu, R. T., De Leo, M. J., Oette, D. H. and Golde, D. W. (1987). *New Engl. J. Med.* 317: 593–8.

Haney, A. F., Muscato, J. J. and Weinberg, J. B. (1981). *Fertil. Steril.* 35: 696–8.

Hardes, G. R., Dobson, A. J., Lloyd, D. M. and Leeder, S. R. (1985). *Cardiology* 72: 23–8.

Harger, J. H., Archer, D. F., Marchese, S. G., Muracca-Clemens, M. and Garver, K. L. (1983). *Obstet. Gynecol.* 62: 574–81.

Hill, J. A. Haimovici, F. and Anderson, D. J. (1987). *J. Immunol.* 139: 2250–4.

Jacoby, D. R., Olding, L. B. and Oldstone, M. B. A. (1984). *Adv. Immunol.* 35: 157–208.

Johnston, P. A., Jansen, M. M., Somers, S. D., Adams, D. O. and Hamilton, T. A. (1987). *J. Immunol.* 138: 1551–8.

Jones, W. R. (1978). In R. R. Macdonald (ed.), *Scientific Basis of Obstetrics and Gynaecology*, 2nd edn. Edinburgh: Churchill Livingstone: 181–210.

Kristensen, B. Ø. (1984). *J. Hypertension* 2: 571–9.

Larsen, B. and Galask, R. P. (1978). *Obstet. Gynecol. Surv.* 33: 297–318.

Lee, M.-L. and Warren, M. K. (1987). *J. Immunol.* 138: 3019–22.

Lippman, S. M. and Meyskens, F. J. (1987). *Ann. Intern. Med.* 107: 499–501.

Lopes-Virella, M. F. and Virella, G. (1985). *Clin. Immunol. Immunopathol.* 37: 377–86.

Lopes-Virella, M., Klein, R.L. and Stevenson, H. C. (1987). *Arteriosclerosis* 7: 176–84.

Mackay, I. R. (1979). In A. Baumgarten and F. F. Richards (eds), Handbook Series in Clinical Laboratory Science Section F; *Immunology*, vol. I, part 2. West Palm Beach: CRC Press: 3–24.

Malinow, M. R. (1984). *Am. Heart J.* 108: 1523–7.

March, L. (1987). *Rheumatol. Int.* 7: 93–100.

Minick, C. R., Fabricant, C. G., Fabricant, J. and Litrenta, M. M. (1979). *Am. J. Pathol.* 96: 673–706.

Mowbray, J. F. and Underwood, J. L. (1985). *Clin. Exp. Immunol.* 60: 1–7.

Mulé, J. J., Yang, J. C., Afreniere, R. L., Shu, S. and Rosenberg, S. A. (1987). *J. Immunol.* 139: 285–94.

Muscato, J. J., Haney, A. F. and Weinberg, J. B. (1982). *Am. J. Obstet. Gynecol.* 144: 503–10.

Nathan, D. G. (1987) *New Engl. J. Med.* 317: 626–8.

Nelson, M., Nelson, D. S., Spradbrow, P. B., Kuchroo, V. K., Jennings, P. A., Cianciolo, G. J. and Snyderman, R. (1985). *Clin. Exp. Immunol.* 61: 109–17.

Nelson, M., Nelson, D. S., Kuchroo, V. K., Spradbrow, P. B. and Jennings, P. A. (1987). *Cancer Immunol. Immunother.* 24: 231–6.

Neta, R., Douches, S. and Oppenheim, J. J. (1986). *J. Immunol.* 136: 2483–5.

Oldham, R. K., Thurman, G. B., Talmadge, J. E., Stevenson, H. C. and Foon, K. A. (1984). *Cancer* 54: 2795–2806.

Olive, D. L., Weinberg, J. B. and Haney, A. F. 1985). *Fertil. Steril* 44: 772–7.

Ozaki, Y., Ohashi, T., Minami, A. and Nakamura, S.-I. (1987). *Infect. Immunity* 55: 1436–40.

Paragh, G., Nagy, J. T., Szondy, E., Fóris, G. and Leövey, A. (1986). *Clin. Exp. Immunol.* 64: 665–72.

Patchen, M. L., D'Alessandro, M. M., Brook, I., Blakeley, W. F. and McVittie, T. J. (1987). *J. Leuk. Biol.* 42: 95–105.

Redman, C. W. G. (1980). In J. P. Hearn (ed.), *Immunological Aspects of Reproduction and Fertility Control*. Lancaster: MTP Press: 83–103.

Rock, T. A. and Zacur, H. A. (1983). *Fertil. Steril.* 39: 123–40.

Rogers, K. A., Hoover, R. L., Castellot, J. J. Jr, Robinson, J. M. and Karnovsky, M. J. (1986). *Am. J. Pathol* 125: 284–91.

Rosenberg, S. A., Lotze, M. T., Muul, L. M., Chang, A. E., Avis, F. P., Leitman, S., Linehan, W. M., Robertson, C. N., Lee, R. E., Rubin, J. T., Seipp, C. A., Simpson, C. G. and White, D. E. (1987). *New Engl. J. Med.* 316: 889–97.

Ross, R. (1986). *New Engl. J. Med.* 314: 488–500.

Ross, R. and Glomset, J. A. (1976). *New Engl. J. Med.* 295: 369–77, 420–5.

Sargent, I. L. and Redman, C. W. G. (1985). *J. Reprod. Immunol.* 7: 95–104.

Schwartz, C. J., Valente, A. J., Sprague, E. A., Kelly, J. L., Suenram, C. A., Graves, D. T., Rozek, M. M., Edwards, E. H. and Delgado, R. (1986). *Sem. Thrombosis Hemostasis* 12: 79–86.

Setiadi, H., Lioté, F. and Wautier, J. L. (1986). *Nouv. Rev. Fr. Hematol.* 28: 339–43.

Sherwood, E. R., Williams, D. L., McNamee, R. B., Jones, E. L., Browder, I. W. and Di Luzio, N. R. (1987). *Int. J. Immunopharmac.* 9: 261–7.

Spradbrow, P. B., Wilson, B. E., Hoffman, D., Kelly, W. R. and Francis, J. (1977). *Vet. Rec.* 100: 376–8.

Taylor, C. and Faulk, W. P. (1981). *Lancet* 2: 68–70.

Thong, Y. H., Steele, R. W., Vincent, M. M., Hensen, S. A. and Bellanti, J. A. (1973). *New. Engl. J. Med.* 289: 604–6.

Trinchieri, G., Rosen, M. and Perussia, B. (1987). *Blood* 69: 1218–24.

Urbaschek, R., Mannel, D. N. and Urbaschek, B. (1987). *Lymphokine Res.* 6: 179–85.

van Rood, J. J. (1986). *Hum. Immunol.* 17: 246–9.

Warner, S. J. C., Auger, K. R. and Libby, P. (1987). *J. Exp. Med.* 165: 1316–31.

West, W. H., Tauer, K. W., Yannelli, J. R., Marshall, G. D., Orr, D. W., Thurman, G. B. and Oldham, R. K. (1987). *New Engl. J. Med.* 316: 898–906.

INDEX

9 0 1 2 3 4 5 6 7 8
A B C D E F G H I J